JANE'S FIGHTING SHIPS

Edited by **Captain John E. Moore**
RN, FRGS

Order of Contents

World Sales Distribution

Jane's Yearbooks,
St. Giles House, 49/50 Poland Street,
London W1A 2LG, England

All the World
except

United States of America and Canada:
Franklin Watts Inc.,
730 Fifth Avenue,
New York, NY 10019.

Editorial communication to:

The Editor, Jane's Fighting Ships
Jane's Yearbooks, St. Giles House, 49/50 Poland Street
London W1A 2LG, England
Telephone 01-437 9844

Advertisement communication to:

Jane's Advertising Department
Haymarket Publishing Group,
Gillow House, 5 Winsley Street,
London W1A 2HG, England
Telephone 01-636 3600

***Classified List of Advertisers**

The various products available from the advertisers in this edition are listed alphabetically in about 350 different headings.

Now .. a submarine

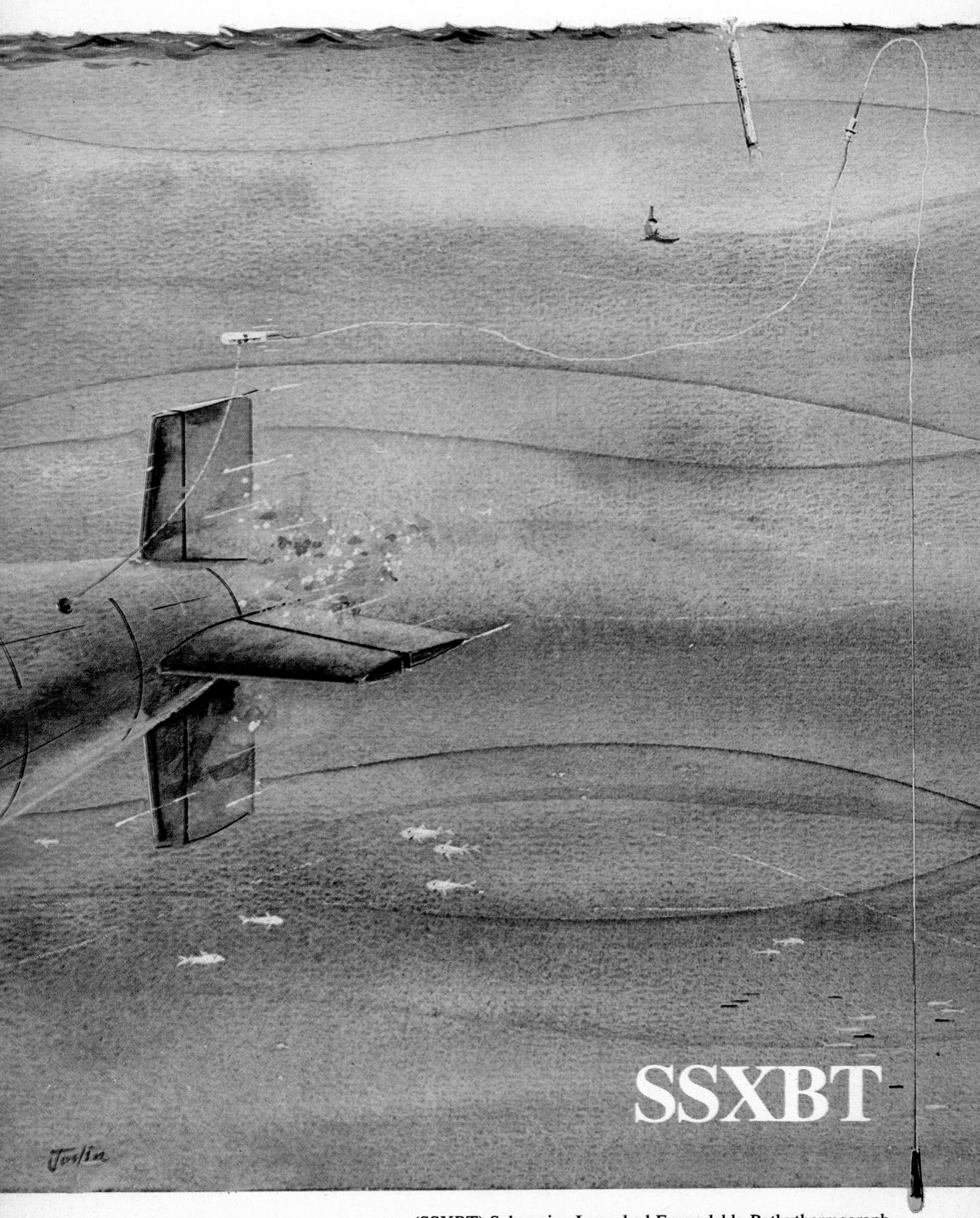

(SSXBT) Submarine Launched Expendable Bathythermograph

launched XBT the SSXBT

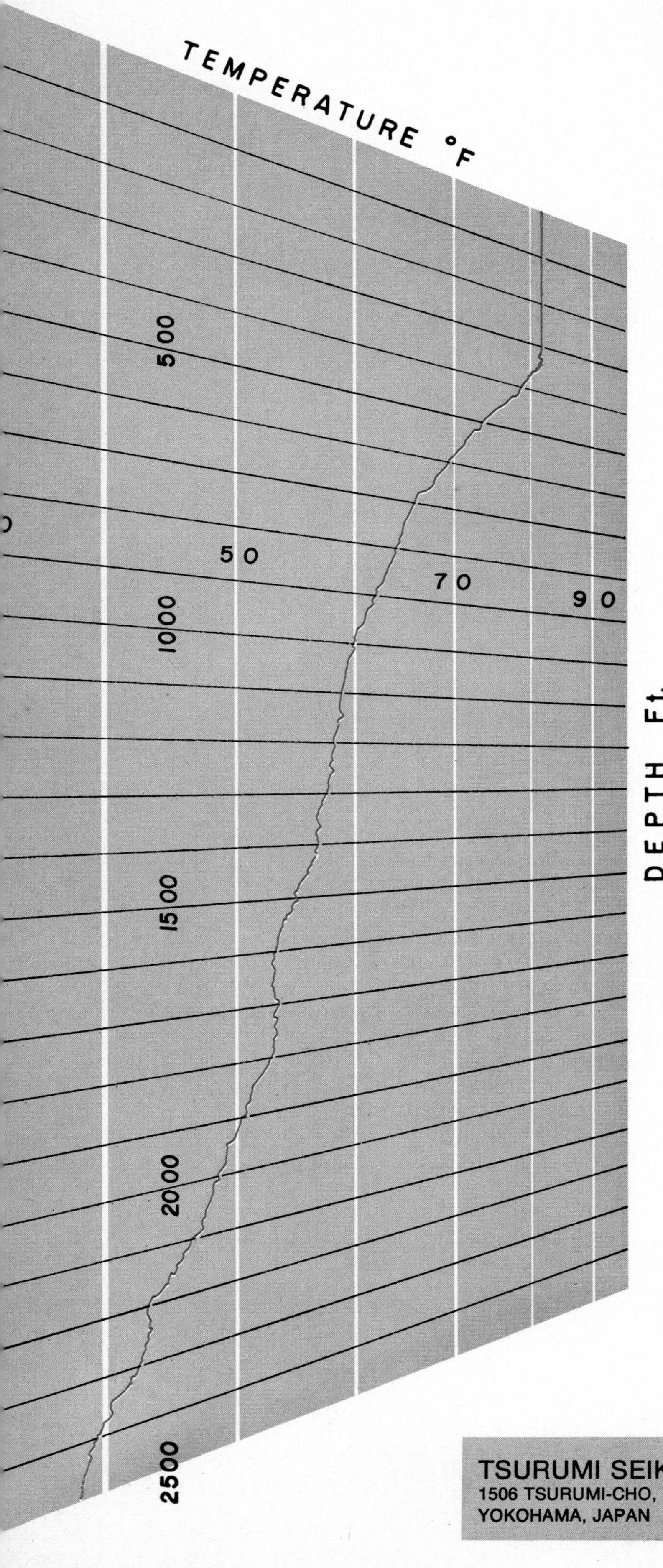

TEMPERATURE °F

50 70 90

DEPTH Ft.

500 1000 1500 2000 2500

The SSXBT is launched from the aft signal ejector of a moving, submerged submarine and transmits temperature data back over a fine wire. The temperature depth profile is displayed on a permanent recording aboard the submarine.

• • •

Designers of the SSXBT

Sippican
OCEANOGRAPHIC SYSTEMS DIVISION
MARION, MASSACHUSETTS 02738
U.S.A.

• •

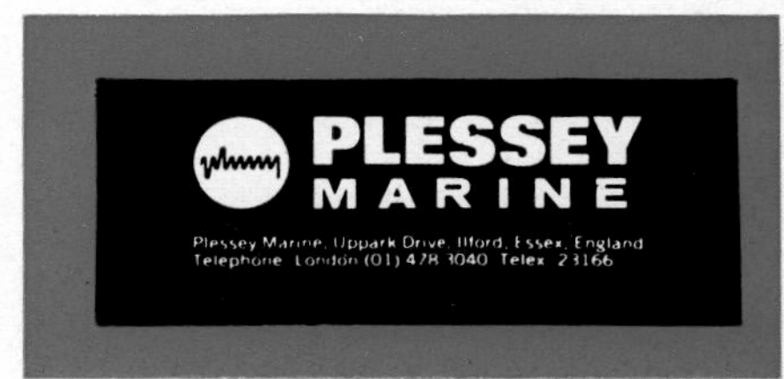

PLESSEY
MARINE
Plessey Marine, Uppark Drive, Ilford, Essex, England
Telephone London (01) 478 3040 Telex 23166

• •

TSURUMI SEIKI CO., LTD.
1506 TSURUMI-CHO, TSURUMI-KU
YOKOHAMA, JAPAN

l'electronique
appliquee
SERVICES COMMERCIAUX
21 - 23 Rue de la VANNE 92120 Montrouge

Alphabetical list of advertisers

1974/75 edition

SCLAR

SHIPBORNE MULTI-ROLE ROCKETS LAUNCHING SYSTEM

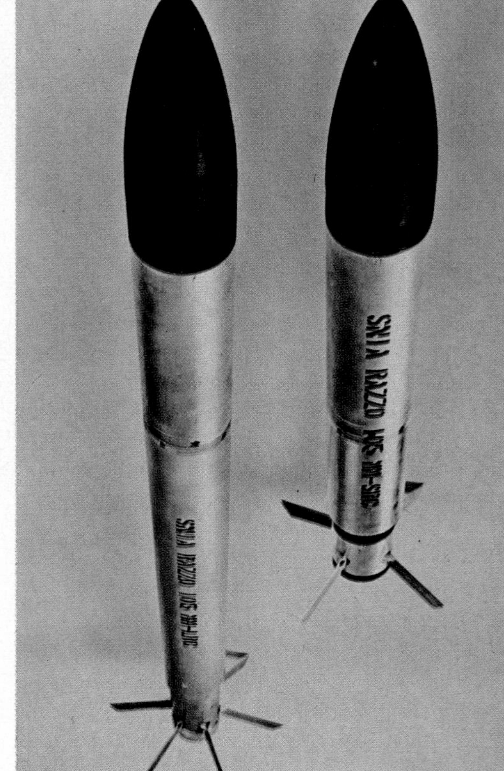

THE SCLAR SYSTEM IS THE LATEST DEVELOPMENT IN THE FIELD OF ROCKET SYSTEM, SPONSORED BY THE ITALIAN NAVY, BEING THE RESULT OF A LENGTHY AND PRODUCTIVE COOPERATION BETWEEN ELETTRONICA SAN GIORGIO - ELSAG, BREDA MECCANICA BRESCIANA AND SNIA VISCOSA.
ITS PRIME TASKS ARE:
PASSIVE DEFENCE FOR THE SHIP AGAINST HOMING MISSILES.
VISUAL FIRE CONTROL IN NIGHT-TIME SURFACE AND SHORE ACTIONS, THIS SYSTEM, WHICH USES A 105 mm ROCKET, HAS BEEN INSTALLED ON SHIPS OF THE ITALIAN NAVY AND OF OTHER EUROPEAN AND EXTRA-EUROPEAN NAVIES.

ELETTRONICA SAN GIORGIO
ELSAG S.p.A.
Weapon Control Systems Department
16155 GENOVA-SESTRI ITALY
v. Hermada 6
Telephone 426.841 - 426.851
Telex 27660 ELSAG

BREDA MECCANICA BRESCIANA S.p.A.
25100 BRESCIA ITALY
v. Lunga 2
Telephone 314.061
Telex 30056 BREDARMI

SNIA VISCOSA S.p.A.
Defence and Aerospace Division
00187 ROMA ITALY
v. Lombardia 31
Telephone 4680
Telex SNIA 61114

Press. Dept. Elsag - ESA 19-74 - Del Pin

ELETTRONICA SAN GIORGIO
ELSAG S.p.A.

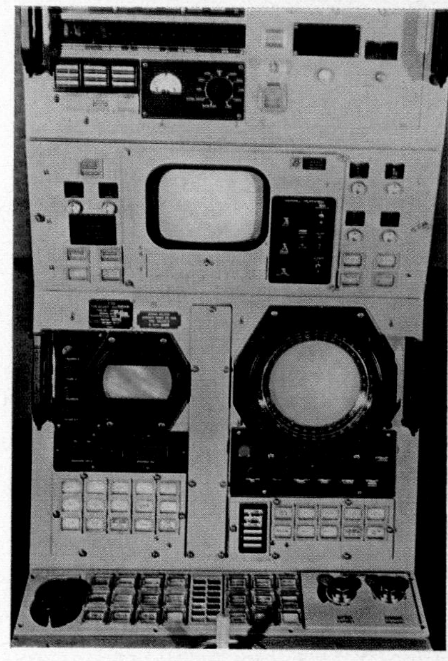

COMBAT SYSTEM ENGINEERING AND SHIPBORNE WEAPON CONTROL SYSTEMS

SINCE 1928 ONE OF THE MOST PROMINENT AND NOW THE LEADING ITALIAN FIRM IN THE FIELD OF DESIGN AND PRODUCTION OF NAVAL FIRE CONTROL SYSTEMS.

MAIN SUPPLIERS OF FIRE CONTROL SYSTEMS TO THE ITALIAN NAVY AND TO A NUMBER OF FOREIGN NAVIES, POSSESSING A SOUND EXPERIENCE IN COMBAT SYSTEM INSTALLATION AND REFITTING.

THE MOST SIGNIFICANT MILITARY PRODUCTION:

« NA 10 » WEAPON CONTROL SYSTEMS.
GUNNERY DATA SYSTEMS.
MULTI-PURPOSE ROCKET CONTROL SYSTEM.
SERVOSYSTEMS.
SPECIAL EQUIPMENT.

ELETTRONICA SAN GIORGIO
ELSAG S.p.A.
Weapon Control Systems Department
16155 GENOVA SESTRI ITALY
Telephone 426.841 - 426.851
via Hermada 6
Telex 27660 ELSAG

Press Dept. Elsag - ESA 17-74 - Del Pino

Alphabetical list of advertisers

1974/75 edition—*continued*

WE HAVE BUILT:

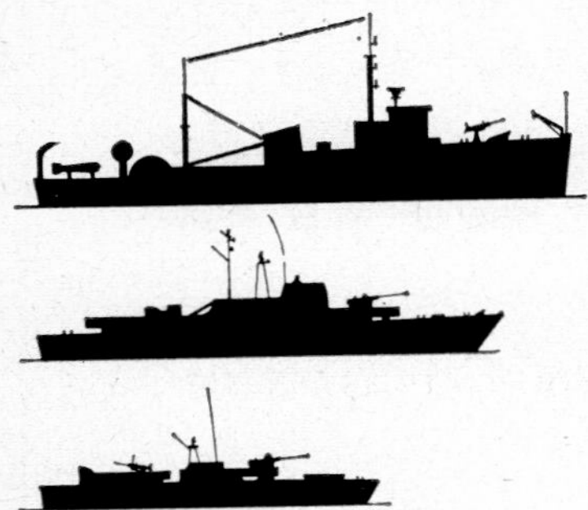

3 Units

6 Units

4 Units

43 Units

NOW BUILDING:

20 45-foot GRP
Patrol Craft for Indian Customs Service

Båtservice Verft a/s

(formerly Boatservice Ltd. a/s)

P.O. BOX 113, N-4501 MANDAL—NORWAY
TELEPHONE: (042) 61011 TELEX: 11862

DIRECTION TECHNIQUE DES CONSTRUCTIONS NAVALES

Design - Development

Production

Engineering

Systems - Missiles

Sophisticated Equipements

Advanced Techniques

Hydraulics - High precision Mechanics
Scientific Computation - Electronics
Metallurgy - High Pressure Technology

E.C.A.N. 16600 Ruelle FRANCE
Téléphone: (45) 95.47.68.
Telex: RUELE 79020

ETABLISSEMENT DES CONSTRUCTIONS ET ARMES NAVALES

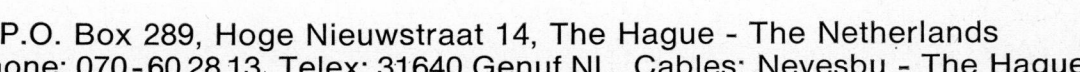

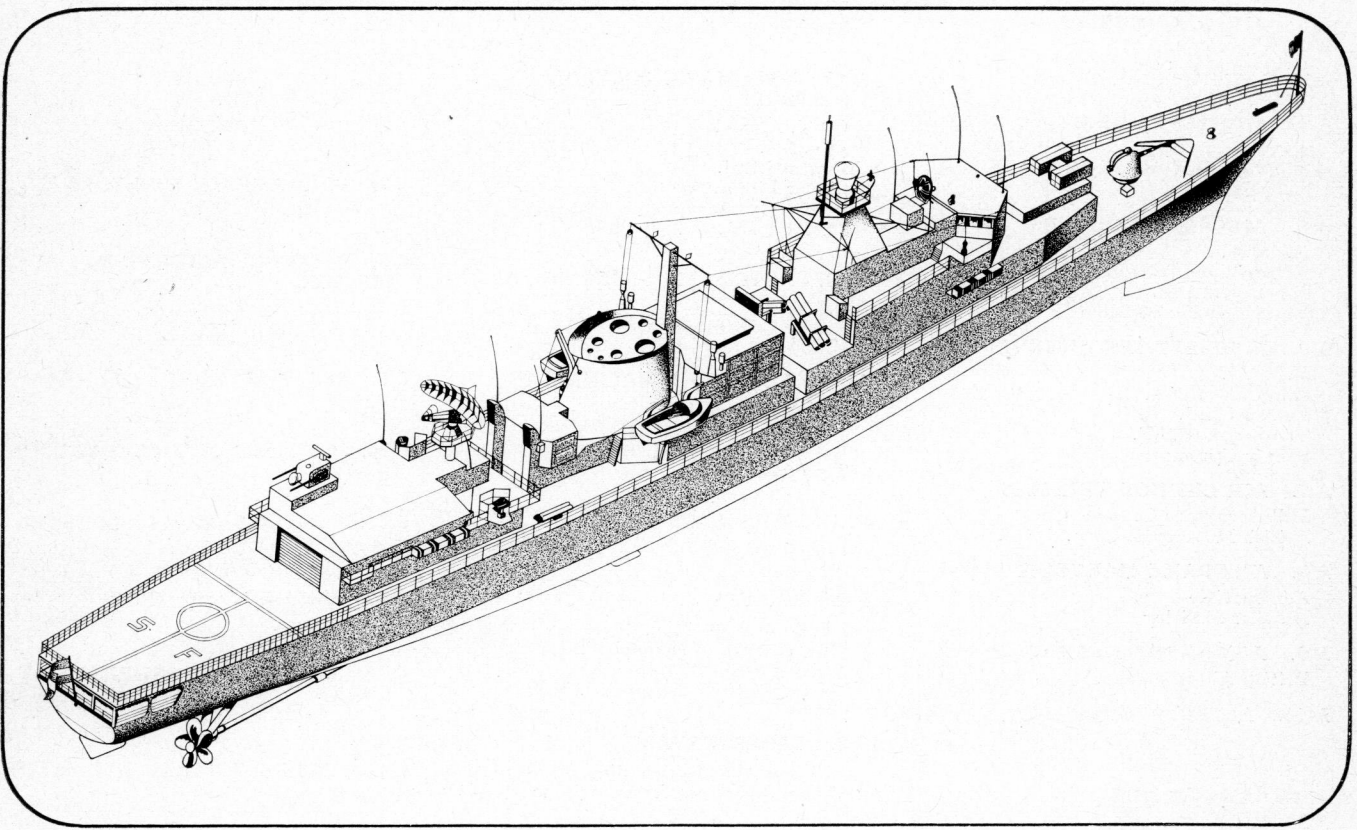

CLASSIFIED LIST OF ADVERTISERS

A 1. ACTIVE INFORMATION SYSTEMS
D.T.C.N.
Ferranti Ltd.
Singer Librascope

A 2. ACTION INFORMATION TRAINERS
Ferranti Ltd.

A 3. AIR COMPRESSORS
C.I.T. Alcatel
Split Shipyard
D.T.C.N.

A 4. AIRCRAFT ARRESTING GEAR
Aerospatiale
MacTaggart, Scott & Co. Ltd.
D.T.C.N.

A 5. AIRCRAFT CARRIERS
D.T.C.N.
Netherlands United Shipbuilding Bureaux Ltd.
Rhine-Schelde Verolme

A 6. AIRCRAFT INSTRUMENTS
D.T.C.N.
Edo Corporation
Ferranti Ltd.
Thompson C.S.F.
Sperry Gyroscope

A 7. AIR CUSHION VEHICLES
Bell Aerospace Canada
British Hovercraft Corp.

A 8. AIRFRAME MANUFACTURERS
Aerospatiale
Hawker Siddeley

A 9. ALIGNMENT EQUIPMENT
British Aircraft Corp.

A 10. ALTERNATORS
Laurence Scott & Electromotors Ltd.
D.T.C.N.

A. 11 AMMUNITION
AB Bofors
Aeromaritime Systems Limited
D.T.C.N.
Sofrexan

A 12. AMMUNITION HOISTS
Blohm & Voss AG
MacTaggart, Scott & Co. Ltd.
D.T.C.N.

A 13. ANTI-SUBMARINE LAUNCHES
D.T.C.N.
Netherlands United Shipbuilding Bureaux Ltd.
Sofrexan
Vosper Thornycroft Group, The
Brooke Marine Ltd.

A 14 ANTI SUBMARINE ROCKET LAUNCHERS
AB Bofors
D.T.C.N.
Sofrexan

A 15. ANTI-SUBMARINE ROCKETS
AB Bofors
D.T.C.N.

A 16. ARMOUR PLATES
AB Bofors
D.T.C.N.

A 17. ASSAULT CRAFT
Blohm & Voss AG
British Hovercraft Corp.
Brooke Marine Ltd.
Cammenga Jachtbouw B.V.
David Cheverton
D.T.C.N.
Vosper Thornycroft Group, The
Netherlands United Shipbuilding Bureaux Ltd.

A 18. ASSAULT SHIPS
Blohm & Voss AG
Brooke Marine Ltd.
David Cheverton
D.T.C.N.
Netherlands United Shipbuilding Bureaux Ltd.
Sofrexan
Vosper Thornycroft Group, The
Yarrow (Shipbuilders) Ltd.

A 19. AUTOMATIC CONTROL SYSTEMS
C.I.T. Alcatel
D.T.C.N.
Ferranti Ltd.
Singer Librascope
Sperry Gyroscope
Thompson C.S.F.

A 20. AUTOMATIC STEERING
C.S.E.E.
Sperry Gyroscope

A 21. AUXILIARY MACHINERY
Blohm & Voss AG
D.T.C.N.
Korody-Colyer Corporation
Termomeccanica

B. 1 BINOCULARS
Barr & Stroud

B 2. BOILERS
Blohm & Voss AG
Howaldtswerke-Deutsche Werft
Rhine-Schelde Verolme
Yarrow (Shipbuilders) Ltd.

B 3. BOOKS (NAVAL)
I.P.C. Business Press Limited
Vosper Thornycroft Group, The

B. 4 BULK CARRIERS
Blohm & Voss AG
David Cheverton
Dubigeon Normandie
Fr. Lürssen Werft
Howaldtswerke-Deutsche Werft
Rhine-Schelde Verolme
Sippican Oceanographic Systems
Split Shipyards

B 5. OCEANOGRAPHIC ELECTRONIC SYSTEMS
Sippican Oceanographic Systems

C 1. CABLE LOOMS (WITH OR WITHOUT)

C 2. CAISSONS
Brooke Marine Ltd.
D.T.C.N.

C 3. CAPSTANS AND WINDLASSES
MacTaggart, Scott & Co. Ltd.
Riva Calzoni

C 4. CAR FERRIES
Bell Aerospace Canada
Blohm & Voss AG
British Hovercraft Corp. Ltd.
Brooke Marine Ltd.
David Cheverton
D.T.C.N.
Dubigeon Normandie
Fr. Lürssen Werft
Rhine-Schelde Verolme
Yarrow (Shipbuilders) Ltd.

C 5. CARGO HANDLING EQUIPMENT
Blohm & Voss AG
D.T.C.N.
MacTaggart, Scott & Co. Ltd.

C 6. CARGO SHIPS
Batservice Verft A/S
Blohm & Voss AG
Brooke Marine Ltd.
David Cheverton
D.T.C.N.
Dubigeon Normandie
Fr. Lürssen Werft
Howaldtswerke-Deutsche Werft
Rhine-Schelde Verolme

C 7. CARGO SPACE MONITORS
D.T.C.N.

C 8. CASTINGS, ALUMINIUM-BRONZE
D.T.C.N.
Rhine-Schelde Verolme

C 9. CASTINGS, HIGH DUTY IRON
D.T.C.N.

C 10. CASTINGS, NON-FERROUS
D.T.C.N.

C 11. CASTINGS, SHELL, MOULDED
D.T.C.N.

C 12. CASTINGS, S.G, IRON
D.T.C.N.

C 13. CASTINGS, S.G. NI-RESIST IRON
D.T.C.N.

C 14. CASTINGS, STEEL
AB Bofors
D.T.C.N.
Rhine-Schelde Verolme

C 15. CATHODIC PROTECTION EQUIPMENT
Marconi Radar Systems Ltd.
Thomson C.S.F.

C 16. CENTRALISED AND AUTOMATIC CONTROL
C.I.T. Alcatel
D.T.C.N.
Thomson C.S.F.

C 17. COASTAL AND INSHORE MINESWEEPERS
Batservice Verft A/S
Bell Aerospace Canada
British Hovercraft Corp.
Brooke Marine Ltd.
Netherlands United Shipbuilding Bureaux Ltd.
Rhine-Schelde Verolme
Sperry Gyroscope
Yarrow (Shipbuilders) Ltd.

C 18. COMPRESSED AIR STARTERS FOR GAS TURBINES AND DIESEL ENGINES
D.T.C.N.
Hatch & Kirk
Korody Colyer Corporation

C 19. COMPRESSORS
C.I.T. Alcatel
D.T.C.N.
Rhine-Schelde Verolme
Split Shipyard

CH-BAC
VOYAGEUR

Designers and Builders of Specialised Ships and Naval Vessels for British, Commonwealth and Foreign Navies.

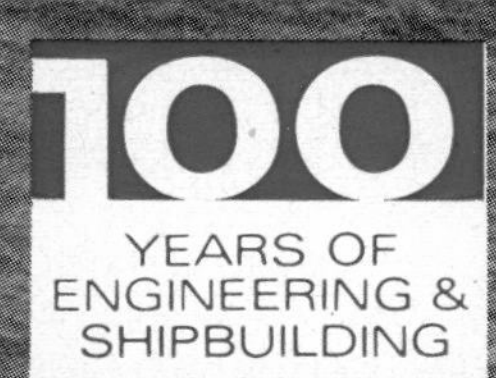

37·5 metre Fast Patrol Craft for undisclosed owners.

33 metre Fast Patol Craft for the Pakistan Navy.

37·5 metre Fast Patrol Craft for the Sultanate of Oman.

33 metre Fast Patrol Craft for the Libyan Arab Republic Navy.

G 16. GUN BOATS
Batservice Verft A/S
Bell Aerospace Canada
Brooke Marine Ltd.
Cammenga Jachtbouw BV
D.T.C.N.
Fairey Marine Ltd.
Fr. Lürssen Werft
Netherlands United Shipbuilding Bureaux Ltd.
L. Rodriquez Shipyard
Sofrexan
Vosper Thornycroft Group, The
Yarrow (Shipbuilders) Ltd.

G 17. GUNS AND MOUNTINGS
AB Bofors
D.T.C.N.
Sofrexan

G 18. GUN MOUNTS
AB Bofors
D.T.C.N.
Sofrexan

G 19. GUN-SIGHTING APPARATUS AND HEIGHT FINDERS
Barr & Stroud
Thomson C.S.F.

G 20. GYROSCOPIC COMPASSES
D.T.C.N.
Sperry Gyroscope
Thomson C.S.F.

H 1. HEAT EXCHANGERS
Blohm & Voss AG
D.T.C.N.
Hatch & Kirk, Inc.
Howaldtswerke-Deutsche Werft
Korody-Colyer Corporation
A. G. Schoonmaker Company Inc.
Split Shipyard
Yarrow (Shipbuilders) Ltd.

H 2. HEATED WINDOWS
Barr & Stroud

H 3. HELM INDICATORS
Laurence Scott & Electromotors Ltd.

H 4. HOVERCRAFT
Bell Aerospace Canada
British Hovercraft Corp.
D.T.C.N.
Vosper Thornycroft Group, The

H 5. HYDRAULIC EQUIPMENT
D.T.C.N.
MacTaggart, Scott & Co. Ltd.
Riva Calzoni
Vosper Thornycroft Group, The

H 6. HYDRAULIC MACHINERY
D.T.C.N.
MacTaggart, Scott & Co. Ltd.
Riva Calzoni

H 7. HYDRAULIC PLANT
MacTaggart, Scott & Co. Ltd.
Riva Calzoni

H 8. HYDROFOILS
Aerospatiale
Blohm & Voss AG
D.T.C.N.
Edo Corporation
L. Rodriquez Shipyard
Vosper Thornycroft Group. The

H 9. HYDROGRAPHIC SURVEY EQUIPMENT
D.T.C.N.
David Cheverton
Edo Corporation
Sofrexan
Van der Heem Electronics N.V.

I 1. INDICATORS, ELECTRIC
D.T.C.N.
Korody-Colyer Corporation
Thomson C.S.F.
Van der Heem Electronics N.V.

I 2. I.F.F. RADAR
Cossor Electronics
D.T.C.N.
Thomson C.S.F.

I 3. IFF Mk 10 SYSTEMS
Cossor Electronics Limited
Thomson C.S.F.

I 4. INFRA-RED MATERIALS
Barr & Stroud
Thomson C.S.F.

I 5. INFRA-RED SYSTEMS
Barr & Stroud
D.T.C.N.
Selenia

I 6. INJECTORS
D.T.C.N.
Hatch & Kirk, Inc.
Korody-Colyer Corporation
A. G. Schoonmaker Company Inc.

I 7. INSTRUMENTS COMPONENTS (MECHANICAL)
D.T.C.N.
Korody-Colyer Corporation
Thomson C.S.F.

I 8. INSTRUMENTS, ELECTRONIC
AB Bofors
Cossor Electronics
D.T.C.N.
Ferranti Ltd.
Sippican Oceanographic Systems
Sperry Gyroscope
Thomson C.S.F.
Van Der Heem Electronics N.V.

I 9. INSTRUMENTS, NAUTICAL
D.T.C.N.
Sperry Gyroscope

I 10. INSTRUMENT PANELS
Ferranti Ltd.
Karlskronavarvet AB
Korody-Colyer Corporation
Thomson C.S.F.
Vosper Thornycroft Group, The

I 11. INSTRUMENT, PRECISION
Barr & Stroud
D.T.C.N.
Ferranti Ltd.
Korody-Colyer Corporation
Sperry Gyroscope

I 12. INSTRUMENTS, TEST EQUIPMENT
Cossor Electronics Limited
D.T.C.N.
Ferranti Ltd.
Korody Colyer-Corporation
Selenia
Singer Librascope
Sperry Gyroscope
Thomson C.S.F.

I 13. INTERIOR DESIGN AND FURNISHING FOR SHIPS
Blohm & Voss AG
Brooke Marine Ltd.
D.T.C.N.
Rhine-Schelde Verolme
Vosper Thornycroft Group, The

I 14. INVERTERS AND BATTERY CHARGERS
D.T.C.N.
Ferranti Ltd.
Vosper Thornycroft Group, The

L 1. LAMPHOLDERS

L 2. LANDING CRAFT
Bell Aerospace Canada
British Hovercraft Corp.
Brooke Marine Ltd.
David Cheverton
D.T.C.N.
Netherlands United Shipbuilding Bureaux Ltd.
Sofrexan
Yarrow (Shipbuilders) Ltd.

L 3. LASER RANGEFINDERS
D.T.C.N.
AB Bofors
Barr & Stroud
Ferranti Ltd.
Selenia
Thomson C.S.F.

L 4. LASER SYSTEMS
Barr & Stroud
D.T.C.N.
Ferranti Ltd.
Selenia
Singer Librascope
Thomson C.S.F.

L 5. LIFTS-HYDRAULIC
D.T.C.N.
MacTaggart, Scott & Co. Ltd.

L 6. LIGHTS AND LIGHTING
D.T.C.N.
Rhine-Schelde Verolme

L 7. LIQUID PETROLEUM GAS CARRIERS
D.T.C.N.
Dubigeon Normandie
Rhine-Schelde Verolme

L 8. LOUDSPEAKER EQUIPMENT
Aeromaritime Systems Limited
Rhine-Schelde Verolme
Thomson C.S.F.

M 1. MACHINED PARTS, FERROUS
Blohm & Voss AG

M 2. MACHINED PARTS NON-FERROUS
Blohm & Voss AG

M 3. MAINTENANCE AND REPAIR SHIPS
Brooke Marine Ltd.
Dubigeon Normandie
Fr. Lürssen Werft
Rhine-Schelde Verolme
Sofrexan
Vosper Thornycroft Group, The

M 4. MARINE ARCHITECTS
Brooke Marine Ltd.
D.T.C.N.
Ingenieurkontor Lübeck
Netherlands United Shipbuilding Bureaux Ltd.
Rhine-Schelde Verolme
Vosper Thornycroft Group, The

M 5. MARINE FUELS AND LUBRICANTS

M 6. MARINE ENGINE MONITORING AND DATA RECORDING SYSTEM
Decca Radar Ltd.

M 7. MARINE RADAR
Decca Radar Ltd.
D.T.C.N.
Hollandse Signaalapparaten B.V.
Selenia
Sofrexan
Thomson C.S.F.

M 8. MATERIALS HANDLING EQUIPMENT
D.C.T.N.
MacTaggart, Scott & Co. Ltd.

M 9. MERCHANT SHIPS
Blohm & Voss AG
Brooke Marine Ltd.
D.T.C.N.
Dubigeon Normandie
Fr. Lürssen Werft
Rhine-Schelde Verolme
Split Shipyard

M 10. MICROPHONE EQUIPMENT
C.I.T. Alcatel
D.T.C.N.
Thomson C.S.F.

M 11. MINELAYERS
Blohm & Voss AG
Brooke Marine Ltd.
D.T.C.N.
Dubigeon Normandie
Netherlands United Shipbuilding Bureaux Ltd.
Rhine-Schelde Verolme
Sofrexan
Vosper Thornycroft Group, The

M 12. MINESWEEPERS
Batservice Verft A/S
Blohm & Voss AG
British Hovercraft Corp.
Brooke Marine Ltd.
D.T.C.N.
Edo Corporation
Netherlands United Shipbuilding Bureaux Ltd.
Sofrexan
Sperry Gyroscope
Thomson C.S.F.
Vosper Thornycroft Group, The
Rhine-Schelde Verolme

M 13. MISSILE CONTROL SYSTEMS
Aerospatiale
C.I.T. Alcatel
D.T.C.N.
Ferranti Ltd.
Selenia
Singer Librascope
Sperry Gyroscope
Thomson C.S.F.

M 14. MISSILE INSTALLATIONS
Aerospatiale
British Aircraft Corporation
C.S.E.E.
D.T.C.N.
Selenia
Thomson C.S.F.

M 15. MISSILE LAUNCHING SYSTEMS
Aerospatiale
British Aircraft Corporation
C.I.T. Alcatel
D.T.C.N.
Selenia
Singer Librascope
Sofrexan

M 16. MISSILE SHIPS
Blohm & Voss AG
British Hovercraft Corp.
Brooke Marine Ltd.
D.T.C.N.
Fr. Lürssen Werft
Netherlands United Shipbuilding Bureaux Ltd.
Rhine-Schelde Verolme
Sofrexan
Vosper Thornycroft Group, The
Yarrow (Shipbuilders) Ltd.

M 17. MODEL MAKERS AND DESIGNERS
Ingenieurkontor Lübeck
Netherlands United Shipbuilding Bureaux Ltd.
Split Shipyard
Vosper Thornycroft Group, The
Yarrow (Shipbuilders) Ltd.

M 18. MODEL TEST TOWING TANK SERVICE
D.T.C.N.

M 19. MOTOR CONTROL GEAR
Korody-Colyer Corporation
Thomson C.S.F.

M 20. MOTOR STARTERS
Hatch & Kirk, Inc.
Korody-Colyer Corporation
Thomson C.S.F.

M 21. MOTOR TORPEDO BOATS
Batservice Verft A/S
Brooke Marine Ltd.
D.T.C.N.
Dubigeon Normandie
Fr. Lürssen Werft
Sofrexan
Thomson C.S.F.
Vosper Thornycroft Group, The
Yarrow (Shipbuilders) Ltd.

M 22. MOTORS, ELECTRIC
Thomson C.S.F.

M 23. MOVING WEIGHT STABILISERS

M 24. MULTI PLAN PLUG

M 25. MINE COUNTER MEASURES
Sperry Gyroscope

N 1. NAVAL GUNS
AB Bofors
D.T.C.N.
Sofrexan

N 2. NAVAL RADAR
Cossor Electronics
Decca Radar Ltd.
D.T.C.N.
Hollandse Signaalapparaten B.V.
Selenia
Sofrexan
Sperry Gyroscope
Thomson C.S.F.

N 3. NAVIGATION AIDS
D.T.C.N.
Decca Radar Ltd.
Sofrexan
Sperry Gyroscope
Thomson C.S.F.

N 4. NIGHT VISION SYSTEMS
Barr & Stroud
D.T.C.N.
Singer Librascope
Sofrexan
Thomson C.S.F.

N 5. NON-MAGNETIC MINESWEEPERS
D.T.C.N.
Dubigeon Normandie
Netherlands United Shipbuilding Bureaux Ltd.
Rhine-Schelde Verolme
Sofrexan
Sperry Gyroscope
Vosper Thornycroft Group, The

O 1. OCEANOGRAPHIC SURVEY SHIPS
Brooke Marine Ltd.
D.T.C.N.
Netherlands United Shipbuilding Bureaux Ltd.
Rhine-Schelde Verolme
Sofrexan
Van Der Heem Electronics N.V.
Yarrow (Shipbuilders) Ltd.

O 2. OIL DRILLING RIGS
C.I.T. Alcatel
Howaldtswerke-Deutsche Werft

O 3. 'OILFREE' COMPRESSORS

O 4. OIL FUEL HEATERS
Blohm & Voss AG

O 5. OIL FUEL SYSTEMS AND BURNERS

O 6. OIL RIG SUPPLY VESSELS AND WORK BOATS
Batservice Verft A/S
Brooke Marine Ltd.
David Cheverton
Dubigeon Normandie
Yarrow (Shipbuilders) Ltd.

O 7. OPTICAL EQUIPMENT
Barr & Stroud
D.T.C.N.
Singer Librascope

O 8. OPTICAL FILTERS
Barr & Stroud
D.T.C.N.

O 9. ORDNANCE
AB Bofors
Sofrexan

P 1 PARTS FOR DIESEL ENGINES
Blohm & Voss AG
C.R.M. Fabbrica Motori Marini
D.T.C.N.
Grandi Motori Trieste
Hatch & Kirk, Inc.
Korody-Colyer Corporation
Rhine-Schelde Verolme
A. G. Schoonmaker Company Inc.

P 2. PASSENGER SHIPS
Batservice Verft A/S
Blohm & Voss AG
Brooke Marine Ltd.
D.T.C.N.
Howaldtswerke-Deutsche Werft
Rhine-Schelde Verolme
L. Rodriquez Shipyard
Split Shipyard

P 3. PATROL BOATS, LAUNCHES, TENDERS AND PINNACES
Bell Aerospace Canada
British Hovercraft Corp.
Brooke Marine Ltd.
Cammenga Jachtbouw BV
David Cheverton
D.T.C.N.
Dubigeon Normandie
Fairey Marine Ltd.
Netherlands United Shipbuilding Bureaux Ltd.
Sofrexan
Vosper Thornycroft Group, The

P 4. PERISCOPE FAIRINGS
D.T.C.N.
Edo Corporation
MacTaggart Scott Co. Ltd.

P 5. PERISCOPES
Barr & Stroud
D.T.C.N.
Sofrexan

P 6. PIPES, COPPER AND BRASS
D.T.C.N.
Rhine-Schelde Verolme

P 7. PIPES, SEA WATER
Rhine Schelde-Verolme

P 8. PIPE BENDING MACHINES

P 9. PISTONS, PISTON RINGS AND GUDGEON PINS
D.T.C.N.
Hatch & Kirk, Inc.
Korody-Colyer Corporation
Rhine-Schelde Verolme

P 10. PLOTTING TABLES
Hollandse Signaalapparaten B.V.
Sofrexan

P 11. PLUGS AND SOCKETS
Rhine-Schelde Verolme
Thomson C.S.F.

P 12. PONTOONS, SELF PROPELLED
Brooke Marine Ltd.
David Cheverton
Netherlands United Shipbuilding
Bureaux Ltd.

P 13. PRESSURE VESSELS
Netherlands United Shipbuilding
Bureaux Ltd.
Yarrow Shipbuilders) Ltd.

P 14. PROPELLENTS
AB Bofors

P 15. PROPELLERS, SHIPS'
AB Bofors
D.T.C.N.
Sofrexan
Split Shipyard

P 16. PROPELLERS, SHIPS' RESEARCH
D.T.C.N.
Vosper Thornycroft Group, The

P 17. PROPULSION MACHINERY
Blohm & Voss AG
D.T.C.N.
Korody Colyer Corporation
M.T.U. (Motoren und Turbinen Union)
Netherlands United Shipbuilding
Bureaux Ltd.
Rhine Schelde Verolme
Ruston Paxman Diesels Ltd.
Sofrexan

P 18. PUBLISHERS
I.P.C. Business Press Limited
Macdonald and Jane's

P 19. PUMPS
D.T.C.N.
Korody-Colyer Corporation
MacTaggart Scott Co. Ltd.
A. G. Schoonmaker Company Inc.
Unelec

P 20. PUMPS, COMPONENT PARTS
Korody-Colyer Corporation
A. G. Schoonmaker Company Inc.

R 1. RADAR AERIALS
British Aircraft Corp.
Cossor Electronics
D.T.C.N.
Decca Radar Ltd.
Hollandse Signaalapparaten B.V.
Thomson C.S.F.

R 2. RADAR FOR FIRE CONTROL
Cossor Electronics
Ferranti Ltd.
Hollandse Signaalapparaten B.V.
Marconi Radar Systems Ltd.
Selenia
Sperry Gyroscope C.S.F.
Thomson C.S.F.

R 3. RADAR FOR HARBOUR SUPERVISION
Decca Radar Ltd.
Hollandse Signaalapparaten B.V.
Selenia
Thomson C.S.F.

R 4. RADAR FOR NAVIGATION WARNING INTERCEPTION
D.T.C.N.
Hollandse Signaalapparaten B.V.
Selenia
Thomson C.S.F.

R 5. RADIO, AIR
R.F. Communications
Thomson C.S.F.

R 6. RADIO EQUIPMENT
D.T.C.N.
Marconi Communications Systems Ltd.
Thomson C.S.F.

R 7. RADIO TRANSMITTERS AND RECEIVERS
Ferranti Ltd.
Marconi Communications Systems Ltd.
Sofrexan
Thomson C.S.F.

R 8. RADOMES
British Aircraft Corporation
D.T.C.N.
Thomson C.S.F.

R 9. RAMJETS
Aerospatiale

R 10. RANGEFINDERS
Barr & Stroud
Sofrexan
Thomson C.S.F.

R 11. RE-ENTRY DEVICE

R 12. RELOCALISATION DEVICE
C.I.T. Alcatel

R 13. REMOTE CONTROLS
Howaldtswerke-Deutsche Werft
Thomson C.S.F.
Vosper Thornycroft Group, The

R 14. REMOTE POWER CONTROL SYSTEMS

R 15. REPLACEMENT PARTS FOR DIESEL ENGINES
Blohm & Voss AG
Chantiers de l'Atlantique
Hatch & Kirk, Inc.
Korody-Colyer Corporation
MacTaggart Scott Co. Ltd.
Rhine-Schelde Verolme
A. G. Schoonmaker Company Inc.

R 16. RESEARCH SHIPS
Bell Aerospace (Canada)
Brooke Marine Ltd.
D.T.C.N.
Dubigeon Normandie
Netherlands United Shipbuilding
Bureaux Ltd.
Rhine-Schelde Verolme
Sofrexan
Yarrow (Shipbuilders) Ltd.

R 17. REVERSE REDUCTION GEARS OIL OPERATED
Hatch & Kirk, Inc.
Korody-Colyer Corporation

R 18. REVERSING ENGINES, STEAM AND AIR OPERATED

R 19. REVERSING GEARS
C.R.M. Fabbrica Motori Marini
Korody-Colyer Corporation

R 20. ROLL DAMPING FINS
Blohm & Voss AG
Vosper Thornycroft Group, The

R 21. RUDDERS
Howaldtswerke-Deutsche Werft
Rhine-Schelde Verolme
Yarrow (Shipbuilders) Ltd.

S 1. SALVAGE AND BOOM VESSELS
Brooke Marine Ltd.
David Cheverton
Netherlands United Shipbuilding
Bureaux Ltd.
Sofrexan
Yarrow (Shipbuilders) Ltd.

S 2. SCIENTIFIC INSTRUMENTS
Barr & Stroud
D.T.C.N.
Ferranti Ltd.
Thomson C.S.F.

S 3. SEALS (MECHANICAL)

S 4. SHIP BUILDERS AND SHIP REPAIRERS
Blohm & Voss AG
Brooke Marine Ltd.
Cantiere Navali Del Tirreno e Riuniti
D.T.C.N.
Dubigeon Normandie
Fr. Lürssen Werft
Howaldtswerke-Deutsche Werft
L. Rodriquez Shipyard
Rhine-Schelde Verolme
Split Shipyard
Vosper Thornycroft Group, The
Yarrow (Shipbuilders) Ltd.

S 5. SHIP AND SUBMARINE DESIGN
Brooke Mariñe Ltd.
Dubigeon Normandie
D.T.C.N.
Howaldtswerke-Deutsche Werft
Ingenieurkontor Lübeck
Netherlands United Shipbuilding
Bureaux Ltd.
Rhine-Schelde Verolme
Vosper Thornycroft Group, The

S 6. SHIP MACHINERY

Blohm & Voss AG
D.T.C.N.
M.T.U. (Motoren-und-Turbinen-Union)
Rhine Schelde Verolme
Yarrow (Shipbuilders) Ltd.

S 7. SHIPS MAGNETIC COMPASS TEST TABLES

Barr & Stroud

S 8. SHIP STABILISERS

Blohm & Voss AG
D.T.C.N.
Vosper Thornycroft Group, The

S 9. SHIP SYSTEMS ENGINEERING

Alinavi
D.T.C.N.
Netherlands United Shipbuilding Bureaux Ltd.
Rhine-Schelde Verolme
Singer Librascope
Vosper Thornycroft Group, The

S 10. SHIPS BRASS FOUNDRY FOR SONAR AND RADAR

C.S.E.E.
D.T.C.N.
Van Der Heem Electronics N.V.

S 11. SIMULATORS

C.I.T. Alcatel
D.T.C.N.
Ferranti Ltd.
Laurence Scott & Electromotors Ltd.
Sofrexan
Van Der Heem Electronics N.V.

S 12. SLIP RING ASSEMBLIES

S 13. SMOKE INDICATORS

Barr & Stroud
Sofrexan

S 14. SOCKETS AND PLUGS, ELECTRIC WATERTIGHT

Thomson C.S.F.

S 15. SOCKETS AND PLUGS, MULTI-PIN PATTERNS

Thomson C.S.F.

S 16. SOCKET TERMINATIONS

Thomson C.S.F.

S 17. SONAR EQUIPMENT

British Aircraft Corporation
C.I.T. Alcatel
D.T.C.N.
Edo Corporation
Hollandse Signaalapparaten B.V.
Plessey Company Ltd.
Sippican Oceanographic Systems
Sofrexan
Thomson C.S.F.
Van Der Heem Electronics Ltd.

S 18. SONAR EQUIPMENT (PASSIVE ACTIVE-INTERCEPT)

C.I.T. Alcatel
D.T.C.N.
Hollandse Signaalapparaten B.V.
Plessey Company Ltd.
Selenia
Sofrexan
Thomson C.S.F.
Van Der Heem Electronics N.V.

S 19. SONAR EQUIPMENT, HULL FITTINGS AND HYDRAULICS

C.I.T. Alcatel
D.T.C.N.
Plessey Company Ltd.

S 20. SPARE PARTS FOR DIESEL ENGINES

Blohm & Voss AG
C.R.M. Fabbrica Motori Marini
D.T.C.N.
Grandi Motori Trieste
Hatch & Kirk, Inc.
Korody-Colyer Corporation
Rhine Schelde Verolme
A. G. Schoonmaker Company Inc.

S 21. SPEED BOATS

Batservice Verft S/A
Bell Aerospace Canada
Brooke Marine Ltd.
Cammenga Jachtbouw B.V.
David Cheverton
D.T.C.N.
Fairey Marine Ltd.
Fr. Lürssen Werft
L Rodriquez Shipyard
Sofrexan
Vosper Thornycroft Group, The

S 22. STABILISING EQUIPMENT

Blohm & Voss AG
Ferranti Ltd.
Vosper Thornycroft Group, The

S 23. STABILISING EQUIPMENT FOR FIRE CONTROL

Ferranti Ltd.
Hollandse Signaalapparaten B.V.

S 24. STEAM-RAISING PLANT, CONVENTIONAL

Blohm & Voss AG

S 25. STEAM-RAISING PLANT, NUCLEAR

D.T.C.N.

S 26. STEAM TURBINES

Blohm & Voss AG
Howaldtswerke-Deutsche Werft

S 27. STEEL, ALLOY AND SPECIAL

AB Bofors

S 28. STEEL FORGINGS, PLATES AND SECTIONS, STAMPINGS

AB Bofors
Rhine Schelde Verolme

S 29. STEEL, MANGANESE, WEAR RESISTING

AB Bofors

S 30. STEERING GEAR

Rhine Schelde Verolme

S 31. STRESS RELIEVING

Yarrow (Shipbuilders) Ltd.

S 32. SUBMARINE DISTRESS BUOY

Barr & Stroud
D.T.C.N.
Sofrexan
Thomson C.S.F.

S 33. SUBMARINE FIRE CONTROL

C.I.T. Alcatel
D.T.C.N.
Singer Librascope
Sofrexan
Sperry Gyroscope

S 34. SUBMARINE PERISCOPES

Barr & Stroud
D.T.C.N.
Dubigeon Normandie
Sofrexan
Thomson C.S.F.

S 35. SUBMARINES

D.T.C.N.
Howaldtswerke-Deutsche Werft
Ingenieurkontor Lübeck
Netherlands United Shipbuilding Bureaux Ltd.
Split Shipyard
Rhine Schelde Verolme

S 36. SUBMARINES (CONVENTIONAL)

D.T.C.N.
Dubigeon Normandie
Ingenieurkontor Lübeck
Netherlands United Shipbuilding Bureaux Ltd.
Rhine Schelde Verolme
Sofrexan

S 37. SUPERHEATERS

Blohm & Voss AG
D.T.F.N.
Yarrow (Shipbuilders) Ltd.

S 38. SUPPORT SERVICES

David Cheverton
Vosper Thornycroft Group, The

S 39. SURVEY EQUIPMENT

D.T.C.N.

S 40. SWITCHBOARDS

Blohm & Voss AG
Plessey Company Ltd., The
Vosper Thornycroft Group, The
Whipp & Bourne Ltd.

S 41. SWITCHBOARDS AND SWITCHGEAR

Vosper Thornycroft Group, The
Whipp & Bourne Ltd.

T 1. TACTICAL TRAINING SIMULATORS

D.T.C.N.
Ferranti Ltd.
Hollandse Signaalapparaten B.V.
Marconi Radar Systems Ltd.
Van Der Heem Electronics N.V.

T 2. TANKERS

Batservice Verft A/S
Blohm & Voss AG
Howaldtswerke-Deutsche Werft
Rhine Schelde Verolme
Split Shipyard
Yarrow (Shipbuilders) Ltd.

T 3. TANKERS (SMALL)

David Cheverton
Dubigeon Normandie
Fr. Lürssen Werft
Rhine-Schelde Verolme
Split Shipyard
Yarrow (Shipbuilders) Ltd.

T 4. TANKS, OIL AND WATER STORAGE

D.T.C.N.
Howaldtswerke-Deutsche Werft
Split Shipyard

T 5. TECHNICAL PUBLICATIONS

Vosper Thornycroft Group, The

T 6. TELECOMMUNICATION EQUIPMENT

C.I.T. Alcatel
D.T.C.N.
Sofrexan
Thomson C.S.F.

T 7. TELEGRAPH SYSTEMS

Thomson C.S.F.

T 8. TELEMOTORS

D.T.C.N.

T 9. TELEPHONES, BATTERY-LESS

T 10. TELEPHONES, LOUD-SPEAKING

T 11. TENDERS

Blohm & Voss AG
Brooke Marine Ltd.
David Cheverton
Fr. Lürssen Werft
Netherlands United Shipbuilding Bureaux Ltd.
Vosper Thornycroft Group, The

T 12. TEST EQUIPMENT FOR FIRE CONTROL SYSTEMS

Hollandse Signaalapparaten N.V.
Singer Librascope
Thomson C.S.F.

T 13. TEXTILE FIBRES

D.T.C.N.

T 14. TORPEDO CONTROL SYSTEMS

C.I.T. Alcatel
D.T.C.N.
Hollandse Signaalapparaten N.V.
Sofrexan
Sperry Gyroscope
Thomson C.S.F.

T 15. TORPEDO CRAFT BUILDERS

Batservice Verft A/S
Brooke Marine Ltd.
C.I.T. Alcatel
D.T.C.N.
Netherlands United Shipbuilding Bureaux Ltd.
Vosper Thornycroft Group, The
Yarrow (Shipbuilders) Ltd.

T 16. TORPEDO DEPTH AND ROLL RECORDERS

Barr & Stroud
D.T.C.N.

T 17. TORPEDO ORDER AND DEFLECTION CONTROL

C.I.T. Alcatel
D.T.C.N.

T 18. TORPEDO SIDE-LAUNCHERS

C.I.T. Alcatel
D.T.C.N.
Sofrexan

T 19. TORPEDOES AND TORPEDO TUBES

D.T.C.N.
Plessey Company Ltd.
Sofrexan

T 20. TRAINING EQUIPMENT

C.I.T. Alcatel
D.T.C.N.
Ferranti Ltd.
Hollandse Signaalapparaten B.V.
Sofrexan
Van Der Heem Electronics N.V.

T 21. TRAWLERS

Brooke Marine Ltd.
David Cheverton
D.T.C.N.
Dubigeon Normandie
Yarrow (Shipbuilders) Ltd.

T 22. TUGS

Brooke Marine Ltd.
David Cheverton
Dubigeon Normandie
Yarrow (Shipbuilders) Ltd.

T 23. TURBINE GEARS

D.T.C.N.

T 24. TURBINES

Blohm & Voss AG
D.T.C.N.
Yarrow (Shipbuilders) Ltd.

T 25. TURBINES, EXHAUST

D.T.C.N.

T 26. TURBINES, GAS MARINE

D.T.C.N.
Yarrow (Shipbuilders) Ltd.

T 27. TURBINES, STEAM MARINE

Blohm & Voss AG
D.T.C.N.
Yarrow (Shipbuilders) Ltd.

U 1. UNDERWATER LIGHTS

Sofrexan

U 2. UNDERWATER TELEVISION EQUIPMENT

Edo Corporation
Sofrexan
Thomson C.S.F.

V 1. VALVES AND COCKS

Cockburns Ltd.
Split Shipyard

V 2. VALVES AND COCKS, HYDRAULICS

Cockburns Ltd.
MacTaggart, Scott & Co. Ltd.
Split Shipyard

V 3. VALVES, AUTOMATIC PLATE OR DISC

Cockburns Ltd.

V 4. VALVES, BUTTERFLY FLUID AND VENTILATION

D.T.C.N.
Cockburns Ltd.

V 5. V/STOL AIRCRAFT

Hawker Siddeley

V 6. VOLTAGE REGULATORS, AUTOMATIC

D.T.C.N.
Ferranti Ltd.
Korody-Colyer Corporation

W 1. WARSHIP REPAIRERS

AB Bofors
Brooke Marine Ltd.
D.T.C.N.
Fr. Lürssen Werft
Howaldtswerke-Deutsche Werft
Netherlands United Shipbuilding Bureaux Ltd.
Rhine-Schelde Verolme
Vosper Thornycroft Group, The
Yarrow (Shipbuilders) Ltd.

W 2. WARSHIPS

Blohm & Voss AG
Brooke Marine Ltd.
D.T.C.N.
Fr. Lürssen Werft
Netherlands United Shipbuilding Bureaux Ltd.
Rhine-Schelde Verolme
Sofrexan
Vosper Thornycroft Group, The
Yarrow (Shipbuilders) Ltd.

W 3. WATER TUBE BOILERS

Blohm & Voss AG
D.T.C.N.
Rhine-Schelde Verolme
Yarrow (Shipbuilders) Ltd.

W 4. WEAPON SYSTEMS

AB Bofors
Aerospatiale
D.T.C.N.
Ferranti Ltd.
Hollandse Signaalapparaten B.V.
Plessey Company Ltd.
Selenia
Sofrexan
Sperry Gyroscope
Thomson C.S.F.
Vosper Thornycroft Group, The

W 5. WEAPON SYSTEMS (SONAR COMPONENTS)

D.T.C.N.
Edo Corporation
Plessey Company Ltd.
Sippican Oceanographic Systems
Sofrexan
Thomson C.S.F.
Van Der Heem Electronics N.V.
Vosper Thornycroft Group, The

W 6. WELDING, ARC, ARGON ARC OR GAS

D.T.C.N.
Rhine-Schelde Verolme
Yarrow (Shipbuilders) Ltd.

W 7. WINCHES

MacTaggart, Scott & Co. Ltd.

X 1. X-RAY WORK

Split Shipyard

Y 1. YACHTS (POWERED)

Brooke Marine Ltd.
David Cheverton
Cammenga Jachtbouw B.V.
Dubigeon Normandie
Fairey Marine Ltd.
Fr. Lürssen Werft
Vosper Thornycroft Group, The
Yarrow (Shipbuilders) Ltd.

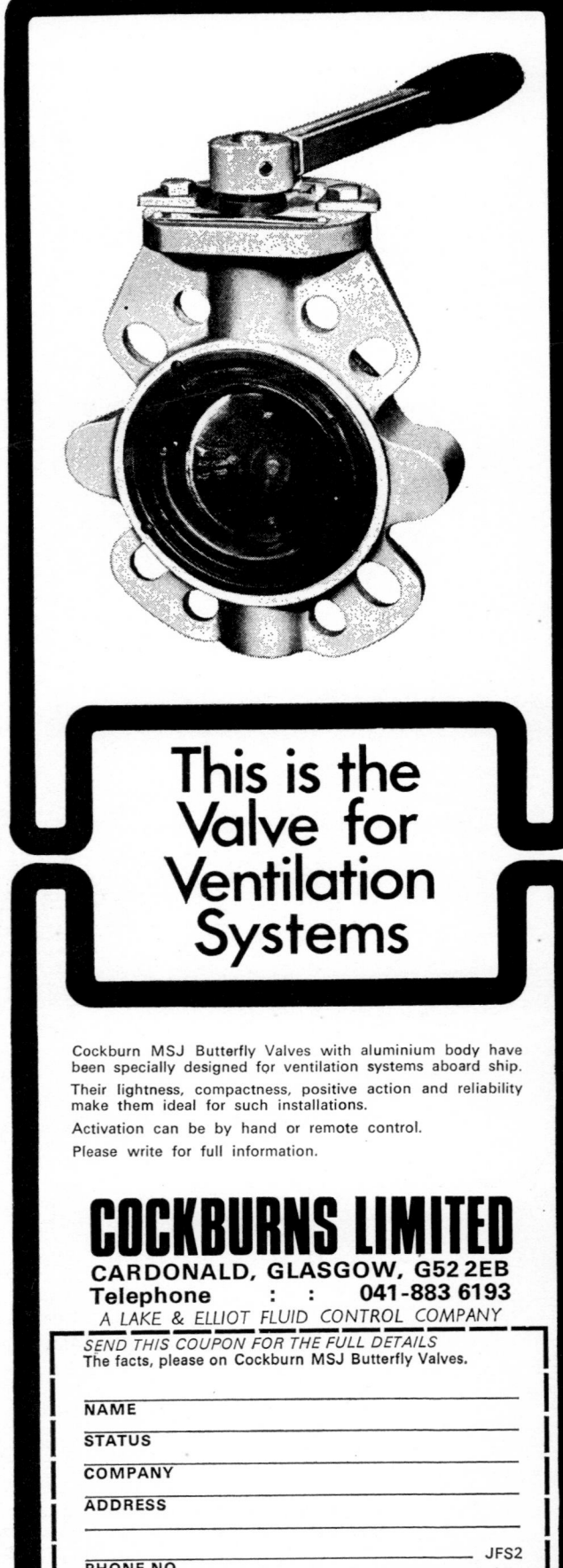

Some things ...like Edo excellence ...never change

In 1935 Edo floats crossed Antarctica with Bernt Balchen on Lincoln Ellsworth's Polar Star. Today, Edo sonar routinely dives under the Polar ice cap aboard the nuclear submarines of the U.S. Navy. In 46 years our standard of excellence has never been lowered ... in Edo systems developed for antisubmarine warfare, oceanography, mine countermeasures, strike warfare, airborne navigation, hydrodynamics and airframes, command and control. And speaking of sonar, sonar designed and built by Edo is standard equipment aboard all the nuclear-powered submarines of the U.S. Navy and many of our modern destroyers.

Edo EDO Corporation
College Point, N.Y. 11356

Harrier

The V/STOL Harrier has landed and taken off from a wider range of ships than any other fixed-wing aircraft. Here are just some of them.

The implications for maritime tactics are enormous – because Harrier puts combat jet power within reach of more

Carriers.

seaborne forces than ever before.

At sea, or on land, Harrier changes everything.

1 *Foch,* France. 27,300 tons.
2 *Guam,* U.S.A. 18,300 tons.
3 *Jeanne d'Arc,* France. 12,365 tons.
4 *Blake,* Great Britain. 12,100 tons.
5 *Dedalo,* Spain. 15,800 tons.
6 *25 de Mayo,* Argentina. 19,900 tons.
7 *Green Rover,* Great Britain. 11,520 tons.
8 *Andrea Doria,* Italy. 6,500 tons.

HAWKER SIDDELEY AVIATION

Kingston upon Thames, England
Hawker Siddeley Group supplies mechanical, electrical and aerospace equipment with world-wide sales and service.

TRITON radar antenna surveillance,
radar of VEGA system.

VEGA

Surveillance and Weapon Control System for Surface Fighting Ships

MISSIONS

- □ Surface and air surveillance
- □ Display and exploitation of ECM data
- □ Designation of surface and air targets
- □ Control of Weapons:
  - all-calibre guns (against surface, air or shore targets)
  - surface-to-surface missiles such as EXOCET and OTOMAT
  - torpedoes
  - surface-to-air missiles (SEA-CAT, SEA-SPARROW, CROTALE)

DESIGN

- □ Modularity allowing to select the configuration best fit for the ship's mission and armament
- □ Effective antijamming protection
- □ Perfect adaptation to modern operational requirements
- □ Ease of use
- □ High reliability and maintainability

THOMSON-CSF

DIVISION RADARS DE SURFACE
1, RUE DES MATHURINS / B.P. 10
92222 BAGNEUX / FRANCE / TÉL. 655.11.22

1970

We predict that you'll need this sound ray path analyser for Sonar operations.

The SPI-03 is efficient, reliable and, above all, versatile. Use it to predict the optimum mode for fixed transducer operation and VDS transducer depth for surface ships: to predict optimum listening and escape depths for submarines: to predict optimum transducer depths for helicopters and effective operating areas for sonobuoys. As a trainer, use it to teach sonar operators in acoustic ray path relationship.

CONVERGENCE ZONE

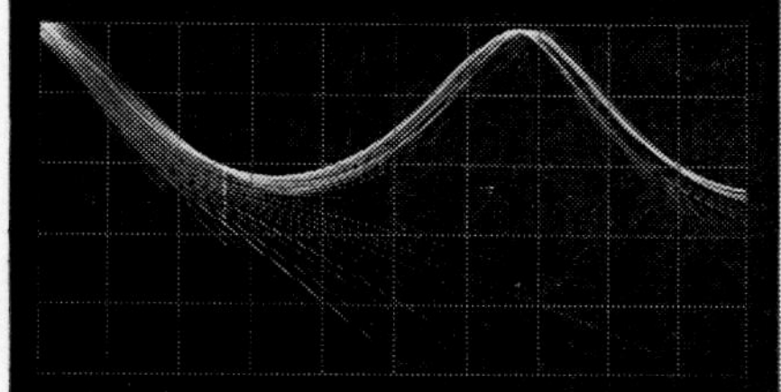

Bottom reflections off

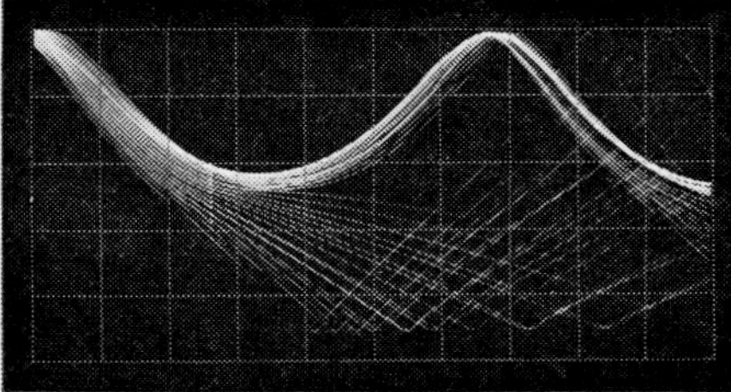

Bottom reflections on

PREDICTION FOR VDS ADJUSTMENT

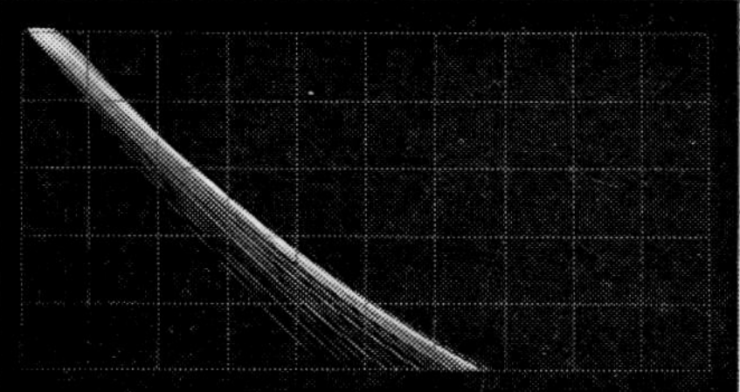

Hull mounted sonar

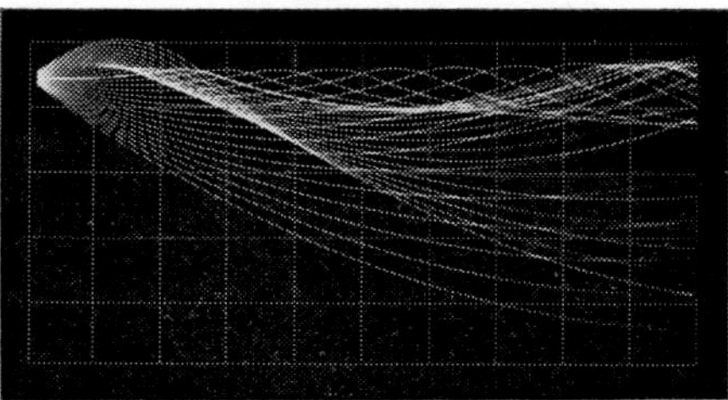

Variable depth sonar, same conditions

SOUND CHANNELS

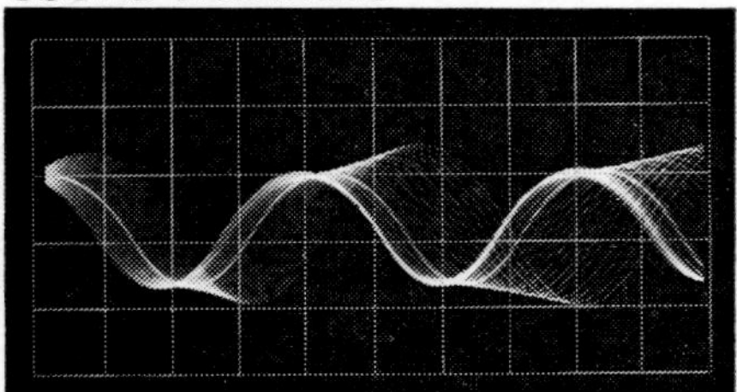

Deep sound channel

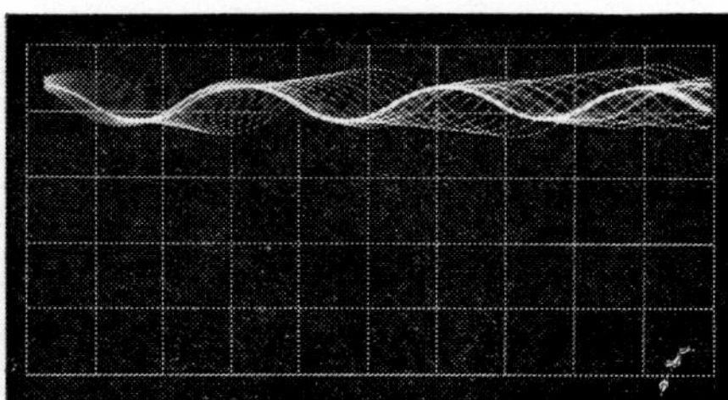

Shallow sound channel

It features:

7 in x 3½ in sound ray path CRT display
5 adjustable water layers and constant gradient in the sixth or bottom layer
maximum calculation time 74ms.
adjustable beam widths from 5° - 40°
5-position test switch
easy alignment and maintenance
compact construction
all solid state.

For full details, please ask for our SPI-03 leaflet.

Program:

- Sound ray path analysers
- Sonar
- Shipborne simulators
- Shorebased training systems
- Echo sounders
- Sub bottom profilers

sonar systems

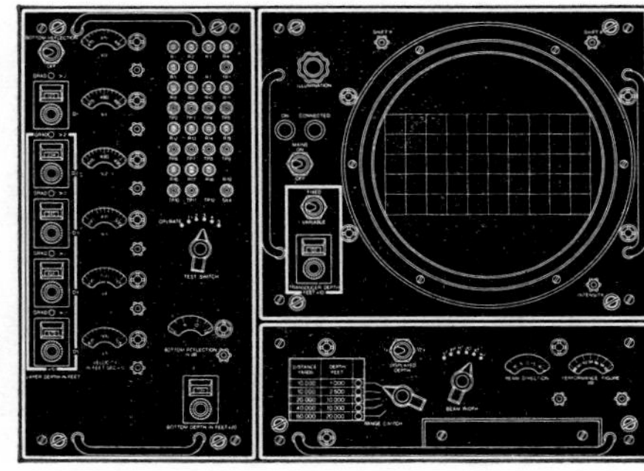

VAN DER HEEM ELECTRONICS B.V.
P.O. BOX 1060, THE HAGUE,
THE NETHERLANDS

A MEMBER OF THE
PHILIPS GROUP OF COMPANIES

H2

Paxman Power. Serving 42 navies.

Paxman Ventura and Valenta high-speed, lightweight diesels provide main propulsion or auxiliary power in a wide range of warships in service with 42 navies.
Built to the most rigorous standards, they meet ASR requirements and range in output from 750 to 4,000 reliable brake horsepower.
For more information, write now for details.

Paxman power

Ruston Paxman Diesels Limited
Paxman Works
Hythe Hill, Colchester
Essex CO1 2HW
Tel: 0206 5151

ORION RTN 10 X
pulse radar for
naval fire control systems
First introduced in 1959, the fire control radars of the fast growing ORION family are now in operational use with several Navies.
The RTN-10X is the latest model of this highly successful series of radars, incorporating state-of-the-art technologies and offering optimal operational efficiency. The RTN-10X is now in large scale production for various Navies.
Continuous development effort ensures that the ORION family keeps abreast with new operational requirements.
Retrofit kits have also been developed for the RTN-10X to update the facilities of the equipment already in service.
SELENIA
INDUSTRIE ELETTRONICHE ASSOCIATE S.p.A.
Missile and Avionic Systems Division
Via Tiburtina Km. 12,400 ROME ITALY
AN IRI-STET GROUP COMPANY

WHIPP and BOURNE

2,000 Amp 'IFA'
Loose Circuit Breaker

the BIG name in switchgear

When it comes to switchgear our name stands out above all others. We may not be the largest company but our reputation for reliability is second to none.

Whipp & Bourne High Fault Level Heavy Current 415 Volt AIR CIRCUIT BREAKERS are designed for use in Industry, Power Stations, Marine, Chemical, Steel Works and Traction application.

With a breaking capacity up to 57MVA and a current rating up to 4,000 amperes they can be supplied as loose circuit breakers or as complete switchboards to comply with relevant B.S. specifications.

Whipp & Bourne switchgear is thoroughly checked right through from first design to final installation to give you switchgear you can rely on.

2,000 Amp A.C.
Breaker Tilted

Write for technical literature:
Whipp & Bourne Ltd.
Castleton, Rochdale,
Lancashire, England.
Telephone: Rochdale 32051 (10 lines)
Telex: 63442
(Whipborn, Casltn.)

THE SUBMARINES

BUILT BY
SHIPYARD •SPLIT•
SPLIT - YUGOSLAVIA

Metastream main propulsion couplings are being fitted to Type 21 and Type 42 machinery and will also be fitted to the future advanced fighting ships. They accommodate misalignment due to thermal expansion, hull flexure and distortion from underwater shock. The non-lubricated dry couplings maintain their high degree of dynamic balance, minimising vibration in high speed and arduous conditions.

The world's first all gas-turbine major warship, H.M.S. Exmouth, uses Metastream couplings in her main propulsion machinery of two Proteus and one Olympus gas turbines.

Metastream flexible couplings are also used in:

ROYAL NAVY *G.P. Frigates, One gas and one steam turbine. H.M.S. Zulu, Nubian, Gurkha, Eskimo, Tartar, Ashanti, Mohawk. G.M.D. Destroyers. Four gas and four steam turbines. H.M.S. London, Hampshire, Kent, Devonshire, Fife, Glamorgan. Type 82 Destroyer. Two steam and two Olympus turbines. H.M.S. Bristol.*

IRANIAN NAVY *Mark 5 Frigates Olympus turbine*

LIBYAN NAVY *Mark 7 Frigates Olympus turbine*

MALAYSIAN NAVY *Yarrow Frigate Olympus turbine*

BRAZILIAN NAVY *Mark 10 Frigate Olympus turbine*

METASTREAM **flexible couplings for main propulsion machinery up to 30,000 s.h.p.**

FLEXIBOX LIMITED Nash Road, Trafford Park Manchester M17 1SS Tel: 061-872 1477 Telex: 667281

1969
YARROW
warship builders
to the
world
YARROW (SHIPBUILDERS) LTD. SCOTSTOUN, GLASGOW G14 0XN Telephone: 041-959 1207 Telex: 77357

Hoverborne Strikepower

BH.7 Mk.6

Instant Reaction — Quick Target Contact

All-weather Availability — Formidable Firepower

Equipped with surface/surface missiles and a large calibre radar-controlled gun, the 60-knot BH.7 Mk.6 provides an instant response to emergencies.

Outpacing displacement craft, it ensures quick target contact taking a direct line towards its objective regardless of reefs, shoals, sandbanks and tidal variations.

The BH.7 Mk.6 is a twin-engine development of the well-proven BH.7 already in use with the Royal Navy and Imperial Iranian Navy and it enjoys the same all-weather performance.

It also combines the high speed amphibious qualities inherent in all BHC craft with the low speed patrol performance and firepower of conventional patrol boats.

The BH.7 Mk.6 represents an invaluable asset to coastal defence forces and is now available to the Navies of the World.

Can you afford to ignore it?

For further information please contact:

british hovercraft corporation

EAST COWES · ISLE OF WIGHT · ENGLAND
Telephone: Cowes 4121

A member of the Westland Group of Companies—
5 times winner of the Queen's Award to Industry

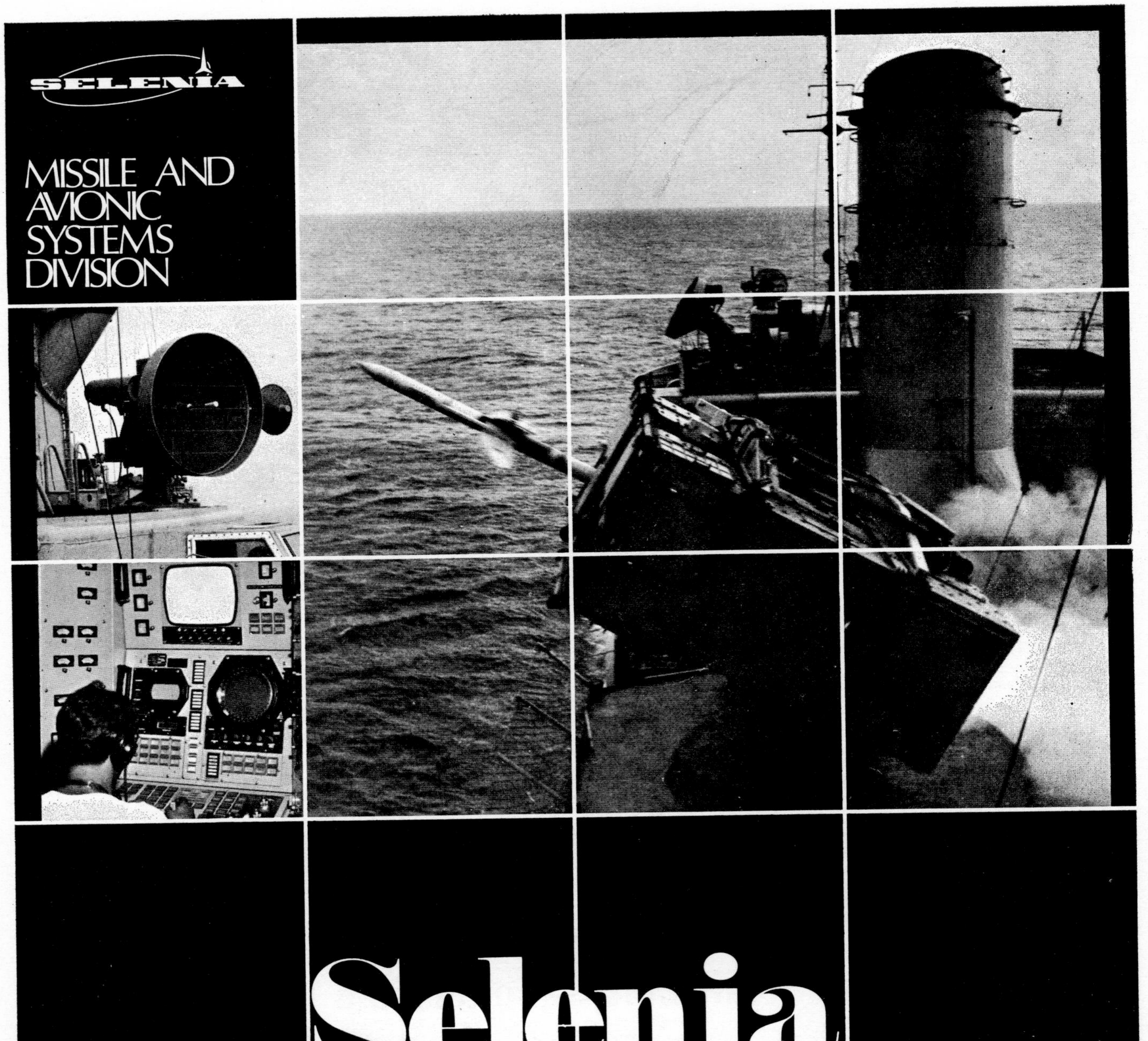

For over three decades, Librascope has helped to pioneer technological advancements in all aspects of Naval weapon systems. Our first product was an aircraft weight and balance computer for use in aircraft operation. From this beginning in mechanical linkage computers, Librascope worked with the Navy to develop electro-mechanical analog computers for Naval antiaircraft and antisubmarine weapon control systems. The alliance between Librascope and the Navy has paid off in progress. Today, virtually every ASW weapon control system installed aboard surface ships and submarines of the U. S. Navy was designed and manufactured by Librascope.

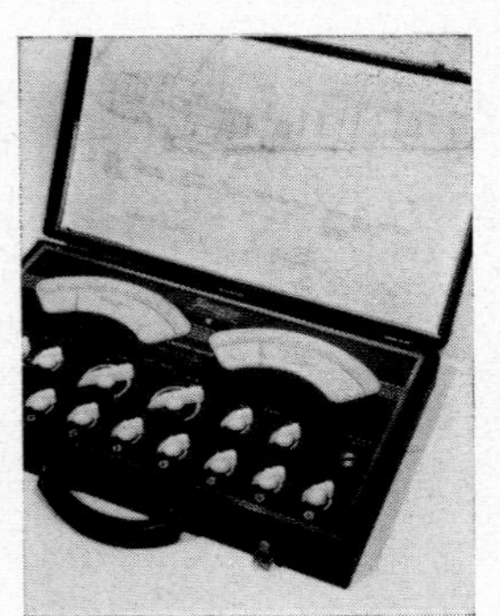

To keep pace with the rapidly

Good ideas...

OFFICIAL U.S. NAVY PHOTO

"Kara" class cruiser Nikolayev (USSR)

JANE'S FIGHTING SHIPS

FOUNDED IN 1897 BY FRED T. JANE

EDITED BY
CAPTAIN JOHN E. MOORE RN, FRGS

1974-75

I.S.B.N. 0-531-02743-0
L. of C. Cat. Card No. 74-4783

JANE'S YEARBOOKS

FRANKLIN WATTS, INC.
NEW YORK

St. Giles House, 49/50 Poland Street, London, W1A 2LG

JANE'S FIGHTING SHIPS 1974-75

EDITED BY

CAPTAIN JOHN E. MOORE

The sections on United States of America, Philippines, South Korea, South Vietnam, and Taiwan China were edited and compiled by:

NORMAN POLMAR

CONTENTS

FOREWORD

Why do nations have navies? This has been one of the recurrent queries in the large number of letters and reviews received during the last year. In the previous edition it was pointed out that the use and purpose of navies varied largely with the size, situation and interests of the countries concerned. Some governments have, despite extensive coastlines, opted for what is little more than coastguard forces. Others have put their resources into small attack-craft carrying powerful missile armaments and, therefore, capable of exercising considerable influence in restricted areas. At the back of all such thinking lies a sense of insecurity in a world rendered unstable by so many factors. Rampant nationalism, the support of murder and piracy by some heads of state, the uneasy balance between the super-powers, the problems of the supply of raw-materials and oil, the international financial position are just some of the factors contributing to this endemic unease. When this is followed by the increasing frequency of minority governments in the non-totalitarian countries, all harassed to varying degrees by the problems, both financial and social, of world inflation, the possibility of friction, internal and external, increases. No sane person would wish matters to go further but miscalculation or the opportunist actions of unskilled leaders could so easily bring about catastrophe. The mindless chanting of the inept, the deprived, the impotent masses, might well generate sufficient heat for the tinder to ignite. If this were to happen the naval participation might be of even greater importance than in the past. In the unmarked, unpopulated oceans covering three-quarters of the globe the most savage battles would affect the world's populations only by their results.

It is in this framework that we must view the world's fighting ships and hope that their presence may act as a curb and a preventive to that more violent action which could threaten all the world's population. Politicians' statements vary with situations, yet, in a naval setting, where ten years may elapse between the conception of a ship and its completion, and a further twenty before her replacement, a thread of policy must be discernible.

Of the two super-powers the more complex problem to Western observers is the Soviet Union and her sea-power. The restrained and, I hope, objective remarks made about this fleet in last year's edition were commented upon in the first-ever review accorded to "JANE'S FIGHTING SHIPS" in the Soviet press. Under the heading, "Tendentious Approach", the reviewer, Captain Shokarev, criticised those remarks for failing to emphasise the "role of the Soviet Navy in the defence of peace" and "the recognition of its noble mission by the peoples of the world". This is indeed a true statement because there is no certainty of the former and little evidence for the latter. Navies have, traditionally, except in certain sinister cases, found their main purpose in the protection of trade. In the case of the Soviet Union the expansion of their Merchant Fleet (now fifth in world ranking) preceded that of their Navy and is employed primarily as an earner of hard currency rather than as the vital life-line which such a fleet provides to many other countries. Seven years ago Admiral Gorshkov commented that, "The Soviet Navy has been converted, in the full sense of the word, into an offensive type of long-range armed force". More recently he has emphasised the role of the Navy which he commands as being, "to protect State interests on the seas". This thinking is sensibly in line with what appears to be the present-day Soviet policy of ensuring the security of the State by all means available. One of these is the possession of preponderant military forces, another the pursuit of detente, a necessary move to allay fears and to gain time. In such a pattern the increase in the Soviet Research and Development programme by well over half in the last five years makes logical sense—whereas in the West every penny for Defence has to be fought for, in the Soviets the battle appears to be more for allocation than provision. In this struggle the Navy has clearly won a very strong position and moved steadily to a position unknown fifteen years ago. Admiral Gorshkov's plans are now apparently set on the provision of a fleet for all purposes, strong in all arms, a "balanced" fleet in which due attention is given to the men as well as the ships and their weapons. With some 80% of the junior ratings being conscripts called up at 18 for a three year period, and with problems in providing adequate senior ratings, a great deal must devolve upon the officers. These form a highly trained volunteer force which, with increased deployment abroad, is clearly learning fast. Nevertheless, manpower must be a continual, and possibly increasing, problem for the High Command.

The ships they man have not changed greatly in the last year, although they remain a very powerful fighting force, amply justifying Admiral Gorshkov's seven-year-old claim. The next few months will see the emergence of *Kiev*, a ship with all outward appearance of being an aircraft-carrier, yet classified by Captain Shokarev as an anti-submarine cruiser. At 35,000 tons she must be the largest cruiser ever built, and the strictures on aircraft-carriers' movements through the Turkish Straits, as laid down in the Montreux Convention, come rather unkindly to mind. With a capability for operating both VTOL aircraft and helicopters, she will provide a much-needed strengthening of the "balance" in the Soviet fleet.

To provide *Kiev* with support in a task-force is the "Kara" class cruiser of 10,000 tons and the increasing number of "Krivak" class destroyers The first of these, *Nikolayev*, is a cruiser of formidable power with her own helicopter and double the strength of missile-power possessed by the "Krivaks". A single vessel of the "Kara" class could well engage a squadron of attacking aircraft—with both VDS and an A/S helicopter available she possesses a sound ability in the event of submarine attack. A "Krivak", although lacking her own helicopter, is more than a match for any Western destroyer and, in any event, could outrun anything opposed to her. *Kiev*, *Nikolayev* and a group of "Krivaks" would need a very numerous force of Western ships to oppose them.

The last year has seen the emergence of the first "Delta" class ballistic-missile submarine, and the acknowledgement of the "Delta II", a giant amongst big submarines, possibly carrying at least the accepted sixteen missiles of other submarines with this capability. These missiles, the SS-N-8, have a range of 4,200 nautical miles giving them a capability of covering the whole of North America and the rest of NATO without the parent submarine leaving the Norwegian Sea.

Much smaller than these huge craft, but showing a most interesting phase of Soviet thought are two new classes—one a nuclear boat, the other, the "Tango" class, a diesel submarine. Where these will fit into the present pattern of "Echo" class with long-range missiles, "Charlie"/"Papa" class with short-range missiles and, closer in, the torpedo-firing "Victor" class, is yet to be seen, but their existence shows a continuing desire for change and, possibly, improvement.

It is easy to prove any point by juggling the figures, but in considering the effectiveness of any fleet, figures must be considered in the context of many other factors, making the whole a very complicated equation. Men, morale, missiles, motivation, speed, range, self-protection against aircraft, missiles and submarines, submarine silence and diving depths are but some of these factors. In the Soviet surface fleet only one in five ships is missile armed but their average age is only about 8 years as compared with some 15 for the non-missile ships. In the submarine world one in four of the order of battle is nuclear-propelled but their average age is 9.5 compared with nearly 16 for the diesel boats. The missile ships and nuclear submarines provide the most formidable element of the navy but, assuming a ship's life to be about 20 years, a considerable replacement programme must be planned if the fleet's world-wide presence is to be

maintained in the future. The Soviet Navy leads the world in seaborne missile armament, both strategic and tactical, both ship and submarine launched. Their shore-based air-force is second to none, they have large mine-warfare forces and a considerable amphibious capability. Possible weak-nesses, which are certainly being most actively examined, lie in their manpower and, consequently, technical mainten-ance, submarine silencing, anti-submarine operations, ship-borne aircraft and custom-built fleet supply ships, although this last is now being remedied. Thus the Soviets possess a navy with great strengths but certain important weaknesses. They have, nevertheless, proved themselves capable of continued and world-wide presence, with all the political value which comes from this.

The other super-power Navy is the USN, whose problems have been much in the news recently. As the main implement of the Nixon doctrine there could be many calls upon it. As the predominant partner in the NATO naval forces, a partnership in which too many of the other nations are below their numerical commitments, with fleets oriented to national needs, it bears a desperately heavy burden. As the maritime guardian of a nation which annually imports some $70 billion worth of goods to satisfy both internal needs and those of its exporters it would be heavily stretched if those sea-lines were threatened. In a democratic system, with a large proportion of the population living 1,000 miles from the sea and unaware of its vital importance to their country, the obtaining of funds to provide the navy needed for these tasks is becoming increasingly difficult. The demands of other departments, social services, education, are so often seen as of far greater importance than defence in a country still heavily disillusioned by the events in Viet-Nam. All this comes at a time when the strength of the navy, in numbers of ships, has been very nearly halved in the last few years. From a fleet of near 1,000 ships in 1968 it has been reduced today to 514 as a matter of direct policy. The 2nd World War is nearly thirty years away but a large number of ships left on the strength at its conclusion are now reaching the end of their lives. Rather than expending huge sums on their rejuvenation and retention, the US Navy has made a conscious decision to dispose of the old and the less valuable, thus freeing funds for an imaginative building programme, which, in the next six or seven years, could provide a fleet more nearly adequate to its country's needs. This programme would make good the serious gap in it's surface-to-surface missile armament with the introduction of Harpoon, and would go some way to redressing its present inferior balance in nuclear submarines and would provide adequate carrier and amphibious forces to provide, as the Soviets once described it, "a guarantee against imperialistic provocations off foreign shores".

The present force goal for the Fleet Submarine (SSN) programme is 90 boats, a figure which should be reached by the early 1980's, thus leaving the USN some 30-40 submarines short of the USSR at current building rates. Replacement, a limited number of shipyards and the planned Ballistic Missile Submarine (SSBN) programme will preclude any significant increase in these numbers. The tendency has been for a steady increase in size of SSNs and, with little progress in submarine reactor design, this has resulted in a degrading of underwater performance. At present US SSNs do not possess an anti-ship-missile capability such as the USSR has had since the first "Whisky" class modifica-tion some 15 years ago but consideration is being given to the building of a class of cruise-missile boats which could well be larger than the "Los Angeles" (SSN 688) class. In the meantime a submarine version of the Harpoon missile with a maximum range of 60 miles is under development. Other plans under discussion apparently include a smaller SSN and an advanced diesel-driven boat with possible outlets in the export markets.

In the SSBN field the 41 submarines of the USN are at present armed with either Polaris or Poseidon missiles. The construction of the first of the Trident class SSBNs has been authorised, for completion probably in 1978, and with nine more to follow under current plans. The whole programme has been split into two phases, the first to provide a 3-4,000 mile missile which could be used in both Poseidon SSBNs and Trident and the second to produce a 6,000 mile weapon suitable only for the Trident class. In addition to this programme funds have been requested to design a smaller SSBN which would be needed by the 1980's to replace the then ageing Poseidon fleet.

In the surface fleet the most important programme is that of the aircraft carriers. With fourteen carriers in the list the USN is at its lowest level for twenty-five years. All these ships will have the capability for both normal fixed-wing and A/S operations, thus filling the gap left by the disposal of the specialised Anti-Submarine Carriers. By the 1980's the number of modern carriers in service will be reduced to twelve. A replacement programme for the mid-1980's (CVX) is being planned. These ships may be smaller than the current nuclear propelled carriers of the "Nimitz" class of which the third has now been authorised.

In addition to the main aircraft-carrier force eight Sea-Control Ships are planned, a recognition of the necessity to have aircraft afloat with the fleet. These ships, in some ways comparable to the escort-carriers of World War II, are planned to be single-screw 26 knot ships carrying V/STOL aircraft and helicopters in a 14,000 ton hull with a minimum outfit of weapons and sensors. At approximately the cost of one "Spruance" class destroyer these ships seem to represent a good return for their cost.

The "Spruance" class, thirty of which are due for delivery in the late 1970's do not, however, represent anywhere near such a good return for $100 million. Apparently built around the SQS-26 sonar they undoubtedly will have an anti-submarine capability but little else, lacking, in a missile age, both anti-ship missiles and long-range surface-to-air missiles. A comparison with the Soviet "Kresta II" class of approximately the same tonnage shows the "Spruance" to be outclassed in all aspects except for anti-submarine operations and the possession of gas-turbines. This is a class of highly expensive ships which only too clearly reflects the prevalent viewpoint that technology must be got to sea and used at any cost. Under such conditions the hub of all naval actions and operations, tactical thought, is at times inhibited, at others forgotten. No doubt the SQS-26 is a highly-specialised instrument, efficient so far as hull-mounted sonars can be. On the other hand it will provide the captain of a nuclear submarine, who anyhow probably possesses a speed advantage, with a highly efficient beacon for attack or evasion. With the acknowledged menace of the A/S helicopter to submarines, the "Spruance's" single LAMPS helicopter may, in fact, prove to be her most efficient weapon during the periods it is airborne.

Five more nuclear-propelled so-called "frigates" will be commissioned in the coming years, ships whose cost is now estimated at $275 million and, once again fitted with SQS-26 sonar. With an additional 3,000 tons over the "Spruance" class these two classes have the advantages of nuclear propulsion and a reasonable surface-to-air missile capability which, presumably, could operate in an anti-ship role. Unfortunately the two ships of the "California" class carry no helicopters, although the later "Virginia" class have two. It is difficult to see the justification for these ships—nuclear-propelled, they can escort the CVNs, adding marginally in the case of the "Virginias" to the latter's own helicopter potential. On their own they could be highly expensive hostages if involved with ships armed with anti-ship missiles, or determined submariners. This may be another case of the technologists overcoming the tacticians.

Another controversial design was that of the "Knox" class, known as Ocean Escorts (DE's). The first of this class commissioned in 1969 to an original design which incorpor-ated a single shaft giving barely 28 knots, a single 5 inch gun, an ASROC launcher, a DASH helicopter, and SQS-26 sonar. Subsequent modifications have provided for a Sea-Sparrow close-range AA missile launcher, the substitu-tion of a LAMPS helicopter for the unmanned DASH and, in some ships, the addition of a surface-to-surface missile capability. At a final cost of some $20 million these ships

are now becoming a more valuable addition to the fleet. As there are forty-six of them this is clearly to be hoped for by the Pentagon.

With the knowledge that a world-wide presence requires numbers, possibly at the expense of some weapon systems, the USN has requested a programme of Patrol Frigates (PF). These are smaller, less expensive ships in which greater emphasis will be laid on anti-missile and anti-ship capabilities with a saving on A/S sensors and weapons by the substitution of SQS-56 sonar for SQS-26 and the deletion of ASROC. These should provide an effective class of some 50 ships in the late 1970's and early 1980's, which, backed by Patrol Missile Boats (PHM) and the proposed 6,000 ton DGX design will provide the USN with a sound surface escort force on the sealanes and in areas of conflict.

In the amphibious role the USN has reduced from 165 ships during the Viet-Nam war to some 60 fully up-to-date vessels at the present time. New additions are 5 ships of the "Tarawa" class (LHA) which combine a full-length flight deck, a docking well for landing craft and accommodation for 1,700 troops. The USN is well provided in this respect and now that all their amphibious ships have a helicopter facility the continual problem of mine-clearance in shallow waters can be met by the embarkation of Sea-Stallion helicopters.

In a fleet which today has only ten active fleet mine-sweepers the introduction of this helicopter has been of great significance. Air transportable in C5A "Galaxies" or operable from most ships provided with helicopter facilities, they provide a highly mobile MCM force, which proved itself off North Viet-Nam in 1973.

So far we have seen the expenditure of great sums on a fleet reduced from over 900 ships to 514 today. This is the result of careful analysis which runs in tandem with an amount of original and constructive thought unusual in Western circles. Beyond the nuclear aircraft-carrier, the Sea Control Ships, the "Trident" SSBNs, the Sea Stallion helicopters, comes the challenging concept of the DSX, a surface-effect-ship of 2,000 tons. So far only two 100 ton research craft have been built—the aim is to produce a vessel with rigid sidewalls for deep-water operation which will overcome the many problems, including among others those of water-seals, control-systems and water-jet inlets thus providing the USN with a new concept of operation in all areas of naval affairs, which could place it many years ahead of any apprehended rivals. Of those countries to whom a navy is today essential the USA is one of the foremost, and the USN is probably also in the van of navies subjected to misinformed, illogical and irrational attacks by some of those who depend upon it most.

Another navy plagued by the philosophy that the majority of savings should be borne by the country's defences is Great Britain. Here, for reasons of their own, demands for a halving of defence expenditure are continually noised by the Left Wing and this, at a time of increasing instability, reflects either an inability to see the truth or a resolution to render the country helpless in the face of determined imperialism abroad, interference with fishing rights and the grab for oceanic resources. The British are rapidly reaching a position of "what we have we cannot hold", including North Sea Oil and the second largest indigenous Merchant Fleet in the World. The future of the Royal Navy is at present unknown to the public—the new Government has delayed until the autumn any definite statement on defence.

There have been few advances in the make-up of this fleet during the last year. The first "command cruiser", with a similarity to the Escort Carrier of thirty years ago and to the USN's Sea Control Ship (but costing more than twice as much as the latter), was laid down on 20th July, 1973. Whether any successors to this ship will be authorised is so far unknown—as is the possibility of a full complement of Harrier aircraft. Concurrently with this building programme run those of the Type 42 destroyers and the frigates of Types 21 and 22. As is the case with the larger ships of the USN programme these are all costly ships which, as weapon systems, compare unfavourably with those currently in production by the USSR. Although each has a single Lynx helicopter, surface-to-surface missiles are planned only for the Type 22 although the Sea Dart in the Type 42 has an alternative anti-ship capability. It appears that the Royal Navy's major problems of lack of numbers of both warships and embarked aircraft have not yet been solved. At the same time the Royal Fleet Auxiliary, PAS and RMAS are well provided to handle a considerable fleet with their traditional efficiency.

Across the Channel apparently no such inhibitions affect the naval staff. Plans announced in France this year include a nuclear-propelled aircraft carrier, a new class of nuclear Fleet submarines and, to match numbers with a world-wide role, a large programme of Type A69 and A70 avisos. Support for this fleet, growing in quantity and quality, is provided by an equivalent building plan for the support services so that, in a very few years, the French will possess the strongest fleet in Western Europe.

On either side of France there are major plans reaching maturity. West Germany's strength in submarines and missile craft is growing rapidly whilst in Spain the next five years will see her fleet augmented by a new aircraft-carrier, missile-armed destroyers and fast-attack-craft, corvettes and patrol craft. These are realistic programmes designed to modernise and augment fleets required for the protection of home-waters and their sea-lines of communication.

In the Mediterranean other countries have plans to meet the same needs—Italy, with splendid ships already at sea, is building new frigates and submarines, Greece is placing emphasis on submarines and fast-attack-craft whilst Turkey continues an all-round improvement and modernisation.

A similar emphasis on smaller craft and submarines can be seen in the Latin-American fleets whilst in the East of Suez area notable increases are taking place in the navies of the Persian Gulf. Iran, recognising the value of hover-craft, is rapidly expanding her fleet and its capabilities, and many small craft swell the numbers in her neighbours' harbours. Pakistan, too, has received fast-attack-craft from China, whilst India, in the shade of her recent successful nuclear detonation, is increasing her numbers of both British and Soviet designed ships. Four more submarines from Russia will be arriving as India discusses plans for building submarines in her own yards.

Finally, the complex situation in the Far East deserves close attention. With the approaches from the West through the Malacca Straits covered by missile-armed craft of both Singapore and Malaysia, with Australia suffering a dangerously reduced naval building programme and New Zealand barely capable of protecting her own coastline and harbours, the time for withdrawal of US land forces approaches. Many factors are intertwined in this region: the removal of American forces from South Korea and possibly Taiwan; Sino-Soviet problems on the Amur and Issuri rivers; Soviet activity on China's Western borders and in Afghanistan; the problem of oil beneath the seas surrounding China and Japan; and the still violent situation in South East Asia are but some of these. With a powerful Soviet Pacific Fleet to the North of her, China's naval building programme is hardly a surprise. With the world's largest fleet of Light Forces she is now moving fast into the field of missile-armed destroyers and frigates, giving her a deep-water capability not previously known, and a chance to demonstrate her power abroad, if this suits her policies. Her submarine programme containing not only a considerable number of new "Romeo" class commissioning each year but also with the new "Han" and "Ming" class under construction, is most impressive. The "Han", possibly nuclear-propelled, if allied to China's knowledge of missile and nuclear-weapon technology could be the precursor of a ballistic-missile submarine in the next ten years. There is no doubt that China is having, and will have, problems with such a fleet, but she has shown remarkable abilities in overcoming difficulties in the past. With her great resources and a powerful national motivation today's fleet may well be only the forerunner of one of the world's great navies of the near future.

On the farther side of the China Sea Japan is building up a

well-found, so-called "Maritime Self Defence Force". With the new ships of the "Haruna" class carrying three A/S helicopters and the "DD 168" class armed with both anti-ship and anti-air missiles, earlier deficiencies are being made good. There is still no sign, however, of any form of fighter cover beyond the range of land-based aircraft nor of the very necessary fleet support ships which the MSDF now lacks.

The Western Pacific poses many problems. They may all be resolved peacefully; even the inevitable reunion of the two Koreas might be accomplished without bloodshed, though this seems to be one of the main danger areas. If any form of conflict should break out the navies of the powers involved will certainly be in the van, for in a water world there will be much for them to do.

The world-wide picture is a sombre one, overshadowed by a universal resort to violence hitherto unequalled except in the event of a major war. The world monetary system is in jeopardy whilst inflation remains rampant and governmental funds are as hard-hit as those of private citizens. The question of availability and the cost of fossil fuels threaten the industrial capacity of the Western nations and the mobility of the fleets which protect them. Much remains to be done in the nuclear research field and its products have not yet provided the cheap power so confidently forecast some years ago. With this background the exploitation of the West's enormous coal reserves has been gravely neglected and much capital is needed to revive the mines. The costs of raw materials and the metals needed for shipbuilding have increased beyond reasonable expectation. At the same time modern technology has produced a series of devices which absorb greater and greater quantities of money and pose ever more complex problems—the nuclear propelled submarine, the missile and its controlling radars, electronic counter measures, to mention a few. At present these result in naval designs which are entirely reactive to the likely oppositions' designs. Surely what is needed is the use of that most widely-available commodity, original thought, to guide and control such technical advances. The capacity of the human mind to outwit mechanical devices is age-old—today the intelligent submariner can circumvent most sonar systems, the clever pilot most radars, the designer of propulsion equipment most power problems, the naval architect most major difficulties of ship construction. It is time, once again, for simplicity and clarity of thought to win the day, for originality to have its chance over complexity and for tactics to dictate the path of technology. The planning process in too many naval staffs is still hog-tied by institutional rigidities, a screening system more efficient than the current plethora of committees is needed to counter-balance the thrust of the technologists, systems analysis must take its proper and subordinate place to experience and understanding and navies must accept the fact that the computer should be the servant of the man.

As pointed out earlier the problems of today's navies can be listed under a few major headings. Firstly comes the over-all question of hull design and here it would seem that simplicity and innovation are needed to meet the major needs of ships of the future within the availability of funds. With manpower absorbing over half the total cost of a ship during her life the size of complements must be reduced. This can be achieved by building smaller ships with smaller control systems. These latter are already available for certain aircraft and could, with a measure of determination, be converted for maritime use. The saving of space and manpower would result in a less costly hull and a reduction in the need for power and fuel. Anti-ship and anti-aircraft missiles, a minimal gun armament and an anti-submarine capability are necessary. That missiles themselves can be mounted in small hulls has been proved in the various classes of fast attack craft, which, too, can also mount guns of adequate calibre. The anti-submarine problem has its best solution in a combination of other submarines and helicopters. Vast hull-mounted sonars absorb a high proportion of the ship's initial cost and could be replaced by the sonar capability of an air component. Space must therefore be provided for the helicopters which, even with increased availability and operating time, should be at least duplicated in each ship. From this brief review the needs are clear—a comparatively small hull whose dimensions are dictated by the need to carry at least two helicopters, armed with both types of missile and a gun, all of which would be controlled by aircraft-type systems, and freed from the enormous cost of large hull-mounted sonars. With modern materials, welding techniques and design knowledge the possibility of this ship being of a catamaran-type, thus providing a reasonable operating base for her aircraft, merits investigation. Large rigid-side-walled surface-effect ships are now on the drawing board as an alternative but may be prohibitively expensive.

A new approach to the enormously costly aircraft-carrier is needed by many navies if the essential fixed-wing aircraft are to be kept at sea in areas not covered by land-based machines. Commercial design and construction provide high-speed ships of large size with small crews for mercantile use. There seems no logical objection to the conversion of these designs for naval use—ships cheap to build and operate, with minimal sensor and weapon fits in the same manner as the USN sea control ships.

A third type of ship, smaller than the foregoing, is required for the manifold tasks continually placed upon a fleet. Once again these ships must be a compromise between adequate size for sea-keeping and the need for reduced manpower and building costs. The use of encapsulated missiles, which can be embarked when needed, would reduce maintenance problems and the need for space-saving would dictate the embarkation of only one helicopter. A number of commercial designs for such ships already exist and they would relieve the more complex and costly vessels of the many mundane duties which they now perform. Where high speed is essential, for instance in missile pickets, and should the surface-effect-ships prove too expensive, the RCN has already developed and proved a hydrofoil design in the *Bras d'Or* which would effectively meet this requirement.

Submarines have already been noted, as has the tendency for nuclear boats to increase in size because of increased sensor and weapon fits. Unless a major advance in reactor design is achieved this vicious circle of bigger boats for new and increased weapon systems, followed by larger reactors to maintain performance seems bound to continue. Smaller reactors will certainly cost more and perhaps it is this factor which is bringing the diesel-propelled submarine back into consideration in some of the major navies.

It is for submarines that the fuel-cell has often been discussed. At present insufficient advance has been made in the design of fuel-cells to make them an early contender as a means of propulsive power. But the possibilities need further examination, as do those of liquified-coal in countries dependent on external oil supplies. The USN has already carried out trials at sea with this form of fuel but little appears to have been done by other navies which are backed by large coal stocks.

This review has, it is hoped, answered the opening question of, "Why do nations have navies?" As well as what they will and could be in the future. In brief, fleets are needed in this unsettled world to protect a nation's maritime interests, be these trade-routes, oil-rigs, fishing rights or any of a dozen other matters, they are needed to protect a country's coast-line, they provide support for political actions abroad and in wartime their duty is to deny the enemy the use of the oceans whilst ensuring their availability for their own shipping. In a world of inflation and monetary instability the fleets required must be of a minimum cost concurrent with their ability to fulfil their numerous tasks. This can be achieved only by applying original thought, not only to their design, but also to their operation. The future is be-devilled by many problems, not least of which was stated by Lenin on 27 November, 1920—"As long as capitalism and socialism remain side by side we cannot live peacefully—the one or the other will be the victor in the end".

John E. Moore

ACKNOWLEDGEMENTS

In my second year as Editor more and more contributors have come forward, making my task that much easier. To all of them I am most deeply indebted, whether their information has concerned a single ship, a whole navy or wide-ranging comments on the book in its entirety. In some cases these comments have arrived too late for publication and I regret having to file them for use in the next edition, rather than include them here. Preparation for a new edition starts in December and copy is sent to the printers, in alphabetical order, from January onwards. If correspondents can meet the similar deadlines to those required of me it would be a great help. Some data and photographs are, I know, not available until later and every effort will be made to include them but such alterations are expensive and do not help in the publisher's battle to keep prices down.

As ever the Ministries in various countries have given great assistance, sometimes directly and sometimes through their attaches in London. To them all I offer my most sincere thanks. Without their aid it would be impossible to do full justice to the fleets of their countries. Conversely, there is little point in criticisms being levelled at Fighting Ships, as was done in a recent Moscow review, if the Government of that country flatly refuses its co-operation.

As always it is very difficult to single out some contributors who have rendered particularly valuable help but, if the others will excuse me and accept my deep gratitude, I must mention the following, Contre Amiral M. J. Adam CVO, CBE, Dr. Giorgio Arra, Herr Siegfried Breyer, Commander A. Fraccaroli, Lieutenant-Commander A. Hague VRD, Mr. G. K. Jacobs, Captain F. de Blocq van Kuffeler, Mr. S. L. Morison, Mr. J. S. Rowe, Mr. C. W. E. Richardson, Lieutenant Toshio Tamura, Senor J. Taibo, Mr. R. F. Winfield.

So far as the production is concerned I have had continual help from my wife whose quick eye and ready memory have frequently saved me from disaster. So too has Mrs Jean Parsons, my secretary, who has never complained at the strange requests and copy which she has had to handle. Once again the production staff of Jane's Yearbooks, led by Mervyn Worthington, have made up the book with tact and understanding whilst, in Huddersfield, the compositors of Netherwood Dalton & Co Ltd, the printers have not only deciphered the very complicated copy but have also put right a number of my errors in the galley stage.

As before the other naval annuals have played their part; *Almanacco Navale*, edited by Dr Giorgio Giorgerini and Signor Augusto Navi, *Floltentaschenbuch* edited by Herr Gerhard Albrecht, *Marinkalender* edited by Captain Allan Kull. Lastly, but for a special reason, comes *Flottes de Combat* edited for the last year by M. Henri le Masson in collaboration with M. J. Labale-Couhat. Henri le Masson's contribution to naval writings has been quite exceptional and all those concerned with Fighting Ships join his many friends in wishing him well in the future.

The United States section has been compiled by Mr. Norman Polmar for the seventh consecutive year and he has also been responsible for the sections on South Korea, Philippines, Taiwan and South Vietnam. His gratitude for providing assistance in the preparation of this edition goes particularly to Admiral Elmo R. Zumwalt, Jnr, formerly Chief of Naval Operations; Vice Admiral Frank H. Price, Jnr, Captains John W. King, Jnr, and Gerald H. Barkalow, and Lieutenant Commander William T. Dannerheim of the Ship Acquisition and Improvement Division, Office of the Chief of Naval Operations; Captain Donald Keach, Deputy Director of Naval Laboratories, Mr Robert Carlisle, Chief Yeoman H. L. Johnson, Miss Anna Urban, and Mrs Sandra Morrison of the Office of Navy Information; Mr. Richard C. Bassett and Mrs. Eleanor Prentiss of the Naval Ship Systems Command; Mr. H. A. Taylor of the Bureau of Naval Personnel; Captain Berry L. Meaux and Miss Elizabeth Segedi of the Public Information Division, US Coast Guard; Mr Raymond Wilcove of the National Oceanic and Atmospheric Administration; and especially, Messrs Samuel L. Morison, A. D. Baker III, Henri Le Masson, Stefan Terzibaschitsch, and Giorgio Arra.

Contributions for the next edition, which is already in preparation, should be sent as soon as possible to:

Captain J. E. Moore, RN,
Editor, Jane's Fighting Ships,
Elmhurst,
Rickney,
Hailsham,
Sussex BN27 1SF,
England.

THE USE OF JANE'S FIGHTING SHIPS

There have been further changes in this edition:

(a) The silhouette section has been altered to include scales and the country or countries of origin of the ships;

(b) The Type designation of ships has been simplified to provide a more ready means of comparison between navies. This has inevitably meant a designation which, from time to time, differs from that given by the ship's own navy. Where this is considered important a note has been made to that effect;

(c) The State of the Fleet has been altered to provide lists of ships in the active fleet, those under construction and those proposed;

(d) The Naval Aircraft and Missile section has been split into its main components for ease of reference.

Improvements and corrections will be found throughout the book, but as always, there is much to do and any comments and suggestions are most welcome.

John E. Moore

We put you in the precise place at the precise time

S.G. Brown and Magnavox

advanced and proven integrated navigation systems

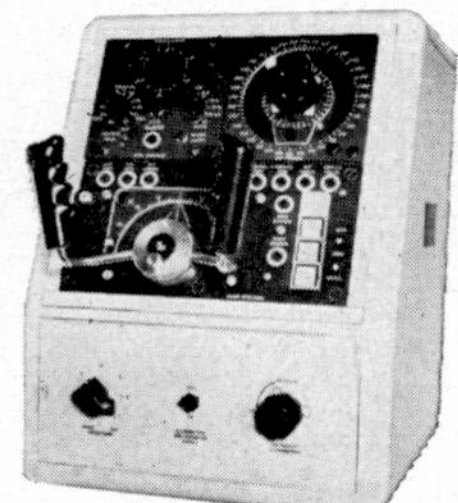

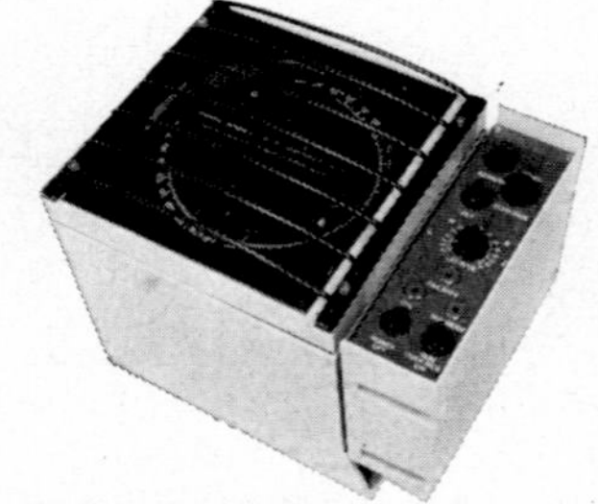

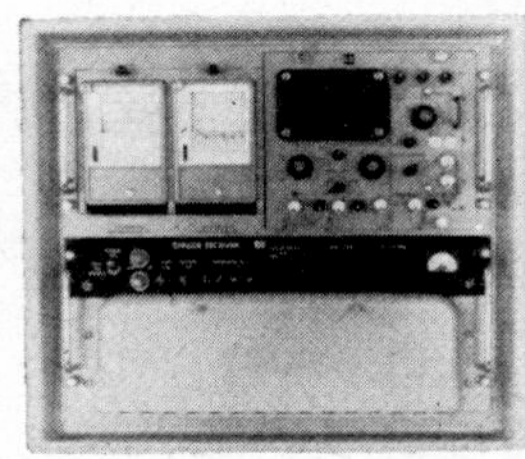

Satellite Navigation
Operational independence from shore based facilities. 24 hour day operation – up to 30 fixes per day. High accuracy fixes establishing position within 100 ft (static), 0.2 nm underway in all weather conditions anywhere in the world. Entirely automatic in operation – no operator intervention to achieve results.

Autopilot and Hand Steering
Fewer manual controls. Improved manoeuvring in autopilot mode. Weather helm automatically applied. Rudder positioning servo loop completely self-contained in steering flat. Helm demand fed to servo loop as analogue signals. Loss of any one helm demand does not affect overall rudder control.

Mk 12 Gyro Compass
Automatic start from single switching action. Low magnetic signature. Remote Control for North seeking/ directional modes. Modular construction and solid-state circuitry. Fail-safe protection circuits. Electrically independent coarse/fine synchro transmission for integrating with retransmission units for radars, direction/finders, repeaters etc.

Omega Navigation Receiver
Automatic continuous tracking position fixing. Hands-off operation. Accuracies of better than one nautical mile during day and two nautical miles at night are typical. Two chart recorders display the percentage of lane representing three lines of position from four OMEGA transmitters.

For further information contact the Marketing Manager.

HAWKER SIDDELEY

S. G. BROWN LTD.

GREYCAINE ROAD, WATFORD, HERTS., WD2 4XU, ENGLAND. Telephone: Watford 27241. Cables: Sidbrownix, Watford. Telex: 23408

Hawker Siddeley Group supplies mechanical, electrical and aerospace equipment with world-wide sales and service.

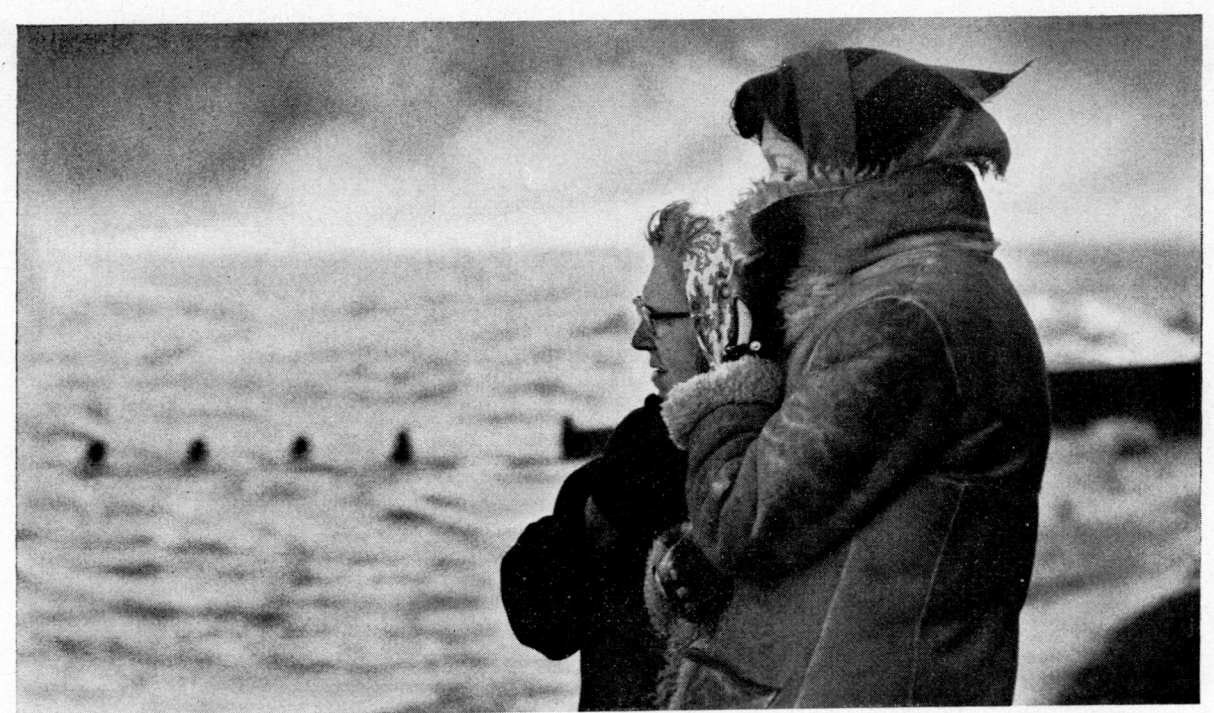

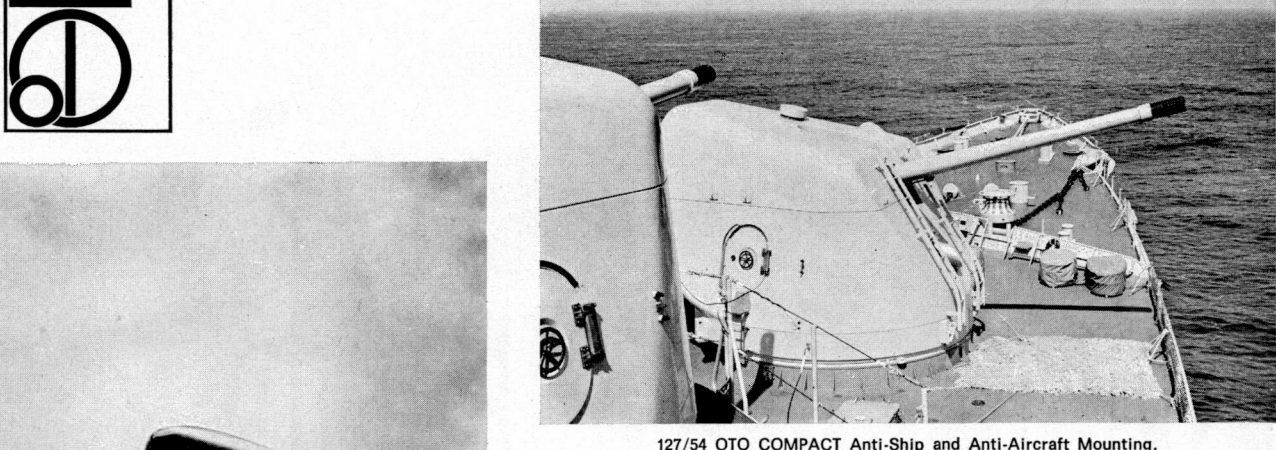

DIESEL ENGINE SPECIALISTS

SERVING NAVAL & COMMERCIAL VESSELS THROUGHOUT THE WORLD SINCE 1945

HK

HATCH & KIRK INC.

Seattle, Wash.

Shop facilities for engine rebuilding, diesel fuel injection, repair and calibration, and hydraulic governor overhaul. In addition over 60,000 square feet of covered Diesel Engine Parts warehoused to guarantee you clean, quality parts at Hatch & Kirk Inc.

Oakland, Calif.

There are over 27,000 square feet of covered Diesel Engine Parts inventoried to serve you from the Oakland warehouse of Hatch & Kirk Inc.

Wilmington, Calif.

There are shop facilities for the repair and calibration of Diesel Fuel Pumps and injectors and Hydraulic Governors. Plus over 50,000 square feet of covered Diesel Fuel Injection Parts, Governors, Bosch Electrical products at Diesel Control Inc. a division of Hatch & Kirk Inc.

Fast Efficient Service

THE LARGEST STOCKS OF DIESEL ENGINE PARTS IN THE UNITED STATES

ALCO—ATLAS—ALLIS CHALMERS (BUDA)
BALDWIN—CLEVELAND 268A, 278A, 258S
COOPER BESSEMER—ELECTROMOTIVE 567
ENTERPRISE—FAIRBANKS MORSE—GRAY MARINE (64HN9)—GM 71
MURRAY & TREGURTHA 02D—NORDBERG—PACKARD (GAS)
SUPERIOR—HILL—JOSHUA HENDY

DE LAVAL SEPARATORS & SHARPLES SEPARATORS

WOODWARD GOVERNORS & MARQUETTE GOVERNORS

REVERSE REDUCTION GEARS

FAWICK FALK—SNOW NABSTEDT (JOES GEAR)—TWIN DISC—CAPITOL

HATCH & KIRK INC.

5111 LEARY AVE. N.W. • SEATTLE, WASHINGTON 98107
PHONE (206) SU 3-2766 • TELEX 032-414

Please send me . . . . copy/copies of the 1974 Edition of the Directory of Shipowners, Shipbuilders & Marine Engineers, price £8.50 ($21.25) each inclusive of postage

☐ Remittance enclosed

☐ Please bill me/my company

Name ______________________

Job Title ______________________

Company ______________________

Address ______________________

____

____

Registered No. 113326 England.
Registered office
IPC Industrial Press Limited,
33-40 Bowling Green Lane,
London EC1R 0NE

Address to :
Sundry Sales Dept,
IPC (Sales & Distribution) Ltd,
40 Bowling Green Lane,
London EC1R 0NE

☐ I would like to subscribe to MarineWeek
Please send me details

With the Blue Book your answer is literally overleaf. The 1974 Directory of Shipowners, Shipbuilders & Marine Engineers – the first and still the best – provides the latest invaluable information you need at the turn of a page. By any other method it could take you hours. Personnel, telex numbers, shipbuilders and repairers, containerisation – even an address when all you have is a telegraphic code – It's all there, in the 1974 Blue Book.

Order Now!

your answer overleaf

in the 1974 Directory of Shipowners, Shipbuilders & Marine Engineers

It can save you hours!

Jane's Pocket Books

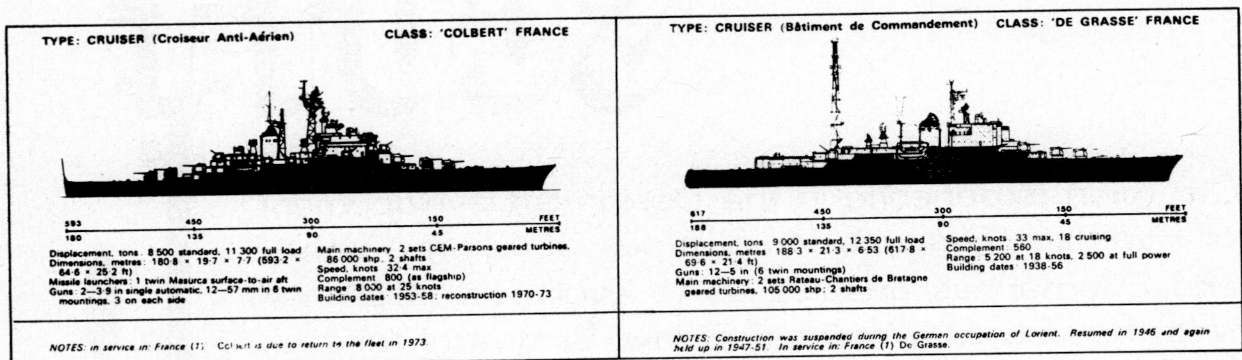

TYPE: CRUISER (Croiseur Anti-Aérien)
CLASS: 'COLBERT' FRANCE
593 450 300 150 FEET
180 135 90 45 METRES
Displacement, tons: 8 500 standard, 11 300 full load
Dimensions, metres: 180·8 × 19·7 × 7·7 (593·2 × 64·6 × 25·2 ft)
Missile launchers: 1 twin Masurca surface-to-air aft
Guns: 2—3·9 in single automatic, 12—57 mm in 6 twin mountings, 3 on each side
Main machinery: 2 sets CEM-Parsons geared turbines, 86 000 shp, 2 shafts
Speed, knots: 32·4 max
Complement: 800 (as flagship)
Range: 8 000 at 25 knots
Building dates: 1953-58; reconstruction 1970-73
NOTES: in service in: France (1). Colbert is due to return to the fleet in 1973.
TYPE: CRUISER (Bâtiment de Commandement)
CLASS: 'DE GRASSE' FRANCE
617 450 300 150 FEET
188 135 90 45 METRES
Displacement, tons: 9 000 standard, 12 350 full load
Dimensions, metres: 188·3 × 21·3 × 6·53 (617·8 × 69·6 × 21·4 ft)
Guns: 12—5 in (6 twin mountings)
Main machinery: 2 sets Rateau-Chantiers de Bretagne geared turbines, 105 000 shp; 2 shafts
Speed, knots: 33 max, 18 cruising
Complement: 560
Range: 5 200 at 18 knots, 2 500 at full power
Building dates: 1938-56
NOTES: Construction was suspended during the German occupation of Lorient. Resumed in 1946 and again held up in 1947-51. In service in: France (1) De Grasse.

All Pocket Books are $4\frac{1}{4}'' \times 7''$

Jane's Pocket Book of Major Combat Aircraft

J. W. R. Taylor

The first of a series of aircraft Pocket Books by the team responsible for *Jane's All the World's Aircraft*. They are intended as easy-to-handle working aids for people whose job or delight it is to recognise aircraft, and the information given for each type is that which will best assist in identifying it. The books will be illustrated by the finest available photographs, reproduced as large and as clearly as possible, backed up by high-quality three-view line drawings.

356 04372 X £1.50 (PVC) 264pp
356 04371 1 £1.95 (cloth)

Jane's Pocket Book of Commercial Transport Aircraft

J. W. R. Taylor

The second book in the series of aircraft Pocket Books describes and illustrates all major types of airliners and business aircraft seen throughout the world.

356 04376 2 £1.50 (PVC) 264pp
356 04375 4 £1.95 (cloth)

Jane's Pocket Book of Military Transport and Training Aircraft

J. W. R. Taylor

This book, which is complementary to the *Pocket Book of Major Combat Aircraft*, describes aircraft used for carrying military cargo.

356 04374 6 £1.75 (PVC) 264pp
356 04373 8 £2.50 (cloth)

The author of the above titles in the series is also the editor of **Jane's All the World's Aircraft.**

Jane's Pocket Book of Modern Tanks and Armoured Fighting Vehicles

Christopher Foss

Gives full particulars of post-war tanks and AFVs, including armament, dimensions, speed, range and type of engine. Each is illustrated by a full-page photograph. By the author of *Armoured Fighting Vehicles of the World.*

356 04654 0 £1.75 (PVC) 200pp
356 04653 2 £2.50 (cloth)

Jane's Pocket Book of Airship Development

Lord Ventry and Eugene M. Kolesnik

A detailed, illustrated guide to all classes of airship ever produced, ranging from Captain Renard's pioneering attempts in 1884 to the lighter-than-air craft of today. There are illustrations of every model, some of them never before published. Lord Ventry is the world's leading expert on airships, and his co-author is also an authority in this field.

356 04656 7 £1.75 (PVC) 264pp
356 04655 9 £2.50 (cloth)

Jane's Pocket Book of Major Warships

Captain John E. Moore

Will be indispensable to all those concerned with ship recognition. All major classes of warships are described and illustrated. The editor is a former Deputy Director of Naval Intelligence and the present editor of **Jane's Fighting Ships.**

356 04238 3 £1.50 (PVC) 280pp
356 04241 3 £1.95 (cloth)

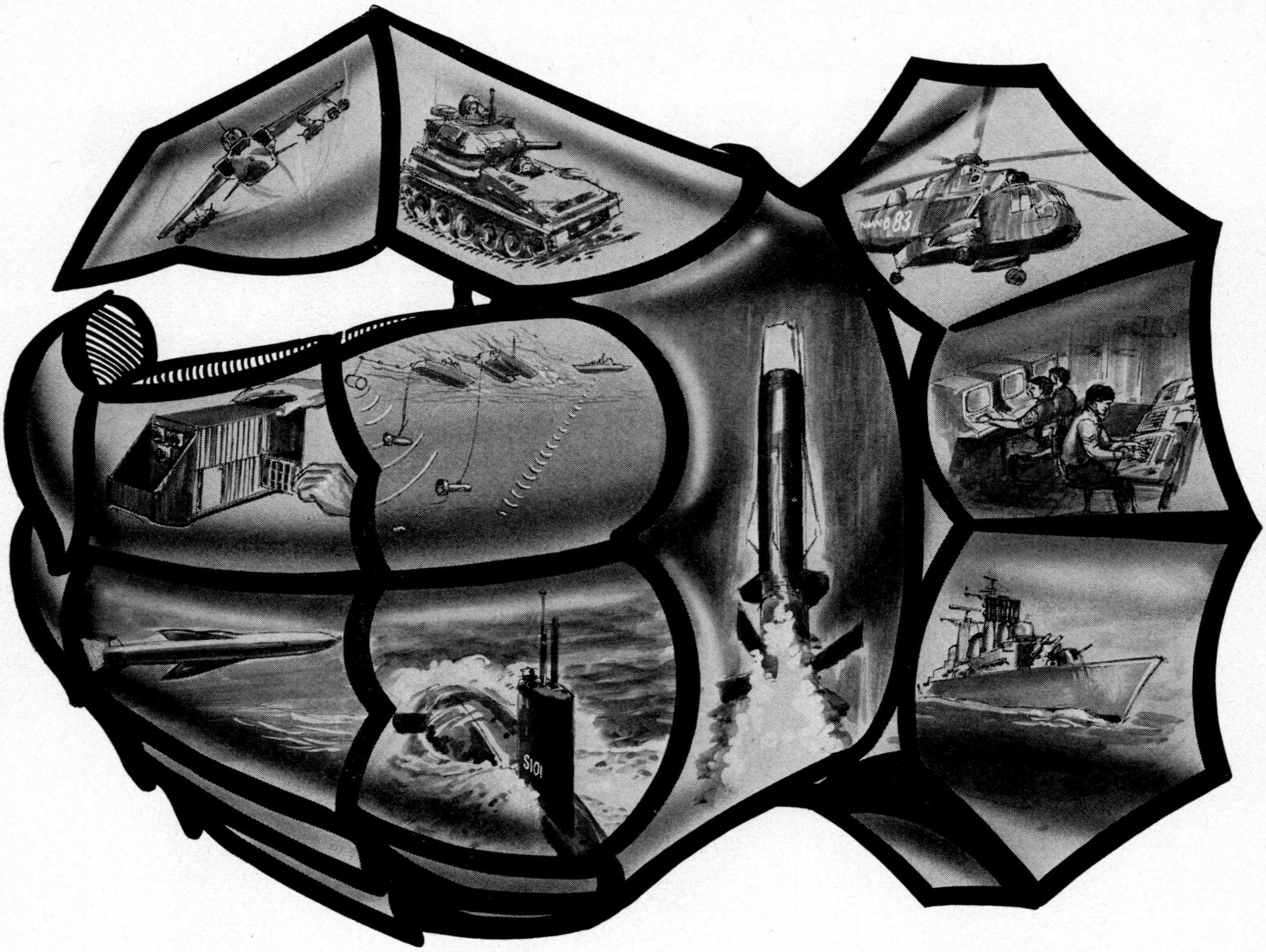

IDENTIFICATION SILHOUETTES

Scale shown against each type or class as appropriate

BATTLESHIP

Scale: 177 Feet to 1 Inch

IOWA CLASS (USA)

AIRCRAFT CARRIERS

Scale: 138 Feet to 1 Inch

COLOSSUS CLASS (ARGENTINA, BRAZIL, FRANCE)

Scale : 140 Feet to 1 Inch

MAJESTIC CLASS (AUSTRALIA, INDIA)

Scale: 173 Feet to 1 Inch

CLEMENCEAU CLASS (FRANCE)

Scale: 147 Feet to 1 Inch

BULWARK CLASS (UK)

AIRCRAFT CARRIERS

Scale: 169 Feet to 1 Inch

ARK ROYAL CLASS (UK)

Scale: 154 Feet to 1 Inch

HERMES CLASS (UK)

Scale: 225 Feet to 1 Inch

ENTERPRISE CLASS (USA)

Scale: 179 Feet to 1 Inch

ESSEX AND HANCOCK CLASS (USA)

AIRCRAFT CARRIERS

Scale: 207 Feet to 1 Inch

FORRESTAL CLASS (USA)

Scale: 118 Feet to 1 Inch

IWO JIMA CLASS (USA)

Scale: 212 Feet to 1 Inch

KITTY HAWK (USA)

Scale: 195 Feet to 1 Inch

MIDWAY CLASS (USA)

SUBMARINES

CRUISERS

Scale: 266 Feet to 1 Inch

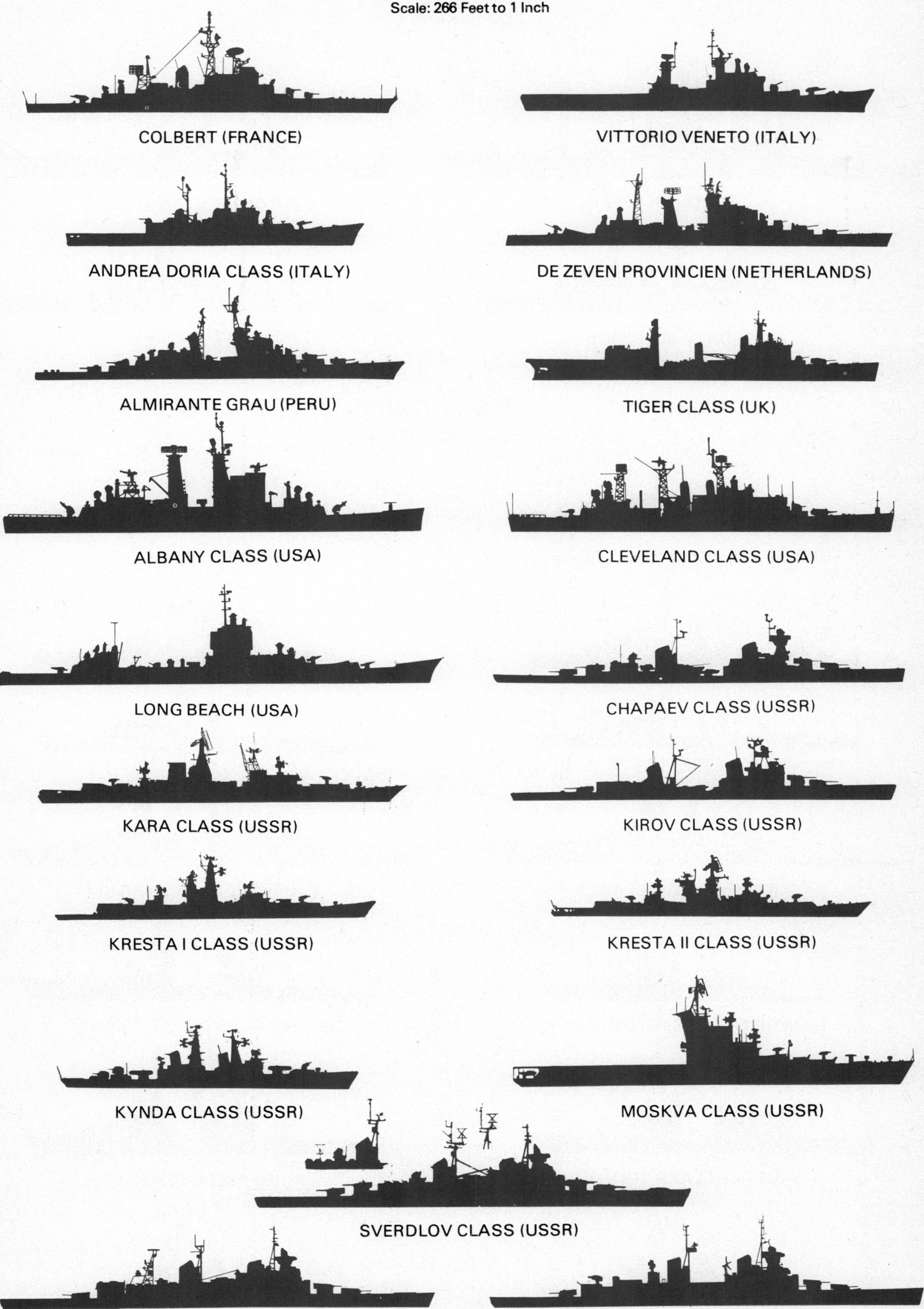
COLBERT (FRANCE)
VITTORIO VENETO (ITALY)
ANDREA DORIA CLASS (ITALY)
DE ZEVEN PROVINCIEN (NETHERLANDS)
ALMIRANTE GRAU (PERU)
TIGER CLASS (UK)
ALBANY CLASS (USA)
CLEVELAND CLASS (USA)
LONG BEACH (USA)
CHAPAEV CLASS (USSR)
KARA CLASS (USSR)
KIROV CLASS (USSR)
KRESTA I CLASS (USSR)
KRESTA II CLASS (USSR)
KYNDA CLASS (USSR)
MOSKVA CLASS (USSR)
SVERDLOV CLASS (USSR)
ZHDANOV (USSR) CONVERTED SVERDLOV CLASS
DZERZHINSKI (USSR) MODIFIED SVERDLOV CLASS

CRUISERS

Scale: 160 Feet to 1 Inch

TRUXTON (USA)

CALIFORNIA CLASS (USA)

COUNTY CLASS (UK)

BRISTOL (UK)

DESTROYERS

Scale: 161 Feet to 1 Inch

IROQUOIS CLASS (CANADA)

ACONIT (FRANCE)

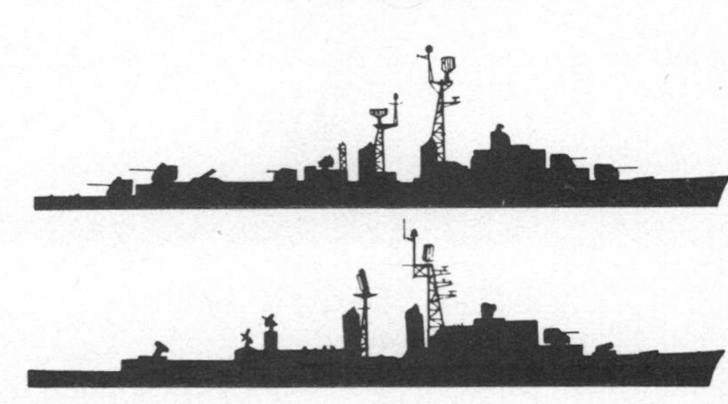

SURCOUF CLASS (FRANCE)

SUFFREN CLASS (FRANCE)

TOURVILLE CLASS (FRANCE)

HAMBURG CLASS (W. GERMANY)

LUTJENS CLASS (W. GERMANY)

AUDACE CLASS (ITALY)

IMPAVIDO CLASS (ITALY)

FLETCHER CLASS (USA)

DESTROYERS

Scale: 160 Feet to 1 Inch

ALLEN M. SUMNER CLASS (USA, ARGENTINA, GREECE, IRAN, SPAIN, TAIWAN)

ADAMS CLASS (USA)

SHEFFIELD CLASS (UK AND ARGENTINA)

FORREST SHERMAN CLASS (CONVERTED) (USA)

FORREST SHERMAN CLASS (USA)

GEARING CLASS (USA, GREECE, TAIWAN AND TURKEY)

GEARING CLASS (FRAM 2)(USA, GREECE, TAIWAN AND TURKEY)

MITSCHER CLASS (USA)

SPRUANCE CLASS (USA)

KANIN CLASS (USSR)

KASHIN CLASS (USSR)

KILDIN CLASS (USSR)

KOTLIN CLASS (USSR) (WITH HELICOPTER PLATFORM)

KOTLIN CLASS (USSR)

SAM KOTLIN (USSR)

SKORY CLASS (USSR)

KRIVAK CLASS (USSR)

KRUPNY CLASS (USSR)

TALLIN CLASS (USSR)

FRIESLAND/HOLLAND CLASS (NETHERLANDS)

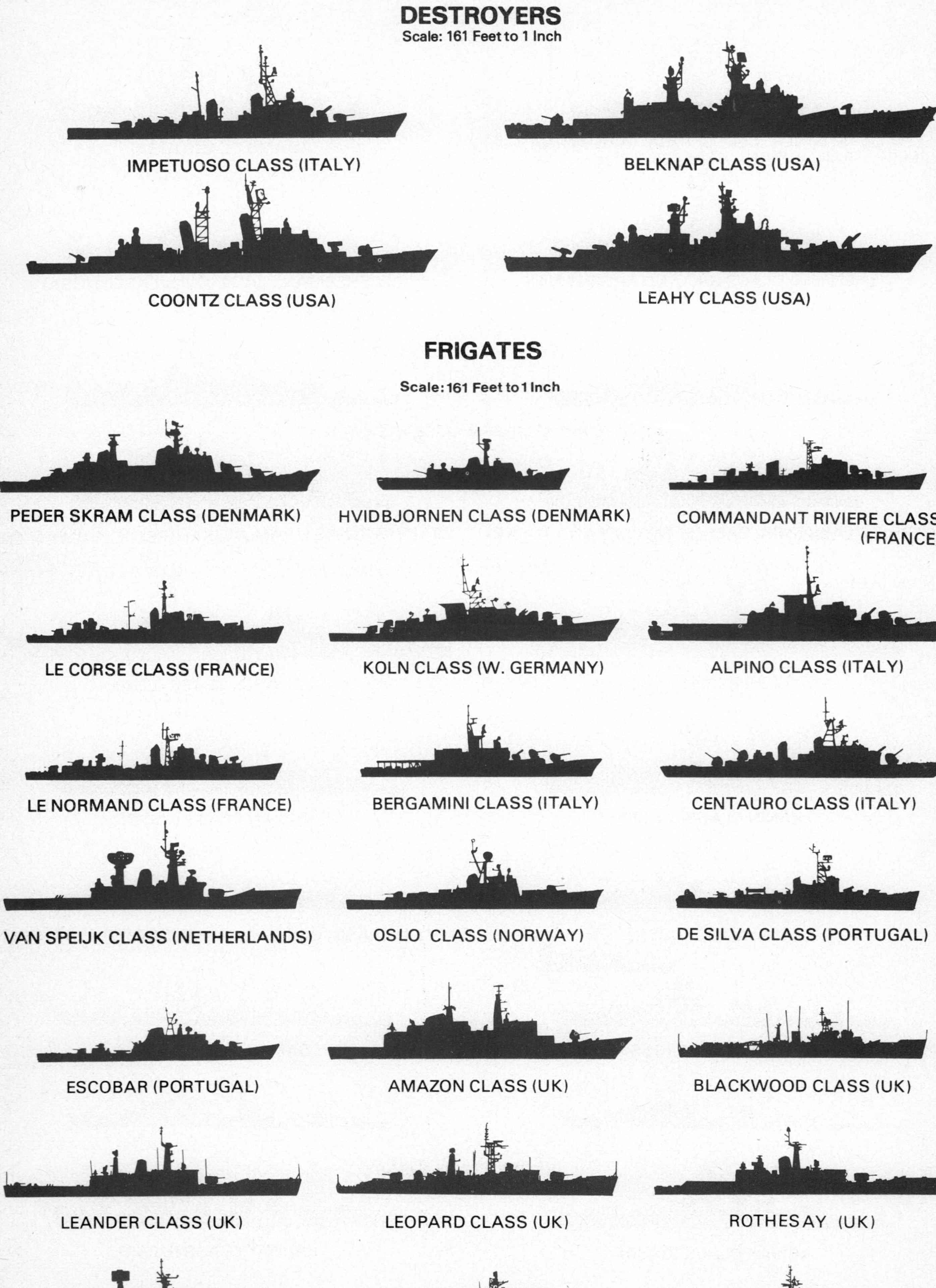

DESTROYERS
Scale: 161 Feet to 1 Inch
IMPETUOSO CLASS (ITALY)
BELKNAP CLASS (USA)
COONTZ CLASS (USA)
LEAHY CLASS (USA)
FRIGATES
Scale: 161 Feet to 1 Inch
PEDER SKRAM CLASS (DENMARK)
HVIDBJORNEN CLASS (DENMARK)
COMMANDANT RIVIERE CLASS (FRANCE)
LE CORSE CLASS (FRANCE)
KOLN CLASS (W. GERMANY)
ALPINO CLASS (ITALY)
LE NORMAND CLASS (FRANCE)
BERGAMINI CLASS (ITALY)
CENTAURO CLASS (ITALY)
VAN SPEIJK CLASS (NETHERLANDS)
OSLO CLASS (NORWAY)
DE SILVA CLASS (PORTUGAL)
ESCOBAR (PORTUGAL)
AMAZON CLASS (UK)
BLACKWOOD CLASS (UK)
LEANDER CLASS (UK)
LEOPARD CLASS (UK)
ROTHESAY (UK)
SALISBURY CLASS (UK)
TRIBAL CLASS (UK)
WHITBY CLASS (UK)

FRIGATES

Scale : 160 Feet to 1 Inch

ANNAPOLIS CLASS (CANADA)

MACKENZIE CLASS (CANADA)

ST. LAURENT CLASS (CANADA)

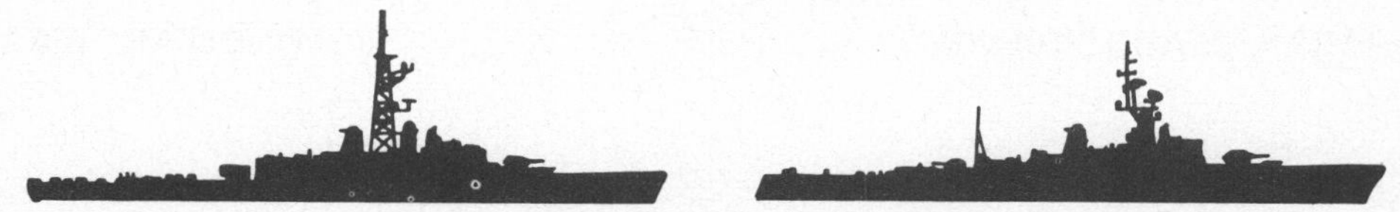

RESTIGOUCHE CLASS (CANADA)

Scale: 125 Feet to 1 Inch

A69 (FRANCE)

KOLA CLASS (USSR)

RIGA CLASS (USSR)

BROOKE CLASS (USA)

KNOX CLASS (USA)

GARCIA CLASS (USA)

MIRKA CLASS (USSR)

CORVETTES

Scale: 110 Feet to 1 Inch

ALBATROS/TRITON CLASS (DENMARK, ITALY)

THETIS CLASS (W. GERMANY)

CRISTOFARO CLASS (ITALY)

WOLF CLASS (NETHERLANDS)

COUTINHO CLASS (PORTUGAL)

POTI CLASS (USSR)

PETYA CLASS (USSR)

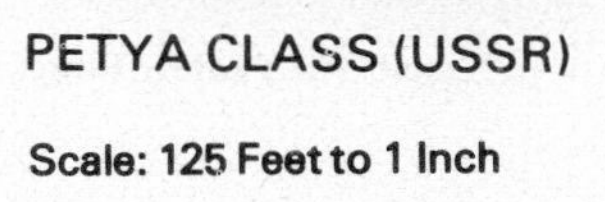

Scale: 125 Feet to 1 Inch

GRISHA CLASS (USSR)

NANUCHKA CLASS (USSR)

SOI CLASS (USSR)

AMPHIBIOUS FORCES

Scale: 170 Feet to 1 Inch

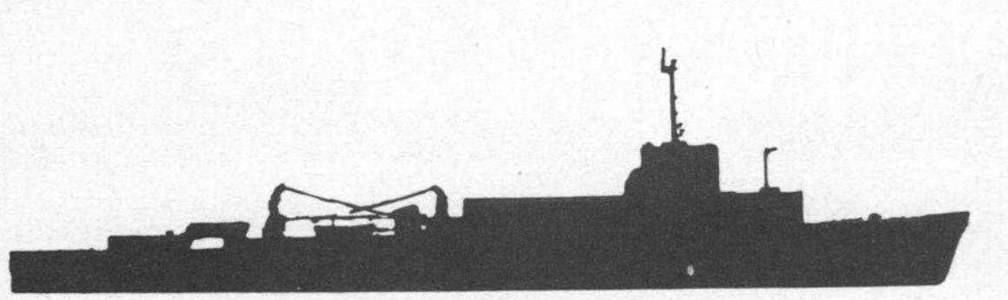

OURAGAN CLASS (FRANCE)

JEANNE D'ARC (FRANCE)

FEARLESS CLASS (UK)

AUSTIN CLASS (USA)

NEWPORT CLASS (USA)

THOMASTON CLASS (USA)

Scale: 117 Feet to 1 Inch

SIR LANCELOT CLASS (UK)

Scale: 148 Feet to 1 Inch

RALEIGH CLASS (USA)

Scale: 157 Feet to 1 Inch

ALLIGATOR CLASS (USSR)

POLNOCNY CLASS (USSR, POLAND)

MP8 CLASS (USSR)

LIGHT FORCES

Scale: 58 Feet to 1 Inch

JAGUAR CLASS (W. GERMANY)

TYPE 143 (W GERMANY)

TYPE 148 (W GERMANY)

STORM CLASS (NORWAY)

TJELD CLASS (NORWAY, GREECE)

KOMAR CLASS (USSR)

OSA 1 & 2 CLASS (USSR)

SHERSHEN CLASS (USSR, EGYPT, E. GERMANY, YUGOSLAVIA)

P. CLASS (P6, 8 and 10 — USSR, CHINA, CUBA, EGYPT, E. GERMANY, GUINEA, INDONESIA)

Scale: 125 Feet to 1 Inch

STENKA CLASS (USSR)

MINE WARFARE FORCES

Scale: 111 Feet to 1 Inch

FALSTER CLASS (DENMARK)

GOR CLASS (NORWAY)

ABDIEL (U.K.)

MINE WARFARE FORCES

Scale: 97 Feet to 1 Inch

CIRCE (FRANCE)

KRAKE (E.GERMANY)

KONDOR (E.GERMANY)

LINDAU CLASS (W. GERMANY)

SCHUTZE CLASS (W. GERMANY, BRAZIL)

KASADA (JAPAN)

DOKKUM WILDERVANK (NETHERLANDS, ETHIOPIA)

KROGULEC (POLAND)

ALMANZORA (SPAIN)

TON (UK, ARGENTINA, AUSTRALIA, GHANA, INDIA, MALAYSIA, S.AFRICA)

AGILE (USA, BELGIUM, FRANCE, ITALY, NETHERLANDS, PORTUGAL, SPAIN & URUGUAY)

AUK (USA, S.KOREA, NORWAY, PERU, TAIWAN, PHILLIPINES, URUGUAY)

BLUEBIRD (USA, BELGIUM, DENMARK, FRANCE, GREECE, IRAN, INDONESIA, ITALY, KOREA, JAPAN, NETHERLANDS, NORWAY, PAKISTAN, PORTUGAL, PHILLIPINES, TAIWAN, SPAIN, THAILAND, TURKEY, S. VIETNAM)

NATYA CLASS (USSR)

SASHA CLASS (USSR)

T-43 CLASS (USSR)

T-58 CLASS (USSR)

T301 CLASS (USSR)

VANYA CLASS (USSR)

YURKA CLASS (USSR)

SUPPORT SHIPS

Scale: 156 Feet to 1 Inch

ZINNIA (BELGIUM)

GODETIA (NETHERLANDS & BELGIUM)

RHEIN CLASS (W. GERMANY)

PRESERVER CLASS (CANADA)

DON CLASS (USSR)

LAMA CLASS (USSR)

UGRA CLASS (USSR)

ENGADINE (UK)

Scale: 85 Feet to 1 Inch

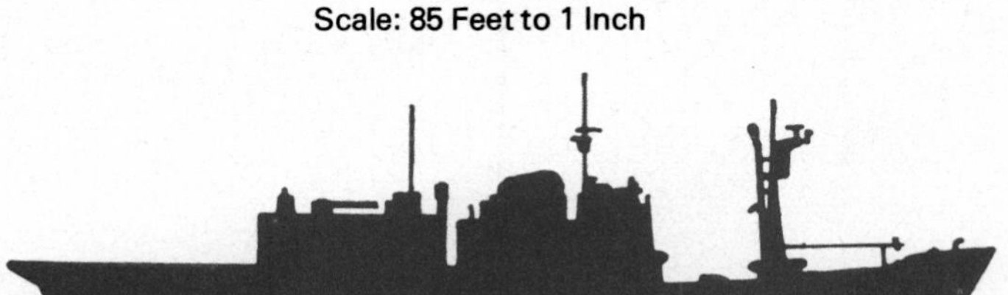

ENDURANCE (UK)

Scale: 206 Feet to 1 Inch

DEUTSCHLAND (W. GERMANY)

Scale: 152 Feet to 1 Inch

BORIS CHILIKIN CLASS (USSR)

Scale: 160 Feet to 1 Inch

SAN GIORGIO (ITALY)

Scale: 200 Feet to 1 Inch

TRIUMPH (UK)

ABU DHABI

SEA WING, ABU DHABI DEFENCE FORCE

Administration

Sea Wing Commander:
Commander G. A. St. G. Poole

Personnel

1974: 150 officers and men

The Sea Wing of the Abu Dhabi Defence Force was formed in March 1968. The Wing's function is to patrol territorial waters and oil installations in Abu Dhabi marine areas. The Wing is locally recruited with the exception of some ex-Royal Naval Officers, and Officers on secondment from the Pakistan Navy.

LIGHT FORCES

3 "KAWKAB" CLASS (COASTAL PATROL CRAFT)

BANIYAS (July 1969) **KAWKAB** (Jan 1969) **THOABAN** (Jan 1969)

Displacement, tons	32
Dimensions, ft (*m*)	57 × 16·5 × 4·5 (*17·4 × 5·1 × 1·4*)
Guns	2—20 mm (single)
Main engines	2 Caterpillar diesels. 750 bhp = 19 knots
Range, miles	300 at 10 knots
Complement	11 (2 officers, 9 men)

Built by Keith Nelson & Co. Ltd, Bembridge, Isle of Wight. Launch dates above. Of glass fibre hull construction.

THOABAN *1970, Abu Dhabi Defence Force*

6 "DHAFEER" CLASS (COASTAL PATROL CRAFT)

DHAFEER (Feb 1968)
DURGHAM (Sep 1968)
GHADUNFAR (May 1968)
HAZZA (May 1968)
MURAYJIB (Feb 1970)
TIMSAH (Sep 1968)

Displacement, tons	10
Dimensions, ft (*m*)	41 × 12 × 3·5 (*12·5 × 3·7 × 1·1*)
Guns	1 × 7·62 MG, 2 light MG
Main engines	2 Cummins diesels; 370 bhp = 19 knots
Range, miles	150 at 12 knots
Complement	6 (1 officer, 5 men)

All built by Keith Nelson & Co Ltd, Bembridge, Isle of Wight. Of glass fibre hull construction. Launch dates above.

DURGHAM *1970, Abu Dhabi Defence Force*

ALGERIA

Strength of the Fleet

9 FAC Missile
6 FAC Patrol
12 FAC Torpedo
2 Minesweepers (Ocean)
1 Training Ship

Personnel

1974: Total 3 500 (250 officers and cadets and 3 250 men)

Bases

Algiers, Annaba, Mers el Kebir

Mercantile Marine

Lloyd's Register of Shipping: 17 vessels of 56 523 tons gross

LIGHT FORCES

3 Ex-SOVIET "OSA" CLASS (F.A.C. MISSILE)

Displacement, tons	165 standard; 200 full load
Dimensions, ft (*m*)	128·7 × 25·1 × 5·9 (*39·3 × 7·7 × 1·8*)
Missiles	4 SSN 2A (Styx)
Guns	4—30 mm (2 twin)
Main engines	3 diesels; 13 000 hp = 32 knots
Range, miles	800 at 25 knots
Complement	25

One boat was delivered by USSR on 7 Oct 1967. Two others have been reported since.

"Osa" I Class

6 Ex-SOVIET "KOMAR" CLASS (F.A.C. MISSILE)

Displacement, tons	70 standard; 80 full load
Dimensions, ft (*m*)	83·7 × 19·8 × 5·0 (*25·5 × 6·0 × 1·5*)
Missiles	2 SSN 2A (Styx)
Guns	2—25 mm (twin)
Main engines	4 diesels, 4 shafts, 4 800 hp = 40 knots
Range, miles	400 at 30 knots

Acquired in 1967 from USSR.

6 Ex-SOVIET "SO I" CLASS (F.A.C. PATROL)

Displacement, tons	215 light; 250 normal
Dimensions, ft (*m*)	138·6 × 20·0 × 9·2 (*42·3 × 6·1 × 2·8*)
Guns	4—25 mm (2 twin mounts)
A/S weapons	4—5 barrelled rocket launchers
Main engines	3 diesels; 6 000 bhp = 29 knots
Complement	30
Range, miles	1 100 at 13 knots

Delivered by USSR on 7 and 8 Oct 1967, first two, and the other four since 1968.

Soviet "SOI" Class

12 Ex-SOVIET "P6" CLASS (F.A.C. TORPEDO)

Displacement, tons	66 standard; 75 full load
Dimensions, ft (*m*)	84·2 × 20·0 × 6·0 (*25·7 × 6·1 × 1·8*)
Tubes	2—21 inch plus mines or depth charges
Guns	4—25 mm (twin)
Main engines	4 Diesels, 4 shafts, 4 800 hp = 43 knots
Range, miles	450 at 30 knots
Complement	25

Six were acquired from the USSR in 1964. Two more boats reported to be in reserve were received from Egypt in 1963.

MINE WARFARE FORCES

2 Ex-SOVIET "T 43" CLASS (MINESWEEPERS, OCEAN)

Displacement, tons	500 standard; 610 full load
Dimensions, ft (*m*)	190·2 × 28·2 × 6·9 (*58·0 × 8·6 × 2·1*)
Guns	4—37 mm (twin); 4—25 mm (twin)
Main engines	2 Diesels; 2 shafts; 2 000 hp = 17 knots
Range, miles	1 600 at 10 knots
Complement	40

T 43 *Class* (& Radar Picket)

Soviet "T 43" *Class*

TRAINING SHIP (*Ex-Coastal Minesweeper*)

SIDI FRADJ (ex- *Darfour*)

Displacement, tons	215 standard; 270 full load
Dimensions, feet	136 oa × 24·5 × 6
Guns	1—3 in; 2—20 mm AA
Main engines	Diesels; 1 000 bhp = 13 knots

Two ex-US BYMS type coastal minesweepers were presented to Algeria by Egypt to form the nucleus of the new Algerian Navy. Both *Darfour* (ex-BYMS 2041) and *Tor* (ex-BYMS 2175) arrived in Algiers on 4 Nov 1962, being handed over on 6 Nov and renamed *Sidi Fradj* and *Djebel Aures*, respectively, but the latter was wrecked off Algiers in Apr 1963 and *Sidi Fradj* has been used as a training ship since 1965. Now considered obsolescent.

ALBANIA

Strength of the Fleet

4 Corvettes	2 Minesweepers (Ocean)	4 Oilers
4 Submarines	6 Minesweepers (Inshore)	20 Small Auxiliaries
42 FAC (Torpedo)	10 MSB	

Bases

Durazzo (Durresi) and Valona (Vlora)

Personnel

(a) 1974: Total 3 000 including 300 coastal frontier guards.
(b) Ratings on 3 years military service.

Mercantile Marine

Lloyd's Register of Shipping:
17 vessels of 56 523 tons gross

CORVETTES

4 Ex-USSR "KRONSTADT" CLASS

Displacement, tons	310 standard; 380 full load
Dimensions, ft (*m*)	170·6 × 21·5 × 9·0 (*52·0 × 6·5 × 2·7*)
Guns	1—3·5 in (*85 mm*); 2—37 mm AA (single); 6—12·7 AA MG (3 vertical twin)
A/S weapons	2 depth charge projectors; 2 DC rails
Main engines	3 Diesels; 3 shafts; 3 300 bhp = 24 knots
Range, miles	1 500 at 12 knots
Complement	65

Equipped for minelaying: 2 rails; about 40 mines. Four were transferred from the USSR in 1958. Albania sent two for A/S updating in 1960 and two others in 1961.

RADAR. Surface search—Ball Gun. Navigation—Neptun. IFF—High Pole.

"KRONSTADT" Class Ex-USSR

"KRONSTADT" Class

SUBMARINES

4 Ex-USSR "W" CLASS

Displacement, tons	1 030 surface; 1 180 dived
Dimensions, ft (*m*)	240·0 × 22·0 × 15·0 (*73·2 × 6·7 × 4·6*)
Tubes	6—21 in (4 bow, 2 stern); 18 torpedoes or 40 mines
Main engines	Diesels; 4 000 bhp; 2 shafts = 17 knots surface Electric motors; 2 500 hp = 15 knots dived
Range, miles	13 000 at 8 knots surfaced
Complement	60

Three of the four "W" class submarines are operational and one is now used as a stationary training hulk. All are based at Vlore. Two were transferred from the USSR in 1960, and two others were reportedly seized from the USSR in mid-1961 upon the withdrawal of Soviet ships from their Albanian base.

RADAR. Snoop Plate.

"WHISKY" *Class*

LIGHT FORCES

12 USSR "P-4" CLASS (F.A.C. TORPEDO)

Displacement, tons	25
Dimensions, feet	62·3 × 11·5 × 5·6 (*19·0 × 3·5 × 1·7 metres*)
Guns	2 or 4—12·7 mm AA MG (see notes)
Tubes	2—18 in (*450 mm*)
Main engines	2 Diesels; 2 Shafts; 2200bhp = 50 knots

Six were transferred from the USSR in 1956 (with radar and 2—12·7 mm MG) and six from China, three in April 1965 and three in Sep 1965, without radar and 4—12·7 mm MG (2 twin). Radar now fitted.

"P-4" Class Ex-USSR

30 Ex-CHINESE "HU CHWAN" CLASS (F.A.C. TORPEDO)

Displacement, tons	45
Dimensions, ft (*m*)	71 × 14·5 × 3·1 (*21·8 × 4·5 × 0·9*)
Guns	2—14·5 mm (twin vertical)
Torpedo tubes	2—21 inch
Main engines	2 M50 Diesels; 2 shafts; 2 200 hp = 55 knots

Built in Shanghai and transferred as follows: 6 in 1968, 15 in 1969, 2 in 1970 and 7 in 1971.

RADAR. Skinhead.

MINE WARFARE FORCES

2 Ex-USSR "T 43" CLASS (MINESWEEPERS, OCEAN)

Displacement, tons	500 standard; 610 full load
Dimensions, ft (*m*)	190·2 × 28·2 × 6·9 (*58·0 × 8·6 × 2·1*)
Guns	4—37 mm AA (2 twin); 4—25 mm AA
Main engines	2 Diesels; 2 shafts; 2 000 bhp = 17 knots
Range, miles	1 600 at 10 knots
Complement	40

"T 43" class fleet minesweepers acquired from the USSR. Transferred in Aug 1960.

"T 43" Class Ex-USSR

6 Ex-USSR "T 301" CLASS (MINESWEEPERS—INSHORE)

Displacement, tons	150 standard; 180 full load
Dimensions, ft (*m*)	128·0 × 18·0 × 4·9 (*39·0 × 5·5 × 1·5*)
Guns	2—37 mm AA; 2—25 mm AA
Main engines	2 diesels; 2 shafts; 1 440 bhp = 17 knots
Range, miles	2 200 at 10 knots
Complement	25

Transferred from USSR—two in 1957, two in 1959 and two in 1960.

"T 301" Class Ex-USSR

10 Ex-SOVIET "PO 2" CLASS (MSB)

Displacement, tons	40 to 45 standard; 45 to 50 full load
Dimensions, ft (*m*)	82·0 × 16·7 × 5·6 (*25 × 5·1 × 1·7*)
Guns	2—25 mm or 2—13 mm
Main engines	Diesels = 30 knots

There are reports of some 10 PO2 class in service and possibly 3 ex-Italian MS 501. The PO2 class, though primarily Minesweeping boats are also general utility craft. They were transferred as follows: 4 in 1957, 3 in 1958-59, 3 in 1960.

DEGAUSSING SHIP

1 Ex-USSR "SEKSTAN" CLASS

Dimensions, ft (*m*)	134·0 × 40·0 × 14·0 max (*40·9 × 12·2 × 4·3*)
Main engines	Diesels; 400 bhp = 11 knots
Complement	35

Built in Finland in 1956. Transferred from the USSR in 1960.

OILERS

2 Ex-USSR "KHOBI" CLASS

Displacement, tons	800
Measurement, tons	1 600 deadweight; 1 500 oil
Dimensions, ft (*m*)	220·0 × 33·0 × 15·0 (*67·1 × 10·1 × 4·6*)
Main engines	2 diesels; 1 600 bhp = 12 knots

Launched in 1956. Transferred from the USSR in Sep 1958 and Feb 1959. In addition to the above there are reported to be a number of small auxiliaries.

RADAR. Neptun.

1 Ex-USSR "TOPLIVO 1" CLASS

Displacement, tons 280

Transferred from the USSR in March 1960. Similar to "Khobi" class in appearance though smaller.

1 Ex-USSR "TOPLIVO 3" CLASS

Displacement, tons 275

Transferred from the USSR in 1960. Funnel aft.

TENDERS

There are reported to be a dozen or so harbour and port tenders including YPs, a water carrier and torpedo recovery vessel of the Soviet "Poluchat 1" class. The "Atrek" class submarine tender transferred from USSR in 1961 as a depot ship was converted into a merchant ship.

TUGS

Several small tugs are employed in local duties or harbour service.

ARGENTINA

Naval Board

Commander of the Navy and Chief of Naval Operations:
Rear Admiral E. E. Massera

Chief of Naval Staff:
Rear Admiral A. Lambruschini

Diplomatic Representation

Naval Attaché in London and The Hague and Head of the Argentine Naval Mission in Europe:
Rear Admiral R. G. Franke

Naval Attaché in Washington:
Rear Admiral D. R. H. De La Riva

Naval Attaché in Paris:
Captain J. C. Malagani

Personnel

(a) 1974: 31 125 (2 615 officers, 16 510 petty officers and ratings and 12 000 conscripts)
(b) Volunteers plus 14 months national service

Deletions and Transfers

Attack Carrier (medium)

1/1971 *Independencia*

Destroyers

1971 *Buenos Aires, Misiones, San Luis*
1973 *Entre Rios, San Juan, Santa Cruz*

Frigates
1973 *Juan B Azopardo*

Minesweeper Support Ship

1971 *Corrientes*

Submarines

1972 *Santa Fe* (ex-*Lamprey*) *Santiago del Estero* (ex-*Macabi*), scrapped for spares

Amphibious Forces

1971 *BDI 15, BDM 1*
1973 *BDI 1, EDVP 4, 5, 6, 11, 20, 22, 27,*

Survey Ships

1970 *Commodoro Augusto Lasserre*
1973 *Ushuia* sunk in collision

Oilers

1971 *Punta Rasa, Punta Lara*

Tugs

1971 *Querendi*

Prefix to Ships' Names

"A.R.A." (Armada Republica Argentina)

Strength of the Fleet

Type	*Active*	*Building*
Attack Carrier (Medium)	1	—
Cruisers	3	—
Destroyers	8	2
Corvettes	12	—
Patrol Submarines	2	2
Landing Ships (Tank)	5	—
Landing Craft (Tank)	1	—
Minor Landing Craft	19	—
Fast Attack Craft (Gun)	2	—
Fast Attack Craft (Torpedo)	2	—
Large Patrol Craft	3	—
Minesweepers (Coastal)	4	—
Minehunters	2	—
Survey Ships	3	3
Survey Launches	2	—
Transports	5	—
Oiler (Underway Replenishment)	1	—
Oilers (Fleet Support)	2	—
Icebreaker	1	—
Training Ship	1	—
Salvage Ship	1	—
Tugs	13	2

MERCANTILE MARINE

Lloyd's Register of Shipping:
351 vessels of 1 452 552 tons gross

AIRCRAFT CARRIER

1 Ex-BRITISH "COLOSSUS" CLASS

Name	*Builders*	*Laid down*	*Launched*	*Completed*
25 DE MAYO (ex-*HNMS Karel Doorman*, ex-*HMS Venerable*)	Cammell Laird & Co Ltd Birkenhead	3 Dec 1942	30 Dec 1943	17 Jan 1945

Displacement, tons	15 892 standard; 19 896 full load
Length, feet (*metres*)	630 (*192·0*) pp 693·2 (*211·3*) oa
Beam, feet (*metres*)	80 (*24·4*)
Draught, feet (*metres*)	25 (*7·6*)
Width, feet (*metres*)	121·3 (*37·0*) overall
Hangar:	
Length, feet (*metres*)	455 (*138·7*)
Width, feet (*metres*)	52 (*15·8*)
Height, feet (*metres*)	17·5 (*5·3*)
Aircraft	Capacity 21; operates with variable complement of S-2 Trackers, A-4Q Skyhawks and S-61 Sea King ASW helicopters
Guns, AA*	10—40 mm
Main engines	Parsons geared turbines; 40 000 shp; 2 shafts
Boilers	4 three-drum; working pressure 400 psi (*28·1 kg/cm²*); Superheat 700°F (*371°C*)
Speed, knots	24·25 designed
Oil fuel, tons	3 200
Range, miles	12 000 at 14 knots ,6 200 at 23 knots
Complement	1 500

GENERAL
Purchased from Great Britain on 1 Apr 1948 and commissioned in the Royal Netherlands Navy on 28 May 1948. Damaged by boiler fire on 29 Apr 1968. Sold to Argentina on 15 Oct 1968 and refitted at Rotterdam by N. V. Dok en Werf Mij Wilton Fijenoord. Commissioned in the Argentine Navy on 12 Mar 1969. Completed refit on 22 Aug 1969 and sailed for Argentina on 1 Sep 1969. With modified island superstructure and bridge, lattice tripod radar mast, and tall raked funnel, she differs considerably from her former appearance and from her original sister ships in the British, Australian, Brazilian, French and Indian navies.

ENGINEERING. The turbine sets and boilers are arranged *en echelon*, the two propelling-machinery spaces having two boilers and one set of turbines in each space, on the unit system. She was reboilered in 1965-1966 with boilers removed from HMS *Leviathan*. During refit for Argentina in 1968-1969 she received new turbines, also from HMS *Leviathan*.

RECONSTRUCTION. Underwent extensive refit modernisation in 1955-1958 including angled flight deck and steam catapult, rebuilt island, mirror sight landing system, and new anti-aircraft battery of ten 40 mm guns, at the Wilton-Fijenoord Shipyard, at a cost of 25 million guilders. Conversion completed in July 1958.

RADAR
Search: Two Philips LWO series early warning radars with associated height finders of VI series for air interception.
Tactical: DA Series tactical and navigation radar.

DRAWING. Starboard elevation and plan. Redrawn in 1971. Scale: 105 feet = 1 inch

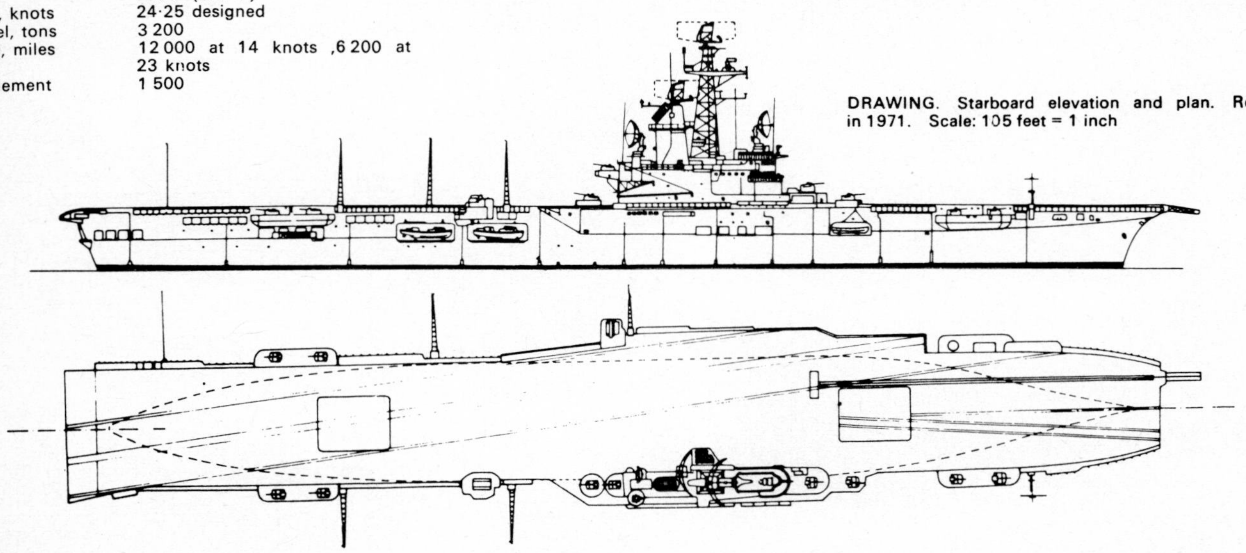

25 DE MAYO (Harrier VTOL aircraft demonstration on flight deck) *1970, Argentine Navy*

25 DE MAYO *1970, Wright & Logan*

CRUISERS

2 Ex-US "BROOKLYN" CLASS

Name	No.	Builders	Laid down	Launched	Completed
GENERAL BELGRANO (*ex-17 de Octubre, ex-Phoenix,* CL 46)	C 4	New York S.B. Corp Camden	15 Apr 1935	12 Mar 1938	18 Mar 1939
NUEVE DE JULIO (*ex-Boise,* CL 47)	C 5	Newport News S.B. & D.D. Co	1 Apr 1935	3 Dec 1936	1 Feb 1939

Displacement, tons	*Gen. Belgrano:* 10 800 standard; 12 650 normal; 13 645 full load *Nueve de Julio:* 10 500 standard 12 300 normal; 13 645 full load
Length, feet (*metres*)	608·3 (*185·4*) oa
Beam, feet (*metres*)	69 (*21·0*)
Draught, feet (*metres*)	24 (*7·3*) max
Aircraft	2 helicopters
Missiles, AA	2 quadruple "Sea Cat" launchers (*General Belgrano* only)
Guns, surface	15—6 in (*153 mm*) 47 cal; 8—5 in (*127 mm*) 25 cal.
Guns, AA	20—40 mm; 16—20 mm (*Gen. Belgrano*); 20—40 mm (*Nueve de Julio*)
Guns, saluting	4—47 mm
Armour	Belt 4 in—1½ in (*100—38 mm*) Decks 3 in+2 in (*76+51 mm*) Turrets 5 in—3 in (*127—76 mm*) Conning Tower 8 in (*203 mm*)
Main engines	Parsons geared turbines; 100 000 shp; 4 shafts
Boilers	8 Babcock & Wilcox Express type
Speed, knots	32·5 (when new)
Range, miles	7 600 at 15 knots
Oil fuel (tons)	2 200
Complement	1 200

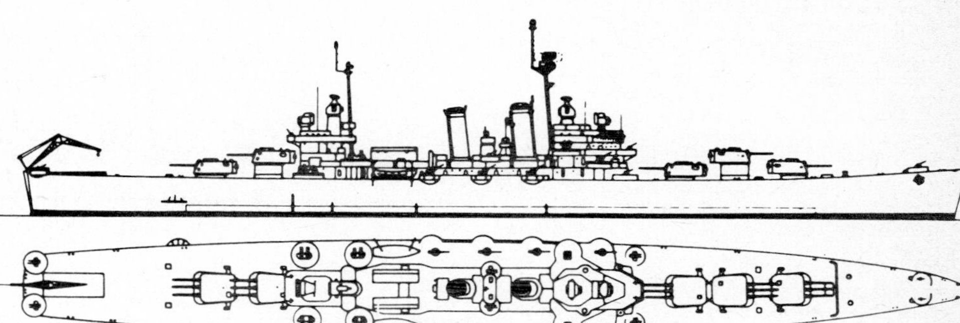

DRAWING: Starboard elevation and plan. Re-drawn in 1971. Scale 120 feet = 1 inch. "Sea-cats" abreast bridge in *General Belgrano* only.

GENERAL
Former cruisers of the United States Navy "Brooklyn" class. Superstructure was reduced, bulges added, beam increased, and mainmast derricks and catapults removed. Purchased from the United States in 1951 at a cost of $7 800 000 representing 20 per cent of their original cost plus the expense of reconditioning them. Both were transferred to the Argentine Navy on 12 Apr 1951. *General Belgrano* was commissioned under the name *17 de Octubre* at Philadelphia on 17 Oct 1951. *9 de Julio* was commissioned into the Argentine Navy at Philadelphia on 11 Mar 1952. *9 de Julio* refers to 9 July 1816, when the Argentine provinces signed the Declaration of Independence. *17 de Octubre* was renamed *General Belgrano* in 1956 following the overthrow of President Peron the year before.

RADAR
Search: LWO and DA Series (Signaal).

HANGAR. The hangar in the hull right aft accommodates two helicopters together with engine spares and duplicate parts, though 4 aircraft was the original complement.

GENERAL BELGRANO — *1973, Argentine Navy*

Name	No.	Builders	Laid down	Launched	Completed
LA ARGENTINA	C 3	Vickers Armstrongs Ltd, Barrow-in-Furness	Jan 1936	16 Mar 1937	31 Jan 1939

Displacement, tons	6 000 standard; 7 610 normal; 8 630 full load
Length, feet (*metres*)	510 (*155·5*) pp; 541·2 (*164·9*) oa
Beam, feet (*metres*)	56·5 (*17·2*)
Draught, feet (*metres*)	16·5 (*5·0*) max
Guns, surface	9—6 in (*153 mm*)
Guns, AA	14—40 mm
Torpedo tubes	6—21 in (*533 mm*) tripled
Armour	Side and C.T. 3 in (*76 mm*); deck and gunhouses 2 in (*51 mm*)
Main engines	Parsons geared turbines 5 4000 shp; 4 shafts
Boilers	4 Yarrow; 300 psi (*21 kg/cm²*)
Speed, knots	30 originally—now 25
Range, miles	7 500 at 12 knots
Oil fuel (tons)	1 500
Complement	800

GENERAL
Designed as Training Cruiser. Cost 6 000 000 gold pesos (about £1 750 000).

GUNNERY. Original 4 inch guns were removed in 1950 and 40 mm guns added.

DRAWING. Starboard elevation and plan. Re-drawn in 1971. Scale 113 feet = 1 inch (1 : 1 500).

LA ARGENTINA — *1969, Argentine Navy*

DESTROYERS

2 NEW CONSTRUCTION TYPE 42

Name	No.	Builders	Laid down	Launched	Commissioning
HERCULES	D 01	Vickers, Barrow in-Furness	16 June 1971	24 Oct 1972	mid 1975
SANTISSIMA TRINIDAD	D 02	AFNE, Rio Santiago	11 Oct 1971	Mar 1974	1976

Displacement, tons: 3 500 full load
Length, feet (*metres*): 392·0 (*119·5*) wl; 410·0 (*125·0*) oa
Beam, feet (*metres*): 47·0 (*14·3*)
Draught, feet (*metres*): 22·0 (*6·7*)
Missile launchers: 2 "Sea Dart" (1 twin)
Aircraft: 1 Lynx helicopter
Guns: 1—4·5 in automatic; 2—20 mm Oerlikon
Main engines: Rolls Royce Olympus gas turbines for full power; Rolls Royce Tyne gas turbines for cruising; 2 shafts; 50 000 shp
Speed, knots: 30 designed
Range, miles: 4 000 at 18 knots
Complement: 300

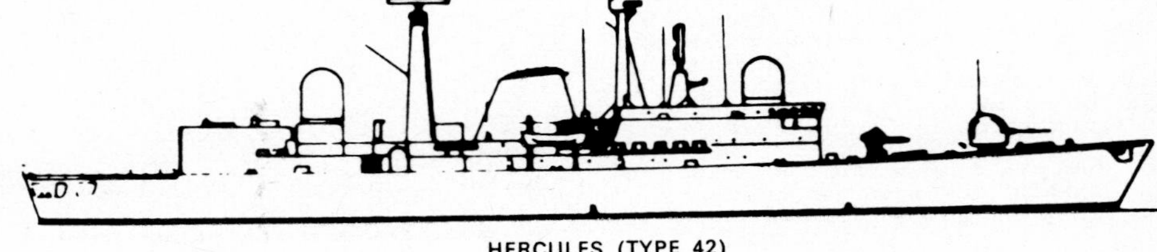

HERCULES (TYPE 42)

GENERAL
Guided missile armed destroyers of the British "Type 42". The Argentine Navy signed the contract with Vickers Ltd, Barrow-in-Furness, announced on 18 May 1970, for the construction of these two ships, one to be built in Great Britain and the other in Argentina with British oversight of construction.

5 Ex-US "FLETCHER" CLASS

Name	No.	Builders	Laid down	Launched	Commissioning
BROWN (ex-USS *Heermann*, DD 532)	D 20	Bethlehem Steel Co, San Francisco	8 May 1942	5 Dec 1942	6 July 1943
ESPORA (ex-USS *Dortch*, DD 670)	D 21	Federal S.B. & D.D. Co, Port Newark	2 Mar 1943	20 June 1943	7 Aug 1943
ROSALES (ex-USS *Stembel*, DD 644)	D 22	Bath Iron Works Corporation, Bath, Maine	21 Dec 1942	8 May 1943	16 July 1943
DOMECQ GARCIA (ex-USS *Braine*, DD 630)	D 23	Bath Iron Works Corp.	12 Oct 1942	7 Mar 1943	11 May 1943
ALMIRANTE STORNI (ex-USS *Cowell*, DD 547)	D 24	Bethlehem Co, San Pedro	7 Sep 1942	18 Mar 1943	23 Aug 1943

ex-Fletcher

ALMIRANTE STORNI — 1972, *Argentine Navy*

Displacement, tons: 2 100 standard; 3 050 full load
Length, feet (*metres*): 376·5 (*114·8*) oa
Beam, feet (*metres*): 39·5 (*12·0*)
Draught, feet (*metres*): 12·2 (*3·7*) mean; 18 (*5·5*) max
Guns, surface: 4—5 in (*127 mm*) 38 cal.
Guns, AA: 6—3 in (*76 mm*) 50 cal.
Torpedo tubes: 5—21 in (*533 mm*) quintupled
A/S depth charges: 2 fixed Hedgehogs; 1 DC rack
A/S torpedo racks: 2 side-launching
Main engines: 2 sets GE or AC geared turbines 60 000 shp; 2 shafts
Boilers: 4 Babcock & Wilcox
Speed, knots: 35
Range, miles: 6 000 at 15 knots
Oil fuel (tons): 650
Complement: 300

GENERAL
First three transferred to the Argentine Navy on 1 Aug 1961. *Espora* is of the later "Fletcher" class. Last pair transferred 17 Aug 1971. *Brown* is division leader. USS *Knapp* (D 653) is also reported transferred as source of spare parts.
RADAR. Search: L Band SPS 6. Tactical: C Band SPS 10. Fire Control: X Band, antenna on Director.

2 Ex-US "ALLEN M. SUMNER" CLASS

Name	No.	Builders	Launched	Commissioning
BOUCHARD (ex-USS *Borie* DD 704)	D 26	Federal SB & DD Co.	4 July 1944	21 Sep 1944
SEGUI (ex-USS *Hank* DD 702)	D 25	Federal SB & DD Co.	21 May 1944	28 Aug 1944

Displacement, tons: 2 200 standard; 3 320 full load
Length, feet (*metres*): 376·5 (*114·8*) oa
Beam, feet (*metres*): 40·9 (*12·5*)
Draught, feet (*metres*): 19 (*5·8*)
Guns: 6—5 in (*127 mm*) 38 cal; DP (twin) 4—3 in (*Hank* only)
A/S Weapons: 2 Triple torpedo tubes (Mk 32); 2 ahead-firing Hedgehogs; Facilities for small helicopter
Main engines: 2 geared turbines; 60 000 shp; 2 shafts
Boilers: 4
Speed, knots: 34
Range, miles: 3 865 at 11 knots; 990 at 31 knots
Complement: *Bouchard* 291; *Segui* 331

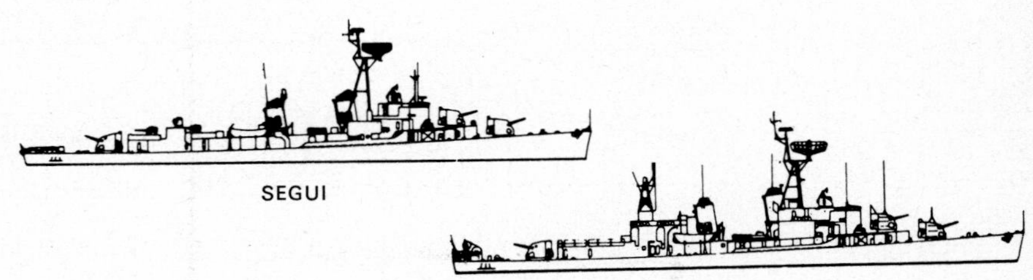

SEGUI

BOUCHARD

Transferred to Argentina 1 July 1972. *Bouchard* has been modernised with VDS, helicopter facilities and hangar.

RADAR (*Bouchard*). SPS 10, SPS 40 and GFCS Mk 25.
SONAR (*Bouchard*). SQA 10A, SQS 30.

1 FRAM II "GEARING" CLASS

Name	No.	Builders	Laid down	Commissioning
PY (ex-USS *Perkins* DD 877)	D 27	Consolidated Steel Corpn.	7 Dec 1944	5 Apr 1945

Displacement, tons: 2 425 standard; approx 3 500 full load
Length, feet (*metres*): 390·5 (*119·0*)
Beam, feet (*metres*): 40·9 (*12·4*)
Draught, feet (*metres*): 19·0 (*5·8*)
Guns: 6—5 inch (*127 mm*), 38 cal. DP (twins)
A/S weapons: 2 Fixed Hedgehogs; 2 triple torpedo tubes (Mk 32); Facilities for small helicopter
Main engines: 2 geared Westinghouse turbines
Boilers: 4 Babcock & Wilcox
Speed, knots: 31·5
Range, miles: 6 150 at 11 knots; 1 475 at 30 knots
Complement: 275

PY

Transferred by sale 15 Jan 1973.

RADAR. SPS 10, SPS 40 and GFCS Mk 25.
SONAR. SQS 23.

SUBMARINES

2 TYPE 209 NEW CONSTRUCTION

SALTA S 31 **SAN LUIS** S 32

Displacement, tons	980 surface; 1 230 dived
Length, feet (*metres*)	183·4 (*55·9*)
Beam, feet (*metres*)	20·5 (*6·25*)
Draught, feet (*metres*)	17·9 (*5·4*)
Torpedo tubes	8—21 in; bow tubes (with reloads)
Main machinery	Diesel electric; MTU Diesels, 4 generators; 1 shaft; 5 000 hp
Speed, knots	22 dived, 10 surfaced
Complement	32

Built in sections by Howaldswerke Deutsche Werft AG, Kiel from the IK 68 design of Ingenieurkontor, Lübeck. Sections are shipped to Argentina for assembly at Tandanor, Buenos Aires. *Salta* launched 21 Nov 1972 and *San Luis* May 2 1973. Both to commission in 1974.

SALTA *1973, Argentine Navy*

2 "GUPPY (IA and II)" CLASS

SANTA FE (ex-USS *Catfish* SS 339) S 21
SANTIAGO DEL ESTERO (ex-USS *Chivo* SS 341) S 22

Displacement, tons	1 870 surface; 2 420 (*Santa Fe*); 2 540 (*Santiago*) dived
Length, feet (*metres*)	307·5 (*93·8*) oa
Beam, feet (*metres*)	27·2 (*8·3*)
Draught, feet (*metres*)	18·0 (*5·5*) (*Santa Fe*); 17·0 (*5·2*) (*Santiago*)
Torpedo tubes	10—21 in (*533 mm*); 6 fwd, 4 aft
Main machinery	3 diesels; 4 800 shp; 2 electric motors; 5 400 shp; 2 shafts
Speed, knots	18 surfaced; 15 dived
Range, miles	12 000 at 10 knots
Oil fuel, tons	300
Complement	82-84

SANTA FE *1972, Argentine Navy*

GENERAL
Both of the "Balao" class built by Electric Boat Co being launched on 19 Nov 1944 and 14 Jan 1945 and commissioned on 19 Mar 1945 and 28 April 1945, respectively. *Catfish* was modified under the Guppy II programme (1948-50) and *Chivo* under the Guppy 1A programme (1951). Both transferred to Argentina at Mare Island on 7 Jan 1971.

AMPHIBIOUS FORCES

1 Ex-US LANDING SHIP (TANK)

CANDIDO DE LASALA Q 43 (ex-USS *Gunston Hall, LSD* 5)

Displacement, tons	5 480 standard; 9 375 full load
Dimensions, feet	457·8 oa × 72·2 × 18·0
Guns	12—40 mm AA
Main engines	2 Skinner Unaflow; 2 shafts; 7 400 shp = 15·4 knots
Boilers	2 Two drum
Range, miles	8 000 at 15 knots
Complement	Accommodation for 326 (17 officers and 309 men)

GENERAL
Built by Moor Dry Dock Co, Oakland, Calif. Laid down on 28 Dec 1942, launched on 1 May 1943 and completed on 10 Nov 1943. Arcticized in 1948/9. Transferred from the US Navy on 1 May 1970. Carries 14 LCA and has helicopter facilities.

CANDIDO DE LASALA *1973, Argentine Navy*

3 Ex-US LST TYPE

CABO SAN GONZALO Q 44 (ex-US *LST* 872)
CABO SAN ISIDRO Q 46 (ex-US *LST* 919)
CABO SAN PIO Q 50 (ex-US *LST* 1044)

Displacement, tons	2 366 beaching; 4 080 full load
Dimensions, feet	316 wl; 328 oa × 50 × 14
Main engines	2 diesels; 2 shafts; 1 800 bhp = 11 knots
Oil fuel (tons)	700
Range, miles	9 500 at 9 knots
Complement	80

GENERAL
Built by Puget Sound Bridge and Dredging Co, Seattle, USA. Launched in 1944. Transferred 1946-47. All ships have two rudders.

MEDIUM LANDING SHIPS

Of the former United States landing ships, (medium) BDM 2 (ex-USN *LSM* 86) was converted into a minelayer support vessel in 1968.

1 LANDING SHIP (TANK)

CABO SAN ANTONIO Q 42

Displacement, tons	4 300 light; 8 000 full load
Dimensions, feet	445 oa × 62 × 16·5
Guns	6—3 in (3 twin)
Main engines	Diesels; 2 shafts; 13 700 bhp = 11 knots
Complement	124

Built at the AFNE Rio Santiago. Designed to carry a helicopter and two landing craft. Launched 1968, completed 1973. To commission in 1974. Modified US "Suffolk County" Class.

1 Ex-US LCT TYPE

BDI Q 56 (ex-USS *LCIL* 583)

Displacement, tons	230 light; 387 full load
Dimensions, feet	153 wl; 159 oa × 23·2 × 5
Guns	2—20 mm AA (only in BDI 4)
Main engines	8 sets diesels; 3 200 bhp = 14 knots. Two reversible propellers
Oil fuel, tons	110
Range, miles	6 000 at 12 knots
Complement	30

Used for training.

BDI *1970 Argentine Navy*

19 MINOR LANDING CRAFT

LCM 1 **LCM 2** **LCM 3** **LCM 4**

It was stated in Jan 1971 that four LCMs built in the USA had been incorporated in the Fleet.

EDVP 1, 3, 7, 8, 9, 10, 12, 13, 17, 19, 21, 24, 28, 29, 30

Displacement, tons	12
Dimensions, feet	39·5 × 10·5 × 5·5
Main engines	Diesel, 9 knots

Ex USN LCVPs. Transferred 1946.

LIGHT FORCES

2 FAST ATTACK CRAFT (GUN)

INTREPIDA ELPR 1 **INDOMITA** ELPR 2

Displacement, tons	240
Dimensions, ft (*m*)	164 × 24 (*50 × 7·3*)
Guns	1—3 in (*76 mm*) Otomelara AA, 2—40 mm AA
Torpedo tubes	Designed for 2—21 inch
Main engines	Diesels; 4 shafts; speed 40 knots
Complement	35

These two fast patrol vessels were ordered in 1970 and were built by Lürssen, Bremen, (Vegesack). Of Combattante II type. *Intrepida* launched 12 Dec 1973 and *Indomita* May 1974. Both to commission later in 1974.

3 "LYNCH" CLASS (LARGE PATROL CRAFT)

EREZCANO GC 23 **LYNCH** GC 21 **TOLL** GC 22

Displacement, tons	100 normal; 117 full load
Dimensions, feet	90 × 19 × 6
Gun	1—20 mm
Main engines	2 Maybach Diesels; 2 700 bhp = 22 knots
Complement	16

GENERAL
Patrol craft operated by the Prefectura Naval Argentina. GC 31 of similar size but different type, see photograph below.

GC 31 *1971*

LYNCH *1969, Argentine Navy*

2 EX-US "HIGGINS CLASS" (FAC—TORPEDO)

ALAKUSH P 82 **TOWORA** P 84

Displacement, tons	45
Dimensions, feet	78·7 × 9·8 × 4·6
Guns	2—40 mm; 4—MG
Torpedo launchers	4—21 inch
Rocket launchers	2 sextuple sets
Main engines	3 Packard; 4 050 hp = 45 knots
Range, miles	1 000 at 20 knots
Complement	12

The last of a class of nine. Given names in 1972.

MINE WARFARE FORCES

6 Ex-BRITISH "TON" CLASS

(MINESWEEPERS (COASTAL) and MINEHUNTERS)

CHACO (ex-HMS *Rennington*)	M 5
CHUBUT (ex-HMS *Santon*)	M 3
FORMOSA (ex-HMS *Ilmington*)	M 6
NEUQUEN (ex-HMS *Hickleton*)	M 1
RIO NEGRO (ex-HMS *Tarlton*)	M 2
TIERRA DEL FUEGO (ex-HMS *Bevington*)	M 4

Displacement, tons	360 standard; 425 full load
Dimensions, ft (*m*)	140 pp; 153 oa × 28·8 × 8·2 (*46·3 × 8·8 × 2·5*)
Guns	1—40 mm AA
Main engines	2 Diesels; 2 shafts; 3 000 bhp = 15 knots
Oil fuel (tons)	45
Range, miles	2 300 at 13 knots; 3 000 at 8 knots
Complement	Minsweepers 27; Minehunters 36

Former British coastal minesweepers of the "Ton" class. Of composite wooden and non-magnetic metal construction. Purchased in 1967. In 1968 *Chaco* and *Formosa* were converted into minehunters in HM Dockyard, Portsmouth, and the other four were refitted and modernised as minesweepers by the Vosper Thornycroft Group with Vosper activated fin stabiliser equipment.

CHACO (HUNTER) *1972, Argentine Navy*

NEUQUEN (SWEEPER) *1971, Argentine Navy*

CORVETTES

2 "KING" CLASS

Displacement, tons	913 standard; 1 000 normal; 1 032 full load
Length, feet (*metres*)	252·7 (*77·0*)
Beam, feet (*metres*)	29 (*8·8*)
Draught, feet (*metres*)	7·5 (*2·3*)
Guns, surface	3—4·1 (*105 mm*)
Guns, AA	4—40 mm Bofors; 2—MG
A/S	4—DCT
Main engines	2—Werkspoor 4-stroke diesels; 2 500 bhp; 2 shafts
Speed, knots	18
Oil fuel (tons)	90
Range, miles	6 000 at 12 knots
Complement	130

Name	*No.*	*Builders*	*Laid down*	*Launched*	*Completed*
KING	P 21	Astillero Nav. Rio Santiago	Dec 1938	Dec 1943	28 July 1946
MURATURE	P 20	Astillero Nav. Rio Santiago	June 1938	July 1945	18 Nov 1946

KING *1970, Argentine Navy*

KING, MURATURE

GENERAL
Both built at Astillero Nav. Rio Santiago. Named after Captain John King, an Irish follower of Admiral Brown, who distinguished himself in the war with Brazil, 1826-28; and Captain Murature, who performed conspicuous service against the Paraguayans at the Battle of Cuevas on Aug 6 1865. Used for cadet training.

Corvettes—*continued*

2 Ex-US ATF TYPE

COMANDANTE GENERAL IRIGOYEN
(ex-USS *Caliuilla*, ATF 152) A 1
COMANDANTE GENERAL ZAPIOLA
(ex-USS *Arpaho*, ATF 68) A 2

Displacement, tons	1 235 standard; 1 675 full load
Dimensions, ft (*m*)	195 wl; 205 oa × 38·2 × 15·3 (*62·5 × 11·6 × 4·7*)
Guns	4—40 mm AA (2 twin); 2—20 mm
Main engines	4 sets diesels with electric drive; 3 000 bhp = 16 knots
Complement	85

Former US fleet ocean tugs of the "Cherokee" class. Fitted with powerful pumps and other salvage equipment. Both built by Charleston S.B. & D.D. Co, Charleston, S.C. Launched on 2 Nov 1944 and 22 June 1942, respectively, and completed on 10 Mar 1945 and 20 Jan 1943. Transferred to Argentina at San Diego, California, in 1961. Classified as tugs until 1966 when they were re-rated as patrol vessels.

COMANDANTE GENERAL ZAPIOLA — *1973, Argentine Navy*

6 Ex-US ATA TYPE

ALFEREZ SOBRAL (ex-USS *Catawba*, *ATA* 210) A 9
CHIRIGUANO (ex-US *ATA* 227) A 7
COMODORO SOMELLERA (ex-USS *Salish ATA* 187) A 10
DIAGUITA (ex-US *ATA* 124) A 5
SANAVIRON (ex-US *ATA* 228) A 8
YAMANA (ex-US *ATA* 126) A 6

Displacement, tons	689 standard; 800 full load
Dimensions, ft (*m*)	134·5 wl; 143 oa × 34 × 12 (*43·4 × 10·4 × 3·6*)
Guns	1—40 mm; 2—20 mm AA
Main engines	Diesel-electric; 1 500 bhp = 12·5 knots
Oil fuel (tons)	154
Range, miles	16 500 at 8 knots
Complement	49

YAMANA — *1969, Argentine Navy*

Former US auxiliary ocean tugs. Built by Levingstone Shipbuilding Co, Orange, Texas, USA, in 1945. *Diaguita* and *Yamana* are fitted as rescue ships. A 5, A 6, A 7 and A 8 bear names of South American Indian tribes. Classified as ocean salvage tugs until 1966 when they were re-rated as patrol vessels. A 9 and A 10 were transferred on 10 Feb 1972. A 9 operated by Coast Guard.

SPIRO GC 12 (ex-Bouchard class)

Displacement, tons	560 normal; 650 full load
Dimensions, feet	197 oa × 24 × 11½
Guns	4 40 mm
Main engines	2 MAN Diesels; 2 000 bhp = 13 knots
Complement	77

GENERAL
Former minesweeper of the "Bouchard" class, now operated by the Prefectura Naval Argentina. Built by the Rio Santiago Navy Yard. Launched on 7 June 1937. Sister ships *Bouchard*, *Py* and *Seaver* were transferred to the Paraguayan Navy. They were the first warships built in Argentine yards.

SPIRO — *1969, Argentine Navy*

SURVEY SHIPS

COMODORO RIVADAVIA

Displacement, tons	655
Dimensions, ft (*m*)	167 × 28·9 × 8·5 (*50·9 × 8·8 × 2·6*)
Main engines	2 Werkspoor Diesels = 12 knots
Complement	30

Building by Mestrina, Tigre, Argentina. Laid down 17 July 1971, launched 2 Dec 1972, to commission late 1974. Rated as "Buque Hidrográfico Auxiliar".

1 NEW CONSTRUCTION SURVEY SHIP

Displacement, tons 1 960 standard

To be laid down in 1974 at Alianza, Avellaneda.

Survey Ships—*continued*

1 NEW CONSTRUCTION OCEANOGRAPHIC SHIP

Displacement, tons	2 100 standard
Dimensions, ft (*m*)	249 × 43·4 × 14·9 (*75·9* × *13·2* × *4·5*)
Engines	1 Diesel; 2 600 hp = 12 knots

To be laid down at Astarsa, San Fernando in 1974.

ISLAS ORCADAS (ex-USS *Eltanin*, T-AGOR 8)

Displacement, tons	2 036 light; 4 942 full load
Dimensions, ft (*m*)	262·2 oa × 51·5 × 18·7 (80 × 15·7 × 5·7)
Main engines	Diesel electric; 3 200 bhp; 2 shafts = 12 knots
Complement	12 officers, 36 men, 38 scientists

Built by Avondale Marine Ways, New Orleans, delivered 2 Aug 1957. Converted for Antarctic Research 1961. Operated in conjunction by Argentine Navy, US National Science Foundation and Argentine National Directorate of the Antarctic.

2 Ex-US TUG TYPE

GOYENA (ex- USS *Dry Tortuga*) A 3
THOMPSON (ex-USS *Sombrero Key*) A 4

Displacement, tons	1 863 full load
Dimensions, ft (*m*)	191·3 × 37 × 18 (*58·3* × *11·3* × *5·5*)
Guns	2—40 mm Bofors (twin); 2—20 mm (single)
Main engines	2 Enterprise Diesels; 2 250 bhp = 12 knots
Oil fuel, tons	532
Complement	60

Built by Pendleton Shipyard Co, New Orleans. Launched in 1943 and leased to Argentina in 1965. Temporarily used as survey ships.

THOMPSON *1973, Argentine Navy*

1 AUXILIARY SAILING SHIP

EL AUSTRAL (ex-US *Atlantis*) Q 7

Displacement, tons	571
Dimensions, feet	110 pp 141 oa × 27 × 20
Main engines	Diesel; 400 bhp
Oil fuel (tons)	22
Complement	19

GENERAL
Built by Burmeister & Wain, Copenhagen. Launched and completed in 1931. Incorporated into the Argentine Navy on 30 April ,1966. Acquired from USA. Officially rated as *Buque Oceanagrafico*.

CORMORAN

Coastal survey launch of 102 tons with complement of 19, built in 1963.

PETREL

Coastal survey launch of 50 tons with complement of 9, built in 1965.

TRANSPORTS

BAHIA AGUIRRE Q 2 **BAHIA BUEN SUCESO** Q 6 **BAHIA THETIS** Q 8

Displacement, tons	3 100 standard; 5 000 full load
Dimensions, ft (*m*)	334·7 × 47 × 13·8 (*95·1* × *14·3* × *7·9*)
Guns (Q8 only)	2—4·1 in; 2—40 mm Bofors AA; 2—20 mm AA; 4—47 mm saluting
Main engines	2 sets Nordberg diesels; 2 shafts; 3 750 bhp = 16 knots
Oil fuel (tons)	500 (Q8); 442 (Q6), 355 (Q2)
Complement	100

Transport—*cont.*

GENERAL
Built by Canadian Vickers, Halifax, Nova Scotia. *Bahia Buen Suceso* was completed in June 1950. The first two are troop transports. *Bahia Thetis* is used as a training ship and armed (see above).

BAHIA THETIS *1967, Werner Schiefer*

SAN JULIAN (ex-*FS* 281) B 7

Displacement, tons	930
Dimensions, feet	176 × 32·5 × 11
Main engines	2 sets diesels; 2 shafts; 1 000 bhp = 10 knots
Oil fuel (tons)	75
Complement	40

GENERAL
Ex-US Army small cargo carrier. Built by Wheeler Shipbuilding Corpn. Launched in 1944. It was officially stated in May 1960 that this vessel, formerly rated as a transport was to be converted into a salvage vessel, but in Dec 1961 it was officially stated that she would continue to be a transport ship.

SALVAGE SHIP

GUARDIAMARINA ZICARI (ex-*Tehuelche*, ex-HMS *Kingfisher*, ex-*King Salvor*) (Q81)

Displacement, tons	1 600
Dimensions, feet	200·2 pp; 216 oa × 37·8 × 13
Main engines	Triple expansion, 2 shafts; 1 500 ihp = 12 knots
Oil fuel, (tons)	310
Complement	82

GENERAL
Former British submarine rescue ship. Built as an Admiralty ocean salvage vessel by Wm. Simons & Co. Ltd. Renfrew, Scotland, and laid down on 17 May 1941, launched on 18 May 1942 and completed on 17 July 1942. Converted into a Submarine Rescue Bell and Target ship in 1953-54. Paid off as Bell Rescue Ship in 1958 and subsequently employed as Submarine Support Ship and Tender. Purchased from Great Britain in Dec 1960, and sailed from Chatham to Argentina in Apr 1961, and renamed *Tehuelche*, Again renamed *Guardiamarina Zicari* in Apr 1963.

GUARDIAMARINA ZICARI *Argentine Navy*

PUNTA DELGADA (ex-*Sugarland*, ex-*Nanticoke, AOG 66*) B 16 (FLEET SUPPORT)

Displacement, tons	5 930 standard; 6 090 full load
Dimensions, feet	325 × 48·2 × 20
Main engines	Westinghouse diesel; 1 shaft; 1 400 bhp = 11·5 knots
Oil fuel (tons)	150
Range, miles	9 000 at 11 knots
Complement	72

GENERAL
Named after geographical location. USMS type T1-M-BT1. Built by St. John's River SB Corp, Jacksonville, Fla. Launched on 7 Apr 1945.

OILERS

PUNTA MEDANOS B 18 (UNDERWAY REPLENISHMENT)

Displacement, tons	14 352 standard; 16 331 full load
Measurement, tons	8 250 deadweight,
Dimensions, feet	470 pp; 502 oa × 62 × 28·5
Main engines	Double reduction geared turbines. 2 shafts; 9 500 shp = 18 knots (over 19 knots attained on trials)
Boilers	2 Babcock & Wilcox two-drum integral furnace water-tube
Oil fuel (tons)	1 500
Range, miles	13 700 at 15 knots
Complement	99

GENERAL
Built by Swan, Hunter & Wigham Richardson Ltd, Wallsend on-Tyne. Launched on 20 Feb 1950. Completed on 10 Oct 1950. A unit of the Argentine Navy available as a training vessel for personnel. She embodied experience gained in previous fleet oilers, and was, when completed the finest equipped and fastest of her type afloat. Fitted for fuelling warships at sea. Boilers built under licence by the Wallsend Slipway & Engineering Company. Steam conditions of 400 lb. per sq. in pressure and 750 deg F.

PUNTA MEDANOS *1973, Argentine Navy*

PUNTA ALTA B 12 (FLEET SUPPORT)

Displacement, tons	1 600 standard; 1 900 full load
Measurement, tons	800 deadweight
Dimensions, feet	210 × 33·8 × 12·5
Main engines	Diesel; 1 shaft; 1 850 bhp = 8 knots
Oil fuel (tons)	146

GENERAL
Built at Puerto Belgrano. Launched in 1937. Named after a headland.

TRAINING SHIP

LIBERTAD Q 2

Displacement, tons	3 025 standard; 3 765 full load
Dimensions, feet	262 wl; 301 oa × 47 × 21·8
Guns	1—3 in; 4—40 mm AA; 4—47 mm saluting
Main engines	2 Sulzer diesels; 2 400 bhp = 13·5 knots
Complement	370 (crew) plus 150 cadets

GENERAL
Built in the state owned shipyards at Rio Santiago. Launched on 20 June 1956. She is the largest sail training ship in the world and set up the fastest crossing of the N. Atlantic under sail in 1966 a record which still stands.

LIBERTAD *1971*

ICEBREAKER

GENERAL SAN MARTIN Q 4

Displacement, tons	4 854 standard; 5 301 full load
Measurement, tons	1 600 deadweight
Dimensions, feet	279 × 61 × 21
Guns	1—4 in; 2—40 mm AA Bofors
Aircraft	1 reconnaissance aircraft and 1 helicopter
Main engines	4 diesel-electric; 2 shafts; 7 100 hp = 16 knots
Range, miles	35 000 at 10 knots
Oil fuel (tons)	1 100
Complement	160

GENERAL
Built by Seebeck Yard of Weser AG. Launched on 24 June 1954. Completed in Oct 1954. Fitted for research. New second radar mast fitted on after end of the hanger in late 1972.

TUGS

GUAYCURU R 33 **QUILMES** R 32

Displacement, tons	368 full load
Dimensions, feet	107·2 × 24·4 × 12·5
Main engines	Skinner Unaflow engines; 645 ihp = 9 knots
Boilers	Cylindrical
Oil fuel (tons)	52
Range, miles	2 200 at 7 knots
Complement	14

GENERAL
"Quilmes" class tugs built at Rio Santiago, Argentina, in the State Naval Shipyards. Laid down on 23 Aug and 15 Mar 1956 respectively, launched on 27 Dec 1959 and 8 July 1957 and completed on 29 July and 30 Mar 1960.

PEHUENCHE R 29 **TONOCOTE** R 30

Displacement, tons	330
Dimensions, feet	105 × 24·7 × 12·5
Main engines	Triple expansion; 600 ihp = 11 knots
Boiler	2
Oil fuel (tons)	36
Range, miles	1 200 at 9 knots
Complement	13

GENERAL
Both built in Rio Santiago Naval Yard. Commissioned for service in 1954.

MATACO R 3 **TOBA** R 4

Displacement, tons	600
Measurement, tons	339 gross
Dimensions, feet	130·5 pp; 137 wl; 139 oa × 28·5 × 11.5
Main engines	Triple expansion; 2 shafts; 1 200 ihp = 12 knots
Boilers	2
Oil fuel (tons)	95
Range, miles	3 900 at 10 knots
Complement	34

GENERAL
Both built by Hawthorn Leslie, Ltd, Hebburn-on-Tyne. Launched on 24 Jan 1928 and 23 Dec 1927, respectively. Both completed in Mar 1928.

HUARPE R 12

Displacement, tons	370
Dimensions, feet	107 × 27·2 × 12
Main engines	Triple expansion; 800 ihp
Boilers	1 cylindrical (Howaldt Werke)
Oil fuel (tons)	58
Complement	13

GENERAL
Built by Howaldt Werke in 1927. Entered service in the Argentine Navy in 1942.

CALCHAQUI	R 6 (ex-US 445)	**CHULUPI**	R 10 (ex-US 426)
CAPAYAN	R 16 (ex-US 443)	**MOCOVI**	R 5 (ex-US 441)
CHAQUILLAN	R 18 (ex-US 444)	**MORCOYAN**	R 19 (ex-US 448)

Displacement, tons	70
Dimensions, feet	67 × 14 × 13
Main engines	Diesel; 310 bhp = 10 knots
Oil fuel (tons)	8·7
Complement	5

Built in USA and allocated the above pennant numbers in 1969.

Note. Two harbour tugs building by Vicente Forte will enter service in 1974.

AUSTRALIA

Minister for Defence (and Navy):
Hon. Mr. L. H. Barnard, MP

Chairman of the Chiefs of Staff:
Admiral Sir Victor Smith, KBE. CB, DSC

Naval Authorities

Chief of Naval Staff:
Vice-Admiral H. D. Stevenson, CBE

Chief of Naval Personnel:
Rear-Admiral G. J. Willis

Chief of Naval Technical Services:
Rear-Admiral M. P. Reed

Chief of Supply and Works:
Rear-Admiral A. G. McFarlane

Deputy Chief of the Naval Staff:
Rear-Admiral G. V. Gladstone, DSC *

Director, Joint Staff (DOD):
Rear-Admiral A. M. Synnot, CBE

Secretary, Department of the Navy:
Mr. Samuel Landau, CBE, MA

Senior Appointments

Flag Officer Commanding Austalian Fleet:
Rear-Admiral D. C. Wells, CBE

Flag Officer Commanding East Australian Area:
Rear-Admiral W. J. Dovers, CBE, DSC

Diplomatic Representation

Australian Naval Representative in London:
Captain David W. Leach, CBE, MVO

Naval Attaché in Washington:
Commodore R. Percy

Naval Attaché in Tokyo:
Captain P. M. Rees

Navy Estimates

$A
1971-72: 270 244 000 *
1972-73: 293 094 000 *
1973-74: 319 994 000 *
*includes United States Credits

Personnel

1 January 1972: 17 000 officers and sailors
1 January 1973: 17 128 officers and sailors
1 January 1974: 16 743 officers and sailors

Prefix to Ships' Names

HMAS. Her Majesty's Australian Ship

Strength of the Fleet

Type	*Active*	*Building*
Attack Carrier (Medium)	1	—
Destroyers	5 (3DDG)	—
Frigates	6	—
Patrol Submarines	4	2
MCM Vessels	6	—
Large Patrol Craft	19	—
Survey Ships	4	1
Fleet Support Ships	2	—
Landing Craft	8	—
Small Craft	7	—

Mercantile Marine

Lloyd's Register of Shipping:
370 vessels of 1 184 010 tons gross

Naval Procurement and Modernisation

The 3 Destroyers which were to have been built at Williamstown were deferred in August 1973. Foreign-built alternatives are being examined to fill the acknowledged requirement. At the same time plans for the Support ship *Protector* were deferred whilst a cheaper solution was sought.

3 Destroyers (DLGs *Hobart, Perth* and *Brisbane*) to be modernized at a cost of $A33 million (see class notes). Older frigates to have extended refits
10 Sea King helicopters in lieu of 20 Wessex at a cost of $A43 million (delivery in 1974)
6 Lynx helicopters at a cost of $A4 million

Naval Bases

Sydney (FOCEA) and Jervis Bay. Brisbane (NOC Queensland) and Cairns. Darwin (NOC.NT). Cockburn Sound (completing 1978) (NOC.WA).

Naval Shipyards

Building at Williamstown (Melbourne) and Cockatoo Island (Sydney). Refits at Garden Island (Sydney).

Fleet Air Arm

Squadron	*Aircraft*
HT 723	Iroquois and Scout helos
VC 724	A4G and TA4G Skyhawks. Macchi Trainers (Training, FRU and trials)
HT 725	Wessex 31B helos (training and FRU)
VF 805	A4G Skyhawks (Front line strike)
VS 816	S2E Trackers (Front line A/S)
HS 817	Wessex 31B helos (Front line A/S)
VC 851	S2E Trackers, HS748 and DC-3's (training, communication and FRU)

Disposals

ex-Carrier

Sydney	For disposal 20.7.73

Destroyers

Arunta	sank in tow to breaker 13.2.69
Tobruk	left Sydney for Taiwan 10.4.72
Anzac	1974

Frigates

Barcoo	left Sydney for Taiwan 17.3.72
Culgoa	left Sydney for Taiwan 17.3.72
Quickmatch	left Sydney for Japan 10.4.72
Quiberon	left Sydney for Japan 6.7.72
Gascoyne	left Sydney for Taiwan 6.7.72

Miscellaneous

Paluma	Sales List 31.3.73
Karakara	(Hulk) scuttled 30.1.73
SDBs 1321, 1324, 1325	1972

PENNANT LIST

Aircraft Carrier

Melbourne	21

Submarines

Oxley	57
Otway	59
Onslow	60
Ovens	70

Destroyers

Perth	38
Hobart	39
Brisbane	41
Vendetta	08
Vampire	11

Frigates

Yarra	45
Parramatta	46
Stuart	48
Derwent	49
Swan	50
Torrens	53

Training Ship

Duchess	154

Minehunters

Snipe	1102
Curlew	1121

Minesweepers (Coastal)

Hawk	1139
Teal (O)	1152
Ibis (O)	1183
Gull (O)	1185

Survey Ships

Moresby	73
Diamantina	266
Flinders	312
Kimbla	314

Support Ships

Supply	195
Stalwart	215

Landing Craft

Brunei	127
Labuan	128
Tarakan	129
Wewak	130
Salamaua	131
Buna	132
Berano	133
Balikpapan	134

Reserve Training Ships

Banks	244
Bass	247

Patrol Boats

Advance	83
Assail	89
Attack	90
Barbette	97
Barricade	98
Bayonet	101
Aitape (P)	84
Ladava (P)	92
Lae (P)	93
Madang (P)	94
Samarai (P)	85
Aware	91
Ardent	87
Bombard	99
Buccaneer	100
Archer	86
Adroit	82
Arrow	88
Acute	81

Notes
O=Operational Reserve
P=Papua-New Guinea Division

AIRCRAFT CARRIER

Name	*No.*	*Builders*	*Laid down*	*Launched*	*Commissioned*
MELBOURNE (ex-*Majestic*)	21	Vickers-Armstrong, Barrow-in-Furness	15 Apr 1943	28 Feb 1945	28 Oct 1955

1 MODIFIED "MAJESTIC" CLASS

Displacement, tons	16 000 standard; 19 966 full load
Length, feet (*metres*)	650·0 (*198·1*)wl; 701·5 (*213·8*)oa
Beam, feet (*metres*)	80·2 (*24·5*) hull
Draught, feet (*metres*)	25·5 (*7·8*)
Width, feet (*metres*)	80·0 (*24·4*) flight deck 126·0 (*38·4*) oa including 6 deg angled deck and mirrors
Hangar, feet (*metres*)	444×52×17·5 (*135·3×15·8×5·3*)
Aircraft	8 Sky Hawk jet fighters; 6 Tracker aircraft; 10 Westland Wessex A/S helicopters (see *Aircraft* notes)
Guns, AA	12—40 mm (4 twin, 4 single) Bofors
Boilers	4 Admiralty 3-drum type
Main engines	Parsons single reduction geared turbines; 2 shafts; 42 000 shp
Speed, knots	24; sea speed 23 max
Range, miles	12 000 at 14 knots; 6 200 at 23 knots
Complement	1 335 (includes 347 Carrier Air Group personnel); 1 070 (75 officers and 995 sailors) as Flagship

MELBOURNE — *1973, Royal Australian Navy*

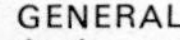

GENERAL
At the end of the Second World War, when she was still incomplete, work on this ship was brought to a standstill pending a decision as to future naval requirements. When full-scale work was resumed during 1949-55, and after her design had several times been re-cast, she underwent reconstruction and modernisation in Great Britain, including the fitting of the angled deck, steam catapult and mirror deck landing sights, and was transferred to the RAN on completion. She was commissioned and renamed at Barrow-in-Furness on 28 Oct 1955, sailed from Portsmouth on 5 Mar 1956, and arrived at Fremantle, Australia, on 23 April 1956. She became flagship of the Royal Australian Navy at Sydney on 14 May 1956. She cost £A8 309 000.

AIRCRAFT. The aircraft complement formerly comprised 8 Sea Venom jet fighters, 17 Gannet turbo-prop anti-submarine aircraft, and 2 Sycamore helicopters, later 4 Sea Venom, 6 Gannet and 10 Wessex A/S helicopters. Fourteen S2E Tracker anti-submarine aircraft and ten A4G Skyhawk fighter/bombers were purchased in 1966 in the USA (in service 1967) at a cost of $A46 000 000. Another 10 A4G Skyhawk (including 2 TA4G Trainers) were delivered during 1971. *Melbourne* now carries Skyhawks, Trackers and Wessex.

MODERNISATION. *Melbourne* completed her extended refit during 1969 at a cost of over $A8 750 000 to enable her to operate with S2E [illegible] and A4G Skyhawk aircraft, and to improve [illegible]bility. In 1971 the catapult was rebuilt and a bridle-catcher fitted, and the flight deck was strengthened. Under refit from November 1972 to July 1973.

RADAR. Search: Philips LWO series early warning and associated height finders for aircraft direction. Tactical: Type 293 Target Indication and surface warning. E.W.: Electronic intelligence and warfare equipment also fitted. Carrier controlled approach Radar. (Dome on island.)

DRAWING. Starboard elevation and plan as converted with the angled deck. Scale: 120 feet = 1 inch.

MELBOURNE — *1972, Royal Australian Navy*

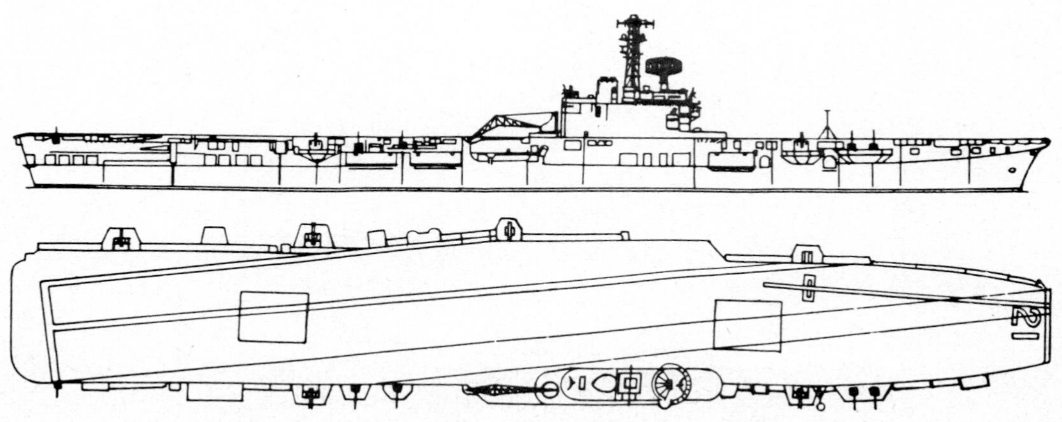

DESTROYERS

DDL Programme

On 22 August 1973 the Australian Government deferred the programme for building 3 new 4 200 ton destroyers. This programme (already severely pruned) was to have been for Australian designed and built replacements for the more elderly frigates. Further decisions on this programme, the need for which the Government has endorsed, will be made later in 1974 after other solutions, using foreign ships, have been examined and costed.

3 "PERTH" CLASS (DLGs)

Name	No.	Builders	Laid down	Launched	Commissioned
BRISBANE	41	Defoe Shipbuilding Co, Bay City, Mich.	15 Feb 1965	5 May 1966	16 Dec 1967
HOBART	39	Defoe Shipbuilding Co, Bay City, Mich.	26 Oct 1962	9 Jan 1964	18 Dec 1965
PERTH	38	Defoe Shipbuilding Co, Bay City, Mich.	21 Sep 1962	26 Sep 1963	17 July 1965

Displacement, tons	3 370 standard; 4 618 full load
Length, feet (*metres*)	431·0 (*131·4*)wl; 437·0 (*132·2*)oa
Beam, feet (*metres*)	47·1 (*14·3*)
Draught, feet (*metres*)	20·1 (*6·1*)
Missile launchers	1 single for "Tartar" (see Modernisation note)
A/S weapons	2 single launchers for long range "Ikara" system
Guns	2—5 in (*127 mm*) 54 cal, dp, single-mount, rapid fire
Torpedo tubes	6 (2 triple) for A/S torpedoes
Boilers	4 Foster Wheeler "D" type; 1 200 psi; 950°F
Main engines	2 GE double reduction turbines; 2 shafts; 70 000 shp
Speed, knots	35
Range, miles	6 000 at 14 knots 1 600 at 30 knots
Complement	333 (21 officers, 312 sailors)

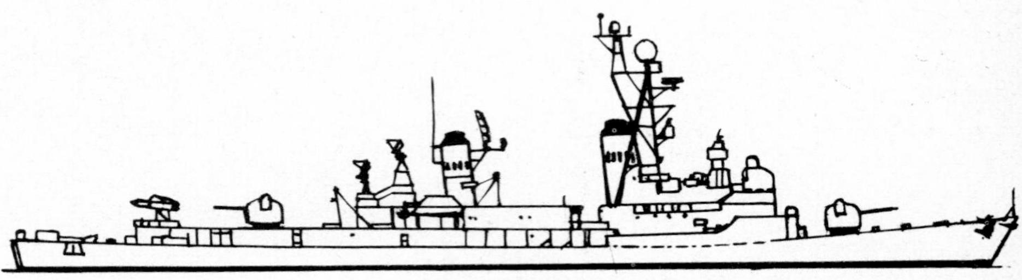
BRISBANE, HOBART, PERTH

GENERAL
On 6 Jan 1962, in Washington, US defence representatives and Australian military officials (on behalf of the Royal Australian Navy) and executives of the Defoe Shipbuilding Company, of Bay City, Michigan, signed a $A25 726 700 contract for the construction of two guided-missile destroyers (shipbuilding cost only). On 22 Jan 1963 it was announced by the Navy Minister in Canberra, Australia, that a third guided-missile destroyer was to be built in USA for Australia. The first of their kind for the Australian Navy, they constitute the 1st Destroyer Squadron, RAN. All three ships have been in action off Vietnam where they served with the US 7th fleet.

COST. Original estimate $A12 800 000 to $A14 000 000 each (with missiles and electronics $A40 000 000 each). The total cost of *Perth* was reported to be $A50 000 000.

DESIGN. Generally similar to the US "Charles F. Adams" class, but they differ by the addition of a broad deckhouse between the funnels enclosing the Ikara anti-submarine torpedo-carrying missile system, and the mounting of a single-arm launcher, instead of a twin, for the Tartar surface-to-air guided missiles. They have a new hull design with aluminium superstructures. The most recent habitability improvements have been incorporated into their construction, including air conditioning of all living spaces.

MODERNISATION. The modernisation of all three ships has been undertaken at Hunters Point, San Francisco. *Hobart* and *Perth* have been completed and *Brisbane* follows. The first stage of this modernisation consists of fitting Mk 10 mountings for the 5 inch armament. The second stage, to be carried out in Australia, will complete the installation of a computerised and automated command and control system (NCDA) and allow for the use of Standard missiles from the Tartar mounting.

RADAR. Search: SPS 40 and 3 D SPS 52 for aircraft. Tactical: SPS 10 surface search and tactical radar. Fire Control: C Band for Tartar system, X band for guns.

PERTH — *1971, Royal Australian Navy*

HOBART — *1973, Royal Australian Navy*

Destroyers—*continued*

3 "DARING" CLASS (DD)

Name	No.	Builders	Begun	Launched	Completed
VAMPIRE	11	Cockatoo Island Dockyard, Sydney	1 July 1952	27 Oct 1956	23 June 1959
VENDETTA	08	HMA Naval Dockyard, Williamstown	4 July 1949	3 May 1954	26 Nov 1958
DUCHESS	154	John I. Thornycroft & Co. Southampton	2 July 1948	9 Apr 1951	23 Oct 1952

Displacement, tons	2 800 standard; 3 600 full load
Length, feet (*metres*)	366 (*111·3*)pp; 388·5 (*118·4*)oa
Beam, feet (*metres*)	43 (*13·1*)
Draught, feet (*metres*)	12·8 (*3·9*)
Guns, surface	6—4·5 in (*115 mm*) in 3 twin turrets, two forward and one aft
Guns, AA	6—40 mm (2—40 mm in *Duchess*)
A/S weapons	1 3-barrelled DC mortar (see *Design* notes)
Boilers	2 Foster Wheeler; 650 psi; 850°F
Main engines	English Electric geared turbines; 2 shafts; 54 000 shp
Speed, knots	30·5
Range, miles	3 700 at 20 knots; 3 000 at 20 knots (*Duchess*).
Oil fuel, tons	584
Complement	320 (14 officers, 306 sailors)

GENERAL
The above particulars refer to *Vampire* and *Vendetta*, which constitute the 2nd Destroyer Squadron, R.A.N. *Vampire* and *Vendetta* are the largest destroyers ever built in Australia. They were ordered in 1946. Their sister ship, *Voyager*, the prototype of the class, collided with the aircraft carrier *Melbourne* and sank off the southern coast of New South Wales on the night of 10 Feb 1964. She was replaced by the British destroyer *Duchess*, lent to Australia by the United Kingdom for four years on 8 May 1964, later extended to 1971 and purchased by RAN in 1972.
Four large destroyers of this type were originally projected, to have been named after the Royal Australian Navy's famous "Scrap Iron Flotilla" of destroyers during the Second World War, but *Waterhen* was cancelled in 1954.

DESIGN. *Vampire* and *Vendetta* were of similar design, (including all welded construction) to that of the "Daring" class, built in Great Britain, but were modified to suit Australian conditions and have "Limbo" instead of "Squid" anti-submarine mortars. The superstructure is of light alloy, instead of steel, to reduce weight.

VAMPIRE, VENDETTA

MODERNISATION. *Vampire* completed in Dec 1971. *Vendetta* started half-life refit on 2 May 1973. The $20 million programme for both ships includes new Mk 22 fire-control systems, new LW02 air-warning and navigation radars, new action-information centre, modernised communications, fitting modernised turrets, improved habitability, the fitting of an enclosed bridge and new funnels. These alterations are being carried out by Williamstown Dockyard.

RADAR. Philips LW02 early warning, (not *Duchess*).

Note. *Duchess* has been converted for training purposes, including the removal of X-turret and Squid to make way for new upper-deck classrooms. She retains her forward battery radar (Type 293 and X-band fire control) and sonar (in maintenance). Completion March 1974.

VENDETTA *1973, Royal Australian Navy*

DUCHESS (after conversion) *1974, Royal Australian Navy*

FRIGATES

6 "RIVER" CLASS

Name	No.	Builders	Laid down	Launched	Commissioned
YARRA	45	Williamstown Naval Dockyard, Melbourne	9 Apr 1957	30 Sep 1958	27 July 1961
PARRAMATTA	46	Cockatoo Island Dockyard, Sydney	3 Jan 1957	31 Jan 1959	4 July 1961
STUART	48	Cockatoo Island Dockyard, Sydney	20 Mar 1959	8 Apr 1961	28 June 1963
DERWENT	49	Williamstown Naval Dockyard, Melbourne	16 June 1958	17 Apr 1961	30 Apr 1964
SWAN	50	Williamstown Naval Dockyard, Melbourne	18 Aug 1965	16 Dec 1967	20 Jan 1970
TORRENS	53	Cockatoo Island Dockyard, Sydney	18 Aug 1965	28 Sep 1968	19 Jan 1971

Displacement, tons	2 100 standard; 2 700 full load
Length, feet (*metres*)	360·0 (*109·7*) pp; 370·0 (*112·8*) oa
Beam, feet (*metres*)	41·0 (*12·5*)
Draught, feet (*metres*)	17·3 (*5·3*)
Missile launchers	1 quadruple for "Seacat"
A/S weapons	1 launcher for "Ikara" long range system 1 "Limbo" 3-barrelled DC mortar
Guns, dual purpose	2—4·5 in (*115 mm*)
Boilers	2 Babcock & Wilcox; 550 psi; 850°F
Main engines	2 double reduction geared turbines; 2 shafts; 30 000 shp
Speed, knots	30
Range, miles	4 500 at 12 knots
Complement	247 (13 officers, 234 sailors) in *Swan* and *Torrens*; 250 (13 officers, 237 sailors) in other four ships

PARRAMATTA — *1973, John Mortimer*

GENERAL
The design of the first four is basically similar to that of British "Type 12", the last pair to that of the "Leander" frigates. All are modified by the Royal Australian Navy to incorporate improvements in equipment and habitability. *Stuart* was the first ship fitted with the "Ikara" anti-submarine guided missile; trial ship for the system. *Derwent* was the first RAN ship to be fitted with "Seacat". The variable depth sonar has been removed from *Derwent* and *Stuart*. Note difference in silhouette between *Swan* and *Torrens* and the earlier ships of the class, the former pair having a straight-run upper deck.

MODERNISATION. Some, at least, of this class will shortly be modernised. This will include improved accommodation consequent on a reduction in crew, new fire control systems, an improved Ikara system and, possibly, the fitting of Mulloka a new and improved Australian sonar.

RADAR. Search: All ships fitted with Philips LWO series of L Band early warning radars. Type 293 combined air and surface warning, except *Swan* and *Torrens* which have Philips/HSA X Band radar. Fire Control: MRS 3 or HSA systems, X Band radar.

SWAN, TORRENS

DERWENT

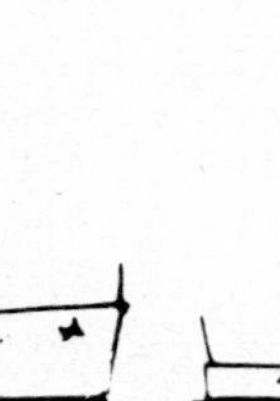

STUART

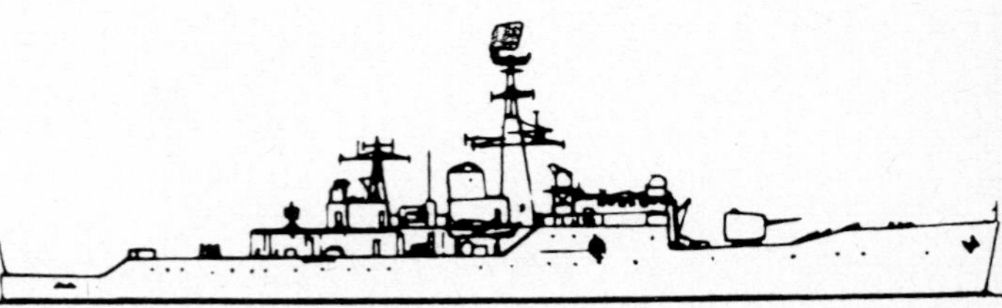

PARRAMATTA, YARRA.

SWAN — *1973, John Mortimer*

SUBMARINES

4 + 2 "OXLEY" CLASS (BRITISH "OBERON" CLASS)

Name	No.	Builders	Laid down	Launched	Commissioned
ONSLOW	60	Scotts' Shipbuilding & Eng Co Ltd, Greenock	4 Dec 1967	3 Dec 1968	22 Dec 1969
OTWAY	59	Scotts' Shipbuilding & Eng Co Ltd, Greenock	29 June 1965	29 Nov 1966	23 Apr 1968
OVENS	70	Scotts' Shipbuilding & Eng Co Ltd, Greenock	17 June 1966	4 Dec 1967	18 Apr 1969
OXLEY	57	Scotts' Shipbuilding & Eng Co Ltd, Greenock	2 July 1964	24 Sep 1965	18 Apr 1967
ORION		Scotts' Shipbuilding & Eng Co Ltd, Greenock	6 Oct 1972	Due 1974	Due 1975
OTAMA		Scotts' Shipbuilding & Eng Co Ltd, Greenock	1973	Due 1975	Due 1976

Displacement, tons: 1 610 standard; 2 196 surface; 2 417 submerged (revised official figures)
Length, feet (*metres*): 241 (*73·5*) pp; 295·5 (*90·1*) oa
Beam, feet (*metres*): 26·5 (*8·1*)
Draught, feet (*metres*): 18 (*5·5*)
Torpedo tubes: 8—21 in (*533 mm*) (6 bow, 2 stern)
Main engines: 2 Admiralty Standard Range diesels, 3 600 bhp; 2 shafts; 2 electric motors, 6 000 shp; Electric drive
Speed, knots: 16 surface; 18 dived (official figure)
Oil fuel, tons: 300
Range, miles: 12 000 at 10 knots
Complement: 62 (7 officers, 55 sailors)

ONSLOW, OTWAY, OVENS, OXLEY

GENERAL
It was announced by the Minister for the Navy on 22 Jan 1963 that four submarines of the "Oberon" class were to be built in British shipyards under Admiralty supervision at an overall cost of £A5 000 000 each. These were to constitute the 1st Submarine Squadron, R.A.N. based at HMAS Platypus, Neutral Bay, Sydney. Subsequently two more were ordered in October 1971 for delivery in 1975-76.

NAMES. *Oxley* and *Otway* are named after two earlier RAN submarines, completed in 1927. *Otama* is the Queensland aboriginal word for Dolphin, *Onslow* is a town in Western Australia, *Ovens* was an early explorer and *Orion* is named after the constellation.

R.N. SQUADRON. The last unit of the Fourth Submarine Squadron of the Royal Navy, *Trump*, was withdrawn from Balmoral, Sydney in Jan 1969.
Odin arrived in Australian waters in Dec 1972 for a three year attachment to the RAN.

OXLEY *1971, Royal Australian Navy*

ONSLOW *1973, John Mortimer*

MINE WARFARE SHIPS

6 "TON" CLASS (MODIFIED)

CURLEW (ex-HMS *Chediston*, ex-*Montrose*) 1121
GULL (ex-HMS *Swanston*) 1185
HAWK (ex-HMS *Somerleyton*, ex-*Gamston*) 1139
IBIS (ex-HMS *Singleton*) 1183
SNIPE (ex-HMS *Alcaston*) 1102
TEAL (ex-HMS *Jackton*) 1152

Displacement, tons: 375 standard; 445 full load (revised official figures)
Dimensions, feet: 140 pp; 152 oa × 28·8 × 8·2
Guns: 2—40 mm AA, *Curlew* and *Snipe* 1—40 mm
Main engines: Napier Deltic diesels; 2 shafts; 3 000 bhp = 16 knots
Range, miles: 2 300 at 13 knots; 3 000 at 8 knots
Complement: 34 (4 officers; 30 sailors); Minehunters 38 (3 officers, 35 sailors)

"Ton" class coastal minesweepers. Purchased from the United Kingdom in 1961, and modified in British Dockyards to suit Australian conditions. Turned over to the Royal Australian Navy, commissioned and re-named on 21 Aug, 19 July, 18 July, 7 Sept, 11 Sept, and 30 Aug respectively. Mirlees diesels were replaced by Napier Deltic, and ships air conditioned and fitted with stabilisers. Sailed from Portsmouth to Australia on 1 Oct 1962. Constitute the 1st Mine Countermeasures Squadron. *Curlew* and *Snipe* have been converted into minehunters.

FUTURE. It is understood that replacements for these ships are being considered.

HAWK *1970, Royal Australian Navy*

PATROL BOATS

19 "ACUTE" CLASS

Australia

ACUTE	81	**ARCHER**	86	**ASSAIL**	89	**BANDOLIER**	95	**BAYONET**	101
ADROIT	82	**ARDENT**	87	**ATTACK**	90	**BARBETTE**	97	**BOMBARD**	99
ADVANCE	83	**ARROW**	88	**AWARE**	91	**BARRICADE**	98	**BUCCANEER**	100

New Guinea

AITAPE	84	**LADAVA**	92	**LAE**	93	**MADANG**	94	**SAMARAI**	85

Displacement, tons	146 full load
Dimensions, feet	107·5 oa × 20 × 7·3 (max)
Guns	1—40 mm; 2 medium MG (no guns in *Aware, Bandolier* and *Madang*)
Main engines	Paxman 16 YJCM Diesels 3 500 hp; 2 shafts = 21-24 knots
Complement	19 (3 officers, 16 sailors). New Guinea boats: 2 officers 14 sailors

LAE — *1972, Royal Australian Navy*

Five patrol boats for the formation of the New Guinea coastal security force and fifteen for general duties were built. Steel construction. Builders: Evans Deakin & Co, Pty Ltd, Brisbane, and Walkers Ltd, Maryborough. Ordered in Nov 1965. First vessel was originally scheduled for delivery in Aug 1966, but was not launched until Mar 1967. Cost $A800 000 each.

TRANSFERS. *Bandolier* transferred to Indonesia after refit in 1973. Archer will be transferred later in 1974.

SILHOUETTE OF "ACUTE" CLASS after modification

OCEANOGRAPHIC AND SURVEY SHIPS

1 NEW CONSTRUCTION

COOK 291

Displacement, tons	1 910 standard; 2 650 full load
Length, feet (*metres*)	317·5 (*91·2*)
Beam, feet (*metres*)	44·0 (*13·4*)
Draught, feet (*metres*)	15·1 (*4·6*)
Main engines	Diesels; 2 shafts; 3 400 bhp
Speed, knots	17
Oil fuel, tons)	640
Range, miles	11 000 at 14 knots
Complement	150 including 13 scientists

GENERAL
Intended to replace HMAS *Diamantina*. She will have dual hydrographic and oceanographic roles. The after part of the ship will contain research equipment and facilities. Accommodation for 13 scientists. Work on her is starting in 1974 with completion planned 3-4 years later.

COOK — *1972, Official, revised artists impression*

Name	*No.*	*Builders*	*Laid down*	*Launched*	*Commissioned*
MORESBY	573	State Dockyard, Newcastle NSW	June 1961	7 Sep 1963	6 Mar 1964

Displacement, tons	1 714 standard; 2 351 full load
Length, feet (*metres*)	284·5 (*86·7*) pp; 314·0 (*95·7*) oa
Beam, feet (*metres*)	42·0 (*12·8*)
Draught, feet (*metres*)	15·0 (*4·6*)
Guns	2—40 mm Bofors AA (single)
Aircraft	1 Westland Scout Helicopter
Main engines	Diesel-electric; 3 diesels; 3 990 bhp; 2 electric motors; 2 shafts; 5 000 shp = 19 knots
Complement	146 (13 officers, 133 sailors)

GENERAL
The Royal Australian Navy's first specifically designed survey ship. Built at a cost of £A2 000 000 ($A4 000 000).

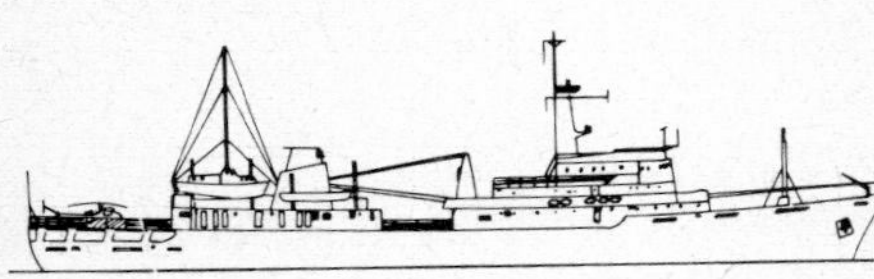

MORESBY

Name	*No.*	*Builders*	*Laid down*	*Launched*	*Completed*
DIAMANTINA	266 (ex-F 377)	Walkers Ltd, Maryborough, Queensland	12 Apr 1943	6 Apr 1944	27 Apr 1945

Displacement, tons	1 340 standard; 2 127 full load
Length, feet (*metres*)	283 (*86·3*) pp; 301·3 (*91·8*) oa
Beam, feet (*metres*)	36·7 (*11·2*)
Draught, feet (*metres*)	12·5 (*3·8*)
Guns	1—40 mm
Boilers	2 Admiralty 3-drum
Main engines	Triple expansion 5 500 ihp; 2 shafts
Speed, knots	19·5
Range, miles	7 700 at 12 knots
Complement	125 (6 officers, 119 sailors)

GENERAL
Frigate converted in 1959-60 for survey and completed conversion for oceanographic research in June 1969. The conversion included the provision of special laboratories. Sister ship *Lachlan* was sold to the Royal New Zealand Navy.

ARMAMENT. The two 4-inch guns and two "Squid" A/S mortars in "B" position were removed. The forward 4-inch gun was in "A" position with the 40 mm gun superimposed.

DIAMANTINA

Survey Ships—*continued*

Name	*No.*	*Builders*	*Laid down*	*Launched*	*Commissioned*
FLINDERS	312	HMA Dockyard Williamstown	11 June 1971	29 July 1972	27 Apr 1973

Displacement, tons 750
Dimensions, feet 161 × 33 × 12
Main engines 2 Paxman Ventura Diesels, total hp 1 680
Speed, knots 13·5
Range, miles 5 000 at 9 knots
Complement 38 (4 officers, 34 men)

Similar in design to *Atyimba* built for the Philippines, she replaced *Paluma* in April 1973, the latter having been running steadily since her conversion from stores tender in 1959. *Flinders* is based at Cairns, with her primary responsibility in the Barrier Reef area.

FLINDERS *1973, Royal Australian Navy*

KIMBLA A 314

Displacement, tons 762 standard; 1 021 full load
Dimensions, feet 150 pp; 179 oa × 32 × 12 mean
Main engines Triple expansion; 1 shaft; 350 ihp
Speed, knots 9·5
Complement 40 (4 officers, 36 men)

Built as a boom defence vessel by Walkers Ltd, Maryborough. Laid down 4 Nov 1953, launched 23 Mar 1955, completed 26 Mar 1956. Converted to trials vessel in 1959. Guns were removed (1—40 mm; 2—20 mm).

SUPPORT SHIPS

Note. On 22 August 1973, the Australian Government decided, amongst other things, that the construction of the third ship of this type, the 600 ft *Protector* should not go on. Examination of cheaper alternatives is in hand.

STALWART 215

Displacement, tons 10 000 standard; 15 500 full load
Length, feet (*metres*) 515·5 (*157·1*) oa
Beam, feet (*metres*) 67·5 (*20·6*)
Draught, feet (*metres*) 29·5 (*9·0*)
Missiles Provision for Seacat
Guns, AA 4—40 mm (2 twin)
Main engines 2 Scott-Sulzer 6-cyl turbo-diesels 2 shafts; 14 400 bhp
Speed, knots 20
Complement 396 (23 officers and 373 sailors)

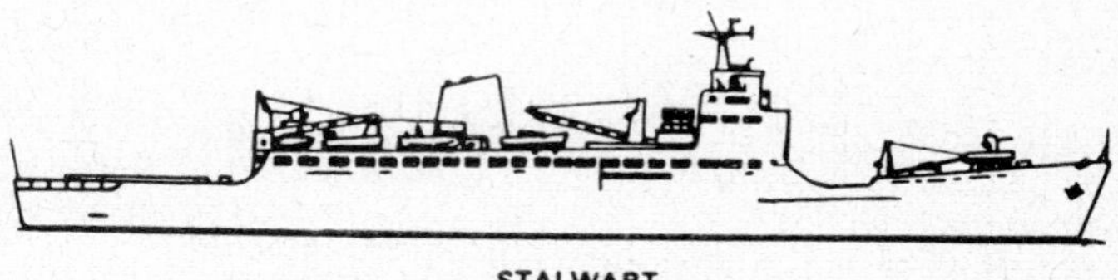

STALWART

GENERAL
Largest naval vessel designed and built in Australia. Built at Cockatoo Island Dockyard by Vickers (Australia) Pty Ltd, Sydney. Ordered on 11 Sep 1963. Laid down in June 1964 and launched on 7 Oct 1966. Commissioned 9 Feb 1968. Designed to maintain destroyers and frigates, and advanced weapons systems, including guided missiles. She has a helicopter flight deck and is defensively armed. High standard of habitability. Formerly rated as Escort Maintenance Ship. Redesignated Destroyer Tender in 1968. Cost officially estimated at just under $A15 000 000.

STALWART *1972, Royal Australian Navy*

SUPPLY (ex-*Tide Austral*) 195

Displacement, tons 15 000 standard; 25 941 full load
Measurement, tons 17 600 deadweight; 11 200 gross
Dimensions, feet 550 pp; 583 oa × 71 × 32 max
Guns 6—40 mm AA (2 twin, 2 single)
Main engines Double reduction geared turbines; 15 000 shp = 17·25 knots
Complement 13 officers, 187 sailors

Built for Australia by Harland & Wolff, Ltd, Belfast. Launched 1 Sep 1954, completed March 1955. British "Tide" Class. Lent to Great Britain until 1 Sep 1962, when *Tide Austral* was re-named HMAS *Supply* and commissioned in the Royal Australian Navy at Portsmouth 15 Aug 1962. Sailed for Australia 1 Oct 1962.

SUPPLY *1972, Royal Australian Navy*

AMPHIBIOUS FORCES

8 LANDING CRAFT (HEAVY) (LCH)

BRUNEI	127 (5.1.73)	**SALAMAUA**	131
LABUAN	128 (9.3.73)	**BUNA**	132
TARAKAN	129 (15.6.73)	**BETANO**	133
WEWAK	130 (10.8.73)	**BALIKPAPAN**	134

Displacement, tons 310 light; 503 full load
Dimensions, ft (*m*) 146 × 33 × 6·5 (*44·5 × 10·1 × 1·9*)
Guns 2 0·5 in MG
Main engines 2 GM Diesels. Twin screw = 10 knots
Complement 13 (2 officers, 11 men)

Originally this class was ordered for the Army with whom *Balikpapan* remained until mid-1974. All now transferred to RAN. Known commissioning dates in brackets.

BRUNEI *1973, Royal Australian Navy*

DIVING TENDERS

OTTER (ex-*Wintringham*) Y 299 **SEAL** (ex-*Popham*) Y 298
PORPOISE (ex-*Neasham*) Y 280

Displacement, tons 120 standard; 159 full load
Dimensions, feet 100 pp × 22 × 5·8
Main engines 2 Paxman diesels; 1 100 bhp = 14 knots
Range, miles 2 000 at 9 knots; 1 500 at 12 knots
Complement 7 (can accommodate 14 divers)

Transferred from the Royal Navy in 1966-67, these ex-inshore Minesweepers were converted to Diving Tenders and attached to the Diving School at Sydney.

SEAL *1971, Royal Australian Navy*

GENERAL PURPOSE VESSELS

BANKS (16 Feb 1960) **BASS** (25 May 1960)

Displacement, tons 207 standard; 255 and 260 full load respectively
Dimensions, feet 90 pp; 101 oa × 22 × 8
Main engines Diesels; speed = 10 knots
Complement 14 (2 officers, 12 sailors)

"Explorer" class. Of all steel construction. *Banks* was fitted for fishery surveillance and *Bass* for surveying, but both were used for other duties, including reserve training. Both built by Walkers, Maryborough. Completion dates in brackets.

TORPEDO RECOVERY VESSELS

TRV 253, 254, 255

Displacement, tons 91·6
Dimensions, feet 88·5 × 20·9 × 4·5
Main engines 3 GM Diesels; 890 = 13 knots
Complement 9 (1 officer, 8 men)

All built at Williamstown—completed between Jan 1970 and Apr 1971.

TRV 254 *1973, Royal Australian Navy*

TUG

BRONZEWING

Displacement, tons 250
Dimensions, feet 98·8 oa × 21·2 × 8·2
Main engines Diesel; 1 shaft; 480 bhp = 10 knots

Launched by Mort's Dock, Sydney 25 June 1946.

501 502 503 504

Displacement, tons 47·5
Dimensions, feet 50 × 15 ×
Main engines 2 GM Diesels; 340 bhp = 8—9 knots
Complement 3

First pair built by Stannard Bros. Sydney in 1969 and second pair by Perrin Engineering Brisbane in 1972.

AUSTRIA

Diplomatic Representation

Defence Attaché in London:
Brigadier General H. Wingelbauer

RIVER CRAFT

A Danube River patrol is run by the Austrian Army.

1 PATROL CRAFT

NIEDERÖSTERREICH

Displacement, tons 71
Dimensions, ft (*m*) 96·8 × 17·8 × 3·6 (*29·4 × 5·4 × 1·1*)
Guns 1—20 mm SPz Mk 66 Oerlikon in a turret; 1—12·7 mm MG; 1—Mk 42 MG; 2—8·4 cm PAR 66 "Carl Gustav" AT rifles
Main engines 2 V 16 Diesels; 1 600 hp = 22 knots
Complement 9

Built by Korneuberg Werft AG. Fully welded.

1 PATROL CRAFT

OBERST BRECHT

A smaller edition of *Nieder-österreich*.

NIEDERÖSTERREICH *1973, Herres Film*

3 Ex-US "M3" PATROL CRAFT

Even smaller riverine craft.

BAHAMAS

PATROL CRAFT

4 60 ft GRP TYPE

ACKLINS **ANDROS** **GLENTHIRA** **SAN SALVADOR**

Displacement, tons	30 standard approx
Dimensions, feet	62·0 oa × 15·8 × 4·6
Guns	1 MG forward; 2 LMG on bridge
Main engines	2 Caterpillar diesels = 20 knots
Complement	11

"60 ft" Keith Nelson patrol craft built by Vosper Thornycroft in glass reinforced plastic, delivered in 1970 as the first four units of the Bahamas Police Marine Division. With air-conditioned living spaces, these craft are designed for patrol amongst the many islands of the Bahamas Group. The foredeck is specially strengthened for a 20 mm MG with light MGs in sockets either side of the bridge.

ANDROS *1972, Vosper Thornycroft*

BAHRAIN

2 PATROL CRAFT

HOWRA **JIDA**

Displacement, tons	15
Dimensions, feet	45·5 × 12 × 3
Main engines	2 Diesels; 1 080 bhp = 23 knots

BANGLADESH

Administration

Minister for Air Shipping and Waterways,
General Osmani

Chief of staff
Commander Nurul Huq

Administrative Officer
Captain Kashedul Islam Chowdhury

Strength:	3 Armed River Steamers 1 Poluchat class
Personnel:	700—1000
Bases:	Chittagong, Kulna, Dacca

The Bangladesh Navy was the last of the three services to be formed, Commander Nurul Huq (a 37 year old engineering specialist trained at Manadon Royal Naval Engineering College) being appointed Chief of Staff at the end of March 1972. The first armed river steamer was commissioned by General Osmani on 12 June 1972 as P101. Two more, P102 and 103, were commissioned in late July being followed by P104, an ex-Soviet Poluchat class. Four Soviet Vanya class coastal minesweepers will be operating in Bangladesh waters until 1974. It is possible that these will be transferred to the navy on completion of their current tasks, but meanwhile the Bangladesh authorities are enquiring abroad for new construction tenders, presumably to carry our their stated intention of building up a force of gunboats and destroyers/ frigates. The activities of the Soviet Navy in this area suggest that, if adequate credit is not available in Western countries, the Bangladesh navy may be based on Russian ships.

3 ARMED RIVER STEAMERS

P 101 **P 102** **P 103**

Displacement, tons	100 tons (approx)
Dimensions, feet	100 × 18 × 6 (approx)
Guns	1—25 mm

1 Ex-SOVIET POLUCHAT PATROL BOAT

P 104

Displacement, tons	100 standard
Dimensions, feet	98·4 × 19·0 × 5·9
Guns	2—25 mm

GENERAL
As no other announcement has been made it is assumed that this ship has been transferred by India.

BARBADOS

PATROL CRAFT

1 65 ft (COASTAL PATROL CRAFT)

3 40 ft "GUARDIAN" CLASS (COASTAL PATROL CRAFT)

BELGIUM

Naval Board

Chief of Naval Staff:
Rear Admiral J. P. L. van Dyck

Diplomatic Representation

Naval, Military and Air Attaché in London:
Colonel (BEM) Jules Kaisin

Naval, Military and Air Attaché in Washington:
Colonel (BEM) de Wilde

Naval, Military and Naval Attaché in Paris:
Colonel (BEM) Hugo Rel

Personnel

(a) 1972: 330 officers and 4 681 men
1973: 330 officers and 4 700 men
1974: 330 officers and 3 875 men
(b) 15 months Military Service

Strength of the Fleet

Type	*Active*	*Building/Planned*
Frigates	—	4
Minesweepers (Ocean)	7	—
Minesweepers (Coastal)	9	—
Minesweepers (Inshore)	14	—
Support Ships	2	—
River Patrol Boats	6	—
Research Ships	2	—
Auxiliary and Service Craft	13	—

Mercantile Marine

Lloyd's Register of Shipping:
236 vessels of 1 161 609 tons gross

FRIGATES

4 "E-71" CLASS

Name	*Pennant No.*	*Builders*	*Laying down*	*Completion*
WEST HINDER	F 900	Cockerill, Hoboken	1974	1976
WEST DIEP	F 901	Cockerill, Hoboken	1974	1977
WANDELAAR	F 902	Boelswerf, Temse	1975	1977
WIELINGEN	F 903	Boelswerf, Temse	1975	1978

Displacement, tons	1 500 standard; 1 828 full load
Length, feet (*metres*)	317·0 (*96·6*)
Beam, feet (*metres*)	38·6 (*11·8*)
Draught, feet (*metres*)	17·2 (*5·3*)
Guns	1—3·9 in (*100 mm*) AA Twin 40 mm or 1—57 mm aft
Missiles	1 NATO Sea Sparrow SAM; with 8 tubes; 4 Exocet SSM
Torpedo Launchers	2 L-5 Torpedo Launchers
A/S Rocket Launchers	1—6 × 375 mm LR Bofors
Rocket Launchers	2—8-barrelled Corvus dual-purpose ECM/flare launchers
Main engines	CODOG—1 Rolls Royce Olympus TM3 gas turbine; 28 000 bhp; 2 Cockerill CO-240 diesels 6 000 bhp. Twin vp propellers
Speed, knots	28 (15 on 1 diesel, 20 on 2 diesels)
Range, miles	3 000 at 18 knots; 5 000 at 14 knots
Complement	15 officers, 145 men

GENERAL
This compact, well-armed class of frigate is the first break by the Belgian Navy from their previous MCM-only interest. These ships, from which a helicopter has now been deleted, will be valuable coastal units. All to be fitted with hull-mounted sonar and fin stabilisers.

ELECTRONICS. Albatros missile and gun control system with Elsag NA-10 gun fire control sub-system.

MISSILES (SAM). Sea Sparrow RIM 7H-2 manufactured under licence by Selenia.

RADAR. Plessey AWS-2 surveillance—HSA Mk 22 fire control—2 Selenia Orion RTN-10X trackers with Albatros continuous wave—navigation radar.

TYPE E 71 FRIGATE — *1973, Belgian Navy*

MINE WARFARE FORCES

7 U.S. MSO (Ex-AM) TYPE 498

(MINESWEEPERS (OCEAN) and MINEHUNTER)

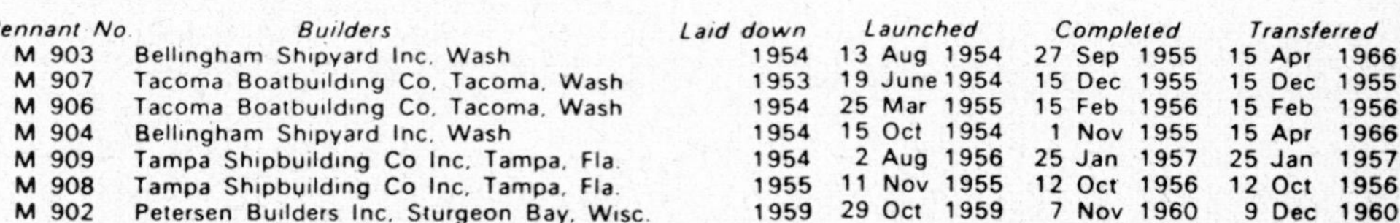

Name	*Pennant No*	*Builders*	*Laid down*	*Launched*	*Completed*	*Transferred*
A.F. DUFOUR (ex-*Lagen*, M 950 ex-*MSO* 498)	M 903	Bellingham Shipyard Inc, Wash	1954	13 Aug 1954	27 Sep 1955	15 Apr 1966
ARTEVELDE (ex-*MSO* 503, ex-*AM* 503)	M 907	Tacoma Boatbuilding Co, Tacoma, Wash	1953	19 June 1954	15 Dec 1955	15 Dec 1955
BREYDEL (ex-*MSO* 504, ex-*AM* 504)	M 906	Tacoma Boatbuilding Co, Tacoma, Wash	1954	25 Mar 1955	15 Feb 1956	15 Feb 1956
DE BROUWER (ex-*Namsen*, M 951, ex-*MSO* 499)	M 904	Bellingham Shipyard Inc, Wash	1954	15 Oct 1954	1 Nov 1955	15 Apr 1966
F. BOVESSE (ex-*MSO* 516, ex-*AM* 516)	M 909	Tampa Shipbuilding Co Inc, Tampa, Fla.	1954	2 Aug 1956	25 Jan 1957	25 Jan 1957
G. TRUFFAUT (ex-*MSO* 515, ex-*AM* 515)	M 908	Tampa Shipbuilding Co Inc, Tampa, Fla.	1955	11 Nov 1955	12 Oct 1956	12 Oct 1956
VAN HAVERBEKE (ex-*MSO* 522)	M 902	Petersen Builders Inc, Sturgeon Bay, Wisc.	1959	29 Oct 1959	7 Nov 1960	9 Dec 1960

Displacement, tons	720 standard; 780 full load
Length, feet (*metres*)	165·0 (*50·3*) wl; 172·5 (*52·6*) oa
Beam, feet (*metres*)	35·0 (*10·7*)
Draught, feet (*metres*)	11·0 (*3·4*)
Guns	1—40 mm AA
Main engines	2 GM diesels; 2 shafts; 1 600 bhp
Speed, knots	14 approx
Range, miles	2 400 at 12 knots; 3 000 at 20 knots
Oil fuel, tons	50
Complement	72 (5 officers, 67 men)

Wooden hulls and non-magnetic structure. Capable of sweeping mines of all types. Diesels of non-magnetic stainless steel alloy. Controllable pitch propellers.
Artevelde was converted to Minehunter in 1972.

VAN HAVERBEKE — *1971, Giorgio Arra*

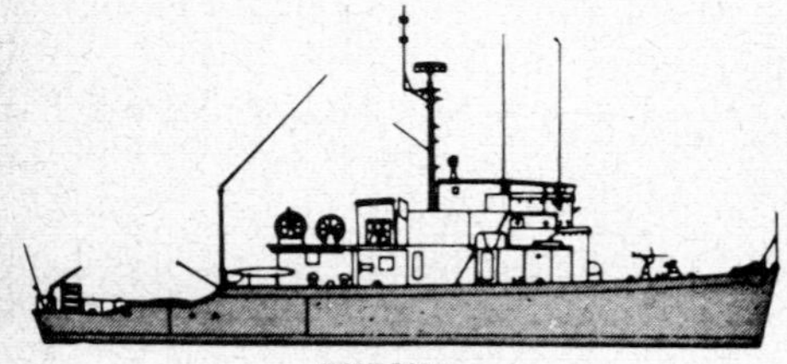

DUFOUR

MINESWEEPERS (COASTAL)

9 U.S. MSC (ex-AMS) TYPE 60 (MINESWEEPERS—COASTAL)

M 929 HEIST
M 931 KNOKKE
M 933 KOKSIJDE
M 932 NIEUWPOORT
M 930 ROCHEFORT
M 927 SPA
M 928 STAVELOT
M 934 VERVIERS (ex-*MSC* 259)
M 935 VEURNE (ex-*MSC* 260)

VERVIERS (minehunter) *12/1973 C. & S. Taylor*

Displacement, tons	330 light; 390 full load
Dimensions, feet	139 pp; 144 oa × 27·9 × 7·5 (8 max)
Guns	1—40 mm AA
Main engines	2 GM Diesels; 2 shafts; 880 bhp = 13·5 knots max
Oil fuel, tons	28
Range, miles	2 700 at economical speed (10·5 knots)
Complement	39

Coastal minesweepers with wooden hulls and constructed throughout of materials with the lowest possible magnetic signature. M 910-925, 934 and 935 were built in USA, under MDAP, and M 926-933 of same type were built in Belgium with machinery and equipment from USA. M 934 (ex-MSC 259) transferred 19 June 1956, M 935 (ex-MSC 260) was transferred on 7 Sep 1956. M 926 to 933 were all laid down in 1953-54 and launched and completed in 1954-55. *Verviers* and *Veurne* converted to minehunters with active rudders.

RECLASSIFICATION. *Mechelen*, M 926, former coastal minesweeper of this class, was re-rated as a research ship and re-numbered A 962 in 1968 (see next page).

MINESWEEPERS (INSHORE)

14 "HERSTAL" CLASS (MINESWEEPERS—INSHORE)

M 485 ANDENNE (ex-*MSI* 97) May 1958
M 484 DINANT (ex-*MSI* 96) 5 Apr 1958
M 471 HASSELT May 1958
M 478 HERSTAL (ex-*MSI* 90) 6 Aug 1956
M 479 HUY (ex-*MSI* 91) 17 Nov 1956
M 472 KORTRYK May 1957
M 473 LOKEREN 18 May 1957
M 476 MERKSEM 5 Apr 1958
M 477 OUDENAERDE May 1958
M 483 OUGREE (ex-*MSI* 95) 16 Nov 1957
M 480 SERAING (ex-*MSI* 92) Mar 1957
M 475 TONGEREN 16 Nov 1957
M 474 TURNHOUT 7 Sep 1957
M 482 VISE (ex-*MSI* 94) 7 Sep 1957

VISE *1971, Belgian Navy*

Displacement, tons	160 light (190 full load)
Dimensions, feet	106·7 pp; 113·2 oa × 22·3 × 6 (7 max)
Guns	1—13 mm AA
Main engines	2 diesels; 2 shafts; 1 260 bhp = 15 knots max
Oil fuel (tons)	18
Range, miles	2 300 at 10 knots
Complement	17

MSI type. Modified AMI "100-foot" class. All built in Belgium. The first four MSI were launched in 1956. *Herstal* and *Temse* were both launched at the Mercantile Marine Yard, Kruibche, on 6 Aug 1956, followed by another pair in 1956, and four more pairs in 1957 (see launch dates above). *Herstal* was completed in June 1957.

The first group of eight (M 478 to 485) was a United States "off shore order", the remaining eight (M 470 to 477) being financed under the Belgian Navy Estimates.

SUPPORT SHIPS

ZINNIA A 961

Displacement, tons	1 705 light; 2 435 full load
Length, feet (*metres*)	299·2 (*91·2*) pp; 309 (*94·2*) wl; 326·4 (*99·5*) oa
Beam, feet (*metres*)	49·9 (*14·0*)
Draught, feet (*metres*)	11·8 (*3·6*)
Guns	3—40 mm AA (single)
Aircraft	1 helicopter
Main engines	2 Cockerill V 12 RT 240 CO diesels; 5 000 bhp; 1 shaft
Speed, knots	20 max; 18 sea
Oil fuel, tons	500
Range, miles	4 400 at 14 knots
Complement	125

Laid down at Hoboken by J. Cockerill on 8 Nov 1966. Launched on 6 May 1967. Completed on 12 Sep 1967. Controllable pitch propeller. Design includes a platform and a retractable hangar for one light liaison-helicopter. Rated as Command and Logistic Support Ship.

ZINNIA *1973 Belgian Navy*

Support Ships—*continued*

GODETIA A 960

Displacement, tons	1 700 light; 2 300 full load
Dimensions, feet	289 wl; 301 oa × 46 × 11·5
Guns	4—40 mm (2 twin) AA
Aircraft	Provision for light helicopter
Main engines	4 ACEC—MAN diesels; 2 shafts; 5 400 bhp = 19 knots max
Oil fuel, tons	500
Range, miles	4 500 at 15 knots
Complement	100 plus 35 spare billets

Built at Temse by J. Boel and Sons. Laid down on 15 Feb 1965, launched on 7 Dec 1965 and completed on 2 June 1966. Controllable pitch propellers. Provided with a platform which can take a light liaison-helicopter, and has Royal Apartments.

GODETIA *1972, Belgian Navy*

RIVER PATROL BOATS

LEIE **LIBERATION** **MEUSE** **SAMBRE** **SCHELDE** **SEMOIS**

Displacement, tons	25 light; 27·5 full load
Dimensions, feet	75·5 pp; 82 oa × 12·5 × 3 feet (*Liberation* 85·5 × 13·1 × 3·2)
Guns	2—13 mm MG
Main engines	2 diesels; 2 shafts; 440 bhp = 19 knots
Complement	7

Built at the Theodor Shipyards of Regensburg, Germany, in 1953, except *Liberation* in 1954. *Dender, Ourthe* and *Rupel* were officially deleted from the list in 1965. *Yser* was deleted from the list on 27 Aug 1969 and sold on 9 Sep 1969.

LEIE *1970, John G. Callis*

RESEARCH SHIPS

ZENOBE GRAMME A 958

Displacement, tons	149
Dimensions, feet	92/76 × 22·5 × 7 feet
Main engines	1 MWM diesel; 1 shaft; 200 bhp = 10 knots
Complement	14

Auxiliary sail schooner. Built by J. Boel in Temse, Belgium, in 1961. Designed for scientific research.

Research Ships—*continued*

MECHELEN A 962 (ex-M 926)

Displacement, tons	330 light; 390 full load
Dimensions, feet	139 pp; 144 oa × 27·9 × 7·5 (8 max)
Main engines	2 GM diesels; 2 shafts; 880 bhp = 13·5 knots max
Oil fuel (tons)	28
Radius, miles	2 700 at economical speed (10·5 knots)
Complement	39

Former coastal minesweeper built in 1954. Re-rated as a research ship in 1968.

MECHELEN *1970, Belgian Navy*

TUGS

SUB-LIEUTENANT VALCKE A 950

Displacement, tons	110
Dimensions, feet	78·8 pp; 95 oa × 21 × 5·5
Main engines	1 diesel; 1 shaft; 600 bhp = 12 knots
Complement	14

Built in Haarlem, Netherlands in 1951.

There are also two port tugs, *Bij* and *Krekel*, displacement 71 tons, length 57·8 feet 2 Voith-Schneider propellers, 400 hp; three harbour tugs, *Hommel* and *Wesp*, displacement 22 tons, length 43 feet, with 300 bhp diesels and Voith-Schneider propellers. built in Germany in 1953; and *Mier*, displacement 17·5 tons, length 41 feet, with 90 bhp diesels and Voith-Schneider propellers, built in Belgium in 1962.

AUXILIARY CRAFT

HARBOUR CRAFT. There are three barges, namely *FN 4, FN 5* and *FN 6*, displacement 300 tons, length, 105 feet, built in the Netherlands; the ammunition ship *Ekster*, displacement 140 tons, length 118 feet, built in Belgium in 1953; two diving cutters, ZM 3 and ZM 4, displacement 8 tons, length 33 feet, built in Belgium in 1953; and the harbour transport cutter *Spin*, displacement 32 tons, length 47·8 feet, with 250 bhp diesels = 8 knots and Voith-Schneider propeller, built in the Netherlands in 1958.

BOLIVIA

Senior Appointment

Rear Admiral Alberto Albarracin

Personnel

(a) 1974: 1 500 officers and men
(b) 12 months selective military service

Prefix to Ships Names

FNB

A small navy used for patrolling Lake Titicaca.

1 TRANSPORT

COLONEL ALAROA M 08

16 PATROL CRAFT

Of various sizes.

BRAZIL

Naval Board

Chief of Naval Staff:
Admiral J de Carvalho Jordão
Chief of Naval Material:
Admiral A de Negreiros Jannuzzi
Chief of Naval Personnel:
Admiral G de Azevedo Henniug

Diplomatic Representation

Naval Attaché in London
Captain Wilson Mourão Santos

Naval Attaché in Washington:
Rear Admiral Roman Gomes Leite Labarthe

Naval Attaché in Paris:
Captain Odyr Marques Buarque de Gusmão

Personnel

1971: 40 600 (3 800 officers and 36 800 men) including marines

1972: 42 125 (3 264 officers and 38 861 men) including marines and auxiliary corps.

1973: 44 339 (3 591 officers and 40 746 men) including marines and auxiliary corps.
1974: 49 600 (3 887 officers and 45 713 men) including marines and auxiliary corps.
(b) 1 years National service

Strength of the Fleet

Type	*Active*	*Building*
Attack Carrier (medium)	1	—
Cruiser	1	—
Destroyers	15	6
Frigates	3	—
Corvettes	10	—
Submarines (Patrol)	8	2
Landing Ships	2	—
Monitor and Gunboats	9	—
River Patrol Ships	5	—
Minesweepers (Coastal)	8	2
Survey Ships	6	—
Survey Launches	11	—
S/M Rescue Ships	1	—
Repair Ship	1	—
Oilers	2 (1 small)	—
Transports	4	—
Tugs	3	—
Floating Docks	3	—

Disposals

Cruiser

1973 *Barroso*

Destroyers

1973 *Amazonas, Mariz, E. Barros, Piaui, Santa Catarina*

Frigates

1973 *Baependi, Bracui*

Submarines

1972 *Rio Grande do Sul* (ex-*Sandlance*) for alongside training. *Bahia* (ex-*Plaice*)

Light Forces

1971 *Piraju, Piranha*
1972 *Paraguaçu*
1973 *Pirague*

Tankers

1970. *Raza* and *Rijo*

Prefix to Ship's Names

These vary, indicating the type of ship e.g N Ae L = Aircraft Carrier; CL = Light Cruiser; CT = Destroyer; F = Frigate.

Proposed New Construction

1 Helicopter Carrier	10 LCM
3 A-A Frigates	1 Survey Ship
4 Coastal Patrol Craft	3 Tugs
1 Replenishment Oiler	
4 LVC	
4 LCVP	

Naval Bases

There are naval bases at Rio de Janeiro, Belém, Natal, and Salvadore, and a River base at Ladario. The Naval Base is at Cabo Frio.

Naval Aviation

A Fleet Air Arm was formed on 26 January 1965. Current strength of helicopters: 3 SH-3D, 3 SH-1-S58 Sikorsky, 3 UH-2-Westland Wasp 5 UH-5-Whirlwind Mk III, 10 IH-2A-Hughes 200, 1 IH-2B-Hughes 300.

Note. Investigations in hand over replacement of certain of these helicopters. Fixed-wing Aircraft are operated by Brazilian Air Force prersonnel.

Mercantile Marine

Lloyd's Register of Shipping:
469 vessels of 2 103 319 tons gross

ATTACK CARRIER (MEDIUM)

1 Ex-BRITISH TYPE
("COLOSSUS" CLASS)

Name	*Pennant No.*	*Builders*	*Laid down*	*Launched*	*Completed*	*Reconstructed*
MINAS GERAIS (ex-HMS *Vengeance*)	A 11	Swan, Hunter & Wigham Richardson, Ltd, Wallsend on-Tyne	16 Nov 1942	23 Feb 1944	15 Jan 1945	Verolme Dock, Rotterdam, 1957-60

Displacement, tons	15 890 standard; 17 500 normal; 19 890 full load (see *Displacement* note)
Length, feet (*metres*)	630 (*192·0*) pp; 695 (*211·8*) oa
Beam, feet (*metres*)	80 (*24·4*)
Draught, feet (*metres*)	21·5 (*6·6*) mean; 24·5 (*7·5*) max
Flight deck,	
Length, feet (*metres*)	690 (*210·3*)
Width, feet (*metres*)	121 (*37·0*) oa as reconstructed
Height, feet (*metres*)	39 (*11·9*) above water line
Catapults	1 steam
Aircraft	20 aircraft including 7 S2A, 4 Sea Kings
Guns, AA	10—40 mm (2 quadruple, 1 twin)
Guns, saluting	2—47 mm
Boilers	4 Admiralty 3-drum type; Working pressure 400 psi (*28 kg/cm²*); max superheat 700°F (371°C)
Main engines	Parsons geared turbines; 2 shafts; 40 000 shp
Speed, knots	24; 25·3 on trials after reconstruction
Range, miles	12 000 at 14 knots; 6 200 at 23 knots
Oil fuel, tons	3 200
Complement	1 000 (1 300 with air group)

MINAS GERAIS *1971, Brazilian Navy*

GENERAL AND CONVERSION
Served in the British Navy from 1945 onwards. Insulated for tropical service and partially air-conditioned. Fitted out in late 1948 to early 1949 for experimental cruise to the Arctic. Lent to the Royal Australian Navy early in 1953, returned to the Royal Navy in Aug 1955. Purchased by the Brazilian Government on 14 Dec 1956. Reconstructed at Verolme Dock, Rotterdam (Verolme United Shipyard's Rozenburg yard) from summer 1957 to Dec 1960. The conversion and overhaul included the installation of the angled deck, steam catapult, mirror sight deck landing system, armament fire control and radar equipment. The ship was purchased for $9 000 000 and the reconstruction cost $27 000 000. Commissioned in the Brazilian Navy at Rotterdam on 6 Dec 1960. Left Rotterdam for Rio de Janeiro on 13 Jan 1961. Used primarily for anti-submarine aircraft and helicopters.

ENGINEERING. Engines and boilers arranged *en echelon*, the two propelling machinery spaces having one set of turbines and two boilers installed side by side in each space, on the unit system. Maximum speed at 120 rpm. Steam capacity was increased when the boilers were retubed during reconstruction in 1957-60.

ELECTRICAL. During reconstruction an alternating current system was installed with a total of 2 500 kW supplied by four turbo-generators and one diesel generator.

RADAR. Air Surveillance SPS 12; Surface Search SPS 4; FD SPS 8B; Air Control SPS 8A; Fire Control SPG 34; Navigation MP 1402.

OPERATIONAL. Single track catapult for launching, and arrester wires for recovering, 20 000 lb aircraft at 60 knots. Catapult accelerator gear port side forward.

HANGAR. Dimensions: length, 445 feet; width, 52 feet; clear depth, 17·5 feet. Aircraft lifts: 45 feet by 34 feet. During reconstruction in 1957-60 new lifts replaced the original units.

DISPLACEMENT. Before reconstruction: 13 190 tons standard; 18 010 tons full load.

Aircraft Carrier—*continued*

DRAWING. Starboard elevation and plan. Re-drawn in 1971. Scale: 107 feet = 1 inch

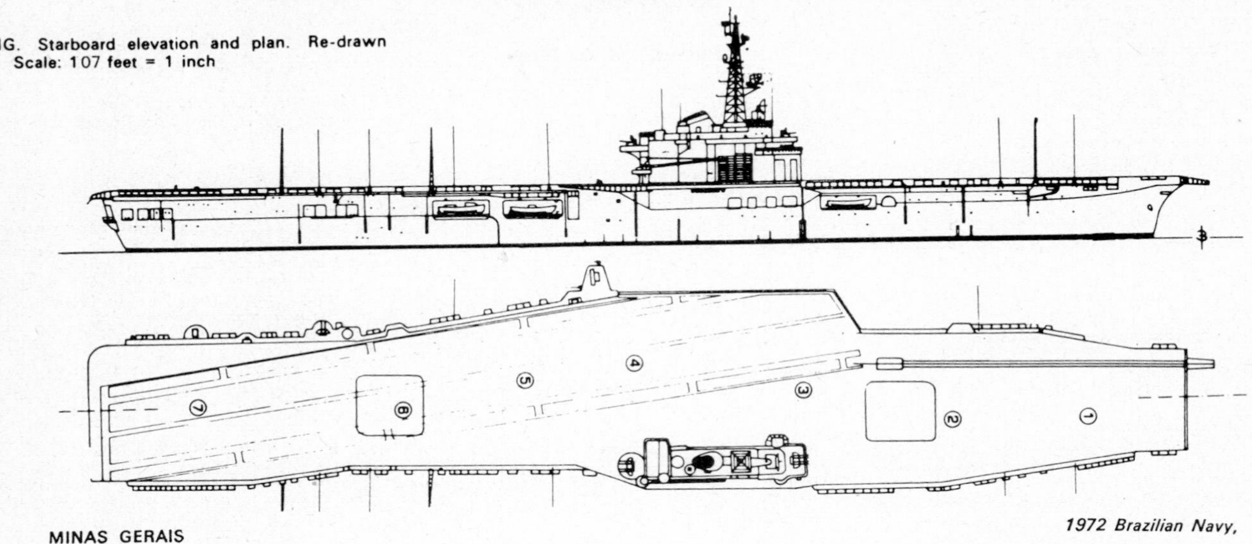

MINAS GERAIS

1972 Brazilian Navy,

CRUISER

Name	*Pennant No.*	*Builders*	*Laid down*	*Launched*	*Completed*
TAMANDARÉ (ex-USS *St. Louis CL* 49)	C 12	Newport News S. B. & DD. Co.	10 Dec 1936	15 Apr 1938	10 Dec 1939

Displacement, tons	10 000 standard; 13 500 full load
Length, feet (*metres*)	608·5 (*185·5*) oa
Beam, feet (*metres*)	69 (*21·0*)
Draught, feet (*metres*)	24 (*7·3*) max
Aircraft	1 Helicopter (see *Hangar notes*)
Guns, surface	15—6 in (*153 mm*) (47 cal (5 triple)
Guns, dual purpose	8—5 in (*127 mm*) 38 cal (4 twin)
Guns, AA	28—40 mm, 8—20 mm
Armour, inches (*mm*)	Belt 5 in—1½ in (*127 mm—38 mm*); Decks 3 in—2 in (*76 mm—51 mm*); Turrets 5 in—3 in (*127 mm—76 mm*); C.T. 8 in (*203 mm*)
Boilers	8 Babcock & Wilcox Express
Main engines	Parson's geared turbines; 100 000 shp; 4 shafts
Speed, knots	32·5
Range, miles	14 500 at 15 knots
Oil fuel, tons	2 100
Complement	975

TAMANDARÉ

1972, Brazilian Navy

GENERAL
"St. Louis class". Transferred from USA on 29 Jan 1951.

HANGAR. The hangar in the hull right aft could originally accommodate 6 aircraft if necessary together with engine spares and duplicate parts, though 4 aircraft was the normal capacity.

RADAR. SPS 12 search and SPS 10 tactical radar.

DRAWING. Starboard elevation and plan: Re-drawn in 1971. Scale: 121 feet = 1 inch.

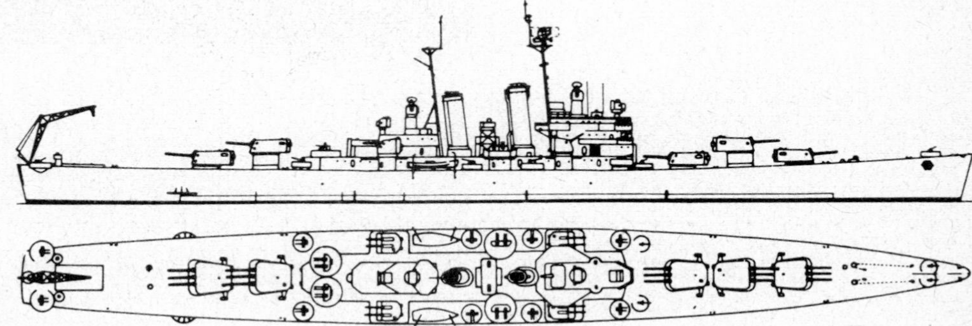

Destroyers—*continued*

2 Ex-US "GEARING" (FRAM I) CLASS

Name	Pennant No.	Builder	Launched	Completed
MARCILIO DIAS (ex-USS *Henry W. Tucker* DD 875)	D 25	Consolidated Steel	8 Nov 1944	12 Mar 1945
MARIZ E. BARROS (ex-USS *Brinkley Bass* DD 887)	D 26	Consolidated Steel	26 May 1945	1 Oct 1945

Displacement, tons	2 425 standard; 3 500 full load
Length, feet (*metres*)	390·5 (*119·0*)
Beam, feet (*metres*)	40·9 (*12·4*)
Draught, feet (*metres*)	19 (*5·8*)
Guns	4—5 inch (*127 mm*) 38 cal DP (twin)
A/S weapons	1 Asroc 8-tube launcher; 2 triple Mk 32 torpedo launchers; facilities for small helicopter
Main engines	2 GE geared turbines; 60 000 shp; 2 shafts
Boilers	4 Babcock & Wilcox
Speed, knots	34
Range, miles	5 800 at 15 knots
Complement	274 (14 officers, 260 men)

GEARING (FRAM I) CLASS

GENERAL
Enlarged "A. M. Sumner" class—14 feet longer. Fitted with VDS. Transfrered 3 Dec 1973.

RADAR. SPS-10 and SPS 40.

SONAR. SQS-23.

FRIGATES

3 ex-US DE TYPE "BERTIOGA" CLASS

Name	Pennant No.	Laid down	Launched	Completed
BAURU (ex-USS *McAnn*, DE 179)	U 28 (ex-D 18)	17 May 1943	22 Aug 1943	11 Oct 1943
BENEVENTE (ex-USS *Christopher*, DE 100)	U 30 (ex-D 20)	7 Dec 1942	June 1943	23 Oct 1943
BOCAINA (ex-USS *Marts*, DE 174)	U 32 (ex-D 22)	26 Apr 1943	8 Aug 1943	3 Sep 1943
	U 31 (ex-D 23)	3 May 1943	5 Sep 1943	24 Sep 1943

Displacement, tons	1 240 standard; 1 900 full load
Length, feet (*metres*)	306 (*93·3*) oa
Beam, feet (*metres*)	36·7 (*11·2*)
Draught, feet (*metres*)	12 (*3·7*)
Guns, dual purpose	3—3 in (*76 mm*)
Guns, AA	2—40 mm, 4—20 mm
Torpedo tubes	3—21 in (*533 mm*)
A/S weapons	2 DC racks
Main engines	4 GM diesels; 2 electric motors; diesel-electric drive; 2 shafts; 6 000 bhp
Speed, knots	21
Range, miles	11 500 at 11 knots
Oil fuel, tons	300
Complement	200

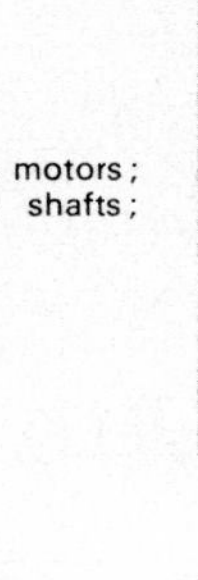

BAEPENDI — *1970, Brazilian Navy*

BERTIOGA *Class*

GENERAL
Former US "Bostwick" class destroyer escorts, transferred in 1944. Built by Federal, Port Newark. Formerly designated CTE (Destroyer Escorts) but reclassified as *Avisos Oceanicos* in 1965.

CORVETTES

10 "IMPERIAL MARINHEIRO" CLASS

ANGOSTURA	V 20	**FORTE DE COIMBRA**	V 18	**IPIRANGA**	V 17
BAHIANA	V 21	**IGUATEMI**	V 16	**MEARIM**	V 22
CABOCLO	V 19	**IMPERIAL MARINHEIRO**	V 15	**PURUS**	V 23
				SOLIMOES	V 24

Displacement, tons	911 standard
Dimensions, feet	184 × 30·5 × 11·7
Guns	1—3 in, 50 cal; 4—20 mm AA
Main engines	2 Sulzer diesels; 2 160 bhp = 16 knots
Oil fuel (tons)	135
Complement	60

All built in the Netherlands, launched in 1954-55, and incorporated into the Brazilian Navy in 1955. Actually fleet tugs. Equipped for the fighting.

IMPERIAL MARINHEIRO *Class*

SOLIMOES — *1972, Brazilian Navy*

SUBMARINES

3 NEW CONSTRUCTION BRITISH "OBERON" CLASS

HUMAITA **TONELERO**
RIACHUELO

Displacement, tons	1 610 standard estimated; 2 060 full buoyancy surface; 2 200 normal surface; 2 420 submerged, official figure
Length, feet (*metres*)	295·5 (*90·1*) overall
Beam, feet (*metres*)	26·5 (*8·1*)
Draught, feet (*metres*)	18·0 (*5·5*)
Tubes	8—21 in (*533 mm*), 6 bow and 2 stern for homing torpedoes
Main engines	2 Admiralty Standard Range 1 16-cyl diesels; 3 680 bhp; 2 electric motors; 6 000 shp; 2 shafts; electric drive
Speed, knots	15 on surface max; 17·5 submerged designed
Complement	70 (6 officers and 64 men)

GENERAL
In 1969 it was announced that two submarines of the British "Oberon" class were ordered from Vickers, Barrow. The third boat was ordered in 1972. *Humaita* was laid down 3 Nov 1970, launched 5 Oct 1971 and completed 18 June 1973. *Tonelero* was laid down 18 Nov 1971, launched 22 Nov 1972. *Riachuelo* was laid down 26 May 1973. Diesels by Vickers Shipbuilding Group. Electric motors by AEI-English Electric. Sonar, modern navigational aids and provision for modern fire control system developed by Vickers.

HUMAITA *1973, Vickers Ltd*

2 Ex-US "GUPPY III" TYPE

AMAZONAS (ex-USS *Greenfish*, SS 351) S16
GOIAS (ex-USS *Trumpetfish*, SS 425) S15

Displacement, tons	1 975 standard; 2 450 dived
Length, feet (*metres*)	326·5 (*99·4*)
Beam, feet (*metres*)	27 (*8·2*)
Draught, feet (*metres*)	17 (*5·2*)
Torpedo tubes	10—21 in; 6 bow 4 stern
Main machinery	4 Diesels; 6 400 hp/2 electric motors; 5 400 hp; 2 shafts
Speed, knots	20 surface, 15 dived
Complement	85

Converted in 1960-62. *Greenfish* built by Electric Boat Co, completing 7 June 1946. *Trumpetfish* built by Cramp Shipbuilding Co, completing on 29 Jan 1946. S 15 transferred 19 Dec 1973, S 16 on 15 Oct 1973.

SONAR. BQR-2 array, BQG-4 (PUFFS) fire control sonar (fins on casing).

AMAZONAS *1969, USN*

5 Ex-US "GUPPY II" TYPE

BAHIA (ex-USS *Sea Leopard* SS 483) S 12
CEARA (ex-USS *Amberjack* SS 522) S 14
GUANABARA (ex-USS *Dogfish* SS 350) S10
RIO DE JANEIRO (ex-USS *Odax* SS 484, ex-*Guanabara*) S 13
RIO GRANDE DO SUL (ex-USS *Grampus* SS 523) S 11

Displacement, tons	1 870 standard; 2 420 dived
Length, feet (*metres*)	307·5 (*93·8*) oa
Beam, feet (*metres*)	27·2 (*8·3*)
Draught, feet (*metres*)	18 (*5·5*)
Torpedo Tubes	10—21 in (6 bow, 4 stern)
Main engines	3 diesels, 4 800 shp; 2 motors; 5 400 shp; 2 shafts
Speed, knots	18 surfaced; 15 dived
Range, miles	12 000 at 10 knots (surfaced)
Complement	82

GENERAL
Dogfish built by Electric Boat Co. Commissioned 29 April 1946. *Odax* and *Sea Leopard* built by Portsmouth Navy Yard, commissioned 11 July 1945 and 11 June 1945 respectively. *Grampus* and *Amberjack* built in Boston Navy Yard and commissioned 26 Oct 1949 and 4 March 1946 respectively. Transferred 13 May 1972 (*Rio Grande do Sul*), 10 July 1972 (*Rio de Janeiro*), 28 July 1972 (*Guanabara*), 27 Mar 1973 (*Bahia*), 17 Oct 1973 (*Ceará*).

RIO GRANDE DO SUL *1972, Brazilian Navy*

AMPHIBIOUS FORCES

1 TANK LANDING SHIP (ex-USS "SUFFOLK COUNTY" CLASS)

DUQUE DE CAXIAS G 26 (ex-USS *Grant County* LST 1174)

Displacement, tons	3 828 light; 7 804 full load
Dimensions, ft (*m*)	445 oa × 62 × 16·9 (*135·7 × 18·9 × 5·2*)
Guns	2—3 in 50 cal (twins)
Main engines	Diesels; 13 700 shp; 2 shafts; CP propellers = 17·2 knots
Complement	175 (11 officers, 164 men)
Troops	App. 575

Built by Avondale, New Orleans. Launched 12 Oct 1956 and transferred 15 Jan 1973.

1 TANK LANDING SHIP (LST) (511-1152 Series)

GARCIA D'AVILA G 28 (ex-USS *Outagamie County* LST 1073)

Displacement, tons	1 653 standard; 2 366 beaching; 4 080 full load
Dimensions, feet	316 wl; 328 oa × 50 × 14
Guns	8—40 mm AA (2 twin, 4 single)
Main engines	GM diesels; 2 shafts; 1 700 bhp = 11·6 knots
Complement	119
Troops	147

Transferred on loan to Brazil by USN 24 May 1971, purchased 1 Dec 1973.

GARCIA D'AVILA *1973, Brazilian Navy*

LIGHT FORCES

1 THORNYCROFT TYPE (RIVER MONITOR)

PARNAIBA U 17 (ex-P 2)

Displacement, tons	620 standard; 720 full load
Dimensions, feet	180·5 oa × 33·3 × 5·1 max
Guns	1—3 in, 50 cal; 2—47 mm; 2—40 mm AA; 6—20 mm AA
Armour	3 in side and partial deck protection
Main engines	2 Thornycroft triple expansion; 2 shafts; 1 300 ihp = 12 knots
Boilers	2 three drum type, working pressure 250 psi
Oil fuel, tons	70
Range, miles	1 350 at 10 knots
Complement	90

Built at Rio de Janeiro. Laid down on 11 June 1936. Launched on 2 Sep 1937 and completed in Nov 1937. In Mato Grosso Flotilla. Rearmed with the above guns in 1960.

PARNAIBA *1971, Brazilian Navy*

Light Forces—*continued*

2 PEDRO TEIXEIRA CLASS (RIVER PATROL SHIPS)

PEDRO TEIXEIRA
RAPOSO TAVARES

Displacement, tons	700 standard
Dimensions, feet	203·4 × 30·7 × 6·3
Guns	1—40 mm AA 2—81 mm mortars 6—·50 cal MG
Main engines	4 diesels; 2 shafts = 16 knots

Both built in Arsenal de Marinha, Rio de Janeiro. Helicopter platforms fitted. *Teixeira* launched 14 Oct 1970. Both commissioned 17 Dec. 1673.

3 RORAIMA CLASS (RIVER PATROL SHIPS)

AMAPA **RORAIMA** **RONDONIA**

Displacement, tons	340 standard
Dimensions, feet	147·6 × 27·7 × 4·2
Guns	1—40 mm AA 2—81 mm mortars 6—·50 cal MGs
Main engines	Diesels; 2 shafts = 14 knots

Built by Shipyard Maclaren, Brazil. Completion in 1974.

6 "PIRATINI" CLASS (GUNBOATS)

PAMPEIRO (ex-USN PGM 118)	P 12	**PIRAJA** (ex-USN PGM 110)	P 11
PARATI (ex-USN PGM 119)	P 13	**PIRATINI** (ex-USN PGM 109)	P 10
PENEDO (ex-USN PGM 120)	P 14	**POTI** (ex-USN PGM 121)	P 15

Displacement, tons	105 standard;
Dimensions, feet	95 × 19 × 6
Guns	3—·50 cal MG; 1—81 mm mortar
Main engines	4 diesels; 1 100 bhp = 17 knots
Range, miles	1 700 at 12 knots
Complement	15 officers and men

Six coastal gunboats of the "Piratini" class were built in the Arsenal de Marinha do Rio de Janeiro under offshore agreement. *Piratini* entered service in Nov 1970 and the remainder between Mar and Oct 1971.

POTI *1972, Brazilian Navy*

PIRAQUE *1968, Brazilian Navy*

MINE WARFARE FORCES

4 + 2 "ARATU" CLASS (MINESWEEPERS—COASTAL)

ANHATOMIRIM M 16
ARACATUBA M 18
ARATU M 15
ATALAIA M 17

Displacement, tons	230 standard; 280 full load
Dimensions, feet	154·9 × 23·6 × 6·9
Guns	1—40 mm AA
Main engines	4 Maybach diesels; 2 shafts; 4 500 bhp = 24 knots
Range, miles	710 at 20 knots
Complement	31

Builders: Abeking & Rasmussen, Lemwerder. First four ordered in Apr 1969 and another pair in Nov 1973. Four more are projected. *Aratu* and *Anhatomirim* entered service on 5 May 1971 and 30 November 1971 respectively, the other pair 13 Dec. 1972.

ARATU *1972, Brazilian Navy*

ARATU *Class*

4 JAVARI CLASS (MINESWEEPERS—COASTAL)

JAVARI (*ex* USS *Cardinal*) M 11
JUTAI (*ex* USS *Egret*) M 12

Displacement, tons	270 standard; 350 full load
Dimensions, feet	136 × 24·5 × 8 max
Guns	4—20 mm in two twin mountings
A/S weapons	2 DCT
Main engines	2 GM diesels; 2 shafts; 1 000 bhp = 15 knots
Oil fuel (tons)	16
Range, miles	2 300 at 8·5 knots
Complement	50

GENERAL
Of wooden construction. Both launched in 1942-43. Originally known in USA as Auxiliary Motor minesweepers (AMS). Reclassified as Minesweepers, Coastal (old), MSC (o), in Feb 1955. *Javari*, ex-*Cardinal*, MSCo 4 and, *Jutai*, ex-*Egret*, MSCo 13, were transferred to Brazil by USA at Charleston Naval Shipyard on 15 Aug 1960 as the nucleus of a Brazilian mine force, and renamed after Brazilian rivers. *Jackdaw* MSCo 21, was transferred in Jan 1963, and *Grackle* MSCo 13, in Apr 1963. Used for patrol and escort duties.

JURUENA *1972, Brazilian Navy*

SURVEY SHIPS

2 FRIGATE TYPE

Name	*Pennant No.*	*Laid down*	*Launched*	*Completed*
CANOPUS	H 22	13 Dec 1956	20 Nov 1957	15 Mar 1958
SIRIUS	H 21	13 Dec 1956	30 July 1957	1 Jan 1958

Displacement, tons	1 463 standard; 1 800 full load
Dimensions, feet	236·2 pp; 246 wl; 255·7 oa × 39·3 × 12.2
Guns	1—3 in AA; 4—20 mm MG
Main engines	2 Sulzer diesels; 2 shafts; 2 700 bhp = 15·75 knots
Range, miles	12 000 at cruising speed of 11 knots
Complement	102

GENERAL
Built by Ishikawajima Heavy Industries Co. Ltd., Tokyo, Japan. Helicopter platform aft. Special surveying apparatus, echo sounders, Raydist equipment, sounding machines installed, and helicopter, landing craft (LCVP), jeep, and survey launches carried. All living and working spaces are air-conditioned. Controllable pitch propellers.

SIRIUS *1970, Brazilian Navy*

3 COASTAL TYPE

Name	*Pennant No.*	*Laid down*	*Launched*	*Commissioned*
ARGUS	H 31	12 Dec 1955	6 Dec 1957	29 Jan 1959
ORION	H 32	12 Dec 1955	5 Feb 1958	11 June 1959
TAURUS	H 33	12 Dec 1955	7 Jan 1958	23 Apr 1959

Displacement, tons	250 standard; 300 full load
Dimensions, feet	138 pp; 147·7 oa × 20 × 6·6
Guns	2—20 mm AA
Main engines	2 diesels coupled to two shafts; 1 200 bhp = 15 knots
Oil fuel, tons	35
Range, miles	1 200 at 15 knots

All built by Arsenal da Marinha, Rio de Janeiro.

TAURUS *1972, Brazilian Navy*

ALMIRANTE SALDANHA U 10 (ex-NE 1)

Displacement, tons	3 325 standard; 3 825 full load
Dimensions, feet	262 pp; 307·2 oa × 52 × 18·2 mean
Main engines	Diesel; 1 400 bhp = 11 knots
Range, miles	12 000 at 10 knots
Complement	356

Former training ship with a total sail area of 25 990 sq ft and armed with four 4-in guns one 3-in AA gun and four 3-pounders. Built by Vickers Armstrongs Ltd, Barrow. Launched on 19 Dec 1933. Cost £314 500. Instructional minelaying gear was included in equipment. The single 21-in torpedo tube was removed. Re-classified as an Oceanographic Ship (NOc) Aug 1959, and completly remodelled by 1964. A photograph as sailing ship appears in the 1952-53 to 1959-60 editions.

ALMIRANTE SALDANHA *1972, Brazilian Navy*

SURVEY LAUNCHES

CAMOCIM	H 16	**ITACURUSSA**	H 15	**PARAIBANO**	H 11
CARAVELAS	H 17	**JACEGUAI**	H 14	**RIO BRANCO**	H 12

Displacement, tons	32 standard; 50 full load
Dimensions, feet	52·5 × 15·1 × 4·3
Main engines	1 diesel; 165 bhp = 11 knots
Range, miles	600 at 11 knots

FAROLEIRO SANTANA	H 28	**FAROLEIRO AREAS**	H 27
FAROLEIRO NASCIMENTO	H 30	**MESTRE JOÃO DOS SANTOS**	H 13
CASTELHANOS	H 24		

Note. Buoy-tender *Almirante Graca Arnaha* ordered in 1971 in Brazil.

TYPE 1 SUBMARINE RESCUE SHIP

GASTAO MOUTINHO K 10 (ex-USS *Skylark* ASR 20)

Displacement, tons	1 235 standard; 1 740 full load
Dimensions, feet	205 oa × 38·5 × 15·3
Main engines	Diesel electric; 1 shaft; 3 000 bhp = 14 knots
Complement	85

Built by Charleston SB & DD Co. and converted to present form in 1957. Fitted with special pumps, compressors and submarine rescue chamber. Fitted for helium-oxygen diving. Transferred 30 June 1973.

REPAIR SHIP

BELMONTE G 24 (ex-USS *Helios*, ARB 12, ex-*LST* 1127)

Displacement, tons	1 625 light; 2 030 standard; 4 100 full load
Dimensions, feet	316 wl; 328 oa × 50 × 11
Guns	8—40 mm AA
Main engines	GM diesels; 2 shafts; 1 800 bhp = 11·6 knots
Oil fuel, tons	1 000
Range, miles	6 000 at 9 knots

GENERAL
Former United States battle damage repair ship. Built by Maryland DD Co, Baltimore Md. Laid down on 23 Nov 1944. Launched on 14 Feb 1945. Completed on 26 Feb 1945. Loaned to Brazil by USA in Jan 1962 under MAP.

BELMONTE — *1974, Brazilian Navy*

OILERS

MARAJÓ G 27

Measurement, tons	10 500 deadweight
Dimensions, feet	440·7 × 63·3 × 24
Main engines	Diesel; one shaft = 13·6 knots
Capacity, *cu metres*	14 200
Complement	80
Range, miles	9 200 at 13 knots

Laid down on 13 Dec 1966 and launched on 31 Jan 1968. Built by Ishikawajima Do Brasil-Estaleisos SA. Completed on 22 Oct 1968.

MARAJÓ — *1972, Brazilian Navy*

Oilers—*continued*

POTENGI G 17

Displacement, tons	600
Dimensions, feet	175·5 pp; 178·8 oa × 24·5 × 6
Main engines	Diesels, 2 shafts; 550 bhp = 10 knots
Oil, tons	450
Complement	19

Built at the Papendrecht yard in the Netherlands. Launched on 16 Mar 1938. Employed in the Mato Grosso Flotilla on river service.

TRANSPORTS

4 "PEREIRA" CLASS

Name	*Pennant No.*	*Laid down*	*Launched*	*Completed*
ARY PARREIRAS	G 21	13 Dec 1955	24 Aug 1956	29 Dec 1956
BARROSO PEREIRA	G 16	13 Dec 1953	10 Aug 1954	1 Dec 1954
CUSTÓDIO DE MELLO	U 26	13 Dec 1953	10 June 1954	30 Dec 1954
SOARES DUTRA	G 22	13 Dec 1955	13 Dec 1956	23 Mar 1957

Displacement, tons	4 800 standard; 7 300 full load
Measurement, tons	4 200 deadweight; 4 879 gross (Panama)
Dimensions, feet	362 pp; 391·8 oa × 52·5 × 20·5 max
Guns	4—3 in (U 26); 2—3 in (others); 2/4—20 mm
Main engines	Ishikawajima double reduction geared turbines; 2 shafts; 4 800 shp = 17·67 knots (sea speed 15 knots)
Boilers	2 Ishikawajima two drum water tube type, oil fuel
Complement	127 (Troop capacity 497)

GENERAL
All built in Japan by Ishikawajima Heavy Industries Co, Ltd, Tokyo. Transports and cargo vessels. Flush deckers with forecastle and long poop. Elevator type helicopter landing platform aft. Troop carrying capacity for 497, with commensurate medical, hospital and dental facilities. Working and living quarters are mechanically ventilated with partial air conditioning. Refrigerated cargo space 15 500 cubic feet. Can carry 4 000 tons of cargo. *Barroso Pereira* and *Custódio de Mello* were incorporated into the Brazilian Navy on 22 Mar 1955 and 8 Feb 1955 respectively. Formerly armed with eight 40 mm AA guns. *Custódio de Mello* has been classified as a training ship since July 1961.

SOARES DUTRA — *1972, Brazilian Navy*

TUGS

TRIDENTE R 22 (ex-*ATA 235*)
TRITÃO R 21 (ex-*ATA 234*)
TRIUNFO R 23 (ex-*ATA 236*)

Displacement, tons	534 standard; 835 full load
Dimensions, feet	133·7 wl; 143 oa × 33 × 13·2
Guns	2—20 mm AA
Main engines	GM diesel-electric; 1 500 hp = 13 knots

GENERAL
All built by Gulfport Boiler & Welding Works, Inc, Port Arthur, Texas, and launched in 1954. Ex-US *ATRs*. Nos. *Tridente* R 22, *Tritao* R 21, *Triunfo* R 23 (ex-R1, R 2, R 3).

TRIDENTE — *1972, Brazilian Navy*

FLOATING DOCKS

3 FLOATING DOCKS

CIDADE DE NATAL (ex-AFDL 39)

Displacement, tons	7 600
Length, feet (*metres*)	390·3 (119)
Beam, feet (*metres*)	86·9 (26·5)
Capacity, tons	2 800

Concrete floating dock loaned to Brazil by USN ,10 Nov. 1966.

ALMIRANTE JERONYMO GONCALVES (ex-AFDL 4)

Displacement, tons	3 000
Length, feet (*metres*)	200 (52·6)
Beam, feet (*metres*)	44 (13·4)
Capacity, tons	1 000

Steel floating dock acquired by Brazil from USN, 10 Nov. 1966.

AFONSO PENA (ex-*ARD* 14)

Displacement, tons	5 200
Dimensions, feet	402·0 × 81·0

Formerly the United States auxiliary repair dry dock *ARD* 14. Transferred from the US Navy to the Brazilian Navy and allocated the name *Ceara* in 1968.

BRUNEI

Askar Melayu Diraja Brunei (Royal Brunei Malay Regiment) Flotilla:
Commanding Officer: Lieutenant Commander P. G. King, R.N.

FAST ATTACK CRAFT (MISSILE)

PAHLAWAN

Displacement, tons	95 standard; 114 full load
Dimensions, feet	90·0 pp; 96·0 wl; 99·0 oa × 25·2 × 7·0
Missiles	8—SS 12 on 2 launchers
Guns	1—40 mm; 1—20 mm Hispano Suiza
Main engines	3 Bristol Siddeley Proteus gas turbines; 3 shafts; 12 750 bhp = 57 knots max; 2 diesels for cruising and manoeuvring
Range, miles	450 at full speed; 2 300 at 10 knots
Complement	20

Ordered from Vosper Ltd, Portsmouth, England, on 10 Dec 1965. Launched on 5 Dec 1966. Completed 19 Oct 1967. Constructed of resin bonded timber with aluminium alloy superstructure. Missile launchers fitted in May 1972.

PAHLAWAN *1968, Vosper Thornycroft Limited*

COASTAL PATROL CRAFT

MASNA **SALEHA** **NORAIN**

Displacement, tons	25
Dimensions, feet	62·0 × 16·0 × 4·5
Guns	2—20 mm Hispano Suiza; 2 MG
Main engines	2 GM diesels; 1 240 bhp = 26 knots *max*
Range, miles	600 at 23 knots
Complement	8

These boats were built specially for the Flotilla by Vosper Thornycroft (Private) Ltd. Singapore. Fitted with Decca 202 radar. *Norain*, last of the three, completed August 1972. Named after Brunei princesses.

NORAIN *1972, Vosper Thornycroft*

Another Coastal Patrol Craft of improved design—71 feet in length with 2 MTU diesels of 1 250 hp each giving a speed of 32 knots and armed with 2—20 mm guns—was ordered in May 1973 for delivery in 1974 by Vospers (Singapore). All wood construction with laminated frames.

ARMED LAUNCHES

BENDAHARA **KEMAINDERA** **MAHARAJALELA**

Displacement, tons	10
Dimensions, feet	47·0 × 12·0 × 3·0
Guns	2 MG
Main engines	2 GM diesels; 334 bhp = 20 knots
Range, miles	200
Complement	6

Rated as armed motor launches. Fitted with Decca 202 radar.

HOVERCRAFT

SRN 6 with a speed of 60 knots and a range of 150 miles armed with one machine gun There are also 25 armed river boats, it was officially stated in Jan 1972.

BULGARIA

Naval Board

Commander-in-Chief, Navy:
Rear-Admiral Yanakiev

Diplomatic Representation

Naval, Military and Air Attaché in London:
Lt. Colonel Dimitar Toskov

Strength of the Fleet

Type	*Active*	*Building*
Frigates	2	—
Corvettes	2	—
Patrol Submarines	4	—
FAC (Missile)	2	—
FAC (Patrol)	6	—
FAC (Torpedo)	12	—
Minesweepers (Ocean)	2	—
Minesweepers (Coastal)	4	—
Minesweepers (Inshore)	2	—
Minesweeping Boats	24	—
Landing Craft	20	—
Auxiliaries	several	—

Personnel

(a) 1974: 9 000 officers and ratings
(b) 3 years national service

Mercantile Marine

Lloyd's Register of Shipping:
159 vessels of 756 749 tons gross

FRIGATES

2 "RIGA" CLASS

DRUZKI **SMELI**

Displacenemt, tons	1 200 standard; 1 600 full load
Length, feet (*metres*)	298·8 (*91·0*) oa
Beam, feet (*metres*)	33·7 (*10·2*)
Draught, feet (*metres*)	11·0 (*3·4*)
Guns	3—3·9 in (*100 mm*); 4—37 mm
A/S Weapons	2 16 barrelled rocket launchers 4 DCT
Tubes	3—21 in (*533 mm*)
Main engines	Geared turbines; 2 shafts; 25 000 shp
Speed, knots	28
Range, miles	2 500 at 15 knots
Complement	150

Transferred from USSR in 1957-8.

RADAR. Search—Slim Net; Navigation—Neptun; IFF—High Pole A; FC—Wasphead/Sunvisor A.

"Riga" Class

CORVETTES

2 "KRONSTADT" CLASS

Displacement, tons	310 standard; 380 full load
Dimensions, ft (*m*)	70·6 × 21·5 × 9·0 (*52·0 × 6·5 × 2·7*)
Guns	1—3·5 in; 2—37 mm AA; 4—25 mm AA
A/S weapons	Depth charge throwers
Main engines	3 Diesels; 3 shafts; 3 300 hp = 24 knots
Oil fuel, tons	20
Range, miles	1 500 at 12 knots
Complement	65

Transferred from USSR in 1957. Pot Drum Radar.

KRONSTADT Class

SUBMARINES (PATROL)

2 Ex-USSR ROMEO CLASS

Displacement, tons	1 100 surfaced; 1 600 dived
Dimensions, ft (*m*)	246 × 24 × 14·5 (*75 × 7·3 × 5·8*)
Torpedo tubes	6—21 in bow tubes
Main Machinery	2 Diesels; 4 000 hp; 2 main motors; 4 000 hp
Speed, knots	17 surfaced, 14 dived
Complement	65

Transferred in 1972. Snoop Plate radar.

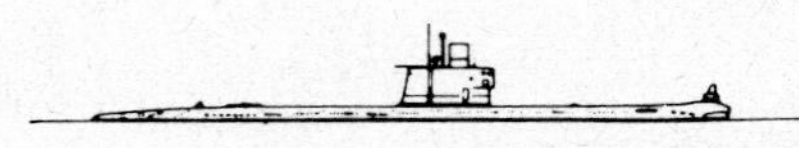

"Romeo" *Class*

SUBMARINES —*continued*

2 Ex-USSR "WHISKY" CLASS

POBEDA **SLAVA**

Displacement, tons	1 030 surface; 1 180 submerged
Dimensions, ft (*m*)	240 × 22 × 15 (*73·2 × 6·7 × 4·6*)
Torpedo tubes	6—21 in (*533 mm*), 4 bow, 2 stern
Main machinery	2 Diesels 4 000 hp 2 Main Motors 2 500 hp
Speed, knots	17 surfaced; 15 dived
Range miles	13 000 at 8 knots (surface)
Complement	60

Transferred from the USSR in 1958. Snoop Plate radar

"Whisky" Class

LIGHT FORCES

3 "OSA I" CLASS (FAST ATTACK CRAFT—MISSILE)

Displacement, tons	165 standard; 200 full load
Dimensions, ft (*m*)	128·7 × 25·1 × 5·9 (*39·3 × 7·7 × 1·8*)
Missile launcher	4 in two pairs abreast for "SS-N-2" system
Guns	4—30 mm (2 twin, 1 forward, 1 aft)
Main engines	3 diesels; 13.000 bhp = 32 knots
Range, miles	800 at 25 knots
Complement	25

Reported to have been transferred from the USSR in 1970-71.

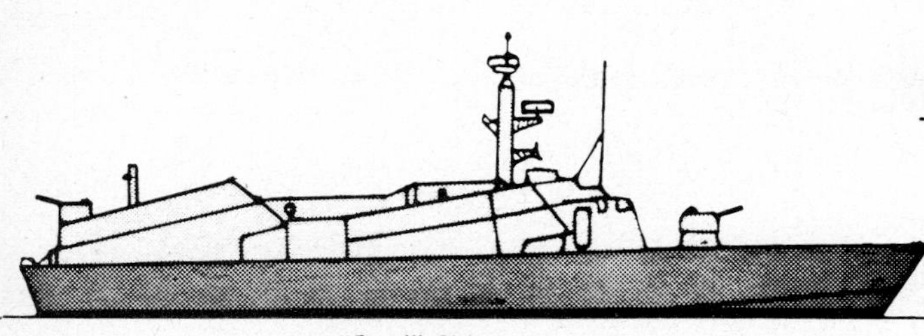

"Osa I" Class

6 "SO I" CLASS (FAST ATTACK CRAFT—PATROL)

Pennants 41-46

Displacement, tons	215 light; 250 full load
Dimensions, ft (*m*)	138·6 × 20·0 × 9·2 (*42·3 × 6·1 × 2·8*)
Guns	4—25 mm (2 twin)
A/S weapons	4 five-barrelled ahead throwing MBU launchers
Main engines	3 diesels; 6 000 bhp = 29 knots
Range, miles	1 100 at 13 knots
Complement	30

Steel hulled patrol vessels transferred from USSR in 1963.

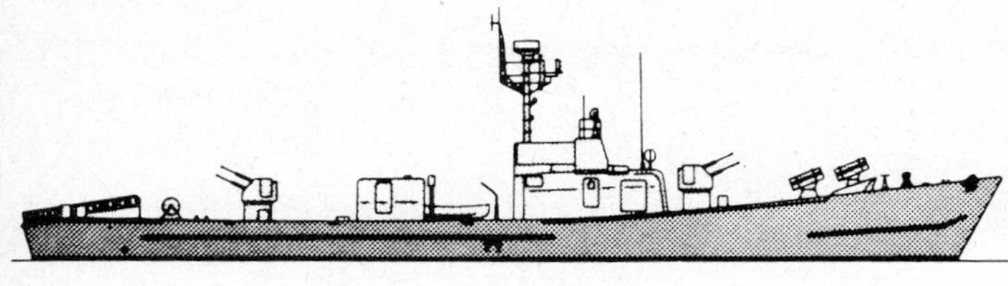

SO I Class

4 "SHERSHEN" CLASS (FAST ATTACK CRAFT—TORPEDO)

Displacement, tons	150 standard; 160 full load
Dimensions, ft (*m*)	115·5 × 23·1 × 5·0 (*35·2 × 7·1 × 1·5*)
Guns	4—30 mm AA (2 twin)
Tubes	4—21 in (single)
A/S armament	12 DCs
Main engines	3 Diesels; 3 shafts; 13 000 bhp = 41 knots
Complement	16

Transferred in 1971. Pot Drum and Drum Tilt Radar. High Pole A IFF.

"Shershen" Class

8 "P 4" CLASS (FAST ATTACK CRAFT—TORPEDO)

Displacement, tons	25 full load
Dimensions, ft (*m*)	62·7 × 11·6 × 5·6 (*25·5 × 6·0 × 1·8*)
Guns	2—25 mm AA
Torpedo tubes	2—18 in
Main engines	2 diesels; 2 shafts; 2 200 bhp = 50 knots

Transferred from the USSR in 1956.

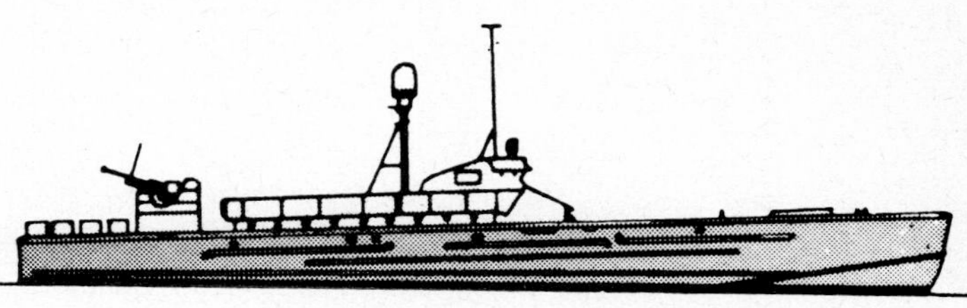

"P 4" Class

MINE WARFARE FORCES

2 "T 43" CLASS (MINESWEEPERS—OCEAN)

Displacement, tons	500 standard; 610 full load
Dimensions, ft (*m*)	190·2 × 28·2 × 6·9 (*58·0 × 8·6 × 2·1*)

4 "VANYA" CLASS (MINESWEEPERS—COASTAL)

36, 37, 38, 39

Displacement, tons	250 standard; 275 full load
Dimensions, ft (*m*)	130·7 × 24 × 6·9 (*39·9 × 7·3 × 2·1*)

2 "T 301" CLASS (MINESWEEPERS—INSHORE)

Displacement, tons	150 standard; 180 full load
Dimensions, ft (*m*)	128 × 18 × 4·9 (*39 × 5·5 × 1·5*)
Guns	2—37 mm AA; 2—MG
Main engines	2 diesels; 2 shafts; 1 440 hp = 17 knots
Range, miles	2 200 at 10 knots

Transferred from the USSR in 1955. These have probably reached the end of their seagoing lives. Two recently deleted.

24 "PO 2" CLASS TYPE (MSB)

Former Soviet craft. 12 were reported to have been acquired in 1950 and 12 in 1956 for general purpose duties.

LANDING CRAFT

10 "VYDRA" CLASS

Displacement, tons	300 standard; 500 full load
Dimensions, ft (*m*)	157·4 × 24·6 × 7·2 (*48 × 7·5 × 2·2*)
Main engines	2 diesels; 2 shafts; 400 bhp = 10 knots

Transferred from the USSR in 1970.

10 MFP TYPE

Dimensions, ft (*m*)	164·0 oa × 20·0 × 6·6 (*50 × 6·1× 2·0*)
Gun	1—37 mm AA or none

Built in Bulgaria in 1954. Based on a German Second World War MFP design.

AUXILIARIES

A number of auxiliaries, harbour oilers and tugs have been reported.

BURMA

Administration

Vice-Chief of Staff, Defence Services (Navy):
Commodore Thaung Tin

Diplomatic Representation

Naval, Military and Air Attaché in London:
Lieutenant-Colonel Kyee Myint

Naval, Military and Air Attaché in Washington:
Colonel Tin Htut

Strength of the Fleet

Type	*Active*	*Building*
Frigates	2	—
Corvettes	4	—
Fast Attack Craft	5	—
River Patrol Craft	35	—
Gunboats	37	—
Survey Vessels	2	—
Auxiliaries	11	—

Personnel

(a) 1974: 6 200 (300 officers and 5 900 ratings) including reserves plus 800 marines
(b) 2 years national service

Mercantile Marine

Lloyd's Register of Shipping:
40 vessels of 54 877 tons gross

FRIGATES

1 Ex-BRITISH "RIVER" CLASS

Name	*Builders*	*Laid down*	*Launched*	*Completed*
MAYU (ex-HMS *Fal*)	Smiths Dock Co Ltd, South Bank-on-Tees, Middlesborough, England	20 May 1942	9 Nov 1942	2 July 1943

Displacement, tons	1 460 standard; 2 170 full load
Length, feet (*metres*)	283 (*86·3*) pp; 301·3 (*91·8*) oa
Beam, feet (*metres*)	36·7 (*11·3*)
Draught, feet (*metres*)	12 (*3·7*)
Guns, dual purpose	1—4 in (*102 mm*)
Guns, AA	4—40 mm
Boilers	2—three drum type
Main engines	Triple expansion 5 500 ihp; 2 shafts
Speed, knots	19
Range, miles	4 200 at 12 knots
Oil fuel (tons)	440
Complement	140

"River" class frigate. Acquired from Great Britain and renamed in March 1948.

MAYU *Burmese Navy*

1 Ex-BRITISH "ALGERINE" CLASS

Name	*Builders*	*Laid down*	*Launched*	*Completed*
YAN MYO AUNG (ex-HMS *Mariner*, ex-*Kincardine*)	Port Arthur Shipyards, Canada	26 Aug 1943	9 May 1944	23 May 1945

Displacement, tons	1 040 standard; 1 335 full load
Length, feet (*metres*)	225 (*68·6*) pp; 235 (*71·6*) oa
Beam, feet (*metres*)	35·5 (*19·8*)
Draught, feet (*metres*)	11·5 (*3·5*)
Guns, surface	1—4 in (*102 mm*)
Guns, AA	4—40 mm
Boilers	2 three-drum type
Main engines	Triple expansion 2 000 shp; 2 shafts
Speed, knots	16·5
Range, miles	4 000 at 12 knots
Complement	140

Former ocean minesweeper in the British Navy, used as escort vessel. Handed over to Burma in London and renamed *Yan Myo Aung*, on 18 Apr 1958. Fitted for minelaying and can carry 16 mines, eight on each side.

YAN MYO AUNG *1964, Burmese Navy*

CORVETTES

1 Ex-US PCE TYPE

YAN TAING AUNG, PCE 41 (ex-USS *Farmington*, PCE 894)

Displacement, tons	640 standard; 903 full load
Dimensions, ft (*m*)	180 wl ;184 oa × 33 × 9·5 (*56 × 10· 1× 2·9*)
Guns	1—3 in, 50 cal dp; 2—40 mm AA (1 twin); 8—20 mm AA (4 twin)
A/S weapons	1 hedgehog; 2 DCT; 2 DC tracks
Main engines	GM diesels; 2 shafts; 1 800 bhp = 15 knots

Former US Patrol ship (escort). Built by Willamette Iron & Steel Corp, Portland, Oregon. Laid down on 7 Dec 1942, launched on 15 May 1943 and completed 10 Aug 1943. Transferred on 18 June 1965.

1 Ex-US MSF TYPE

YAN GYI AUNG, PCE 42 (ex-USS *Craddock*, MSF 356)

Displacement, tons	650 standard; 945 full load
Dimensions, ft (*m*)	180 wl; 184·5 oa × 33 × 9·8 (*56 × 10·1 × 2·8*)
Guns	1—3 in 50 cal single forward; 4—40 mm AA (2 twin); 4—20 mm AA (2 twin)
Main engines	Diesels; 2 shafts; 1 710 shp = 14·8 knots
Range, miles	4 300 at 10 knots

Former US steel hulled fleet minesweeper of the "Admirable" class. Built by Willamette Iron & Steel Corp, Portland, Oregon. Laid down on 10 Nov 1943 and launched on 22 July 1944. Transferred at San Diego on 31 Mar 1967.

2 BURMESE-BUILT TYPE

NAGAKYAY **NAWARAT**

Displacement, tons	400 standard; 450 full load
Dimensions, ft (*m*)	163 × 26·8 × 5·8 (*49·7 × 8·2 × 1·8*)
Guns	2—25 pdr QF; 2—40 mm AA
Main engines	2 Paxman-Ricardo turbo-charged diesels; 2 shafts; 1 160 bhp = 12 knots
Complement	43

Built at the Government Dockyard, Dawbon, Rangoon, Burma, *Nagakyay* was completed on 3 Dec 1960 and *Nawarat* on 26 Apr 1960.

NAGAKYAY *1962, Burmese Navy*

LIGHT FORCES

5 SAUNDERS ROE FAST ATTACK CRAFT

T 201 (ex-*PTS 101*) **T 202** (ex-*PTS 102*) **T 203** (ex-*PTS 103*) **T 204** (ex-*PTS 104*) **T 205** (ex-*PTS 105*)

Displacement, tons	50 standard; 64 full load
Dimensions, ft (*m*)	67 pp; 71·5 oa × 19·5 × 6 max (*21·8 × 5·9 × 1·8*)
Guns	As MGB: 1—4·5 in; 1—40 mm AA; As MTB: 2—20 mm AA
Tubes	As MTB: 4—21 in
Main engines	2 Napier Deltic diesels; 5 000 shp = 42 knots
Complement	13

T 202 *1966, Burmese Navy,*

Interchangeable motor torpedo boats/motor gunboats built by Saunders Roe (Anglesey) Ltd, England. Convertible craft of aluminium construction, with riveted skin and aluminium alloy framework. As well as main engines, auxiliary power is also provided by diesels. The Saunders-Roe slow-speed electric drive was fitted to facilitate manoeuvring in the confined inland waters where the craft may be required to operate. Armament and layout of the vessels were similar to the British fast patrol boats of the "Dark" Class. The cost including engines, equipment, and spares of the five boats was over £1 800 000. T 201 was launched 24 Mar 1956. All were completed in 1956-57.

10 BURMESE-BUILT RIVER PATROL CRAFT

Small craft, 50 feet long, built in Burma in 1951-52.

25 YUGOSLAV-BUILT RIVER PATROL CRAFT

Small craft, 52 feet long, acquired from Yugoslavia in the mid 1960's.

GUN BOATS

4 Ex-BRITISH LCG (M) TYPE

INDAW **INLAY** **INMA** **INYA**

Displacement, tons	381
Dimensions, ft (*m*)	154 oa × 22·5 × 7·8 (*47·1 × 6·8 × 2·4*)
Guns	2—25 pdr; 2—2 dpr
Main engines	Paxman Ricardo diesels; 2 shafts; 1 000 bhp = 13 knots
Complement	39

Former British landing craft, gun (medium) *LCG* (M). Employed as gunboats.

INMA *Burmese Navy*

2 IMPROVED YUGOSLAV TYPE GUNBOATS

Y 311 **Y 312**

Dimensions approximately as Y-type above. Built in Burma 1969.

Gunboats—*cont.*

10 YUGOSLAVIAN-BUILT "Y" TYPE GUNBOATS

Y 301 Y 302 Y 303 Y 304 Y 305 Y 306 Y 307 Y 308 Y 309 Y 310

Displacement, tons	120
Dimensions, ft (*m*)	100 pp; 104·8 oa × 24 × 3 (*32 × 7·3 × 0·9*)
Guns	2—40 mm AA; 1—2 pdr
Main engines	2 Mercedes-Benz diesels; 2 shafts; 1 000 bhp = 13 knots
Complement	29

All ten of these boats were completed in 1958 at the "Uljanik" Shipyard, Pula, in Yugoslavia. For detailed building dates see 1966-67 and earlier editions.

Y 310 *1964, Burmese Navy*

8 GUNBOATS (ex-TRANSPORTS)

SABAN **SAGU** **SEINDA** **SETKAYA** **SETYAHAT** **SHWEPAZUN** **SHWETHIDA** **SINMIN**

Displacement, tons	98
Dimensions, ft (*m*)	94·5 × 22 × 4·5 (*28·8 × 6·7 × 1·4*)
Guns	1—40 mm; 3—20 mm
Main engines	Crossley ERL—6 diesel; 160 bhp = 12 knots
Complement	32

SHWEPAZUN *1971, Burmese Navy*

6 US-BUILT PGM TYPE GUNBOATS

PGM 401 **PGM 402** **PGM 403** **PGM 404** **PGM 405** **PGM 406**

Displacement, tons	100
Dimensions, ft (*m*)	95 × 19 × 5 (*29 × 5·8 × 1·5*)
Guns	1—40 mm AA; 2—0·5 US Browning MG
Main engines	4 GM diesels; 2 shafts; 1 000 bhp = 16 knots
Complement	17

Built by the Marinette Marine Corporation, USA. Ex-US PGM 43-46, 51 and 52 respectively. Machinery comprises 2-stroke, 6-cylinder, tandem geared twin diesel propulsion unit—1 LH and 1 RH; 500 bhp per unit.

PGM 401 *1962, Burmese Navy*

Gunboats—*cont.*

7 Ex-UNITED STATES CGC TYPE GUNBOATS

MGB 101 MGB 102 MGB 104 MGB 105 MGB 106 MGB 108 MGB 110

Displacement, tons	49 standard; 66 full load
Dimensions, ft (*m*)	78 pp; 83 oa × 16 × 5·5 (*25·3 × 4·9 × 1·7*)
Guns	1—40 mm AA; 1—20 mm AA
Main engines	4 GM diesels; 2 shafts; 800 bhp = 11 knots
Complement	16

Ex-USCG 83-ft type cutters with new hulls built in Burma. Completed in 1960. For detailed building dates see 1966-67 and earlier editions. Machinery comprises 2-stroke, 6 cylinder, tandem geared, twin diesel propulsion units—1 LH and 1 RH drive; 400 bhp per unit. Three of this class are reported to have been sunk.

MGB 102 *1962, Burmese Navy*

SURVEY VESSELS

THU TAY THI

Ocean Survey ship, 204 feet overall and 1 100 tons displacement, acquired from Yugoslavia in the mid-1960's. Complement 99.

YAY BO (UBHL 807)

Coastal survey vessel, possibly Dutch built with complement of 25 and a displacement of 108 tons.

SUPPORT SHIP

YAN LON AUNG

Light forces support ship of 520 tons, acquired from Japan in 1967.

TRANSPORTS

PYIDAWAYE

Measurement tons	2 217·31 gross
Dimensions, ft (*m*)	270 × 47 × 15 (*82·3 × 14·3 × 4·6*)
Main engines	Fleming & Ferguson triple expansion 2 000 ihp
Boilers	2 Scotch (return type)
Range, miles	2 000
Complement	88

Former passenger ship. In service since 1962. Bears the Burmese naval ensign.

PYIDAWAYE *1964, Burmese Navy*

1 Ex-US LCU TYPE

LCU 1626 (ex-USS *LCU 1626*)

Displacement, tons	200 light; 342 full load
Dimensions, ft (*m*)	135·2 oa × 29 × 5·5 (*41·2 × 8·8 × 1·7*)
Main engines	Diesels; 2 shafts; 1 000 bhp = 11 knots

Ex-US utility landing craft. Transferred under MAP in 1967. Used as transport.

8 Ex-US LCM TYPE

LCM 701 LCM 702 LCM 703 LCM 704 LCM 705 LCM 706 LCM 707 LCM 708

Displacement, tons	28
Dimensions, ft (*m*)	56 × 14 × 4 (*17·0 × 4·3 × 1·2*)
Main engines	2 Gray Marine diesels; 225 bhp

US-built LCM type landing craft. Used as local transports for stores and personnel.

CAMEROON

Personnel

1974: 300 officers and men

Base

Douala

Mercantile Marine

Lloyd's Register of Shipping: 16 vessels of 2 895 tons gross

LIGHT FORCES

5 COASTAL PATROL CRAFT

VIGILANT (ex-*VC 6*, P 756) **AUDACIEUX** (ex-*VC 8*, P 758)

Displacement, tons	75 standard; 82 full load
Dimensions, ft (*m*)	104·2 × 15·5 × 5·5 (*31·8 × 4·7 × 1·7*)
Guns	2—20 mm AA
Main engines	Mercedes-Benz diesels; 2 shafts; 2 700 bhp = 28 knots
Range, miles	1 500 at 15 knots
Complement	15

Former French seaward defence motor launches of the VC type. Built by Constructions Mécaniques de Normandie, Cherbourg. Completed in 1957-58 *Vigilant* was officially handed over from France to the Republic of Cameroon on 7 Mar 1964.

ALFRED MOTTO

Displacement, tons	80 approx.
Dimensions, ft (*m*)	110 × 16 (*33·6 × 4·9*)

ALFRED MOTTO *1973, Y. Bertrand*

BRIGADIER M'BONGA TOUNDA

Displacement, tons	20 full load
Dimensions, ft (*m*)	60 × 13·5 × 4 (*18·3 × 4·1 × 1·2*)
Guns	1—12·7 mm MG
Main engines	Caterpillar Diesel; 2 shafts; 540 bhp = 21 knots
Complement	8

Built by Ch Navals de L'Esterel in 1967. Customs duties.

VALEUREUX

Displacement, tons	45 full load
Dimensions, ft (*m*)	78·1 × 16·3 × 5·1 (*23·8 × 5·0 × 1·6*)
Guns	2—20 mm AA
Main engines	2 Diesels; 2 shafts; 960 hp = 25 knots
Complement	9

Built by Ch Navals de L'Esterel in 1970.

2 LCVP

Built by Ateliers et Chantiers de l'Afrique Equatoriale, near Libreville, Gabon

2 LCM

Built by Carena, Abaidjan, Ivory Coast.

2 SERVICE CRAFT

Locally built.

CANADA

Ministerial

Minister of National Defence:
The Hon. James Richardson MP

Senior Naval Appointments

Chief of Maritime Operations:
Rear Admiral R. H. Leir

Commander, Maritime Command:
Rear Admiral D. S. Boyle, CD

Commander, Maritime Forces, Pacific:
Rear Admiral R. J. Pickford, CD

Diplomatic Representation

Senior Naval Liaison Officer, London:

Captain (N) J. W. Mason, CD

Canadian Forces Attaché and Senior Naval Liaison Officer, Washington:
Commodore A. L. Collier, DSC, CD

Canadian Forces Attaché (Naval) Moscow:
L.t Col. W. Draper, CD

Navy Estimates

1971-72: $348 000 000
1972-73: $363 000 000
1973-74: $394 300 000

Personnel

(a) 1971: 16 906 (2 379 officers, 14 527 men and women)
1972: 15 223 (2 590 officers, 12 633 men and women)
1973: 16 003 (1 985 officers, 14 018 men and women)
(b) Voluntary Service

Establishment

The Royal Canadian Navy was officially established on 4 May 1910, when Royal Assent was given to the Naval Service Act.

Strength of the Fleet

Type	*Active*	*Building*
Destroyers (DDH)	4	—
Frigates (some with helicopters)	15	—
Patrol Submarines	4	—
Replenishment Ships	3	—
Small Oilers	2	—
Patrol Escorts (Small)	6	—
Research Ships	6	—
Diving Support Ships and Tenders	3	—
Gate Vessels	4	—
Tugs (Large)	12	—
Tugs (Small)	13	—
Police Patrol Vessels	31	—
Hydrofoil	1	—

Air Arm

In an integrated force there is no specific Fleet Air Arm, but a squadron of Sea King helicopters provides for ships' needs.

Bases

Halifax and Esquimalt

Disposals

Attack Carrier (medium)
1970 *Bonaventure* paid off 1 April, towed to Taiwan for scrap, leaving Halifax 27 October

Destroyers

1971 *Algonquin* left Victoria BC for Taiwan 21 April
Crescent left Victoria BC for Taiwan 21 May

Frigates

1973 *St. Laurent, Columbia, St. Croix*

Maintenance Ships
1972 *Cape Breton* and *Cape Scott* reduced to hulks

Research Vessels

1972 *Fort Frances*

Tugs

1973 *St. John, Oakwood*

Police Patrol Vessels

1973 *Fort Steele, Victoria, Burin, Interceptor, Nanaimo, Tahsis, Westview*

Mercantile Marine

Lloyd's Register of Shipping:
1 235 vessels of 2 422 802 tons gross

PENNANT NUMBERS

Destroyers

Iroquois	280
Huron	281
Athabaskan	282
Algonquin	283

Frigates

Saguenay	206
Skeena	207
Ottawa	229
Margaree	230
Fraser	233
Assiniboine	234
Chaudiere	235
Gatineau	236
Restigouche	257
Kootenay	258
Terra Nova	259
Mackenzie	261
Saskatchawan	262
Yukon	263
Qu'appelle	264
Annapolis	265
Nipigon	266

Submarines

Ojibwa	72
Onandaga	73
Okanagan	74
Rainbow	75

Replenishment Ships

Provider	AOR 508
Protecteur	AOR 509
Preserver	AOR 510
Dundalk	AOC 501
Dundurn	AOC 502

Research Vessels

Sackville	AGOR 113
Bluethroat	AGOR 114
Endeavour	AGOR 171
Quest	AGOR 172
Kapuskasing	AGOR 173
Laymore	AGOR 516

Patrol Escort (PFL)

Fundy	159
Chignecto	160
Thunder	161
Cowichan	162
Miramichi	163
Chaleur	164

Gate Vessels

Porte St. Jean	180
Porte St. Louis	183
Porte de la Reine	184
Porte Quebec	185

Tugs

Heatherton	ATA 527
Riverton	ATA 528
Clifton	ATA 529
St. Anthony	ATA 531
St. Charles	ATA 533
Glenside	YTB 500
Glenbrook	YTB 501
Glenevis	YTB 502
Glendyne	YTB 503
Glenlivet II	YTB 504
Eastwood	YMT 550
Greenwood	YMT 551
Mannville	YTS 577
Listerville	YTS 578
Parkesville	YTS 579
Merrickville	YTS 581
Adamsville	YTS 582
Beamsville	YTS 583
Lawrenceville	YTS 584
Marysville	YTS 585
Queensville	YTS 586
Plainsville	YTS 587
Youville	YTS 588
Loganville	YTS 589
Otterville	YTS 590

Miscellaneous

Granby	FSE 180

DESTROYERS (DDH)

4 "IROQUOIS" CLASS (DDH)

Name	No.	Builders	Laid down	Launched	Completion
ALGONQUIN	283	Davie SB Co, Lauzon	1 Sep 1969	27 Nov 1970	30 Sept 1973
ATHABASKAN	282	Davie SB Co, Lauzon	1 June 1969	mid Apr 1971	30 Nov 1972
HURON	281	Marine Industries Ltd, Sorel	15 Jan 1969	3 Apr 1971	16 Dec 1972
IROQUOIS	280	Marine Industries Ltd, Sorel	15 Jan 1969	28 Nov 1970	29 July 1972

Displacement, tons	4 200 full load
Length, feet (*metres*)	398 (*121·3*) pp 426 (*129·8*) oa
Beam, feet (*metres*)	50 (*15·2*)
Draught, feet (*metres*)	14·5 (*4·4*)
Aircraft	2 "Sea King" CHSS-2 A/S helicopters
Missiles	(see note)
Gun, dual purpose	1—5 in (*127 mm*) 54 cal LA, single Oto-Melara
A/S	1 Mk 10 "Limbo"
Torpedo tubes	2 triple Mk 32 for A/S homing torpedoes
Main engines	Gas turbines; 2 Pratt & Whitney FT4A2 50 000 shp + 2 Pratt & Whitney FT12AH3 7 400 shp for cruising; 2 shafts
Speed, knots	29 +
Range, miles	4 500 at 20 knots
Complement	245 (20 officers, 225 men) (plus air unit, 12 officers + 30 men)

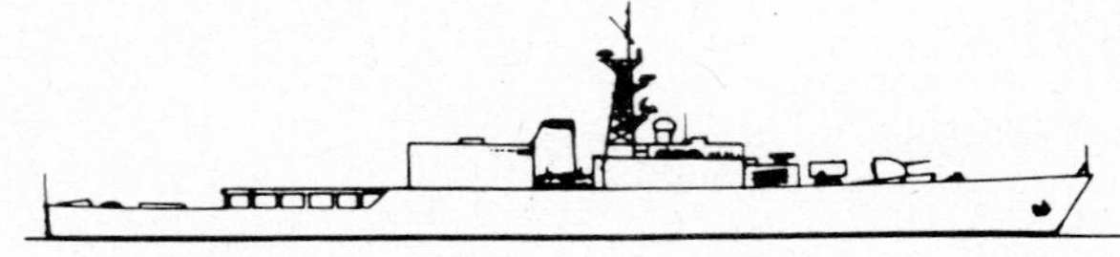
IROQUOIS *Class* (twin funnels)

GENERAL
These ships have the same hull design, dimensions and basic characteristics as the large general purpose frigates cancelled at the end of 1963 (see particulars and illustration in the 1963-64 edition). Designed as anti-submarine ships, they are fitted with variable depth and hull sonar, landing deck equipped with double hauldown and Beartrap, flume type anti-rolling tanks to stabilise the ships at low speed, pre-wetting system to counter radio-active fallout, enclosed citadel, and bridge control of machinery.

ENGINEERING. The gas turbines feed through a Swiss double reduction gearbox to two five bladed CP propellers.

ELECTRONICS. Mk 22 Weapon System Control by Hollandse Signaal.

MISSILES. Launch system (GMLS) by Raytheon for Mk III Sea Sparrow missiles. Two quadruple launchers in forward end of the superstructure.

RADAR. SPQ 2D Surface warning and Navigation SPS 501 (SPS 12) long range warning M 22 fire control.

SONAR. SQS 505 Hull mounted in 14 ft dome VDS. 18 ft towed body aft. SQS 501 Bottomed target classification.

TORPEDOES. The Mk 32 tubes are to be used with Mk 46 torpedoes.

IROQUOIS — *1973, Canadian Forces*

HURON — *1973, Canadian Forces*

FRIGATES

2 "ANNAPOLIS" CLASS

Name	No.	Builders	Work started	Launched	Completed
ANNAPOLIS	265	Halifax Shipyards Ltd, Halifax	July 1960	27 Apr 1963	19 Dec 1964
NIPIGON	266	Marine Industries Ltd, Sorel Q	Apr 1960	10 Dec 1961	30 May 1964

Displacement, tons	2 400 standard; 3 000 full load
Length, feet (*metres*)	371·0 (*113·1*) oa
Beam, feet (*metres*)	42·0 (*12·8*)
Draught, feet (*metres*)	14·4 (*4·4*)
Aircraft	1 CHSS-2 "Sea King" helicopter
Guns, AA	2—3 in (*76 mm*) 50 cal (1 twin)
A/S weapons	1 Mk 10 "Limbo" in after well
Boilers	2 water tube
Main engines	Geared turbines; 2 shafts; 30 000 shp
Speed, knots	28 (official figure) 30 trials
Range, miles	4 750 at 14 knots
Complement	246 (12 officers, 234 ratings)

These two ships represented the logical development of the original "St Laurent" class, through the "Restigouche" and "Mackenzie" designs. Due to the erection of a helicopter hangar and flight deck, and variable depth sonar only one "Limbo" mounting could be installed. Also the 50 cal 3 inch mounting had to be moved forward to replace the 70 cal mounting in the original design.

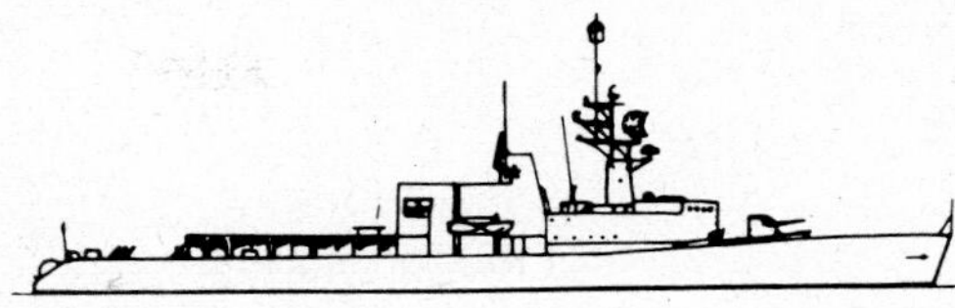

ANNAPOLIS, NIPIGON

CLASSIFICATION. Officially classified as DDH.

CONSTRUCTION. As these are largely prefabricated no firm laying down date is officially given. Work on hull units started under cover long before components were laid on the slip.

RADAR. Search: SPS 12. Tactical: SPS 10. Fire Control: X Band.

NIPIGON *1971, Canadian Forces*

4 "MACKENZIE" CLASS

Name	No.	Builders	Laid down	Launched	Completed
MACKENZIE	261	Canadian Vickers Ltd, Montreal	15 Dec 1958	25 May 1961	6 Oct 1962
QU'APPELLE	264	Davie Shipbuilding & Repairing	14 Jan 1960	2 May 1962	14 Sep 1963
***SASKATCHEWAN**	262	Victoria Machinery (and Yarrow)	16 July 1959	1 Feb 1961	16 Feb 1963
YUKON	263	Burrard DD & Shipbuilding	25 Oct 1959	27 July 1961	25 May 1963

Displacement, tons	2 380 standard; 2 890 full load
Length, feet (*metres*)	366·0 (*111·5*) oa
Beam, feet (*metres*)	42·0 (*12·8*)
Draught, feet (*metres*)	13·5 (*4·1*)
Guns, AA	4—3 in (*76 mm*) 2 twin (70 cal fwd, 50 cal aft)
A/S weapons	2 Mk 10 "Limbo" in well aft
Main engines	Geared turbines; 2 shafts; 30 000 shp
Boilers	2 water tube
Speed, knots	28
Range, miles	4 750 at 15 knots
Complement	245 (12 officers, 233 ratings)

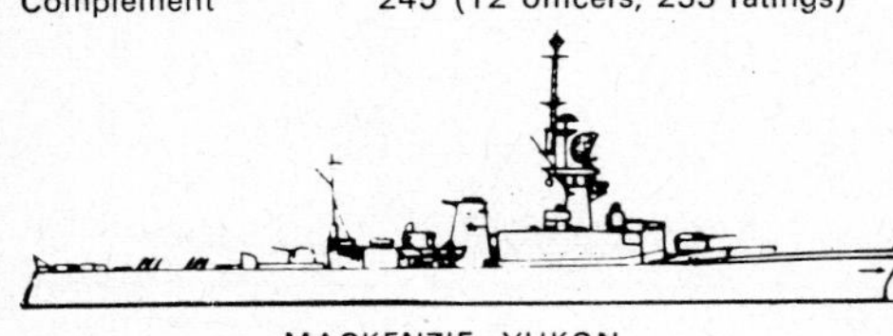

MACKENZIE, YUKON

QU'APPELLE

MACKENZIE *1970, Canadian Forces*

CLASSIFICATION. Officially classified as DDE.

RADAR. Search: SPS 12. Tactical: SPS 10. Fire Control: X Band.

**Saskatchewan* was launched by Victoria Machinery Depot Co Ltd, but completed by Yarrow's Ltd.

3 "RESTIGOUCHE" CLASS

Name	No.	Builder	Laid down	Launched	Completed
CHAUDIERE	235	Halifax Shipyards Ltd	30 July 1953	13 Nov 1957	14 Nov 1959

Displacement, tons	2 370 standard; 2 880 full load
Length, feet (*metres*)	366·0 (*111·5*) oa
Beam, feet (*metres*)	42·0 (*12·8*)
Draught, feet (*metres*)	13·5 (*4·1*)
Guns, AA	4—3 in (*76 mm*) 2 twin
A/S weapons	2 Mk 10 "Limbo" in well aft
Main engines	Geared turbines; 2 shafts; 30 000 shp
Boilers	2 water tube
Speed, knots	28
Range, miles	4 750 at 14 knots
Complement	248 (12 officers, 236 ratings)

CHAUDIERE *1970 Canadian Forces*

CLASSIFICATION Officially classified as DDE.

RADAR. Search: SPS 12. Tactical: SPS 10. Fire Control: X Band.

4 "IMPROVED RESTIGOUCHE"

Name	No.	Builder	Laid down	Launched	Completed
GATINEAU	236	Davie Shipbuilding & Repairing	30 Apr 1953	3 June 1957	17 Feb 1959
KOOTENAY	258	Burrard DD & Shipbuilding	21 Aug 1952	15 June 1954	7 Mar 1959
RESTIGOUCHE	257	Canadian Vickers, Montreal	15 July 1953	22 Nov 1954	7 June 1958
TERRA NOVA	259	Victoria Machinery Depot Co	14 Nov 1952	21 June 1955	6 June 1959

Displacement, tons	2 390 standard; 2 900 full load
Length, feet (*metres*)	371·0 (*113·1*)
Beam, feet (*metres*)	42·0 (*12·8*)
Draught, feet (*metres*)	14·1 (*4·3*)
Guns, AA	2—3 in (*76 mm*) 70 cal forward
A/S weapons	ASROC aft and 1 Mk 10 "Limbo" in after well
Main engines	Geared turbines; 2 shafts; 30 000 shp
Boilers	2 water tube
Speed, knots	28 plus
Range, miles	4 750 at 14 knots
Complement	250 (13 officers, 237 ratings)

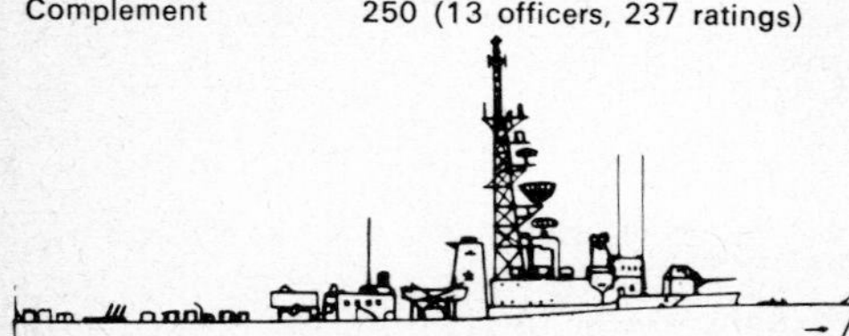
GATINEAU

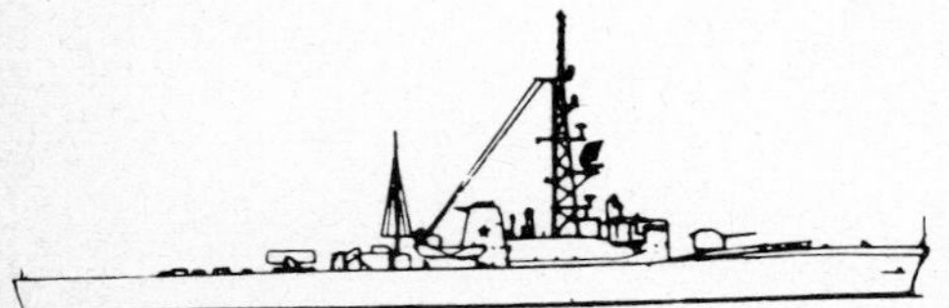
RESTIGOUCHE

GATINEAU *1972, Canadian Forces*

CLASSIFICATION. Officially classified as DDE.

CONVERSION. These four ships were refitted with ASROC aft and lattice foremast. Work included removing the after 3 inch 50 cal twin gun mounting and one "Limbo" A/S Mk 10 triple mortar, to make way for ASROC and variable depth sonar. Dates of refits, *Terra Nova* was completed on 18 Oct 1968; *Gatineau* completed in 1972 and *Kootenay* and *Restigouche* in 1973.

RADAR. Search: SPS 12. Tactical: SPS 10. Fire Control: X Band.

6 "ST. LAURENT" CLASS

Name	No.	Builders	Laid down	Launched	Completed
SAGUENAY	DDE 206	Halifax Shipyards, Ltd, Halifax	4 Apr 1951	30 July 1953	15 Dec 1956
SKEENA	DDE 207	Burrard Dry Dock & Shipbuilding	1 June 1951	19 Aug 1952	30 Mar 1957
OTTAWA	DDE 229	Canadian Vickers, Ltd, Montreal	8 June 1951	29 Apr 1953	10 Nov 1956
MARGAREE	DDE 230	Halifax Shipyards Ltd, Halifax	12 Sep 1951	29 Mar 1956	5 Oct 1957
***FRASER**	DDE 233	Yarrows Ltd, Esquimalt, B.C.	11 Dec 1951	19 Feb 1953	28 June 1957
ASSINIBOINE	DDE 234	Marine Industries Ltd, Sorel, Q	19 May 1952	12 Feb 1954	16 Aug 1956

Displacement, tons	2 260 standard; 2 800 full load
Length, feet (*metres*)	366·0 (*111·5*) oa
Beam, feet (*metres*)	42·0 (*12·8*)
Draught, feet (*metres*)	13·2 (*4·0*)
Aircraft	1 CHSS Sea King helicopter
Guns, AA	2—3 in (*76 mm*) 50 cal (1 twin)
A/S weapons	1 Mk 10 "Limbo" in after well
Main engines	English Electric geared turbines; 2 shafts; 30 000 shp
Boilers	2 water tube
Speed, knots	28·5
Range, miles	4 570 at 12 knots
Complement	250 (13 officers, 237 ratings)

GENERAL
The first major warships to be designed in Canada. In design, much assistance was received from the Royal Navy (propelling machinery of British design) and the US Navy.

**Fraser* was launched by Burrard Dry Dock & Shipbuilding but completed by Yarrows Ltd.

CLASSIFICATION. Officially classified as DDH.

GUNNERY. Original armament was 4—3 inch, 50 cal AA (2 twin), 2—40 mm AA (single), and 2 "Limbo" mortars.

RADAR. Search: SPS 12. Tactical: SPS 10.

RECONSTRUCTION. All have helicopter platforms and VDS. Twin funnels were fitted to permit forward extension of the helicopter hangar.

Gunhouses are of fibreglass. In providing helicopter platforms and hangars it was possible to retain only one three barrelled "Limbo" mortar and only one twin 3-inch gun mounting. Dates of recommissioning after conversion: *Assiniboine* 28 June 1963, *Ottawa* 21 Oct 1964, *Saguenay* 14 May 1965, *Skeena* 15 Aug 1965, *Margaree* 15 Oct 1965, *Fraser* 31 Aug 1966.

Fraser has lattice radar mast by the funnels.

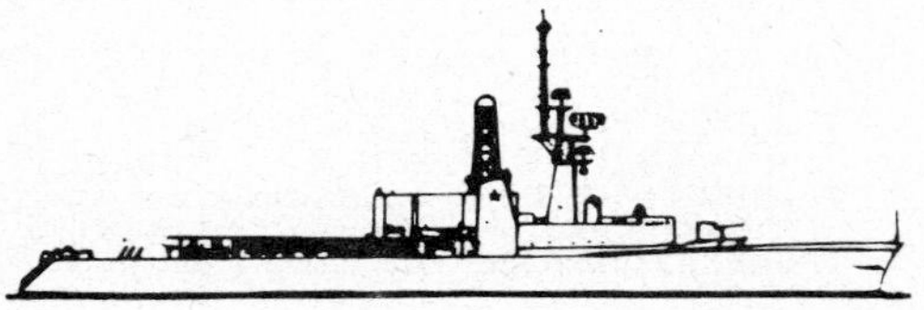
FRASER

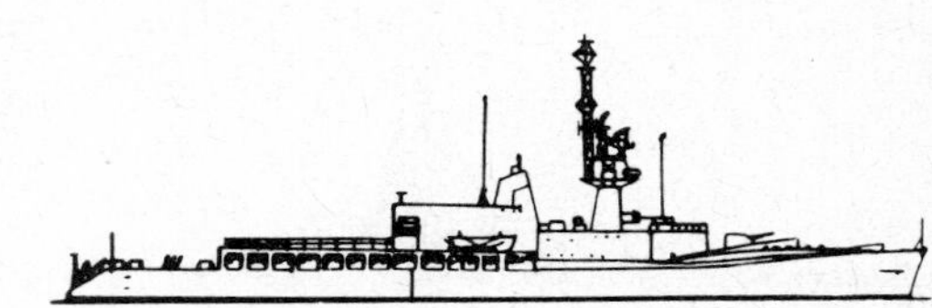
SAGUENAY, SKEENA, OTTAWA, MARGAREE, ASSINIBOINE.

SKEENA *1971, Wright & Logan*

SUBMARINES

3 BRITISH-BUILT "OBERON" CLASS

(PATROL SUBMARINES)

Name	No.	Builders	Laid down	Launched	Commissioned
OJIBWA (ex-*Onyx*)	72	HM Dockyard, Chatham	27 Sep 1962	29 Feb 1964	23 Sep 1965
OKANAGAN	74	HM Dockyard, Chatham	25 Mar 1965	17 Sep 1966	22 June 1968
ONONDAGA	73	HM Dockyard, Chatham	18 June 1964	25 Sep 1965	22 June 1967

Displacement, tons	2 060 full buoyancy surface; 2 200 normal surface; 2 420 dived
Length, feet (*metres*)	241 (*73·5*) pp; 294·2 (*90·0*) oa
Beam, feet (*metres*)	26·5 (*8·1*)
Draught, feet (*metres*)	18 (*5·5*)
Torpedo tubes	8—21 in (*533 mm*), 6 bow and 2 stern
Main machinery	2 Admiralty Standard Range diesels; 3 680 bhp; 2 shafts; 2 electric motors; 6 000 hp
Speed, knots	12 on surface; 17 dived
Complement	65 (7 officers, 58 ratings)

GENERAL
On 11 April 1962 the Minister of National Defence announced that Canada was to buy three Oberon class submarines in UK. The first of these patrol submarines was obtained by the Canadian Government from the Royal Navy construction programme. She was laid down as *Onyx* but launched as *Ojibwa*. The other two were specific Canadian orders. There were some design changes to meet specific new needs including installation of RCN communications equipment and increase of air-conditioning capacity to meet the wide extremes of climate encountered in Canadian operating areas.

ELECTRONICS. The equipment includes sonar with fore casing mounted array and X band surveillance radar installations.

NAMES. The name *Ojibwa* is that of a tribe of North American Indians now widely dispersed in Canada and the USA and one of the largest remnants of aboriginal population. *Okanangan* and *Onondaga* are also well known Canadian Indian tribes.

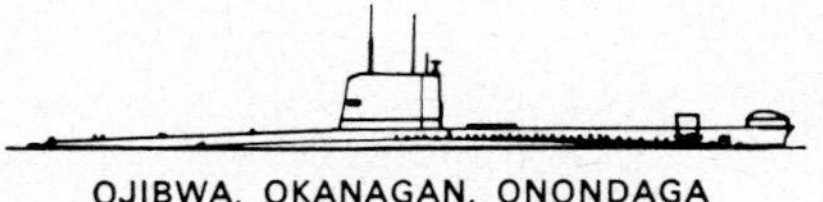

OJIBWA, OKANAGAN, ONONDAGA

OKANAGAN — *1969, Canadian Maritime Command*

ONONDAGA — *1970 Canadian Maritime Command*

1 Ex-US "TENCH" CLASS

(PATROL SUBMARINE)

RAINBOW SS 75 (ex-USS *Argonaut* SS 475)

Displacement, tons	1 800 surface; 2 500 dived
Length, feet (*metres*)	311·2 (*95·0*)
Beam, feet (*metres*)	27·2 (*8·2*)
Draught, feet (*metres*)	17·1 (*5·2*)
Torpedo tubes	10—21 in (*533 mm*) 6 fwd, 4 aft
Main machinery	6 500 hp diesels; 4 610 hp motors
Speed, knots	20 on surface; 10 dived
Range, miles	12 000 at 10 knots surfaced
Complement	82 (8 officers, 74 men)

RAINBOW — *1970, Canadian Maritime Command*

GENERAL
Built by Navy Yard, Portsmouth, New Hampshire. Laid down on 28 June 1944, launched on 1 Oct 1944 and completed on 15 Jan 1945. Purchased in Dec 1968 as a replacement for *Grilse*. Commissioned on 2 Dec 1968. Based at Esquimalt for anti-submarine training.

RAINBOW

REPLENISHMENT SHIPS

Name	No.	Builders	Laid down	Launched	Completed
PRESERVER	AOR 510	Saint John Dry Dock Co Ltd, N.B.	17 Oct 1967	29 May 1969	30 July 1970
PROTECTEUR	AOR 509	Saint John Dry Dock Co Ltd, N.B.	17 Oct 1967	18 July 1968	30 Aug 1969

Displacement, tons 9 000 light; 24 000 full load
Measurement, tons 22 100 gross; 13 250 deadweight
Length, feet (*metres*) 546 (*168·4*) oa
Beam, feet (*metres*) 76 (23·2)
Draught, feet (*metres*) 30 (*9.1*)
Guns, AA 2—3 in (*76 mm*)
A/S launcher 1 Sea Sparrow fitted
Aircraft 3 CHSS-2 helicopters
Boilers 2 forced draught water tube
Main engines Geared turbine; 21 000 shp; 1 shaft
Range, miles 4 100 at 20, 7 500 at 11·5 knots
Complement 227 (15 officers, 212 ratings)

GENERAL
Contract price $47 500 000 for both ships. In design they are an improvement on that of the prototype *Provider*. They could carry spare anti-submarine helciopters, military vehicles and bulk equipment for sealift purposes. 12 000 tons fuel, 1 250 tons ammunition.

PRESERVER *1971, Canadian Forces*

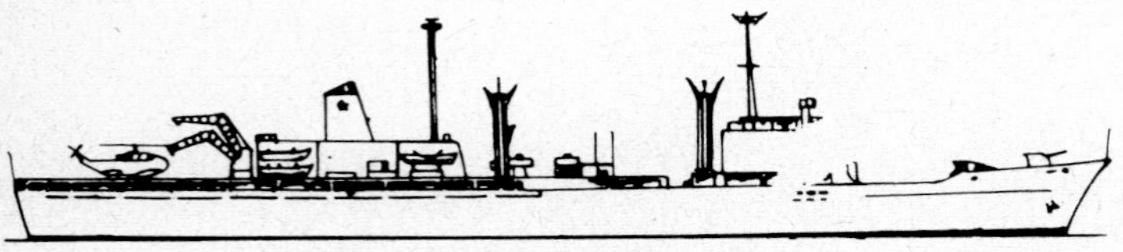
PRESERVER, PROTECTEUR

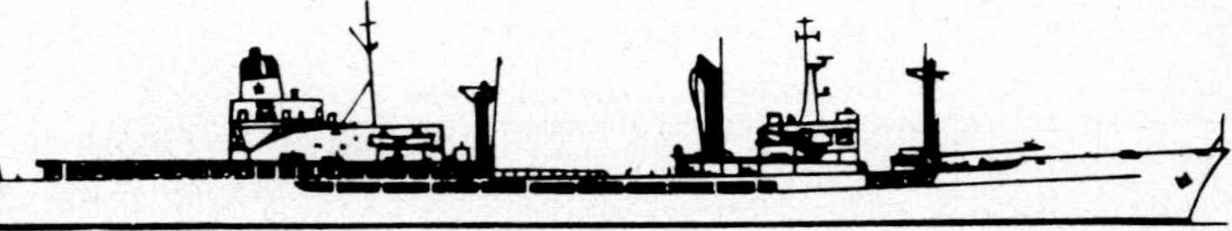
PROVIDER

PROVIDER AOR 508

Displacement, tons 7 300 light; 22 700 full load
Measurement, tons 20 000 gross; 14 700 deadweight
Length, feet (*metres*) 523 (*159·4*) pp; 555 (*169·2*) oa
Beam, feet (*metres*) 76 (*23·2*)
Draught, feet (*metres*) 32 (*9·8*) max
Aircraft 3 CHSS Sea King helicopters
Boilers 2 water tube
Main engines Double reduction geared turbine 21 000 shp; 1 shaft
Speed, knots 20
Range, miles 5 000 at 20 knots
Oil fuel, (tons) 1 200
Complement 142 (11 officers, 131 ratings)

GENERAL
Built by Davie Shipbuilding Ltd, Lauzon, Quebec. Preliminary construction work began in Sep 1960. Laid down on 1 May 1961. Launched on 5 July 1962. Commissioned on 28 Sep 1963. Cost $15 700 000.

PROVIDER *1971, Canadian Forces*

DESIGN. The helicopter flight deck is aft with the hangar at the same level and immediately below the funnel. Three Sea King helicopters can be accommodated in the hangar. The flight deck can receive the largest and heaviest helicopters. A total of 20 electro-hydraulic winches are fitted on deck for ship-to-ship movements of cargo and supplies, as well as shore-to-ship requirements when alongside.

2 "DUN" CLASS OILERS

DUNDALK AOC 501 **DUNDURN** AOC 502

Displacement, tons 950
Dimensions, feet 178·8 × 32·2 × 13
Main engines Diesel; 700 bhp = 10 knots

Small tankers, classed as fleet auxiliaries.

DUNDURN *1969, courtesy Mr. G. R. Hooper (Master)*

MAINTENANCE SHIPS

2 "CAPE" CLASS

Name	No.	Builders	Laid down	Launched	Completed
CAPE BRETON	100	Burrard Dry Dock Co, Vancouver, BC	5 July 1944	7 Oct 1944	25 Apr 1945
CAPE SCOTT	101	Burrard Dry Dock Co, Vancouver, BC	8 June 1944	27 Sep 1944	20 Mar 1945

Displacement, tons 8 580 standard; 11 270 full load
Dimensions, feet 441·5 × 57 × 20 mean at standard displacement.

GENERAL
Alongside Base Ships for FMU'S on each coast. They are decommissioned and no further operational role is planned. These ships, with a number of sisters, were originally built in Canada for the R.N.

CAPE SCOTT *1971, Canadian Forces*

RESEARCH VESSELS

BLUETHROAT AGOR 114

Displacement, tons	785 standard; 870 full load
Dimensions, feet	150·7 pp; 157 oa × 33 × 10
Main engines	Diesel; 2 shafts; 1 200 bhp = 13 knots

Authorised under 1951 Programme. Built by Geo. T. Davie & Sons Ltd, Lauzon PQ. Laid down on 31 Oct 1952. Launched on 15 Sep 1955. Completed on 28 Nov 1955 as mine and Loop Layer. In 1957 she was rated Controlled Minelayer, NPC 114. Redesignated as Cable Layer (ALC) in 1959, and as Research Vessel (AGOR) and GP craft in 1964.

SACKVILLE AGOR 113

Displacement, tons	1 085 standard; 1 350 full load
Dimensions, feet	190 pp; 205 oa × 33 × 14·5
Main engines	Triple expansion; 2 750 ihp = 16 knots
Boilers	2 SE

Built by St. John Dry Dock Co, NB. Launched on 15 May 1941. Completed on 30 Dec 1941. Ex-"Flower" class corvette converted to loop layer. Employed by Bedford Institute for oceanographic work.

KAPUSKASING AGOR 173

Displacement, tons	1 040 standard; 1 335 full load
Dimensions, feet	225 oa × 35 × 11 max
Main engines	Triple expansion; 2 shafts; 2 000 ihp = 16·5 knots
Boilers	2, of 3-drum type

Completed July 22 1943. Former "Algerine" class Ocean Minesweeper. *Kapuskasing* was lent to Dept of Mines and Technical Surveys. and returned to Naval Service in Nov 1972.

QUEST AGOR 172

Displacement, tons	2 130
Dimensions, feet	235 oa × 42 × 15·5
Aircraft	Light helicopter
Main engines	Diesel electric; 2 shafts; 2 950 shp = 16 knots max; Bow thruster propeller
Range, miles	10 000 at 12 knots
Complement	55

Built by Burrard Dry Dock Co, Vancouver for the Naval Research Establishment of the Defence Research Board for acoustic, hydrographic and general oceanographic work. Capable of operating in heavy ice in the company of an icebreaker. Construction began in 1967. Launched on 9 July 1968. Completed on 21 Aug 1969. Based at Halifax.

QUEST *1972, Canadian Forces*

ENDEAVOUR AGOR 171

Displacement, tons	1 560
Dimensions, feet	215 wl; 236 oa × 38·5 × 13
Aircraft	1 light helicopter
Main engines	Diesel electric; 2 shafts; 2 960 shp = 16 knots
Range, miles	10 000 at 12 knots
Complement	10 officers, 13 scientists, 25 ratings (plus helicopter pilot and engineer)

A naval research ship designed primarily for anti-submarine research. Flight deck 48 by 31 feet. Stiffened for operating in ice-covered areas. Built by Yarrows Ltd, Esquimalt, BC. Accepted for service on 9 Mar 1965. She is able to turn in 2·5 times her own length. Her crowsnest is fitted with engine and steering controls for navigation in ice. A bulbous bow reduces pitch and she has anti-roll tanks. Two 9-ton Austin-Weston telescopic cranes are fitted. There are two oceanographical winches each holding 5 000 fathoms of wire, two bathythermograph winches and a deep-sea anchoring and coring winch. She has acoustic insulation in her machinery spaces.

ENDEAVOUR *1970, Canadian Maritime Command*

LAYMORE AGOR 516 (ex-AKS 516)

Measurement, tons	560 gross, 262 net
Dimensions, feet	176·5 × 32 × 8
Main engines	GM diesels; 1 000 bhp = 10·8 knots

Former coastal supply vessel, rated as fleet auxiliary and designated AKS. Converted to research vessel 2 Aug 1965 to Mar 1966 and reclassified AGOR.

MISCELLANEOUS

6 "BAY" CLASS Ex-CMS (PFL)

Displacement, tons	390 standard; 412 full load
Dimensions, feet	140·0 pp; 152·0 oa × 28·0 × 7·0 aft
Gun	1—40 mm AA
Main engines	2 GM V-12 diesels; 2 shafts; 2 400 bhp = 16 knots
Oil fuel, tons	52
Range, miles	4 500 at 11 knots
Complement	38 (3 officers, 35 ratings)

Extensively built of aluminium, including frames and decks. There were originally 14 vessels of this class. Named after Canadian straits and bays. Designation changed from AMC to MCB in 1954. After a period as training ships they were redesignated as Patrol Escorts (small) (PFL) in 1972.

GRANBY FSE 180 (ex-*Victoriaville*, DE 320) (DIVING SUPPORT SHIP)

Displacement, tons	1 570 standard; 2 360 full load (as frigate)
Dimensions, feet	310·5 oa × 36·5 × 16·0
Guns, surface	2—4 in (1 twin)
Guns, AA	6—40 mm (4 single, 1 twin) as frigate
A/S weapons	2 "Squid" triple barrelled depth charge mortars
Boilers	2 Admiralty 3-drum type
Main engines	Triple expansion; 2 shafts; 5 500 ihp = 19 knots max
Range, miles	9 600 at 12 knots
Complement	140 (as frigate)

Depot ship for Fleet Diving Unit, Atlantic.

1 ANTI-SUBMARINE HYDROFOIL (FHE)

BRAS D'OR

Displacement, tons	180
Dimensions, feet	150·8 × 21·5 × 23 (hull borne draught) × 7·5 (60 knots draught on foils)
Main engines	Pratt & Whitney FT4A-2 gas turbine on foils; 22 000 shp = 60 knots Davey Paxman Diesel when hull borne; 2 000 shp = 15 knots

A prototype craft designed by De Havilland Aircraft (Canada). After very successful trials she was laid up ashore at Halifax in 1971.

BRAS D'OR *1971, USN*

YMT 11 **YMT 12** (DIVING TENDERS)

Displacement, tons	110
Dimensions, feet	88 × 20 × 4·8 mean
Main engines	GM diesels; 228 bhp = 10·75 knots

YMT 11 was completed in Jan 1962 and YMT 12 on 7 Aug 1963, both by Ferguson Industries Ltd, Picton, Nova Scotia. They can dive four men at a time to a depth of 250 feet and are fitted with a recompression chamber.
There are small diving tenders YMT 6, YMT 8, YMT 9 and YMT 10, 70 tons, 75 × 18·5 × 8·5 feet, 2 diesels 165 bhp. YMT 1 (46 ft) was transferred to the Naval Research Establishment as a yard craft. YMT 2 and YMT 7 are 46 ft wooden hulled single screw vessels. Two new diving tenders, YSD 1 and YSD 2, entered service in 1965.
Also torpedo recovery vessels *Nimpkish*, YMR 120, and *Songhee*, YMR 1. The yacht *Oriole*, QW 3, used for officer cadet training has been in commission since 1953.

FUNDY *1972, Canadian Maritime Command, Official*

Miscellaneous—*continued*

4 "PORTE" CLASS (GATE VESSELS)

Name	*No.*	*Builders*	*Laid down*	*Launched*	*Completed*
PORTE DE LA REINE	184	Victory Machinery	4 Mar 51	28 Dec 51	19 Sep 52
PORTE QUEBEC	185	Burrard Dry Dock	15 Feb 51	28 Aug 51	7 Oct 52
PORTE ST. JEAN	180	Geo. T. Davie	16 May 50	21 Nov 50	4 June52
PORTE ST. LOUIS	183	Geo. T. Davie	21 Mar 51	22 July 52	28 Aug 52

Displacement, tons 429 full load
Dimensions, feet 125·5 × 26·3 × 13
Guns 1—40 mm AA
Main engines Diesel; A/C Electric; 1 shaft; 600 bhp = 11 knots
Complement 3 officers; 20 ratings

Of trawler design. Multi-purpose vessels used for operating gates in A/S booms, fleet auxiliaries, anti-submarine netlayers for entrances to defended harbours. Can be fitted for minesweeping. Designation changed from YNG to YMG in 1954. All four used during summer for training Reserves. *Port Dauphine* was taken over by the Coast Guard.

PORTE DE LA REINE *1971, Canadian Forces*

TUGS

2 "SAINT" CLASS

Name	*No.*	*Laid down*	*Launched*	*Completed*
SAINT ANTHONY	ATA 531	15 July 1954	2 Nov 1955	22 Feb 1957
SAINT CHARLES	ATA 533	28 Apr 1954	10 July 1956	7 June 1957

Displacement, tons 840 full load
Dimensions, feet 151·5 × 33 × 17
Guns 2—40 mm Bofors AA
Main engines Diesel; 1 shaft; 1 920 bhp = 14 knots

Ocean tugs. Authorised under the 1951 Programme. All built by the St. John Dry Dock Co.

SAINT JOHN *1970, Canadian Maritime Command*

3 "NORTON" CLASS

CLIFTON (ATA 529) **HEATHERTON** (ATA 527) **RIVERTON** (ATA 528)

Displacement, tons 462
Dimensions, feet 104 pp; 111·2 oa × 28 × 11
Main engines Dominion Sulzer diesel; 1 000 bhp = 11 knots
Complement 17

Large harbour tugs. *Clifton* was launched on 31 July 1944.

5 "GLEN" CLASS

GLENBROOK YTB 501
GLENDYNE YTB 503
GLENEVIS YTB 502
GLENLIVET II YTB 504
GLENSIDE YTB 500

Dimensions, feet 80 × 20·7 × 7·2 (aft full load)
Main engines Diesel; 300 bhp = 9 knots

Big harbour tugs. *Glenlivet II* is loaned to Halifax Department of Public Works.

2 "WOOD" CLASS

EASTWOOD YMT 550 **GREENWOOD** YMT 551

Dimensions, feet 60 oa × 16 × 5 (aft full load)
Main engines 250 hp = 10 knots

Medium harbour tugs. Used as A/S Target Towing Vessels. Launched 1944. Other medium harbour tugs are:

FT1, FT2. Employed as fire tugs, Hull numbers YMT 556 and 557 respectively. Sister fire tug FT3; YMT 558, was taken out of service on 31 Mar 1964 and transferred to Dept of Public Works, St. John's Newfoundland.

Tugs—*continued*

13 "VILLE" CLASS

ADAMSVILLE YTS 582
BEAMSVILLE YTS 583
LAWRENCEVILLE YTS 584
LISTERVILLE YTS 578
LOGANVILLE YTS 589
MANNVILLE YTS 577
MARYSVILLE YTS 585
MERRICKVILLE YTS 581
OTTERVILLE YTS 590
PARKSVILLE YTS 579
PLAINSVILLE YTS 587
QUEENSVILLE YTS 586
YOUVILLE YTS 588

Dimensions, feet 40 × 10·5 × 4·8
Main engines Diesel; 1 shaft; 150 bhp

Small harbour tugs. Majority employed on towing duties at Esquimalt and Halifax.

R.C.M. POLICE PATROL VESSELS

3 75ft PATROL VESSELS

CENTENNIAL **STANDOFF** **NICHOLSON**

Displacement, tons 55
Dimensions, feet 75 oa × 17 × 6·5
Main engines 2 diesels; 1 400 bhp = 16 knots
Complement 6

Of wood construction. *Nicholson* and *Standoff* built by Smith & Rhuland, Lunenburg NS and completed in 1968 and 1967 respectively, *Centennial* completed in 1973 by A. F. Theriault & Sons Ltd, Meteghan, NS. Intended for service on the Atlantic Coast.

8 65 ft PATROL VESSELS

ACADIAN **ADVERSUS** **ALERT** **CAPTOR** **DETECTOR** **GANGES** **MASSET** **TOFINO**

STANDOFF *1973, RCMP*

Displacement, tons 48
Dimensions, feet 65 × 15 × 4
Main engines 1 Cummins diesel; 1 shaft; 410 bhp = 12 knots

Coastal patrol police boats built for service on the East and West coasts.

2 55 ft PATROL VESSELS

LITTLE BOW II **SIDNEY**

Displacement, tons 27
Dimensions, feet 55 × 14 × 4
Main engines 2 General Motors Diesels; 600 bhp = 16 knots

Coastal patrol vessels built for service on west coast.

9 PATROL VESSELS (GREAT LAKES)

BRULE **DAWSON** **LAC LA RONGE** **MANYBERRIES** **MOOSOMIN II** **OUTLOOK** **VALLEYFIELD II** **WHITEHORSE** **YELLOWKNIFE**

Ranging from 25 to 41 feet and with speeds up to 30 knots these are all of glass fibre construction except for *Brule, Lac La Ronge* and *Valleyfield*.

8 PATROL VESSELS (WEST COAST)

ADVANCE **ATHABASCA** **DUFFERIN** **DUNCAN** **PEARKES** **REGINA** **RELIANCE** **SLIDEOUT**

Ranging from 25 to 52 feet. In addition there is the 41 ft Patrol Vessel *Fort Macleod* on the East Coast.

CANADIAN COAST GUARD

Administration

Minister of Transport:
Hon Jean Marchand MP, PC

Deputy Minister of Transport:
Mr. O. G. Stoner, BA

Administrator, Marine Transportation Administration:
Dr. P. Camu

Commandant (Canadian Coast Guard):
Captain I. Green

Establishment

In January 1962 all ships owned and operated by the Federal Department of Transport with the exception of pilotage and canal craft, were amalgamated into the Canadian Coast Guard, a civilian service.

Ships

The Canadian Coast Guard comprises 140 ships and craft of all types (including 61 barges). They operate in Canadian waters from the Great Lakes to the northernmost reaches of the Arctic Archipelago.

There are heavy icebreakers, icebreaking ships for tending buoys and lighthouses, marine survey craft, weather-oceanographic ships, and many specialized vessels for tasks such as search and rescue, cable lifting and repair, marine research and shallow-draft operations in areas such as the Mackenzie River system and some parts of the Arctic.

The Ship Building and Heavy Equipment Branch of the Department of Defence Productions arranges for the design, construction and repair of Coast Guard ships and also provides this service for a number of other Canadian Government departments.

Principal bases for the ships are the department's 11 District offices, located at— St. John's, Newfoundland; Dartmouth, N.S.; Saint John, N.B.; Charlottetown, P.E.I.; Quebec and Sorel, Que.; Prescott and Parry Sound, Ont.; Victoria and Prince Rupert, B.C.; and at Hay River, on Great Slave Lake.

Flag

The Canadian Coast Guard has its own distinctive jack, a red maple leaf on a white ground at the hoist and two gold dolphins on a blue ground at the fly.

Canadian Coast Guard vessels have white funnels with a red band at the top and the red maple leaf against the white.

Missions

The Canadian Coast Guard carries out the following missions:

1. Icebreaking and Escort. Icebreaking is carried out in the Gulf of St. Lawrence and River St. Lawrence and the Great Lakes in winter to assist shipping and fc. flood control, and in Arctic waters in summer.
2. Icebreaker-Aids to Navigation Tenders. Installation, supply and maintenance of fixed and floating aids-to-navigation in Canadian waters.
3. Organize and provide icebreaker support and some cargo vessels for the annual Northern sealift which supplies bases and settlements in the Canadian Arctic and Hudson Bay.
4. Provide and operate special patrol cutters and lifeboats for marine search and rescue.
5. Provide and operate survey and sounding vessels for the St. Lawrence River Ship Channel.
6. Provide and operate weatherships for Ocean Station "Papa" in the Pacific.
7. Provide and operate vessel for the repairing of undersea cables.
8. Provide and operate vessel for environmental research.
9. Provide and operate vessel for Marine Traffic Control on the St. Lawrence river.
10. Operate a small fleet of aircraft primarily for aids to navigation ice reconnaissance, and pollution control work.

Fleet Strength

Heavy Icebreakers	5
Medium Icebreakers	1
Medium Icebreaking aid to navigation vessels	7
Light Icebreaking aid to navigation vessels	8
Ice strengthened aid to navigation vessels	4
Aid-to-navigation tenders	10
Northern supply vessels	2
Search and Rescue—Offshore patrol cutters	8
Great Lakes patrol cutters	3
Shore-based hovercraft	1
Shore-based lifeboats	6
Shore-based launches	6
St. Lawrence light icebreaking survey and sounding vessel	1
St. Lawrence ship channel survey and sounding vessels	6
Weather ships for ocean station Papa in the Pacific	2
Cable repair ship	1
Environmental research vessel	1
St. Lawrence River marine traffic control vessel	1
Training vessels	2
Total	75

Aircraft

Fixed wing	1
Helicopters	28

WEATHER SHIPS

Name	*Laid down*	*Launched*	*Completed*
QUADRA	Feb 1965	4 July 1966	Mar 1967
VANCOUVER	Mar 1964	29 June 1965	4 July 1966

Displacement, tons: 5 600 full load
Dimensions, feet: 361·2 pp; 404·2 oa × 50 × 17·5
Aircraft: 1 helicopter
Main engines: Turbo-electric; 2 shafts; 7 500 shp = 18 knots
Boilers: 2 automatic Babcock & Wilcox D type
Range, miles: 8 400 at 14 knots
Complement: 96

Turbo-electric twin screw weather and oceanographic vessels for Pacific Ocean service. Both built by Burrard Drydock Limited, North Vancouver, B.C. They have bow water jet reaction system to assist steering at slow speeds. Flume stabilization systems are fitted. They are turbo-electric powered, with oil-fired boilers to provide the quiet operation needed for vessels housing much scientific equipment. Their complement includes 15 technical officers such as meteorologists, oceanographers and electronics technicians.

VANCOUVER — *1970, Canadian Coast Guard*

JOHN CABOT

Displacement, tons: 6 375 full load
Dimensions, feet: 313·3 × 60 × 21·5
Aircraft: 1 helicopter
Main engines: Diesel-electric; 2 shafts; 9 000 shp = 15 knots
Range, miles: 10 000 at 12 knots
Complement: 85 officers and men

Combination cable repair ship and icebreaker. Built by Canadian Vickers Limited, Montreal. Laid down in May 1963, launched on 15 Apr 1964 and completed in July 1965. Designed to repair and lay cable over the bow only. For use in East Coast and Arctic waters. Bow water jet reaction manoeuvring system, heeling tanks and Flume stabilisation system. Three circular storage holds handle a total of 400 miles of submarine cable. Personnel include technicians and helicopter pilots.

JOHN CABOT — *1970, Canadian Coast Guard*

NORTHERN SUPPLY VESSELS

2 FORMER TANK LANDING CRAFT (LCT 8s)

EIDER **SKUA**

Measurement, tons	1 083 to 1 104 gross
Dimensions, feet	225 pp; 231·2 oa × 38 × 3
Main engines	Diesel; 1 000 shp = 9 knots

Converted LCT (8)s, acquired from Great Britain in 1957-61. Built by Harland & Wolff, Belfast (*Puffin* and *Raven*) and Sir Wm. Arrol & Co Ltd, Glasgow (*Eider*). All completed in 1946.

SKUA *Canadian Coast Guard*

2 FORMER TANK LANDING CRAFT (LCT 4s)

MARMOT **MINK**

Displacement, tons	586 full load
Dimensions, feet	187·2 × 33·8 × 4
Main engines	Diesel; 920 shp = 8 knots

Converted LCT (4)s acquired from Great Britain in 1958. Completed in 1944. Formerly officially rated as Steel Landing Craft for Northern Service, now re-rated as Aids to Navigation Tenders, in reserve.

MINK *1963, Canadian Coast Guard*

ICEBREAKERS

LOUIS S. ST. LAURENT

Displacement, tons	13 000 full load
Dimensions, feet	366·5 oa × 80 × 31
Aircraft	2 helicopters
Main engines	Turbo-electric; 3 shafts; 24 000 shp = 17·75 knots *trials*
Range, miles	16 000 miles at 13 knots cruising speed
Complement	Total accommodation for 216

This new icebreaker for service in the Arctic and the Gulf of St. Lawrence was built at Canadian Vickers Limited, Montreal. She is larger than any of the former Coast Guard icebreakers. This triple screw ship with a steam turbo-electric propulsion system is the world's most powerful non-nuclear powered icebreaker. She has a helicopter hangar below the flight deck, with an elevator to raise the two helicopters to the deck when required. She was launched on 3 Dec 1966 and completed in Oct 1969. She is officially rated as a heavy icebreaker.

LOUIS S. ST. LAURENT *1971, Canadian Coast Guard*

Icebreakers—*continued*

NORMAN MCLEOD ROGERS

Displacement, tons	6 320 full load
Dimensions, feet	295 oa × 62·5 × 20
Aircraft	1 helicopter
Landing craft	2
Main engines	4 diesels and 2 gas turbines powering 2 electric motors; 2 shafts; 12 000 shp = 15 knots
Complement	55

A new type of icebreaker for use in the Gulf of St Lawrence and East Coast waters. Built at the yard of Canadian Vickers Limited, Montreal. This is the world's first application of gas turbine electric propulsion for booster power in an icebreaker. Completed in Oct 1969. Officially rated as a Heavy Icebreaker.

NORMAN MCLEOD ROGERS *1970, Canadian Coast Guard*

JOHN A. MACDONALD

Displacement, tons	9 160 full load
Measurement, tons	6 186 gross
Dimensions, feet	315 × 70 × 28
Main engines	Diesel-electric; 15 000 shp = 15·5 knots designed

Completed by Davie Shipbuilding Limited, Lauzon Port Quebec, in Sep 1960. Officially rated as a heavy icebreaker.

JOHN A. MACDONALD *1971, Canadian Coast Guard*

MONTCALM **WOLFE**

Displacement, tons	3 005 full load
Measurement, tons	2 022 gross
Dimensions, feet	220 × 48 × 16
Main engines	Steam reciprocating; 4 000 ihp = 13 knots

Wolfe was built by Canadian Vickers Limited, Montreal, and completed in Nov 1959, *Montcalm* was built by Davie Shipbuilding Ltd, Lauzon, P.Q., and completed in June 1957. Officially rated as Medium Icebreaking Aids to Navigation Vessels.

MONTCALM ***1972, Canadian Coast Guard***

Icebreakers—*continued*

CAMSELL

Displacement, tons	3 072 full load
Measurement, tons	2 020 gross
Dimensions, feet	223·5 × 48 × 16
Main engines	Diesel-electric; 4 250 shp = 13 knots

Completed by Burrard Dry Dock Company Limited, Vancouver, BC in Oct 1959. Officially rated as Medium Icebreaking Aids to Navigation Vessel.

CAMSELL *1972, Canadian Coast Guard*

SIR HUMPHREY GILBERT

Displacement, tons	3 000 full load
Measurement, tons	1 930 gross
Dimensions, feet	220 × 48 × 16·3
Main engines	Diesel-electric; 4 250 shp = 13 knots

Completed by Davie Shipbuilding Limited, Lauzon, Port Quebec, in June 1959. Officially rated as Medium Icebreaking Aids to Navigation Vessel.

SIR HUMPHREY GILBERT *1970, Canadian Coast Guard*

LABRADOR

Displacement, tons	6 490 full load
Measurement, tons	3 823 gross
Dimensions, feet	269·0 pp; 290·0 oa × 63·5 × 29·0
Aircraft	Provision for 2 helicopters
Main engines	Diesel-electric; 10 000 shp = 16 knots

Built by Marine Industries Limited, Sorel, Quebec. Ordered in Feb 1949, laid down on 18 Nov 1949, launched on 14 Dec 1951 and completed for the Royal Canadian Navy on 8 July 1954, but transferred to the Department of Transport in Feb 1958. Officially rated as a Heavy Icebreaker. She was the first naval vessel to traverse the North West passage and circumnavigate North America, when she was Canada's largest and most modern icebreaker. High-tensile steel sides 1·6 inches thick and heeling tanks. Aircraft hanger and flight deck aft for operating helicopters. Carries two landing craft strengthened to resist ice. Latest navigational devices, and equipped with instruments for hydrography, oceanography, meteorology, cosmic ray research, ice reconnaissance and other scientific purposes. Fitted with Denny Brown stabilisers. Propelling machinery can be controlled from bridge. She was transferred, on loan to the Department of Transport and subsequently acquired from the Royal Canadian Navy outright. Mounting for two 40 mm guns forward, but guns were removed.

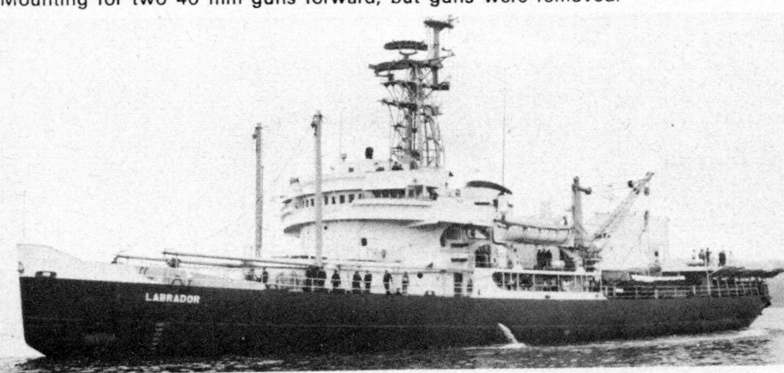

LABRADOR *1970, Canadian Coast Guard*

d'IBERVILLE

Displacement, tons	9 930 full load
Measurement, tons	5 678 gross
Dimensions, feet	310 × 66·5 × 30·2
Main engines	Steam reciprocating; 10 800 ihp = 15 knots

Completed by Davie Shipbuilding Limited Lauzon, Port Quebec, in May 1953. Officially rated as a Heavy Icebreaker.

ERNEST LAPOINTE

Displacement, tons	1 675 full load
Measurement, tons	1 179 gross
Dimensions, feet	184 × 36 × 15·5
Main engines	Steam reciprocating; 2 000 iph = 13 knots

Completed by Davie Shipbuilding Limited, Lauzon, Port Quebec in Feb 1941. Officially rated as St. Lawrence Ship Channel Icebreaking Survey and Sounding Vessel.

N. B. McLEAN

Displacement, tons	5 034 full load
Measurement, tons	3 254 gross
Dimensions, feet	277 × 60·5 × 19·6
Main engines	Steam reciprocating; 6 500 ihp = 13 knots

Completed by Halifax Shipyards Limited, Halifax, NS, in 1930. Officially rated as Medium Icebreaker.

GRIFFON

Displacement, tons	3 096
Dimensions, feet	234 × 49 × 15·5
Main engines	Diesel; 4 000 bhp; 13·5 knots

Completed in Dec 1970 by Davie Shipbuilding Ltd, Lauzon, Quebec. Officially rated as a Medium Icebreaking Aid to Navigation Vessel.

J. E. BERNIER

Displacement, tons	3 096
Dimensions, feet	231 × 49 × 16
Aircraft	1 helicopter
Main engines	Diesel Electric; 4 250 bhp = 13·5 knots (trial speed)

Built by Davie Shipbuilding Co, Ltd, Lauzon, Quebec; completed in Aug 1967. Officially rated as Medium Icebreaking Aid to Navigation Vessel.

SIMCOE

Displacement, tons	1 300 full load
Dimensions, feet	179·5 × 38 × 12
Main engines	Diesel-electric; 2 000 shp = 12 knots

Completed by Canadian Vickers in 1962. Officially rated as Ice Strengthened Aid to Navigation Vessel.

SIMON FRASER **TUPPER**

Displacement, tons	1 876 full load
Measurements, tons	1 357 gross
Dimensions, feet	204·5 × 42 × 14
Main engines	Diesel-electric; 2 900 shp = 13·5 knots designed

Simon Fraser was completed by Burrard Dry Dock Company Limited, N. Vancouver in Feb 1960 and *Tupper* by Marine Industries Limited, Sorel, Quebec in Dec 1959. Both officially rated as Light Icebreaking Aid to Navigation Vessels.

THOMAS CARLETON

Displacement, tons	1 532 full load
Dimensions, feet	180 × 42 × 13
Main engines	Diesel; 2 000 bhp = 12 knots

Built by Saint John Dry Dock Limited Saint John, NB. Completed in 1960. Officially rated as a light Icebreaking Aid to Navigation Vessel.

ALEXANDER HENRY

Displacement, tons	2 497 full load
Measurements, tons	1 647 gross
Dimensions, feet	210 × 43·5 × 16
Main engines	Diesel; 3 550 bhp = 13 knots designed

Built by Port Arthur Shipbuilding Limited, Port Arthur. Completed in July 1959. Officially rated as a Medium Icebreaking Aid to Navigation Vessel.

EDWARD CORNWALLIS

Displacement, tons	3 700 full load
Measurement, tons	1 965 gross
Dimensions, feet	259 × 43·5 × 18
Main engines	Steam reciprocating; 2 800 ihp = 13·5 knots designed

Built by Canadian Vickers Limited, Montreal. Completed in Dec 1949. In reserve. Officially rated as a Light Icebreaking Aid to Navigation Vessel.

EDWARD CORNWALLIS *1971, Canadian Coast Guard*

WALTER E. FOSTER

Displacement, tons	2 715 full load
Measurement, tons	1 672 gross
Dimensions, feet	229·2 × 42·5 × 16
Main engines	Steam reciprocating; 2 000 ihp = 12·5 knots

Built by Canadian Vickers, Limited, Montreal. Completed in Dec 1954. Officially rated as a Light Icebreaking Aid to Navigation Vessel.

SIR WILLIAM ALEXANDER

Displacement, tons	3 555 full load
Measurements, tons	2 153 gross.
Dimensions, feet	227·5 × 45 × 17·5
Main engines	Diesel electric; 4 250 shp = 15 knots designed

Built by Halifax Shipyards, Limited, Halifax. Completed in June 1959. Equipped with Flume Stabilisation System. Officially rated as a Medium Icebreaking Aid to Navigation Vessel.

DEPOT SHIP

NARWHAL

Measurement, tons	2 064 gross
Dimensions, feet	251·5 × 42·0 × 12·0
Main engines	Diesel; 2 000 bhp
Range, miles	9 200 cruising
Complement	32

Built by Canadian Vickers, Montreal. Completed in July 1963. Officially rated as Sealift Stevedore Depot Vessel.

NARWHAL *1970, Canadian Coast Guard*

SEARCH AND RESCUE CUTTERS

ALERT

Displacement, tons	2 025
Dimensions, feet	234·3 × 39·9 × 15·1
Aircraft	1 helicopter
Main engines	Diesel Electric; 7 716 hp = 18·75 knots
Range, miles	6 000

Completed by Davie Shipbuilding Ltd Lauzon Dec 1969. Officially rated as offshore Patrol Cutter.

ALERT *1971, Canadian Coast Guard*

DARING (ex-*Wood*, ex-MP 17)

Displacement, tons	600 standard
Dimensions, feet	178 oa × 29 × 9·2
Main engines	2 Fairbanks- Morse diesels; 2 shafts; 2 660 bhp = 16 knots

Corvette type. Built by Geo. T. Davie and Sons Ltd Lauzon, Quebec. Completed in July 1958. Used for patrol on the east coast of Canada, this ship is built of steel, strengthened against ice, with aluminium superstructure. Transferred from the Royal Canadian Mounted Police Marine Division to the Ministry of Transport in 1971, and renamed *Daring*.

DARING (ex-*Wood*) *1966, Director of Marine Services*

RACER RALLY RAPID READY RELAY RIDER

Measurement, tons	153 gross
Dimensions, feet	95·2 × 20 × 6·5
Main engines	Diesel; 2 400 bhp = 20 knots designed

Built by Yarrows Ltd, Esquimalt, BC; Davie Shipbuilding Ltd, Lauzon, PQ; Ferguson Industries, Picton, NS; Burrard Dry Dock, Vancouver; and Kingston Shipyard, respectively. All completed in 1963. *Rider*, completed for the Dept of Fisheries, was taken over by the Coast Guard in Mar 1969. *Rapid* was placed in reserve in 1970

SPINDRIFT SPRAY SPUME

Measurement, tons	57 gross
Dimensions, feet	70 × 16·8 × 4·7
Main engines	2 diesels; 1 500 bhp = 19 knots designed

Built by Cliff Richardson Boats Ltd. Meaford, Ont; J. J. Taylor & Sons, Ltd, Toronto; and Grew Ltd, Penetanguishene, Ont, respectively. Completed in 1963-64 for service on Great Lakes Patrol.

SPINDRIFT *1966, Canadian Coast Guard, Official*

SUPPLY VESSELS

BARTLETT PROVO WALLIS

Displacement, tons	1 620
Dimensions, feet	189·3 × 42·5 × 12·5
Engines	Diesel; 1 760 bhp = 12 knots

In service since 1970. Classed as Ice Strengthened Aid to Navigation Vessels.

MONTMORENCY

Displacement, tons	1 006 full load
Measurement, tons	750 gross
Dimensions, feet	163 × 34 × 11
Main engines	Diesel; 1 200 bhp

Built by Davie Shipbuilding Limited, Lauzon, Port Quebec. Completed in Aug 1957. Officially rated as an Ice Strengthened Aid to Navigation Vessel.

MONTMAGNY

Displacement, tons	565 full load
Dimensions, feet	148·0 × 29·0 × 8·
Main engines	Diesels; 1 000 bhp

Built by Russel Bros. Owen Sound, Ont. Completed in May 1963.

MONTMAGNY *1970, Canadian Coast Guard*

VERENDRYE

Displacement, tons	400 full load
Dimensions, feet	125·0 × 26·0 × 7·0
Main engines	Diesels; 760 bhp

Built by Geo. T. Davie & Sons.Ltd, Lauzon. Completed in Oct 1959.

ALEXANDER MACKENZIE SIR JAMES DOUGLAS

Displacement, tons	720 full load
Dimensions, feet	150·0 × 30·0 × 10·3
Main engines	Diesels; 1 000 bhp

564 tons gross. Built by Burrard Dry Dock Vancouver and completed 1950 and Nov 1956 respectively. These two, and *Montmagny* and *Verendrye*, are officially rated as Aid to Navigation Tenders.

SURVEY AND SOUNDING VESSELS

VILLE MARIE

Displacement, tons	493 full load
Dimensions, feet	134·0 × 28·0 × 9·5
Main engines	Diesel electric; 1 000 hp

BEAUFORT

Displacement, tons	767 full load
Dimensions, feet	167·5 × 24·0 × 9·0
Main engines	Diesels; 1 280 bhp

NICOLET

Displacement, tons	935 full load
Dimensions, feet	166·5 × 35·0 × 9·6
Main engines	Diesels; 1 350 bhp

DETECTOR

Displacement, tons	584 full load
Dimensions feet	140·0 × 35·0 × 10·0
Main engines	Steam reciprocating

Beaufort and *Ville Marie* were completed in 1960. There are also two smaller vessels *Glenada* and *Jean Bourdon* for the St. Lawrence Ship Channel.

ENVIRONMENTAL RESEARCH VESSEL

PORTE DAUPHINE

Displacement, tons	447
Dimensions, feet	119·3 × 25 × 11·3
Main engines	Diesel; 1 shaft; 600 bhp = 12·5 knots

Former gate vessel of the "Porte" class in the Royal Canadian Navy, taken over in 1958.

DUMIT ECKALOO MISKANAW TEMBAH

Four vessels to assist navigation in Mackenzie River operations. Small tug/buoy tender type.

MALLARD MOORHEN

Shore based craft: For search and rescue and patrol duties: Six lifeboats (CG 101-106), six launches (*Mallard, Moorhen*, CG 110-113) and one Hovercraft (CG 021).

CHILE

MINISTERIAL

Minister of National Defence:
Vice-Admiral Patricio Carvajal Prado

Naval Board

Commander in-Chief of the Navy:
Admiral José Toribio Merino Castro

Chief of the Naval Staff:
Rear-Admiral Hugo Cabezas

Diplomatic Representation

Chief of the Chilean Naval mission in Great Britain and Naval Attaché in London. The Hague and Stockholm:
Vice-Admiral Oscar Buzeta

Chief of the Chilean Naval Mission in USA and Naval Attaché in Washington:
Vice-Admiral Luis Eberhard

Personnel

(a) 1972: 20 000 (1 200 officers, 18 300 ratings, 500 marines)
1973: 22 000 (1 300 officers, 18 500 ratings, 2 200 marines)
1974: 22 000 (1 300 officers, 18 500 ratings, 2 200 marines)

(b) 1 year national service

Disposals

Frigates

1973 *Riquelme*

Submarines

1972 *Thomson*

Landing Craft

1971 *Bolados* (LCU 95)

Strength of the Fleet

Type	*Active*	*Building*
Cruisers	3	—
Destroyers	4 (+?2)	—
Frigates	3	2
Patrol Submarines	1	2
Landing Ships (Tank)	2	—
Repair Ships (ex-LST)	2	—
Landing Ships (M)	3	—
Landing Craft (U)	2	—
Fast Attack Craft (T)	4	—
Large Patrol Craft	5	—
Survey Ship	1	—
Sail Training Ship	1	—
Transports	2	—
Oilers	3	—
Floating Docks	2	—
Tugs	7	—

Mercantile Marine

Lloyd's Register of Shipping:

138 vessels of 383 886 tons gross

CRUISERS

	No.	*Builders*	*Laid down*	*Launched*	*Completed*
LATORRE (ex-*Göta Lejon*)	CL 04	Eriksberg Mekaniska Verkstad, Göteborg	27 Sep 1943	17 Nov 1945	15 Dec 1947

Displacement, tons	8 200 standard; 9 200 full load
Length, feet (*metres*)	590·5 (*180·0*) wl; 597 (*182·0*) oa
Beam, feet (*metres*)	54 (*16·5*)
Draught, feet (*metres*)	21·5 (*6·6*) max
Guns, surface	7—6 in (*150 mm*) 53 cal.
Guns, AA	4—57 mm; 11—40 mm
Tubes	6—21 inch
Armour	3 in—5 in (*75—125 mm*)
Main engines	2 sets De Laval geared turbines; 100 000 shp; 2 shafts
Boilers	4 Swedish 4-drum type
Speed, knots	33 designed
Complement	610

Scale 1 inch = 118 ft.

GENERAL
Radar control arrangements were installed for 6-inch guns. Fitted for minelaying with a capacity of 120 mines. Reconstructed in 1951-52, modernised in 1958, with new radar, 57 mm guns etc.

GUNNERY. The 6 inch guns are high angle automatic anti-aircraft weapons with an elevation of 70 degrees.

RADAR. Search: LWO 3, Type 227. Tactical: Type 293. Fire Control: X band.

TRANSFER. Purchased by Chile from Sweden July 1971.

LATORRE — *1973, Chilean Navy*

2 "PRAT" CLASS

Name	*No.*	*Builders*	*Laid down*	*Launched*	*Commissioned*
O'HIGGINS (ex-USS *Brooklyn*, CL 40)	CL 02	New York Navy Yard	12 Mar 1935	30 Nov 1936	18 July 1938
PRAT (ex-USS *Nashville*, CL 43)	CL 03	New York S.B. Corp.	24 Jan 1935	2 Oct 1937	25 Nov 1938

Displacement, tons	
O'Higgins	9 700 standard; 13 000 full load
Prat	10 000 standard; 13 500 full load
Length, feet (*metres*)	608·3 (*185·4*) oa
Beam, feet (*metres*)	69 (*21·0*)
Draught, feet (*metres*)	24 (*7·3*) max
Aircraft	1 Bell helicopter
Guns, surface	15—6 in (*153 mm*) 47 cal (5 triple); 8—5 in (*127 mm*) 25 cal (single)
Guns, AA	28—40 mm; 24—20 mm
Armour, inches (*mm*)	Belt 4 in—1½ in (*102—38*); Decks 3 in+2 in (*76+51*); Turrets 5 in—3 in (*127—76*); C.T. 8 in (*203*)
Boilers	8 Babcock & Wilcox Express type
Main engines	Parsons geared turbines 100 000 shp; 4 shafts
Speed, knots	32·5
Range, miles	14 500 at 15 knots
Oil fuel (tons)	2 100
Complement	888 to 975 (peace)

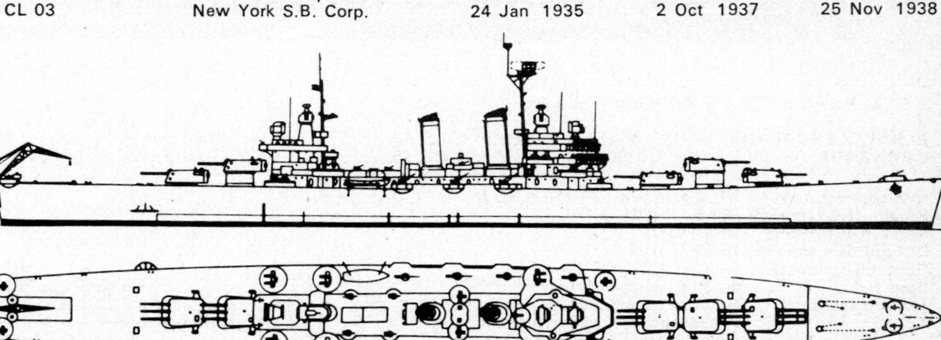

Cruisers—*continued*

Former "light" cruisers of the US "Brooklyn" Class. Purchased from the United States in 1951 at a price representing 10 per cent of their original cost ($37 000 000) plus the expense of reconditioning them.

HANGER. The hanger in the hull right aft could accommodate 6 aircraft if necessary together with engine spares and duplicate parts, though 4 aircraft was the normal capacity. Above the hanger two catapults were mounted as far outboard as possible, and a revolving crane was placed at the stern extremity overhanging the aircraft hatch.

RADAR. Search: SPS 12. Tactical: SPS 10.

DRAWING. Starboard elevation and plan. Drawn in 1971. Scale: 121 feet = 1 inch

PRAT — *1971, Chilean Navy.*

DESTROYERS

2 "ALMIRANTE" CLASS

Name	No.	Builders	Laid down	Launched	Commissioned
RIVEROS	DDG 18	Vickers-Armstrong Ltd, Barrow	12 Apr 1957	12 Dec 1958	31 Dec 1960
WILLIAMS	DDG 19	Vickers-Armstrong Ltd, Barrow	20 June 1956	5 May 1958	26 Mar 1960

Displacement, tons	2 730 standard; 3 300 full load
Length, feet (*metres*)	402 (*122·5*) oa
Beam, feet (*metres*)	43 (*13·1*)
Draught, feet (*metres*)	13·3 (*4·0*)
Missiles, AA	4 Exocet Launchers Quadruple launcher for "Seacat"
Guns, AA	4—4 in (*102 mm*); 5—40 mm
A/S	2 Squid 3-barrelled DC mortars
Torpedo tubes	5—21 in (*533 mm*) quintupled
Boilers	2 Babcock & Wilcox
Main engines	Parsons Pametrada geared turbines 54 000 shp; 2 shafts
Speed, knots	34·5
Range, miles	6 000 at 16 knots
Complement	266

GENERAL
Ordered in May 1955. Layout and general arrangements are conventional. Bunks fitted for entire crew. Both modernised by Swan Hunter, *Williams* in 1971 and *Riveros* in 1973.

ELECTRICAL. The electrical system is on alternating current. Galleys are all electric. There is widespread use of fluorescent lighting. Degaussing cables are fitted.

RADAR. Plessey AWSI and Target Indication radar with A10 autonomous displays being fitted at refits.

MISSILES. British "Seacat" radar controlled short range surface-to-air weapon installations were fitted at the Chilean Navy Yard at Talcahuano in 1964. Exocet fitted during 1971-72 modernisations.

GUNNERY. The four inch guns are disposed in four single mountings, two superimposed forward and two aft. They are automatic with a range of 12 500 yards (11 400 metres) and an elevation of 75 degrees.

WILLIAMS — *1972, Wright & Logan*

WILLIAMS, RIVEROS

OPERATIONAL. The operations room and similar spaces are air-conditioned. Twin rudders. Ventilation and heating system designed to suit Chilean conditions, extending from the tropics to the Antarctic.

RIVEROS — *1971, Chilean Navy*

2 Ex-US "FLETCHER" CLASS

	No.	Builder	Launched	Commissioned
BLANCO ENCALADA (ex-USS *Wadleigh* DD 689)	DD 14	Bath Iron Works Corpn. Bath	7 Aug 1943	19 Oct 1943
COCHRANE (ex-USS *Rooks*, DD 804)	DD 15	Todd Pacific Shipyards	6 June 1944	2 Sep 1944

Displacement, tons	2 100 standard; 2 750 full load
Length, feet (*metres*)	376·5 (110·5) oa
Beam, feet (*metres*)	39·5 (12·0)
Draught, feet (*metres*)	18 (5·5) max
Guns, dual purpose	4—5 in (127 *mm*) 38 cal.
Guns, AA	6—3 in (*76 mm*) 50 cal.
Torpedo tubes	5—21 in (quintupled)
A/S	2 Hedgehogs; 2 side launching torpedo racks; 1 DC rack; 6 "K" DCT
Boilers	4 Babcock & Wilcox
Main engines	2 Westinghouse geared turbines; 60 000 shp; 2 shafts
Range, miles	5 000 at 15 knots; 1 260 at 30 knots
Oil fuel (tons)	650
Speed, knots	35
Complement	250 (14 officers, 236 men). Accommodation for 324 (24 officers, 300 men)

BLANCO ENCALADA, COCHRANE

Destroyers—*continued*

GENERAL
Former United States destroyers of the "Fletcher" class. Transferred to Chile under the Military Aid Program in 1963. Three more destroyers were scheduled for transfer from the United States Navy to the Chilean Navy under a new transfer law signed by the President of the United States in 1966. The ships were to have been refitted and modernised and adapted to Chilean requirements before transfer to the new flag, but the four Frigates of the "Serrano" class were transferred instead.

RADAR. Search: SPS 6. Tactical: SPS 10. Fire Control: X Band.

Note. Negotiations in hand for transfer of two ex-US "Allen M. Sumner" class (Fram II) in 1974.

COCHRANE *1972, Chilean Navy*

FRIGATES

2 BRITISH "LEANDER" CLASS

Name	*No.*	*Builders*	*Laid down*	*Launched*	*Commissioned*
CONDELL	PFG 06	Yarrow & Co. Ltd	5 June 1971		
LYNCH	PFG 07	Yarrow & Co Ltd	6 Dec 1972		

Displacement, tons	2 500 standard; 2 962 full load
Length, feet (*metres*)	360·0(*109·7*)wl; 372·0(*113·4*) oa
Beam, feet (*metres*)	43·0 (*13·1*)
Draught, feet (*metres*)	18·0 (*5·5*) max (props)
Aircraft	1 light helicopter
Missile launchers	4 Exocet launchers 1 quadruple "Seacat"
Guns, duel purpose	2—4·5 in (1 twin)
Boilers	2
Main engines	2 geared turbines; 30 000 shp
Speed, knots	30
Range, miles	4 500 at 12 knots
Complement	263

GENERAL
Ordered from Yarrow & Co Ltd, Scotstoun in the modernisation programme of the Chilean Navy. Until the Swedish cruiser was acquired *Condell*, laid down on 5 June 1971, was to have been named *Latorre*.

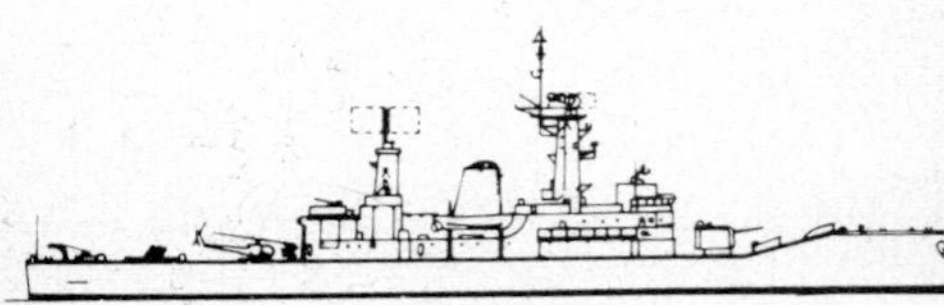
CONDELL, LYNCH

CONDELL *1973, Yarrow & Co Ltd*

3 APD TRANSPORT TYPE

SERRANO APD 26 (ex-USS *Odum* APD 71, ex-DE 670)
ORELLA APD 27 (ex-USS *Jack C. Robinson* APD 72, ex-DE 671)
RIQUELME APD 28 (ex-USS *Joseph E. Campbell* APD 49, ex-DE 70)
URIBE APD 29 (ex-USS *Daniel Griffin* APD 38, ex-DE 54)

Displacement, tons	1 400 standard; 2 130 full load
Length, feet (*metres*)	300·0 (*91·4*) wl; 306·0 (*93·3*) oa
Beam, feet (*metres*)	37·0 (*11·3*)
Draught, feet (*metres*)	12·6 (*3·8*)
Guns	1—5 in 38 cal dp; 6—40 mm AA
Main engines	GE turbo-electric; 2 shafts; 12 000 shp = 23·6 knots 2 turbines 6 000 hp each 2 generators 4 500 kW each
Boilers	2 Foster Wheeler "D" type
Range, miles	5 000 at 15 knots 2 000 at 23 knots
Complement	209

ORELLA *1970, Chilean Navy*

GENERAL
These former destroyer escort transports were purchased from the USA, transferred at Orange, Texas 25 Nov 1966 (first two) and Norfolk Va 1 Dec 1966 (*Uribe*). They have been modernised, *Requelme* was also transferred but is being used for provision of spare parts.

SUBMARINES

2 BRITISH "OBERON" CLASS

Name	*No.*	*Builder*	*Laid down*	*Launched*	*Completion*
O'BRIEN	SS 22	Scotts Greenock	17 Jan 1971	21 Dec 1972	Mid-1974
HYATT	SS 23	Scotts Greenock	10 Jan 1972	26 Sep 1973	Late 1974

Displacement, tons	1 610 standard; 2 030 surface; 2 410 submerged
Length, feet (*metres*)	241·0 (*73·5*) pp; 295·2 (*90·0*) oa
Beam, feet (*metres*)	26·5 (*8·1*)
Draught, feet (*metres*)	18·1 (*5·5*)
Torpedo tubes	8—21 in (*533 mm*)
Main machinery	2 diesels 3 680 bhp; 2 electric motors 6 000 shp; 2 shafts, electric drive
Speed, knots	12 surface, 17 submerged

Ordered from Scott's Shipbuilding & Engineering Co, Ltd, Greenock, late 1969 as part of a new fleet replacement and modernisation programme.

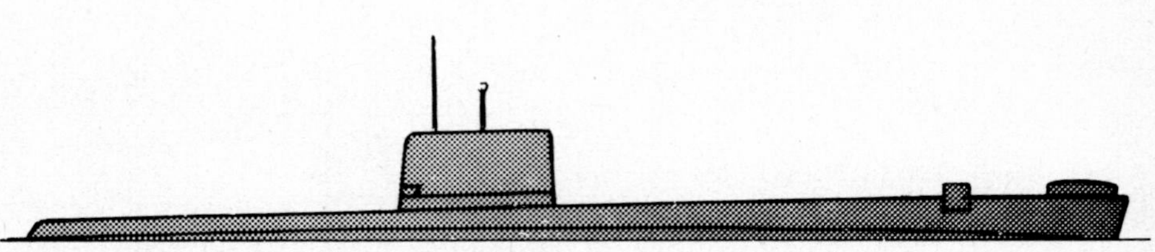

OBERON *Class*

1 Ex-US "BALAO" CLASS

SIMPSON SS 21 (ex-USS *Spot*, SS 413)

Displacement, tons	1 526 standard; 1 816 surface; 2 425 submerged
Length, feet (*metres*)	311·6 (*95·0*)
Beam, feet (*metres*)	27·0 (*8·2*)
Draught, feet (*metres*)	17·0 (*5·2*)
Torpedo tubes	10—21 in (*533 mm*), 6 bow; 4 stern
Main machinery	6 500 hp GM 2-stroke diesels; 4 610 hp electric motors
Speed, knots	20 on surface, 10 submerged
Complement	80

Built at Mare Island Navy Yard. *Simpson*, launched on 20 May 1944 and completed on 3 Aug 1944, was transferred end of 1961. Streamlined fleet type. *Thomson*, of same class, was paid off for spares in September 1972.

SIMPSON *1972, Chilean Navy*

AMPHIBIOUS FORCES

2 ex-US LANDING SHIPS (LST)

COMANDANTE ARAYA LST 89 (ex-USS *Nye County*, LST 1067)
COMANDANTE HEMMERDINGER LST 88 (ex-USS *New London County* LST 1066)

Displacement, tons	1 653 standard; 4 080 full load
Dimensions, feet	328 × 50 × 14
Main engines	GM Diesels; 1 700 shp; 2 shafts = 11·6 knots
Complement	approx. 40

Transferred 29 Aug 1973.

MOREL LSM 92 (ex-USS *Aloto, LSM 444*)

Displacement, tons	743 standard; 1 095 full load
Dimensions, feet	196·5 wl; 203·5 oa × 34·5 × 7·3
Main engines	Diesel; 2 shafts; 2 800 bhp = 12 knots
Oil fuel (tons)	60
Range, miles	2 500 at 9 knots
Complement	60

Former United States ... ...um landing ship launched in 1945. *Aspirante Morel* (ex-*Aloto*) was leased to Chile on 2 Sep 1960 at Pearl Harbour to replace the older LSM of the same name.

MOREL *1972, Chilean Navy*

DIAZ LCU 96 (ex-LCU 1396) **TELLEZ** LCU 93 (ex-LCU 1458)

Displacement, tons	143 to 160 light; 309 to 329 full load
Dimensions, feet	105 wl; 119 oa × 32·7 × 5 max
Main engines	Diesel; 3 shafts; 675 bhp = 10 knots
Oil fuel (tons)	11
Range, miles	700 at 7 knots
Complement	12

Former United States tank landing craft of the LCT (6) type. Launched in 1944. Transferred in 1960.

ELICURA LSM 90 **OROMPELLO** LSM 94

Displacement, tons	290 light; 750 full load
Dimensions, feet	138 wl; 145 oa × 34 × 12·8
Main engines	Diesels; 2 shafts; 900 bhp = 10·5 knots
Oil fuel (tons)	77
Range, miles	2 900 at 9 knots
Complement	20

Orompello wqs built for the Chilean Government by Dade Drydock Corporation, Miami, Florida, and transferred on 15 Sep 1964. *Elicura* was built at Talcahuano, launched on 21 April 1967, and handed over on 10 Dec 1968.

OROMPELLO *1971, Chilean Navy*

REPAIR SHIP

AGUILA LST 91, ex-ARV 135 (ex-USS *Aventinus*, ARVE 3, ex-LST 1092)
TORO LST 97 (ex-USS LST 277)

Displacement, tons	1 625 light; 4 100 full load
Dimensions, feet	316 wl; 328 oa × 50 × 11·2
Guns	8—40 mm AA
Main engines	GM diesels; 2 shafts; 1 800 bhp = 11·6 knots

Aguila was United States aircraft repair ship (Engine). Built by American Bridge Co. Ambridge, Pa. Laid down on 8 Jan 1945, launched on 24 Mar 1945, and completed on 19 May 1945. Transferred to the Chilean Navy by USA in 1963 under the Military Aid Program. Also used as a destroyer tender and submarine repair ship. *Toro* transferred 2 Feb 1973.

LIGHT FORCES

FRESIA PTF 81 **GUACOLDA** PTF 80 **QUIDORA** PTF 82 **TEGUALDA** PTF 83

(FAST ATTACK CRAFT—TORPEDO)

Displacement, tons	134
Dimensions, feet	118·1 × 18·4 × 7·2
Guns	2—40 mm AA
Tubes	4—21 in
Main engines	Diesels; 2 shafts; 4 800 bhp = 32 knots
Range, miles	1 500 at 15 knots
Complement	20

Built in Spain at Cadiz to German Lürssen design. *Fresia* and *Guacolda* were delivered on 9 Dec 1965 and 30 July 1965, respectively, *Quidora* and *Tegualda* in 1966.

FRESIA *1971, Chilean Navy*

PAPUDO PC 37 (LARGE PATROL CRAFT)

Displacement, tons	450
Dimensions, feet	173·0 × 23·0 × 12·0
Guns	1—40 mm; 4—20 mm
A/S weapons	1 Hedgehog; 4 "K" DCT; 1 DC rack
Complement	69 (4 officers, 65 men)

Built in Asmar, Talcahuano, Chile. Completed 27 Nov 1971.

PAPUDO *1972, Chilean Navy*

	Pennant No.	Launched
LAUTARO (ex-USS *ATA 122*)	PP 62	27 Nov 1942
LIENTUR (ex-USS *ATA 177*)	PP 60	5 June 1944

(LARGE PATROL CRAFT)

Displacement, tons	534 standard; 835 full load
Dimensions, feet	134·5 wl; 143 oa × 33 × 13·2 max
Guns	1—3 in AA; 2—20 mm AA
Main engines	GM diesel-electric; 1 500 shp = 12·5 knots
Oil fuel, tons	187
Complement	33

Former United States Navy auxiliary ocean tugs of the ATA type ("Maricopa" class), originally ocean rescue tugs (ATRs), transferred to the Chilean Navy and reclassified as patrol vessels. Built by Levingstone Shipbuilding Co, Orange, Texas, USA.

Light Forces—*continued*

LAUTARO *1969, Chilean Navy*

ALDEA ATF 63 (ex-US *ATF* 98, *Arikara*) (LARGE PATROL CRAFT)

Displacement, tons	1 235 standard; 1 675 full load
Dimensions, feet	195·0 wl; 205·0 oa × 38·5 × 15·5 max
Guns	1—3 in 50 cal AA
Main engines	Diesel Electric; 1 shaft; 3 000 bhp = 15 knots
Complement	85

Former USN fleet ocean tug, launched on 22 June 1943. Transferred on 7 Jan 1971.

ALDEA *1972, Chilean Navy*

FUENTEALBA WPC 75 **ODGER** WPC 76 (LARGE PATROL CRAFT)

Displacement, tons	215 max
Dimensions, feet	80 × 21 × 9
Guns	1—20 mm AA
Main engines	One Cummins diesel 340 hp = 9 knots
Range, miles	2 600 at 9 knots
Complement	19

Both these vessels were built in Chile by Astilleros Y Maeslronzas De La Armada (ASMAR); *Fuentealba* was completed in 22 July 1966 and *Odger* 21 April 1967.

FUENTEALBA *1972, Chilean Navy*

SURVEY SHIP

YELCHO (ex-USS *Tekesta,* ATF 93) Pennant No. AGS 64

Displacement, tons	1 235 standard; 1 675 full load
Dimensions, feet	195 wl; 205 oa × 38·5 × 15·3 max
Guns	2—40 mm AA
Main engines	4 diesels/Diesel electric; 1 shaft; 3 000 bhp = 16 knots
Complement	85

Former United States fleet ocean tug of the ATF type ("Apache" class) fitted with powerful pumps and other salvage equipment. *Yelcho* was built by Commercial Iron Works, Portland, Oregon, laid down on 7 Sep 1942, launched on 20 Mar 1943, completed on 16 Aug 1943, and loaned to Chile by the USA on 15 May 1960, having since been employed as Antarctic research ship and surveying vessel.

YELCHO *1972, Chilean Navy*

TRAINING SHIP

ESMERALDA (ex-*Don Juan de Austria*) BE 43

Displacement, tons	3 040 standard; 3 673 full load
Dimensions, feet	308·8 oa; 260 pp × 43 × 23 max
Guns	2—57 mm
Sail area	Total 26 910 sq feet
Main engines	1 Fiat Auxiliary diesel; 1 shaft; 1 400 bhp = 11 knots
Range, miles	8 000 at 8 knots
Complement	271 plus 80 cadets

ESMERALDA *1971, A. & J. Pavia*

Training Ships—*continued*

Four-masted schooner completed in 1952. Built in Spain by the Echevarrieta Yard, Cadiz, and originally intended for the Spanish Navy. Transferred to Chile on 12 May 1953. Near sister ship of *Juan Sebastian de Elcano* in the Spanish Navy. Similar to the Brazilian training ship *Almirante Saldanha* before her major reconstruction. Replaced transport *Presidente Pinto* as training ship.

TRANSPORTS

AQUILES AP-47 (ex-Danish *Tjaldur*)

Displacement, tons	2 660 registered; 1 462 net; 1 395 dw
Dimensions, feet	288 × 44 × 17
Main engines	1 Slow Burmeister and Wain Diesel; 3 600 bhp = 16 knots
Range, miles	5 500 at 16 knots
Complement	60 crew plus 447 troops

Ex-Danish MV *Tjaldur* built in 1953 by Aalborg Verft, Denmark, bought by Chile in 1967.

AQUILES *1968, Chilean Navy*

PILOTO PARDO AP 45

Displacement, tons	1 250 light; 2 000 standard; 3 000 full load
Dimensions, feet	269 × 39 × 15
Aircraft	1 helicopter
Guns	1—101·6/50; 2—20 mm
Main engines	2 diesel-electric; 2 000 hp = 14 knots
Complement	44 (plus 24 passengers)
Range, miles	6 000 at 10 knots

Built by Haarlemsche Scheepsbouw Mij, Haarlem, Netherlands. Antarctic patrol ship, transport and research vessel with reinforced hull to navigate in ice. Officially listed as transport. Delivered in 1959.

PILOTO PARDO *1969, Chilean Navy*

OILERS

BEAGLE AOG 54 (ex-AOG 8 USS *Genesee*)

Displacement, tons	4 240 standard
Dimensions, feet	310 × 48·7 × 16
Guns	2—3 inch 50 cal; 4—20 mm
Range, miles	6 670 at 10 knots

Transferred on loan 5 July 1972.

BEAGLE *1972, Chilean Navy*

Oilers—*continued*

ARAUCANO AO 53

Displacement, tons 17 300
Measurement, tons 18 030 deadweight
Dimensions, feet 497·6 × 74·9 × 28·8
Guns 4—40 mm
Main engines B and W diesels; 10 800 bhp = 15·5 knots (17 on trials)
Range, miles 12 000 at 15·5 knots

Naval tanker built by Burmeister & Wain, Copenhagan, Denmark. Launched on 21 June 1967.

ARAUCANO *1972, U.S. Navy*

ALMIRANTE JORGE MONTT AO 52

Displacement, tons 9 000 standard; 17 500 full load
Measurement, tons 11 800 gross; 17 750 deadweight
Dimensions, feet 548 × 67·5 × 30
Main engines Rateau Bretagne geared turbine; 1 shaft; 6 300 shp = 14 knots
Boilers 2 Babcock & Wilcox
Range, miles 16 500 at 14 knots

Naval supply tanker. Built by Ateliers et Chantiers de la Seine Maritime, Le Trait, France Laid down in 1954. Launched on 14 Jan 1956. Completed in Mar 1956.

ALMIRANTE JORGE MONTT *1969, Chilean Navy*

FLOATING DOCK

2 ex-US ARD

MUTILLA ARD 132 (ex-US *ARD 32*) — (ex-US *ARD 25*)

Displacement, tons 5 200
Capacity, tons 3 000
Dimensions, feet 492 × 84 × 5·7 to 33·2 feet

Mutilla leased to Chile 15 May 1960. *ARD 25* transferred 20 Aug 1973.

TUGS

COLO COLO ATA 73

Displacement, tons 790
Dimensions, feet 126·5 × 27·0 × 12·0 mean
Main engines Triple expansion; 1 050 shp = 11 knots
Oil fuel, tons 155

Built by Bow, McLachlan & Co, Paisley. Formerly classed as coastguard vessel. Rebuilt in 1962-63. Of four sister ships *Janequeo* was withdrawn from service in 1958, *Sobenes* in 1965, *Galvarino* in 1968 and *Cabrales* in 1971.

ANCUD (YT 104) **CORTEZ** (YT 128) **REYES** (YT 120)
CAUPOLICAN (YT 127) **MONREAL** (YT 105)

Fortuna (YT 123) and *Galvez* (YT 102) were withdrawn from service in 1965, *Moctezuma* (YT 108) in 1968 and *Ugarte* (YT 107) in 1971. *Yagan* (YT 126) was lost in 1964 while assisting a merchant ship during a storm.

1 Ex-US FLEET TUG

ALDEA ATF 63 (ex-*Arikara* ATF 98)

Displacement, tons 1 235 standard; 1 675 full load
Dimensions, feet 205 oa × 38·5 × 15·5
Gun 1—3 in
Main engines Diesel electric; 1 shaft; 3 000 bhp = 16 knots
Complement 85

Transferred in 1971.

CHINA

Administration

Commander-in-Chief of the Navy:
Vice-Admiral Hsiao Ching Kuang

Diplomatic Representation

Defence and Naval Attaché in London:
Mr. Shih Hsin-Jen

Personnel

(a) 1974: 170 000 officers and men, including 25 000 naval air force and 28 000 marines
(b) 4 years national service

Pennant Numbers

Block numbering system:—
Submarines: 100 series; Major Surface Ships; 200 series; Amphibious Ships: 300 series

Bases

Northern Fleet: Tsingtao, Lu Shun
Eastern Fleet: Shanghai, Chusan
Southern Fleet: Huan Pu, Chan Chiang
(The fleet is split with about half in the Eastern Fleet, the remainder divided between the other two)

Mercantile Marine

Lloyd's Register of Shipping:
323 vessels of 1 478 992 tons gross

Strength of the Fleet

Type	*Active*	*Building (Estimated)*
Destroyers (DDG)	5	2
Frigates	14 (7 with missiles)	1 ?
Corvettes	30	4
Fleet Submarines	1	?
Missile-Firing Submarines	1	—
Patrol Submarines	49	4
Fast Attack Craft (Missile)	80	15
Fast Attack Craft (Gun)	455	20 ?
Fast Attack Craft (Torpedo)	150	—
Minesweepers (Ocean)	16	—
Minesweepers (Coastal)	10	2 ?
Landing Ships LST	15	—
LSM's	18	2 ?
LSIL's	15	—
LCM's	15	—
LCT's	450	—
Survey & Research Ships	8	—
Range Instrumentation Ships	4	?
Supply Ships	8 (+?12)	—
Oilers (small)	8	—
Boom Defence Vessels	6	—
Escorts (old)	13	—
Coast Defence Vessels (Old)	6	—
River Defence Vessels (Old)	13	—
Repair Ship	1	—
Misc. Small Craft	375	—

The Chinese Navy

Despite setbacks under the Manchus, the Chinese have possessed a navy in some force since 200BC. In addition they have had the will and capability to use their fleet, as their expeditions to the Persian Gulf and Africa in the 15th Century bear witness. So today's navy has a tradition older than any other except the Greek and Italian and a modern, rapidly expanding force capable of operations abroad. In the following pages the Chinese Navy is shown in two parts—the new fleet of Hsiao Ching Kuang and the antique remnants of the Nationalist navy. While studying these it must be remembered that not only is there a steady building programme of all classes in the modernised Chinese Yards but also the Chinese have an advanced nuclear and missile capability. This combination will make the Chinese navy, already twice as strong in manpower as the Royal Navy, an important element in the future balance of power East of Suez.

Chinese Naval Air Force

With 20 000 officers and men and over 450 aircraft, this is a considerable land-based naval air force. Equipped with about 400 MIG 17 and 19 (and possibly MIG 21) fighter aircraft and SA2-SAM, with 100 IL 28 Torpedo bombers, Tu-2 bombers, Madge flying boats, Hound M14 helicopters and transport and communication aircraft this is primarily a defensive force. Chinese ingenuity should find little difficulty in getting a proportion of these aircraft afloat, particularly in view of the increasing tempo of their shipbuilding programme.

"THE NEW NAVY"

DESTROYERS

5 + 2 "LUTA" CLASS

246 + 4

Displacement, tons	3 250 standard; 3 750 full load
Dimensions, ft (*m*) (approx)	450 × 45 × 15 (*137·3* × *13·7* × *4·6*)
Missile launchers	2 Twin SSN-2 type
Guns	4—130 mm (2 twins) 8—57 mm 8—25 mm
A/S weapons	2—A/S rocket launchers
Main engines	Geared turbines
Speed	32+
Range, miles (estimated)	4 000 at 15 knots
Complement (approx)	300

New Construction DDG *1972 Chinese*

GENERAL
Most of the above figures are approximate, designed to show the anticipated capability of this new class, which is being built in Luta yard Shanghai (and other yards).

COMPLETION. 1 in 1971, 2 in 1972, 2 in 1973.

RADAR. Air search, Slim Net., Cross Slot: Fire Control, Guns, Wasphead; Missiles: Square Tie: Navigation: Neptun.

New Construction

FRIGATES

1 + 1(?) "KIANGTUNG" CLASS

Displacement, tons: 1 500—2 000 tons standard
Dimensions, ft (*m*): 350 × 40 approx (*106* × *12*)
Missile launchers: 1 or 2 Twin SS-N 2
Guns: 2 or 4 twin 3·9 inch (*100 mm*)

The first unit reported as laid down in 1971 for launch in 1973.

4 Ex-SOVIET "GORDY" CLASS

ANSHAN 201
CHANG CHUN 202
CHI LIN 203
FU CHUN 204

Displacement, tons	1 657 standard; 2 040 full load
Length, feet (*metres*)	357·7 (*109·0*) pp; 370 (*112·8*) oa
Beam, feet (*metres*)	33·5 (*10·2*)
Draught, feet (*metres*)	13 (*4·0*)
Missile launchers	1 twin SSN—2
Guns	4—5·1 in (*130 mm*); 8—37 mm
A/S	8 DCT
Main engines	Tosi geared turbines 48 000 shp; 2 shafts
Boilers	3-drum type
Speed, knots	36
Oil fuel (tons)	540
Range, miles	800 at 36 knots; 2 600 at 19 knots
Complement	250

CHANG CHUN (before conversion) *Hajime Fukaya*

GENERAL
Gordy Type 7 of Odero-Terni-Orlando design. All launched in 1936-41. Fitted for minelaying. Two transferred in Dec 1954 and two in July 1955.

CONVERSION. Three have been converted already and the fourth is in hand for completion (probably) in 1974. The alterations consist of the replacement of the torpedo tubes by a twin SS-N-2 launcher and the fitting of twin 37 mm mounts in place of the original singles.

RADAR. Air Search: Cross Bird. Fire Control: Square Tie. Navigation: Neptun. IFF: Skipole.

5 "KIANGNAN" CLASS

209 214 231 232 233

Displacement, tons	1 000 standard; 1 350 full load
Length, feet (*metres*)	298 (*90·8*)
Beam, feet (*metres*)	33·5 (*10·2*)
Draught, feet (*metres*)	11 (*3·4*)
Guns, dual purpose	3—3·9 in (*100 mm*) 56 cal, 1 fwd, 2 aft; 6 or 8—37 mm (twin); 4 or 8—25 mm (twin)
A/S weapons	Depth charges
Main engines	Diesels; 9 000 shp
Speed, knots	30
Complement	175

GENERAL
Built at Canton and Shanghai between 1965 and 1969.

The Communist Chinese Navy embarked on a new building programme of which this class was the first. These good-sized ships with a deep-water capability are a sensible complement to the growing submarine fleet and the enormous number of short range missile boats and FPBs with which the Chicom navy is now equipped.

RADAR. Fire Control: Sun Visor.

4 "RIGA" CLASS

CH'ENG TU 205
KUEI LIN 206
KUEI YANG 207
K'UN MING 208

Displacement, tons	1 200 standard; 1 600 full load
Length, feet (*metres*)	298·8 (*91*) oa
Beam, feet (*metres*)	33·7 (*10·2*)
Draught, feet (*metres*)	10 (*3·0*)
Missile launchers	1 twin SSN—2 (see *Conversion* note)
Guns	3—3·9 in (*100 mm*) (single) 4—37 mm
A/S	4 DC projectors
Torpedo tubes	3—21 in (*533 mm*) (see *Conversion* note)
Mines	50 capacity, fitted with rails
Main engines	Geared turbines 25 000 shp; 2 shafts
Boilers	2
Speed, knots	28
Oil fuel (tons)	300
Range, miles	2 500 at 15 knots
Complement	150

"Riga" Class *1971*

GENERAL
First of the class, launched on 28 Apr 1956 at Hutang Shipyard, Shanghai, had light tripod mast, but was later converted with heavier mast and larger bridge as in the other three. Second vessel was launched on 26 Sep 1956. Third vessel was built at Shanghai and the fourth in 1957. Similar to the Soviet "Riga" class destroyer escorts. Two were redesigned with modified superstructure.

CONVERSION. Two started conversion in 1971 for the replacement of the torpedo tubes by a twin SSN-2 launchers.

Radar. Surface warning: Slim Net. Fire Control: Sun Visor for Guns, Square Tie for missiles; Navigation; Neptun.

CORVETTES

20 "KRONSTADT" TYPE SUBMARINE CHASERS

Nos. 251 252 253 261 262 263 264 265 266 286 + 10

Displacement, tons	310 standard; 380 full load
Dimensions, ft (*m*)	170·6 × 21·5 × 9 (*52* × *6·5* × *2·7*)
Guns	1—3·5 in; 2—37 mm AA; 6—12·7 mm AA
A/S weapons	2 Rocket launchers; 2 DC racks
Mines	2 rails for 8-10 mines
Main engines	Diesels; 2 shafts; 3 300 shp; speed 24 knots
Range, miles	1 500 at 12 knots
Complement	65

Six built in 1950-53 were received from USSR in 1956-57. Remainder were built at Shanghai and Canton, with 12 completed in 1956. The last was assembled by 1957.

RADAR. Ball Gun, Skinhead.

KRONSTADT class firing Rocket Launchers *1972*

10 + 4 "HAI NAN" CLASS

Displacement, tons	500 standard
Dimensions, ft (*m*)	200 × 25 × 9 (*61* × *7·6* × *2·7*)
Guns	2—3 in (fore and aft); 4/6—25 mm (twins)
Main engines	Geared turbines; 3 300 shp (estimated)
Speed, knots	About 20

Chinese built. Low freeboard. The 25 mm guns are abaft the bridge. Programme started 1963-64 and continues. Skinhead Radar.

SUBMARINES

Note. In 1973 the visit to West Germany from Peking of a party led by Professor Chang Wei highlighted Chinese interest in nuclear propulsion for ships. It also suggests that the Chinese may be meeting design problems as such visits are rare events. However, reports suggest the construction of at least one nuclear submarine. This combined with the known Chinese capability to build liquid-fuelled rockets of the MRBM, IRBM and ICBM types and the completion of a solid-propellant factory, suggests that last year's forecast of a Chinese ballistic-missile nuclear submarine within the 1970's may not be out of the question.

1 "HAN" CLASS

This is the first report of a possible Chinese nuclear submarine. With an Albacore hull it was probably laid down in 1971-72. Its construction may have been delayed if the problems mentioned in the note above have been encountered.

1 "MING" CLASS

Displacement, tons	Possibly about 1 500 tons standard
Length, feet	Possibly about 250 feet
Armament	Possibly 6—21 in tubes
Main machinery	Probably diesels and main motors

Believed to have been laid down in 1971-72 which would give an operational date around late 1974 or 1975.

1 "GOLF" CLASS

(BALLISTIC MISSILE TYPE)

Displacement, tons	2 350 surface; 2 800 dived
Length, feet (*metres*)	320·0 (*97·5*)
Beam, feet (*metres*)	25·1 (*7·6*)
Draught, feet (*metres*)	22·0 (*6·7*)
Missile launchers	3 vertical tubes
Torpedo tubes	10—21 in (*533 mm*) bow
Main machinery	3 diesels, total 6 000 hp; 3 shafts 3 electric motors, total 6 000 hp
Speed, knots	20 surface; 17 dived
Range, miles	22 700 surface cruising
Complement	86 (12 officers, 74 men)

Ballistic missile submarine similar to the Soviet "G" class. Built at Dairen in 1964. The missile tubes are fitted in the conning tower. It is not known whether this boat has been fitted with missiles, although it is possible and well within Chinese technical capability (see note above concerning SLBM's)

"Golf" Class 1972

24 SOVIET "ROMEO" CLASS

(PATROL TYPE)

Displacement, tons	1 100 surface; 1 600 dived
Length, feet (*metres*)	246·0 (*75·0*)
Beam, feet (*metres*)	24 (*7·3*)
Draught, feet (*metres*)	14·5 (*4·4*)
Torpedo tubes	6—21 in (bow) 18 torpedoes
Main machinery	2 Diesels, total 4 000 hp; 2 Electric motors, total 4 000 hp; 2 shafts
Speed, knots	17 surface; 14 dived
Complement	65

The Chinese are now building their own Soviet design "Romeo" class submarines possibly at a rate of 4 a year.

"Romeo" Class 1972

21 SOVIET "WHISKY" CLASS

(PATROL TYPE)

Displacement, tons	1 030 surface; 1 180 dived
Length, feet (*metres*)	240 (*73·2*)
Beam, feet (*metres*)	22 (*6·7*)
Draught, feet (*metres*)	15 (*4·6*)
Torpedo tubes	6—21 in (*533 mm*); 4 bow 2 stern (20 torpedoes or 40 mines)
Main machinery	Diesel-electric; 2 shafts; 4 000 bhp diesels; 2 500 hp electric motors
Speed, knots	17 surface; 15 dived
Range, miles	13 000 at 8 knots surfaced
Complement	60

Medium size streamlined, long range submarines similar to the "Whisky" class built in the USSR. Equipped with snort. Assembled from Soviet components in Chinese yards between 1956 and 1964.

3 Ex-SOVIET "S-1" CLASS

(PATROL TYPE)

S 113 **S 114** +1

Displacement, tons	840 surface; 1 050 submerged
Length, feet (*metres*)	256 (*78·0*)
Beam, feet (*metres*)	21 (*6·4*)
Draught, feet (*metres*)	13 (*4·0*)
Torpedo tubes	6—21 in (*533 mm*)
Main machinery	4 200 hp diesels; 2 200 hp electric motors
Speed, knots	19 surface; 8·5 submerged
Range, miles	9 800 at 9 knots
Oil fuel, tons	105
Complement	50

Launched in 1939. Transferred from the USSR in 1955.

'Whisky" Class 1972

1 Ex-SOVIET "M-V" CLASS

(COASTAL PATROL TYPE)

Displacement, tons	350 surface; 420 submerged
Length, feet (*metres*)	167·3 (*51·0*)
Beam, feet (*metres*)	16·0 (*4·9*)
Draught, feet (*metres*)	12·1 (*3·7*)
Guns, AA	1—45 mm 1 MG
Torpedo tubes	2—21 in (*533 mm*)
Main machinery	1 000 hp diesels; 800 hp electric motors
Speed, knots	13 surface; 10 submerged
Range, miles	4 000 at 8·5 knots
Oil fuel, tons	21
Complement	24

Designed for coastal operations, latterly used for training and instruction but nearing the end of its life. Four were transferred from the USSR in 1954-55.

COLOMBIA

Administration

Fleet Commander:
Vice Admiral Jaime Parra Ramirez

Chief of Naval Operations:
Rear Admiral Eduardo Wills Olaya

Chief of Naval Staff:
Rear Admiral Alfonso Diaz Osorio

Diplomatic Representative

Naval Attaché in Washington:
Captain Hernando Salas Ramirez

Personnel

(a) 1974: 700 officers and 6 500 men
(b) 1 year's national service

Strength of the Fleet

Type	*Active*	*Building*
Destroyers	5	—
Frigates	4	—
Submarines	2 (70 tons)	2
Coastal Patrol Craft	25	—
Survey Vessels	4	—
Transports	6	—
Oilers	3	—
Training Ship	1	—
Tugs	13	—
Floating Docks	2	—
Floating Workshop	1	—

Disposals

Frigate

1973 *Almirante Padilla*

Oilers

1970 *Tumaco, Barran Cabermeja*

Prefix to Ships' Names

Ships names are prefaced by the letters "ARC" (Armada Republica de Colombia)

Mercantile Marine

Lloyd's Register of Shipping
54 vessels of 223 881 tons gross

DESTROYERS

2 MODIFIED "HALLAND" CLASS

Name	*No.*	*Builders*	*Laid down*	*Launched*	*Completed*
SIETE DE AGOSTO	06	Götaverken, Göteberg	Nov 1955	19 June 1956	31 Oct 1958
VEINTE DE JULIO	05	Kockums Mek Verkstads A/B, Malmo	Oct 1955	26 June 1956	15 June 1958

7 DE AGOSTO *1971, Colombian Navy*

20 DE JULIO *1970, Colombian Navy*

Displacement, tons	2 650 standard; 3 300 full load
Length, feet (*metres*)	380·5 (*116·0*)pp; 397·2 (*121·1*)oa
Beam, feet (*metres*)	40·7 (*12·4*)
Draught, feet (*metres*)	15·4 (*4·7*)
Guns	6—4·7 in (*120 mm*) (3 twin turrets); 4—40 mm (single)
Torpedo tubes	4—21 in (*533 mm*)
A/S weapons	1 quadruple DC rocket launcher
Main engines	De Laval double reduction geared turbines; 2 shafts; 55 000 shp
Speed, knots	30 nominal, 16 economical
Boilers	2 Penhöet, Motala Verkstad; 568 psi; 840°F
Range, miles	445 at full power
Oil fuel, tons	524
Complement	260 (20 officers, 240 men)

GENERAL
Modified Swedish "Halland" Class ordered in 1954. The hull and machinery are similar to the Swedish class but they have different armament (six 4·7 inch instead of four, no 57 mm guns, four 40 mm guns instead of six, and four torpedo tubes instead of eight) and different accommodation arrangements. They have an anti-submarine rocket projector, more radar and communication equipment, and air conditioned living spaces, having been designed for the tropics.

ENGINEERING. Although the designed speed was 35 knots, it is officially stated that the maximum sustained speed does not exceed 25 knots.

RADAR. Search: HSA LWO 3—SGR 114. Tactical: HSA DA 02—SGR 105. Fire Control: X Band, probably HSA M 20 series.

1 Ex-FLETCHER"" CLASS

Name	*No.*	*Builders*	*Laid down*	*Launched*	*Completed*
ANTIOQUIA (ex-USS *Hale*, DD 642)	DD 01	Bath Iron Works Corporation, Bath, Maine	23 Nov 1942	4 Apr 1943	15 June 1943

Displacement, tons	2 050 standard; 2 952 full load
Length, feet (*metres*)	369·0 (*112·5*)pp; 376·5 (*114·8*)oa
Beam, feet (*metres*)	39·5 (*12·0*)
Draught, feet (*metres*)	18·0 (*5·5*) max
Guns	4—5 in (*127 mm*) 38 cal; 6—3 in (*76 mm*) 50 cal (3 twin)
Torpedo tubes	5—21 in (*533 mm*) quintupled
A/S weapons	2 fixed Hedgehogs; 1 DC rack 2 side-launching torpedo racks
Main engines	2 sets GE geared turbines; 2 shafts; 60 000 shp
Speed, knots	35
Boilers	4 Babcock & Wilcox; 565 psi; 850°F
Range, miles	6 000 at 14 knots
Oil fuel, tons	650
Complement	300

Former US destroyer of the "Fletcher class". Transferred from the US Navy at Boston, Massachussetts, on 23 Jan 1961.

RADAR. Search: SPS 6. Tactical: SPS 10. Fire Control: X Band.

ANTIOQUIA *1970, Colombian Navy*

Destroyers—*continued*

2 Ex-US "ALLEN M. SUMNER" CLASS

	Builder	Launched	Commissioned
CALDAS (ex-USS *Willard Keith* DD 775)	Bethlehem (San Pedro)	29 Aug 1944	27 Dec 1944
SANTANDER (ex-USS *Waldron* DD 699)	Federal SB Co		

Displacement, tons	2 200 standard; 3 320 full load
Length, feet (*metres*)	376 (*114·8*) oa
Beam, feet (*metres*)	40·9 (12·4)
Draught, feet (*metres*)	19 (*5·8*)
Guns	6—5 in (twins); 4—3 in (twins) (*Caldas* only)
A/S Weapons	2 Fixed Hedgehogs; 2 triple torpedo tubes (Mk 32) Facilities for small helicopter (*Santander* only)
Main engines	2 geared turbines; 2 shafts; 60 000 shp
Boilers	4
Speed, knots	34
Range, miles	2 400 at 25 knots; 4 800 at 15 knots
Complement	274

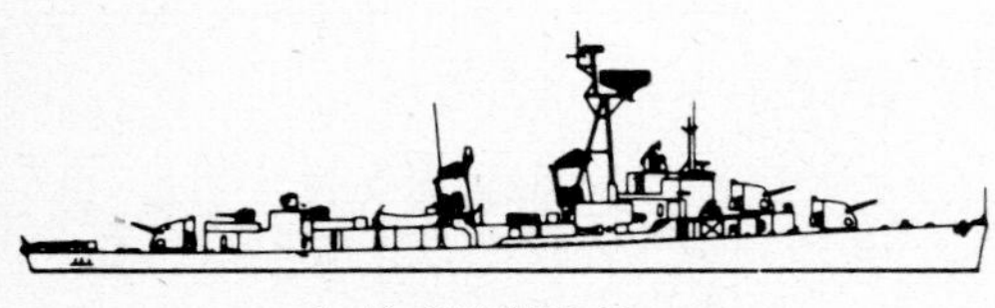
A. M. SUMNER Class

Caldas transferred 1 July 1972 on sale. Santander on 30 Oct. 1973.

FRIGATES

3 Ex-US APD's

ALMIRANTE BRION (ex-USS *Burke APD* 65, ex-*DE* 215)	DT 07
ALMIRANTE TONO (ex-USS *Bassett APD* 73, ex-*DE* 672)	DT 04
CORDOBA (ex-USS *Ruchamkin LPR* 89, ex-*APD* 89, ex-*DE* 228)	DT 15

GENERAL
Almirante Tono was built by Consolidated Steel Co, Orange, Tex, laid down on 28 Nov 1943, launched on 15 Jan 1944, completed on 23 Feb 1945 and transferred at Boston, Mass, on 6 Sep 1968. *Almirante Brion* was built by Philadelphia Navy Yard, laid down on 1 Jan 1943, launched on 3 Apr 1943, completed on 20 Aug 1943 and transferred on 8 Dec 1968. *Cordoba* was built by Philadelphia Navy Yard, laid down on 14 Feb 1944, launched on 15 June 1944 and transferred on 24 Nov 1969. DT 07 now serving as riverine hospital ship. for attending native population. Secondary armament removed to make way for 30 beds.

ALMIRANTE BRION — *1971, Colombian Navy*

1 Ex-US "DEALEY" CLASS

BOYACA DE 16 (ex-USS *Hartley* DE 1029)

Displacement, tons	1 450 standard; 1 914 full load
Dimensions, feet	314·5 oa × 36·8 × 13·6
Guns	2—3 in; 50 cal
A/S Weapons	2 triple torpedo tubes
Main engines	1 De Laval geared turbine; 20 000 shp; 1 shaft
Boilers	2 Foster Wheeler
Speed, knots	25
Complement	165

Built by New York SB Corpn, Commissioned 26 June 1957. Transferred 8 July 1972.

SUBMARINES

2 TYPE 209 PATROL SUBMARINES

Displacement, tons	1 000 surface; 1 290 dived
Length, feet (*metres*)	183·4 (*55·9*)
Beam, feet (*metres*)	20·5 (*6·25*)
Torpedo tubes	8—21 in bow with reloads
Main engines	Diesel electric; 1 shaft; 5 000 hp
Speed, knots	22 dived

Building by Howaldtswerke, Kiel. Ordered in 1971. Possible delivery 1974.

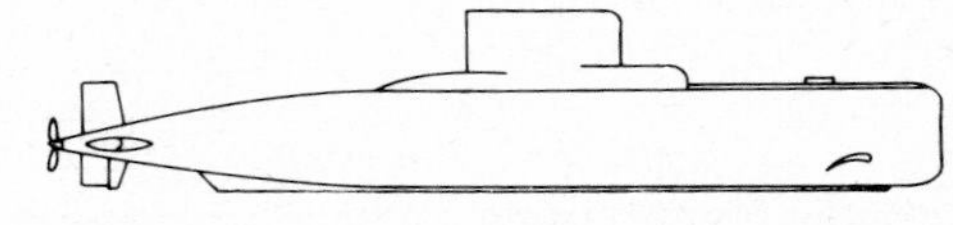
TYPE 209 — *1973, IKL*

2 MIDGET SUBMARINES

These boats, purchased from Italy and of about 70 tons were delivered in July-August 1972 for assembly in Cartagena.

LIGHT FORCES

CARLOS ALBAN
JORGE SOTO DEL CORVAL
NITO RESTREPO

Displacement, tons	100
Main engines	2 Diesels = 19 knots

First of class entered service in 1971.

CARLOS ALBAN — *1971, Colombian Navy, Official*

25 COASTAL PATROL CRAFT

CARLOS E. RESTREPO AN 206
ESTEBAN JARAMILLO AN 205
PEDRO GUAL AN 204

Displacement, tons	85
Dimensions, feet	107·8 pp × 18 × 6
Guns	1—20 mm AA
Main engines	2 Maybach diesels; 2 450 bhp = 26 knots

Built by Werft Gebr. Schurenstedt KG Bardenfleth in 1964.

PEDRO GUAL — *1965, Colombian Navy*

OLAYA HERRERA AN 203

Displacement, tons	40
Dimensions, feet	68·8 pp × 12·8 × 3·5
Guns	1—·50 mm Browning AA
Main engines	2 Merbens diesels; 570 bhp = 20 knots

Built by Astilleros Magdalena Barranquilla, in 1960.

GENERAL RAFAEL REYES AN 01 **GENERAL VASQUES COBO** AN 02

Displacement, tons	146
Dimensions, feet	118 pp; 124·7 oa × 23 × 5
Guns	1—40 mm
Main engines	2 Maybach diesels; 2 400 bhp = 18 knots

Built by Lürssen Werft, Vegesack. Launched on 10 Nov and 27 Sep 1955, respectively. Delivered in May 1956.

ESPARTANA GC 100

Displacement, tons	50
Dimensions, feet	90 wl; 96 oa × 13·5 × 4
Guns	1—20 mm AA
Main engines	2 diesels; 300 bhp = 13·5 knots

Launched on 22 June 1950 at Cartagena Naval Dockyard.

CAPITAN R. D. BINNEY GC 101

Displacement, tons	23
Dimensions, feet	67 × 10·7 × 3·5
Main engines	Diesels; 115 bhp = 13 knots

Built at Cartagena in 1947. Buoy and lighthouse inspection boat. Named after first head of Colombian Naval Academy, Lt-Commander Ralph Douglas Binney, RN.

Light Forces—*continued*

ALBERTO RESTREPO LR 125 (1 Oct 1952)
CARLOS GALINDO LR 128 (1954)
HUMBERTO CORTES LR 126 (26 Nov 1952)
JUAN LUCIO LR 122 (2 May 1953)

Displacement, tons 35
Dimensions, feet 76·8 pp; 81·8 oa × 12 × 2·8
Guns 1—20 mm AA; 4 MG
Main engines 2 GM diesels; 260 bhp = 13 knots
Complement 13

Built at Cartagena. Launch dates above.

ALFONSO VARGAS LR 123 (3 July 1952)
FRITZ HAGALE LR 124 (19 July 1952)

Displacement, tons 33
Dimensions, feet 72 pp; 76 oa × 12 × 2·8
Guns 1—20 mm AA; 4 GM
Main engines 2 GM diesels 280 bhp = 13 knots
Complement 10

Built at Cartagena naval base. Designed for operations on rivers. Named after naval officers. Launch dates above.

DILIGENTE LR 132
INDEPENDIENTE LR 134
PALACE LR 130
TORMENTOSA LR 136
TRIUNFANTE LR 133
VALEROSA LR 137
VENGADORA LR 131
VOLADORA LR 135

Launched af the Naval Base, Cartagena, in 1952-54. The boats vary in detail.

3 "ARAUCA" CLASS GUNBOATS

ARAUCA CF 37 **LETICIA** CF 36 **RIOHACHA** CF 35

Displacement, tons 184 full load
Dimensions, feet 163·5 oa × 23·5 × 2·8
Gun 2—3 in, dp, 50 cal; 4—20 mm
Main engines 2 Caterpillar diesels; 916 bhp = 14 knots
Range, miles 1 890 at 14 knots
Complement 43 (*Leticia* 39 and 6 orderlies)

Built by Union Industrial de Barranquilla (Unial) Colombia. Launched in 1955. Completed in 1956. *Leticia* has been equipped as a hospital ship with 6 beds.

RIOHACHA *1966, Colombian Navy*

1 BARRANQUILLA CLASS GUNBOAT

CARTAGENA CF 33

Displacement, tons 142
Dimensions, feet 130 pp; 137·8 oa × 23·5 × 2·8 max
Guns 2—3 in; 1—20 mm AA; 4 MG
Main engines 2 Gardner semi-diesels; 2 shafts working in tunnels; 600 hp = 15·5 knots
Oil fuel (tons) 24
Complement 39

Built by Yarrow & Co. Ltd., Scotstoun, Glasgow, and launched on 22 Mar 1930. Sister ship *Santa Marta,* CF 32, was withdrawn from service in Dec 1962. and Barranquilla in 1970.

CARTAGENA *1971, Colombian Navy*

SURVEY VESSELS

SAN ANDREAS (ex-USS *Rockville,* PCER 851) LC 151

Displacement, tons 674 standard; 858 full load
Dimensions, feet 180·0 wl; 184·5 oa × 33·6 × 7·0
Main engines 2 diesels; 2 shafts; 1 800 bhp = 15 knots
Complement 60

Former US patrol rescue escort vessel built by Pullman Standard Car Mfg Co. Chicago, laid down on 18 Oct 1943, launched on 22 Feb 1944, completed on 15 May 1944. acquired on 5 June 1969 for conversion to a surveying vessel.

Survey Vessels—*continued*

GORGONA FB 161

Displacement, tons 560
Dimensions, feet 135 × 29·5 × 9·3
Main engines 2 Nohab diesels; 910 bhp = 13 knots

Built by Lidingoverken, Sweden. Launched in May 1954. Formerly classified as a tender.

GORGONA *1971, Colombian Navy*

QUINDIO

Displacement, tons 380 light; 600 full load
Dimensions, feet 131 × 29·8 × 9
Main engines 2 diesels; 300 hp = 10 knots
Complement 17

Launched in 1943. Originally small cargo ship.

BOCAS DE CENIZA

Displacement, tons 675
Complement 20

Launched in 1943.

TRANSPORTS

CIUDAD DE QUIBDO TM 43

Displacement, tons 633
Dimensions, feet 165 × 23·5 × 9
Main engines 1 Main diesel; 1 shaft; 390 bhp = 11 knots
Oil fuel (tons) 32
Complement 12

Built by Gebr. Sander Delfzijl, in the Netherlands.

CIUDAD DE QUIBDO *1971, Colombian Navy*

BELL SALTER (ex-*Souris,* ex-*Leccarmaro II*). TM 41.

Displacement, tons 60
Dimensions, feet 82 × 14 × 5·5
Main engines 2 GM diesels; 1 500 rpm; speed 8 knots

HERNANDO GUTIERREZ TF 52
MARIO SERPA TF 51
SOCORRO (ex-*Alberto Gomez*)

Displacement, tons 70
Dimensions, feet 82 × 18 × 2·8
Main engines 2 GM diesels; 260 bhp = 9 knots
Oil fuel (tons) 4
Range, miles 650 at 9 knots
Complement 12 (berths for 48 troops and medical staff)

River transports. Launched at Cartagena in 1954, 1953 and 1955 respectively. Named after Army Officers. *Socorro* was converted in July 1967 into a floating surgery. *Hernando Gutierrez* and *Mario Serpa* were also converted into dispensary ships in 1970.

RAFAEL MARTINEZ

Displacement, tons 38
Dimensions 57·5 oa × 15 × 8
Main engines 2 six-cylinder diesels = 120 bhp

OILERS

COVENAS (ex-MT *Randfonn*) BT 65

Measurement, tons	22 096 gross; 5 096 net; 14 000 deadweight
Dimensions, feet	515·3 oa × 64 × 30·5 max
Main engines	Diesel; 1 shaft; 6 000 bhp = 14·5 knots
Complement	49 (7 officers, 42 men)

Built by Gotaverken in 1950. Acquired in 1966. Capacity 136 250 barrels. The oiler *Antonio de Arevalo* was withdrawn from service in 1967.

COVENAS *1971, Colombian Navy*

MAMONAL (ex-US *Tonti*, AOG 76) BT 62
SANCHO JIMENO (ex-*Transmere*, ex-USS *Kiamichi*, AOG 73) BT 63

Displacement, tons	5 984 full load
Measurement, tons	3 150 gross; 3 925 deadweight; 2 063 net
Dimensions, feet	309 wl, 325 oa × 48·2 × 21·7
Main engines	Diesel; 1 shaft; 800 bhp = 10 knots
Complement	33

Built by Todd Shipyard, Houston, and St. John's River S.B. Corp., Jacksonville, respectively. *Sancho Jimeno* was purchased in 1952. *Mamonal* was transferred in Jan 1965.

SANCHO JIMENO *1970, Colombian Navy*

TRAINING SHIP

GLORIA

Displacement, tons	1 300
Dimensions, feet	212 × 34·8 × 21·7
Main engines	Auxiliary diesel; 500 bhp = 10·5 knots

Sail training ship. Built at Bilbao in 1968. Barque rigged. Hull is entirely welded. Sail area: 1 675 sq yards (*1,400 sq. metres*).

GLORIA *1971, Colombian Navy*

TUGS

PEDRO DE HEREDIA (ex-USS *Choctaw*, ATF 70) RM 72

Displacement, tons	1 235 standard; 1 764 full load
Dimensions, feet	195 wl; 205 oa × 38·5 × 15·5 max
Main engines	4 diesels, electrical drive; 3 000 bhp = 16·5 knots

Former United States ocean tug of the "Apache" class. Launched on 18 Oct 1942.

PEDRO DE HEREDIA *1971, Colombian Navy*

BAHIA HONDA RM 74 (ex-USS *Umpqua* ATA 209)
BAHIA UTRIA RM 75 (ex-USS *Kalmia* ATA 184)

Displacement, tons	534 standard; 858 full load
Dimensions, feet	133·9 wl; 143·0 oa × 33·9 × 8·0
Gun	1—3 in dp
Main engines	2 GM diesel-electric; 1 shaft; 1 500 bhp = 13 knots
Complement	45

184 launched 29 Aug 1944 **209** launched 2 Feb 1945

Transferred from the United States Navy on 1 July 1971 on lease.

TENIENTE SORZANO

Displacement, tons	54
Dimensions, feet	60 pp; 65·7 oa × 17·5 × 9
Main engines	6-cylinder diesel; 240 bhp

ANDAGOYA RM 71

Displacement, tons	100
Main engines	Caterpillar diesel; 80 bhp = 8 knots

Launched in 1928. Re-engined in 1955.

ABADIA MENDEZ

Displacement, tons	39
Dimensions, feet	52·5 × 11 × 4
Main engines	Caterpillar diesel; 80 bhp = 8 knots

Built in Germany in 1924. Harbour tug. There are also the harbour tug, *La Colombiana* and the river tug *Joves Fiallo*, RR 90.

CANDIDO LEGUIZAMO
CAPITAN ALVARO RUIZ
CAPITAN CASTRO
CAPITAN RIGOBERTO GIRALDO
CAPITAN VLADIMAR VALEK
TENIENTE LUIS BERNAL

Displacement, tons	50
Dimensions, feet	63 × 14 × 2·5
Main engines	2 GM diesels; 260 bhp = 9 knots

TENIENTE MIGUEL SILVA RM 89

Dimensions, feet	73·3 × 17·5 × 3
Main engines	2 diesels; 260 bhp = 9 knots

River tug. Built by Union Industrial (Unial) of Barranquilla.

FLOATING DOCKS AND WORKSHOP

RODRIGUEZ ZAMORA (ex-USN ARD 28)

Displacement, tons	6 700 full load
Capacity, tons	3 000
Dimensions, feet	488 × 81
Complement	109

Auxiliary Floating Dock.

MANUEL LARA

Small Floating Dock.

CAPITAN ELOY MANTILLA (ex-USN YR 66)

Displacement, tons	516 standard
Dimensions, feet	150 × 34
Complement	24

Floating Workshop.
In addition there is the repair craft *Victor Cubillos*.

CONGO

The Republic of Congo, which became independent on 15 Aug 1960, formed a naval service, but the patrol vessel *Reine N'Galifowou* (ex-French P 754) which was transferred 16 Nov, 1962 was returned to France on 18 Feb 1965 and then re-transferred to Senegal as *Siné Saloum*. Since 1970, at least twelve river patrol boats have been delivered and are run by a small naval group 150 strong.

Mercantile Marine

Lloyd's Register of Shipping: 5 vessels of 1 210 tons gross

COSTA RICA

Mercantile Marine

Lloyd's Register of Shipping: 14 vessels of 9 062 tons gross

3 COASTAL PATROL CRAFT

401, 402, 430

Displacement, tons	10
Length, feet	40
Gun	1 MG

Built in early 1950's.

CUBA

Senior Appointment

Commander in Chief May Aldo, Santamaria

Personnel

(a) 1974: 6 000 (380 officers 220 subordinate officers and 5 400 men)
(b) 3 years national service

Standard of Efficiency

The US embargo on exports to Cuba has been running for over a decade. As a result all ex-USN ships in the Cuban Navy must be suffering from lack of spares, though some may have been stripped to provide for others. Soviet support for Cuba's armed forces, which replaced that of the USA, currently runs at about £10m a year, of which the Navy has a fair share. This, combined with the training received during Soviet visits, suggests that the standard of tactical and material efficiency may be higher than some imagine.

Naval Establishments

Naval Academy:
At Mariel, for officers and cadets

Naval school:
At Morro Castle, for petty officers and men

Naval Bases:
Mariel and Cienfuegos

Naval Airforce

A helicopter force of 15 Mi-4 (Hound) from USSR is in existence.

Mercantile Marine

Lloyd's Register of Shipping:
271 vessels of 416 306 tons gross

Disposals

Cruiser (so-called)

1972 *Cuba*

Frigates

1973 *Antonio Maceo, Jose Marti, Maximo Gomez*

Light Forces

1973 *Donotivo, Matanzas*

"THE NEW NAVY"

CORVETTES

12 Ex-USSR "SO I" CLASS

Displacement, tons	215 standard; 250 full load
Dimensions, ft (*m*)	138·6 × 20 × 9·2 (*42·3 × 6·1 × 2·8*)
Guns	4—25 mm (2 twin)
A/S weapons	4 five-barrelled rocket launchers
Main engines	3 diesels; 6 000 bhp = 29 knots
Range, miles	1 100 at 13 knots
Complement	30

Six were transferred from the USSR by Sep 1964, and six more in 1967.

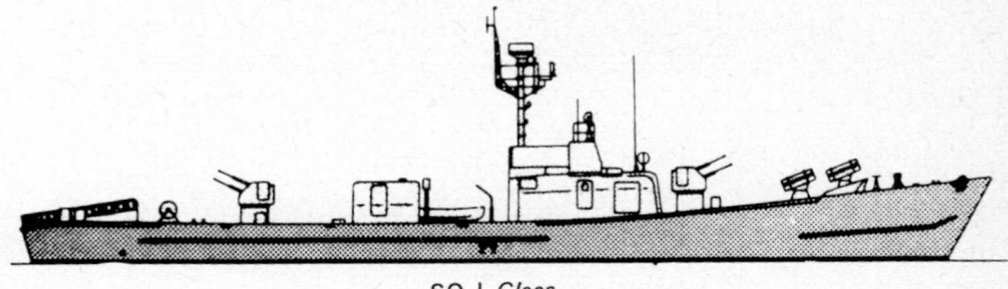

SO I *Class*

6 Ex-USSR "KRONSTADT" CLASS

Displacement, tons	310 standard; 380 full load
Dimensions, ft (*m*)	170·6 × 21·3 × 9 (*52·0 × 6·5 × 2·7*)
Guns	1—3·5 in; 2—37 mm AA; 4—25 mm AA
A/S weapons	1 DC thrower
Mines	6 on two racks at the stern
Main engines	3 diesels; 3 shafts; 3 030 hp = 24 knots
Range, miles	1 500 at 12 knots
Complement	65

Former Soviet submarine chasers reported transferred from the USSR in 1962.

RADAR. Surface; Skinhead or Ballgun. Navigation; Don 2 × 3 IFF; High Pole A.

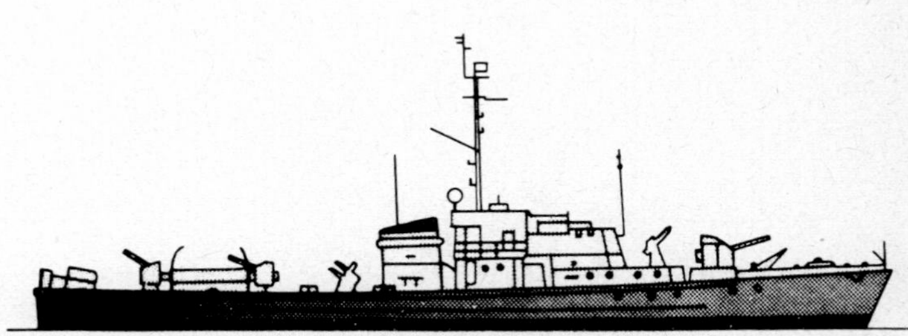

KRONSTADT *Class*

LIGHT FORCES

2 Ex-USSR "OSA" CLASS (FAST ATTACK CRAFT—MISSILE)

Displacement, tons	165 standard; 200 full load
Dimensions, ft (*m*)	128·7 × 25·1 × 5·9 (*39·3 × 7·7 × 1·8*)
Missiles	4 SSN-2 launchers in two pairs
Guns	4—30 mm (2 twin, 1 forward, 1 aft)
Main engines	3 diesels; 13 000 bhp = 32 knots
Range, miles	800 at 25 knots
Complement	25

Two boats of this class were transferred to Cuba from the USSR in January 1972. With the obvious rundown of the ex-USN ships in the Cuban Navy and the determination of the Cuban Government to maintain an Independent Naval presence in the Caribbean, these could be the forerunners of further reinforcements. With the "Komar" class units there are now twenty hulls mounting 44 of the proven and effective "Styx" missiles in a highly sensitive area.

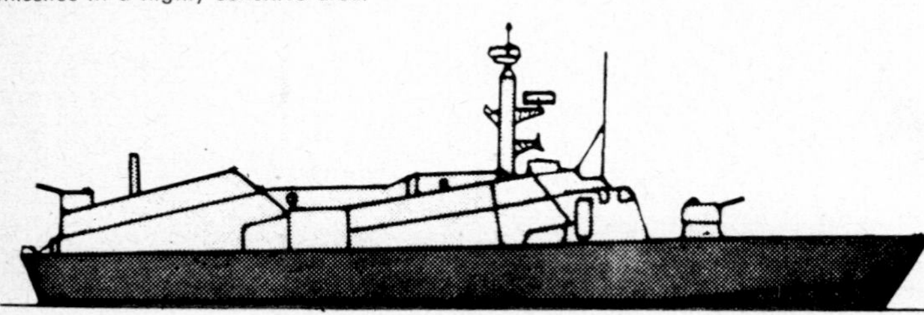

OSA *Class*

18 Ex-USSR "KOMAR" CLASS (FAST ATTACK CRAFT—MISSILE)

Displacement, tons	70 standard; 80 full load
Dimensions, ft (*m*)	83·7 × 19·8 × 5·0 (*25·5 × 6·0 × 1·8*)
Missiles	2 SSN-2 launchers
Guns	2—25 mm AA
Main engines	4 diesels; 4 shafts; 4 800 bhp = 40 knots
Range, miles	400 at 30 knots

First twelve transferred in 1962. Last pair arrived in Dec 1966.

KOMAR CLASS *1970 USN*

12 Ex-USSR "P 6" CLASS (FAST ATTACK CRAFT—TORPEDO)

Displacement, tons	66 standard; 75 full load
Dimensions, ft (*m*)	84·2 × 20 × 6 (*25·7 × 6·1 × 1·8*)
Guns	4—25 mm AA (two twin)
Tubes	2—21 in (two single)
Main engines	4 diesels; 4 shafts; 4 800 hp = 43 knots
Range, miles	450 at 30 knots
Complement	25

Transferred in 1962. Pothead or Skinhead Radar. Can carry mines or depth charges in place of torpedo tubes.

P 6 *Class*

Light Forces—*continued*

12 Ex-USSR "P 4" CLASS (FAST ATTACK CRAFT—TORPEDO)

Displacement, tons	25
Dimensions, ft (*m*)	62·7 × 11·6 × 5·6 (*19·1 × 3·5 × 1·7*)
Guns	2—25 mm AA
Tubes	2—18 in
Main engines	2 diesels; 2 200 bhp; 2 shafts = 50 knots

Former Soviet motor torpedo boats, transferred from the USSR in 1962-64.

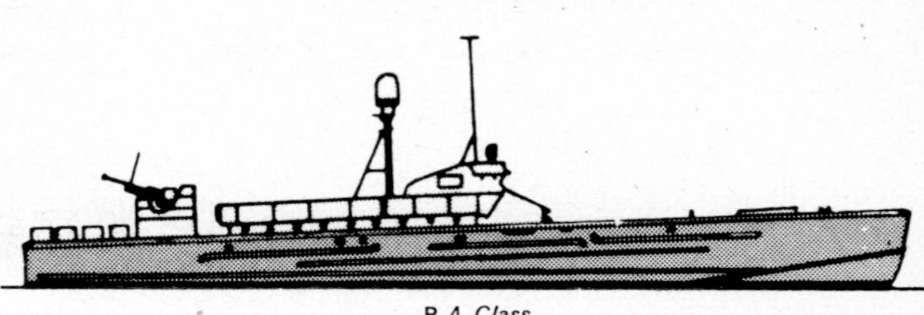

P 4 *Class*

1 Ex-US PCE TYPE ESCORT PATROL VESSEL

SIBONY (ex-USS *PCE 893*) PE 302

Displacement, tons	640 standard; 903 full load
Dimensions, feet	180 wl; 184·5 oa × 33 × 9·5
Guns	1—3 in dp; 3—40 mm AA; 4—20 mm AA
A/S weapons	Hedgehog; DCT and racks
Main engines	12 cylinder diesels; 2 shafts; 1 800 bhp = 14 knots
Complement	99

Built in USA. Completed 1943-44. Refitted at Key West 1956.

HABANA *GC* 107 (ex-*SC* 1291) **ORIENTE** *GC* 104 (ex-*SC* 1 000)
LAS VILLAS *GC* 106 (ex-*SC* 1290) **PINAR DEL RIO** *GC* 108 (ex-*SC* 1301)

Displacement, tons	95
Dimensions, feet	107·5 wl; 111 oa × 17 × 6.5
Guns	2—20 mm AA
Main engines	GM diesels; 2 shafts; 1 000 bhp = 15 knots

Built in the United States by Dingle Boat Works (*Oriente*), W.A. Robinson, Inc, Ipswich, Mass. (*Havana* and *Las Villas*), and Perkins & Vaughn Inc, Wickford, RI (*Pinar del Rio*).

HABANA *Cuban Navy*

LEONCIO PRADO *GC* 101

Displacement, tons	80
Dimensions, feet	110 × 17·7 × 6·2
Gun	1—20 mm AA
Main engines	2 sets 8-cycle, 2 stroke diesels; 1 000 bhp = 15 knots
Oil fuel	2 232 gallons

Built at Havana. Launched in 1946. Of wooden hulled construction.

LEONCIO PRADO *1966, Cuban Navy*

Light Forces—*continued*

GC 11 (ex-USCGC 83351) **GC 13** (ex-USCGC 83385) **GC 14** (ex-USCGC 83395)

Displacement, tons	45
Dimensions, feet	83 × 16 × 4·5
Guns	1—20 mm AA
Main engines	2 Sterling Viking petrol motors; 1 200 hp = 18 knots
Complement	12

Former *CS* of same numbers. Built in USA. Ex-Coast Guard Cutters. Launched in 1942-43. Of wooden hulled construction. Received from US Navy in March 1943. Rated as *Guardacostas*, 83 ft.

GC 32 (ex-USCGC 56191) **GC 33** (ex-USCGC 56190) **GC 34** (ex-USCGC 56192)

Displacement, tons	45
Dimensions, feet	83 × 16 × 4·5
Guns	1—20 mm AA
Main engines	2 Superior diesels; 460 bhp = 12 knots
Complement	12

Built in USA. Ex-Coast Guard cutters. Launched in 1942-43.

R 41 (ex-*PT* 715) **R 42** (ex-*PT* 716)

Displacement, tons	35
Dimensions, feet	71 × 19·2 × 5
Guns	2 MG
Main engines	2 Packard gas engines; 3 shafts; 3 600 bhp = 35 knots

Former US motor torpedo boats of the PT type. Built in the USA by Annapolis Yacht Yard Inc, Annapolis, Md. Launched on 9 July 1945 (R 41) and 17 July 1945 (R 42). Sunk during a hurricane on 5 Oct 1948, but were salvaged and put into service as sea-air rescue craft.

SV 7 **SV 8** **SV 9** **SV 10** **SV 12** **SV 14**

Dimensions, feet	Length 40
Gun	1—50 cal MG
Main engines	2 GM diesels; speed 25 knots

Later boats of the SV type assigned to naval stations for coastal patrol. Equipped with radar.

SV 1 **SV 2** **SV 3** **SV 4** **SV 5** **SV 6**

Displacement, tons	6·15
Dimensions, feet	32 × 10 × 2·8
Main engines	2 Chrysler Crown, 230 bhp = 18 knots

Auxiliary patrol boats for port patrol, launched in 1953.

ENRIQUE COLLAZO (ex-*Joaquin Godoy*)

Displacement, tons	815
Dimensions, feet	211 × 24 × 9
Main engines	Triple expansion; 2 shafts; 672 ihp = 8 knots

Built at Paisley, Scotland. Launched in 1906. Acquired in 1950 from Cuban mercantile marine. Lighthouse tender.

BERTHA SF 10

Displacement, tons	98
Dimensions, feet	104 × 19 × 11
Main engines	2 Gray Marine diesels; 450 bhp = 10 knots

Launched in 1944. Lighthouse tender.

10 DE OCTUBRE (ex-*ATR* 4) RS 210

Displacement, tons	852 standard; 1 315 full load
Dimensions, feet	155 wl 165·5 oa × 33·3 × 16
Main engines	Triple expansion; 1 600 ihp = 12 knots
Boilers	2 Babcock & Wilcox D-type; oil burning

Former US ocean rescue tug. Built in the USA. Launched in 1943. Largely of wooden construction.

GRANMA A 11

Yacht which landed in Cuba on 2 Dec 1956 with Dr Fidel Castro and the men who began the liberation war. Historic vessel incorporated into the Navy as an auxiliary.

A1 **A2** **A3**

Displacement, tons	60
Dimensions, feet	74 × 15 × 5
Gun	1 MG
Main engines	2 diesels

CYPRUS

LIGHT FORCES

Mercantile Marine

Lloyd's Register of Shipping: 589 vessels of 2 935 775 tons gross

6 "P 4" CLASS

Displacement, tons	25
Dimensions, ft (*m*)	62·7 × 11·6 × 6·5 (*19·1 × 3·5 × 1·7*)
Guns	2—25 mm
Tubes	2—18 in
Main engines	2 diesels; 2 200 bhp; 2 shafts = 50 knots

Four of these were transferred by USSR in Oct 1964 and two in Feb 1965. Also reported that two extra engines have been supplied since that time.

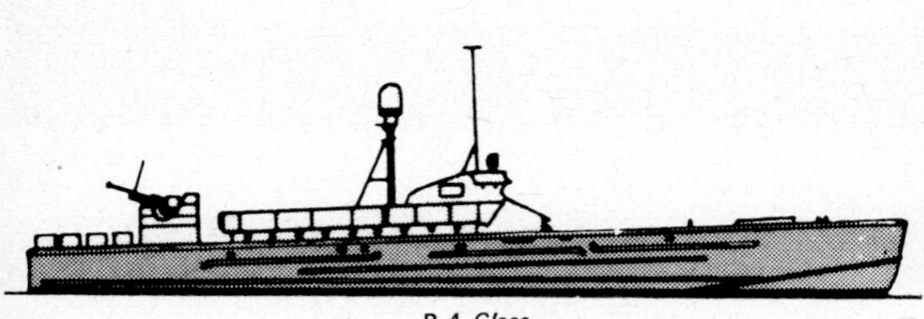

P 4 *Class*

2 Ex-GERMAN "R" TYPE

Displacement, tons	125
Dimensions, feet	124 × 19 × 4·5
Guns	1—40 mm; 1—20 mm
Main engines	2 MAN diesels; 1 800 bhp = 20 knots

Originally three of this class were taken up from mercantile use and re-armed. One was destroyed by Turkish air attack on 8 Aug 1964 at Xeros. It was reported that there are 10 small craft of about 50 tons, armed with one or two 20 mm guns.

No. 15 *1972, Dr. Giorgio Arra*

DENMARK

Administration

Commander-in-Chief:
Vice-Admiral S. Thostrup, RDN

Diplomatic Representation

Defence Attaché, London:
Colonel H. H. Prince Georg of Denmark, CVO

Assistant Defence Attaché, London:
Captain I. E. Eriksen, RDN

Defence Attaché, Washington:
Colonel P. B. Nissen, RDAF

Personnel

(a) January 1974: 6 000 officers and men (Reserve of 3 000 Maritime Home Guard)
(b) 9 months National service

Disposals

Large Patrol Craft

1972 *Alholm*

Tenders

1970 *Hollaenderdybet, Kongedybet*

Icebreaker

1972 *Lillebjørn*

Strength of the Fleet

Type	*Active*	*Building*
Frigates	6	1
Corvettes	4	—
Submarines (Patrol)	6	—
Fast Attack Craft (Missile)	—	8
Fast Attack Craft (Torpedo)	16	—
Large Patrol Craft	22	—
Coastal Patrol Craft	16	2
Minelayers	7	—
Minesweepers (Coastal)	8	—
Minesweepers (Inshore)	4	—
Depot Ships	2	—
Oilers (Small)	2	—
Icebreakers	3	—
Royal Yacht	1	—

Navy Estimates

1970-71: 441 800 000 Kr.
1971-72: 478 500 000 Kr.
1972-73: 520 400 000 Kr.
1973-74: 583 600 000 Kr.

Prefix to Ships Names

Names prefixed by HDMS

Naval Bases

Copenhagen, Århus, Grønnedal (Greenland)

New Programme

In November 1973 the Danish Navy started discussions with Yarrow Ltd and Vosper Thornycroft Ltd of UK to consider the possible construction of frigates either in the UK or under licence in Denmark. Up to 3 to 4 ships have been mentioned of Type 5 or Type 21.

Farvands Direktoratet

This Directorate of Waters (under the MOD) now controls the Pilot Service, Lighthouse Service, and Lifeboat service. In future the Icebreakers and SAR helicopters will probably come under this Directorate.

Mercantile Marine

Lloyd's Register of Shipping:
1 362 vessels of 4 106 525 tons gross

FRIGATES

2 "PEDER SKRAM" CLASS

Displacement, tons	2 030 standard; 2 720 full load
Length, feet (*metres*)	354·3 (108) pp; 396·5 (*112·6*) oa
Beam, feet (*metres*)	39·5 (*12*)
Draught, feet (*metres*)	11·8 (*3·6*)
Guns, surface	4—5 in (*127 mm*) 38 cal
Guns, AA	4—40 mm
A/S weapons	DC
Main engines	CODOG; 2 shafts:— 2 GM 16-567 D diesels; 4 800 hp; 2 Pratt & Whitney PWA GG 4A-3 gas turbines; 44 000 hp total output
Speed, knots	28 designed; over 30 max; 18 economical sea
Complement	112

Name	*No.*	*Builders*	*Laid down*	*Launched*	*Completed*
HERLUF TROLLE	F 353	Helsingörs J. & M.	18 Dec 1964	8 Sep 1965	16 Apr 1967
PEDER SKRAM	F 352	Helsingörs J. & M.	25 Sep 1964	20 May 1965	30 June 1966

GENERAL
Fast frigates of Danish design built at Helsingör. They were to have been armed. additionally to guns, with three 21 inch torpedo tubes and the "Terne" anti-submarine weapon. There is space on the quarter deck for installation of Sea Sparrow in 1974-75.

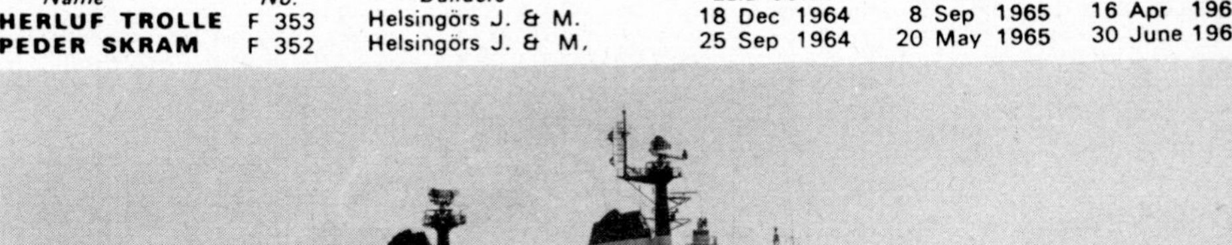

HERLUF TROLLE — *1972, Royal Danish Navy.*

RADAR. Search: Two S Band air and surface search. Tactical: X Band. Fire Control: Three X Band and Contraves.

4 "HVIDBJØRNEN" CLASS

Name	*No.*	*Builders*	*Laid down*	*Launched*	*Completed*
FYLLA	F 351	Aalborg Værft	27 June 1962	18 Dec 1962	10 July 1963
HVIDBJØRNEN	F 348	Aarhus Flydedok	4 June 1961	23 Nov 1961	15 Dec 1962
INGOLF	F 350	Svendborg Værft	5 Dec 1961	27 July 1961	27 July 1963
VÆDDEREN	F 349	Aalborg Værft	30 Oct 1961	6 Apr 1962	19 Mar 1963

Displacement, tons	1 345 standard; 1 650 full load
Length, feet (*metres*)	219·8 (*67·0*) pp; 238·2 (*72·6*) oa
Beam, feet (*metres*)	38·0 (*11·6*)
Draught, feet (*metres*)	16 (*4·9*)
Aircraft	1 Alouette III helicopter
Gun, dual purpose	1—3 in (*76 mm*)
Main engines	4 GM 16—567C diesels; 6 400 bhp; 1 shaft
Speed, knots	18
Range, miles	6 000 at 13 knots
Complement	75

GENERAL
Ordered in 1960-61. Of frigate type for fishery protection and surveying duties in the North Sea, Faroe Islands and Greenland waters. They are equipped with a helicopter platform aft.

RADAR. Search: S Band combined air and surface Navigation: X Band.

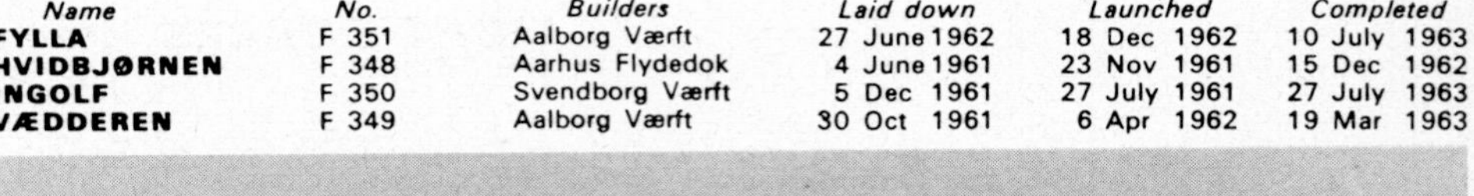

FYLLA — *1972, Royal Danish Navy*

1 MODIFIED "HVIDBJØRNEN" CLASS

Length, feet (*metres*)	244 (*74·4*) oa
Beam, feet (*metres*)	39 (*11·8*)
Draught, feet (*metres*)	15 (*4·5*)
Aircraft	1 Alouette III helicopter
Gun, DP	1—3 in (*76 mm*)
Main engines	4 B.W. Alpha diesels; 7 440 bhp; 1 shaft
Speed, knots	18
Complement	60

Laid down in 1970 for completion Oct 1975.

CORVETTES

4 "TRITON" CLASS

Displacement, tons	760 standard; 873 full load
Length, feet (*metres*)	242·8 (*74·0*) pp; 250·3 (*76·3*) oa
Beam, feet (*metres*)	31·5 (*9·6*)
Draught, feet (*metres*)	9 (*2·7*)
Guns, surface	2—3 in (*76 mm*)
Guns, AA	1—40 mm
A/S	2 Hedgehogs; 4 DCT
Main engines	2 Ansaldo Fiat 409T diesels 4 400 bhp; 2 shafts
Speed, knots	18 designed, 20 max 16 sea
Range, miles	3 000 at 18 knots
Complement	110

GENERAL
All four vessels were built in Italy for the Danish Navy under the United States "offshore" account. Sisters of the Italian "Albatros" class.

RADAR. Search: Plessey AWS 1. Navigation: S Band.

CLASSIFICATION. Officially classified as corvettes in 1954, but have "F" pennant numbers like frigates.

Name	*No.*	*Builders*	*Launched*	*Transferred*
BELLONA	F 344	Naval Meccanicia, Castellammare	9 Jan 1955	31 Jan 1957
DIANA	F 345	Cantiere del Tirreno, Riva, Trigoso	19 Dec 1954	30 July 1955
FLORA	F 346	Cantiere del Tirreno, Riva, Trigoso	25 June 1955	28 Aug 1956
TRITON	F 347	Cantiere Navali di Taranto	12 Sep 1954	10 Aug 1955

FLORA — *1972, Royal Danish Navy*

SUBMARINES

2 "NARHVALEN" CLASS

Displacement, tons	370 surface; 450 dived
Length, feet (*metres*)	144·4 (*44·3*)
Beam, feet (*metres*)	15 (*4·6*)
Draught, feet (*metres*)	12·5 (*3·8*)
Torpedo tubes	8—21 in (*533 mm*) bow,
Main machinery	2 MB Diesels; 1 500 bhp surface; 2 electric motors; 1 500 bhp dived
Speed, knots	12 surface; 17 dived
Complement	22

These coastal submarines are similar to the German Improved Type 205 and were built under licence at the Royal Dockyard, Copenhagen with modifications for Danish needs. They are fitted with snort and radar.

Name	*No.*	*Laid down*	*Launched*	*Completed*
NARHVALEN	S 320	16 Feb 1965	10 Sep 1968	27 Feb 1970
NORDKAPEREN	S 321	20 Jan 1966	18 Dec 1969	22 Dec 1970

NARHVALEN — *1970, Royal Danish Navy*

4 "DELFINEN" CLASS

Displacement, tons	550 standard; 595 surface; 643 submerged
Length, feet (*metres*)	117·2 (*54·0*)
Beam, feet (*metres*)	15·4 (*4·7*)
Draught, feet (*metres*)	13·1 (*4·0*)
Torpedo tubes	4—21 in (*533 mm*)
Main machinery	2 Burmeister & Wain diesels; 1 200 bhp surface; electric motors; 1 200 hp submerged
Speed, knots	15 surface and submerged
Range, miles	4 000 at 8 knots
Complement	33

Built in the Royal Dockyard, Copenhagen. Equipped with snort and radar.

Name	*No.*	*Laid down*	*Launched*	*Completed*
DELFINEN	S 326	1 July 1954	4 May 1956	16 Sep 1958
SPÆKHUGGEREN	S 327	1 Dec 1954	20 Feb 1957	27 June 1959
SPRINGEREN	S 329	3 Jan 1961	26 Apr 1963	22 Oct 1964
TUMLEREN	S 328	22 May 1956	22 May 1958	15 Jan 1960

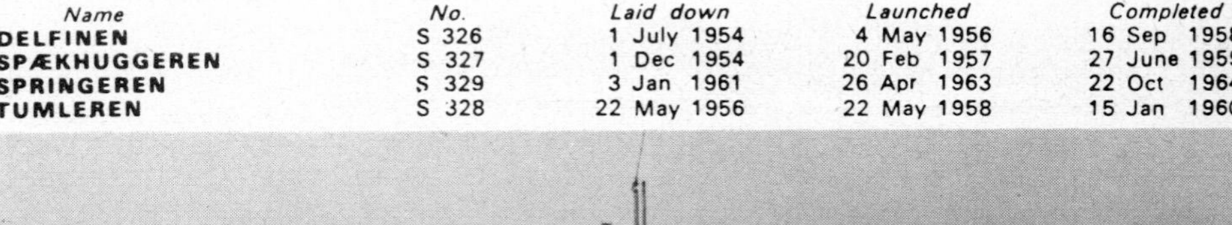

SPRINGEREN — *1972, Royal Danish Navy*

LIGHT FORCES

8 200 ton TYPE (FAST ATTACK CRAFT—MISSILE)

Displacement, tons	220
Dimensions, feet	151 × 24 × 8
Guided weapons	To be installed
Guns	1—76 mm Oto Melara or 1—57 mm L 70 Bofors
Torpedo tubes	4—21 in
Main engines	CODAG arrangement of 3 Rolls Royce Proteus gas turbines plus diesels for cruising on wing shafts
Speed, knots	40 max approx

First four ordered in 1971 to complete in 1975-76. Further four now building. Lürssen Werft design. Basically similar to "Combattante II" class. Controllable pitch propellers. All building at Frederikshavn Vaerft and Flydedok.

2 NEW CONSTRUCTION (COASTAL PATROL CRAFT)

2 Patrol craft for Greenland service.

1 "FYRHOLM" CLASS (COASTAL PATROL CRAFT)

LINDHOLM Y 374 (ex-*MSK* 6)

Displacement, tons	68
Dimensions, feet	65·7 × 16·8 × 7·5
Main engines	Diesel; 120 bhp = 9 knots

Built by Sydhavns Vaerft. Launched in 1945.

1 "ALHOLM" CLASS (LARGE PATROL CRAFT)

ERTHOLM Y 371 (ex-*MSK* 3)

Displacement, tons	70
Dimensions, feet	69 × 17 × 9
Gun	1—20 mm AA
Main engines	Diesel; 120 bhp = 10 knots

Built by Frederikssund Vaerft. Launched in 1945.

Light Forces—*continued*

4 "FALKEN" CLASS (FAST ATTACK CRAFT—TORPEDO)

Name	Pennant No.	Laid down	Launched	Completed
FALKEN	P 506	1 Nov 1960	19 Dec 1961	4 Oct 1962
GLENTEN	P 507	3 Jan 1961	15 Mar 1962	15 Dec 1962
GRIBBEN	P 508	15 May 1961	18 July 1962	26 Apr 1963
HØGEN	P 509	1 Sep 1961	4 Oct 1962	6 June 1963

Displacement, tons 119
Dimensions, feet 118 × 17·8 × 6
Guns 1—40 mm AA; 1—20 mm AA
Tubes 2—41 in (side)
Main engines 3 diesels; 3 shafts; 9 000 bhp = 40 knots
Complement 23

Ordered under US offshore procurement in the Military Aid Programme. All built at the Royal Dockyard, Copenhagen. Named after birds.

GRIBBEN *1970, Royal Danish Navy*

6 "FLYVEFISKEN" CLASS (FAST ATTACK CRAFT—TORPEDO)

FLYVEFISKEN P 500 **HAVKATTEN** P 502 **MAKRELEN** P 504
HAJEN P 501 **LAXEN** P 503 **SVÆRDFISKEN** P 505

Displacement, tons 110
Dimensions, feet 120 × 18 × 6
Guns 1—40 mm AA; 1—20 mm AA
Tubes 2—21 in
Main engines 3 diesels; 3 shafts; 7 500 bhp = 40 knots
Complement 22

Three built in Royal Dockyard, Copenhagen, three in Frederikssund Vaerft. All units are named after fishes. Ordered in 1952, laid down in 1953 and launched in 1954-55.

SVÆRDFISKEN *1970, Royal Danish Navy*

6 "SØLØVEN" CLASS (FAST ATTACK CRAFT—TORPEDO)

Name	Pennant No.	Laid down	Launched	Completed
SØLØVEN	P 510	27 Aug 1962	19 Apr 1963	June 1964 *
SØRIDDEREN	P 511	4 Oct 1962	22 Aug 1963	June 1964 *
SØBJORNEN	P 512	9 July 1963	19 Aug 1964	Sep 1965
SØHESTEN	P 513	5 Sep 1963	31 Mar 1965	June 1966
SØHUNDEN	P 514	18 Aug 1964	12 Jan 1966	Dec 1966
SØULVEN	P 515	30 Mar 1965	27 Apr 1966	Mar 1967

Displacement, tons 95 standard; 114 full load
Dimensions, feet 90 pp; 96 wl; 99 oa × 25·5 × 7
Guns 2—40 mm Bofors AA
Tubes 4—21 in (side)
Main engines 3 Bristol Siddeley Proteus gas turbines; 3 shafts; 12 750 bhp = 54 knots
GM diesels on wing shafts for cruising = 10 knots
Range, miles 400 at 46 knots
Complement 29

The design is a combination of the "Brave" class hull form and "Ferocity" type construction. *Søløven* ("Sea Lion") and *Søridderen* ("Sea Knight") were built by Vosper Limited, Portsmouth, England (*delivered to the Royal Danish Navy on 12 and 10 Feb 1965, respectively); and the remaining four under licence by the Royal Dockyard, Copenhagen.

SØULVEN *1970, Royal Danish Navy*

9 "BARSØ" CLASS (LARGE PATROL CRAFT)

BARSØ Y 300 **SAMSØ** Y 303 **FARØ** Y 306
DREJØ Y 301 **THURØ** Y 304 **LAESØ** Y 307
ROMSØ Y 302 **VEJRØ** Y 305 **ROMØ** Y 308

Displacement, tons 155
Dimensions, feet 83·7 × 19·7 × 9·8
Speed 11 knots

Rated as patrol cutters. First six launched and completed in 1969. Remainder in 1972-73.

FARØ *1973, Royal Danish Navy*

2 "MAAGEN" CLASS (LARGE PATROL CRAFT)

MAAGEN (Y 384) **MALLEMUKKEN** Y 385

Displacement, tons 190
Dimensions, feet 88·5 × 21·7 × 9·5
Guns 1—40 mm AA
Main engines 385 hp; 1 shaft; speed 11 knots

Of steel construction. Built at Helsingør, laid down 15 Jan 1960, launched 1960.

1 "SKARVEN" CLASS (LARGE PATROL CRAFT)

TEJSTEN Y 383

Displacement, tons 130
Dimensions, feet 82 × 20·7 × 9·4
Gun 1—37 mm
Main engines Alfa Diesel; 180 bhp = 9 knots

Of wooden construction. Built by Holbaek Skibsbyggeri. Launched 1951. For service in Greenland waters.

9 "DAPHNE" CLASS (LARGE PATROL CRAFT)

Name	Pennant No.	Laid down	Launched	Completed
DAPNHE	P 530	1 Apr 1960	10 Nov 1960	19 Dec 1961
DRYADEN	P 531	1 July 1960	1 Mar 1961	4 Apr 1962
HAVFRUEN	P 533	15 Mar 1961	4 Oct 1961	20 Dec 1962
HAVMANDEN	P 532	15 Nov 1960	16 May 1961	30 Aug 1962
NAJADEN	P 534	20 Sep 1961	20 June 1962	26 Apr 1963
NEPTUN	P 536	1 Sep 1962	29 May 1963	18 Dec 1963
NYMFEN	P 535	1 Apr 1962	1 Nov 1962	4 Oct 1963
RAN	P 537	1 Dec 1962	10 July 1963	15 May 1964
ROTA	P 538	19 July 1963	25 Nov 1963	20 Jan 1965

Displacement, tons 170
Dimensions, feet 121·3 × 20 × 6·5
Gun 1—40 mm AA
A/S weapons 2—51 mm rocket launchers, depth charges
Main engines Diesels; 2 shafts; 2 600 bhp = 20 knots (plus 1 cruising engine; 100 bhp)
Complement 23

All built at the Royal Dockyard, Copenhagen. 4 built under US offshore programme.

NEPTUN *1970, Royal Danish Navy*

Light Forces—*continued*

7 "FÆNØ" CLASS (COASTAL PATROL CRAFT)

ASKØ MHV 81 (ex-Y 386, ex-M 560, ex-MS 2)
BAAGØ MHV 84 (ex-Y 387, ex-M 561, ex-MS 3)
ENØ MHV 82 (ex-Y 388, ex-M 562, ex-MS 5)
FÆNØ MHV 69 (ex-M 563, ex-MS 6)
HJORTØ MHV 85 (ex-Y 389, ex-M 564, ex-MS 7)
LYØ MHV 86 (ex-Y 390, ex-M 565, ex-MS 8)
MANØ MHV 83 (ex-Y 391, ex-M 566, ex-MS 9)

Displacement, tons 74
Dimensions, feet 78·8 × 21 × 5
Guns 1—20 mm
Main engines Diesel; 1 shaft; 350 bhp = 11 knots

Of wooden construction. All launched in 1941. Former inshore minesweepers. Used by the Maritime Home Guard.

FÆNO *1969, Royal Danish Navy*

3 MHV TYPE

MHV 60 **MHV 71** **MHV 72**

Displacement, tons 76
Guns 1—20 mm AA
Main engines 200 bhp = 10 knots

Built in 1958. Patrol boats and training craft for the Naval Home Guard. Of the fishing cutter type. Formerly designated DMH, but allocated MHV numbers in 1969. In addition there are some 20 small vessels of the trawler and other types.

5 "Y" TYPE

Y 338 **Y 339** **Y 343** **Y 354** **Y 359**

Miscellaneous patrol cutters (ex-fishing vessels) all built in 1944-45. Y 342 and Y 347 were removed from the list in 1971.

MHV 72 *1973, Royal Danish Navy*

MINE WARFARE FORCES

4 "FALSTER" CLASS MINELAYERS

Name	*No.*	*Builders*	*Laid down*	*Launched*	*Completed*
FALSTER	N 80	Nakskov Skibsvaerft	12 Apr 1962	19 Sep 1962	7 Nov 1963
FYEN	N 81	Frederikshavn Værft	12 Apr 1962	3 Oct 1962	18 Sep 1963
MØEN	N 82	Frederikshavn Værft	4 Oct 1962	6 Mar 1963	29 Apr 1964
SJÆLLAND	N 83	Nakskov Skibsværft	17 Jan 1963	14 June 1963	7 July 1964

Displacement, tons 1 900 full load
Length, feet (*metres*) 238 (*72·5*) pp; 252·6 (*77·0*) oa
Beam, feet (*metres*) 41 (*12·5*)
Draught, feet (*metres*) 10 (*3·0*)
Missiles To be fitted with Seasparrow 1974-75
Guns, dual purpose 4—3 in (*76 mm*), 2 twin mountings
Mines 400
Main engines 2 GM—567D 3 diesels; 4 800 shp 2 shafts
Speed, knots 17
Complement 120

GENERAL
Minelayers of a novel Scandinavian-NATO design. Ordered in 1960-61. All are named after Danish islands. The steel hull is flush-decked with a raking stem, a full stern and a prominent knuckle forward. The super structure has a block outline surmounted by a squat streamlined funnel, two light lattice masts, high angle director control towers fore and aft and whip aerials. The hull has been specially strengthened for ice navigation.

RADAR. Search: C Band low coverage. Navigation: S and X Band.

SJÆLLAND *1972 Royal Danish Navy*

1 "LANGELAND" CLASS COASTAL MINELAYER

LANGELAND N 42
Displacement, tons 310 standard; 332 full load
Dimensions, feet 133·5 oa; 128·2 pp × 23·7 × 7·2
Guns 2—40 mm; 2—20 mm Madsen
Main engines Diesel; 2 shafts; 385 bhp = 11·6 knots
Complement 37

Built at the Royal Dockyard, Copenhagen. Laid down in 1950. Launched on 17 May 1950. Completed in 1951.

LANGELAND *1973, Royal Danish Navy*

2 "LOUGEN" CLASS COASTAL MINELAYERS

LAALAND N 40 **LOUGEN** N 41

Displacement, tons	240 standard; 260 full load
Dimensions, feet	105·5 × 21·2 × 6·5
Guns	2—20 mm AA
Main engines	B & W diesel; 2 shafts; 350 bhp = 10 knots
Complement	31

Built at the Royal Dockyard, Copenhagen. Both laid down in 1940, launched in 1941 and completed in 1946. The old coastal minelayer *Lindormen*, N 39, was officially stricken from the list in 1970.

LAALAND *1973, Royal Danish Navy*

8 "SUND" CLASS (MINESWEEPERS—COASTAL)

AARØSUND (ex-*AMS* 127) M 571
ALSSUND (ex-*AMS* 128) M 572
EGERNSUND (ex-*AMS* 129) M 573
GRØNSUND (ex-*MSC* 256) M 574
GULDBORGSUND (ex-*MSC* 257) M 575
OMØSUND (ex-*MSC* 221) M 576
ULVSUND (ex-*MSC* 263) M 577
VILSUND (ex-*MSC* 264) M 578

Displacement, tons	350 standard; 376 full load
Dimensions, feet	138 pp; 144 oa × 27 × 8·5
Guns	2—20 mm
Main engines	Diesels; 2 shafts; 1 200 bhp = 13 knots
Range, miles	2 500 at 10 knots
Complement	35

MSC (ex-AMS) 60 class NATO coastal minesweepers all built in USA. Completed in 1954-56. *Aarøsund* was transferred on 24 Jan 1955, *Alssund* on 5 Apr 1955, *Egernsund* on 3 Aug 1955, *Grønsund* on 21 Sep 1956, *Guldborgsund* on 11 Nov 1956, *Omøsund* on 20 June 1956, *Ulvsund* on 20 Sep 1956 and *Vilsund* on 15 Nov 1956.

Guldborgsund has been fitted with a charthouse between bridge and funnel and is employed on surveying duties.

GULDBORGSUND *1973, Royal Danish Navy*

4 "VIG" CLASS (MINESWEEPERS—INSHORE)

Name	*No.*	*Laid down*	*Launched*	*Completed*
ASVIG	M 579	22 Apr 1959	11 May 1960	6 Sep 1961
MOSVIG	M 580	22 Apr 1959	14 Sep 1960	25 Oct 1961
SANDVIG	M 581	11 May 1960	1 Mar 1961	1 Feb 1962
SAALVIG	M 582	14 Sep 1960	14 July 1961	30 Apr 1962

Displacement, tons	180
Dimensions, feet	113·5 × 22·5 × 6·2
Guns	2—20 mm AA
Main engines	2 diesels; 2 shafts; 11 000 bhp = 13 knots
Range, miles	2 000 at 9 knots
Complement	18

All built at the Royal Dockyard, Copenhagen.

MOSVIG *1970, Royal Danish Navy*

SLEIPNER

A 200 ton torpedo recovery/transporter.

DEPOT SHIPS

HJÆLPEREN (ex-US *LSM* 500) A 563

Displacement, tons	1 030 standard; 1 170 full load
Dimensions, feet	203·5 oa × 34·5 × 8·3
Guns	2—40 mm
Main engines	Diesels; 2 shafts; 2 800 bhp = 12 knots
Complement	60

Former United States medium landing ship. Built by Brown Shipbuilding Co, Houston, Texas. Laid down on 17 Mar 1945. Launched on 7 Apr 1945. Completed on 17 May 1945. Transferred to the Royal Danish Navy on 15 May 1953. Depot and repair ship for motor torpedo boats.

HJÆLPEREN *1971, Royal Danish Navy*

HENRIK GERNER (ex-M/S *Hammershus*) A 542

Displacement, tons	2 200 standard
Dimensions, feet	252·7 × 40 × 18·3
Main engines	Burmeister & Wain diesel; speed = 15 knots
Complement	230

Former Danish passenger ship. Built in 1936. Transferred to the Royal Danish Navy on 8 Jan 1964, refitted at the Royal Dockyard, Copenhagen, and commissioned as a depot ship for submarines.

HENRIK GERNER *1971, Royal Danish Navy*

OILERS

RIMFAXE (ex-US *YO* 226) A 568 **SKINFAXE** (ex-US *YO* 229) A 569

Displacement, tons	422 light; 1 390 full load
Dimensions, feet	174 oa × 32 × 13·2
Main engines	1 GM diesel; 560 bhp = 10 knots
Complement	23

Yard oilers transferred to the Royal Danish Navy from the USA on 2 Aug 1962.

RIMFAXE *1971, Royal Danish Navy*

ICEBREAKERS

Note. Icebreakers are controlled by the Ministry of Trade and Shipping, but are maintained by RDN at Frederikshavn in summer.

ELBJØRN

Displacement, tons	893 standard; 1 400 full load
Dimensions, feet	156·5 × 40·3 × 14·5
Main engines	Diesels; electric drive; 3 600 bhp = 12 knots

Built in 1953. Recently used by RDN for surveying in summer.

DANBJØRN **ISBJØRN**

Displacement, tons	3 685
Dimensions, feet	252 × 56 × 20
Main engines	Diesels; Electric drive; 11 880 bhp = 14 knots
Complement	34

Built in 1965.

DANBJØRN 1970, Royal Danish Navy

STOREBJØRN

Displacement, tons	2 540
Dimensions, feet	197 × 49·2 × 19

Built in 1931.

ROYAL YACHT

DANNEBROG A 540

Displacement, tons	1 130
Dimensions, feet	246 oa × 34 × 11·2
Guns	2—37 mm
Main engines	2 sets Burmeister & Wain 8 cylinder; 2 cycle diesels. 1 800 bhp = 14 knots
Complement	57

Built at the Royal Dockyard, Copenhagen. Launched on 10 Oct 1931.

DANNEBROG *1971, Royal Danish Navy*

DOMINICAN REPUBLIC

Administration

Under Secretary for the Navy:
Commodore Francisco A. Amiama Castillo

Chief of Naval Staff:
Commodore Manuel A. Logroño Contin

Vice-Chief of Naval Staff:
Captain Francisco A. Marte Victoria

Personnel

(a) 1974: 3 810 officers and men
(b) Selective

Strength of the Fleet

Type	*Active*	*Projected*
Frigates	3	—
Corvettes	2	5(?)
Large Patrol Craft	5	—
Coastal Patrol Craft	7	—
LSM	1	—
LCU	2	—
Minesweepers (Ocean)	2	—
Survey Vessels	2 (1 launch)	—
Oilers (Small)	2	—
Tugs (Large)	4	—
Tugs (Harbour)	8	—

Disposals

Destroyers

1972 *Duarte*

Corvettes

1972 *Gerardo Jansen, Juan Bautista Cambiaso, Juan Bautista Maggiola*

Mercantile Marine

Lloyd's Register of Shipping:
18 vessels of 9 381 tons gross

FRIGATES

2 Ex-US "TACOMA" CLASS

Name	*Pennant No.*	*Builders*	*Laid down*	*Launched*	*Completed*
CAP. GENERAL PEDRO SANTANA (ex-*Presidente Troncoso*, ex-USS *Knoxville*, PF 64)	453 (ex-F 104)	Kaiser S.Y. Richmond, Cal.	14 Nov 1943	20 Jan 1944	27 May 1944
GREGORIO LUPERON (ex-*Presidente Peynado*, ex-USS *Pueblo*, PF 13)	452 (ex-F 103)	Leatham D. Smith S.B. Co, Wis.	15 Apr 1943	10 July 1943	29 Apr 1944

Displacement, tons	1 430 standard; 2 415 full load
Length, feet (*metres*)	298·0 (*90·8*) wl; 304·0 (*92·7*) oa
Beam, feet (*metres*)	37·5 (*11·4*)
Draught, feet (*metres*)	12·0 (*3·7*); 13·7 (*4·2*)
Guns	3—3 in (*76 mm*) single; 4—40 mm (2 twin); 6—20 mm; 4—0·5 in (*12·7 mm*) MG (2 twin)
Main engines	Triple expansion; 2 shafts; 5 500 ihp
Speed, knots	19 (designed)
Boilers	2 of three-drum type
Oil fuel, tons	760
Range, miles	9 500 at 12 knots
Complement	140

Formerly United States patrol frigates, PF of the "Tacoma" class similar to the contempory British frigates of the "River" class. Transferred from the US Navy to the Dominican Republic Navy in 1949. Renamed in 1962.

Probably soon to be paid off.

GREGORIO LUPERON *1972, Dominican Navy*

1 Ex-CANADIAN "RIVER" CLASS

MELLA (ex-*Presidente Trujillo*, ex-HMS *Carlplace*) 451

Displacement, tons	1 400 standard; 2 125 full load
Length, feet (*metres*)	301·5 (*91·9*)
Beam, feet (*metres*)	36·7 (*11·2*)
Draught, feet (*metres*)	12·0 (*3·7*) mean
Guns	1—4 in; 2—47 mm; 1—40 mm; 4—20 mm (2 twin)
Main engines	Triple expansion; 2 shafts; 5 500 ihp
Speed, knots	20
Boilers	2 of three-drum type
Oil fuel, tons	645
Range, miles	4 200 at 12 knots
Complement	195 (15 officers, 130 ratings, 50 midshipmen)

MELLA *1972, Dominican Navy*

Built by Davies SB & Repairing Co, Lauzon, Canada. Launched on 6 July 1944. Completed on 13 Dec 1944. Transferred to the Dominican Navy in 1946. Modified for use as Presidential Yacht with extra accommodation and deck-houses built up aft. Pennant number as a frigate was F 101, but as the Presidential Yacht it was no longer worn. Now carries pennant number 451 as training ship. Renamed *Mella* in 1962. Used for training midshipmen.

CORVETTES

2 Ex-CANADIAN "FLOWER" CLASS

Name	Pennant No.	Builders	Launched	Completed
CRISTOBAL COLON (ex-HMCS *Lachute*)	401 (ex-C 101)	Morton Ltd, Quebec City, P.Q.	9 June 1944	24 Oct 1944
JUAN ALEJANDRO ACOSTA (ex-HMCS *Louisbourg*)	402 (ex-C 102)	Morton Ltd, Quebec City, P.Q.	13 July 1943	13 Dec 1943

Displacement, tons	1 060 standard; 1 350 full load
Length, feet (*metres*)	193·0 (*58·8*) pp; 208·0 (*63·4*) oa
Beam, feet (*metres*)	33·0 (*10·0*)
Draught, feet (*metres*)	13·3 (*4·0*) mean
Guns, surface	1—4 in (*102 mm*)
Guns, AA	*C. Colon:* 2—40 mm (twin) 6—20 mm; 4—0·5 in MG (2 twin) *J. A. Acosta*: 1—40 mm; 6—20 mm; 2—0·5 in MG
Main engines	Triple expansion; 2 750 ihp
Speed, knots	16
Boilers	2 of three-drum type
Oil fuel, tons	282
Range, miles	2 900 at 15 knots
Complement	53

Built in Canadian shipyards under the emergency construction programme during the Second World War. Transferred to the Dominican Navy in 1947. Pennant numbers were changed in 1968, 300 being added to all numbers and letter C suppressed.

JUAN ALEJANDRO ACOSTA *1972, Dominican Navy*

LIGHT FORCES

3 Ex-USCG WPC TYPE (LARGE PATROL CRAFT)

	Pennant No.	Launched
INDEPENDENCIA (ex-USCGC *Icarus*)	204 (ex-P 105)	1931
LIBERTAD (ex-*Rafael Atoa*, ex-USCGC *Thetis*)	205 (ex-P 106)	1931
RESTAURACION (ex-USCGC *Galathea*)	203 (ex-P 104)	1932

Displacement, tons	337 standard
Dimensions, feet	165·0 × 26·2 × 9·5
Guns	1—3 in; 1—40 mm AA; 1—20 mm AA
Main engines	2 Diesels; 1 280 bhp = 15 knots
Range, miles	1 300 at 15 knots
Complement	49 (5 officers, 44 men)

Ex-US Coastguard Cutters. *Independencia* was completed by Bath Iron Works in 1932, and *Restauracion* by John H. Machis & Co, Camden, NJ, in 1933.

RESTAURACION *1972, Dominican Navy*

1 US PGM TYPE (LARGE PATROL CRAFT)

BETELGEUSE (ex-US *PGM* 77) GC 102

Displacement, tons	145·5
Dimensions, feet	101·5 × 21·0 × 5·0
Guns	1—40 mm; 4—20 mm AA (2 twin); 2—0·5 in 50 cal MG
Main engines	4 diesels; 2 shafts; 2 200 bhp = 2. knots
Range, miles	1 500 at 10 knots
Complement	20

Built in the USA and transferred to the Dominican Republic under the Military Aid Programme. Completed in 1966 by Peterson Builders. Transferred on 14 Jan 1966.

BETELGEUSE *1972, Dominican Navy*

2 "ATLANTIDA" CLASS (COASTAL PATROL CRAFT)

PUERTO HEMOSA LA 7 **ATLANTIDA** LA 8

4 "BELLATRIX" CLASS (COASTAL PATROL CRAFT)

BELLATRIX GC 106 **CAPELLA** GC 108 **PROCYON** GC 103

+ 1

Displacement, tons	60
Dimensions, feet	85 × 18 × 5
Guns	3—·5 mg
Main engines	2 GM Diesels; 500 bhp = 18·7 knots

Built by Sewart Seacraft Inc. at Berwick, Louisiana. Transferred to the Dominican Navy by USA, *Bellatrix* on 18 Aug 1967, *Procyon* on 1 May 1967 and *Capella* on 15 Oct 1968. Fourth of class delivered May 1972.

BELLATRIX *1970, Dominican Navy*

CAPITAN ALSINA GC 105 (ex-RL 101) (LARGE PATROL CRAFT)

Displacement, tons	100 standard
Dimensions, feet	92·0 wl; 104·8 oa × 19·2 × 5·8
Guns	2—20 mm AA
Main engines	2 GM diesels; 2 shafts; 1 000 hp = 17 knots
Complement	20

Of wooden construction. Launched in 1944. Named as above in 1957.

CAPITAN ALSINA

RIGEL GC 101 (ex-US AVR) (COASTAL PATROL CRAFT)

Displacement, tons	27 standard; 32·2 full load
Dimensions, feet	63·0 × 15·5 × 5·0
Guns	2—50 cal MG
Main engines	General Motors V8—71 diesels = 18·5 knots
Complement	9

Originally built in 1953. Reconditioned by NAUSTA, Keywest, USA.

MINESWEEPERS (OCEAN)

2 Ex-US MSF TYPE

SEPARACION (ex-USS *Skirmish*, MSF 303) BM 454 **TORTUGERO** (ex-USS *Signet*, MSF 302) BM 455

Displacement, tons	650 standard; 900 full load
Dimensions, feet	180·0 wl; 184·5 oa × 33·0 × 14·5
Guns	1—3 in; 2—40 mm AA; 6—20 mm AA
Main engines	2 diesels; 2 shafts; 1 710 bhp = 14 knots
Range, miles	5 600 at 9 knots
Complement	90 (8 officers, 82 men)

Former US fleet minesweepers of the "Admirable" class. Purchased on 13 Jan 1965.

SEPARACION *1972, Dominican Navy*

AMPHIBIOUS FORCES

1 Ex-US LSM

SIRIO (ex-USS *LSM* 483) 301 (ex-BA 104)

Displacement, tons	734 standard; 1 100 full load
Dimensions, feet	196 wl; 203·5 oa × 34 × 10 mean
Main engines	2 General Motors diesels; 2 shafts; 1 800 bhp = 14 knots
Oil fuel, tons	164
Complement	30

Ex-United States *LSM* (Medium Landing Ship). Built by Brown Shipbuilding Co, Houston, Texas. Laid down on 17 Feb 1945, launched on 10 Mar 1945 and completed on 13 April 1945. Transferred to the Dominican Navy in 1960. Refitted in Dominican Republic in 1970.

SIRIO *1968, Dominican Navy*

2 LCUs

ENRIQUILLO (ex-*17 de Julio*) 303 (ex-LA 3) **SAMANA** 302 (ex-LA 2)

Displacement, tons	150 standard; 310 full load
Dimensions, feet	105 wl; 119·5 oa × 36 × 3 mean
Guns	1 AA, 50 cal
Main engines	3 General Motors diesels; 441 bhp = 8 knots
Oil fuel, tons	80
Complement	17

Both built by Astilleros Navales Dominicanos in 1957-58. The new *Samana*, LA 2, replaced the *Samana* LA 2 lost in bad weather. *Enriquilla* (ex-17 *de Julio*) was launched on 24 Oct 1957. Renamed in 1962.

SAMANA *1972, Dominican Navy*

SURVEY VESSELS

CAPOTILLO (ex-*Camillia*) (ex-FB 101) 1

Displacement, tons	337
Dimensions, feet	117 × 24 × 7·8
Main engines	2 Diesels; 880 bhp = 10 knots
Complement	29

Built in the United States in 1911. Acquired from the United States Coast Guard in 1949. Underwent a major refit in Dominican Republic in 1970.

Survey Vessels—*continued*

CAONABO LA 5

Displacement, tons	12
Dimensions, feet	53 × 9 × 4
Main engines	2 motors; 500 hp = 14 knots
Complement	6

Acquired for the Hydrographic Service of the Navy in 1960.

CADNABO *1971*

OILERS

2 Ex-US YO TYPE

CAPITAN W ARVELO BT 4 (ex-USS *YO 215*) **CAPITAN BEOTEGUI** BT 5 (ex-US *YO 213*)

Displacement, tons	370 light; 1 400 full load
Dimensions, feet	174·0 × 32·0 × 13·0
Guns	1—20 mm
Main engines	1 Fairbanks-Morse diesel; 525 bhp = 8 knots max
Capacity	6 570 barrels
Complement	27

Former United States self-propelled fuel oil barges. Both built by Ira S. Bushey & Sons, Inc, Brooklyn, New York. Loaned by the USA in Mar 1964.

TUGS

1 Ex-US "APACHE" CLASS

MACORIX RM 21 (ex-USS *Kiowa* ATF 72)

Displacement, tons	1 235 standard; 1 675 full load
Dimensions, feet	195 wl; 205 oa × 38·5 × 15·5
Gun	1—3 in 50 cal LA
Main engines	Diesel-electric; 1 shaft; 3 000 bhp = 15 knots
Complement	85

Built in USA—launched 5 Nov 1942. Carries additional salvage equipment. Transferred 16 Oct 1972.

MACORIX *1970, USN*

1 Ex-US "MARICOPA" CLASS

CAOMABO RM 18 (ex-USS *Sagamore* ATA 208)

Displacement, tons	534 standard; 835 full load
Dimensions, feet	143 oa × 33·9 × 13
Guns	1—3 in 50 cal
Main engines	2 GM diesel-electric; 1 shaft; 1 500 bhp = 13 knots

Transferred 1 Feb 1972.

2 "HERCULES" CLASS

HERCULES RP 12 (ex-R 2) **GUACANAGARIX** RP 13 (ex-R 5)

Displacement, tons	200 (approx)
Dimensions, feet	70·0 × 15·6 × 9·0
Main engines	1 Caterpillar motor; 500 hp; 1 225 rpm
Complement	8 to 11

Small tugs of coastal type built by Astilleros Navalis Dominicos in 1960.

BOHECHIO RP 16 **CONSUELO** RP 18 **HAINA** RP 17
CALDERAS RP 19 **MAGUANA** RP 14 (ex-R 10) **SANTANA** RP 15 (ex-R 7)
+1 ex-US YTL **ISABELA** PR 20 (ex-R 1)

Small tugs for harbour and coastal use. Not all of uniform type and dimensions.

ECUADOR

Administration

Minister of Defence:
Senor Luis Robles Plaza

Commander-in-Chief of the Navy:
Rear Admiral Reinaldo Vallejo Vivas

Diplomatic Representation

Naval Attaché in London:
Vacant

Naval Attaché in Washington:
Commander M. Valviviezo

Strength of the Fleet

Type	Active	Building
Frigates	3	—
Corvettes	2	—
Fast Attack Craft (Patrol)	3	3
Large Patrol Craft	2	—
Coastal Patrol Craft	6	—
LSM's	2	—
Survey Ship	1	—
Tugs	3	—
Supply Ship (Small)	1	—
Auxiliary Dock	1	—
Miscellaneous	3	—

New Construction

The Ecuadorian Navy, after considering the purchase of two "Whitby" class frigates from UK is now investigating new construction frigates.

Disposals

Frigates
1972 *Guayas*

Prefix to ships Names

The names of Ecuadorian naval vessels are prefaced by "BAE".

Establishments

The Naval Academy is in Salinas

Naval Bases

Guayaquil, Salinas, San Lorenzo and Galapagos

Personnel

(a) 1974: Total 3 800 (300 officers and 3 500 men)
(b) Two years selective National Service

Mercantile Marine

Lloyd's Register of Shipping:
23 vessels of 75 975 tons gross

FRIGATES

1 Ex-US APD TYPE

25 DE JULIO D 1 (ex-E 12) (ex-*Enright*, APD 66, ex-DE 216)

Displacement, tons	1 400 standard; 2 130 full load
Dimensions, feet	306·0 oa × 37·0 × 12·6
Guns	1—5 in 38 cal; 4—40 mm
A/S weapons	DC racks
Boilers	2 "D" Express
Main engines	GE geared tubines with electric drive; 2 shafts; 12 000 shp = 23 knots
Range, miles	2 000 at 23 knots
Complement	204

Former US high speed transport (modified destroyer escort). Built by the Navy Yard, Philadelphia, Pa. Laid down on 22 Feb 1943, launched on 29 May 1943 and completed on 21 Sep 1943. Transferred to Ecuador on 14 July 1967 under MAP. Could carry 162 troops.

25 DE JULIO *1968, Ecuadorian Navy*

2 Ex-BRITISH "HUNT" CLASS (TYPE 1)

Name	Pennant No.	Builders	Laid down	Launched	Completed
PRESIDENTE ALFARO (ex-HMS *Quantock*)	D 2 (ex-D 01)	Scotts' S.B. & Eng Co Ltd, Greenock	26 July 1939	22 Apr 1940	6 Feb 1941
PRESIDENTE VELASCO IBARRA (ex-HMS *Meynell*)	D 3 (ex-D 02)	Swan Hunter & Wigham Richardson, Wallsend	10 Aug 1939	7 June 1940	30 Dec 1940

Displacement, tons	1 000 standard; 1 490 full load
Length, feet (*metres*)	272·3 (*83·0*) pp; 280 (*85·4*) oa
Beam, feet (*metres*)	29 (*8·8*)
Draught, feet (*metres*)	14 (*4·3*)
Guns, surface	4—4 in (*102 mm*)
Guns, AA	2—20 mm
A/S weapons	DC throwers, DC racks
Boilers	2 Admiralty 3-drum
Main engines	Parsons geared turbines (by Wallsend Slipway in *Presidente Velasco Ibarra*) 19 000 shp; 2 shafts
Speed, knots	23
Range, miles	2 000 at 12 knots; 800 at 25 knots
Oil fuel (tons)	280
Complement	146

PRESIDENTE ALFARO *1970, Ecuadorian Navy*

Former British frigates (ex-escort destroyers) of the "Hunt" class, Type 1, purchased by Ecuador from Great Britain on 18 Oct 1954, and refitted by J. Samuel White & Co. Ltd. Cowes, Isle of Wight. *Quantock* was taken over by the Ecuadorian Navy in Portsmouth Dockyard on 16 Aug 1955, when she was renamed *Presidente Alfaro*. Sister ship *Meynell* was transferred to the Ecuadorian Navy and renamed *Presidente Velasco Ibarra* in Aug 1955.

CORVETTES

2 Ex-US PCE TYPE

ESMERALDAS P 21 (ex-E 22, ex-E 03) (ex-USS *Eunice*, PCE 846)
MANABI P 22 (ex-E 23, ex-E 02) (ex-USS *Pascagoula*, PCE 874)

Displacement, tons	640 standard; 903 full load
Dimensions, feet	180 wl; 184·5 oa × 33 × 9·5
Guns	1—3 in dual purpose; 6—40 mm AA
A/S weapons	4 DCT; 2 DC Racks
Main engines	GM diesels; 2 shafts; 1 800 bhp = 15·4 knots
Range, miles	4 300 at 10 knots
Complement	100 officers and men

Former United States patrol vessels (180 ft Escorts) completed on 4 Mar 1944 and 31 Dec 1943 respectively and transferred from the US Navy to the Ecuadorian Navy on 29 Nov amd 5 Dec 1960.

MANABI *1972, Ecuadorian Navy*

LIGHT FORCES

3 + 3 "MANTA" CLASS (FAST ATTACK CRAFT—PATROL)

MANTA LT 91 **TENA** LT 93 **TULCAN** LT 92

Displacement, tons	119 standard; 134 full load
Dimensions, feet	119·4 × 19·1 × 6·6
Guns	1—40 mm AA; 1—20 mm AA
Torpedo tubes	2—21 inch
Machinery	Diesels; 3 shafts; 9 000 bhp = 35 knots
Range, miles	700 at 30 knots; 1 500 at 15 knots
Complement	19

Built by Lürssen Werft, Bremen 1970-71. 3 Further boats of this class are under construction.

MANTA *1972, Ecuadorian Navy*

2 Ex-US PGM TYPE (LARGE PATROL CRAFT)

GUAYAQUIL (ex-US *PGM* 76) LC 62 (ex-LC 72)
QUITO (ex-US *PGM* 75) LC 61 (ex-LC 71)

Displacement, tons	130 standard; 147 full load
Dimensions, feet	101 oa × 21 × 6
Guns	1—40 mm AA; 2—20 mm
Main engines	4 diesels; 2 shafts; 2 200 bhp = 21 knots
Range, miles	1 500 at cruising speed
Complement	15

US built. Transferred to the Ecuadorian Navy under MAP on 30 Nov 1965.

GUAYAQUIL *1967, Ecuadorian Navy*

6 ML TYPE (COASTAL PATROL CRAFT)

LSP 1 **LSP 2** **LSP 3** **LSP 4** **LSP 5** **LSP 6**

Displacement, tons	45 standard; 64 full load
Dimensions, feet	76·8 × 13·5 × 4·2 mean (6·3 max)
Guns	Light MG AA
Main engines	Bohn & Kähler diesel; 2 shafts; 1 200 bhp = 22 knots
Range, miles	550 at 16 knots
Complement	9

Built by Hermann Havighorst, Bremen-Blumenthal. Ordered in 1954. First two were delivered in Aug 1954 and the remainder in 1955. Pennant Nos. LP 81 to LP 86.

LSP 6 *1963, Ecuadorian Navy*

SURVEY SHIP

ORION (ex-USS *Mulberry*, AN 27) 101

Displacement, tons	560 standard; 805 full load
Dimensions, feet	146 wl; 163 oa × 30·5 × 11·8 max
Guns	1—3 in AA
Main engines	Diesel-electric; 800 bhp = 13 knots
Complement	35

Former United States netlayer. Built by Commercial Iron Works, Portland, Oregon. Launched on 26 Mar 1941. Loaned by US under MAP. Transferred to Ecuador in Nov 1965.

AMPHIBIOUS SHIPS

JAMBELI (ex-USS *LSM* 539) T 31 **TARQUI** (ex-USS *LSM* 555) T 32

Displacement, tons	743 beaching; 1 095 full load
Dimensions, feet	196·5 wl; 203·0 oa × 34·0 × 10
Guns	2—40 mm AA
Range, miles	2 500 at 12 knots
Main engines	Diesels; 2 shafts; 2 800 bhp = 12·5 knots

Amphibious Ships—*continued*

Former US Landing Ships. Medium. *Jambeli* was laid down by Brown S.B. Co, Houston, on 10 May 1945.,*Tarqui* was laid down by the Navy Yard, Charleston, SC on 3 Mar 1945 and launched on 22 Mar 1945. Purchased from USA in 1958 and transferred to the Ecuadorian Navy at Green Cove Springs, Florida in Nov 1958. Crew 60.

JAMBELI *1967, Ecuadorian Navy*

TUGS

CAYAMBE (ex-*Lois Rios*, ex-USS *Cusabo, ATF* 155) R 101 (ex-R 51, ex-R 01)

Displacement, tons	1 235 standard; 1 675 full load
Dimensions, feet	195 wl; 205 oa × 38·5 × 15·5 max
Guns	1—3 in; 4—40 mm AA; 2—20 mm AA
Main engines	4 diesels with electric drive; 3 000 bhp = 16·5 knots
Complement	85

Former US "Apache" class fleet ocean tug. Launched on 26 Feb 1945. Fitted with powerful pumps and other salvage equipment. Transferred to Ecuador by lease on 2 Nov 1960 and renamed *Los Rios*. Again renamed *Cayambe* in 1966.

CAYAMBE *1970, Ecuadorian Navy*

SANGAY (ex-*Loja*) R 102 (ex-R 52)

Displacement, tons	295 light; 390 full load
Dimensions, feet	107 × 26 × 14
Main engines	Fairbanks Morse diesel; speed = 12 knots

Built in 1952. Acquired by the Ecuadorian Navy in 1964. Renamed in 1966.

COTOPAXI (ex-*R. T. Ellis*) R 103 (ex-R 53)

Displacement, tons	150
Dimensions, feet	82 × 21 × 8
Main engines	Diesel; 1 shaft; 650 bhp = 9 knots

Former US tug. Built by Equitable Building Co, Incorp. Purchased from the United States in 1947.

MISCELLANEOUS

CALICUCHIMA (ex-US *FS* 525) T 34 (ex-T 42) (SUPPLY SHIP).

Displacement, tons	650 light; 950 full load
Dimensions, feet	176 × 32 × 14 max
Main engines	Diesels; 2 shafts; 500 bhp = 11 knots

Former United States small cargo ship of the Army FS type. Leased to Ecuador on 8 Apr 1963 and purchased in April 1969. Provides service to the Galapagos Islands.

2 Ex-USN YP

ISLA DE LA PLATA UT 111 **ISLA DE PUNA** UT 112

Transferred 1962. Coastguard utility boats.

PUTU MAYO BT 62 (ex-USN YR 34)

Repair barge leased July 1962.

ATAHUALPA (ex-US *YW* 131) T 33 (ex-T 41, ex-A 01) (WATER BOAT)

Displacement, tons	415 light; 1 235 full load
Dimensions, feet	174·0 × 32·0 × 15·0
Main engines	GM diesels; 750 bhp = 11·5 knots

Built by Leatham D. Smith SB Co, Sturgeon Bay in 1945. Transferred from USA in Mar 1963. Acquired by the Ecuadorian Navy on 2 May 1963.

AMAZONAS (ex-US *ARD* 17) (AUXILIARY DOCK)

Measurement, tons	3 500 lifting capacity
Dimensions, feet	491·7 oa × 81·0 oa × 32·9 max

Former United States auxiliary floating dock. Built in 1943-44. Transferred on loan on 7 Jan 1961. Suitable for docking destroyers and landing ships. Dry dock companion craft YFND 20 was leased on 2 Nov 1961.

Note. 1 40 ft CGB transferred by USA 1971.

EGYPT

Administration

Commander Naval Forces:
Commodore Fuad Zekry

Diplomatic Representation

Assistant Defence Attaché in London:
Colonel (Navy) Mohammed Abdel Meguid Azab

Personnel

(a) 1974: 15 000 officers and men, including the Coast Guard
(b) 3 years National Service

Strength of the Fleet

Type	*Active*	*Building*
Destroyers	5	—
Frigates	3	—
Corvettes	12	—
Submarines (patrol)	12	—
Fast Attack Craft (Missile)	12	—
Fast Attack Craft (Torpedo)	36	—
LCU's	14	—
Minesweepers (Ocean)	10	—
Minesweepers (Inshore)	2	—
Training Ships	2	—
Tugs	4	—

Bases

Alexandria, Port Said, Mersa Matru and Berenice (Ras Banas) on the Red Sea

Mercantile Marine

Lloyd's Register of Shipping

137 vessels of 268 747 tons gross

DESTROYERS

4 Ex-USSR "SKORY" CLASS

AL NASSER
AL ZAFFER
DAMIETTE
SUEZ

Displacement, tons	2 600 standard; 3 500 full load
Length, feet (*metres*)	395·2 (*120·5*)
Beam, feet (*metres*)	38·7 (*11·8*)
Draught, feet (*metres*)	15·1 (*4·6*)
Guns, surface	4—5·1 in (*130 mm*) 50 cal. 2—3·4 in (*88 mm*); 8—37 mm (unmodified); 4—57 mm (quad); 4—37 mm (twins) (modified)
A/S weapons	4 DCT (unmodified) 2—12 barrelled MBU 2500A (Modified)
Torpedo tubes	10—21 in (*533 mm*) in two mounts (unmodified); 1 mounting with 5 tubes (modified)
Mines	80 can be carried
Boilers	3
Main engines	Geared turbines; 2 shafts; 60 000 shp
Speed, knots	35
Range, miles	4 000 at 15 knots
Complement	260

SKORY 1966

Former Skory class destroyers of the Soviet Navy. Launched in 1951. *Al Nasser* and *Al Zaffer* were delivered to the Egyptian Navy on 11 June 1956 at Alexandria. Two more were delivered at Alexandria in Jan 1962. In April 1967 one pair was exchanged for ships with modified secondary and A/S armament.

RADAR. Search: Probably S Band. Tactical: Probably C Band. Fire Control: Hawkscreech.

1 Ex-BRITISH "Z" CLASS

Name	*Builders*	*Laid down*	*Launched*	*Completed*
EL FATEH (ex-HMS *Zenith*)	Wm. Denny & Bros Dumbarton	19 May 1942	5 June 1944	22 Dec 1944

EL FATEH (ex-HMS *Zenith*)

Displacement, tons	1 730 standard; 2 575 full load
Length, feet (*metres*)	350 (*106·8*) wl; 362·8 (*110·6*) oa
Beam, feet (*metres*)	35·7 (*10·9*)
Draught, feet (*metres*)	17·1 (*5·2*) max
Guns, dual purpose	4—4·5 in (*115 mm*)
Guns, AA	6—40 mm
A/S weapons	4 DCT
Boilers	2 Admiralty 3-drum
Main engines	Parsons geared turbines; 2 shafts; 40 000 shp
Speed, knots	36·75 designed; 31·25 sea
Radius, miles	2 800 at 20 knots
Oil fuel, tons	580
Complement	250

GENERAL
Purchased from Great Britain in 1955. Before being taken over by Egypt, *El Fateh* was refitted by John I. Thornycroft & Co Ltd, Woolston, Southampton in July 1956, subsequently modernised by J. S. White & Co Ltd, Cowes completing July 1964.

RADAR. Search: Type 960 Metric wavelength. Tactical: Type 293. S Band. Fire Control: X Band.

EL FATEH

FRIGATES

1 EX-BRITISH "BLACK SWAN" CLASS

Name	*No.*	*Builders*	*Laid down*	*Launched*	*Completed*
TARIK (ex-*Malek Farouq*, ex-HMS *Whimbrel*)	42	Yarrow & Co Ltd, Glasgow	31 Oct 1941	25 Aug 1942	13 Jan 1943

Displacement, tons	1 490 standard; 1 925 full load
Length, feet (*metres*)	283 (*86·3*) pp; 299·5 (*91·3*) oa
Beam, feet (*metres*)	38·5 (*11·7*)
Draught, feet (*metres*)	14·0 (*4·3*) max
Guns, surface	6—4 in (*102 mm*)
Guns, AA	4—40 mm; 2—20 mm
A/S weapons	4 DCT
Boilers	2 three-drum type
Main engines	Geared turbines; 2 shafts; 4 300 shp
Speed, knots	19·75 designed; 18 sea
Range, miles	4 500 at 12 knots
Oil fuel, tons	370
Complement	180

Transferred from Great Britain in Nov 1949. As flotilla leader she had a broad band painted on her funnel and a thinner flotilla band.

TARIK

MINEWARFARE FORCES

6 Ex-USSR "T 43" CLASS (MINESWEEPERS—OCEAN)

ASSIUT
BAHAIRA
CHARKIEH
DAKHALIA
GHARBIA
SINAI

Displacement, tons	500 standard; 610 full load
Dimensions, feet	190·2 × 28·2 × 6·9 (*58·0 × 8·6 × 2·1*)
Gun	4—37 mm; 4—25 mm
Main engines	2 diesels; 2 shafts; 2 000 hp = 17 knots
Range, miles	1 600 at 10 knots
Complement	40

Three were transferred from the Soviet Navy and delivered to Egypt 1956-59, and three since 1970. *Miniya* was sunk by Israeli air attack in the Gulf of Suez on 6 Feb 1970 but was later replaced.

T 43 *Class*

4 Ex-USSR "YURKA" CLASS (MINESWEEPERS—OCEAN)

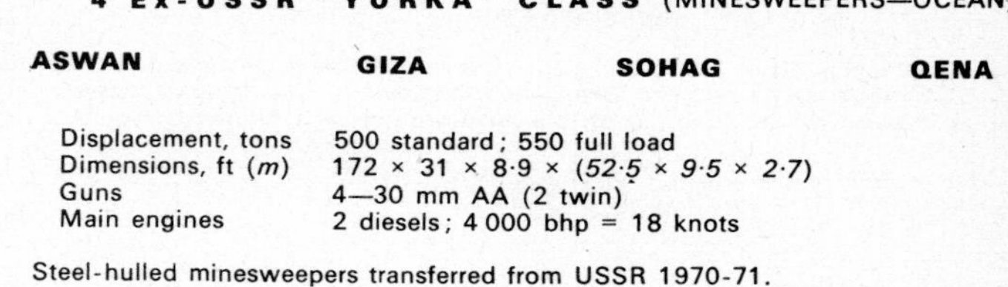

ASWAN **GIZA** **SOHAG** **QENA**

Displacement, tons	500 standard; 550 full load
Dimensions, ft (*m*)	172 × 31 × 8·9 × (*52·5 × 9·5 × 2·7*)
Guns	4—30 mm AA (2 twin)
Main engines	2 diesels; 4 000 bhp = 18 knots

Steel-hulled minesweepers transferred from USSR 1970-71.

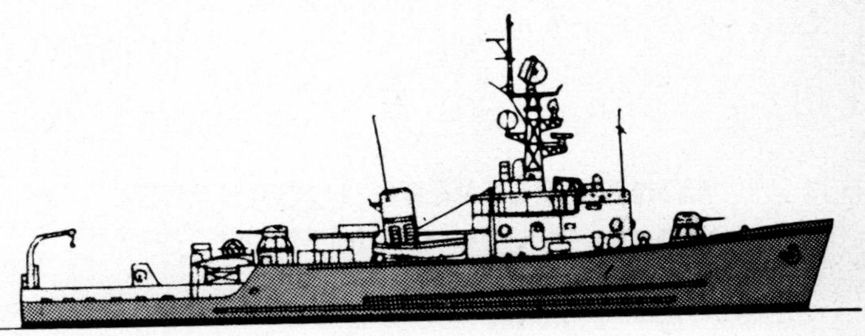

YURKA *USSR*

2 Ex-USSR "T 301" CLASS (MINESWEEPERS—INSHORE)

Displacement, tons	130 standard; 180 full load
Dimensions, ft (*m*)	124·6 × 19·7 × 4·9 (*39 × 5·5 × 1·5*)
Guns	2—37 mm; 2—MG
Main engines	2 Diesels; 2 shafts; 1 440 hp = 17 knots
Range, miles	2 200 at 10 knots
Complement	30

Reported to have been transferred by the USSR to Egypt in 1962; a third ship may have been transferred later.

MISCELLANEOUS

1 Ex-BRITISH "BANGOR" CLASS

A number of Soviet fleet tugs was reported transferred to the Egyptian Navy in 1966

4 Ex-USSR "OKHTENSKY" CLASS TUGS

NASR (ex-HMS *Bude*)

Displacement, tons	672 standard; 900 full load
Dimensions, feet	180·0 oa × 28·5 × 9·5
Guns	1—4 in; 1—3 in; 2—40 mm AA
A/S weapons	2 DCT
Main engines	Triple expansion; 2 shafts; 2 400 ihp = 16 knots (designed) sea speed 14 knots
Boilers	2 Admiralty 3-drum type
Oil fuel, tons	170
Range, miles	4 300 at 10 knots
Complement	60

Former "Bangor" class fleet minesweeper acquired from Great Britain. Built by Lobnitz & Co, Ltd, Renfrew. Laid down on 2 April 1940, launched on 4 Sep 1940 and completed on 12 Dec 1941, now virtually a hulk.

1 Ex-BRITISH "FLOWER" CLASS

EL SUDAN (ex-*Mallow*, ex-*Partizanka*, ex-*Nada*)

Displacement, tons	1 060 standard; 1 340 full load
Length, feet (*metres*)	190 (*57·9*) pp; 205 (*62·5*) oa
Beam, feet (*metres*)	33 (*10·0*)
Draught, feet (*metres*)	14·5 (*4·4*) max
Gun, surface	1—4 in (*102 mm*)
Guns, AA	2—20 mm
Boilers	2 SE
Main engines	Triple expansion; 2 750 shp
Speed, knots	16
Range, miles	7 000 at 10 knots
Oil fuel (tons)	230
Complement	85

Former "Flower" class corvette of the British Navy. Taken over by Yugoslavia in 1943 (loaned). Returned to the British Navy early in 1949 and transferred to Egypt on 28 Oct 1949. Now used for training with little sea-going potential.

EL SALVADOR

Personnel

130 officers and men

Mercantile Marine

Lloyds Register of Shipping: 10 vessels of 1 506 tons gross

PATROL BOATS

GC 1 (ex-*Fle-Ja-Lis*) **GC 2** (ex-*Nohaba*)

Displacement, tons	46
Dimensions, feet	72 oa × 16 × 5·5
Guns	1—20 mm
Main engines	2 diesels; 2 shafts; speed = 12 knots
Complement	16

Former British HDML type. Purchased from commercial sources in 1959.

GC 3 **GC 4**

Displacement, tons	14

USCG 40 ft type built in 1950.

GC 5

Displacement, tons	33
Dimensions, ft (*m*)	65 × 16·3 × 5·0 (*19·8 × 4·9 × 1·5*)
Guns	3 MG
Main engines	GM Diesels; 1 600 hp = 25 knots

Built by Sewart, USA in 1967. Transferred Sept 1967.

ETHIOPIA

Administration

The Imperial Ethiopian Navy, founded in 1955, is one of the three Services under the Ministry of National Defence. The Commander-in-Chief is His Imperial Majesty. The Deputy Commander-in-Chief has his Naval Headquarters in Addis Ababa.

Deputy Commander-in-Chief of the Imperial Ethiopian Navy:
Rear Admiral H.I.H. Prince Alexander Desta

Chief of Staff:
Colonel Taye Telahun

Naval Officer in Charge, "Haile Selassie I" Naval Base, Massawa:
Captain P. W. Stewart, RN(Retd)

Naval Establishments

"Haile Selassie I" Massawa: Naval Base and College, established in 1956.
Embaticalla: Marine Commando Training School.
Assab: Naval Base, expanding to include a ship repair facility.

Personnel

1974: 1 380 officers and men

Mercantile Marine

Lloyd's Register of shipping: 25 vessels of 48 903 tons gross

MINESWEEPERS (COASTAL)

1 Ex-NETHERLANDS "WILDERVANK" CLASS

MS 41 (ex-*Elst*, M 829)

Displacement, tons	373 standard; 417 full load
Dimensions, feet	149·8 oa × 28·0 × 7·5
Guns	2—40 mm AA
Main engines	2 diesels; 2 shafts; 2 500 bhp = 14 knots
Oil fuel, tons	25 tons
Radius, miles	2 500 at 10 knots
Complement	38

Western Union type minesweeper of the "Wildervank" class built in the Netherlands in 1954-56. Purchased by Ethiopia and transferred from the Royal Netherlands Navy in 1971.

MS 41 *1972*

TRAINING SHIP

ETHIOPIA (ex-USS *Orca*, AVP 49) A 01

Displacement, tons	1 766 standard; 2 800 full load
Dimensions, feet	300 wl; 310·8 oa × 41 × 13·5 max
Guns	1—5 in 38 cal; 5—40 mm AA
Main engines	2—sets diesels; 2 shafts; 6 080 bhp = 18·2 knots
Complement	215

Former United States seaplane tender. Built by Lake Washington Shipyard, Houghton Wash. Laid down 13 July 1942, launched on 4 Oct 1942 and completed on 23 Jan, 1944. Transferred from the US Navy in Jan 1962.

ETHIOPIA *1972, Imperial Ethiopian Navy*

LIGHT FORCES

5 PGM TYPE (LARGE PATROL CRAFT)

PC 11 (ex-USCG *WVP* 95304) **PC 13** (ex-USN *PGM* 53)
PC 12 (ex-USCG *WVP* 95310) **PC 14** (ex-USN *PGM* 54)
PC 15 (ex-USN *PGM* 58)

Displacement, tons	145·5 full load
Dimensions, feet	101·5 × 21 × 5
Guns	1—40 mm AA; 1—50 cal MG
Main engines	4 diesels; 2 shafts; 2 200 bhp = 21 knots
Range, miles	1 500 at cruising speed
Complement	20

PC 12 *1970, Imperial Ethiopian Navy*

4 "CAROLINE" CLASS (COASTAL PATROL CRAFT)

CAROLINE GB 22 **JOHN** GB 21
JACQUELINE GB 24 **PATRICK** GB 23

Length, feet	40
Guns	2—·50 calibre machine guns
Speed, knots	20 approx
Complement	7

Built by Seward Seacraft Inc, Berwick, La. *Caroline* and *John* were delivered in 1966, *Jacqueline* and *Patrick* in 1967. Their complement is 3 officers and 4 ratings or 2 officers and 5 ratings.

JOHN *1970, Imperial Ethiopian Navy*

LANDING CRAFT

There are 4 of the US LCM type.

LC 34 *1972, Imperial Ethiopian Navy*

FINLAND

Administration

Commander-in-Chief Finnish Navy:
Vice-Admiral J. K. Pirhonen

Diplomatic Representation

Naval Attaché in London:
Captain Erik Wihtol

Naval Attaché in Washington:
Colonel T. O. Lehti

Naval Attache in Moscow:
Colonel Henrik Anttila

Naval Attaché in Paris:
Lieutenant-Colonel Erkki Palmujoki

Personnel

(a) 1972: 2 000 (150 officers and 1 850 ratings)
1973: 2 500 (200 officers and 2 300 ratings)
1974: 2 500 (200 officers and 2 300 ratings)
(b) 9 months National Service

Strength of the Fleet

Type	*Active*	*Building*
Frigates	2	—
Corvettes	2	—
Fast Attack Craft (Missile)	1	—
Fast Attack Craft (Gun)	15	—
Large Patrol Craft	4	—
Transports (LCUs)	11	—
Tugs	6	—
Cable Ship	1	—
Icebreakers	8	2
Coastguard Vessels	14	—

Disposals

COASTGUARD VESSELS

1970 VMV 11, 13, 19 and 20
1971 Aura

Treaty Limitations

The Finnish Navy is limited by the treaty of Paris 1947 to 10 000 tons of ships and 4 500 personnel. Submarines and motor torpedo boats are prohibited.

Hydrographic Department

This office and the Survey Ships come under the Ministry of Trade and Industry.

Coast Guard

All Coast Guard Vessels come under the Ministry of the Interior.

Icebreakers

All these ships work for the Board of Navigation.

Mercantile Marine

Lloyd's Register of Shipping:
390 vessels of 1 545 626 tons gross

ICEBREAKERS

FRIGATES

2 "UUSIMAA" CLASS

HÄMEENMAA **UUSIMAA**

Displacement, tons	1 200 standard; 1 600 full load
Length, feet (*metres*)	298·8 (*91*)
Beam, feet (*metres*)	33·7 (*10·2*)
Draught, feet (*metres*)	11 (*3·4*)
Guns	3—3·9 in (*100 mm*) dp single; 2—40 mm; 2—30 mm (twin)
A/S weapons	1 Hedgehog; 4 DC projectors
Torpedo tubes	3—21 in (*533 mm*)
Mines	50 (capacity)
Main engines	Geared turbines; 2 shafts; 25 000 shp
Speed, knots	28
Boilers	2
Range, miles	2 500 at 15 knots
Complement	150

UUSIMAA *1972, Finnish Navy*

Former Soviet frigates of the "Riga" class. Purchased from the USSR and transferred to the Finnish Navy on 28 Apr 1964 and 12 May 1964, respectively. Armament modified in 1971.

RADAR. Search: Slimnet. Fire Control: Wasphead, Sun Visor A. Navigation: Neptun. IFF: High Pole A.

MATTI KURKI (ex-HMS *Porlock Bay*, ex-*Loch Seaforth*, ex-*Loch Muick*)

Displacement, tons	1 580 standard; 2 420 full load
Length, feet (*metres*)	286·0 (*87·2*) pp; 307·5 (*93·7*) oa
Beam, feet (*metres*)	38·5 (*11·7*)
Draught, feet (*metres*)	15·2 (*4·6*)
Guns	4—4 in (*102 mm*); 2 twin; 6—40 mm AA (2 twin, 2 single)
Main engines	Triple expansion; 2 shafts; 5 500 ihp
Speed, knots	18
Boilers	2 Admiralty 3-drum
Range, miles	9 500 at 12 knots
Oil fuel, tons	724
Complement	160

Former British frigate of the "Bay" class. Built by Charles Hill & Sons, Bristol. Laid down on 22 Nov 1944, launched on 14 June 1945 and completed on 8 Mar 1946. Transferred in Mar 1962. Employed as a training ship (*Koululaiva*).

RADAR. Search and Tactical. Type 293.

MATTI KURKI *1972, Wright & Logan*

CORVETTES

2 "TURUNMAA" CLASS

KARJALA **TURUNMAA**

Displacement, tons	660 standard; 770 full load
Dimensions, ft (*m*)	243·1 × 25·6 × 7·9 (*74·1 × 7·8 × 2·4*)
Guns	1—4·7 in (*120 mm*) automatic dp forward; 2—40 mm AA; 2—30 mm AA (1 twin) aft
A/S weapons	Depth charge projectors
Main engines	CODOG (combined diesel or gas turbine). 3 Mercedes-Benz diesels; 3 990 bhp; 1 Rolls Royce Olympus gas turbine; 22 000 hp = 35 knots
Complement	70

Ordered on 23 Feb 1956 from Wärtsilä-yhtymä Oy Shipyard, Helsinki. Flush-decked. Rocket flare guide rails on sides of 4·7 in turret. Fitted with Vosper Thornycroft fin stabilisers equipment. *Karjala* was launched on 16 Aug 1967 and completed on 21 Oct 1968. *Turunmaa* was launched on 11 July 1967 and completed on 29 Aug 1968.

RADAR. Search and Tactical: X Band. (HSA).

KARJALA *1971, Finnish Navy*

LIGHT FORCES

ISKU (FAST ATTACK CRAFT—MISSILE)

Displacement, tons	115
Dimensions, feet	86·5 × 28·6 × 6·6
Missile launchers	4 SSN-2 system launchers
Guns	2—30 mm (1 twin)
Main engines	4 diesels; 4 800 bhp = 25 knots

Guided missile craft of novel design completed for the Finnish Navy in 1970. Built at the Reposaaron Konepaja. The construction combines a missile boat armament on a landing craft hull. The missile launchers are of similar type to Soviet SSN-2 system.

ISKU *1972, Finnish Navy*

13 "NUOLI" CLASS (FAST ATTACK CRAFT—GUN)

Displacement, tons	45 standard; 64 full load
Dimensions, ft (*m*)	72·2 × 21·7 × 5·0 (*22 × 6·6 × 1·5*)
Guns	1—40 mm; 1—20 mm
A/S weapons	DCs
Main engines	3 diesels; 2 700 bhp = 40 knots
Complement	15

Designed and built by Laivateollisuus, Turku. First four were launched in 1961, five more in 1962, and two more in 1963. Fitted with X Band radar.

NUOLI 13 *1968, Finnish Navy*

2 "VASAMA" CLASS (FAST ATTACK CRAFT—GUN)

VASAMA 1 **VASAMA 2**

Displacement, tons	50 standard; 70 full load
Dimensions, ft (*m*)	67·0 pp; 71·5 oa × 19·5 × 6·0 (*21·8 oa × 5·9 × 1·8*)
Guns	2—40 mm
Main engines	2 Napier Deltic diesels; 5 000 bhp = 42 knots
Complement	20

British "Dark" type built by Saunders Roe (Anglesey) Ltd, Beaumaris, in 1955-57.

VASAMA 2 *1970, Finnish Navy*

VALPAS (LARGE PATROL CRAFT)

Displacement, tons	540
Dimensions, ft (*m*)	159·1 × 27·9 × 12·5 (*48·5 × 8·5 × 3·8*)
Main engines	Diesel; 1 800 bhp = 15 knots

Completed in 1971.

VALPAS *1971, Finnish Navy*

SILMÄ (LARGE PATROL CRAFT)

Displacement, tons	500
Dimensions, ft (*m*)	160·8 × 27·2 × 11·8 (*49 × 8·3 × 3·6*)
Main engines	1 800 bhp = 15 knots

Coast Guard vessel built by Laivateollisuus, Turku, in 1962-63.

SILMÄ *1964, Finnish Navy*

UISKO (LARGE PATROL CRAFT)

Displacement, tons	400
Dimensions, ft (*m*)	141 × 24 × 12·8 (*43 × 7·3 × 3·9*)
Main engines	1 800 bhp = 15 knots

Coast Guard vessel built by Valmet, Helsinki. Launched in 1958. Completed in 1959.

UISKO *Finnish Navy*

TURSAS (LARGE PATROL CRAFT)

Displacement, tons	400
Dimensions, ft (*m*)	131·2 × 23·5 × 14 (*40 × 7·2 × 4·3*)
Guns	1—3 in; 1—40 mm AA; 2—20 mm AA
Main engines	Diesel; 620 bhp = 12 knots

Built by Crichton-Vulkan, Turku. Launched in 1933. Belongs to the Coast Guard.

TURSAS *1968, Finnish Navy*

Light Forces—*continued*

VIIMA

Displacement, tons	135
Dimensions, feet	118·1 × 21·7 × 7·5
Gun	1—20 mm AA
Main engines	3 diesels; 4 050 bhp = 24 knots

Coast Guard patrol boat built by Laivateollisuus, Turku, Finland in 1964.

VIIMA *1971, Finnish Navy*

8 "KOSKELO" CLASS

KAAKKURI **KIILSA** **KOSKELO** **KUOVI** **TELKKA** **KUIKKA** **KURKI** **TAVI**

Displacement, tons	75 standard; 97 full load
Dimensions, feet	95·1 × 16·4 × 4·9
Guns	2—20 mm AA
Main engines	2 Mercedes-Benz diesels; 2 shafts; 1 000 bhp = 16 knots
Complement	8

Built of steel and strengthened against ice, *Koskelo* and *Kuikka* were completed in 1956. Remaining six were completed in 1958-60.

KUIKKA *1968, Finnish Navy*

5 "R" CLASS

RAISIO (No. 4) **RÖYTTA** (No. 5) **RUISSALO** (No. 3)

Displacement, tons	110 standard; 130 full load
Dimensions, feet	108·3 × 18·0 × 5·9
Guns	1—40 mm; 1—20 mm
A/S weapons	1 Squid mortar
Main engines	2 Mercedes-Benz diesels; 2 500 bhp = 17 knots

Built by Laivateollisuus, Turku, in 1959.

RUISSALO *1969, Finnish Navy*

RIHTNIEMI (No. 1) **RYMÄTTYLÄ** (No. 2)

Displacement, tons	90 standard; 110 full load
Dimensions, feet	101·7 × 18·7 × 5·9
Guns	1—40 mm; 1—20 mm
Main engines	2 Mercedes-Benz diesels; 1 400 bhp = 15 knots

Built by Rauma-Repela Shipyard. Ordered in July 1955, launched in 1956 and delivered on 20 May 1957. Controllable pitch propellers.

Light Forces—*continued*

RIHTNIEMI *1968, Finnish Navy*

MINE WARFARE SHIPS

KEIHÄSSALMI

Displacement, tons	360
Dimensions, feet	168 × 23 × 6
Guns	2—40 mm AA; 4—30 mm (twins)
Mines	Up to 100 capacity
Main engines	2 Wärtsilä diesels; 2 shafts; 2 000 bhp = 15 knots
Complement	60

Of improved "Ruotsinsalmi" type, built at Valmet, Helsinki under contract dated June 1955. Launched on 16 Mar 1957. Armament modified in 1972. X Band Search and Tactical radar.

KEIHASSALMI *1972, Finnish Navy*

RUOTSINSALMI

Displacement, tons	310
Dimensions, feet	150 × 23 × 5
Guns	2—40 mm AA; 2—20 mm AA
Mines	Up to 100 capacity
Main engines	2 MAN diesels; 2 shafts; 1 200 bhp = 15 knots
Complement	60

Built by Crichton-Vulcan, Turku. Laid down in 1937. Launched in May 1940. Completed in Feb 1941.

RUOTSINSALMI *1969, Finnish Navy*

MISCELLANEOUS

6 NEW CONSTRUCTION GRP TYPE

(MINESWEEPERS—INSHORE)

Displacement, tons	c. 90
Dimensions, ft (*m*)	84 × 23 (*25·6 × 7*)
Guns	1/2—20 mm
Main engines	2 Diesels; 600 shp
Complement	15

Building in Finland for completion 1974-75.

KORSHOLM (HQ SHIP)

Displacement, tons	650
Dimensions, feet	160·8 × 27·9 × 10·8
Speed, knots	10·5

Converted merchant ship of the small passenger and cargo type. Built in 1931.

Miscellaneous—*continued*

6 "KALA" CLASS

KALA 1-6

Displacement, tons	60
Dimensions, ft (*m*)	81·8 × 26·2 × 6 (*24·9 × 8 × 1·8*)
Main engines	2 diesels; 360 bhp = 9 knots

Launched in 1956. Completed in 1959. Of LCU (utility landing craft) type.

KALA 6 — *1963, Finnish Navy.*

5 "KAVE" CLASS (SMALL TRANSPORTS)

KAVE 1-4 and 6

Displacement, tons	30
Dimensions, ft (*m*)	75·8 × 16·4 × 5·9 (*23·1 × 5 × 1·8*)
Gun	1—20 mm
Main engines	2 Diesels; 370 hp = 9 knots

LCU type. Built 1956-60.

KAVE 4 — *1961, Finnish Navy*

3 "PANSIO" CLASS (TUG TYPE)

PANSIO (1947) **PORKKALA** (1940) **PUKKIO** (1939)

Displacement, tons	162 standard
Dimensions, ft (*m*)	92·0 × 21·5 × 9·0 (*28·1 × 6·6 × 2·7*)
Guns	1—40 mm AA; 1—20 mm AA
Main engines	Diesels; 300 bhp = 9 knots

Built by Valmet, Turku. Launch dates above. Vessels of the tug type used as transports, minesweeping tenders, minelayers and patrol vessels. Can carry 20 mines.

3 "PIRTTISAARI" CLASS TUGS

PIRTTISAARI (ex-*DR* 7) **PYHTÄÄ** (ex-*DR* 2) **PURHA** (ex-*DR* 10)

Displacement, tons	106
Dimensions, ft (*m*)	69 × 20 × 8·5 (*21 × 6·1 × 2·6*)
Gun	1—20 mm
Main engines	1 diesel; 400 bhp = 9 knots

Former US Army Tugs. Launched in 1943-44. General purpose vessels used as minesweepers, minelayers, patrol vessels, tenders, tugs or personnel transports. *DR 2* and *DR 7*, were adapted as the Coast Artillery transports *Pyhtää* and *Pirttisaari* in 1958 and 1959, respectively.

PIRTTISAARI — *1970, Finnish Navy.*

PUTSAARI (CABLE SHIP)

Displacement, tons	430
Dimensions, ft (*m*)	147·6 × 38·5 × 9·8 (*44·8 × 11·7 × 3*)
Main engines	Diesel; 450 bhp = 10 knots

Built by Rauma-Repola, Rauma. Launched in Dec 1965.

ICEBREAKERS

2 NEW CONSTRUCTION

URHO + 1

Displacement, tons	7 800
Dimensions, ft (*m*)	337·8 × 77·1 × 24·6 (*103 × 23·5 × 7·5*)
Aircraft	1 helicopter
Main engines	Diesel-electric; 5 diesels 20 000 bhp = 17 knots
Complement	57

The first icebreaker of new construction considerably larger then the "Tarmo" class icebreaker was ordered on 11 Dec 1970. She is scheduled to be completed in January 1975. The second was ordered on 14 April 1971 for completion in Jan 1976. Fitted with two screws aft, taking 60%of available power and one forward, taking the remainder. Both from the Wärtsilä company.

3 "TARMO" CLASS

TARMO **VARMA** **APU**

Displacement, tons	4 890
Dimensions, ft (*m*)	281·0 × 71·0 × 21·0 (*85·7 × 21·7 × 6·4*)
Aircraft	1 helicopter
Main engines	Wärtsilä-Sulzer diesels; electric drive; 4 shafts (2 screws forward 2 screws aft); 12 000 bhp = 17 knots

Built by Wärtsilä, Helsinki. *Tarmo* was completed in 1963, *Varma* in 1968 (launched 29 Mar) and *Apu* on 25 Nov 1970.

TARMO — *1968, Finnish Navy*

3 "KARHU" CLASS

Displacement, tons	3 540
Dimensions, ft (*m*)	243·2 × 57 × 20 (*74·2 × 17·4 × 6·1*)
Main engines	Diesel-electric; 4 shafts; 7 500 bhp = 16 knots

Built by Wärtsilä, Helsinki. *Karhu* was launched on 22 Oct 1957, and completed at the end of 1958. *Murtaja* was launched on 23 Sep 1958. *Sampo* was completed in 1960. There is also the combined Finnish/West German owned, Finnish manned, icebreaker *HANSA*, of the "Sampo" class, completed on 25 Nov 1966, which operates off Germany in winter and off Finland otherwise.

VOIMA

Displacement, tons	4 415
Dimensions, ft (*m*)	254·8 wl; 274 oa × 63·7 × 20·3 (*77·7; 83·6 × 19·4 × 6·2*)
Main engines	Diesels with electric drive; 4 shafts; 14 000 bhp = 16·5 knots
Oil fuel (tons)	740

Built by Wärtsilä, Helsinki. Launched and completed in 1953. Built for deep-sea work. Two propellers forward and aft.

SISU

Displacement, tons	2 075
Dimensions, ft (*m*)	194·8 wl; 210·2 oa × 46·5 × 16·8 (*59·4; 64·1 × 14·2 × 5·1*)
Guns	2—3·9 in AA
Main engines	2 sets Atlas Polar Diesels with electric drive; 2 shafts and a bow propeller; 4 000 hp = 16 knots
Complement	100

Built by Wärtsilä, Helsinki. Launched on 24 Sep 1938.

COASTGUARD VESSELS

NV 1-10

10 ton craft of 20 knots built 1956-59.

VMV 11, 13, 19, 20

35 ton craft with a 20 mm gun—first pair built 1935, second pair in 1943.

FRANCE

Administration

Conseil Supérieur de la Marine:
Amiraux De Joybert and Iehlé

Vice-Amiraux d'Escadre Bourdais, Daille, Guillou and Brasseur-Kermadec

Vice-Amiraux Joire Noulens and Sanguinetti

C in C Atlantic Theatre (CECLANT) and Préfet Maritime de la Deuxième Région (PREMAR DEUX):
Vice-Amiral d'Escadre Daille

Prefet Maritime de la Première Région (PREMAR UN):
Contre-Amiral Frédéric Moreau

C in C Mediterranean Theatre (CECMED) and Préfet Maritime de la Troisième Région (PREMAR TROIS):
Vice-Amiral d'Escadre Brasseur-Kermadec

C in C French Naval Forces, Polynesia:
Vice-Amiral Claverie

Diplomatic Representation

Naval Attaché in London:
Contre-Amiral François Flohic

Naval Attaché in Washington:
Contre-Amiral Gelinet

Naval Attaché in Moscow:
Capitaine de Vaisseau Cahuac

Naval Attaché in Ottawa:
Capitaine de Frégate Sauvage

Personnel

(a) 1970: 69 300 (4 880 officers 64 420 ratings)
1971: 68 586 (4 732 officers, 63 854 ratings)
1972: 68 308 (4 604 officers, 63 704 ratings)
1973: 67 600 (4 400 officers, 63 200 ratings)
1974: 67 700 (4 500 officers, 63 200 ratings)
(personnel to be increased by 5 000 under the 15-year re-equipment plan)

(b) National Service 12 months

Mercantile Marine

Lloyd's Register of Shipping:
1 376 vessels of 8 288 773 tons gross

Strength of the Fleet

Type	*Active*	*Building or Projected*
Attack Carriers (Medium)	2	1 (Nuclear powered)
Cruisers	2	—
Destroyers	22	4
Frigates	27	12 (+? Type A 70)
Submarines (Strat Missile)	4 1 (Diesel powered)	2
Submarines (Fleet)	—	1
Submarines (Patrol)	19	4
Corvettes	25	—
Fast Attack Craft (Missile)	1	2
Large Patrol Craft	4	—
Coastal Patrol Craft	2	—
LPD	2	—
LST	5	—
LCT	13	—
LCM	14	—
Minesweepers (Ocean)	12	—
Minesweepers (Coastal)	42	—
Minehunters	5	—
Minesweepers (Inshore)	3	—
Surveying Ships	7	—
Coastal Survey Ships	4	—
Inshore Survey Craft	2	—
Tankers (UR)	4	3
Tankers (Support)	5	—
Maintenance Ships	2	—
Depot Ships	5	—
Repair Ships (ex-LCT)	5	—
Trials Ships	3	—
Boom Defence Vessels	15	—
Torpedo Recovery Vessels	2	—
Victualling Supply Ship	1	—
Store Ship	1	—
Light Transports	2	—
Small Transports	14	—
Tenders	8	—
Tugs	54	—
Miscellaneous	14	—

Submarine Service

Now known as Force Océanique Stratégique (FOST) with HQ at Houilles near Paris. SSBN (*SNLE*) force based at Ile Longue Brest with a training base at Roche-Douvres and VLF W/T station at Rosay. Patrol submarines are based at Lorient and Toulon. Plans for nuclear fleet submarines are included in the 15 year plan.

15-Year Re-equipment Plan

This programme provides for the following fleet by 1985:

2 Aircraft carriers
2 Helicopter carriers
30 Frigates or corvettes
35 Avisos
5 SSBN
20 Patrol Submarines (or Fleet)
30 Patrol craft
MHC and MSC as necessary
5 Replenishment Oilers
Logistic Support and Maintenance Ships
2 Assault Ships
Landing Ships and craft
Transports
50 LRMP aircraft
Carrier borne aircraft
Helicopters

1971-75 New Construction Plan

1 Helicopter Carrier
3 Guided Missile Destroyers ("Corvettes") "C 70" Type
3 Guided Missile Destroyers ("Corvettes") "C 67" Type
14 Escorts (officially rated as *Avisos*) "A 69" Type
3 Nuclear Powered Ballistic Missile Submarines
4 Patrol Submarines
2 Patrol Boats (for overseas service)
1 Fleet Replenishment Ship
2 Small Landing Ships (Transports)

Disposals

Sea Control Ship

1974 *Arromanches*

Cruiser

1973 *De Grasse*

Destroyer

6/1971 *Surcouf.* Forward section sank after collision—after section used for spares

Frigate

1971 *Gustave Zédé* (Command Ship)

Submarines

1970 *Eurydice*, Lost
1972 *Sirène* sank at Lorient (subsequently salved)

Survey Ship

1973 *La Coquille*

Service Forces

1972 *Lac Chambon, Lac Tchad*
1973 *Médoc*

Trials Ship

1973 *Arago*

BDV

1972 *Tarantule*

Miscellaneous

1970 6 Water Boats

NAVAL AIR ARM

NAVAL AIR ARM

Squadron Number	*Base*	*Aircraft*	*Task*
	Embarked Squadrons		
4F	Lann Bihoue	BR1050 "Alize"	Patrol & A/S
6F	Nimes Garons	BR1050 "Alize"	Patrol & A/S
11F	Landivisiau	ETD IVM	Fighter Bomber
12F	Landivisiau	F8E "Crusader"	Interceptors
14F	Landivisiau	F8E "Crusader"	Interceptors
16F	Landivisiau	ETD IV P	Reconnaissance
17F	Hyeres	ETD IV M	Fighter Bomber
31F	St. Mandrier	HSS 1	A/S
32F	Lanveoc Poulmic	Super-Frelon	A/S
33F	St. Mandrier	HSS 1	Assault
J. d'Arc	J. d'Arc or St. Mandries	HSS 1	Training
SRL	Landivisiau	MS 760 Paris	Support
	Support Squadrons		
2S	Lann Bihoue	Navajo, Nord 262	Support 1st & 2nd Region
3S	Hyeres	Navajo, Nord 262	Support 3rd Region
10S	St. Raphael	Nord 2504, BR1050 Navajo MS 733	Trials CEPA
20S	St. Raphael	AL 11, AL 111 AL 111 ASM HSSI Super Frelon	Trials CEPA
22S	Lanveoc Poulmic	AL 11, AL 111 AL 111 VSV	Support 2nd Region SAR
23S	St. Mandrier	AL11 AL111	Support 3rd Region SAR
SSD	Dugny	C 54, Nord 262 Navajo	Support

Squadron Number	*Base*	*Aircraft*	*Task*
	Maritime Patrol Squadrons		
21F	Nimes Garons	BR 1150 "Atlantic"	MP
22F	Nimes Garons	BR 1150 "Atlantic"	MP
23F	Lann Bihoue	BR 1150 "Atlantic"	MP
24F	Lann Bihoue	BR 1150 "Atlantic"	MP
25F	Lann Bihoue	Neptune P2H	MP
	Training Squadrons		
55S	Aspretto	Nord 262, SNB 5	Twin-engine conversion
56S	Nimes Garons	C 47	Flying School
59S	Hyeres	ET IV, BR 1050 CM 175 "Zephyr"	Fighter School
SVS	Lanveoc Poulmic	MS 733	Naval School Recreational
Esalat Dax	Dax	AL 11	Helicopter School
	Overseas Detachments		
New Caledonia	Tontouta	C 54, C 47	Support and Liaison
Malagasy	Diego Suarez	C 47	Support and Liaison
	CEP Formations		
Sectal Pac.	Hao	AL 111	Support
27S	Hao	Super-Frelon	Support
12S	Papeete	Neptune P2H	MP

PENNANT NUMBERS

R Aircraft and Helicopter Carriers

97 Jeanne d'Arc
98 Clemenceau
99 Foch

S Submarines

610 Le Foudroyant
611 Le Redoutable
612 Le Terrible
613 L'Indomptable
614 Le Tonnant
631 Narval
632 Marsouin
633 Dauphin
634 Requin
635 Aréthuse
636 Argonaute
637 Espadon
638 Morse
639 Amazone
640 Ariane
641 Daphné
642 Diane
643 Doris
645 Flore
646 Galatée
648 Junon
649 Venus
650 Psyche
651 Sirène
655 Gymnote

C Cruiser

611 Colbert

D Missile Leaders and Destroyers

602 Suffren
603 Duquesne
609 Aconit
610 Tourville
611 Duguay-Trouin
612 De Grasse
622 Kersaint
623 Cassard
624 Bouvet
625 Dupetit Thouars
626 Chevalier Paul
627 Maillé Brézé
628 Vauquelin
629 D'Estrées
630 Du Chayla
631 Casablanca
632 Guépratte
633 Duperré
634 La Bourdonnais
635 Forbin
636 Tartu
637 Jauréguiberry
638 La Galissonnière
710 Georges Leygues
711 Dupleix
712 Montcalm

F Frigates, Escorts and Corvettes

725 Victor Schoelcher
726 Commandant Bory
727 Amiral Charner
728 Doudart de La Grée
729 Balny
733 Commandant Rivière
740 Commandant Bourdais
748 Protet
749 Enseigne Henry
761 Le Corse
762 Le Brestois
763 Le Boulonnais
764 Le Bordelais
765 Le Normand
766 Le Picard
767 Le Gascon
768 Le Lorrain
769 Le Bourguignon
770 Le Champenois
771 Le Savoyard
772 Le Breton
773 Le Basque
774 L'Agenais
775 Le Béarnais
776 L'Alsacien
777 Le Provençal
778 Le Vendéen

M Coastal and Inshore Minesweepers

609 Narvik
610 Ouistreham
612 Alençon
613 Bernéval
615 Cantho
616 Dompaire
617 Garigliano
618 Mytho
619 Vinh-long
620 Berlaimont
621 Origny
622 Autun
623 Baccarat
624 Colmar
632 Pervenche
633 Pivoine
635 Résèda
638 Acacia
639 Acanthe
640 Marjolaine
668 Azalée
669 Bégonia
670 Bleuet
671 Camélia
672 Chrysanthème
674 Cyclamen
675 Eglantine
677 Giroflée
678 Glaieul
679 Glycine
680 Jacinthe
681 Laurier
682 Lilas
683 Liseron
684 Lobelia
685 Magnolia
687 Mimosa
688 Muguet
691 ex-SC 525
703 Antares
704 Algol
707 Véga
710 Pégase
712 Cybele
713 Calliope
714 Clio
715 Circe
716 Ceres
737 Capricorne
740 Cassiopée
741 Eridan
743 Sagittaire
747 Bételgeuse
749 Phénix
750 Bellatrix
751 Dénébola
755 Capella
756 Céphée
757 Verseau
758 Aries
759 Lyre
765 Mercure
773 Violette
784 Géranium
787 Jonquille

P Patrol Vessels, Coastal Escorts

630 L'Intrépide
635 L'Ardent
637 L'Etourdi
638 L'Effronté
639 Le Frondeur
640 Le Fringant
641 Le Fougueux
642 L'Opiniatre
643 L'Agile
644 L'Adroit
645 L'Alerte
646 L'Attentif
647 L'Enjoué
648 Le Hardi
650 Arcturus
651 La Malouine
652 La Lorientaise
653 La Dunkerquoise
654 La Bayonnaise
655 La Dieppoise
656 Altair
657 La Paimpolaise
658 Croix du Sud
659 Canopus
660 Etoile Polaire
661 Jasmin
662 Petunia
730 La Combattante
752 VC2
753 VC3

L Landing Ships

9003 Argens
9004 Bidassoa
9007 Trieux
9008 Dives
9009 Blavet
9021 Ouragan
9022 Orage
9061 LCT
9070 LCT
9071 LCT
9072 LCT
9073 LCT
9074 LCT
9081 Workshop
9082 Workshop
9083 Workshop
9084 Workshop
9091 LCT
9092 LCT
9093 LCT
9094 LCT
9095 LCT
9096 LCT
9097 Issole
9099 LCT

(CTM LCMs 1-14)

A Auxiliaries and Support Ships

603 Henry Poincaré
608 Moselle
610 Ile d'Oléron
614 Falleron
615 Loire
617 Garonne
618 Rance
619 Aber Wrach
620 Jules Verne
621 Rhin
622 Rhône
625 Papenoo
626 La Charente
627 La Seine
628 La Sâone
629 La Durance
630 Lac Tonlé Sap
632 Punaruu
637 Maurienne
638 Sahel
643 Aunis
644 Berry
646 Triton
648 Archimède
649 Etoile
650 La Belle Poule
652 Mutin
653 La Grande Hermine
660 Hippopotame
661 Infatigable
665 Goliath
666 Eléphant
667 Hercule
668 Rhinocéros
669 Tenace
670 Implacable
671 Le Fort
672 Utile
673 Lutteur
674 Centaure
675 Isère
682 Alidade
683 Octant
684 Coolie
685 Robuste
686 Actif
687 Laborieux
688 Valeureux
692 Travailleur
698 Petrel
699 Pelican
701 Aionc
706 Courageux
710 Myosotis
711 Gardénia
716 Oiseau des Iles

A Auxiliaries—*continued*

718 Pachyderme
719 Bélier
724 Belouga
727 Araignée
728 Scorpion
730 Libellule
731 Persistante
733 Saintonge
735 Hibiscus
736 Dahlia
737 Tulipe
738 Capucine
739 Oeillet
740 Hortensia
741 Armoise
742 Paquerette
749 La Prudente
750 La Persévérante
751 La Fidèle
753 La Découverte
755 Commandant Robert Giraud
756 Espérance
757 D'Entrecasteaux
758 La Recherche
759 Marcel Le Bihan
760 Cigale
761 Criquet
762 Fourmi
763 Grillon
764 Scarabée
765 Locuste
766 Estafette
770 Champlain
771 Francis Garnier
777 Luciole
780 L'Astrolabe
781 Boussole
785 Zelée
789 Archéonaute
791 Corail

Y

601 Acajou
604 Ariel
607 Balsa
608 Bambou
612 Bouleau
613 Faune
620 Chataigner
623 Charme
624 Chêne
628 Oukomê
629 Cormier
630 Noyer
635 Equeurdville
638 Marronier
640 Papayer
642 Paguerette
644 Frêne
652 Haut Barr
654 Hétre
655 Hévéat
661 Korrigan
662 Dryade
663 Latainer
664 Lutin
666 Manguier
668 Mélêze
669 Merisier
671 Morgane
686 Palétuvier
688 Peuplier
689 Pin
695 Platane
696 Alphée
706 Chimère
708 Saule
709 Sycomore
710 Sylphe
711 Farfadet
712 Tréberon
713 Faune
717 Ébêne
718 Erable
719 Olivier
720 Santal
735 Merlin
736 Mélusine
738 Marronier
740 Papayer
741 Elfe
743 Palangrin
760 PB
761 PB

AIRCRAFT CARRIERS

2 "CLEMENCEAU" CLASS

Displacement, tons	27 307 normal; 32 780 full load
Length, feet (*metres*)	780·8 (*238·0*)pp; 869·4 (*265·0*)oa
Beam, feet (*metres*)	104·1 (*31·7*) hull (with bulges)
Width, feet (*metres*)	168·0 (*51·2*) oa
Draught, feet (*metres*)	24·6 (*7·5*) 28·2 (*8·6*) screws
Aircraft	**Capacity 40, including jet aircraft. Each carries 3 Flights—1 of *Etendard IV*, 1 of *Crusader*, 1 of Breguet *Alizé***
Catapults	**2 Mitchell-Brown steam, Mk BS 5**
Armour	**Flight deck, island superstructure and bridges, hull (over machinery spaces and magazines)**
Guns	8—3·9 in (*100 mm*) AA automatic in single turrets
Main engines	2 sets Parsons geared turbines; 2 shafts; 126 000 shp
Speed, knots	32 max (33·4 trials); 24 sustained sea
Boilers	6; steam pressure 640 psi (*45 kg/cm²*), superheat 842°F (450°C)
Range, miles	7 500 at 18 knots; 4 800 at 24 knots; 3 500 at full power
Oil fuel, tons	3 720
Complement	2 239 (179 officers, 2 060 men)

Note. It was announced on 22 Jan 1974 that a nuclear-powered aircraft-carrier of some 18 000 tons would be laid down in 1975, to be operational in 1980. It is suggested that this ship might carry Harriers as well as helicopters.

Name	*No.*	*Builders*	*Laid down*	*Launched*	*Completed*
CLEMENCEAU	R 98	Brest	Nov 1955	21 Dec 1957	22 Nov 1961
FOCH	R 99	Chantier de L'Atlantique	Feb 1957	28 July 1960	15 July 1963

CLEMENCEAU *1972, French Navy*

GENERAL
First aircraft carriers designed as such and built from the keel to be completed in France. Authorised in 1953 and 1955, respectively. *Clemenceau* ordered from Brest Dockyard on 28 May 1954 and begun in Nov 1955. *Foch* begun at Chantiers de l'Atlantique a St. Nazaire, Penhoet-Loire, in a special dry dock (contract provided for the construction of the hull and propelling machinery) and completed by Brest Dockyard.

ELECTRONICS. Comprehensive DF and ECM equipment. Both fitted wtih SENIT 4 Tactical data automation system.

FLIGHT DECK. Angled deck incorporated, two lifts, measuring 52·5 × 36 feet, one on the starboard deck edge, two steam catapults for aircraft up to 11 tons, and two deck landing aids. The flight deck measures 543 × 96·8 feet and is angled at 8 degrees.

HANGAR. Dimensions of the hangar are 590·6 × 78·7 × 23·0 feet.

RADAR. One DRBV 20C; One DRBV 23B; Two DRBI 10; One DRBV 50; One DRBC 31.

SONAR. One SQS 505

DRAWING. Starboard elevation and plan. Scale: 118 feet = 1 inch

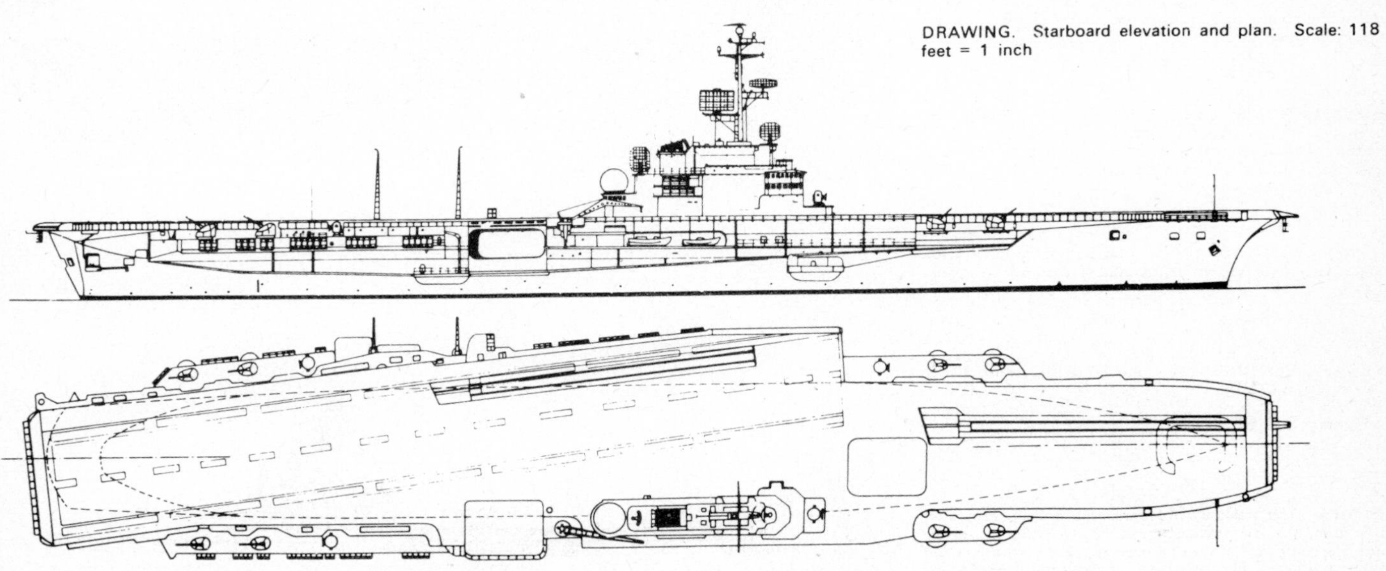

GUNNERY. Originally to have been armed with 24—2·25 inch guns in twin mountings, but the armament was revised to 12—3·9 inch (*100 mm*) in 1956 and to 8—3·9 inch (*100 mm*) in 1958. The 100 mm guns were of a new design. Rate of fire 60 rounds per minute.

BULGES. *Foch* was completed with bulges. These having proved successful, *Clemenceau* was modified similarly on first refit, increasing her beam by 6 feet.

FOCH ***1971, French Navy.***

CRUISERS

Name	No.	Builders	Ordered	Laid down	Launched	Completed
JEANNE D'ARC (ex-*La Résolue*)	R 97	Brest Dockyard	8 Mar 1957	7 July 1960	30 Sep 1961	1 July 1963 (trials) 30 June 1964 (service)

Displacement, tons	10 000 standard; 12 365 full load
Length, feet (*metres*)	564·2 (*172*) pp; 597·1 (*182·0*) oa
Beam, feet (*metres*)	78·7 (*24·0*) hull
Draught, feet (*metres*)	24·0 (*7·3*) max
Flight deck	203·4 × 68·9 (*62·0 × 21·0*)
Aircraft	Heavy A/S helicopters (4 in peacetime as training ship; 8 in wartime)
Guns	4—3·9 in (*100* mm) AA single
Main engines	Rateau-Bretagne geared turbines; 2 shafts; 40 000 shp
Speed, knots	26·5 designed
Boilers	4; working pressure 640 psi (*45 kg/cm²*); 842°F (*450°C*)
Range miles	6 000 at 15 knots
Oil fuel, tons	1 360
Complement	906 (44 officers, 670 ratings and 192 cadets)

GENERAL
Authorised under the 1957 estimates. Used for training officer cadets in peacetime in place of the old training cruiser *Jeanne d'Arc* (which was decommissioned on 28 July 1964 and sold for scrap in Dec 1965 at Brest). In wartime, after rapid modification, she would be used as a commando ship, helicopter carrier or troop transport with commando equipment and a battalion of 700 men. The lift has a capacity of 12 tons. The ship is almost entirely air-conditioned.

MODIFICATIONS. Between first steaming trials and completion for operational service the ship was modified with a taller funnel to clear the superstructure and obviate the smoke and exhaust gases swirling on to the bridges.

ELECTRONICS. The ship is almost as well equipped with electronic apparatus as the aircraft carrier *Clemenceau*.

RADAR. One DRBV 22D; one DRBV 50; one DRBN 32; one DRBI 10.

SONAR. One SQS 503.

NAMES. The name *La Résolue* was only a temporary one until the decommissioning of the training cruiser *Jeanne d'Arc* which was relieved by *La Résolue* in 1964 when the latter ship took the name *Jeanne d'Arc*, on 16 July.

JEANNE D'ARC *1972, courtesy W. A. Fuller, Esq*

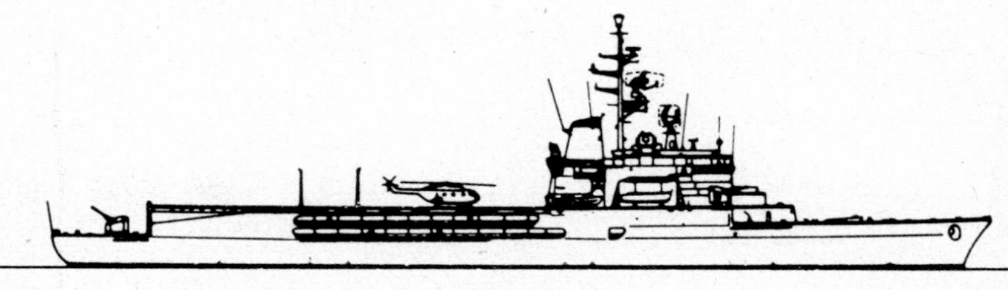

JEANNE D'ARC

JEANNE D'ARC *French Navy*

Name	Pennant No.	Builders	Laid down	Launched	Completed	Commissioned
COLBERT	C 611	Brest Dockyard	Dec 1953	24 Mar 1956 (floated out of dry dock)	1958 (trials end of 1957)	5 May 1959

Displacement, tons	8 500 standard; 11 300 full load
Length, feet (*metres*)	593·2 (*180·8*)
Beam, feet (*metres*)	64·6 (*19·7*)
Draught, feet (*metres*)	25·2 (*7·7*) screws
Missile launchers	1 twin "Masurca" surface-to-air aft
Guns	2—3·9 in (*100 mm*) single automatic; 12—57 mm in 6 twin mountings, 3 on each side
Armour	50—80 mm belt and 50 mm deck
Main engines	2 sets CEM-Parsons geared turbines; 2 shafts; 86 000 shp
Speed, knots	32; 15 economical sea
Boilers	4 Indret multitubular; 640 psi (*45 kg/cm²*); 842°F (450°C)
Range, miles	4 000 at 25 knots
Oil fuel, tons	1 492
Complement	796 (69 officers, 727 men) as Flagship after reconstruction

Provision was made in the original design for her to be fitted with guided missiles. She was equipped as command ship and for radar control of air strikes.

ELECTRONICS. Senit data automation system; Radar intercept equipment; wireless intercept equipment; two Knebworth Corvus dual-purpose launchers for CHAFF.

RECONSTRUCTION. Between April 1970 and October 1972 she underwent a complete reconstruction and rearmament. The gunnery systems were altered to those given above, the "Masurca" surface-to-air missile system was fitted and helicopter facilities were installed on the quarter-deck. Reductions in the original armament schedule saved 80 mill francs from the original refit cost of 350 mill. francs.

MISSILES. *Colbert* carries 48 Masurca missiles. Mk 2 mod 3 semi-active radar homing version.

RADAR. One Decca RM416 (navigation); one DRBV 50 (surveillance); one DRBV 23C (air surveillance); one DRBV 20 (warning); two DRBR 51 (f.c.); one DRBR 32c; two DRBC 31; one DRBI 10D (height-finder).

GUNNERY. Prior to Apr 1970 the armament comprised sixteen 5 inch (*127 mm*) dual purpose guns in eight twin mountings, and twenty 57 mm Bofors anti-aircraft guns in ten twin mountings.

SONAR. Hull mounted set.

COLBERT — *1973, French Navy*

COLBERT — *1973, French Navy*

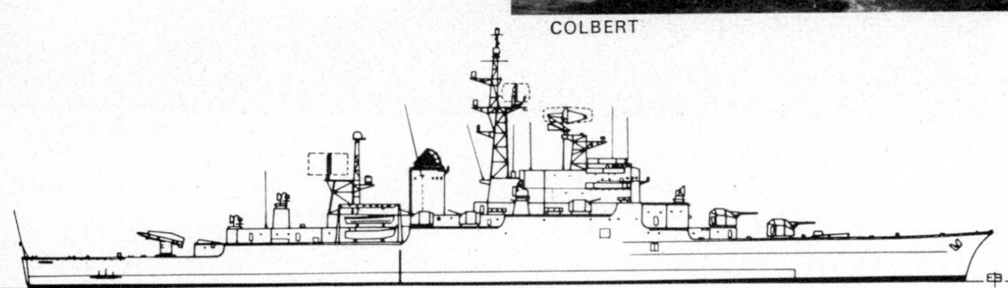

COLBERT — *1973, French Navy*

DESTROYERS

2 "SUFFREN" CLASS

Name	No.	Builders	Laid down	Launched	Trials	Operational
DUQUESNE	D 603	Brest Dockyard	Nov 1964	12 Feb 1966	July 1968	Apr 1970
SUFFREN	D 602	Lorient Dockyard	Dec 1962	15 May 1965	Dec 1965	July 1967

Displacement, tons 5 090 standard; 6 090 full load
Length, feet (*metres*) 517·1 (*157·6*) oa
Beam, feet (*metres*) 50·9 (*15·5*)
Draught, feet (*metres*) 20·0 (*6·1*)
Missile launchers Twin "Masurca" surface-air
Guns 2—3·9 in (*100 mm*) automatic, single AA; 2—30 mm (automatic, single) AA
A/S weapons "Malafon" rocket/homing torpedo single launcher 13 missiles carried
Torpedo tubes 4 (2 each side) for A/S homing torpedoes
Main engines Double reduction geared turbines; 2 shafts; 72 500 shp
Speed, knots 34
Boilers 4 automatic; working pressure 640 psi (*45 kg/cm²*); superheat 842°F (450°C)
Range, miles 5 000 at 18 knots; 2 400 at 29 knots
Complement 426 (38 officers, 388 men)

GENERAL
Ordered under the 1960 Programme. The structure provides best possible resistance to atomic blast. Equipped with gyro controlled stabilisers. Air conditioning of accommodation and operational areas.

ELECTRONICS. *Senit I* action data automatic system.

RADAR. One DRBN 32 search and navigation set; one DRBI 23 L band stacked-beam three dimensional air surveillance and target designator in radome; one DRBV 50 surface surveillance radar; two DRBR 51 Masurca fire control; one DRBC 32A fire control for forward guns

MISSILES. Carry 48 *Masurca* missiles, a mix of Mk 2 Mod 2 beam riders and Mk 2 Mod 3 semi-active homers.

SONAR. One DUBV 23 hull-mounted set and a DUBV 43 VDS.

DUQUESNE 1973 French Navy

DUQUESNE 1973, French Navy

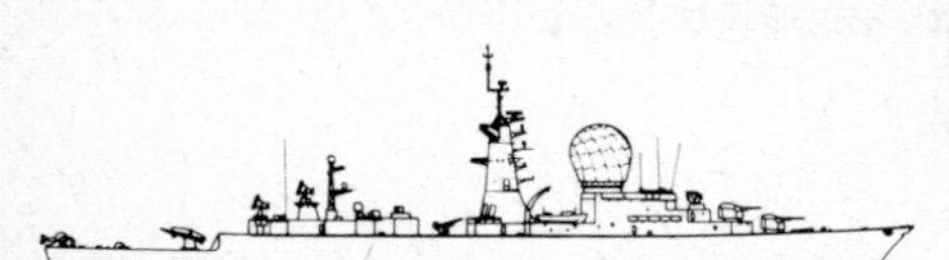

3 "GEORGES LEYGUES" CLASS (C70 TYPE)

GEORGES LEYGUES D 710
DUPLEIX D 711
MONTCALM D 712

Displacement, tons 3 800 standard; 4 100 full load
Dimensions, ft (*m*) 455·9 oa × 45·9 (*139 × 14*)
Aircraft 2 WG 13 "Lynx" helicopters with Mk L6 torpedoes & ASM
Missile launchers 4 "MM 38" ("Exocet"); Masurca in A/A version
Guns 2—3·9 in (*100 mm*)
A/S Weapons Malafon in A/S version
Torpedoes 10 tubes in 2 mountings for Mk L5
Main engines CODOG; 2 Rolls Royce Olympus gas turbines; 2 SEMT-Pielstick diesels; 2 shafts VP screws
Speed, knots 30 (19·5 on diesels)
Complement 242

A new C 70 type of so-called "corvette". Three are included in the new construction programme. *Georges Leygues* laid down June 1974 for trials in 1977 and service in 1978. *Dupleix* to be laid down in 1975 for trials in 1978 and *Montcalm* to be laid down in 1975 for trials 1979.
A total of 24 is planned for completion by 1985, half being an A/S version like *G. Leygues* and half A/A.

HELICOPTER. The Lynx, as well as its A/S role, can have an anti-surface role when armed with 4 AS 12 missiles.

SONAR. One DUBV 23 hull-mounted; one DUBV 43 VDS

Destroyers—*continued*

3 "TOURVILLE" CLASS

(F 67 TYPE ex-C-67A)

Name	*No.*	*Builders*	*Laid down*	*Launched*	*Trials*
TOURVILLE	D 610	Lorient	Mar 1970	13 May 1972	Nov 1972
DUGAY-TROUIN	D 611	Lorient	Jan 1971	1 June 1973	1974
DE GRASSE	D 612	Lorient	1972	1974	1975

Displacement, tons	4 580 standard; 5 745 full load
Length, feet (*metres*)	510·3 (*152·8*) oa
Beam, feet (*metres*)	50·2 (*15·3*)
Draught, feet (*metres*)	18·7 (*5·7*)
Aircraft	2 WG 13 Lynx ASW helicopters
Missile launchers	6 "MM 38" ("Exocet")
Guns	3—3·9 in (*100 mm*) AA
A/S Weapons	"Malafon" rocket/homing torpedo (13 missiles)
Torpedoes	2 mountings for Mk L5
Main engines	Rateau geared turbines; 2 shafts; 54 400 shp
Speed, knots	31
Boilers	4 automatic
Range, miles	5 000 at 18 knots
Complement	303 (25 officers, 278 men)

Developed from the "Aconit" design. Originally rated as "corvettes" but reclassified as "frigates" on 8 July 1971 and given "D" pennant numbers like destroyers.

RADAR. One DRBV 26; one DRBV 51; one DRBC 32D; two Decca Type 1226; Senit.

SONARS. 1 DUBV 23 hull-mounted; one DUBV 43 VDS.

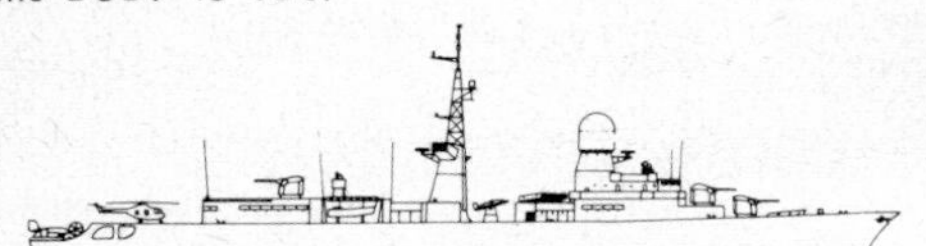

TOURVILLE 1973, *French Navy*

1 TYPE 56

Name	*Pennant No.*	*Builders*	*Laid down*	*Launched*	*Completed*
LA GALISSONNIÈRE	D 638	Lorient Naval Dockyard	Nov 1958	12 Mar 1960	July 1962

Displacement, tons	2 750 standard; 3 740 full load;
Length, feet (*metres*)	435·7 (*132·8*) oa
Beam, feet (*metres*)	41·7 (*12·7*)
Draught, feet (*metres*)	15·4 (*4·7*) aft; 18·0 (*5·5*) screws
Aircraft	1 A/S helicopter
A/S weapons	"Malafon" rocket/homing torpedoes, 1 launcher
Guns	2—3·9 in (*100 mm*) AA automatic, single
Torpedo tubes	6—21·7 in (*550 mm*) ASM, 2 triple for Mks K2 and L3
Main engines	2 sets geared turbines; 2 shafts; 63 000 shp (72 000 on trials, light)
Boilers	4 A & C de B Indret; 500 psi (*35 kg/cm²*); 617°F (*380°C*)
Speed, knots	34 (32 full load)
Range, miles	5 000 at 18 knots
Oil fuel, tons	725
Complement	333 (20 officers, 313 men)

LA GALISSONIÈRE

GENERAL
Designed as a flotilla leader. Same characteristics as regards hull and machinery as T 47 and T 53 types, but different armament. She has a hangar and a platform for landing a helicopter. When first commissioned she was used as an experimental ship for new sonars and anti-submarine weapons.

ARMAMENT. First French combatant ship to be armed with Malafon. This is the reason for the two 3·9 in (*100 mm*) guns instead of the 3 or 4 previously planned. France's first operational guided missile ship.

ELECTRONICS. Tacan beacon and full DF and ECM fit.

RADAR. One DRBN 32; one DRBV 50 search/navigation set; one DRBV 22 L-band search set; one DRBC 32A X band fire-control.

SONAR. One hull-mounted DUBV 23; one DUBV 43 VDS.

LA GALISSONNIÈRE 1972, *A. & J. Pavia*

Destroyers—*continued*

2 TYPE 47 (LEADERS)

Name	Pennant No.	Builder	Laid down	Launched	Completed
CASSARD	D 623	A. C. Bretagne	Nov 1951	12 May 1953	14 Apr 1956
CHEVALIER PAUL	D 626	F. C. Gironde	Feb 1952	28 July 1953	22 Dec 1956

Displacement, tons	2 750 standard; 3 740 full load
Length, feet (*metres*)	421·3 (*128·4*)
Beam, feet (*metres*)	41·7 (*12·7*)
Draught, feet (*metres*)	17·7 (*5·4*)
Guns	6—5 in (*127 mm*) (twins) 4—57 mm AA (twins)
Torpedoes	2 triple mountings (550 mm) for Mk K2 and L3
Main engines	2 geared turbines; 63 000 shp; 2 shafts
Speed, knots	34 (32 fully laden)
Range, miles	5 000 at 18 knots
Oil fuel, tons	800
Complement	291 (15 officers, 276 men)

TYPE 47 (Leaders)

GENERAL
Built of pre-fabricated sections, all welded. Achieved 36 knots on trials.

RADAR. One DRBV 20; one DRBV 11; one DRBV 32; one DRBC 11; one DRBC 34.

SONAR. One DUBV 1; one DUBA 1.

CASSARD (leader type) *1972, Dr. Giorgio Arra*

4 TYPE 47 (DDG)

Name	Pennant No.	Builder	Laid down	Launched	Completed
KERSAINT	D 622	Lorient	June 1951	3 Oct 1953	20 Mar 1956
BOUVET	D 624	Lorient	Nov 1951	3 Oct 1953	13 May 1956
DUPETIT THOUARS	D 625	Brest	Mar 1952	4 Mar 1954	15 Sep 1956
DU CHAYLA	D 630	Brest	July 1953	27 Nov 1954	4 June 1957

Displacement, tons	2 750 standard; 3 740 full load
Length, feet (*metres*)	421·3 (*128·4*)
Beam, feet (*metres*)	41·7 (*12·7*)
Draught, feet (*metres*)	17·7 (*5·4*)
Missiles	Single Mk 13 Tartar launcher (40 missiles—SMI or SMIA)
Guns	6—57 mm AA (twins)
Torpedoes	2 triple mountings (*550 mm*) for Mk K2 and L3
A/S weapons	375 mm Mk 54 projector
Main engines	2 geared turbines; 63 000 shp; 2 shafts
Speed, knots	34 (32 fully laden)
Range, miles	5 000 at 18 knots
Oil fuel, tons	800
Complement	278 (17 officers, 261 men)

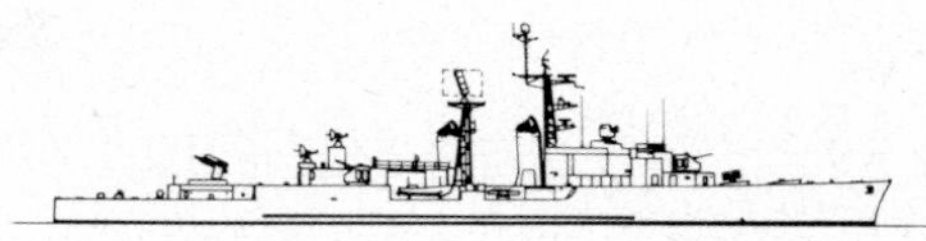

TYPE 47 (DDG)

RADAR. One DRBV 20 (search); one SPS 39A or B; one DRBV 31 (navigation); two SPG 51B (tartar control); one DRBC 31; Senit.

SONARS. One DUBA 1; one DUBV 24.

BOUVET *1972, French Navy*

Destroyers—*continued*

1 TYPE 47 (MODIFIED)

Name	Pennant No.	Builder	Laid down	Launched	Completed
DUPERRÉ	D 633	Lorient	Nov 1954	23 June 1956	8 Oct 1957

Displacement, tons: 2 800 standard; 3 900 full load
Length, feet (*metres*): 435·7 (*132·8*) oa
Beam, feet (*metres*): 41·7 (*12·7*)
Draught, feet (*metres*): 15·4 (*4·7*) aft; 18·0 (*5·5*) screws
Aircraft: 1 WG 13 Lynx helicopter
Missiles: 4 MM 38 Exocet
Gun: 1—3·9 in (*100 mm*)
Torpedo tubes: 1 mounting for Mk L5
Main engines: 2 sets geared turbines; 2 shafts; 63 000 shp (72 000 on trials; light)
Boilers: 4 A & C de B Indret; 500 psi (*35 kg/cm²*); 617°F (*380°C*)
Speed, knots: 34 (32 full load)
Range, miles: 5 000 at 18 knots
Oil fuel, tons: 725
Complement: 255 (16 officers, 239 men)

GENERAL
After serving as trial ship from 1967-71 she was converted at Brest to her present state in 1972-73.

RADAR. One DRBV 26; one DRBV 51; one DRBC 31c; Senit.

SONAR DUBV 23 hull-mounted; DUBV 43 VDS.

DUPERRE

1974 Contre Amiral M. Adam

4 TYPE 53

Name	Pennant No.	Builder	Laid down	Launched	Completed
LA BOURDONNAIS	D 634	Brest	Aug 1954	15 Oct 1955	Mar 1958
FORBIN	D 635	Brest	Aug 1954	15 Oct 1955	1 Feb 1958
TARTU	D 636	At. Chantiers de Bretagne	Nov 1954	2 Dec 1955	5 Feb 1958
JAURÉGUIBERRY	D 637	Gironde	Sept 1954	5 Nov 1955	July 1958

Displacement, tons: 2 750 standard; 3 740 full load
Length, feet (*metres*): 421·3 (*128·4*)
Beam, feet (*metres*): 41·7 (*12·7*)
Draught, feet (*metres*): 17·7 (*5·4*)
Guns: 6—5 in (*127 mm*) (twins); (*Forbin* 4—5 in); 6—57 mm (twin); 2—20 mm
Torpedoes: 2 triple mountings (*550 mm*) for Mk K2 and L3
A/S weapons: 375 mm Mk 54 projector
Main engines: 2 geared turbines; 63 000 shp; 2 shafts
Speed, knots: 34 (32 fully laden)
Range, miles: 5 000 at 18 knots
Oil fuel, tons: 800
Complement: 274 (14 officers, 260 men)

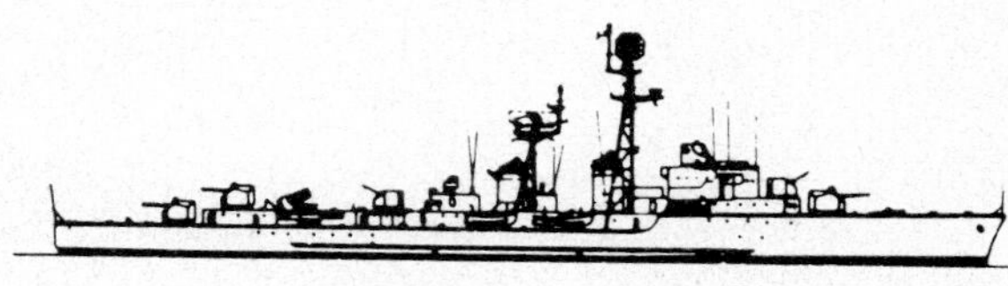
SURCOUF *Class* (Group D)

FORBIN (with helo platform)

1973, French Navy

Destroyers—*continued*

GENERAL
Air-direction ships—*Forbin* has helicopter platform aft in place of Y mount.

RADAR. One DRBV 22A (air search); one DRBI 10A; one DRBV 31; Tacan; Senit.
SONAR. One DUBA 1; one DUBV 24.

JAURÉGUIBERRY

1972, Dr. Giorgio Arra

5 TYPE 47 (ASW)

Displacement, tons	2 750 standard; 3 900 full load
Length, feet (*metres*)	434·6 (*132·5*)
Beam, feet (*metres*)	41·7 (*12·7*)
Draught, feet (*metres*)	14·4 (*4·4*)
Guns	2—3·9 in (*100 mm*) (singles); 2—20 mm
A/S weapons	1 Malafon; 1 375 mm Mk 54 projector
Torpedo tubes	Two triple mountings (*550 mm*) for Mk K2 and L3
Main engines	2 geared turbines; 63 000 shp; 2 shafts
Speed, knots	34 (32 fully laden)
Range, miles	5 000 at 18 knots
Oil fuel, tons	800
Complement	320 (21 officers, 299 men)

Name	*Pennant No.*	*Builder*	*Laid down*	*Launched*	*Completed*
MAILLE BRÉZÉ	D 627	Lorient	Oct 1953	26 Sept 1954	4 May 1957
VAUQUELIN	D 628	Lorient	Mar 1953	26 Sep 1954	3 Nov 1956
D'ESTRÉES	D 629	Brest	May 1953	27 Nov 1954	19 Mar 1957
CASABIANCA	D 631	F. C. Gironde	Oct 1953	13 Nov 1954	4 May 1957
GUÉPRATTE	D 632	A. C. Bretagne	Aug 1953	8 Nov 1954	6 June 1957

TYPE 47 (ASW)

RADAR. One DRBV 22A; one DRBV 50; one DRBN 32; two DRBC 23A; Senit.

SONARS. One DUBV 23 hull mounted; one DUBV 43 VDS.

MAILLE BRÉZÉ

1973 French Navy

1 "ACONIT" CLASS

ACONIT D 609

Displacement, tons	3 500 standard; 3 800 full load
Length, feet (*metres*)	416·7 (*127·0*) oa
Beam, feet (*metres*)	44·0 (*13·4*)
Draught, feet (*metres*)	18·9 (*5·8*) screws
Missiles, A/S	"Malafon" rocket/homing torpedo MM 38 Exocet to be fitted
Guns	2—3·9 in (*100 mm*) AA
A/S weapons	1 quadruple 12 in (*305 mm*) mortar
Torpedoes	2 launchers for Mk L5
Main engines	Rateau geared turbine; 1 shaft; 28 650 shp
Boilers	2 automatic
Speed, knots	27
Range, miles	5 000 at 18 knots
Complement	215 (15 officers, 200 men)

Rated as "Corvette". Laid down at Lorient in Jan 1966 and launched on 7 Mar 1970, commissioned 15 May 1971 for service in 1972.

RADAR. One DRBV 13 (S-band surveillance); one DRBC 32B (X-band fire control); one DRBN 32 (search/navigation set); one DRBV 32A; Senit.

SONAR. One hull-mounted DUBV 23; one VDS type DUBV 43.

ACONIT

1972, French Navy

ACONIT

FRIGATES

9 "COMMANDANT RIVIÈRE" CLASS

Displacement, tons	1 750 standard; 2 250 full load (*Balny* 1 650 standard; 1 950 full load)
Length, feet (*metres*)	321·5 (*98·0*) pp; 338 (*103*) oa
Beam, feet (*metres*)	37·8 (*11·5*)
Draught, feet (*metres*)	12·5 (*3·8*) mean; 14·1 (*4·3*) max
Aircraft	1 light helicopter can land aft
Guns, AA	3—3·9 in (*100 mm*) automatic, singles (*Balny, Henry* and *Bourdais* 2 only); 2—30 mm
A/S	1—12 in (*305 mm*) quadruple mortar
Torpedo tubes	6—21 in (*533 mm*) (triple) for Mk K2 and L3
Main engines	4 SEMT-Pielstick diesels; 16 000 bhp; 2 shafts; (except *Balny:* CODAG; 2 diesels (16 cyl); one TG Turboméca M38; 1 shaft; VP screw).
Speed, knots	25 max (26·6 trials)
Range, miles	4 500 at 15 knots (*Balny* 8 000 at 12 knots)
Complement	215 (15 officers, 200 men)

Name	*No.*	*Launched*	*Completed*
AMIRAL CHARNER	F 727	Mar 1960	Dec 1962
BALNY	F 729	Mar 1962	Feb 1971
COMMANDANT BORY	F 726	Oct 1958	Mar 1964
COMMANDANT BOURDAIS	F 740	Apr 1961	Mar 1963
COMMANDANT RIVIÈRE	F 733	Oct 1958	Dec 1962
DOUDART DE LA GRÉE	F 728	Apr 1961	Mar 1963
ENSEIGN HENRY	F 749	Dec 1963	Jan 1965
PROTET	F 748	Dec 1962	May 1964
VICTOR SCHOELCHER	F 725	Oct 1958	Dec 1962

COMMANDANT RIVIÈRE *Class*

COMMANDANT BORY — *1974 Wright and Logan*

GENERAL
All built by Lorient Dockyard. Fitted for operations under widely differing conditions. Capable of accepting a light helicopter aft. Can carry a force of up to 80 soldiers in an emergency, as well as two 30 ft LCAs. *Balny's* trials continued for several years. *Commandant Bourdais* commissioned as fishery protection ship for Newfoundland and Greenland in Mar 1963. *Commandant Bourdais* and *Enseigne Henry* had helicopter platforms rigged in place of X Gun in 1973-74. *Commandant Bory* had experimental machinery replaced by conventional diesels in 1973. *Victor Schoelcher* acts as training ship. *Com. Belo* class of Portugal is similar.

RADAR. Search: DRBV 22A. Tactical: S Band. Fire Control: X Band DRBC 32A. One DRBV 50; one DRBN 32.

SONAR. One DUBA 3; one SQS 17.

14 "LE NORMAND" CLASS

(E52 TYPE)

Displacement, tons	1 250 standard; 1 702 full load
Length, feet (*metres*)	311·7 (*95·0*) pp; 325·8 (*99·8*) oa
Beam, feet (*metres*)	33·8 (*10·3*)
Draught, feet (*metres*)	11·2 (*3·4*) aft; 13·5 (*4·1*) screws
Guns, AA	6—2·25 in (*57 mm*), in twin mountings (4 only in F 771, 772 773); 2—20 mm
A/S	Sextuple Bofors ASM (*lance-roquettes*) mortar forward (*except* F 776, 777, 778 with 1—12 in (*305 mm*) quadruple mortar) 2 DC mortars; 1 DC rack
Torpedo tubes	12 ASM (4 triple mountings aft) for Mk K2 and L3
Boilers	2 Indret; pressure 500 psi (*35·2 kg/cm²*); superheat 725°F (385°C)
Main engines	Parsons or Rateau geared turbines 20 000 shp
Speed, knots	27 (on trials they exceeded 29 kts)
Range, miles	4 500 at 15 knots
Oil fuel (tons)	310
Complement	205 (13 officers, 192 men)

Name	*No.*	*Builders*	*Laid down*	*Launched*	*Completed*
L'AGENAIS	F 774	Lorient	Aug 1955	23 June 1956	14 May 1958
L'ALSACIEN	F 776	Lorient	July 1956	26 Jan 1957	27 Aug 1960
LE BASQUE	F 773	Lorient	Dec 1954	25 Feb 1956	18 Oct 1957
LE BÉARNAIS	F 775	Lorient	Dec 1955	23 June 1956	18 Oct 1958
LE BRETON	F 772	Lorient	June 1954	2 Apr 1955	20 Aug 1957
LE BOURGUIGNON	F 769	Penhoet	Jan 1954	28 Jan 1956	11 July 1957
LE CHAMPENOIS	F 770	A. C. Loire	May 1954	12 Mar 1955	1 June 1957
LE GASCON	F 767	A. C. Loire	Feb 1954	23 Oct 1954	29 Mar 1957
LE LORRAIN	F 768	F. Ch de la Medit	July 1953	13 Feb 1954	3 Nov 1956
LE NORMAND	F 765	F. Ch. de la Medit	July 1953	13 Feb 1954	3 Nov 1956
LE PICARD	F 766	A. C. Loire	Nov 1953	31 May 1954	20 Sep 1956
LE PROVENCAL	F 777	Lorient	Feb 1957	5 Oct 1957	6 Nov 1959
LE SAVOYARD	F 771	F. Ch. de la Medit	Nov 1953	7 May 1955	14 June 1956
LE VENDÉEN	F 778	F. Ch. de la Medit	Mar 1957	27 July 1957	1 Oct 1960

L'ALSACIEN, LE PROVENCAL, LE VENDÉEN

LE NORMAND *Class*

GENERAL
The E 52 type have similar characteristics to the E 50 type as regards hull and machinery but are easily distinguished in that they have the ASM tubes aft and the heavy hedgehog or ASM howitzer forward while the E 50 type have the ASM torpedo tubes forward. *L'Agenais, L'Alsacien, Le Basque, Le Béarnais, Le Breton, Le Provencal* and *Le Vendéen* have a different arrangement of bridges. *L'Alsacien, Le Provencal* and *Le Vendéen* are of the E 52B type and have the Strombos-Velensi modified funnel cap.

RADAR. Search: DRBV 22A. Fire Control: One DRBV 32; one DRBC 31.

SONAR. One DUBV 24; one DUBA 1 (except 771, 772, 773, one DUBV 1 and one DUBA 1).

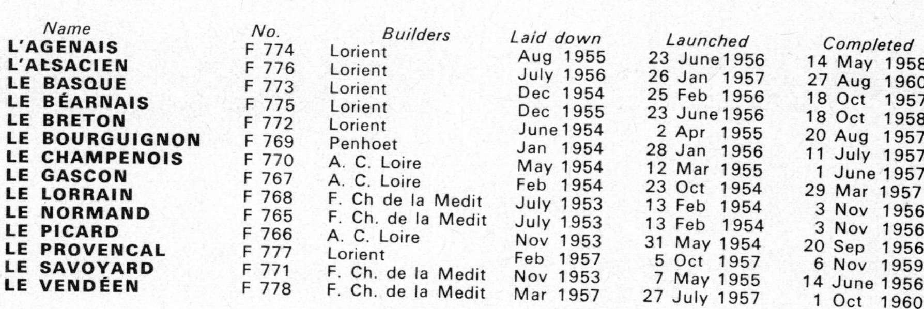

LE VENDÉEN — *1972, Dr. Giorgio Arra*

LE BÉARNAIS — *1972, Dr. Giorgio Arra*

Frigates—*continued*

4 E50 TYPE

Displacement, tons	1 250 standard; 1 528 for trials; 1 702 full load
Length, feet (*metres*)	311·7 (*95·0*) pp; 327·3 (*99·8*) oa
Beam, feet (*metres*)	33·8 (*10·3*)
Draught, feet (*metres*)	13·5 (*4·1*) screws
Guns, AA	6—2·25 in (*57 mm*) (twins); 2—20 mm
A/S weapons	1—375 mm Mk 54 rocket launcher;
Torpedo tubes	12 tubes (four triple mounts forward) for Mk K2 and L3
Main engines	2 Rateau A & C de B geared turbines; 20 000 shp; 2 shafts
Speed, knots	27 (29 on trials); economical speed 14
Range, miles	4 500 at 15 knots
Oil fuel, tons	292
Complement	205 (13 officers, 192 men)

Name	No.	Builders	Laid down	Launched	Completed
LE BORDELAIS	F 764	F. Ch. de la Medit	May 1952	11 July 1953	7 Apr 1955
LE BOULONNAIS	F 763	A. C. Loire	Mar 1952	12 May 1953	5 Aug 1955
LE BRESTOIS	F 762	Lorient Navy Yard	Nov 1951	16 Aug 1952	19 Jan 1956
LE CORSE	F 761	Lorient Navy Yard	Oct 1951	5 Aug 1952	15 Apr 1955

GENERAL
Le Bordelais has Strombos-Velensi type modified funnel cap. *Le Brestois* has similar mast arrangement to that in *Le Provencal*.

GUNNERY. *Le Brestois* had a single 3·9 in (*100 mm*) automatic AA gun mounted in place of the after twin 57 mm mounting for experimental purposes and after her refit, completed in 1963, she retained this mounting.

RADAR. Search: DRBV 20; one DRBN 32; one DRBC 31.

SONAR. One DUBV 1; one DUBA 1.

E 50 Type

LE BRESTOIS (showing 100 mm gun) — *1971, Dr. Giorgio Arra*

LE CORSE (as reactivated) — *1972, Dr. Giorgio Arra*

12 NEW CONSTRUCTION TYPE A69

Displacement, tons	950 standard; 1 170 full load
Length, feet (*metres*)	262·5 (*80·0*) oa
Beam, feet (*metres*)	33·8 (*10·3*)
Draught, feet (*metres*)	9·8 (*3·0*)
Guns	1—3·9 in (*100 mm*) AA; 2—20 mm AA
A/S weapons	1—375 mm Mk 54 Rocket launcher
Torpedoes	4 fixed tubes for Mk L3 and L5
Main engines	2 SEMT Pielstick PC2V diesels; 2 shafts; controllable pitch propellers; 11 000 bhp
Speed, knots	24 (22 with 80% power)
Range, miles	4 500 at 15 knots
Complement	62 (4 officers, 58 men)

Name	No.	Builder	Laid down	Launched	Trials	Service
D'ESTIENNE D'ORVES	F 781	Lorient	Aug 1972	1 June 1973	July 1974	July 1975
AMYOT D'INVILLE	F 782	Lorient	Sep 1973	Sep 1974	July 1975	July 1976
DROGOU	F 783	Lorient	Oct 1973	Sep 1974	Aug 1975	July 1976
DETROYAT	F 784	Lorient	1974	1975	Feb 1976	July 1977
—	F 785	Lorient	1974	1975	Mar 1976	May 1977
+7 future construction						

GENERAL
Primarily intended for coastal A/S operations—officially classified as "Avisos". Also available for overseas patrols and can carry a detachment of 2 officers and 29 men.

RADAR. One Decca type 202 navigation set; one DRBV 51 stabilised surveillance and target designator; One DRBC 32E fire control; one DRBN 32.

SONAR. One hull mounted sonar DUBA 25.

A 69 TYPE (A70 similar hull)

NEW CONSTRUCTION TYPE A70

Very similar to the type A 69, ships of this type are planned for building in the near future with Lorient acting as the lead yard. The details and remarks listed for Type A 69 apply also to Type A 70—in addition the latter will mount two MM 38 Exocet launchers with associated radar.

D'ESTIENNE D'ORVES after launching — *1973, French Navy*

SUBMARINES

5 NUCLEAR POWERED BALLISTIC MISSILE TYPE (SNLE)

Name	No.	Builders	Laid down	Launched	Completion	Operational
LE REDOUTABLE	S 611	Cherbourg Naval Dockyard	30 Mar 1964	29 Mar 1967	Trials 1969	1 Dec 1971
LE TERRIBLE	S 612	Cherbourg Naval Dockyard	24 June 1967	12 Dec 1969	Trials 1971	1 Jan 1973
LE FOUDROYANT	S 610	Cherbourg Naval Dockyard	1969	4 Dec 1971	Trials May 1973	July 1974
L'INDOMPTABLE	S 613 (Q 258)	Cherbourg Naval Dockyard	1971	Aug 1974		Dec 1975
LE TONNANT	S 614 (Q 259)	Cherbourg Naval Dockyard	1973	1975		July 1978

Displacement, tons: 7 500 surface; 9 000 dived
Length, feet (*metres*): 420 (*128·0*)
Beam, feet (*metres*): 34·8 (*10·6*)
Draught, feet (*metres*): 32·8 (*10·0*)
Missile launchers: 16 tubes amidships for "Polaris type ICBM's; range 1 400 miles
Torpedo tubes: 4—21·7 inch (18 torpedoes)
Nuclear reactor: 1 pressurised water-cooled
Main machinery: 2 turbo-alternators; 1 electric motor; 15 000 hp; 1 shaft
Auxiliary propulsion: 1 diesel
Speed, knots: 20 on surface; 25 dived
Complement: Two alternating crews each of 135 (15 officers, 120 men)

GENERAL
Le Redoutable was the first French nuclear powered, ballistic missile armed submarine and the prototype of the "*Force de dissuasion*" of five such vessels which the Navy plans to have in the late 1970s. The diesel has oil bunkerage for a range of 5 000 miles. The decision to build a fourth unit of this class was announced on 7 Dec 1967 and the fifth in Feb 1972. Diving depth over 700 feet.

MISSILES. First boats armed with MSBS M-1 of 18 tons launch weight with a range of 1 400 miles. The last three boats will have M-2 missiles (19·9 tons and 1 875 miles range). Both M-1 and M-2 have a 500 KT head. Further improvements planned include the M-20 missile (M2 with thermonuclear head) and M-4 with a range in the 3 000 mile bracket and fitted with MRV or MIRV. Both these developments are unlikely until the late 1970s.

LE REDOUTABLE *1972, French Navy*

RADAR. *Le Redoutable* is equipped with Calypso X Band radar for navigation and attack. Has passive ECM and DF systems.

REACTOR. The reactor is a natural-water-cooled type running on enriched uranium, feeding twin turbines and two turbo-alternators.

LE REDOUTABLE, LE TERRIBLE, LE FOUDROYANT

1 EXPERIMENTAL MISSILE TYPE

Name	No.	Builders	Laid down	Launched	Completed
GYMNOTE	S 655	Cherbourg Naval Dockyard	17 Mar 1963	17 Mar 1964	17 Oct 1966

Displacement, tons: 3 000 surface; 3 250 dived
Length, feet (*metres*): 275·6 (*84·0*)
Beam, feet (*metres*): 34·7 (*10·6*)
Draught, feet (*metres*): 25 (*7·6*)
Missile launchers: 4 tubes for MSBS
Main machinery: 4 sets 620 kW diesel electric; 2 electric motors; 2 shafts; 2 600 hp
Speed, knots: 11 surface; 10 dived
Complement: 78 (8 officers, 70 men)

An experimental submarine for testing ballistic missiles for the first French nuclear powered deterrent submarines, and for use as an underwater laboratory to prove equipment and arms for nuclear powered submarines.

HULL. *Gymnote* was the hull laid down in 1958 as the nuclear powered submarine Q 244 which was cancelled in 1959. The hull was still available when a trials vessel for the French "Polaris" type missiles was required and was completed as *Gymnote*.

GYMNOTE *1970, French Navy*

Submarines—*continued*

1 NEW CONSTRUCTION FLEET SUBMARINE

SNA 72
It was announced in 1973 that a nuclear-propelled fleet submarine would be included in the 1974 budget. This is to have a single reactor and one screw—studies of the machinery are in progress at Cadarache. Present plans are for a comparatively small boat of some 3 000 tons with a speed of 25 knots plus. She is due to be laid down in 1976. Two squadrons of these submarines are forecast, one to be stationed at Brest and the other at Toulon from 1982.

4 "AGOSTA" CLASS

Name	*Builder*	*Laid down*	*Launched*	*Operational*
AGOSTA	Cherbourg	7 Feb 1972	Jan 1974	April 1976
BÉVÉZIERS	Cherbourg	17 May 1973	Apr 1974	June 1976
LA PRAYA	Cherbourg	1974	Oct 1975	1976
OUESSANT	Cherbourg	1974	Jan 1976	1977

Displacement, tons: 1 200 standard; 1 450 surface; 1 725 dived
Length, feet (*metres*): 221·7 (*67·6*)
Beam, feet (*metres*): 22·3 (*6·8*)
Draught, feet (*metres*): 17·7 (*5·4*)
Tubes: 21·4 in (*550 mm*); 20 reload torpedoes
Main machinery: Diesel-electric; 2 SEMT Peilstick diesels 3 600 hp; 1 main motor 4 600 hp; 1 cruising motor; 1 shaft
Speed, knots: 12 surfaced; 20 submerged
Range, miles: 9 000 at 9 knots (snorting); 350 at 3·5 knots (dived)
Endurance: 45 days
Complement: 50 (7 officers, 43 men)

GENERAL
New type of patrol submarines of high performance, the building of which was announced in 1970 under the third five-year new construction plan 1971-75.

RADAR. Possibly X Band Calypso Th D 1030 or 1031 for search/navigation.

SONAR. DUUA 1 active sonar with transducers forward and aft; DSUV passive sonar with 36 hydrophones; passive ranging; intercept set.

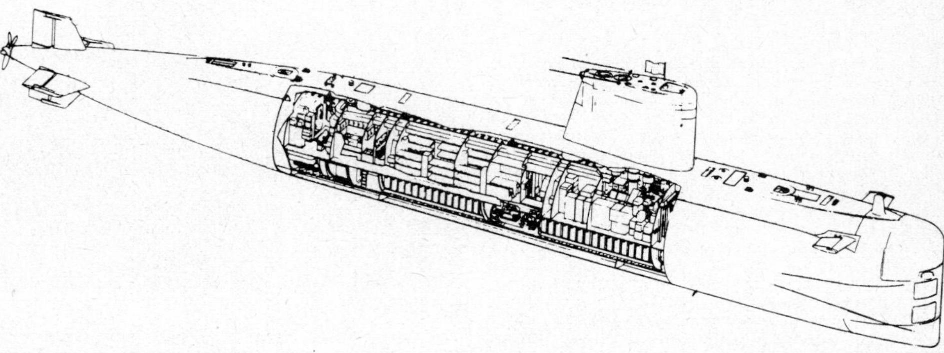

BEVEZIERS *1973, Cols Bleus*

9 "DAPHNÉ" CLASS

Name	*No.*	*Builder*	*Laid down*	*Launched*	*Completed*
DAPHNÉ	S 641	Dubigeon	Mar 1958	20 June 1959	1 June 1964
DIANE	S 642	Dubigeon	July 1958	4 Oct 1960	20 June 1964
DORIS	S 643	Cherbourg	Sep 1958	14 May 1960	26 Aug 1964
FLORE	S 645	Cherbourg	Sep 1958	21 Dec 1960	21 May 1964
GALATÉE	S 646	Cherbourg	Sep 1958	22 Sep 1961	25 July 1964
JUNON	S 648	Cherbourg	July 1961	11 May 1964	25 Feb 1966
VENUS	S 649	Cherbourg	Aug 1961	24 Sep 1964	1 Jan 1966
PSYCHÉ	S 650	Brest	May 1961	28 June 1967	July 1969
SIRÈNE	S 651	Brest	May 1961	28 June 1967	Mar 1970

Displacement, tons: 869 surface; 1 043 dived
Length, feet (*metres*): 189·6 (*57·8*)
Beam, feet (*metres*): 22·3 (*6·8*)
Draught, feet (*metres*): 15·1 (*4·6*)
Torpedo tubes: 12—21·7 in (*550 mm*) 8 bow 4 stern
Main machinery: SEMT-Pielstick diesel-electric 1 300 bhp surface; 1 600 hp motors dived; 2 shafts
Range, miles: 2 700 at 12·5 knots (surfaced); 4 500 at 5 knots (snorting); 3 000 at 7 knots (snorting)
Speed, knots: 13·5 surface; 16 dived
Complement: 45 (6 officers, 39 men)

VENUS (showing new sonar dome) *1972, Dr. Georgio Arra*

GENERAL
Improved "Arethuse" class with diving depth about 1 000 ft (*300 metres*).

MODERNISATION. In hand from 1971 to improve sonar and armament.

RADAR. X Band Calypso II for search/navigation.

SONAR. DUUA 1 active sonar with transducers forward and aft; passive ranging; intercept set.

FOREIGN ORDERS. South Africa (3), Pakistan (3), Portugal (4), Spain (building in Spain) (4).

DORIS ***1972, Dr. Giorgio Arra***

Submarines—*continued*

4 "ARÉTHUSE" CLASS

Name	No.	Programme	Builders	Laid down	Launched	Completed
AMAZONE	S 639	1954	Cherbourg	Dec 1955	3 Apr 1958	1 July 1959
ARÉTHUSE	S 635	1953	Cherbourg	Mar 1955	9 Nov 1957	23 Oct 1958
ARGONAUTE	S 636	1953	Cherbourg	Mar 1955	29 June 1957	11 Feb 1959
ARIANE	S 640	1954	Cherbourg	Dec 1955	12 Sep 1958	16 Mar 1960

Displacement, tons	400 standard; 543 surface; 669 submerged
Length, feet (*metres*)	162·7 (*49·6*)
Beam, feet (*metres*)	19 (*5·8*)
Draught, feet (*metres*)	13·1 (*4·0*)
Torpedo tubes	4—21·7 in (*550 mm*) bow, 4
Main machinery	12-cyl. SEMT-Pielstick diesel-electric; 1 060 bhp surface; 1 300 hp motors dived; 1 shaft
Speed, knots	12·5 surface; 16 dived
Complement	40 (6 officers, 34 men)

GENERAL
An excellent class of small submarines with a minimum number of ballast tanks and a diving depth of about 600 feet.

ARIANE 1972, *Dr. Giorgio Arra*

6 "NARVAL" CLASS

Name	No.	Programme	Builders	Laid down	Launched	Completed
NARVAL	S 631	1949	Cherbourg	June 1951	11 Dec 1954	1 Dec 1957
MARSOUIN	S 632	1949	Cherbourg	Sept 1951	21 May 1955	1 Oct 1957
DAUPHIN	S 633	1950	Cherbourg	May 1952	17 Sep 1955	1 Aug 1958
REQUIN	S 634	1950	Cherbourg	June 1952	3 Dec 1955	1 Aug 1958
ESPADON	S 637	1954	Normand	Dec 1955	15 Sep 1958	2 Apr 1960
MORSE	S 638	1954	Seine Maritime	Feb 1956	10 Dec 1958	2 May 1960

Displacement, tons	1 320 standard; 1 635 surface; 1 910 dived
Length, feet (*metres*)	257·2 (*77·6*)
Beam, feet (*metres*)	25·6 (*7·8*)
Draught, feet (*metres*)	18·5 (*5·4*)
Torpedo tubes	6—21·7 in (*550 mm*) bow; 14 reload torpedoes; capable of minelaying
Main machinery	Diesel electric, three 12-cyl SEMT-Pielstick diesels; two 2 400 hp electric motors; 2 shafts
Speed, knots	15 surface; 18 dived
Range, miles	15 000 at 8 knots (snorting)
Endurance	45 days
Complement	63 (7 officers, 56 men)

GENERAL
Designed as oceangoing standard submarines. Improved versions based on the German XXI type. *Dauphine Marsouin, Narval* and *Requin* were built in seven prefabricated parts each of 10 metres in length.

MORSE (showing modified conning fin) 1972, *Dr. Giorgio Arra*

RECONSTRUCTION. During a five-year reconstruction programme, announced in 1965 and completed by the end of 1970, these submarines, *Requin* in Spring 1967 and *Espadon* and *Morse* in succession at Lorient followed by the other three, were given a new diesel electric power plant as well as new weapon and detection equipment. Sonar similar to that in the *Daphne* class. Alcatel DLT-8-4E torpedo control system. See altered appearance of *Morse* and *Doris*.

ENGINEERING. New main propelling machinery installed on reconstruction during 1965 to 1970 includes diesel-electric drive on the surface with SEMT-Pielstick diesels. The original main machinery was Schneider 4 000 bhp 7 cyl. 2 str. diesels for surface propulsion and 5 000 hp electric motors submerged.

AMPHIBIOUS FORCES

NOTE—SEE BATRAL CLASS UNDER "TRANSPORTS"

2 LANDING SHIPS (DOCK) (TCD)

OURAGAN L 9021 **ORAGE** L 9022

Displacement, tons	5 800 light; 8 500 full load; 15 000 when fully immersed
Length, feet (*metres*)	488·9 (*149·0*)
Beam, feet (*metres*)	70·5 (*21·5*)
Draught, feet (*metres*)	16·1 (*4·9*); 28·5 (*8·7*) max
Guns	2—4·7 in (*120 mm*) mortars; 6—30 mm
Main engines	2 diesels; 2 shafts; 8 640 bhp
Speed, knots	17
Range, miles	4 000 at 15 knots
Complement	239 (16 officers, 223 men)

Built at Brest Dockyard. *Ouragan* was laid down in June 1962, launched on 9 Nov 1963, completed for trials in 1964, and commissioned in Jan 1965. *Orage* was laid down in June 1966, launched on 22 Apr 1967 and completed in Mar 1968. Bridge is on the starboard side. Fitted with a platform for four heavy helicopters. Able to carry EDICs loaded with eleven light tanks each, or 18 loaded LCMs, also 1 500 tons of material and equipment handled by two 35 ton cranes. *Orage* is allocated to the Pacific Nuclear Experimental Centre. Can carry 350 troops normally or 470 for short periods.

SONAR. One SQS-17 in *Ouragan*.

OURAGAN 1970, *Contre Amiral M. Adam*

ORAGE, OURAGAN

ORAGE 1969, *French Navy*

Amphibious Forces—*continued*

5 LANDING SHIPS (TANK)

ARGENS L 9003 **BIDASSOA** L 9004 **BLAVET** L 9009 **DIVES** L 9008 **TRIEUX** L9007

Displacement, tons	1 400 standard; 1 765 normal; 4 225 full load
Dimensions, ft (*m*)	328 oa × 50 × 14 (*102·1 × 15·5 × 3·2*)
Guns	2—40 mm AA; 4—20 mm AA (*Argens, Trieux*) 1—4·7 in mortar; 3—40 mm AA (*Bidassoa, Blavet, Dives*)
Main engines	SEMT-Pielstick diesels; 2 shafts; 2 000 bhp = 11 knots
Range, miles	18 500 at 10 knots
Complement	85 (6 officers and 79 men.) Plus 170 troops (normal)

Built by Chantiers Seine Maritime (*Bidassoa, Dives*) and Chantiers de Bretagne, Nantes (others). Launched on 7 Apr 1959, 30 Dec 1960, 15 Jan 1960, 29 June 1960 and 6 Dec 1958, respectively. All commissioned in 1960-61. Can carry: 4 LCVP's, 1 800 tons of freight, 335 (up to 807 if required) troops (329 in bunks, 552 in hammocks). *Blavet* and *Trieux* are fitted as light helicopter carriers with a hanger before the bridge and can carry two Alouette III.

ARGENS *1971, Dr. Giorgio Arra*

11 LANDING CRAFT (TANK) (EDIC)

L 9091 (7 Jan 1958)
L 9092 (2 Dec 1958)
L 9093 (17 Apr 1958)
L 9094 (24 July 1958)
L 9095 (11 Apr 1958)
L 9096 (11 Oct 1958)
L 9070 (30 Mar 1967)
L 9071 (4 Nov 1967)
L 9072 (1968)
L 9073 (1968)
L 9074 (22 July 1969)

Displacement, tons	250 standard; 670 full load
Dimensions, ft (*m*)	193·5 × 39·2 × 4·5 (*59 × 12 × 1·3*)
Guns	2—20 mm AA
Main engines	MGO diesels; 2 shafts; 1 000 bhp = 8 knots
Range, miles	1 800 at 8 knots
Complement	16 (1 officer, and 15 men)

Seven were built by C. N. Franco Belges, two by Toulon Dockyard, two by La Perrière. Launch dates above. Can carry 11 lorries or 5 Light Fighting Vehicles.

L 9092 *1970, French Navy*

ISSOLE L 9097 (LCT)

Displacement, tons	600 full load
Dimensions, feet	160·8 × 32 × 7·2
Main engines	2 diesels; 1 000 bhp = 12 knots

Built at Toulon in 1957-58. Coaster with bow doors and ramp.

ISSOLE *1969, Godfrey H. Walker*

LCT 9061 (ex-HMS *Buttress*, LCT(8) 4099)

Displacement, tons	657 standard; 1 000 full load
Dimensions, ft (*m*)	231·2 × 39 × 5·9 (*70·5 × 11·9 × 1·8*)
Guns	2—20 mm; 1—120mm mortar
Main engines	4 Paxman diesels; 2 shafts; 1 840 bhp = 9 knots
Complement	29 (2 officers, 27 men)

Former Brirish landing craft bought in July 1965.

14 LCM's

CTM 1 to 14

Displacement, tons	56 standard; 150 full load
Dimensions, ft (*m*)	92·8 × 21 × 3·9 (*28·3 × 6·4 × 1·2*)
Main engines	Hispano diesels; 2 shafts; 225 hp = 9·5 knots
Complement	6

Can carry up to 90 tons in coastal or protected waters.

CORVETTES

14 "LE FOUGUEUX" CLASS

L'ADROIT (5 Oct 1957) P 644
L'AGILE (26 June 1954) P 643
L'ALERTE (5 Oct 1957) P 645
L'ATTENTIF (5 Oct 1957) P 646
L'ARDENT (17 July 1958) P 635
L'EFFRONTÉ (27 Jan 1959) P 638
L'ENJOUÉ (5 Oct 1957) P 647
L'ÉTOURDI (5 Feb 1958) P 637
LE FOUGUEUX (31 May 1954) P 641
LE FRINGANT (6 Feb 1959) P 640
LE FRONDEUR (26 Feb 1959) P 639
LE HARDI (17 Sep 1958) P 648
L'INTRÉPIDE (12 Dec 1958) P 630
L'OPINIATRE (4 May 1954) P642

Displacement, tons	325 standard; 400 full load
Dimensions, ft (*m*)	170 pp × 23 × 6·5 (*53 × 7·3 × 3·1*)
Guns	2—40 mm Bofors AA; 2—20 mm AA (P 641—3 only)
A/S weapons	1 hedgehog; 4 DC mortars; 2 DC racks; (P 641—3 only); 1—120 mm A/S mortar; 2 DC mortars; 2 DC racks (rest)
Tubes	*L'Intrepide* has a tube mounted on the stern
Main engines	4 SEMT-Pielstick diesel engines coupled 2 by 2; 3 240 bhp = 18·6 knots (22 knots on trial)
Range, miles	3 000 at 12 knots; 2 000 at 15 knots
Complement	63 (4 officers, 59 men)

L'Agile, Le Fougueux and *L'Opiniatre* were built in France under a USA offshore order. Five more were built under the 1955 and six under the 1956 estimates. These have a different armament, and modified bridge. *L'Agile* is employed on fishery protection duties.

SONAR. One DUBA 2 (P 641—3); one QCU2. (remainder)

SIMILAR CLASSES. Four "Boavista" class (Portugal) and one in Yugoslavia.

L'INTRÉPIDE (tube on stern) *1972, Dr. Giorgio Arra*

6 "LA DUNKERQUOISE" CLASS

LA DUNKERQUOISE (ex-*Fundy*) P 653
LA MALOUINE (ex-*Cowlcham*) P 651
LA BAYONNAISE (ex-*Chignecto*) P 654
LA PAIMPOLAISE (ex-*Thunder*) P 657
LA DIEPPOISE (ex-*Chaleur*) P 655
LA LORIENTAISE (ex-*Miarmachi*) P 652

Displacement, tons	370 full load; 470 standard;
Dimensions, ft (*m*)	140 pp; 152 oa × 28 × 8·7 (*50 × 9·2 × 2·8*)
Gun	1—40 mm AA
Main engines	General Motors diesels; 2 shafts; 2 500 bhp = 15 knots max
Oil fuel (tons)	52
Range, miles	4 500 at 11 knots
Complement	43 (4 officers, 39 men)

La Bayonnaise (launched 12 May 1952), *La Malouine* (launched 12 Nov 1951) and *La Paimpolaise* (launched 17 July 1953) were transferred to the French flag at Halifax on 1 Apr 1954, *Dunkerquoise* (launched 17 July 1953) on 30 Apr 1954, and *La Dieppoise* (launched 21 June 1952) and *La Lorientaise* (launched in 1953) on 10 Oct 1954. All similar to the "Bay" class in the Royal Canadian Navy. All transferred from minesweeping to overseas patrol operations 1973. They have been air conditioned.

LA DIEPPOISE *1971, French Navy*

5 "SIRIUS" CLASS

ALTAIR P 656
ARCTURUS P 650
CROIX DU SUD P 658
CANOPUS P 659
ÉTOILE POLAIRE P 660

All of "Sirius" class minesweepers (see Minewarfare Section for details) transferred for coastal patrol operations 1973.

LIGHT FORCES

LA COMBATTANTE P 730 (FAST ATTACK CRAFT—MISSILE)

Displacement, tons	180 standard; 202 full load
Dimensions, ft (*m*)	147·8 × 24·2 × 6·5 (*45 × 7·4 × 2·5*)
Gun	1—30 mm AA
Launchers	1 quadruple for SS 11; 1 for 14 flares
Main engines	2 SEMT-Pielstick diesels; 2 shafts; controllable pitch propellers; 3 200 bhp = 23 knots
Range, miles	2 000 at 12 knots
Complement	25 (3 officers, 22 men)

Authorised under the 1960 Programme. Built by Constructions Mécaniques de Normandie. Laid down in April 1962, launched on 20 June 1963, and completed on 1 Mar 1964. Of wooden and plastic laminated non-magnetic construction. Was fitted for trials of the MM 38 missile system (Exocet).

LA COMBATTANTE *1972, Dr. Giorgio Arra*

2 NEW CONSTRUCTION (FAST ATTACK CRAFT—MISSILE)

TRIDENT **GLAIVE**

Displacement, tons	115 standard; 130 full load
Dimensions, ft (*m*)	121·4 × 18 × 5·2 (*37 × 5·5 × 1·6*)
Missiles	6—SS 12
Gun	1—40 mm
Main engines	Diesels; 3 600 hp = 25 knots
Range, miles	1 500 at 15 knots
Complement	15

Laid down in 1973.

1 Ex-US SC TYPE (LARGE PATROL CRAFT)

M 691 (ex-*CH* 101, ex-*SC* 524)

Displacement, tons	110 standard; 138 full load
Dimensions, ft (*m*)	107·5 wl; 110·6 oa × 18·8 × 6·5 (*33·7 × 5·7 × 2*)
Main engines	2 GM diesels; 2 shafts; 1 000 bhp = 15 knots
Complement	25

Of wooden construction. Launched in 1943. Acquired from the USN in 1944.

TRANSFERS
P 699 was transferred to the Ivory Coast Republic and re-named *Patience* (now defunct) and P 700 was transferred to the Senegalian Republic and re-named *Senegal*.

1 FAIRMILE ML TYPE (LARGE PATROL CRAFT)

OISEAU DES ILES A 716

Displacement, tons	140 full load
Dimensions, feet	111·5 × 18·4 × 4·3 (*34 × 5·6 × 1·3*)
Speed, knots	11·5

Former Fairmile motor launch was allocated to the Navy for training frogmen.

2 VC TYPE (COASTAL PATROL CRAFT)

VC 2 P 752 **VC 3** P 753

Displacement, tons	70 standard; 80 full load
Dimensions, ft (*m*)	104·2 × 15·5 × 5·5 (*31·8 × 4·7 × 1·7*)
Guns	2—20 mm AA
Main engines	2 Mercedes-Benz diesels; 2 shafts; 2 700 bhp = 28 knots
Range, miles	1 500 at 15 knots
Complement	15

Completed in 1958 and 1959. Built by the Constructions Mécaniques de Normandie, Cherbourg (VC 3) and Lürssens in Germany (VC 2).

TRANSFERS
VC 1 (P 751). To Mauritania 1969. VC 4 (P 754). To Congo and subsequently to Senegal (*Sine Saloum*) in 1966. VC 5 (P 755). To Senegal (*Casamance*) Jan 1963. VC 5 (P 756). To Cameroon (*Vigilante*) Jan 1964. VC 6 to disposal. VC 7 (P 757). VC 8 (P 758). To Madagascar in 1963, returned and subsequently to Cameroon (*Audacieux*) 1968. VC 9 (P 759). To Ivory Coast (*Perseverance*) 1963. VC 11 (P 761). To Tunisia (*Istiklal*) 1960. VC 12 (P 762) To Morocco (*El Sabiq*) 1960.

VC 3 *1972, Dr. Giorgio Arra*

Y 760 (ex-P 9786) **Y 761** (ex-P 9785)

Displacement, tons	45
Dimensions, feet	79·3 × 14·8 × 4·2
Guns	8—0·5 MG (four twin mountings)
Main engines	2 Daimler-Benz diesels; 2 shafts; 1 000 bhp = 18 knots

Built by Burmeister-Bremen and Bodenwerft-Kressbronn. Completed in 1954.

JASMIN (ex-M 776) P 661 **PETUNIA** (ex-M 789) P 662

2 ex-"Ham" class MSI's used for patrol duties. See Minewarfare Forces for details.

MINE WARFARE FORCES

5 "CIRCE" CLASS (MINEHUNTERS)

CYBELE	M 712	**CALLIOPE**	M 713	**CLIO**	M 714
CIRCE	M 715	**CERES**	M 716		

Displacement, tons	460 standard; 495 normal; 510 full load
Dimensions, ft (*m*)	152·6 × 29·2 × 8·0 (*46·5 × 8·9 × 2·5*)
Gun	1—20 mm
Main engines	Diesels; single axial screw; 1 800 bhp = 15 knots
Range, miles	3 000 at 12 knots
Complement	50 (5 officers, 45 men)

Ordered in 1968. Built by Constructions Mécaniques de Normandie, Cherbourg. *Circe* launched 15 Dec 1970, in service 18 May 1972; *Clio* launched 10 June 1971, in service 18 May 1972; *Calliope* launched 21 Nov 1971, in service 28 Sept 1972; *Cybèle* launched Jan 1972, in service 28 Sept 1972; *Ceres* launched 10 Aug 1972 in service 8 Mar 1973.

MINEHUNTING. All ships are fitted with DUBM 20 minehunting sonar. The 9 foot long PAP is propelled by two electric motors at 6 knots. Fitted with a television camera, thia machine detects the mine and lays its 100 kgm charge nearby. These are then detonated by an ultra-sonic signal.

MINESWEEPING. These ships carry no normal minesweeping equipment.

CERES *1972, French Navy*

12 Ex-US MSO "BERNEVAL" CLASS (MINESWEEPERS—OCEAN)

NARVIK (ex-*AM* 512)	M 609	**MYTHO** (ex-*AM* 475)	M 618
OUISTREHAM (ex-*AM* 513)	M 610	**VINH LONG** (ex-*AM* 477)	M 619
ALENCON (ex-*AM* 453)	M 612	**BERLAIMONT** (ex-*AM* 500)	M 620
BERNEVAL (ex-*AM* 450)	M 613	**AUTUN** (ex-*AM* 502)	M 622
CANTHO (ex-*AM* 476)	M 615	**BACCARAT** (ex-*AM* 505)	M 623
GARIGLIANO (ex-*AM* 452)	M 617	**COLMAR** (ex-*AM* 514)	M 624

Displacement, tons	700 standard; 780 full load
Dimensions, ft (*m*)	165 wl; 171 oa × 35 × 10·3 (*50·3 × 10·7 × 3·2*)
Gun	1—40 mm AA
Main engines	2 GM diesels; 2 shafts; 1 600 bhp = 13·5 knots
Range, miles	3 000 at 10 knots
Complement	56 (4 officers, 52 men)

The USA transferred to France eight new AMs in 1953, and four in 1954. Three more transferred in 1956. *Origny* is classified and fitted as an oceanographic research vessel but is Navy owned and manned. *Bir Hacheim* M614 (ex-*AM* 451) was returned to the US Navy at Brest on 4 Sept 1970 and transferred to Uruguayan Navy, being renamed *Maldonado*.

APPEARANCE. *Autun, Baccarat, Berlaimont, Colmar, Narvik, Origny* and *Ouistreham* have a taller funnel.

AUTUN (tall funnel type) *1971, A. & J. Pavia*

Mine Warfare Forces—*continued*

17 "SIRIUS" CLASS (MINESWEEPERS—COASTAL)

ALGOL (15 Apr 1953)	M 704	**DÉNÉBOLA** (12 July 1956)	M 751
ANTARES (21 Jan 1954)	M 703	**ÉRIDAN** (18 May 1954)	M 741
ARIES (13 Mar 1956)	M 758	**LYRE** (3 May 1956)	M 759
BELLATRIX (21 July 1955)	M 750	**PHÉNIX** (23 May 1955)	M 749
BETELGEUSE (12 July 1954)	M 747	**PÉGASE** (21 June 1955)	M 710
CAPELLA (6 Sep 1955)	M 755	**SAGITTAIRE** (12 Jan 1955)	M 743
CAPRICORNE (8 Aug 1956)	M 737	**VEGA** (14 Jan 1953)	M 707
CASSIOPÉE (16 Nov 1953)	M 740	**VERSEAU** (26 Apr 1956)	M 757
CÉPHÉE (3 Jan 1956)	M 756		

Displacement, tons	365 standard; 424 full load
Dimensions, feet	140 pp; 152 oa × 28 × 8·2
Guns	1—40 mm Bofors AA; 120 mm Oerlikon AA (several have 2—20 mm AA)
Main engines	SIGMA free piston generators and Alsthom or Rateau-Bretagne gas turbines or SEMT-Pielstick 16-cyl fast diesels; 2 shafts; 2 000 bhp = 15 knots (11·5 knots when sweeping)
Oil fuel (tons)	48
Range, mlies	3 000 at 15 knots
Complement	38

Of wooden and aluminium alloy construction. Launch dates above. Of same general characteristics as the British "Ton" class, but of different hull construction. Propelled by Alsthom or Rateau gas turbines with SIGMA free piston generators, except *Aries, Bételgeuse, Capella, Céphée, Lyre, Phénix* and *Verseau*, which have SEMT-Pielstick light diesels. 16 vessels were built under the "off-shore" programme.

TRANSFERS
D 25, D 26 and D 27 were allocated to Yugoslavia. *Fomalhaut, Orion, Pollux* and *Procyon* were returned to the USN in 1970, *Achernar* and *Centaure* in 1971.

ANTARES *1971, courtesy Admiral M. Adam*

24 Ex-US "ACACIA" CLASS (MINESWEEPERS—COASTAL)

PERVENCHE (ex-*AMS* 141)	M 632	**CYCLAMEN** (ex-*AMS* 119)	M 674
PIVOINE (ex-*AMS* 125)	M 633	**EGLANTINE** (ex-*AMS* 117)	M 675
RÉSÉDA (ex-*AMS* 126)	M 635	**GIROFLÉE** (ex-*AMS* 85)	M 677
ACACIA (ex-*AMS* 69)	M 638	**GLAIEUL** (ex-*AMS* 120)	M 678
ACANTHE (ex-*AMS* 70)	M 639	**GLYCINE** (ex-*AMS* 118)	M 679
MARJOLAINE (ex-*Aconit*, ex-*AMS* 66)	M 640	**JACINTHE** (ex-*AMS* 115)	M 680
		LAURIER (ex-*AMS* 86)	M 681
AZALÉE (ex-*AMS* 67)	M 668	**LILAS** (ex-*AMS* 93)	M 682
BÉGONIA (ex-*AMS* 83)	M 669	**LISERON** (ex-*AMS* 98)	M 683
BLEUÉT (ex-*AMS* 116)	M 670	**LOBÉLIA** (ex-*AMS* 96)	M 684
CAMÉLIA (ex-*AMS* 68)	M 671	**MAGNOLIA** (ex-*AMS* 87)	M 685
CHRYSANTHÈME (ex-*AMS* 113)	M 672	**MIMOSA** (ex-*AMS* 99)	M 687
		MUGUET (ex-*AMS* 97)	M 688

Displacement, tons	320 standard; 370 full load
Dimensions, ft (*m*)	136·2 pp; 141 oa × 26 × 8·3 (*43 × 8 × 2·6*)
Guns	2—20 mm AA
Main engines	2 GM diesels; 2 shafts; 1 200 bhp = 13 knots (8 sweeping)
Oil fuel, tons	40
Range, miles	2 500 at 10 knots
Complement	38 (3 officers, 35 men)

GENERAL
The USA agreed in Sep 1952 to allocate to France in 1953, 36 new AMS (later re-designated MSC) under the Mutual Defence Assistance Programme, but only 30 were finally transferred to France in 1953.

ALTERATIONS. *Ajonc* (ex-M 667) A 701 is a diving-school tender and *Gardénia* (ex-M 676) A 711 is a clearance-diving training ship.

TRANSFERS. Three were returned to the USA after delivery to Saigon for Indo-China, and two of these were allocated to Japan (AMS 95 and 144). Three were not delivered, two having been allocated to Spain (139 and 143) and one to Taiwan (140). *Marguerite* (ex-*AMS* 94) was returned to the USN at Toulon in Nov 1969 and transferred to the Uruguayan Navy. renamed *Rio Negro*. *Pavot* (ex-*MSC* 124) and *Renocule* (ex-*MSC* 142) were returned to the USN on 24 March 1970 and transferred to the Turkish Navy. *Coquelicot* (ex-M 673) to Tunisia 1973.

PERVENCHE *1971, Dr. Giorgio Arra*

Minewarfare Forces—*continued*

1 SPECIAL TYPE (DBI) (MINESWEEPER—COASTAL)

MERCURE M 765

Displacement, tons	333 light; 365 normal; 400 full load
Dimensions, ft (*m*)	137·8 pp; 145·5 oa × 27 × 8·5 (*44·4 × 8·3 × 4*)
Guns	2—20 mm AA
Main engines	2 Mercedes-Benz diesels; 2 shafts; Kamewa variable pitch propellers; 4 000 bhp = 15 knots
Oil fuel, tons	48
Range, miles	3 000 at 15 knots
Complement	48

Ordered in France from Mécaniques de Normandie under the "off-shore" programme. Laid down in Jan 1955. Launched on 21 Dec 1957. Completed in Dec 1958.
FOREIGN SALES
Six built for W. Germany.

MERCURE *1968, French Navy*

3 Ex-BRITISH "HAM" CLASS (MINESWEEPERS—INSHORE)

GÉRANIUM (ex-*Tibenham*)	M 784
JONQUILLE (ex-*Sulham*)	M 787
VIOLETTE (ex-*Mersham*)	M 773

Displacement, tons	140 standard; 170 full load
Dimensions, ft (*m*)	100 pp; 106·5 oa × 21·2 × 5·5 (*32·4 × 6·5 × 1·7*)
Gun	1—20 mm Oerlikon AA forward
Main engines	2 Paxman diesels; 550 bhp = 14 knots (9 knots when sweeping)
Oil fuel, tons	15
Complement	12 (2 officers, 10 men)

Former British inshore minesweepers of the "Ham" class transferred to France under the US "off-shore" procurement programme in 1955.

SURVEY SHIPS

D'ENTRECASTEAUX A 757

Displacement, tons	2 400 full load
Dimensions, ft (*m*)	295·2 × 42·7 × 12·8 (*89 × 13 × 3.9*)
Main engines	2 diesel-electric; 1 000 kW; 2 controllable pitch propellers; Speed:15 knots
Auxiliary engines	2 Schottel trainable and retractable
Range, miles	10 000 at 12 knots
Complement	81 (9 officers, 72 men)

This ship was specially designed for oceanographic surveys and built at Brest. Completed 10 Oct 1970. Accommodation for 38 scientists. Hangar for Alouette II helicopter.

D'ENTRECASTEAUX *1971, Courtesy Admiral M. Adam*

ESPÉRANCE (ex-*Jacques Coeur*) A 756
ESTAFETTE (ex-*Jacques Cartier*) A 766

Displacement, tons	956 standard; 1 360 full load
Dimensions, ft (*m*)	196·1 × 32·2 × 14·8 (*63·5 × 9·8 × 5·9*)
Main engines	MAN diesels; 1 850 bhp = 15 knots
Range, miles	7 500 at 13 knots
Complement	29 (5 officers, 24 men)

Former trawlers built in 1962 at Gdynia and purchased in 1968-69. Adapted as survey ships commissioning in 1969 and 1972.

APPEARANCE. *Espérance* has a normal foremast in place of the crane in *Estafette*.

ESTAFETTE *1973, French Navy*

Survey Ships—*continued*

LA RECHERCHE (ex-*Guyane*) A 758

Displacement, tons	810 standard; 910 full load
Dimensions, ft (*m*)	221·5 oa × 34·2 × 13 (*67·5 × 10·4 × 4·5*)
Main engines	1 Werkspoor diesel; 1 535 bhp = 13·5 knots
Range, miles	3 100 at 10 knots
Complement	23 (2 officers, 21 men) (plus 43 surveyors)

Former passenger motor vessel built by Chantiers Zeigler at Dunkirk. Launched on 17 Sep 1951. Purchased in 1960 and converted by Cherbourg Dockyard into a surveying ship. Commissioned into the French Navy in Mar 1961 and her name changed from *Guyane* to *La Recherche*. To improve stability she was fitted with bulges. Now comes under the Colonial ministry.

LA RECHERCHE *1970, French Navy*

2 "BERNEVAL" CLASS

DOMPAIR M 616 **ORIGNY** M 621

Displacement, tons	700 standard; 795 full load
Dimensions, ft (*m*)	171 × 35 × 10·5 (*52·2 × 10·7 × 3·2*)
Gun	1—40 mm
Main engines	2 GM diesels; 2 shafts; 1 600 bhp = 13·5 knots
Range, miles	3 000 at 10 knots
Complement	52

Origny launched Feb 1955 as a Minesweeper—Ocean of "Berneval" class. Converted for Oceanographic research 1961-62. *Dompaire* launched 1955. Converted as survey ship in 1970.

LA DÉCOUVERTE (ex-*Amalthée*, ex-*Plantagenet*, ex-*Barwood*) A 753

Displacement, tons	750 standard; 927 full load
Dimensions, ft (*m*)	159·7 × 30·7 × 13 (*49 × 9·3 × 4·8*)
Main engines	Triple expansion; 720 ihp = 9·5 knots
Boilers	Cylindrical
Range, miles	2 900 at 9 knots
Complement	33 plus 25 surveyors

Formerly the British boom defence vessel HMS *Plantagenet* (ex-*Barwood*) built by Lobnitz & Co Ltd, Renfrew and launched on 23 Feb 1939. She became the commercial oil research ship *Amalthée* under the French flag in 1960. She was purchased for the French Navy in 1969 and converted as a survey ship.

LA DÉCOUVERTE *1970, courtesy Admiral M. Adam*

L'ASTROLABE A 780 **BOUSSOLE** A 781

Displacement, tons	330 standard; 440 full load
Dimensions, ft (*m*)	137·8 × 27 × 8·2 (*42·7 × 8·5 × 2·9*)
Guns	1—40 mm AA; 2 MG
Main engines	2 Baudouin DV.8 diesels; 1 shaft; variable pitch propeller; 800 bhp = 13 knots max
Range, miles	4 000 at 12 knots
Complement	34 (3 officers, 31 men)

Authorised under the 1961 Programme. Specially designed for surveys in tropical waters. Built by Chantiers de la Seine Maritime. Le Trait. Laid down in 1962, launched on 27 May and 11 Apr 1963 respectively, and commissioned in 1964.

L'ASTROLABE *1972, French Navy*

Survey Ships—*continued*

ALIDADE (ex-*Evelyne Marie*) A 682 **OCTANT** (ex-*Michel Marie*) A 683

Displacement, tons	128 standard; 133 full load
Dimensins, ft (*m*)	78 × 20 × 10·5 (*24 × 6·1 × 3·2*)
Main engines	2 diesels; 1 shaft; variable pitch; 200 bhp = 9 knots
Complement	13
Range, miles	2 000 at 7 knots

Two small fishing trawlers purchased by the Navy and converted into survey craft by the Constructions Mécaniques deNormandie at Cherbourg as tenders to *La Recherche*. Wooden hull and steel upperworks. *Alidade* floated up after conversion on 15 Nov 1962 and *Octant* on 20 Dec 1962. Commissioned in 1963.

OCTANT *1970.*

CORAIL A 791 (INSHORE SURVEY CRAFT)

Launched in 1957. 50 tons with complement of 7. Operating in New Caledonia. To be replaced by *Marc Joly* who will take over her name.

ZÉLÉE A 785 (INSHORE SURVEY CRAFT)

Operating as inshore survey launch in French Polynesia.

SERVICE FORCES

1 + 2 NEW CONSTRUCTION (UNDERWAY REPLENISHMENT TANKERS)

LA DURANCE A 629 **+ 2**

Displacement, tons	17 450 standard; 19 950 full load
Dimensions, ft (*m*)	515·9 × 69·5 (*157·3 × 21·2*)
Guns	2—40 mm
Main engines	2 diesels SEMT-Pielstick 16 PC 3; 20 000 hp = 19 knots
Range, miles	9 000 at 15 knots
Complement	149 (45 passengers)

GENERAL
Building at Brest—laid down 1973 for completion in 1976. Beam fuelling both sides as well as astern. Helicopter hangar. Classed as P.R.E. (Pétrolier Pravitailleur d'Escadre).

LA CHARENTE (ex-*Beaufort*) A 626 (UNDERWAY REPLENISHMENT TANKER)

Displacement, tons	7 440 light; 26 000 full load
Dimensions, ft (*m*)	587·2 × 72 × 30·3 (*179 × 21·9 × 9·3*)
Main engines	1 General Electric geared turbine; 1 screw = 17·5 knots
Boilers	2
Complement	70 (6 officers, 64 men)

Former Norwegian tanker built by Haldnes Mek. Verksted Tönsberg in 1957. Purchased by the French Navy in May 1964.

LA CHARENTE *1969, Admiral M. Adam*

ISÈRE (ex-*La Mayenne*, ex-*Caltex Strasbourg*) A 675 (UNDERWAY REPLENISHMENT TANKER)

Displacement, tons	7 440 standard; 26 700 full load
Dimensions, ft (*m*)	559 × 71·2 × 30·3 (*170·4 × 21·7 × 9·3*)
Main engines	1 single geared Parsons turbine; 8 260 shp = 16 knots
Boilers	2
Complement	112 (6 officers, 106 men)

Built by Seine Maritime. Launched on 22 June 1959. Former French tanker. Purchased in 1965. Fitted for beam fuelling as well as stern rig.

Service Forces—*continued*

LA SAONE A 628 **LA SEINE** A 627

(UNDERWAY REPLENISHMENT TANKERS)

Displacement, tons	8 550 light; 24 200 full load
Dimensions, ft (*m*)	525 × 72·5 × 33 (*160 × 22·1 × 10*)
Main engines	Parsons geared turbines; 2 shafts; 15 800 shp = 18 knots
Boilers	3 Penhoet
Complement	200

Ordered as fleet tankers. Completed as merchant tankers in 1948. Returned to the French Navy from charter company in Sep 1953. *La Seine* was fitted as a fleet replenishment ship in 1961, *La Saône* in 1962. They carry 11 500 tons of fuel, 275 tons of food and wine tanks holding 82 000 litres. Fitted with automatic tensioning.

LA SAONE *1972 Dr. Giorgio Arra*

FLEET SUPPORT SHIPS

LAC TONLÉ SAP A 630
(SUPPORT TANKER)

Displacement, tons	800 light; 2 700 full load
Dimensions, ft (*m*)	235 × 37 × 15·8 (*71·7 × 11·3 × 4·8*)
Guns	3—20 mm AA
Main engines	2 Fairbanks-Morse diesels; 1 150 bhp = 11 knots
Range, milrs	6 300 at 11 knots
Complement	37 (2 officers, 35 men)

Ex-US Oil Barge acquired in 1945.

TIANEE *1973, French Navy*

PAPENOO (ex-Norwegian *Bow Queen*) A 625
PUNARUU (ex-Norwegian *Bow Cecil*) A 623 (SUPPORT TANKERS)

Displacement, tons	1 195 standard; 2 927 full load
Dimensions, ft (*m*)	272·2 × 45·6 × 18·0) (*83 × 13·9 × 5·5*)
Main engines	2 Diesels; 1 vp screw; 2 050 hp = 12 knots (bow screw in addition)

Two small oilers added to the navy in late 1969.

ABER-WRACH (ex-*CA* 1) A 619 (SUPPORT TANKER)

Displacement, tons	1 220 standard; 3 500 full load
Dimensions, ft (*m*)	284 oa × 40 × 15·8 (*86·6 × 12·2 × 4·8*)
Gun	1—40 mm AA
Main engines	1 diesel; vp propeller; 3 000 bhp = 12 knots

Built at Cherbourg. Authorised in 1956. Ordered in 1959. Laid down in 1961. The after part with engine room was launched on 24 Apr 1963. The fore part was built on the vacated slip, launched and welded to the after part. Complete hull floated up on 21 Nov 1963. Commissioned in 1966.

ABER WRACH *1970, French Navy*

AUNIS (ex-*Regina Pacis*) A 643 (STORE SHIP)

Displacement, tons	2 900 full load
Dimensions, ft (*m*)	284·5 × 38 × 15 (*86·5 × 11·6 × 4·6*)
Main engines	MAN diesels geared to 1 shaft; 2 400 bhp = 12 knots
Range, miles	4 500 at 12 knots

Built by Roland Werft, Bremen. Launched on 3 July 1956. Purchased in Nov 1966 from Seatto, Ambrosino & Pugliese and converted in Toulon 1972-73. Employed as trials ship in Operation Cormoran.

Fleet Support Ships—*continued*

SAHEL A 638

Displacement, tons	630 light; 1 450 full load
Measurement, tons	650 deadweight
Dimensions, ft (*m*)	176·2 × 29·5 × 14·5 (*53·7 × 9 × 4·5*)
Guns	2—20 mm AA
Main engines	2 diesels; 1 400 bhp = 12 knots

Completed in Aug 1951 by Chantiers Naval de Caen. Fuel carrier.

SAHEL *1972, Dr. Giorgio Arra*

5 "RHIN" CLASS (DEPOT SHIPS)

Name	*No.*	*Laid down*	*Launched*	*Completed*
GARONNE	A 617	Nov 1963	8 Aug 1964	1 Sep 1965
LOIRE	A 615	July 1965	1 Oct 1966	10 Oct 1967
RANCE	A 618	Aug 1964	15 May 1965	5 Feb 1966
RHIN	A 621	May 1961	17 Mar 1962	1 Mar 1964
RHONE	A 622	Feb 1962	8 Dec 1962	1 Dec 1964

Displacement, tons	2 075 standard; 2 445 full load (*Rhin, Rance* and *Rhône*) 2 320 standard (*Garonne and Loire*).
Dimensions,, feet	302·0 pp 331·5 oa × 43·0 × 12·1
Guns	3—40 mm AA (except *Garonne*)
Aircraft	1/3 Alouette helicopter (except *Garonne* and *Loire*)
Landing craft	2 (LCP)
Main engines	2 SEMT-Pielstick diesels; 1 shaft; 3 300 bhp = 16·5 knots
Range, miles	13 000 at 13 knots
Complement	*Rhine* and *Rhône* 71 (5 officers, 66 men) and about 100 technicians; *Rance* 150 (10 officers, 140 men) and about 118 extras; *Garonne* 221 (10 officers, 211 men); *Loire* 175 (13 officers, 162 men)

Designed for supporting various classes of ships. Have a 5 ton crane, carry two LCP (S) and have a helicopter platform (except *Garonne*). *Rhin and Rhône* have a hangar and carry an Alouette helicopter. *Rance* carries three in her hangar and *Loire* has only the helicopter platform. *Garonne* is designed as a Repair Workshop, *Loire* for minesweeper support. *Rance* for laboratory and radiological services, *Rhin* for electronic maintenence and *Rhône* for submarine support. *Loire* and *Rhône* are currently operating in support of North Atlantic fishery patrols.
RADAR. 1 DRBV 50 (in *Rhin* and *Rhône*)

RHIN (LOIRE similar) *1972, Dr. Giorgio Arra*

RHONE *1972, Dr. Giorgio Arra*

RANCE *1969, French Navy*

GARONNE *French Navy*

Fleet Support Ships—*continued*

MAURIENNE (ex-M/S *Brazza*) A 637 (MAINTENANCE SHIPS)
MOSELLE (ex-*Foucauld*) A 608

Displacement, tons	8 200 standard; 8 700 full load
Dimensions, ft (*m*)	480 oa × 62 × 22·3 (*146·3 × 18·9 × 6·9*)
Main engines	2 Doxford diesels; 2 shafts; 8 800 bhp = 15 knots
Complement	177 (7 officers, 170 men)

Former motor passenger ships of the *Chargeurs Réunis* (West Africa Coast Service). Built by Swan, Hunter & Wigham Richardson Ltd, Wallsend-on-Tyne. Launched on 14 Oct and 17 July 1947. Completed in 1948. *Maurienne* was purchased in Nov 1964, converted at Brest in 1965 and admitted to active service on 8 Mar 1966; helicopter landing platform aft. *Moselle* was converted in 1967 (no platform). Used as Base Ships in Pacific Trial Centre.

MOSELLE — *1972, Dr. Giorgio Arra*

JULES VERNE (ex-*Achéron*) A 620 (MAINTENANCE SHIP)

Displacement, tons	6 485 standard; 10 250 full load
Dimensions, ft (*m*)	482·2 × 70·5 × 21·3 (*147 × 21·5 × 6·5*)
Main engines	2 diesels SEMT-Pielstick; 1 shaft; 21 500 hp = 18 knots

Ordered in 1961 budget, originally as an Armament Supply Ship. Role and design changed—now rated as Engineering and Electrical Maintenance Ship. Launched 30 May 1970.

1 REPAIR SHIP (Ex-BRITISH LCT)

Displacement, tons	200 standard; 500 full load
Dimensions, ft (*m*)	187·3 × 38·9 × 4·5 (*57·1 × 11·8 × 1·3*)
Main engines	2 Paxman Diesels; 1 000 hp = 8 knots

Purchased from UK in 1964—used as Mechanical Workshop.

Fleet Support Ships—*continued*

4 REPAIR SHIPS (Ex-LCT)

L 9081 **L 9082** **L 9083** **L 9084**

Displacement, tons	310 standard; 685 full load
Dimensions, ft (*m*)	193·5 × 39 × 5 (*59 × 11·9 × 1·6*)
Main engines	2 Diesels MGO; 1 000 bhp = 8 knots
Range, miles	1 800 at 8 knots

Built in 1964-65 by Ch. N. Franco-Belge. Repair facilities grafted onto LCT hulls. First pair are fitted with mechanical workshops, 9083 with electronic workshops and 9084 is primarily an electrical stores ship.

EDIC 9082 — *1972, Dr. Giorgio Arra*

BERRY (ex-M/S *Médoc*) A 644 (VICTUALLING STORES SHIP)

Displacement, tons	1 148 standard; 2 700 full load
Dimensions, ft (*m*)	284·5 oa × 38 × 15 (*86·7 × 11·6 × 4·6*)
Main engines	2 MWM diesels coupled on one shaft; 2 400 bhp = 15 knots

Built by Roland Werft, Bremen. Launched on 10 May 1958. Purchased in Oct 1964 and refitted in 1964-66.

BERRY — *1969, French Navy*

TRIALS RESEARCH SHIPS

HENRI POINCARÉ (ex-*Maina Marasso*) A 603

Displacement, tons	24 000 full load
Dimensions, ft (*m*)	565·0 pp; 590·6 oa × 72·8 × 28·9 (*180 × 22·2 × 9·4*)
Guns	2—20 mm
Main engines	1 Parsons geared turbine; 1 shaft; 10 000 shp = 15 knots
Boilers	2 Foster Wheeler high pressure water tube
Range, miles	11 800 at 13·5 knots
Complement	305 (21 officers, 9 civilians, 275 men)

Built by Cantieri Riuniti de Adriaricos, Monfalcone. Launched in Oct 1960. Former Italian tanker. Purchased in Sep 1964. Converted in Brest dockyard from 1 Oct 1964 to Mar 1968. To work with the experimental guided missile station in the Landes (SW France). Named after the mathematician and scientist.

AIRCRAFT. Can land on heavy helicopters and has space for two large or five light helicopters in her hangar.

OPERATIONS. She is primarily a missile-range-ship and to enable her to plot the trajectory etc of missiles fired from land or sea she is equipped with three tracking radars, a telemetry station, transit nav-aid, cinetheodolite, infra-red tracking as well as an up-to-date fit of hull-mounted sonar, meteorological and oceanographic equipment.

RADAR. In addition to tracking radars, one DRBV 22D.

HENRI POINCARÉ — *1969, French Navy.*

ILE d'OLÉRON (ex-*München*, ex-*Mur*) A 610

Displacement, tons	5 500 standard; 6 500 full load
Length, feet (*metres*)	350·0 (*106·7*pp; 377·5 (*115·2*)oa
Beam, feet (*metres*)	50·0 (*15·2*)
Draught, feet (*metres*)	21·3 (*6·5*)
Main engines	MAN 6-cylinder diesels; 1 shaft; 3 500 bhp
Speed, knots	14·5
Oil fuel, tons	340
Range, miles	7 200 at 12 knots
Complement	195 (15 officers, 180 men)

Launched in Germany in 1939. Taken as a war prize Formerly rated as a transport. Converted to experimental guided missile ship in 1957-58 by Chantiers de Provence and l'Arsenal de Toulon. Commissioned early in 1959. Equipped with stabilisers.

ILE d'OLÉRON — *1970, French Navy*

ILE D'OLERON

EXPERIMENTAL. When converted was designed for experiments with two launchers for ship to air missiles, the medium range "Masurca" and the long range "Masalca", and one launcher for ship to shore missiles, the "Malaface". Latterly fitted with one launcher for target planes. Now fitted for trials on MM 38 ("Exocet").

RADAR. One DRDV 22C, one DRBV 50, one DRBI 10. The missile system tracking radar operates in C band.

Trials Research Ships—*continued*

TRITON A 646

Displacement, tons: 1 410 standard; 1 510 full load
Dimensions, ft (*m*): 242·7 × 38·9 × 12 (*74 × 11·8 × 3·7*)
Main engines: 2 MGO V Diesels driving a Voith Schneider screw aft; 2 electric motors driving a Voith Schneider forward
Speed, knots: 13
Range, miles: 4 000 at 13 knots
Complement: 62 (4 officers, 41 men + 5 officers and 12 men for diving)

GENERAL
Under sea recovery and trials ship to replace *Elie Monnier*. Equipped with a helicopter platform. Launched at Lorient on 7 Mar 1970 and in service 1972. Support ship for the 2-man submarine *Griffon*.

OPERATIONS. Operated by G.E.R.S. (Groupe d'Etude et de Recherches Sousmarins) for trials of submarines and deep-sea diving equipment. Underwater TV, decompression chamber and laboratories are fitted. Available as submarine rescue ship.

RADAR. Navigational

SONAR. Special equipment for deep operations.

SUBMARINE. The 16 ton *Griffon* can dive to 2 000 feet and be used for deep recovery operations.

TRITON *1972, French Navy*

2 DEEP SUBMERGENCE VEHICLES

ARCHIMÉDE A 648

Built in Toulon. 68·9 feet long with displacement 65 tons. Diving depth 36 000 feet (*11 000 metres*). *Marcel le Bihan* acts as tender.

FNRS 3

Built in Toulon. 52 feet long with displacement 30 tons. Diving depth 13 000 feet (*4 000 metres*).

1 ARCHAELOGICAL RESEARCH CRAFT

ARCHÉONAUTE A 789

Built by Auroux, Arcachon August 1967. 120 tons full load and 96 feet long (*29·3 metres*). For underwater archaeological research carries a complement of 2 officers, 4 men, 3 archaeologists and 6 divers.

1 RADIOLOGICAL RESEARCH CRAFT

PALANGRIN Y 743

Acquired 1969. Of 44 tons with single diesel.

BOOM DEFENCE VESSELS

LA FIDÉLE A 751 **LA PERSÉVÉRANTE** A 750 **LA PRUDENTE** A 749

Displacement, tons: 446 standard; 626 full load
Dimensions, ft (*m*): 142·8 × 32·8 × 9·2 (*43·5 × 10 × 2·8*)
Main engines: 2 Baudoin diesels; 1 shaft; 620 bhp = 10 knots
Range, miles: 4 000 at 10 knots
Complement: 30 (1 officer, 29 men)

Net layers and tenders built by Atel. Ch. La Manche, Dieppe, (*La Fidèle* and *La Prudente*) and Atel. Ch. La Rochelle (*La Persévérante*). Launched on 26 Aug 1968 (*La Fidèle*), 14 May 1968 (*La Persévérante*) and 13 May 1968 (*La Prudente*). Diesel-electric drive, 440 kW. 25 ton lift.

LA PRUDENTE *1970, French Navy*

Boom Defence Vessels— *continued*

1 NEW CONSTRUCTION

TIANEE

Displacement, tons: 842 standard; 905 full load
Dimensions, ft (*m*): 178·1 × 34·8 (*54·3 × 10·6*)
Main engines: Diesel-electric; 2 diesels; 1 shaft = 12 knots
Range, miles: 5 200 at 12 knots
Complement: 37 (1 officer, 36 men)

Built at Brest. Launched 17 Nov 1973. For service in the Pacific. Fitted with lateral screws in bow tunnel.

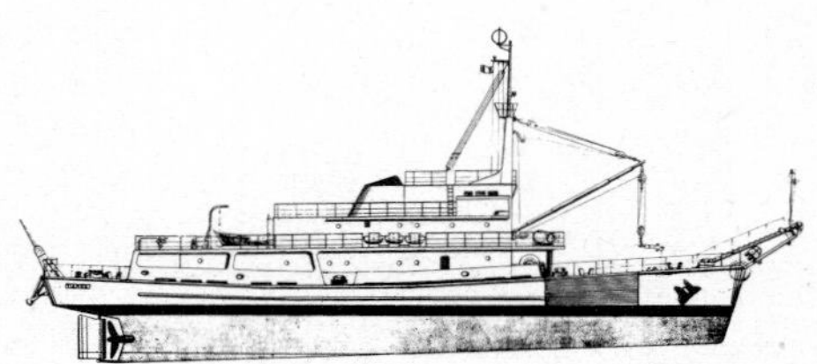

TIANEE *1973, French Navy*

CIGALE (ex-*AN* 98) A 760
CRIQUET (ex-*AN* 96) A 761
FOURMI (ex-*AN* 97) A 762
GRILLON (ex-*AN* 95) A 763
SCARABÉE (ex-*AN* 94) A 764

Displacement, tons: 770 standard; 850 full load
Dimensions, ft (*m*): 151·9 oa × 33·5 × 10·5 (*46·3 × 10·2 × 3·2*)
Guns: 1—40 mm Bofors AA; 4—20 mm AA
Main engines: 2, 4-stroke diesels, electric drive, 1 shaft; 1 600 bhp = 12 knots
Range, miles: 5 200 at 12 knots
Complement: 45

US off-shore order. Sister ship G 6 was allocated to Spain. *Cerberus* transferred to Netherlands and subsequently to Turkey as AG 6. *Criquet* was launched on 3 June 1954, *Cigale* on 23 Sep 1954, *Fourmi* on 6 July 1954, *Grillon* on 18 Feb 1954 and *Scarabée* on 21 Nov 1953.

CIGALE *1971, French Navy*

5 Ex-US AN TYPE NETLAYERS

ARAIGNÉE (ex-*Hackberry*, ex-*Maple*) A 727
LIBELLULE (ex-*Rosewood*) A 730
LOCUSTE (ex-*Locust*) A 765
LUCIOLE (ex-*Sandalwood*) A 777
SCORPION (ex-*Yew*) A 728

Displacement, tons: 560 standard; 850 full load
Dimensions, ft (*m*): 146·0 wl; 163·0 oa × 30·5 × 11·7 (*50 × 9·3 × 4·8*)
Guns: 1—3 in AA; some MG
Main engines: 2 GM diesels; diesel-electric; 1 shaft; 1 300 bhp = 13 knots
Range, miles: 7 200 at 12 knots
Complement: 39 (2 officers, 37 men)

Launched on 6 Mar 1941, 1 Apr 1941, 1 Feb 1941, 6 Mar 1941 and 25 Aug 1941 respectively. *Locuste* was purchased in 1966, *Luciole* in 1967, *Libellule* in 1969. The others were transferred in 1944.

ARAIGNEE *1970, French Navy*

Boom Defense Vessels—*cont.*

MARCEL LE BIHAN (ex-*Greif*) A 759

Displacement, tons	800 standard; 1 250 full load
Dimensions, ft (*m*)	236·2 × 34·8 × 10·5 max (*72 × 10·6 × 3·2*)
Guns	4—20 mm AA (twins)
Main engines	2 GM diesels; 2 shafts; 4 400 bhp = 13 knots
Range, miles	2 500 at 13 knots
Complement	53 (3 officers, 50 men), accommodation for 22 extra hands

Former German aircraft tender. Built by Lubecker Fleudewerke. Launched in 1936. Completed in 1937. Transferred by USA in Feb 1948. 4·1 in gun and 2—40 mm removed. Tender for bathysphere *Archimède.*

MARCEL LE BIHAN *1971, Dr. Giorgio Arra*

COMMANDANT ROBERT GIRAUD

(ex-*Immelmann*) A 755 (ex-F 755)

Displacement, tons	1 142 standard; 1 220 full load
Length, feet (*metres*)	239·0 (*72·9*) pp; 256·0 (*78·0*) oa
Beam, feet (*metres*)	36·0 (*11·0*)
Draught, feet (*metres*)	12·0 (*3·7*)
Main engines	4 MAN diesels; 2 shafts; 5 720 bhp
Range, miles	9 000 at 10 knots
Oil fuel, tons	236
Complement	39

Ex-German aircraft tender. Built by Norderwerft, Hamburg. Launched in Dec 1941. Transferred by Great Britain in Aug 1946, with *Paul Goffeny*. The diesels are coupled two by two with hydraulic transmission on two shafts. Crane lift 18 tons.

PERSISTANTE A 731

Displacement, tons	350
Main engines	500 hp = 8 knots

COMMANDANT ROBERT GIRAUD *1972. Dr. Giorgio Arra*

TORPEDO RECOVERY VESSELS

PÉLICAN (ex-*Kerfany*) A 699

Displacement, tons	362 standatd; 425 full load
Dimensions, ft (*m*)	121·4 × 28·0 × 13·1 (*37 × 8·6 × 4*)
Tubes	One
Main engines	Diesel; 1 shaft; 650 bhp = 11 knots
Complement	19

Built in USA in 1951. Purchased in 1965 and converted from tunny fisher into torpedo recovery craft in 1966.

PÉLICAN *1972, Dr. Giorgio Arra*

PÉTREL (ex-*Cap Lopez*) A 698

Displacement, tons	227 standard; 318 full load
Dimensions, ft (*m*)	98·4 × 25·6 × 11·5 (*30 × 7·8 × 3·5*)
Main engines	2 Baudouin diesels; 1 vp screw; 600 bhp = 10 knots
Complement	19

Built in Daubigeon 1960. Purchased 1965 and converted from tunny fisher to torpedo recovery craft.

TRANSPORTS

2 "BATRAL" TYPE (LIGHT TRANSPORTS)

CHAMPLAIN A 770 **FRANCIS GARNIER** A 771

Displacement, tons	750 standard; 1 250 full load
Dimensions, ft (*m*)	262·4 × 42·6 × 7·5 (*80 × 13 × 2·3*)
Guns	2—40 mm; 2—81 mm Mortars
Main engines	2 Diesels; 2 shafts; 1 800 hp = 16
Range, miles	3 500 at 13 knots
Complement	37

Fitted with bow doors, and stowage for vehicles above and below decks. Helicopter landing platform. Can carry a company of 5 officers and 133 men with 12 vehicles. Built at Brest, launched 17 Nov 1973 for completion 1974.

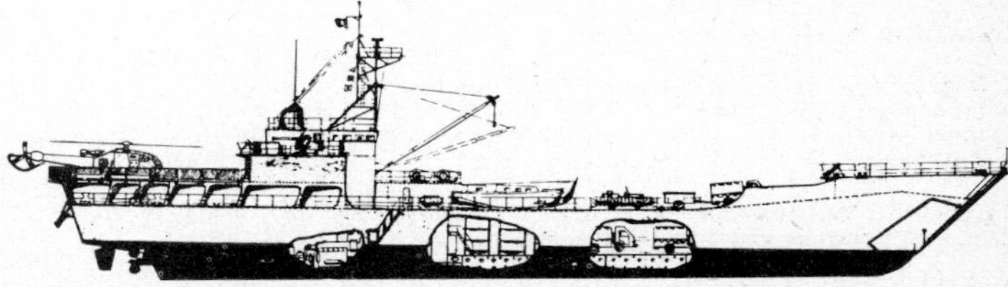

BATRAL TYPE *1974 French Navy*

SMALL TRANSPORTS

(SMALL TRANSPORTS)

ALPHÉE Y 696
ARIEL Y 604
DRYADE Y 662
ELFE Y 741
FAUNE Y 613
KORRIGAN Y 661
MORGANE Y 671

Displacement, tons	195 standard; 225 full load
Dimensions, ft (*m*)	132·8 × 24·5 × 10·8 (*40·5 × 7·5 × 3·3*)
Main engines	2 diesels; 2 shafts; 1 640 bhp = 15 knots
Complement	9

Ariel was launched on 27 Apr 1964. *Korrigan* on 6 Mar 1964, *Alphée* on 10 June 1969. *Elfe* on 14 Apr 1970, *Faune* on 8 Sept 1971 *Dryade* in 1973, *Morgane* in May 1973. All built by S. F. de CN. except Y671 by A. du Mourillon. Can carry 400 passengers.

ALPHÉE *1972, courtesy Admiral M. Adam*

SYLPHE Y 710

Displacement, tons	171 standard; 189 full load
Dimensions, ft (*m*)	126·5 × 22·7 × 8·2 (*38·5 × 6·9 × 2·5*)
Main engines	MGO diesel; 1 shaft; 425 bhp = 12 knots
Complement	9

Small transport for personnel, built by Chantiers Franco-Belge in 1959-60.

Small Transports—*cont.*

SAINTONGE (*ex-Santa Maria*) A 733

Measurements, ton: 300 standard; 990 full weight
Dimensions, ft (*m*): 177× 28 × 10·5 (*54 × 8·5 × 3·2*)
Main engines: 1 diesel; 1 shaft; 760 bhp = 10 knots
Complement: 15

Built by Chantiers Duchesne et Bossière, Le Havre, for a Norwegian owner under the name of *Sven Germa*. Launched on 12 July 1956. Purchased in Apr 1965 from the firm of H. Beal & Co, Fort de France for the Pacific Nuclear Experimental Centre.

FALLERON (*ex-German Welle*) A 614

Displacement, tons: 200 standard; 429 full load
Dimensions, ft (*m*): 128·0 × 22·0 × 7·8 (*39 × 6·7 × 2·3*)
Main engines: 1 Sulzer diesel; 280 bhp = 8 knots
Range, miles: 1 600 at 8 knots
Complement: 11

MÉLUSINE Y 736 — **MERLIN** Y 735

Displacement, tons: 170
Dimensions, ft (*m*): 103·3 × 23·2 × 7·9 (*31·5 × 7·1 × 2·4*)
Main engines: MGO diesels; 2 shafts; 960 bhp = 11 knots

Small transports for 400 personnel built in 1966 by Chantiers Navals Franco-Belges at Chalon sur Saône. Both laid down in Dec 1966 and accepted on 1 June 1968. Their home port is Toulon.

TRÉBÉRON (ex-B 254) Y 712

Displacement, tons: 120 standard; 140 full load
Dimensions, ft (*m*): 82·0 × 19·7 × 9·5 (*25 × 6 × 2·9*)
Main engines: Diesel; 1 shaft; 120 bhp = 8·5 knots

Former German danlayer used as small personnel transport for local port service.

LUTIN (ex-*Georges Clemenceau*) Y 664

Displacement, tons: 68
Main engines: 400 hp = 10 knots

Purchased in 1965. Ex-vedette. Detection school, Toulon.

DIVING TENDERS

Note. Ex-minesweepers *Ajonc* A 701 and *Gardénia* A 711 of "Acacia" class and *Myosotis* A 710 of "Ham" class operate as Diving Tenders.

ARMOISE (ex-M 772)	A 741	**HORTENSIA** (ex-M 783)	A 740
CAPUCINE (ex-M 782)	A 738	**OEILLET** (ex M 774)	A 739
DAHLIA (ex-M 786)	A 736	**PAQUERETTE** (ex-M 775)	A 742
HIBISCUS (ex-M 785)	A 735	**TULIPE** (ex-M 771)	A 737

Ex-MSI's of "HAM" class. See under Minewarfare Forces for details.

BELOUGA A 724 (ex-*Côte d'Argent*)

Displacement, tons: 225 standard; 270 full load
Dimensions, ft (*m*): 85·3 × 22·6 × 9·8 (*26 × 6·9 × 3*)
Main engines: 1 Baudouin DV 8 diesel; 400 bhp = 9·5 knots
Complement: 11 (1 officer, 10 men)

Tunny fisher built 1958. purchased in 1966 for conversion into a diving tender. Used for training groups of up to 16 clearance divers.

SSBN TENDER. A 1 200-ton service lighter of 1 000 hp for nuclear fuel elements of SSBNs was launched on 26 Oct 1967 for delivery in May 1968.

SAIL TRAINING SHIPS

CHIMERE Y 706 — **FARFADET** Y 711

Auxiliary sail training ships built at Bayonne in 1971. Tenders to the Naval School.

LA BELLE-POULE A 650 — **L'ÉTOILE** A 649

Displacement tons: 227
Dimensions, ft (*m*): 128 oa × 23·7 × 11·8 (*32·3 × 7 × 3·2*)
Main engines: Sulzer diesels; 120 bhp = 6 knots

Auxiliary sail vessels. Built by Chantiers de Normandie (Fécamp) in 1932. Accommodation for 3 officers, 30 cadets, 5 petty officers, 12 men. Attached to Navy School.

LA GRANDE HERMINE (ex-*Ménestral*) A 653

Ex sailing fishing boat built in 1936. Purchased in 1963 in replacement for *Dolphin* (ex-*Simone Marcelle*) as the School of Manoeuvre Training ship. Length 46 feet.

MUTIN A 652

A small 57 ton coastal tender built in 1927. Auxiliary diesel and sails attached to the Navigation School.

TUGS

TENACE A 669 — **CENTAURE** A 674

Displacement, tons: 1 080 light; 1 454 full load
Dimensions, ft (*m*): 167·3 oa × 37·8 (*51 × 11·5*)
Main engines: 2 diesels; Kort engines 4 600 hp = 15 knots
Range, miles: 9 500 at 15 knots
Complement: 42

New oceangoing tugs. A 669 built by Joelkers, Hamburg, A 674 built at La Pallice 1972-74.

Tugs—*continued*

2 NEW CONSTRUCTION

Dimensions, ft (*m*): 92·7 × 25 × 13 (*28·3 × 7·6 × 4*)
Main engines: 1 MGO diesel; 1 000 hp = 11 knots

Built at Lorient. Delivery, one at Toulon Jan 1974, one at Brest May 1974.

ACTIF	A 686	**HERCULE**	A 667	**ROBUSTE**	A 685
COURAGEUX	A 706	**LABORIEUX**	A 687	**TRAVAILLEUR**	A 692
LE FORT	A 671	**LUTTEUR**	A 673	**VALEUREUX**	A 688
				UTILE	A 672

Displacement, tons: 230
Dimensions, feet: 92 × 26 × 13
Main engines: 1 MGO diesel; 1 050 bhp = 11 knots
Range, miles: 2 400 miles
Complement: 15

Courageux, Hercule, Robuste and *Valeureux* were completed in 1960 and the other four in 1962-63 at Le Havre, and F. Ch.de la Méditerranée for service at Cherbourg (*Lutteur*). Toulon (*Actif, Robuste* and *Travailleur*) and Brest (*Hercule, Laborieux* and *Valeureux*).

HIPPOPOTAME (ex-*Utrecht*) A 660 — **RHINOCEROS** A 668

Displacement tons: 640
Main engines: Diesel-electric; 1 850 shp = 12 knots

A 660 built as USN ATA of *Maricopa* class. Former Netherlands high sea tug. Built in 1943. Purchased by the French Navy in Jan 1964 to be used at the Experimental Base in the Pacific.

BÉLIER A 719 — **PACHYDERME** A 718

Displacement, tons: 900 standard; 1 185 and 1 115 full load respectively
Main engines: 2 000 ihp = 12 knots
Oil fuel (tons): 180
Range, miles: 3 000

INFATIGABLE (ex- *Polangen*) A 661

Displacement, tons: 715
Main engines: 1 300 ihp = 11 knots

IMPLACABLE (ex-*Fohn II*) A 670

Displacement, tons: 800
Main engines: 1 300 ihp = 11 knots

ÉLÉPHANT (ex-*Bar*) A 666

Displacement, tons: 810 standard; 1 180 full load
Main engines: 2 000 ihp = 12 knots

COOLIE A 684

Displacement, tons: 300
Main engines: 1 000 hp

GOLIATH A 665

Displacement, tons: 380
Main engines: 900 hp

BAMBOU Y 608 — **HAUT-BARR** Y 652

HARBOUR TUGS. Of 200 tons and 11 knots.

29 of 105 tons and 10 knots.

Y 601 *Acajou*, Y 607 *Balsa*, Y 612 *Bouleau*, Y 620 *Chataigner*, Y 623 *Charme*, Y 624 *Chêne*, Y 628 *Oukomé*, Y 629 *Cormier*, Y 630 *Noyer*, Y 635 *Equeurdville*, Y 644 *Frêne*, Y 654 *Hétre*, Y 655 *Hévéa*, Y 663 *Latanier*, Y 666 *Manguier*, Y 668 *Mélêze*, Y 669 *Merisier*, Y 686 *Palétuviér*, Y 688 *Peuplier*, Y 689 *Pin*, Y 695 *Platane*, Y 708 *Saule* Y 709 *Sycomore*, Y 717 *Ebêne*, Y 718 *Erable*, Y 719 *Olivier*, Y 720 *Santal*, Y 738 *Marroneir* Y 740 *Papayer*.

WATER BOATS

OASIS

Displacement, tons: 335 standard; 683 full load
Dimensions, ft (*m*): 164·8 × 27 × 9 (*50·2 × 8·2 × 2·7*)
Guns: 2—20 mm AA
Main engines: Triple expansion; 1 shaft; 875 ihp = 10 knots

Built by A. C. Bretagne.

CATARACTE

Small water carrier of 330 tons and 10 knots.

GERMANY (Federal Republic)

Bundesmarine Administration

Chief of Naval Staff, Federal German Navy:
Vice-Admiral Heinz Kühnle

Commander-in-Chief of the Fleet:
Vice Admiral Paul Hartwig

Diplomatic Representation

Naval Attaché in London
Rear Admiral Dr. W. Schünemann

Naval Attaché in Washington:
Captain Andreas Wiese

Naval Attaché in Paris:
Captain Carl Hoffmann

Personnel

(a) 1970: 39,000 (3 900 officers, 35 100 men)
1971: 35 000 (3 200 officers, 31 800 men)
1972: 35 900 (4 500 officers, 31 400 men)
1973: 36 000 (4 550 officers, 31 450 men)
1974: 36 000 (4 550 officers, 31 450 men)
(Includes Naval Air Arm)
(b) 15 months National Service

Future Development

Interest is being shown by the Naval Staff in various and varied projects.
(a) Development of more powerful ship-to-ship missiles.
(b) Development of SAM's and ASM's.
(c) Installation of coastal missiles.
(d) Construction of 250 ton hydrofoils of US *Tucumcari* type.
(e) New frigates of 2 500 tons with guided weapons to replace Hamburg, Z, and Köln Classes—10 planned.

Strength of the Fleet

Type	*Active*	*Building (Projected)*
Destroyers	11	—
Frigates	6	(10)
Corvettes	6	—
Submarines—Patrol	28	2
Fast Attack Craft (Missile)	12	18
Fast Attack Craft (Torpedo)	29	—
LCU's	22	—
LCM's	28	—
Minesweepers—Coastal	18	—
Minesweepers—Inshore	44	—
Depot Ships	13	—
Repair Ships	3 (1 small)	—
Replenishment Tankers (Small)	6	—
Support Tankers	5	—
Supply Ships	9	—
Ammunition Transports	3	—
Mine Transports	2	—
Training Ship	1	—
Sail Training Ships	2	—
Misc. Tenders	5	—
Rescue Launches	7	—
Tugs—Ocean	16	—
Tugs—Harbour	9	—
*Icebreakers	3	—
*Coastguard Craft	8+	—
*Survey Ships	6	—
*Fishery Protection Ships	7	—
*Experimental Ships	10	—

*Non-naval

Naval Air Arm

6 000 men total
2 LRPM squadrons (15 Breguet Atlantic)
4 Fighter bomber squadrons (60 F104G)
1 Helicopter squadron (re-equipping with 22 Sea King Mk 41—First pair delivered June 1973).
Communication aircraft (20 DO 28)

Mercantile Marine

Lloyd's Register of Shipping:
2,234 vessels of 7 914 679 tons gross

Hydrographic Service

This service is under the direction of the Ministry of Transport, is civilian manned with HQ at Hamburg. Survey ships are listed at the end of the section.

Disposals

Destroyers
1972 Z1

Frigates
1972 *Scharnhorst* and *Gneisenau*

Fast Attack Craft (Torpedo)
1972 *Marder, Weihe*
1973 *Fuchs, Häher, Jaguar, Kranich, Leopard, Luchs, Panther Pinguin, Reiher*

Minelayers
1972 *Bochum, Bottrop* Transferred to Turkey.

Minesweepers Coastal
1973 6 "Vegesack" class

Minesweepers Inshore
6 "Schütze" class

Supply Ship
1972 *Angeln* Transferred to Turkey

DESTROYERS

3 MODIFIED "ADAMS" CLASS DDG

Name	*No.*	*Builders*	*Laid down*	*Launched*	*Completion*
LUTJENS	D 185 (USN-DDG 28)	Bath Iron Works Corp	1 Mar 1966	11 Aug 1967	12 Mar 1969
MÖLDERS	D 186 (USN-DDG 29)	Bath Iron Works Corp	12 Apr 1966	13 Apr 1968	12 Sep 1969
ROMMEL	D 187 (USN-DDG 30)	Bath Iron Works Corp	22 Aug 1967	1 Feb 1969	24 Apr 1970

Displacement, tons	3 370 standard; 4 500 full load
Length, feet (*metres*)	431 (*131·4*) wl; 440 (*134·1*) oa
Beam, feet (*metres*)	47 (*14·3*)
Draught, feet (*metres*)	20 (*6·1*)
Missile launchers	1 "Tartar" single
Guns, dual purpose	2—5 in (*127 mm*) single
A/S launchers	"Asroc"; 2 triple torpedo; 1 DCT
Boilers	4 Combustion Engineering; 1 200 psi (*84·4 kg/cm²*)
Main engines	Geared steam turbines 70 000 shp; 2 shafts
Oil fuel, tons	900
Range, miles	4 500 at 20 knots
Speed, knots	35
Complement	340 (21 officers, 319 men)

LÜTJENS 1974, Federal German Navy

GENERAL

Destroyers basically of the "Charles F. Adams" type; but modified to suit Federal German requirements and practice and presenting a different silhouette. 1965 contract. Cost $43 754 000. Due for modernisation from Autumn 1974, starting with *Rommel*.

RADAR. SPS 52 three dimensional air search and target designator with aerial on after funnel. SPS 50 air surveillance with aerial on mainmast. Two SPG 51 Tartar fire control aerials abaft after funnel. One SPS 10 surface warning set. One GFCS 68 for gun armament Tacan beacon. Satir 2 ADA system (believed similar to Senit 2).

LÜTJENS *Class*

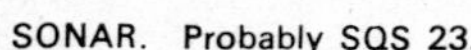
SONAR. Probably SQS 23.

Destroyers—*continued*

ROMMEL *1972*

4 "HAMBURG" CLASS

Name	*No.*	*Builders*	*Laid down*	*Launched*	*Completed*
BAYERN	D 183	H. C. Stülcken Sohn, Hamburg	1961	14 Aug 1962	6 July 1965
HAMBURG	D 181	H. C. Stülcken Sohn, Hamburg	1959	26 Mar 1960	23 Mar 1964
HESSEN	D 184	H. C. Stülcken Sohn, Hamburg	1962	4 May 1963	8 Oct 1968
SCHLESWIG-HOLSTEIN	D 182	H. C. Stülcken Sohn, Hamburg	1959	20 Aug 1960	12 Oct 1964

Displacement, tons	3 400 standard; 4 400 full load
Length, feet (*metres*)	420 (*128*) wl; 439·7 (*134·0*) oa
Beam, feet (*metres*)	44 (*13·4*)
Draught, feet (*metres*)	17 (*5·2*)
Guns, dual purpose	4—3·9 in (*100 mm*) single
Guns, AA	8—40 mm, 4 twin
A/S weapons	2 Bofors 4-barrel DC Mortars; 1 DCT
Torpedo tubes	5—21 in (*533 mm*), 3 bow and 2 stern; 2—12 in for AS torpedoes
Boilers	4 Wahodag; 910 psi (*64 kg/cm²*), 860°F (460°C)
Main engines	2 Wahodag dr geared turbines; 68 000 shp; 2 shafts
Speed, knots	35·8 max; 18 economical sea
Range, miles	6 000 at 13 knots; 920 at 35 knots
Complement	280 (17 officers, 263 men)

GENERAL
All named after countries of the German Federal Republic. Capable of minelaying.

ELECTRONICS. FCS for Bofors A/S launcher, Torpedoes and DC from Hollandse. ECM fitted.

RADAR. All Radar by Hollandse Signaalapparaten. One air warning LW 02/3. One DAO 2 target designator. One nav/surface warning set. Two M45 100 mm fire control sets. Two M45 40 mm fire control sets.

HESSEN *1973, Wright & Logan*

HAMBURG *Class*

BAYERN *1971, Wright & Logan*

Destroyers—*continued*

4 Ex-US "FLETCHER" CLASS

Name	No.	Builders	Laid down	Launched	Completed	German commissioned
Z 2 (ex-USS *Ringgold, DD* 500)	D 171	Federal SB & DD Co, Port Newark	25 June 1942	11 Nov 1942	24 Dec 1942	14 July **1959**
Z 3 (ex-USS *Wadsworth, DD* 516)	D 172	Bath Iron Works Corporation, Maine	18 Aug 1942	10 Jan 1943	16 Mar 1943	6 Oct **1959**
Z 4 (ex-USS *Claxton, DD* 571)	D 178	Consolidated Steel Corporation, Orange	25 June 1941	1 Apr 1942	8 Dec 1942	15 Dec **1959**
Z 5 (ex-USS *Dyson, DD* 572)	D 179	Consolidated Steel Corporation, Orange	25 June 1941	15 Apr 1942	30 Dec 1942	23 Feb **1960**

Displacement, tons	2 100 standard; 2 750 full load
Length, feet (*metres*)	368·4 (*112·3*) wl; 376·5 (*114·8*) oa
Beam, feet (*metres*)	39·5 (*12*)
Draught, feet (*metres*)	18 (*5·5*) max
Guns, dual purpose	4—5 in (*127 mm*) 38 cal.
Guns, AA	6—3 in (*76 mm*) 50 cal., 3 twin mountings
A/S	2 hedgehogs; 1 DC rack
Torpedo tubes	5—21 in (*533 mm*), quintuple bank; 2 ASW tubes
Boilers	4 Babcock & Wilcox; 569 psi (*40 kg/cm²*); 851°F (*455°C*)
Main engines	2 sets GE geared turbines 60 000 shp; 2 shafts
Speed, knots	35 max; 17 economical sea speed
Range, miles	6 000 at 15 knots
Oil fuel (tons)	540
Complement	250

Z1 *Class*

GENERAL
Former US "Fletcher" class destroyers. Their loan from the United States for five years was extended. First ship arrived at Bremerhaven on 14 Apr 1958. *Ringgold* was transferred by the USA at Charleston, S.C. on 14 July 1969. Capable of minelaying.

RADAR. Search: SPS 6. Tactical: SPS 10. Fire Control: GFCS 56 and 68.

Z 3 *1972,*

FRIGATES

6 "KOLN" CLASS

Name	No.	Builders	Launched	Completed
AUGSBURG	F 222	H. C. Stülcken Sohn, Hamburg	15 Aug 1959	7 Apr 1962
BRAUNSCHWEIG	F 225	H. C. Stülcken Sohn, Hamburg	3 Feb 1962	16 June 1964
EMDEN	F 221	H. C. Stülcken Sohn, Hamburg	21 Mar 1959	24 Oct 1961
KARLSRUHE	F 223	H. C. Stülcken Sohn, Hamburg	24 Oct 1959	15 Dec 1962
KÖLN	F 220	H. C. Stülcken Sohn, Hamburg	6 Dec 1958	15 Apr 1961
LUBECK	F 224	H. C. Stülcken Sohn, Hamburg	23 July 1960	6 July 1963

Displacement, tons	2 100 standard; 2 550 full load
Length, feet (*metres*)	360·9 (*110*)
Beam, feet (*metres*)	36·1 (*11·0*)
Draught, feet (*metres*)	11·2 (*3·4*)
Guns, dual purpose	2—3·9 in (*100 mm*)
Guns, AA	6—40 mm; 2 twin and 2 single
A/S	2 Bofors 4-barrel DC mortars (rocket launchers)
Torpedo tubes	2 for ASW torpedoes
Main engines	Combined diesel and gas turbine plant: 4 MAN 16-cyl. diesels, total 12 000 bhp; 2 Brown-Boveri gas turbines, 24 000 bhp; total 36 000 shp; 2 shafts
Speed, knots	32 max; 23 economical sea speed;
Range, miles	920 at full power
Oil fuel, tons	333
Complement	210

GENERAL
Ordered in Mar 1957. All ships of this class are named after towns of West Germany. Capable of minelaying.

LUBECK *1972*

ELECTRONICS. Hollandse FCS for Bofors A/S launchers M9 torpedo fire control.

RADAR. All by Hollandse. One DA 02 target designator. One nav/surface warning set. Two M45 100 mm fire control sets. Two M45 40 mm fire control sets.

ENGINEERING. Each of the two shafts is driven by two diesels coupled and geared to one BBC gas turbine. Controllable pitch propellers. A speed of 32 knots is reported to have been attained on full power trials.

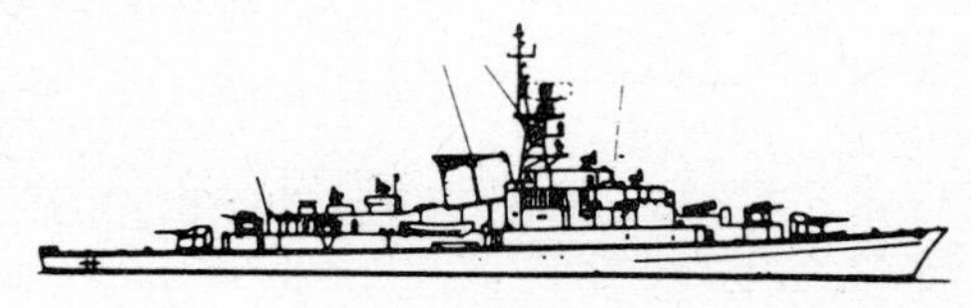
KÖLN *Class*

Frigates—*continued*

BRAUNSCHWEIG *1971, Skyfotos*

CORVETTES

HANS BÜRKNER Y 879

Displacement, tons	982 standard; 1 100 full load
Dimensions, feet	265·2 oa × 30·8 × 10
Guns	2—40 mm AA (twin mounting)
A/S weapons	1 DC mortar (four-barrelled), 2 DC racks
Main Engines	4 MAN diesels; 2 shafts; 13 600 shp = 25 knots
Complement	50

Torpedofangboot. Built by Atlaswerke, Bremen. Launched on 16 July 1961. Completed on 18 May 1963. Named after designer of German pre-First World War battleships.

HANS BÜRKNER *1970*

5 "THETIS" CLASS

HERMES P 6112
NAJADE P 6113
THESEUS P 6115
TRITON P 6114
THETIS P 6111

Displacement, tons	564 standard; 680 full load
Dimensions, feet	229·7 × 27 × 7·5
Guns	2—40 mm AA (twin mounting) (To be replaced by 1—3 in Oto Melara)
A/S weapons	Bofors DC mortar (*Hermes* 2 tubes)
Main engines	2 MAN diesels; 2 shafts; 6 800 bhp = 24 knots
Complement	48

Built by Roland Werft, Bremen-Hemelingen. Some have computer house before bridge. *Thetis* commissioned on 1 July 1961, *Hermes* on 16 Dec 1961, *Najada* on 12 May 1962, *Triton* on 10 Nov 1962, *Theseus* on 15 Aug 1963. Combined nav/surface warning radar. HSA M9 series torpedo control.

THESEUS (blockbridge type) *1970*

NAJADE (forebridge type) *1970, Skyfotos*

SUBMARINES

18 NEW CONSTRUCTION TYPE 206

U 13 S 192
U 14 S 193
U 15 S 194
U 16 S 195
U 17 S 196
U 18 S 197
U 19 S 198
U 20 S 199
U 21 S 170
U 22 S 171
U 23 S 172
U 24 S 173
U 25 S 174
U 26 S 175
U 27 S 176
U 28 S 177
U 29 S 178
U 30 S 179

Displacement, tons	500 nominal, 600 submerged
Length, feet (*metres*)	147·6 (*45·0*)
Beam, feet (*metres*)	15·4 (*4·7*)
Torpedo tubes	8 bow
Main engines	Diesel-electric; 1 shaft; 1 800 hp
Speed, knots	17 max submerged
Complement	22

Authorised on 7 June 1969 from Howaldtswerke Deutsche Werft (8) and Reinstahl Nordseewerke (10).

U 13, U 14, U 16, U 17, U 18, and U 19, were completed in 1973. Launch dates of remainder as follows: U 20, 16 Jan 1973 — U 21, 9 Mar 1973 — U 22, 27 Mar 1973 — U 23, 22 May 1974 — U 24, 24 June 1973 — U 25, 23 May 1973 — U 26, 20 Nov 1973 — U 27, 21 Aug 1973 — U 28, 22 Jan 1974 — U 29, 5 Sep 1973 — U 30, 26 Mar 1974.

U 13 *1973, Howaldtswerke, Kiel*

Submarines—*continued*

11 TYPE 205

U 1 (21 Oct 1961) S 180	**U 7** (29 May 1963) S 186
U 2 (25 Jan 1962) S 181	**U 8** (11 Oct 1963) S 187
U 4 (22 Aug 1962) S 183	**U 9** (20 Oct 1966) S 188
U 5 (22 Nov 1962) S 184	**U 10** (20 July 1967) S 189
U 6 (22 Apr 1963) S 185	**U 11** (9 Feb 1968) S 190
	U 12 (10 Sep 1968) S 191

U I — *1973, Howaldtswerke, Kiel*

Displacement, tons	370 surface; 450 submerged
Length, feet (*metres*)	142·7 (*43·5*) oa
Beam, feet (*metres*)	15·1 (*4·6*)
Draught, feet (*metres*)	13·5 (*4·3*)
Torpedo tubes	8 in bow
Main engines	2 MB diesels; total 1 200 bhp 2 electric motors, total 1 700 bhp; single screw
Speed, knots	10 on surface; 17 submerged
Complement	21

GENERAL
All built by Howaldtswerke, Kiel in floating docks. Original launch dates above. Fitted with schnorkel. First submarines designed and built by Germany since the end of the Second World War. U 4-12 were built to a heavier and improved design. U 1 and U 2 were modified accordingly and refloated on 17 Feb 1967 and 15 July 1966 respectively. U 1 was reconstructed late 1963 to 4 Mar 1965. (See original appearance in the 1962-63 and 1963-64 editions). U 4-8 are sheathed with zinc. U9-12 have hulls of different steel alloys of non-magnetic properties. U 7 snd U 11 entered service on 22 May 1968 and 21 June 1968, respectively. U 12 was completed on 14 Jan 1969. U 3 of this class lent to Norway on 10 July 1962 and temporarily named *Kobben* (S 310), was returned to Germany in 1964 and decommissioned on 15 Sep 1967 for disposal.

different steel alloys of non-magnetic properties. U 7 and U 11 entered service on 22 May 1968 and 21 June 1968, respectively. U 12 was completed on 14 Jan 1969. U 3 of this class lent to Norway on 10 July 1962 and temporarily named *Kobben* (S 310), was returned to Germany in 1964 and decommissioned on 15 Sep 1967 for disposal.

RADAR. French Thomson-CSF Calypso, nav/attack set. Passive DF.

TORPEDO EQUIPMENT. The boats are trimmed by the stern to load through the bow caps. Also fitted for minelaying. Fire control by Hollandse Sig. Mk 8.

1 CONVERTED TYPE XXI

WILHELM BAUER (ex-U 2540) Y 880

Displacement, tons	1 620 surface; 1 820 submerged
Length, feet (*metres*)	252·7 (*77·0*) pp
Beam, feet (*metres*)	21·7 (*6·6*)
Draught, feet (*metres*)	20·3 (*6·2*)
Torpedo tubes	4—21 in (*533 mm*) in bow
Main engines	Diesel-electric drive 2 diesels total 4 200 bhp 2 electric motors total 5 000 hp
Speed, knots	15·5 surface; 17·5 submerged

Launched in 1944 by Blohm & Voss, Hamburg. Sunk on 3 May 1945. Raised in 1957. Rebuilt in 1958-59 at Howaldtswerke, Kiel. Commissioned on 1 Sep 1960. Used for experiments on submarine equipment. Conning tower was modified.

WILHELM BAUER — *1973, Howaldtswerke, Kiel*

LIGHT FORCES

10 NEW CONSTRUCTION TYPE 143

(FAST ATTACK CRAFT—MISSILE)

S 61 P 6111	**S 64** P 6114	**S 67** P 6117	**S 69** P 6119
S 62 P 6112	**S 65** P 6115	**S 68** P 6118	**S 70** P 6120
S 63 P 6113	**S 66** P 6116		

Displacement, tons	295 nominal; 378 full load
Dimensions, ft (*m*)	200·0 × 24·6 × 8·5 (*57 × 7·8 × 2·4*)
Missiles	4 launchers for "Exocet" MM 38
Guns	2—76 mm AA (Italian Oto Melara)
Torpedoes	2—21 in wire guided aft
Main engines	4 MTU diesels; 4 shafts = 38 knots
Range, miles	1 300 at 30 knots 16 000 hp
Complement	40

MODEL TYPE 143 — *1974, Federal German Navy*

GENERAL
Ordered in 1972. To be completed from 1974 to 1976 to replace ten torpedo boats of the "Jaguar" class. Final funds allocated 13 July 1972. First laid down late 1972. Builders; S 61-64, 66, 68 and 70 at Lürssen and S 65, 67 and 69 at Kröger, Rendsburg.

ELECTRONICS.
Believed that data automation system AGIS is being fitted to permit use of Type 143 as control ship for concerted operation of Type 148 boats.

RADAR.
All by Hollandse Signaal. WM 27 in radome for Exocet, gun and torpedo control.

Light Forces—*continued*

20 NEW CONSTRUCTION TYPE 148

(FAST ATTACK CRAFT—MISSILE)

S 41	P 6141	**S 42**	P 6142	**S 43**	P 6143	**S 44**	P 6144
S 45	P 6145	**S 46**	P 6146	**S 47**	P 6147	**S 48**	P 6148
S 49	P 6149	**S 50**	P 6150	**S 51**	P 6151	**S 52**	P 6152
S 53	P 6153	**S 54**	P 6154	**S 55**	P 6155	**S 56**	P 6156
S 57	P 6157	**S 58**	P 6158	**S 59**	P 6159	**S 60**	P 6160

Displacement, tons: 234 standard; 265 full load
Dimensions, ft (*m*): 154·2 × 23·0 × 5·9 (*47 × 7 × 2*)
Missiles: 4 launchers for "Exocet" MM 38
Guns: 1—76 mm AA (Oto Melara); 1—40 mm AA (Bofors)
Main engines: 4 MTU diesels; 4 shafts; 14 400 bhp = 38·5 knots
Oil fuel, tons: 39
Range, miles: 600 at 30 knots
Complement: 30 (4 officers, 26 men)

GENERAL
Ordered in Oct 1970. To be completed from 1973 onwards to replace the "Jaguar" class. All to be operational by end 1975. Builders: Constructions Mecaniques de Normandy, Cherbourg. Eight hulls contracted to Lürssen but all are to fit-out in France. Up to S 49 commissioned by Spring 1974.

Launch and completion dates:

	Launched	*Completion*
S 41	27 Mar 1972	30 Oct 1972
S 42	12 Dec 1972	8 Jan 1973
S 43	7 Mar 1973	9 Apr 1973
S 44	5 May 1973	14 June 1973
S 45	3 July 1973	Aug 1973
S 46	9 Apr 1973	May 1973
S 47	20 Sep 1973	Oct 1973

S 53 and 54 laid down Oct 1973.

RADAR. X-Band nav radar. Triton C-band air and surface search and target designator with IFF aerial POLLUX X-band tracking radar. Thomson-CSF VEGA-POLLUX PCET control system and radar for control of EXOCET, torpedoes and guns. Less sophisticated than type 143.

S 41 — *1974, Federal German Navy*

10 "ZOBEL" CLASS

(TYPE 142 FAST ATTACK CRAFT—TORPEDO)

DACHS	P 6094	**HERMELIN**	P 6095	**OZELOT**	P 6101
FRETTCHEN	P 6100	**HYÄNE**	P 6099	**PUMA**	P 6097
GEPARD	P 6098	**NERZ**	P 6096	**WIESEL**	P 6093
				ZOBEL	P 6092

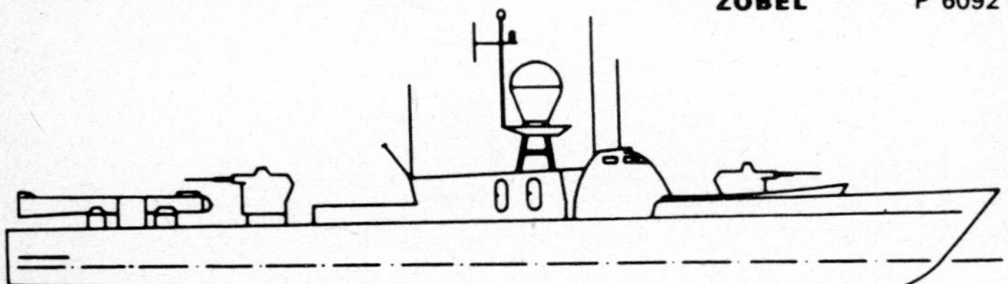

Displacement, tons: 225 full load
Dimensions, ft (*m*): 139·4 × 23·4 × 7·9 (*42·5 × 7·2 × 2·4*)
Guns: 2—40 mm AA Bofors L 70 (single)
Tubes: 2—21 in for Seal wire-guided torpedoes
Main engines: 4 Mercedes-Benz 20 cyl diesels; 4 shafts; 12 000 bhp = 40·5 knots
Complement: 39

Originally units of the "Jaguar" class, but, after conversion, known as the "Zobel" class. Two M 20 series Radars in radome for control of guns and torpedoes. Three built by Kröger, Rendsburg and seven by Lürssen, Vegesack.

DACHS — *1973, Stefan Terzibaschitch*

19 "JAGUAR" CLASS

(TYPE 140-141 FAST ATTACK CRAFT—TORPEDO)

ALBATROS *	P 6069	**GREIF ***	P 6071	**PELIKAN**	P 6086
ALK	P 6084	**HABICHT ***	P 6075	**SEEADLER ***	P 6068
BUSSARD *	P 6074	**ILTIS**	P 6058	**SPERBER ***	P 6076
DOMMEL	P 6091	**KONDOR ***	P 6070	**STORCH**	P 6085
ELSTER	P 6088	**KORMORAN ***	P 6077	**TIGER**	
FALKE *	P 6072	**LÖWE**	P 6065	**WOLF**	P 6062
GEIER *	P 6073				

Displacement, tons: 160 standard; 190 full load
Dimensions, ft (*m*): 139·4 × 23·4 × 7·9 (*42·5 × 7·2 × 2·4*)
Guns: 2—40 mm AA Bofors L 70 (single)
Tubes: 4—21 in (2 torpedo tubes can be removed for 4 mines)
Main engines: Mercedes-Benz 20 cyl or Maybach 16 cyl diesels; 4 shafts; 12 000 bhp = 42 knots
Complement: 39

32 boats were built by Lürssen, Vegesack in 1957-62 and eight by Kröger, Rendsburg in 1958-64. Of composite construction, with steel frames, mahogany diagonal carvel hulls, alloy bulkheads and superstructure. Units marked * are type 141 with Maybach diesels. Remainder are Type 140 with Mercedes-Benz diesels. Ten were converted into Type 142, see above. All to be paid off by 1975 on replacement by Types 143 and 148. Some may be available for foreign sale.

DOMMEL — *1971, Giorgio Arra*

AMPHIBIOUS FORCES

28 LCM TYPE

LCM 1-28

Displacement, tons: 116 standard; 140 full load
Dimensions, ft (*m*): 77·1 × 21·4 × — (*23·5 × 6·5 × —*)
Main engines: 1 320 hp = 10 knots

Similar to US LCM 8 Type. Built 1965-67.

22 LCU TYPE

BARBE	L 790	**FELCHEN**	L 793	**LACHS**	L 762	**SALM**	L 799
BRASSE	L 789	**FLUNDER**	L 760	**MAKRELE**	L 796	**SCHLEI**	L 765
BUTT	L 788	**FORELLE**	L 794	**MURANE**	L 797	**STÖR**	L 766
DELPHIN	L 791	**INGER**	L 795	**PLOTZE**	L 763	**TÜMMLER**	L 767
DORSCH	L 792	**KARPFEN**	L 761	**RENKE**	L 798	**WELS**	L 768
				ROCHEN	L 764	**ZANDER**	L 769

Displacement, tons: 200 light; 430 full load
Dimensions, ft (*m*): 136·5 × 28·9 × 6·9 (*42 × 8·8 × 2·1*)
Gun: 1—20 mm AA
Main engines: GM diesels; 2 shafts; 1 380 bhp = 12 knots
Complement: 17

Similar to the United States LCU (Landing Craft, Utility) type. Provided with bow and stern ramp. Built by Howaldt, Hamburg, 1964-67. To carry 160 tons load.

SCHLEI — *1970, Stefan Terzibaschitsch*

MINE WARFARE FORCES

18 "LINDAU" CLASS (MINESWEEPERS—COASTAL and MINEHUNTERS)

CUXHAVEN	M 1078	**KONSTANZ**	M 1081	**TÜBINGEN**	M 1074
DÜREN	M 1079	**LINDAU**	M 1072	**ULM**	M 1083
FLENSBURG	M 1084	**MARBURG**	M 1080	**VÖLKLINGEN**	M 1087
FULDA	M 1068	**MINDEN**	M 1085	**WIELHEIM**	M 1077
GÖTTINGEN	M 1070	**PADERBORN**	M 1076	**WETZLAR**	M 1075
KOBLENZ	M 1071	**SCHLESWIG**	M 1073	**WOLFSBURG**	M 1082

Displacement, tons	370 standard; 425 full load
Dimensions, feet	137·8 pp; 147·7 oa × 27·2 × 8·5
Gun	1—40 mm AA
Main engines	Maybach diesels; 2 shafts; 4 000 bhp = 17 knots
Complement	46

Lindau, first German built vessel for the Federal German Navy since the Second World War, launched on 16 Feb 1957. Basically of NATO WU type but modified for German requirements. Built by Burmester, Bremen-Berg. Seventeen were built in German yards in 1958-60. The hull is of wooden construction, laminated with plastic glue. The engines are of non-magnetic materials. The first six, *Gonttingen, Koblenz, Lindau, Schleswig, Tubingen* and *Wetzlar*, were modified with lower bridges in 1958-59. *Schleswig* was lengthened by 6·8 feet in 1960—all others in 1960-64. *Fulda* and *Flensburg* were converted into minehunters in 1968-69 as part of a total of twelve ships to be so converted.

KONSTANZ — *1973, C. & S. Taylor*

STIER (decompression chamber) — *1972*

10 "FRAUENLOB" CLASS (MINESWEEPERS—INSHORE)

ACHERON	Y 1661	**FRAUENLOB**	Y 1652	**MEDUSA**	Y 1655
ATLANTIS	Y 1660	**GEFION**	Y 1654	**MINERVA**	Y 1657
DIANA	Y 1658	**LORELEY**	Y 1659	**NAUTILUS**	Y 1653
				UNDINE	Y 1656

Displacement, tons	204 standard; 230 full load
Dimensions, feet	124·7 × 27·2 × 7·2
Gun	1—40 mm AA
Main engines	Diesels = 14 knots
Complement	24

Built by Kröger Werft, Rendsberg. Launched in 1965-67. Completed in 1965-68. Originally designed as *Kustenwachboote* or coastguard boats with "W" pennant numbers. Rated as inshore minesweepers in 1968 with the "M" hull numbers. Re-allocated "Y" numbers in 1970.

FRAUENLOB — *1973, Stefan Terzibaschitsch*

23 "SCHÜTZE" CLASS (MINESWEEPERS—INSHORE)

ATAIR	M 1067	**NEPTUN**	M 1093	**SKORPION**	M 1060
CASTOR	M 1051	**PERSEUS**	M 1090	**SPICA**	M 1059
DENEB	M 1064	**POLLUX**	M 1054	**STEINBOCK**	M 1091
FISCHE	M 1096	**PLUTO**	M 1092	**STIER**	Y 849
GEMMA	M 1097	**REGULUS**	M 1057	**WAAGE**	M 1063
HERKULES	M 1095	**RIGEL**	M 1056	**WEGA**	M 1089
JUPITER	M 1065	**SCHÜTZE**	M 1062	**WIDDER**	M 1094
MARS	M 1058	**SIRIUS**	M 1055		

Displacement, tons	200 standard; 226 full load
Dimensions, feet	144·5 pp; 154·5 oa × 22·3 × 7·2
Guns	1—40 mm AA (some still have the designed 2—40 mm) (except *Stier*)
Main engines	Maybach diesels; 2 shafts; Escher-Wyss propellers; 3 600 bhp = 24·5 knots

Castor, Fische, Gemma, Mars, Pollux, Regulus, Rigel, Schütze, Sirius, Skorpion, Spica, Steinbock, Stier, Waage, and *Wega* were built by Abeking & Rasmussen, Lemwerder; *Deneb, Jupiter, Pluto,* and *Widder* by Schürenstedt, Bardenfl; *Atair, Herkules, Neptun,* and *Perseus* by Schlichting, Travemünde. The design is a development of the "R" boats of the Second World War. All this class are named after stars. *Stier*, former hull number M 1061, carries no weapons, but has a decompression chamber, being security vessel for submarines. All completed in 1959-64.
Formerly classified as inshore minesweepers, but re-rated as fast minesweepers in 1966.

DENEB — *1973, Ste·an Terzibaschitsch*

HOLNIS Y 836 (ex-M 2651) (MINESWEEPER—INSHORE)

Displacement, tons	180
Dimensions, feet	116·8 × 24·3 × 6·9
Guns	1—20 mm AA
Main engines	2 Mercedes-Benz diesels; 2 shafts; 2 000 bhp = 14·5 knots
Complement	21

Now serving for test and evaluation purposes. *Holnis* was launched on 22 May 1965 and completed in 1966 by Abeking & Rasmussen, Lemwerde, as the prototype of a new design of *Binnenminensuchboote* projected as a class of 20 such vessels but she is the only unit of this type, the other 19 boats having been cancelled. Hull number changed from M 2651 to Y 836 in 1970.

HOLNIS — ***1972***

Mine Warfare Forces—*continued*

2 "NIOBE" CLASS (MINESWEEPERS—INSHORE)

HANSA Y 806 **NIOBE** Y 1643

Displacement, tons	150 standard; 180 full load
Dimensions, feet	115·2 × 21·3 × 5·6
Gun	1—40 mm AA
Main engines	*Hansa:* 1 Mercedes-Benz diesel; 1 shaft; 950 bhp = 14 knots *Niobe:* 2 Mercedes-Benz diesels; 2 shafts; 1 900 bhp = 16 knots
Complement	*Hansa* 19; *Niobe* 22

Built by Kröger Werft, Rendsburg. Launch dates above. Completed in 1958. The post-war prototype vessels of the category, formerly designated *Küstenwachboote* or coastal patrol vessels but re-rated as *Binnenminensuchboote* or inshore minesweepers in 1966. Named after former cruisers. *Hansa* serves as support ship for minedivers. *Niobe* (photograph in the 1967-68 edition) serves for test and evaluation purposes.

HANSA *1970, Stefan Terzibaschitsch*

8 "ARIADNE" CLASS (MINESWEEPERS—INSHORE)

AMAZONE	(27 Feb 1963)	Y 1650	**HERTHA**	(18 Feb 1961)	Y 1647
ARIADNE	(23 Apr 1960)	Y 1644	**NIXE**	(3 Dec 1962)	Y 1649
FREYA	(25 June 1966)	Y 1645	**NYMPHE**	(20 Nov 1962)	Y 834
GAZELLE	(14 Aug 1963)	Y 1651	**VINETA**	(17 Sep 1960)	Y 1646

Displacement, tons	184 standard; 210 full load
Dimensions, feet	124·3 × 27·2 × 6·6
Guns	1—40 mm AA
Main engines	2 Mercedes-Benz diesels; 2 shafts; 2 000 bhp = 14 knots
Complement	23

Launch dates above. All completed by Krögerwerft, Rendsburg, in 1960-63. All named after former cruisers, 1897-1900. Formerly classified as patrol boats (*Küstenwachboote*) but re-rated as inshore minesweepers in 1966, and given new M hull numbers in Jan 1968, and Y hull numbers in 1970. In reserve.

FREYA *1970*

SERVICE FORCES

12 "RHEIN" CLASS (DEPOT SHIPS)

DONAU	69	**LECH**	56	**RHEIN**	58
ELBE	61	**MAIN**	63	**SAAR**	65
ISAR	54	**MOSEL**	67	**WERRA**	68
LAHN	55	**NECKAR**	66	**WESER**	62

Displacement, tons	2 370 standard; 2 800 full load except *Lahn* and *Lech* 2 460 standard; 2 680 full load
Length, feet (*metres*)	304·5 (*92·8*) wl; 323·5 (*98·6*) oa
Beam, feet (*metres*)	38·8 (*11·8*)
Draught, feet (*metres*)	11·2 (*3·4*); 12·2 (*3·3*) in *Lahn* and *Lech*
Guns, AA	2—3·9 in (*100 mm*); none in *Lahn, Lech*; 4—40 mm
Main engines	6 Maybach or Daimler diesels; Diesel-electric drive in *Isar, Lahn, Lech, Mosel, Saar* 11 400 bhp; 2 shafts
Speed, knots	21·7 max. 15 economical sea speed
Range, miles	1 625 at 15 knots
Oil fuel, tons	334
Complement	110 (accommodation for 200) 198 (*Lahn* and *Lech*)

RUHR *1973, Federal German Navy*

GENERAL
Elbe, Mosel, Rhein, and *Ruhr* were built by Schliekerwerft, Hamburg, *Isar* by Blohm & Voss, Hamburg, *Weser* by Elsflether Werft, *Neckar* by Lúrssen, Bremen-Vegesack, *Saar* by Norderwerft, Hamburg, *Donau* by Schlichting, Travemunde, *Lahn* and *Lech* by Flender, Lúbeck, *Main, Werra* by Lindenau, Kiel-Friedrichsort. All completed in 1961-64. Rated as Depot Ships for minesweepers (*Isar, Mosel, Saar*), submarines (*Lahn, Lech*), Type 206 submarines (*Rhein*), and motor torpedo boats (others) but these ships with their 3·9 in (*100 mm*) guns could obviously be used in lieu of frigates.

RADAR. All by Hollandse. Search: HSA DA 02. Fire Control: Two HSA M 45 for 100 mm and 40 mm.

STATUS. Five of these comparatively new ships, namely *Donau, Isar, Lahn, Lech* and *Weser,* were placed in reserve by July 1968. This was part of the economy programme announced by the Federal German Navy in Sep 1967.

RHEIN ***Class***

2 Ex-US LST (REPAIR SHIPS)

ODIN (ex-USS *Diomedes, ARB* 11, ex-*LST* 1119) A 512
WOTAN (ex-USS *Ulysses, ARB* 9, ex-*LST* 967) A 513

Displacement, tons	1 625 light; 3 600 full load; (revised official figures)
Dimensions, feet	316 wl; 328 oa × 50 × 11
Guns	4—20 mm AA
Main engines	2 GM diesels, 2 shafts; 1 800 bhp = 11·6 knots
Oil fuel (tons)	600
Range, miles	15 000 at 9 knots

Repair Ships. Transferred under MAP in June 1961. *Odin* commissioned in Jan 1966 and *Wotan* on 2 Dec 1965.

WOTAN ***1970***

MEMMERT Y 805

The small repair ship *Memmert* Y 805 (ex-USN 106, ex-*India*, ex-BP 34), 165 tons, rated as torpedo repair ship, salvage vessel with a derrick.

Service Forces—*cont.*

FRANKENLAND (ex-*Münsterland*, ex-*Powell*) A 1439 (ex-Y 827) (REPLENISHMENT TANKER)

Displacement, tons	16 310
Dimensions, feet	521·8 × 70·2 × 37·5
Main engines	Diesels; 5 800 bhp = 13·5 knots

Built by Lithgows, Glasgow. Launched in 1950. Commissioned on 29 Apr 1959.

FRANKENLAND 1972

2 "EMSLAND" CLASS (REPLENISHMENT TANKERS)

EMSLAND (ex-*Antonio Zotti*) A 1440 (ex-Y 828)
MÜNSTERLAND (ex-*Angela Germona*) A 1441 (ex-Y 829)

Measurement, tons	6 200 gross (*Emsland*); 6 191 (*Münsterland*)
Dimensions, feet	461 × 54·2 × 25·8
Main engines	Diesel; CRDA; 4 800 bhp (*Emsland*); Fiat 5 500 bhp (*Münsterland*) = 13 knots

Built by CRDA Monfalcone, and Ansaldo, Genoa, respectively. Both launched in 1943. Completed in 1947 and 1946 respectively. Purchased in 1960 from Italian owners. Converted in 1960-61 by Schliekerwerft, Hamburg, and Howaldtswerke, Hamburg, respectively. Commissioned 7 Nov 1961 and 16 Oct 1961. Civilian crew.

MÜNSTERLAND 1972

2 "BODENSEE" CLASS (REPLENISHMENT TANKERS)

BODENSEE (ex-*Unkas*) A 1406 (ex-A 54) **WITTENSEE** (ex-*Sioux*) A 1407

Displacement, tons	1 200
Measurement, tons	1 230 deadweight; 980 gross
Dimensions, feet	208·3 × 32·5 × 15
Main engines	Diesels; 1 050—1 250 bhp = 12 knots

Built by P. Lindenau, Kiel-Friedrichsort. Launched on 19 Nov 1955 and on 23 Sep 1958, respectively. Commissioned on 26 Mar 1959.

WITTENSEE 1972

EIFEL (ex-*Friedrich Jung*) A 1429 (REPLENISHMENT TANKER)

Displacement, tons	2 279 light; 4 700 full load
Dimensions, feet	334 × 47·2 × 23·3
Main engines	3 360 hp = 14 knots

Built by Norder-Werft, Hamburg. Launched on 29 Mar 1958. Purchased in 1963 for service in the Bundesmarine. Commissioned on 27 May 1963.

EIFEL 1970

4 "WALCHENSEE" CLASS (SUPPORT TANKERS)

AMMERSEE	A 1425	**WALCHENSEE**	A 1424
TEGERNSEE	A 1426	**WESTENSEE**	A 1427

Displacement, tons	2 000
Dimensions, feet	233 × 36·7 × 13·5
Main engines	Diesels; 2 shafts; 1 400 bhp = 12·6 knots

Built by Lindenau, Friedrichsort. Launched on 22 Sep 1966, 22 Oct 1966, 10 July 1965 and 25 Feb 1966 and commissioned on 2 Mar 1967 23 Mar 1967, 29 June 1966 and 6 Oct 1967 respectively.

WESTENSEE 1971

8 "LÜNEBURG" CLASS (SUPPLY SHIPS)

COBURG	A 1412	**LÜNEBURG**	A 1411	**OFFENBURG**	A 1417
FREIBURG	A 1413	**MEERSBURG**	A 1418	**SAARBURG**	A 1415
GLÜCKSBURG	A 1414	**NIENBURG**	A 1416		

Displacement, tons	3 254
Dimensions, feet	341·2 × 43·3 × 13·8
Guns	4—40 mm AA
Main engines	2 Maybach diesels; 2 shafts; 5 600 bhp = 17 knots
Complement	103

Lüneberg, *Coburg*, *Glücksburg*, *Meersburg* and *Nienburg* were built by Flensburger Schiffbau and Vulkan, Bremen, others by Blohm & Voss, Hamburg. Commissioned on 9 July, 27 May, 9 July, 9 July, 25 June, 1 Aug, 27 May and 30 July, respectively, 1968.

SAARBURG *1974, Federal German Navy*

HARZ (ex-*Claere Jung*) A 1428 (SUPPORT TANKER)

Displacement, tons	1 308 light; 3 696 full load
Dimensions, feet	303·2 × 43·5 × 21·7
Main engines	2 520 hp = 13 knots

Built in 1953 by Norder-Werft, Hamburg. Purchased in 1963 for service as an oiler in the Bundesmarine. Commissioned on 27 May 1963.

HARZ 1970

Service Forces—*continued*

1 "ANGELN" CLASS (SUPPLY SHIP)

DITHMARSCHEN (ex-*Hébé*) A 1409

Measurement, tons	2 101 gross
Dimensions, feet,	296·9 × 43·6 × 20·3
Main engines	Pielstick diesels; 1 shaft; 3 000 bhp = 14 knots
Complement	57

Built by Ateliers et Chantiers de Bretagne, Nantes. Purchased from shipowners S. N. Caënnaise, Caen. Launched on 7 May 1955 and commissioned on 19 Dec 1959.

DITHMARSCHEN *1972, Wright & Logan*

SCHWARZWALD (ex-*Amalthee*) A 1400 (AMMUNITION TRANSPORT)

Measurement, tons	1 667 gross
Dimensions, feet	263·1 × 39 × 15·1
Guns	4—40 mm AA Bofors
Main engines	Sulzer diesel; 3 000 bhp = 15 knots

Built by Ch. Dubigeon, Nantes. Launched on 31 Jan 1956. Purchased from the Soc Navale Caënnaise in Feb 1960.

SCHWARZWALD *1971*

6 "FW" CLASS (WATER BOATS)

FW 1 **FW 2** **FW 3** **FW 4** **FW 5** **FW 6**

Displacement, tons	590 (revised official figure)
Dimensions, feet	144·4 × 25·6 × 8·2
Main engines	MWM diesel, 230 bhp = 9 knots

Built by Germania in 1963-64.

2 "WESTERWALD" CLASS (AMMUNITION TRANSPORTS)

ODENWALD A 1436 **WESTERWALD** A 1435

Displacement, tons	3 460
Dimensions, feet	347·8 × 46 × 12·2
Guns	4—40 mm AA
Main engines	Diesels; 5 600 bhp = 17 knots
Complement	60

Built by Lübecker Masch in 1966-67. *Odenwald* was launched on 5 May 1966 and commissioned on 23 Mar 1967 and *Westerwald* was launched on 25 Feb 1966 and commissioned on 1 Feb 1967.

2 "SACHSENWALD" CLASS (MINE TRANSPORTS)

SACHSENWALD A 1437 **STEIGERWALD** A 1438

Displacement, tons	3 850 full load
Dimensions, feet	363·5 × 45·6 × 11·2
Guns	4—40 mm AA (two twin mountings)
Main engines	2 diesels; 2 shafts; 5 600 hp = 17 knots
Range, miles	3 500 nautical
Complement	65

Built by Blohm & Voss, Hamburg as mine transports. Laid down on 1 Aug 1966 and 9 May 1966. Launched on 10 Dec 1966 and 10 Mar 1967. Both commissioned on 20 Aug 1969. Have mine ports in the stern and can be used as minelayers.

SACHSENWALD *1970*

1 "DEUTSCHLAND" CLASS (TRAINING SHIP)

Name	*No.*	*Builders*	*Laid down*	*Launched*	*Completed*
DEUTSCHLAND	A 59	Nobiskrug, Rendsburg	1959	5 Nov 1960	25 May 1963

Displacement, tons	4 880 normal; 5 500 full load
Length, feet (*metres*)	452·8 (*138·0*) pp; 475·8 (*145·0*) oa
Beam, feet (*metres*)	52·5 (*16·0*)
Draught, feet (*metres*)	15·7 (*4·8*)
A/S weapons	2 Bofors 4-barrel rocket launchers
Guns, dual purpose	4—3·9 in (*100 mm*) single
Guns, AA	6—40 mm; 2 twin and 2 single
Torpedo tubes	4 for A/S; 2 for surface
Boilers	2 Wahodag; 768 psi (*54km/cm²*); 870°F (*465°C*)
Main engines	6 680 bhp diesels (2 Daimler-Benz and 2 Maybach); 2 shafts 8 000 shp double reduction MAN geared turbines; 1 shaft
Speed, knots	22 max (3 shafts); 17 (2 shafts) 14 economical (1 shaft)
Range, miles	1 700 at 17 knots
Oil fuel, tons	230 furnace; 410 diesel
Complement	554 (33 officers, 271 men, 250 cadets)

GENERAL

First West German naval ship to exceed the post-war limit of 3 000 tons. Designed with armament and machinery of different types for training purposes. The name originally planned for this ship was *Berlin*. Ordered in 1956. Carried out her first machinery sea trials on 15 Jan 1963.

DEUTSCHLAND *1974, Federal German Navy*

RADAR. All by Hollandse. Search: HSA LW 02/3. Tactical: HSA DA 02. One nav/surface warning radar. Fire Control: HSA 2 M45 100 mm and 40 mm fire control. HSA fire control for Bofors A/S launcher, torpedoes and DC.

DEUTSCHLAND

GORCH FOCK A 60 (SAIL TRAINING SHIP)

Displacement, tons	1 760 standard; 1 870 full load
Dimensions, feet	229·7 wl; 257 oa × 39·2 × 15·8
Main engines	Auxiliary MAN diesel; 800 bhp = 11 knots
Sail area, sq ft	21 141 (speed of up to 15 knots under sail)
Radius, miles	1 990
Complement	206 (10 officers, 56 ratings, 140 cadets)

Sail training ship of the improved "Horst Wessel" type. Barque rig. Launched by Blohm & Voss, Hamburg, on 23 Aug 1958 and commissioned on 17 Dec 1958. A photograph appears in the 1968-69 to 1970-71 editions.

8 TRVs

TF 101-108

Dimensions, ft (*m*)	81·8 × 16·5 × 3 (*24·9 × 5·0 × 0·9*)
Speed	17 knots

Built in 1966-67.

RESCUE LAUNCHES

4 "KW" TYPE

FL 5 Y 857 (ex-W 11)
FL 6 Y 858 (ex-W 12)
FL 7 Y 859 (ex-W 13)
FL 8 Y 860 (ex-W 14)

Displacement, tons	45 standard; 60 full load
Dimensions, ft (*m*)	93·5 oa × 15·5 × 4·0 (*28·5 × 4·7 × 1·2*)
Guns	2—20 mm
Main engines	2 Mercedes-Benz diesels; 2 000 bhp = 25 knots
Complement	14

Built in 1951-53. All are similar to US Coast Guard 93-ft type.

FL 6 *1968*

FL 9 Y 861 (ex-D 2763) **FL 10** Y 862 (ex-D 2765) **FL 11** Y 963 (ex-D 2766)

Displacement, tons	70
Dimensions, ft (*m*)	95·2 × 15·6 × 4·2 (*29 × 5 × 1·3*)
Main engines	Maybach diesels; 2 shafts; 3 200 bhp = 30 knots
Range, miles	600 at 20 knots

Built by Kröger, Rendsburg. Completing in 1955.

FL 10 *1972*

TUGS

BALTRUM **JUIST** **NORDERNEY**
ELLERBEK **LANGEOOG** **SPIEKEROOG**
HEPPENS **NEUENDE** **WANGEROOGE**

Displacement, tons	854 standard; 1 024 full load
Dimensions, feet	170·6 × 39·4 × 12·8
Gun	1—40 mm AA
Main engines	Diesel-electric; 2 shafts; 2 400 hp = 13·6 knots
Complement	35

Built by Schichau, Bremerhaven. *Wangerooge*, prototype, salvage tug, was launched on 4 July 1966. *Wangerooge* commissioned on 9 Apr 1968, *Langeoog* and *Spiekeroog* on 14 Aug 1968. *Baltrum* on 8 Oct 1968.

NORDWIND Y 834 (SAIL TRAINING SHIP)

Displacement, tons	100
Dimensions, feet	78·8 × 22 × 9
Main engines	Diesel; 150 bhp = 8 knots. (Sail area 2 037·5 sq ft)

Ketch, ex-Kreigsfischkutter (KFK). Photograph in the 1954-55 edition. There are over 70 other sailing vessels of various types serving for sail training and recreational purposes. *Achat, Alarich, Amsel, Argonaut, Borasco, Brigant, Dankwart, Diamont, Dietrich, Drossel Dompfaff, Fafnir, Fink, Flibustier, Freibeuter, Gernot, Geiserich, Geuse, Giselher, Gödicke, Gunnar, Gunter, Hadubrand, Hagen, Hartnaut Hildebrand, Horand, Hunding, Jaspis, Kaper, Klipper, Korsar, Kuchkuch, Lerche, Likendeeler, Magellan, Michel, Mime, Meise, Mistral, Monsun, Nachtigall, Ortwin, Ostwind, Pampero, Pirol, Ruediger, Samum, Saphir, Schirocco, Seeteufel, Siegfried, Siegmund, Siegura Smaragd, Star, Stieglitz, Stortebecker, Taifun, Teja, Topas, Tornadon, Totila Vitalienbrüder, Volker, Walter, Wate, Westwind, Wiking, Wittigo, Zeisig.*

Tugs—*continued*

FEHMARN A 1458 **HELGOLAND** A 1457

Displacement, tons	1 310 standard; 1 619 full load
Dimensions, feet	223·1 × 41·7 × 14·4
Gun	1—40 mm AA
Main engines	Diesel-electric; 4 MWM diesels; 2 shafts; 3 800 hp = 16·6 knots

Bergungsschlepper or salvage tugs. Built by Unterweser, Bremerhaven. Launched on 25 Nov 1965 and 8 Apr 1965 and commissioned on 1 Feb 1967 and 8 Mar 1966.

AMRUM Y 822 **FÖHR** Y 821 **NEUWERK** Y 823 **SYLT** Y 820

Displacement, tons	262 standard
Dimensions, feet	100·7 oa × 25·2
Main engines	1 Deutz diesel 1 100 bhp = 12 knots

Built by Fr. Schichau, Bremerhaven. Launched in 1961. All completed in 1962-63.

PELLWORM (ex-USN 102) 500 tons, 12 knots

HARBOUR TYPE. There are also nine small harbour tugs all completed in 1958-60;— *Blauort* Y 803, *Knechtsand* Y 814, *Langeness* Y 819, *Lütje Horn* Y 812, *Mellum* Y 813, *Nordstrand* Y 817, *Scharhörn* Y 815 *Trischen* Y 818 and *Vogelsand* Y 816 and three completed in 1970 by Schichau, Bremerhaven of 122 tons and 800 hp;- *Neuende, Eller Bek, Heppens.*

ICEBREAKERS

HANSE

Displacement, tons	3 700
Dimensions, feet	243·2 × 57 × 20
Main engines	Diesel-electric; 4 shafts; 7 500 bhp = 16 knots

Built by Wärtsilä Oy, Helsinki, Finland. Laid down on 12 Jan 1965. Launched on 17 Oct 1966. Completed on 25 Nov 1966. Commissioned on 13 Dec 1966. Although owned by West Germany she sails under the Finnish flag, manned by a Finnish crew. Only when the winter is so severe that icebreakers are needed in the southern Baltic will she be transferred under the German flag and command. She is of improved "Karhu" class. She does not belong to the Bundesmarine.

EISBAR A 1402 **EISVOGEL** A 1401

Displacement, tons	560 standard
Dimensions, feet	125·3 oa × 31·2 × 7·9 (15·1 max)
Guns	Can carry 1—40 mm AA Bofors
Main Engines	2 Maybach diesels; 2 shafts; 2 400 bhp = 13 knots

Built by J. G. Hitzler, Lauenburg. Launched on 9 June and 28 Apr 1960, and commissioned on 1 Nov and 11 Mar 1961, respectively.

EISVOGEL *1970*

EXPERIMENTAL SHIPS

EIDER (ex-*Catherine*, ex-*Dochet*) Y 1663 (ex-A 50) (MC TRAINING SHIP)

Displacement, tons	480 standard; 750 full load
Dimensions, feet	164·0 pp; 177·2 oa × 27·5 × 14·0
Guns	1—40 mm AA; 1—20 mm AA (removed in peacetime)
Main engines	Triple expansion; 1 shaft; 750 ihp = 12 knots
Oil fuel, tons	130

Former British "Isles" type minesweeping trawler. Built in Canada by Davie & Sons, Lauzon, in 1942. Employed as a mine clearance training vessel. She has been civilian manned since 1 Jan 1968.

OSTE (ex-USN 101, *Puddefjord*) A 52 (RADAR TRIALS SHIP)

Measurement, tons	567 gross
Dimensions, feet	160 × 29·7 × 17
Guns	2—20 mm AA
Main engines	2 Sulzer diesels; 1 shaft; 1 400 bhp = 14 knots

Built in 1943 at Akers Mekaniske Vaerkstad. Oslo. Taken over from the US Navy, Converted in 1968.

OSTE (as radar testing ship) *1970, Stefan Terzibaschitsch*

EMS (ex-USN 104, ex-*Harle*) Y 1662 (ex-A 53) (DIVING TENDER)

Measurement, tons	660 gross
Dimensions, feet	185·7 oa × 29 × 15·5
Guns	4—20 mm
Main engines	Sulzer diesels; 1 000 bhp = 12 knots

Built in 1941 by Kremer & Sohn, Elmshorn.

EMS *1972*

WALTHER VON LEDEBUR Y 841

Displacement, tons	725
Dimensions, feet	219·8 × 34·8 × 8·9
Main engines	Maybach diesels; 2 shafts; 5 000 bhp = 19 knots

Wooden hulled vessel. Built by Burmester, Bremen-Berg. Launched on 30 June 1966.

WALTHER VON LEDEBUR *1971*

Experimental Ships—*cont.*

4 Ex-COASTAL MINESWEEPERS

ADOLF BESTELMEYER (ex-*BYMS* 2213)
H. C. OERSTED (ex-*Vinstra*, ex-*NYMS* 247)
HERMAN VON HELMOLTZ
RUDOLF DIESEL (ex-*BYMS* 2279)

Displacement, tons	270 standard; 350 full load
Dimensions, feet	136 × 24·5 × 8
Main engines	2 diesels; 2 shafts; 1 000 bhp = 15 knots

Of US YMS type. Built in 1943. *Adlof Bestelmeyer*, Y 881, and *Rudolf Diesel* Y 889, are used for gunnery purposes. *H. C. Oersted*, Y 877, was acquired from the Royal Norwegian Navy. *Herman von Helmholtz*, Y 878, commissioned on 18 Dec 1962, is used as a degaussing ship.

WILHELM PULLWER Y 838 of 130 tons and 19 knots. Built in 1966.

HEINZ ROGGENKAMP Of 785 tons and 12 knots. Built in 1952.

FRIEDRICH VOGE Y 888. Of 179 tons.

KARL KOLLS Y 887. Of 189 tons.

OTTO MEYCKE. Diving Trials.

2 TANK CLEANING VESSELS

FÖRDE **JADE**

Of 600 tons, completed in 1967.

COASTAL PATROL CRAFT

KW 15-20

Same particulars as FL 5-8 (Rescue Launches)

TMI (ex-British MMS)

Displacement, tons	140
Speed, knots	10

Built in 1944.

KW 2, 3 and 8

Displacement, tons	112
Speed, knots	8

Built in 1943. Trawler type used as training ships.

COASTGUARD VESSELS

(BUNDESGRENZSCHUTZ—SEE)

Note. This paramilitary force consists of about 1 000 men who operate the craft below as well as helicopters.

8 LARGE PATROL CRAFT

ALSFELD	BG 16	**ESCHWEGE**	BG 15
BAD BRAMSTEDT	BG 12	**NEUSTADT**	BG 11
BAYREUTH	BG 17	**ROSENHEIM**	BG 18
DUDERSTADT	BG 14	**UELTZEN**	BG 13

Displacement, tons	203
Length, feet (*metres*)	127·1 (*38·5*)
Guns	2—40 mm
Mai nengines	3 Diesels; 4 500 hp = 30 knots

All built between 1969 and late 1970—BG 13 by Schlichting, Travemünde, the remainder by Lürssen, Vegesack. Form two flotillas BG 11-14 the 1st and BG 15-18 the 2nd. A third flotilla of smaller craft has been formed.

SURVEY SHIPS

Note. These ships operate for the Deutsches Hydrographisches Institut, under the Ministry of Transport.

METEOR (Research Ship) 3 085 tons, launched 1964, Complement 55
KOMET (Survey and Research) 1 595 tons, launched 1969, Complement 42
GAUSS (Survey and Research) 1 074 tons, launched 1949, Complement 40
SÜDEROOG (Survey Ship) 211 tons, launched 1956, Complement 16
ATAIR (Survey and Wrecks) 148 tons, launched 1962, Complement 13
WEGA (Survey and Wrecks) 148 tons, launched 1962, Complement 12

7 FISHERY PROTECTION SHIPS

Note. Operated by Ministry of Agriculture and Fisheries.

ANTON DOHRN of 1 950 tons and 15 knots
FRITHJOF of 2 150 tons and 15 knots.
MEERKATZE of 1 000 tons and 12 knots.
NORDENHAM of 975 tons and 16 knots.
POSEIDON of 935 tons and 12 knots.
UTHÖRN of 110 tons and 9 knots
WALTHER HERTWIG of 2 500 tons and 15 knots.

GERMANY (Democratic Republic)

Administration

Commander-in-Chief, Volksmarine:
Vice Admiral Willi Ehm

Chief of Naval Staff:
Rear Admiral Gustav Hesse

Personnel

(a) 1973: 1 700 officers and 15 200 men (including GBK)
1974: 1 750 officers and 15 300 men (including GBK)

(b) 18 months National Service

Strength of the Fleet

Type	*Active*	*Building*
Frigates	2	—
Corvettes	18	—
Fast Attack Craft—Missile	12	—
Fast Attack Craft—Torpedo	55	—
Fast Attack Craft—Patrol	4 (GBK)	—
Landing Craft	18	—
Minesweepers—Ocean	6	—
Minesweepers—Coastal	44	3
Intelligence Ships	3	—
Survey Ships	8	—
Supply Ship	1	—
Support Tankers	3	—
Buoy Tenders	8	—
Ice Breakers	3	—
Tugs	18	—
Tenders	6	—
Training Ships and Craft	12	—
Cable Layer	1	—

GRENZBRIGADE KUSTE (GBK)

The seaborne branch of the Frontier Guards, this is a force of about 3 000 men. Their various craft are difficult to disentangle from those of the Navy, many being taken from that list. Where possible mention of this is made in the notes.

Mercantile Marine

Lloyds Register of Shipping:
432 vessels of 1 219 037 tons gross

FRIGATES

2 Ex-SOVIET "RIGA" CLASS

ERNEST THÄLMANN 141 **KARL MARX** 142

Displacement, tons	1 200 standard; 1 600 full load
Dimensions, feet	298·8 × 33·7 × 11
Guns	3—3·9 in single; 4—37 mm AA twin
Tubes	3—21 in
A/S weapons	4 depth charge projectors; 2 rocket launchers
Main engines	Geared turbines; 2 shafts; 25 000 shp = 28 knots
Oil fuel (tons)	300
Range, miles	2 500 at 15 knots
Complement	150

Designed to carry 50 mines. Sister ships *Friedrich Engels* 124 and *Karl Liebknecht* 123 were scrapped in 1971. A fifth ship of this type was burnt out at the end of 1959 and became a total wreck. Two of these hulks are beached at Warnemünde.

KARL MARX *1965, Werner Kähling*

CORVETTES

4 USSR "SO-I" CLASS

421 422 423 424

Displacement, tons	215 standard; 250 full load
Dimensions, ft (*m*)	138 × 20 × 9·2 (*42·3 × 6·1 × 2·8*)
Guns	4—25 mm AA (2 twin mounts)
A/S weapons	4 MBU 1 800 5 barrelled launchers; 2 DCT
Main engines	3 diesels; 6 000 bhp = 29 knots
Range, miles	1 100 at 13 knots
Complement	30

Fitted with mine rails. These vessels belonged to the coast guard (GBK) but have now been returned to the navy.

G22 *1970, Niels Gartig*

14 "HAI" CLASS

BAD DOBERAN
BÜTZOW
GREVESMÜHLEN
GADEBUSCH
LÜBZ
LUDWIGSLUST
PARCHIM
PERLEBERG
RIBNITZ-DAMGARTEN
STERNBERG
TETEROW
WISMAR

Displacement, tons	300 standard; 370 full load
Dimensions, feet	174 pp; 187 oa × 19 × 10
Guns	4—30 mm (2 twin)
A/S weapons	2 MBU 1 800 5 barrelled launchers
Main engines	2 gas turbines; diesels; 8 000 bhp = 25 knots
Complement	45

Built at Peenewerft, Wolgast. The prototype vessel was completed in 1963. All were in service by the end of 1969, and the programme is now completed. Pennant numbers are in the 400 series.

HAI No. 411 *1971, S. Breyer*

LIGHT FORCES

12 Ex-SOVIET "OSA" CLASS (FAST ATTACK CRAFT—MISSILE)

ARVID HAMACK
AUGUST LÜTTGENS
FRITZ GAST
HEINRICH DORRENBACH
JOSEF SCHARES
KARL MESEBERG
MAX REICHPIETSCH
OTTO TOST
PAUL EISENSCHNEIDER
PAUL WIECZOREK
RICHARD SORGE
RUDOLF EGELHUFER

Displacement, tons	165 standard; 200 full load
Dimensions, feet	128·7 × 25·1 × 5·9
Missile launchers	4 mountings in 2 pairs abreast aft for "Styx"; SSN-2A
Guns	4—30 mm (2 twin, 1 forward, 1 aft)
Main engines	3 diesels; 13 000 hp = 32 knots

Most valuable and powerful boats for coastal operations. Pennant numbers in the 700 series.

OSA CLASS *1965, Reinecke*

15 Ex-SOVIET "SHERSHEN" CLASS

(FAST ATTACK CRAFT—TORPEDO)

ADAM KUCKHOFF
ARTHUR BECKER
BERNHARD BÄSTLEIN
BRUNO KÜHN
EDGAR ANDRÉ
ERNST SCHNELLER
FIETE SCHULZE
FRITZ HECKERT
HANS COPPI
RUDOLF BREITSCHEID
WILHELM FLORIN

Displacement, tons	150 standard; 160 full load
Dimensions, ft (*m*)	115·5 × 23·1 × 5 (*35·2 × 7·1 × 1·5*)
Guns	4—30 mm (2 twin)
A/S weapons	12 DC
Tubes	4—21 in (single)
Main engines	3 Diesels; 13 000 bhp; 3 shafts = 41 knots
Complement	16

Acquired from the USSR. Four were delivered in 1968-69, the first instalment of a flotilla. They do not differ from the Soviet boats of the class. Pennant numbers 811-5, 831-5, 851-5

SHERSHEN *Class*

40 "ILTIS" CLASS (FAST ATTACK CRAFT—TORPEDO)

Displacement, tons	20
Dimensions, ft (*m*)	55·8 × 10·5 × 2·5 (*17 × 3·2 × ·8*)
Tubes	2—21 in (torpedoes fired over stern). Some have three tubes (Type 3) Mines can be carried in place of torpedo tubes
Main engines	Diesels; 3 000 bhp = 30 knots

No guns. Numbered in a 900 series. Several different types of this class exist, varying in hull material and silhouette. eg. Type 1 are flush-decked and Type 2 have a raised forecastle. With the torpedo tubes removed these boats are used to land frogmen and raiding parties. Displacement and dimensions given are for Type 2. Others vary slightly. Built by Mitteldeutschland, starting in 1962.

No. 912 — *1971, S. Breyer*

4 Ex-SOVIET "P6" CLSSS (FAST ATTACK CRAFT—PATROL)

Displacement, tons	66 standard; 75 full load
Dimensions, ft (*m*)	84·2 × 20 × 6 (*25·7 × 6·1 × 1·8*)
Guns	4—25 mm (2 twin mountings)
Main engines	4 diesels; 4 800 bhp; 4 shafts = 43 knots max
Range, miles	450 at 30 knots
Complement	25

Acquired in 1957-60 from the USSR. Originally there were 27. Wooden hull. Most of this class has been scrapped or converted. Four have had their tubes removed and been transferred to the GBK with pennant Nos G81-84. Pot Head radar.

P 6 Class No. 864 (Tubes now removed) — *1970, Niels Gartig*

18 "KB 123" CLASS (PATROL CRAFT)

Displacement, tons	about 25
Dimensions, ft (*m*)	64 × 16·4 × —) (*20 × 5 × —*)

This class (total uncertain) was introduced in 1971for operations on rivers and inland waterways by the GBK. It appears to be fast and unarmed, though small arms are certainly carried.

KB 123 Class — *1972*

AMPHIBIOUS FORCES

6 "ROBBE" CLASS

EBERSWALDE **GRIMMEN** **LÜBBEN**
ELSENHÜTTENSTADT **HOYERSWERDA** **SCHWEDT**

Displacement, tons	600 standard; 800 full load
Dimensions, feet	196·8 × 32·8 × 6·6
Guns	2—57 mm AA (1 twin); 4—25 mm AA (2 twin)
Main engines	Diesels = 12 knots

Amphibious vessels of a type midway between the landing ship and landing craft categories. Launched in 1962-64.

"ROBBE CLASS" — *1971, S. Breyer*

12 "LABO" CLASS

GERHARD PRENZLER **HEINZ WILKOWSKI** **ROLF PETERS**

Displacement, tons	150 standard; 200 full load
Dimensions, feet	131·2 × 27·9 × 5·9
Guns	4—25 mm AA (2 twin)
Main engines	Diesels = 10 knots

Landing craft of a lighter type. Built by Peenewerft, Wolgast. Launched in 1961-63

"LABO" Class — *1969, S. Breyer*

MINE WARFARE FORCES

6 "KRAKE" CLASS (MINESWEEPERS—OCEAN)

BERLIN **HALLE** **KARL-MARX-STADT** **LEIPZIG** **POTSDAM** **ROSTOCK**

Displacement, tons	650 standard
Dimensions, ft (*m*)	229·7 × 26·5 × 12·2 (*70* × *8·1* × *3·7*)
Guns	1—3·4 in; 10—25 mm AA paired vertically
A/S weapons	4 DCT
Mines	Can carry 30
Main engines	Diesels; 2 shafts; 3 400 bhp = 18 knots
Complement	90

Built in 1956-58 at Peenewerft, Wolgast. Four completed in 1958, were originally for Poland. Appearance is different compared with the first type, the squat wide funnel being close to the bridge with lattice mast and radar. Fitted for minelaying. On 1 Mar 1961 they were given the names of the capitals of districts etc, of East Germany. Pennant numbers are 221 to 223 and S11-13.

"Krake" Class No. 222 — *1970, Niels Gartig*

44 "KONDOR" I and II CLASS (MINESWEEPERS—COASTAL)

AHRENSHOOP **ANKLAM** **BERGEN** **BITTERFELD** **BERNAU** **DEMMIN** **DESSAU** **GENTHIN** **GRAAL-MÜRITZ** **GREIFSWALD** **KLÜTZ** **KUHLUNGSBORN** **KYRITZ** **NEURUPPIN** **NEUSTRELITZ** **PASEWALK** **PREROW** **ROBEL** **ROSSLAU** **STRASBURG** **TANGERHÜTTE** **TEMPLIN** **UCKERMUNDE** **VITTE** **WARNEMUNDE** **WEISSWASSER** **WOLGAST** **ZERBST** **ZINGST** + 15

Displacement, tons	245 standard; 280 full load
Dimensions, ft (*m*)	154·2 × 23·0 × 6·6 (*47* × *7* × *2*)
Guns	2—25 mm or 2—30 mm (Kondor I); 6—25 mm (twins) (Kondor II)
Main engines	2 diesels; 2 shafts; 4 000 bhp = 21 knots

GENERAL

A new class of medium fast minesweepers and patrol vessels built at Peenewerft. Five units were operational in 1970 and 15 by the end of 1971. They replace the small minesweepers of the "Schwalbe" class. Type II has additional length and extra MG's. First appearing in 1971. Production continues.

PENNANT NUMBERS

These have been changed with some frequency. At present the following is as near as can be offered:

Type I (Total 19) Prototype-V31. Attached to GBK;-G11-16. G21-26. Conversion for torpedo recovery-B73 and B74. Conversion to AGi's Meteor and Komet.

Type II (Total 25) Prototype-V32. Active minesweepers-331-316, 321-326, 331-336 341-346.

KONDOR II CLASS — *1973, S, Breyer*

INTELLIGENCE SHIPS

METEOR **KOMET**

Both of "Kondor I" Class. For details see under Minewarfare Forces.

HYDROGRAPH

Displacement, tons	500
Dimensions ft (*m*)	167 × 28·8 × — (*50·9* × *8·7* × —)
Main engines	Diesel; 540 hp = 11 knots

Built in 1960 by Volkswerft, Stralsund.

SURVEY SHIPS

ALFRED MERZ **KARL F. GASS**

Built in 1952-55. Of 200 tons and 9·5 knots. Seiner type.

ARKONA **DASSER ORT** **STUBBEN KAMMER**

Built in 1956. Of 55 tons and 10 knots.

JORDAN **MAGNETOLOG**

Built in 1954. Of 135 tons and 10 knots. Similar to "KFK" Class.

FLAGGTIEF

Built in 1953. Of 30 tons and 8 knots

TRAINING SHIPS

2 KS2 CLASS

PARTISAN **PIONIER**

Displacement, tons	79
Main engines	Speed = 13 knots

Built in 1957. Coastal boats rated as *schulschiffe* or training vessels. The 20 boats of the "KS 1" class in the GBK were deleted from the list in 1971.

PIONIER — *1969*

10 TRAINING SHIPS

Sailing vessels and old minesweepers attached to the Naval Academy.

SERVICE FORCES

1 "BASKUNCHAK" CLASS (SUPPLY SHIP)

USEDOM

Displacement, tons	2 500
Dimensions, ft (*m*)	227 × 29 × 12·3 (*70 × 8·9 × 3·8*)
Speed, knots	13

Tanker converted to act as supply ship.

USEDOM *1973, S. Breyer*

3 TYPE 600 (SUPPORT TANKERS)

HIDDENSEE **POEL** **RIEMS**

Displacement, tons	600 DWT
Dimensions, feet	195 oa × 29·5 × 12·5 max
Main engines	2 diesels; 2 800 bhp = 14 knots
Complement	26

Built at Peenewerft, Wolgast, in 1960-61.

RIEMS *1971, S. Breyer*

3 "KUMO" CLASS

RUDEN **RUGEN** **VILM**

Displacement, tons	400
Dimensions, ft (*m*)	118 × 24 × 8·9 (*36 × 7·3 × 2·7*)
Speed, knots	10

Built in mid-1950's. *Rugen* is a torpedo Trials Ship and the other two general tenders.

BUK

Displacement, tons	1 000 standard
Dimensions, ft (*m*)	180·5 × 31·2 × 11·5 (*55 × 9·5 × 3·4*)
Main engines	Diesels = 16 knots

1 Ex-SOVIET "KAMENKA" CLASS

DORNBUSCH

Cable layer of 700 tons with bow rollers.

FREESENDORF

Danlayer built in 1963.

LUMME

Small diving tender. Tug type.

8 BUOY TENDERS

BREITLING **GOLWITZ** **LANDTIEFF** **RAMZOW**
ESPER ORT **GRASS ORT** **PALMER ORT** **ROSEN ORT**

Displacement, tons	158
Dimensions, feet	97 × 20·3 × 6·2
Main engines	1 diesel; 580 hp = 11·5 knots

Delivery 1970-72.

ICEBREAKERS

STEPHAN JANSEN

Of 2 500 tons and 13 knots built in 1965. Of Soviet "Nikitch" class.

EISBAR **EISVOGEL**

Of 550 tons and 12 knots built in 1957.

TUGS

3 "700" CLASS

Of 800 tons and 12 knots.

3 "H" CLASS

H 35 **H 36** **H 37**

Of 700 tons and 14 knots.

WISMAR

Of 700 tons and 14 knots.

11 HARBOUR TUGS

Note. Gesellschaft fúr Sport und Technik (GST) (Association for Sport and Technical Science) controls fifteen training ships—*Ernst Thälman*, a retired "Habicht I" Class minesweeper; *Ernst Schneller*, "Tummler" class; *Partisan*, and *Pionier* of 80 tons; *Freundschaft* of 200 tons; *F. L. Jahn* of 100 tons; and the sail training ships *Wilhelm Pieck, Seid Bereil, Jonny Scheer, Max Reichpietsch II* and *Knechtsand II*.

GHANA

Administration

Commander of the Navy: Commodore Kelvin Dzang

Personnel

(a) 1 300 (150 officers, 1 150 ratings)
(b) Voluntary Service

Naval Base

Tema, near Accra

Mercantile Marine

Lloyd's Register of Shipping: 73 vessels of 165 565 tons gross

CORVETTES

2 "KROMANTSE" CLASS

KROMANTSE F 17 **KETA** F 18

Displacement, tons	380 light; 440 standard; 500 full load
Dimensions, feet	162 wl; 177 oa × 28·5 × 13 (props)
Guns	1—4 in; 1—40 mm AA (see notes)
A/S weapons	1 Squid triple-barrelled depth charge mortar
Main engines	2 Bristol Siddeley Maybach diesels; 2 shafts; 390 rpm; 7 100 bhp = 20 knots (5 700 hp = 18 knots sea)
Oil fuel, tons	60
Range, miles	2 000 at 16 knots; 2 900 at 14 knots
Complement	54 (6 + 3 officers, 45 ratings)

Anti-submarine vessels of a novel type designed by Vosper Ltd, Portsmouth, a joint venture with Vickers-Armstrong's Ltd, one ship being built by each company. Comprehensively fitted with sonar, air and surface warning radar. Vosper roll damping fins, and air conditioning throughout excepting machinery spaces. Generators 360 kW. The electrical power supply is 440 volts, 60 cycles ac. A very interesting patrol vessel design, an example of what can be achieved on a comparatively small platform to produce an inexpensive and quickly built anti-submarine vessel. *Kromantse* was launched by Vosper Ltd at the Camber Shipyard, Portsmouth, on 5 Sep 1963, and commissioned on 27 July 1964. *Keta* was launched at Newcastle on 18 Jan 1965, and commissioned on 18 May 1965.

RADAR. Search. Plessey AWS 1.

KROMANTSE *1971*

MINESWEEPER FORCES

1 Ex-BRITISH "TON" CLASS (MINESWEEPER—COASTAL)

EJURA (ex-*Aldington*) M 16

Displacement, tons	360 standard; 425 full load
Dimensions, feet	140 pp; 153 oa × 28·8 × 8·2
Guns	1—40 mm AA forward; 2—20 mm AA aft
Main engines	Deltic diesels; 2 shafts; 3 000 bhp = 15 knots max
Oil fuel (tons)	45
Range	2 300 at 13 knots
Complement	27

Lent to Ghana by Britain in 1964.

EJURA *1971, Ghana Navy.*

2 Ex-BRITISH "HAM" CLASS (MINESWEEPERS—INSHORE)

AFADZATO (ex-*Ottringham*) M 12 **YOGAGA** (ex-*Malham*) M 11

Displacement, tons	120 standard; 159 full load
Dimensions, feet	100 pp; 107·5 oa × 22 × 5·8
Guns	1—15 mm AA
Main engines	2 Paxman diesels; 1 100 = 14 knots
Oil fuel, tons	15
Range, miles	2 000 at 9 knots
Complement	22

Malham commissioned on 2 Oct 1959, and *Ottringham* commissioned on 30 Oct 1959, sailed for Ghana on 31 Oct 1959, and were transferred from the Royal Navy to the Ghana Navy at Takoradi at the end of Nov 1959 and renamed after hills in Ghana. Fitted with funnel.

YOGAGA *1966, Ghana Navy*

LIGHT FORCES

2 "FORD" CLASS (LARGE PATROL CRAFT)

ELMINA P 13 **KOMENDA** P 14

Displacement, tons	120 standard; 142 full load
Dimensions, feet	110 wl; 117·5 oa × 20 × 7 (screws)
Guns	1—40 mm, 60 cal Bofors AA
A/S weapons	Depth charge throwers
Main engines	2 Davey Paxman diesels; 2 shafts; 1 000 bhp = 18 knots (max).
Complement	19

KOMENDA *1969, Ghana Navy*

3 Ex-USSR "POLUCHAT I" CLASS (COASTAL PATROL CRAFT)

P 20 **P 21** **P 23**

Displacement, tons	86 standard; 91 full load
Dimensions, feet	98 pp × 15 × 4·8
Guns, AA	2—14·5 mm (twin mounting)
Main engines	2 model M50-3 diesels; 2 shafts; 1 600 rpm. 1 200 bhp = 18 knots
Oil fuel, tons	9·25
Range, miles	460 at 17 knots
Complement	16 (2 officers, 14 ratings)

Built in the USSR. Completed in Aug 1963. Acquired in 1967. Sister boat P 22 was scrapped in 1970.

P 23 *1969, Ghana Navy*

ASUANTSI (ex-*MRC* 1122)

Displacement, tons	657
Dimensions, feet	225 pp; 231·3 oa × 39 × 3·3 forward, 5 aft
Main engines	4 Paxman, 1 840 bhp = 9 knots cruising

Acquired from Britain in 1965 and arrived in Ghana waters in July 1965. Used as a base workshop at Teme Naval Base. Is kept operational, and does a fair amount of seatime in general training and exercise tasks.

GREECE

Administration

Chief, Hellenic Navy:
Vice-Admiral P. Avapakis

Deputy Chief:
Rear-Admiral P. Konialis

Commander of the Fleet:
Rear Admiral P. Kalogeropoulos

Strength of the Fleet

Type	*Active*	*Building*
Destroyers	11	—
Frigates	4	—
Corvettes	5	—
Patrol Submarines	7	—
Fast Attack Craft—Missile	4	—
Fast Attack Craft—Torpedo	12	—
Large Patrol Craft	5	—
Landing Ships	14	—
LCU's	8	—
Minelayers—Coastal	2	—
Minesweeper—Coastal	15	—
Survey Vessels	5	—
Support Tankers	2	—
Harbour Tankers	6	—
Salvage Ship	1	—
Repair Ship	1	—
Lighthouse Tenders	2	—
Tugs	10	—

Disposals

Destroyers

1972 *Doxa, Niki* (Gleaves class)

Submarine

1972 *Poseidon*

Patrol Craft

1971 *Antiploiarkhos Laskos, Ploiarchos Meletopoulos*

Minesweepers—Coastel

1972 *Kichu*
1973 *Afroessa, Kalymnos, Karteria, Kerkyra, Papalos, Zakynthos*

Survey Vessel

1973 *A. Idhi*

Minesweeper Depot Ship

1973 *Hermes*

Tugs

1972 *Aegeus*

Water Boat

1972 Kaliroe

Diplomatic Representation

Naval Attaché in London:
Captain I. K. Papageorgiou

Naval Attaché in Washington:
Captain X. Douginas

Naval Attaché in Cairo:
Captain P. Vossos

Naval Attaché in Bonn:
Captain P. Marinos

Prefix to Ship's Names

H.S. (Hellenic Ship)

Personnel

(a) 1974: 17 600 (1 900 officers and 15 700 ratings)
(b) 2 years National Service

Naval Bases

Salamis and Crete

Mercantile Marine

Lloyd's Register of Shipping:
2 536 vessels of 19 295 143 tons gross

DESTROYERS

1 Ex-US "GEARING FRAM II" CLASS
3 Ex-US "GEARING FRAM I" CLASS

Name	*No.*	*Builder*	*Commissioned*	*Transferred*
— (ex-USS *Arnold J. Isbell*, DD 869)	D 214	Bethlehem (Staten Is.)	17 Nov 1945	3 Dec 1973
KANARIS (ex-USS *Stickell*, DD 888)	D 212	Consolidated Steel Corpn.	30 Oct 1945	1 July 1972
KONTOURIOTIS (ex-USS *Rupertus*, DD 851)	D 213	Bethlehem (Quincy)	8 Mar 1946	7 Oct 1973
THEMISTOCLES (ex-USS *Frank Knox*, DD 742)	D 210	Bath Iron Works	11 Dec 1944	3 Feb 1971

Displacement, tons	2 425 standard; 3 500 full load
Length, feet (*metres*)	390·5 (*119·0*) oa
Beam, feet (*metres*)	40·9 (*12·4*)
Draught, feet (*metres*)	19·0 (*5·8*)
Guns	6—5 in (*127 mm*) 38 cal dp (twin) (210 only); 4—5 in (twin) in Fram I's
A/S weapons	2 fixed Hedgehogs, (210 only); 1 ASROC 8-barrelled launcher and facilities for small helicopter in Fram I's
Torpedo tubes	2 triple (Mk 32)
Main engines	2 Westinghouse geared turbines; 2 shafts; 60 000 shp
Boilers	4 Babcock & Wilcox
Speed, knots	34
Range, miles	4 800 at 15 knots
Complement	269 (16 officers, 253 men)

Themistocles was a Fram II Radar Picket conversion, *Kanaris* was a Fram I Radar Picket conversion and the other pair Fram I DD conversions.

THEMISTOCLES (FRAM II) *1972, Helenic Navy*

KANARIS (FRAM I) *1973, Helenic Navy*

Destroyers—*continued*

1 Ex-S "ALLEN M. SUMNER" CLASS

Name	*No.*	*Builder*	*Commissioned*	*Transferred*
MIAOULIS (ex-USS *Ingram*, DD 694)	D 211	Federal SB & DD Co	10 Mar 1944	July 1971

Displacement, tons	2 200 standard; 3 320 full load
Length, feet (*metres*)	376·5 (*114·8*) oa
Beam, feet (*metres*)	40·9 (*12·4*)
Draught, feet (*metres*)	19·0 (*5·8*)
Guns	6—5 in (*127 mm*) 38 cal dp
A/S weapons	2 triple torpedo launchers, Mk 32; 2 ahead throwing hedgehogs
Main engines	2 geared turbines; 2 shafts; 60 000 shp
Boilers	4
Speed, knots	34 approx
Range, miles	4 600 at 15 knots
Complement	269 (16 officers, 94 POs, 159 men)

Former fleet destroyer of the "Allen M. Sumner" class which had been modernised under the FRAM II programme.

MIAOULIS *1973, Hellenic Navy*

6 Ex-US "FLETCHER" CLASS

Name	*No.*	*Builder*	*Laid down*	*Launched*	*Completed*
ASPIS (ex-USS *Conner, DD* 582)	D 06	Boston Navy Yard	16 Apr 1942	18 July 1942	8 June 1943
LONCHI (ex-USS *Hall, DD* 583)	D 56	Boston Navy Yard	16 Apr 1942	18 July 1942	6 July 1943
NAVARINON (ex-USS *Brown, DD* 546)	D 63	Bethlehem (S. Pedro)	27 June 1942	22 Feb 1943	10 July 1943
SFENDONI (ex-USS *Aulick, DD* 569)	D 85	Consolidated Steel Corp, Texas	14 May 1941	2 Mar 1942	27 Oct 1942
THYELLA (ex-USS *Bradford, DD* 545)	D 28	Bethlehem (S. Pedro)	28 Apr 1942	12 Dec 1942	12 June 1943
VELOS (ex-USS *Charette, DD* 581)	D 16	Boston Navy Yard	20 Feb 1941	3 June 1942	18 May 1943

Displacement, tons	2 100 standard; 3 050 full load
Length, feet (*metres*)	376·5 (*114·7*) oa
Beam, feet (*metres*)	39·5 (*12·0*)
Draught, feet (*metres*)	18 (*5·5*) max
Guns, dual purpose	4—5 in (*127 mm*) 38 cal. in *Aspis, Lonchi, Sfendoni* and *Velos*, 5 in *Navarinon* and *Thyella*
Guns, AA	6—3 in (*76 mm*), 3 twin, in *Aspis, Lonchi, Sfendoni* and *Velos*. 10—40 mm (2 quadruple, 1 twin) in *Navarinon* and *Thyella*
A/S weapons	Hedgehogs; DC's
Torpedo tubes	5—21 in (*533 mm*), quintuple bank, in *Aspis, Lonchi, Sfendoni* and *Velos*, none in *Navarinon* and *Thyella*
Torpedo racks	Side-launching for A/S torpedoes
Boilers	4 Babcock & Wilcox; 615 psi (*43·3 kg/cm²*) 800°F (*427°C*)
Main engines	2 sets GE geared turbines; 2 shafts; 60 000 shp
Speed, knots	35 designed, 30 to 32 max
Range, miles	6 000 at 15 knots; 1 260 to 1 285 at 30 to 32 knots
Oil fuel, tons	506
Complement	250

Transferred from USA, *Aspis, Lonchi* and *Velos* at Long Beach, Cal, on 15 Sep 1959, 9 Feb 1960 and 15 June 1959, respectively, *Sfendoni* at Philadelphia on 21 Aug 1959. *Navarinon* and *Thyella* at Seattle, Wash, on 27 Sep 1962. *Aspis* means Shield.

RADAR. Search: SPS 6, SPS 10. Fire Control: GFC 56 and 63 systems.

SFENDONI *1971, Major Aldo Fraccaroli*

FLETCHER Class (4 guns)

FRIGATES

4 Ex-US "BOSTWICK" DE TYPE

Name	*No.*	*Builders*	*Laid down*	*Launched*	*Completed*
AETOS (ex-USS *Slater*, DE 766)	D 01	Tampa SB Co.	9 Mar 1943	13 Feb 1944	1 May 1944
IERAX (ex-USS *Elbert*, DE 768)	D 31	Tampa SB Co	1 Apr 1943	23 May 1944	12 July 1944
LEON (ex-USS *Eldridge*, DE 173)	D 54	Federal SB & DD Co	22 Feb 1943	25 June 1943	27 Aug 1943
PANTHIR (ex-USS *Garfield Thomas*, DE 193)	D 67	Federal SB & DD Co	23 Sep 1943	12 Dec 1943	24 Jan 1944

Displacement, tons	1 240 standard; 1 900 full load
Length, feet (*metres*)	306 (*93·3*) oa
Beam, feet (*metres*)	36·7 (*11·2*)
Draught, feet (*metres*)	14 (*4·3*)
Guns, dual purpose	3—3 in (*76 mm*) 50 cal.
Guns, AA	6—40 *mm*, 3 twin 14—20 *mm*, 7 twin
A/S weapons	Hedgehog; 8 DCT; 1 DC rack
Torpedo racks	Side launching for A/S torpedoes
Main engines	4 sets GM diesel-electric 6 000 bhp; 2 shafts
Speed, knots	19·25 max
Range, miles	9 000 at 12 knots
Oil fuel (tons)	316
Complement	220 (war)

Former US destroyer escorts of the "Bostwick" class. *Aetos* and *Ierax* were transferred on 15 Mar 1951 and *Leon* and *Panthir* on 15 Jan 1951. Their 3—21 inch torpedo tubes in a triple mount were removed. Meanings of names are Eagle, Falcon, Lion and Panther, respectively.

LEON *1972, Hellenic Navy.*

CORVETTES

5 Ex-BRITISH "ALGERINE" TYPE

Name	No.	Builders	Launched
ARMATOLOS (ex-HMS *Aries*)	M 12	Toronto Shipyard	19 Sep 1942
MAHITIS (ex-HMS *Postillion*)	M 58	Redfern Construction Co	14 Nov 1942
NAVMACHOS (ex-HMS *Lightfoot*)	M 64	Redfern Construction Co	31 Aug 1942
POLEMISTIS (ex-HMS *Gozo*)	M 74	Redfern Construction Co	18 Mar 1943
PYRPOLITIS (ex-HMS *Arcturus*)	M 76	Redfern Construction Co	27 Jan 1943

Displacement, tons	1 030 standard; 1 325 full load
Length, feet (*metres*)	225 (*68·6*) oa
Beam, feet (*metres*)	35·5 (*10·8*)
Draught, feet (*metres*)	11·5 (*3·5*) max
Guns, dual purpose	2—3 in (*76 mm*) US Mark 21 (1 in *Pirpolitis*, none in *Mahitis*)
Guns, AA	4—20 mm (US), 2MG
A/S weapons	2 to 4 DCT
Main engines	2 triple expansion; 2 shafts; 2 700 ihp = 16 knots max
Boilers	2 Yarrow, 250 psi (*17·6 kg cm²*)
Oil fuel, tons	235
Range, miles	5 000 at 10 knots; 2 270 at 14·5 knots
Complement	85

Former British ocean minesweepers of the "Algerine" class. Acquired from the Executive Committee of Surplus Allied Material. Latterly employed as Corvettes. The armament of *Mahitis* was removed when she became a training ship. *Armatolos* and *Navmachos* were used as auxiliaries and others as personnel transports.

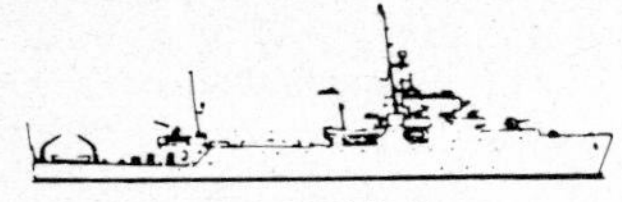

ex-ALGERINE Class

POLEMISTIS — *1971, Hellenic Navy*

SUBMARINES

4 TYPE 209 "GLAVKOS" CLASS

GLAVKOS S 110 **PROTEUS** S 113
NEREUS S 111 **TRITON** S 112

Displacement, tons	990 surfaced; 1 290 dived
Length, feet (*metres*)	177·1 (*54·0*)
Beam, feet (*metres*)	20·3 (*6·2*)
Torpedo tubes	8—21 in (with reloads) bow
Main machinery	Diesel-electric; 4 MTU; Siemens diesel-generators; 1 Siemens electric motor; 1 shaft
Speed	10 surfaced; 22 dived
Range	50 days
Complement	31

GLAVKOS — *1973, Hellenic Navy*

Designed by Ingenieurkontor, Lübeck for construction by Howaldtswerke, Kiel and sale by Ferrostaal Essen all acting as a consortium.
A single-hull design with two ballast tanks and forward and after trim tanks. Fitted with snort and remote machinery control. The single screw is slow revving. Very high capacity batteries with GRP lead-acid cells and battery cooling—by Wilh. Hagen and VARTA. Active and passive sonar, sonar detection, equipment, sound ranging and underwater telephone. Fitted with two periscopes, radar and Omega receiver. Fore-planes retract.
Glavkos launched Sep 1970, completed Sep 1971, Nereus in Sep 1971 and Feb 1972, *Triton* in 1971 and Sep 1972, *Proteus* in 1971 and 1973.

TRITON — *1973, Hellenic Navy*

1 Ex-US "BALAO" CLASS

Name	No.	Builder	Completed	Transferred
TRIAINA (ex-USS *Scabbard Fish* SS 397)	S 86	Portsmouth Navy Yard	29 Apr 1944	26 Feb 1965

Displacement, tons	1 816 surface; 2 425 submerged
Length, feet (*metres*)	311·5 (*94·9*) oa
Beam, feet (*metres*)	27·0 (*8·2*)
Draught, feet (*metres*)	17·0 (*5·2*)
Torpedo tubes	10—21 in (*533 mm*), 6 bow, 4 stern
Main engines	6 500 bhp diesels (surface) 4 610 hp motors (submerged)
Speed, knots	20 on surface, 10 submerged
Range, miles	12 000 at 10 knots (surface)
Complement	85

Originally one of the wartime "Balao" class later having a streamlined fin fitted.

TRIAINA — *1970, Hellenic Navy*

Submarines—*continued*

1 Ex-US "GUPPY IIA" CLASS

Name	*No.*	*Builder*	*Completed*	*Transferred*
PAPANIKOLIS (ex-USS *Hardhead* SS 365)	S 114	Manitowoc SB Co.	Apr 1944	26 July 1972

Displacement, tons	1 840 standard; 2 445 dived
Length, feet (*metres*)	306 (*93·2*)
Beam, feet (*metres*)	27 (*8·3*)
Draught, feet (*metres*)	17 (*5·2*)
Torpedo tubes	10—21 inch; 6 bow, 4 stern
Main engines	3 Diesels; 4 800 shp/2 Motors, 5 400 shp; 2 shafts
Speed	17 surface; 15 dived
Range, miles	12 000 at 10 knots (surface)
Complement	84

Hardhead built by Manitowoc SB Co. Commissioned April 1944. Transferred 26 July 1972.

PAPANIKOLIS *1973, Hellenic Navy*

1 Ex-US "GUPPY III" CLASS

Name	*No.*	*Builder*	*Completed*	*Transferred*
KATSONIS (ex-USS *Remora* SS 487)	S 115	Portsmouth Navy Yard	3 Jan 1946	29 Oct 1973

Displacement, tons	1 975 standard; 2 450 dived
Dimensions, ft (*m*)	326 × 27 × 17 (*99·4 × 8·2 × 5·2*)
Torpedo tubes	10—21 in; 6 bow 4 stern
Main machinery	4 Diesels; 6 400 hp;—2 electric motors; 5 400 shp; 2 shafts
Speed, knots	20 surface; 15 dived
Range, miles	12 000 at 10 knots (surfaced)
Complement	85

Originally of the wartime "Tench" class, subsequently converted under the Guppy II programme and, in 1961-62 to Guppy III. Amongst other modifications this involved the fitting of BQG-4 Sonar (Puffs) for dived fire-control, in addition to the BQR-2 array sonar.

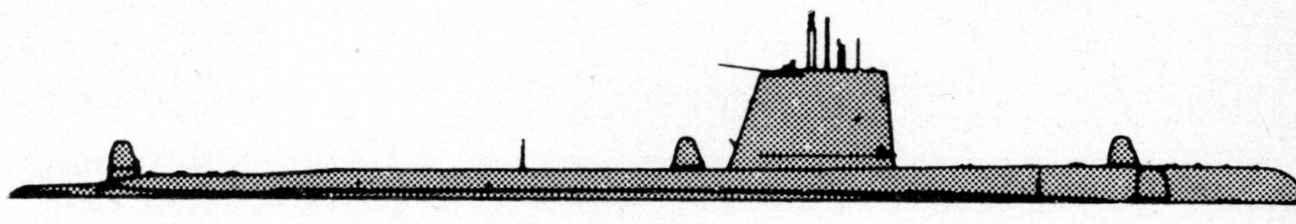

GUPPY III

LIGHT FORCES

4 "LA COMBATTANTE" CLASS

(FAST ATTACK CRAFT—MISSILES)

CALYPSO P 54 **EUNIKI** P 55 **KYMOTHOI** P 53 **NAVSITHOI** P 56

Displacement, tons	234 standard; 255 full load
Dimensions, feet	154·2 × 23·3 × 8·2
Missiles	4 MM 38 Exocet surface-to-surface
Guns	4—35 mm AA (2 twin)
Torpedo tubes	2 aft for wire-guided torpedoes
Main engines	4 diesels; 4 shafts; 12 000 bhp = 36·5 knots
Oil fuel, tons	39 bunkerage
Range, miles	850 at 25 knots
Complement	40 (4 officers, and 36 men)

Ordered in 1969 from Constructions Mécaniques de Normandie Cherbourg.

Calypso launched 26 Apr 1971, completed Apr 1972. *Euniki* launched 8 Sept 1971, completed June 1972. *Kymothoi* launched 26 Jan 1971, completed Dec 1971. *Navsithoi* launched 20 Dec 1971 completed July 1972.

NAVSITHOI *1973, Hellenic Navy*

5 "SILBERMÖWE" CLASS (FAST ATTACK CRAFT—TORPEDO)

DOLPHIN (ex-*Sturmmöwe*) P 15
DRAKON (ex-*Silbermöwe*) P 16
FOINIX (ex-*Eismöwe*) P 27
POLIKOS (ex-*Raubmöwe*) P 17
POLIDEFKIS (ex-*Wildschwan*) P 18

Displacement, tons	119 standard; 155 full load
Dimensions, feet	116·1 × 16·7 × 5·9
Torpedo tubes	2—21 in
Guns	1—40 mm AA; 2—20 mm AA (1 twin)
Main engines	3 diesels; 3 shafts; 9 000 bhp = 38 knots

Old S-Boote taken over from Germany 17 Dec 1968. Built by Lurssen, Vegesack, 1951-56.

5 "TJELD" CLASS (FAST ATTACK CRAFT—TORPEDO)

ANDROMEDA P 21
KASTOR P 23
KYKØNOS P 24
PIGASSOS P 25
TOXOTIS P 26

Displacement, tons	69 standard; 76 full load
Dimensions, feet	75 pp; 80·4 oa × 24·6 × 6·9
Torpedo tubes	4—21 in
Guns	2—40 mm AA
Main engines	2 Napier Deltic T 18-37 K diesels; 3 100 bhp = 43 knots
Complement	22

Andromeda and *Imionos* were taken over in Feb 1967 from Mandal, Norway. *Kastor* and *Kykonos*, and the third pair, *Pigassos* and *Toxotis*, were delivered in succession in 1967.

ANDROMEDA *1971, Hellenic Navy*

1 VOSPER "BRAVE" CLASS (FAST ATTACK CRAFT—TORPEDO)

ASTRAPI P 20 (ex-*Strahl* P 6194)

Displacement, tons	95 standard; 110 full load
Dimensions, feet	96 (full); 99 oa × 25 × 7 (props)
Torpedo chutes	4—21 in side launching
Guns	2—40 mm AA
Main engines	3 Bristol Siddeley Marine Proteus gas turbines; 3 shafts; 12 750 bhp = 55·5 knots

ASTRAPI *1972, Hellenic Navy*

Light Forces—*continued*

Built by Vosper, Portsmouth. Launched on 10 Jan 1962. Commissioned in Federal German Navy on 21 Nov 1962. Transferred to Royal Hellenic Navy in Apr 1967. Refitted by Vosper in 1968. Of similar design to British "Brave" class.

1 VOSPER "FEROCITY" CLASS

(FAST ATTACK CRAFT—TORPEDO)

AIOLOS P 19 (ex-*Pfeil* P 6193)

Displacement, tons	75 standard; 80 full load
Dimensions, feet	92 wl; 95 oa × 23·9 × 6·5
Torpedo chutes	4—21 in side launching
Guns	2—40 mm AA
Main engines	2 Bristol Siddeley Marine Proteus gas turbines; 2 shafts; 8 500 bhp = 50 knots

Built by Vosper, Portsmouth. Launched on 26 Oct 1961. Commissioned in German Navy on 27 June 1962. Transferred to Royal Hellenic Navy in Apr 1967. Refitted by Vosper in 1968. Based on design of Vosper prototype *Ferocity*.

AIOLOS *1972, Hellenic Navy*

3 PGM TYPE

ANTIPLOIARKHOS PEZOPOULOS (ex-*PGM* 21, ex-*PC* 1552) P 70
PLOTARKHIS ARSLANOGLOU (ex-*PGM* 25, ex-*PC* 1556) P 14
PLOTARKHIS CHADZIKONSTANDIS (ex-*PGM* 29, ex-*PC* 1565) P 96

Displacement, tons	335 standard; 439 full load
Dimensions, feet	170 wl; 174·7 oa × 23 × 10·8 (max)
Guns	1—3 in; 6—20 mm AA
A/S weapons	Hedgehog; side launching torpedo racks; depth charges
Main engines	2 GM diesels; 2 shafts; 3 600 bhp = 19 knots

All launched in 1943-44. Acquired from USA in Aug 1947. The two 40 mm AA guns were removed and a hedgehog was installed in 1963.

ANTIPLOIARKHOS PEZOPOULOS *1973, Hellenic Navy*

2 LSSL TYPE

PLOTARKHIS MARIDAKIS (ex-USS *LSSL* 65) L 94 (ex-P 94)
PLOTARKHIS VLACHAVAS (ex-USS *LSSL*) 35 L 95 (ex-P 95)

Displacement, tons	257 standard; 395 full load
Dimensions, feet	157·0 × 23·2 × 5·7
Guns	1—3 in; 4—40 mm AA (2 twin); 4—20 mm AA
Main engines	Diesels; 2 shafts; 1 600 bhp = 14·4 knots

Built by Albina Engine & Machinery Works Inc. Portland, Oreg, and Commercial Iron Works, Portland, and launched on 14 Nov and 17 Sep 1944, respectively. *Plotarkhis Vlachavas* was transferred from USA on 12 Aug 1957 and *Plotarkhis Maridakis* in June 1958. Given L instead of P pennant numbers in 1971

AMPHIBIOUS FORCES

1 Ex-US LSD

NAFKRATOUSSA (ex-USS *Fort Mandan, LSD* 21) L 153

Displacement, tons	4 790 light; 9 375 full load
Dimensions, feet	457·8 oa × 72·2 × 18 max
Guns	8—40 mm AA
Main engines	Geared turbines; 2 shafts; 7 000 shp = 15·4 knots
Boilers	2

Built at Boston Navy Yard. Laid down on 2 Jan 1945. Launched on 22 May 1945 Completed on 31 Oct 1945. This dock landing ship taken over from USA in 1971 replacing the previous *Nafkratoussa* (ex-*Hyperion*, ex-*LSD* 9) out of service in 1971 as Headquarters ship of Captain, Landing Forces.

NAFKRATOUSSA *1973, Hellenic Navy*

8 Ex-US LST's

KRITI (ex-USS *Page County, LST* 1076) L 171
IKARIA (ex-USS *Potter County, LST* 1086) L 154
LESBOS (ex-USS *Boone County, LST* 389) L 172
RODOS (ex-USS *Bowman County, LST* 391) L 157
SYROS (ex-USS *LST* 325) L 144
CHIOS (ex *LST* 35) L 195
LIMNOS (ex *LST* 36) L 158
SAMOS (ex *LST* 33) L 179

Displacement, tons	1 653 standard; 2 366 beaching; 4 080 full load
Dimensions, ft (*m*)	328 × 50 × 14 (*100 × 15·3 × 2·9*)
Guns	8—40 mm; 6—20 mm (*Rodos* 10—40 mm)
Main engines	2 GM diesels; 2 shafts; 1 700 bhp = 11·6 knots
Range, miles	9 500 at 9 knots
Complement	93 (8 officers, 85 men)

Former United States tank landing ships. Cargo capacity 2 100 tons. *Ikaria, Lesbos* and *Rodos* were transferred to the Royal Hellenic Navy on 9 Aug 1960. *Syros* was transferred on 29 May 1964 at Portsmouth, Virginia, under MAP. *Kriti* was transferred in Mar 1971. Last three under lease-lend in 1943.

LIMNOS *1972, Hellenic Navy*

Amphibious Forces—*continued*

5 Ex-US LSM's

IPOPLIARKHOS CRYSTALIDIS (ex-USS *LSM* 541) L 165
IPOPLIARKHOS DANIOLOS (ex-USS *LSM* 227) L 163
IPOPLIARKHOS GRIGOROPOULOS (ex-USS *LSM* 45) L 161
IPOPLIARKHOS ROUSSEN (ex-USS *LSM* 399) L 164
IPOPLIARKHOS TOURNAS (ex-USS *LSM* 102) L 162

Displacement, tons	743 beaching; 1 095 full load
Dimensions, feet	196·5 wl; 203·5 oa × 34·2 × *8·3*
Guns	2—40 mm AA; 8—20 mm AA
Main engines	Diesel direct drive; 2 shafts; 3 600 bhp = 13 knots

Former US Medium Landing Ships. *LSM* 541 and *LSM* 557 were handed over to Greece at Salamis on 30 Oct 1958 and *LSM* 45, *LSM* 102, *LSM* 227 and *LSM* 399 at Portsmouth, Virginia on 3 Nov 1958. All were renamed after naval heroes killed during World War 2.

IPOPLIARKHOS TOURNAS *1971, Hellenic Navy*

Amphibious Forces—*continued*

8 Ex-US LCU's

LCU 763 (*Kithnos*)
LCU 677 (*Sifnos*)
LCU 827 (*Sciathos*)
LCU 852 (*Skopelos*)
LCU 971 (*Kimolos*)
LCU 1229 (*Kea*)
LCU 1379 (*Karpathos*)
LCU 1382 (*Kassos*)

Displacement, tons	143 standard; 309 full load
Dimensions, feet	105 wl; 119 oa × 32·7 × 5 max
Guns	2—20 mm AA
Main Engines	Diesel; 3 shafts; 440 bhp = 8 knots
Complement	13

Former US Utility Landing Craft of the *LCU* (ex-*LST* (6)) type. *Sciathos* and *Scopelos* were acquired in 1959. *Kea, Kithnos* (original No. 149) and *Sifnos* were transferred from USA in 1961. and *Karpathos* (original No. 146) *Kassos* and *Kimolos* in 1962. These LCUs are referred to by their hull numbers and not by name. There are also 13 LCMs and 34 *LCVPs*. all transferred from USA

LCU 763 *1971, Hellenic Navy*

MINE WARFARE FORCES

2 COASTAL MINELAYERS

AKTION (ex-*LSM* 301, ex-MMC 6) N 04
AMVRAKIA (ex-*LSM* 303, ex-MMC 7) N 05

Displacement, tons	720 standard; 1 100 full load
Dimensions, feet	203·5 oa × 34·5 × 8·3 max
Guns	8—40 mm dp (4 twin); 6—20 mm AA (single)
Mines	Capacity 100 to 130
Main engines	2 diesels; 2 shafts; 3 600 bhp = 12·5 knots
Range, miles	3 000 at 12 knots
Complement	65

Former US Medium Landing Ships. Both built at Charleston Naval Shipyard. *Aktion* was launched on 1 Jan 1945 and *Amvrakia* on 14 Nov 1944. Converted in the USA into all purpose seagoing minelayers for the Royal Hellenic Navy. Underwent extensive rebuilding from the deck up. Twin rudders. Transferred on 1 Dec 1953.

AMVRAKIA *1970, Hellenic Navy*

10 Ex-US "BLUEBIRD" CLASS (MINESWEEPERS—COASTAL)

AEDON (ex-*MSC* 310) M 248
AIGLI (ex-*MSC* 299) M 246
ARGO (ex-*MSC* 317) M 213
AVRA (ex-*MSC* 318) M 214
ALKYON (ex-*MSC* 319) M 211
DAFNI (ex-*MSC* 307) M 247
DORIS (ex-*MSC* 298) M 245
KICHLI (ex-*MSC* 308) M 241
PLEIAS (ex-*MSC* 314) M 240
KISSA (ex-*MSC* 309) M 242

Displacement, tons	320 standard; 370 full load
Dimensions, feet	138 pp; 144 oa × 28 × 8·2
Guns	2—20 mm AA (twin)
Main engines	2 GM diesels; 2 shafts; 880 bhp = 13 knots
Complement	39

Built in USA for Greece. *Aedon, Aigli, Dafni, Doris, Kichli* and *Kissa*, were completed and transferred in 1964-65, *Argo* and *Avra* in 1968, *Alkyon* and *Pleias* in 1969-70. Built of wood and non-magnetic materials.

DORIS *1971, Hellenic Navy*

5 ex.-US MSC TYPE 60

ANTIOPI (ex-Belgian *Herve*, *M* 921, ex-USS *MSC* 153) M 205
ATALANTI (ex-Belgian *St. Truiden*, *M* 919 ex-USS *MSC* 169) M 202
NIOVI (ex-Belgian *Laroche*, *M* 924. ex-USS *MSC* 171) M 254
FAEDRA (ex-Belgian *Malmedy*, *M* 922, ex-USS *MSC* 154) M 206
THALIA (ex-Belgian *Blankenberge*, *M* 923, ex-USS *MSC* 170) M 210

Displacement, tons	330 standard; 402 full load
Dimensions, feet	145·0 oa × 27·9 × 8·0 feet
Guns	2—20 mm Oerlikon (1 twin)
Main engines	2 GM diesels; 2 shafts; 900 bhp = 14 knots
Complement	38 officers and men

Former Belgian vessels taken over on 29 July 1969 (*Herve* and *St. Truiden*) and 26 Sep 1969 (*Laroche, Malmedy* and *Blankenberge*).

NIOVI *1971, Michael D. J. Lennon*

SURVEY VESSELS

ATALANTI

Of 383 tons, launched in 1954 with a complement of 35.

VEGAS (ex-*BYMS* 2078) A 478

Of 350 tons and with a complement of 33.

Former coastal minesweeper of the wooden hulled BYMS type.

ANEMOS A 469 (ex-German *KFK KW7*)

Displaced 112 tons, was launched in 1944 and has a complement of 16. Added to the Navy List in 1969.

HEFAISTOS (ex-USS *Josiah Willard Gibbs*, T-AGOR 1, ex-USS *San Carlos*, AVP 51) A 413

Displacement, tons	1 750 standard; 2 800 full load
Dimensions, feet	300·0 wl; 310·8 oa × 41·2 × 13·5
Main engines	2 Fairbanks-Morse diesels. 2 shafts; 6 080 bhp = 18 knots
Complement	75 (10 officers and 65 men)

Former US seaplane tender converted for oceanographic research. Built by Lake Washington Shipyard, Houghton, Wash. Laid down on 7 Sep 1942, launched on 20 Dec 1942 and completed on 21 Mar 1944. Transferred to the Hellenic Navy on 7 Dec 1971.

HEFAISTOS *Dr. Giorgio Arra*

1 SURVEYING LAUNCH

Of 25 tons, launched in 1940. Complement 9.

SERVICE FORCES

2 SUPPORT TANKERS

ARETHOUSA (ex-USS *Natchaug, AOG* 54) A 377
ARIADNI (ex-USS *Tombigbee, AOG* 11) A 414

Displacement, tons	1 850 light; 4 335 full load
Measurement, tons	2 575 deadweight; cargo capacity 2 040
Dimensions, feet	292 wl; 310·8 oa × 48·5 × 15·7 max
Guns	4—3 in dp; 50 cal
Main engines	GM diesels; 2 shafts; 3 300 bhp = 14 knots
Complement	43 (6 officers, 37 men)

Former US petrol carriers. A 377 built by Cargill Inc, Savage, Minn. Laid down on 15 Aug 1944. Launched on 16 Dec 1944. Transferred from the USA to Greece under the Mutual Defense Assistance Program at Pear Harbour, Hawaii in July 1959. A 414 transferred 7 July 1972.

ARETHOUSA *1972, Hellenic Navy*

Service Forces—*cont.*

ZEUS (ex-YOG 98) A 372 (PETROL CARRIER)

Dimensions, feet 165 × 35 × 10

Former US yard petrol carrier. Launched in 1944. Capacity 900 tons.

SIRIOS (ex-*Poseidon*, ex-*Empire Faun*) A 345 (HARBOUR TANKER)

Formerly on loan from Great Britain, but purchased outright in 1962. This ship was renamed *Sirios* when the name *Poseidon* was given to the submarine *Lapon* acquired from the USA in 1958. Capacity 850 tons.

VIVIES A 471 (HARBOUR TANKER)

Originally a water carrier. Capacity 687 tons.

PROMETHEUS A 374 (HARBOUR TANKER)

Launched in 1959. Capacity 520 tons.

KRONOS (ex-*Islay*, ex-*Dresden*) A 373 (HARBOUR TANKER)

Displacement, tons 311 Capacity 110 tons

ORION (ex-US tanker Y 126) A 376 (HARBOUR TANKER)

Formerly small United States yard tanker. Capacity 700 tons.

ORION *1969, Hellenic Navy*

SOTIR (ex-*Salventure*) A 384 (SALVAGE SHIP)

Displacement, tons	1 440 standard; 1 700 full load
Measurement, tons	1 112 gross
Dimensions, feet	216 oa × 37·8 × 13 max
Main engines	Triple expansion; 2 shafts; 1 500 ihp = 12 knots
Oil fuel (tons)	310
Complement	60

Former British Royal Fleet Auxiliary ocean salvage vessel of the "Salv" class. On loan from Great Britain. Equipped with a decompression chamber.

SOTIR *1972, Dr Giorgio Arra*

SAKIPIS (ex-*KNM Ellida*, ex-USS *ARB* 13, ex-USS *LST* 50) A 329 (REPAIR SHIP)

Displacement, tons	3 800 standard; 5 000 full load
Dimensions, feet	316 wl; 328 oa × 50 × 11 max
Guns	12—40 mm AA; 12—20 mm AA
Main engines	GM diesels; 2 shafts; 1 800 bhp = 10 knots
Complement	200

Former US tank landing ship. Built by Dravo Corporation, Pittsburgh. Laid down on 29 Aug 1943, launched on 16 Oct 1943, completed on 27 Nov 1943. Converted to a repair ship in 1952 by Puget Sound Bridge & Dry Dock Co. Taken over by the Royal Norwegian Navy at Seattle on 14 Nov 1952. Returned to the US Navy on 1 July 1960. Transferred to Greece on 16 Sep 1960 at Bergen Norway.

SAKIPIS *1972, Hellenic Navy.*

THETIS (ex-USS *AN* 103) A 307 (NETLAYER)

Displacemetn, tons	680 standard; 805 full load
Dimensions, feet	146 wl; 169·5 oa × 33·5 × 11·8 max
Guns	1—40 mm AA; 4—20 mm AA
Main engines	MAN diesels; 1 shaft; 1 400 bhp = 12 knots
Complement	48

Built by Krúger, Rendsburg as a US offshore order. Launched in 1959. Taken over by the Royal Hellenic Navy on 9 Apr 1960.

THETIS *1971, Hellenic Navy*

SKYROS A 485

Displacement, tons	350

Acts as Lighthouse Tender.

ST LYKOUDIS (ex-*Chania*, ex-HMS *Nasturtium*) A 481

Displacement, tons	1 020 standard; 1,280 full load
Dimensions, feet	190 pp; 205 oa × 33 × 14·5
Main Engines	Triple expansion; 2 750 ihp = 14 knots
Boilers	2 SE
Oil fuel (tons)	230

Former corvette of the British "Flower" type. Launched in 1940. Sold to Greece as a merchant ship in 1948. Now acts as Lighthouse Tender.

ST. LYKOUDIS *1969, Hellenic Navy*

11 TUGS

ACCHILEUS (ex-*Confident*)
AIAS
ANTAIOS (ex-*Busy*)
ATLAS (ex-*F* 5)
ATROMITOS A 410
CIGAS
MINOTAVROS (ex-*Theseus*, ex-*ST* 539)
PERSEUS (ex-*ST772*)
ROMALEOS
TITAN
SAMSON (ex-*F* 16)

Heraklis was officially deleted from the list in 1966, *Aegeus* in 1968, *Kentravros* in 1969 and *Aegeus* in 1972.

5 WATER BOATS

ILIKI **KASTORIA** **STYMFALIA** **TRICHONIS** **VOLVI**

Capacity: *Iliki* and *Stymfalia* 120 tons, *Trihonis* 300 tons, *Volvi* 350 tons, *Kastoria* 520 tons.

GABON

Personnel

(a) 1974: 100 officers and men
(b) Volunteers

Mercantile Marine

Lloyd's Register of Shipping: 9 vessels of 12 428 tons gross

Bases

Libreville, Port Gentil

PATROL BOATS

PRESIDENT ALBERT BERNARD BONGO

Displacement, tons	80
Dimensions, ft (*m*)	104 × 19 × 5 (*32 × 5·8 × 1·5*)
Guns	2—20 mm
Main engines	2 MTU diesels; 2 700 hp = 30 knots
Range, miles	1 500 at 15 knots
Complement	17 (3 officers, 14 ratings)

Built by Chantiers Naval de l'Esterel. Delivered March 1972. Fitted with radar and echo sounder.

PRESIDENT ALBERT BERNARD BONGO *1972, Chanters Navals de Liesterel*

PRESIDENT LEON M'BA GCO 1

Displacement, tons	85 standard
Dimensions, ft (*m*)	92 × 20·5 × 5 (*28 × 6·3 × 1·5*)
Guns	1—75 mm; 1—12·7 mm MG
Main engines	Diesel = 12·5 knots
Complement	16

Built in Gabon, launched on 16 Jan 1968

BOUET-WILLAUMEZ (ex-HDML 1021).

Displacement, tons	40
Dimensions, ft (*m*)	70·8 × 15·3 × 5·9 (*21·6 × 4·7 × 1·8*)
Guns	2—20 mm AA
Main engines	2 Diesels; 300 hp = 12·5 knots
Complement	8

Launched in 1943. Transferred in 1961 by France and still, apparently, going strong.

NOTE. Plans exist for a 60 ft Patrol Boat and four LCVP s.

GRENADA

Note. Grenada was granted self-government, in association with Great Britain (who was responsible for her defence) on 3 March 1967. Full self-government was achieved in February 1973.

Mercantile Marine

Lloyd's Register of Shipping: 2 vessels of 226 tons gross

PATROL BOAT

Displacement, tons	15
Dimensions, ft (*m*)	40 × 12 × 2 (*12·2 × 3·7 × ·6*)
Guns	3 MG
Main engines	2 Diesels; 370 hp = 22 knots

Delivered by Brooke Marine, Lowestoft early in 1972.

GUATEMALA

On 5 Jan 1959 Guatemala announced the establishment of a navy for coastguard work. Subsequently the navy was assigned missions of search and rescue and the support of amphibious operations. The commissioning of a Marine Elevator (Synchrolift) at Santo Tomás on 23 June 1973 (230 ton lift) has greatly improved this navy's repair facilities.

Personnel

(a) 1974: 400 (50 officers and 350 men, including 10 officers and 200 men of the Marines)
(b) 2 years National Service

Bases

Santo Tomás de Castillas (Atlantic); Sipacate (Pacific)

Mercantile Marine

Lloyd's Register of Shipping: 6 vessels of 8 222 tons gross

2 COASTAL PATROL CRAFT

UTATLAU P 851 — P 852

Displacement, tons	42
Dimensions, ft (*m*)	85 × 18·7 × 3 (*25·9 × 5·7 × ·9*)
Guns	2 MG
Main engines	2 GM Diesels; 2 200 bhp = 23 knots
Range, miles	400 at 12 knots
Complement	12 (2 officers, 10 ratings)

Built by Sewart, Florida to "Commercial Cruiser" design.

P 851 — *1973, Guatamalian Navy*

3 65ft COASTAL PATROL CRAFT

P 651 **P 652** **P 653**

Displacement, tons	32
Dimensions,ft (*m*)	64·5 × 17 × 3 (*19·7 × 5·2 × ·9*)
Guns	2 MG
Main engines	2 GM Diesels = 25 knots
Complement	10 (2 officers, 8 ratings)

Built by Halter (US). Delivered 1972.

2 63ft COASTAL CRAFT (ex-SAR CRAFT)

P 631 **P 632**

Displacement, tons	32
Dimensions, ft (*m*)	63·3 × 15·4 × 3 (*19·3 × 4·7 × 0·9*)
Guns	2 MG
Main engines	2 GM Diesels 8V71 = 25 knots
Complement	10 (2 officers, 8 men)

2 Ex-USCG UTILITY BOATS MK IV

P 401 **XIMICHE** P 402

Transferred Aug 1963.

2 28ft COASTAL PATROL CRAFT

P 281 **P 282**

Striker Utility Patrol Craft modified for one GM 6-53 Diesel.

1 Ex-US LCM 6 MK VI

CHIMALTENANGO 561

Transferred Jan 1966.

1 Ex-US REPAIR BARGE YR 40

Transferred July 1962.

GUINEA

Personnel

1974: 350 officers and men

Mercantile Marine

Lloyd's Register of Shipping: 9 vessels of 15 538 tons gross

LIGHT FORCES

4 Ex-USSR "P 6" CLASS (FAST ATTACK CRAFT—TORPEDO)

Displacement, tons	66 standard; 75 full load
Dimensions, ft (*m*)	84·2 × 20·0 × 6·0 (*25·7 × 6·1 × 1·8*)
Guns	4—25 mm AA
Tubes	2—21 in (or mines or depth charges)
Main engines	4 Diesels; 4 shafts; 4 800 bhp = 43 knots
Range, miles	450 at 30 knots
Complement	25

It seems unlikely that the torpedo armament is operational.

2 Ex-USSR "POLUCHAT I" CLASS (COASTAL PATROL CRAFT)

P 215 **P 425**

Displacement, tons	86 standard; 91 full load
Dimensions, ft (*m*)	98·0 pp × 15·0 × 4·8 (*29·9 × 4·6 × 1·5*)
Guns	2—14·5 mm AA (1 twin)
Main engines	2 diesels; 2 shafts; 1 200 bhp = 18 knots
Oil fuel, tons	9·25
Range, miles	460 at 17 knots
Complement	16 (2 officers, 14 ratings)

4 Ex-USSR "MO VI" CLASS (COASTAL PATROL CRAFT)

Displacement, tons	64 standard; 73 full load
Dimensions, ft (*m*)	83·6 × 19·7 × 4·0 (*25·5 × 6 × 1·2*)
Guns	4—25 mm (twin)
A/S weapons	DC mortars and racks
Main engines	4 Diesels; 4 shafts; 4 800 hp = 40 knots

Transferred 1972-73. Radar—Pot Head.

LANDING CRAFT

2 SMALL UTILITY TYPE

Recent visits by considerrable numbers of Soviet ships may have increased these numbers.

GUYANA

Mercantile Marine

Lloyd's Register of Shipping: 42 vessels of 13 735 tons gross

PATROL LAUNCHES

Mercantile Marine

Lloyd's Register of Shipping: 42 vessels of 13 735 tons gross

JAGUAR **MARGAY** **OCELOT**

Displacement, tons	10
Dimensions, ft (*m*)	40 × 12 × 3·5 (*12·2 × 3·7 × 1·1*)
Guns	7·62 mm general purpose machine guns
Main engines	2 Cummins diesels; 370 hp = 19 knots
Range, miles	150 at 12 knots
Complement	6

They have glass fibre hulls with aluminium superstructures. Completed 29 Apr 1971 (*Jaguar*) 21 May 1971 (*Margay*), 22 June 1971 (*Ocelot*).

Note. Three 110 ft Patrol craft ordered in 1970. No more news..

HAITI

Personnel

(a) 1974: Total 300 (40 officers and 260 men)
(b) Voluntary service

COAST GUARD VESSELS

DESSALINES (ex-USS *Tonawanda, AN* 89) GC 10

Displacement, tons	650 standard; 785 full load
Dimensions, feet	168·5 × 33 × 10·8
Main engines	Busch-Sulzer diesel-electric; 1 500 shp = 12 knots

Former United States Navy netlayer of the "Cohoes" class. Built by Leatham D· Smith S.B. Co. Launched on 14 Nov 1944. Loaned to Haiti in 1960 for five years.

AMIRAL KILLICK (ex-USCG *Black Rock, WAGL* 367) GC 7

Displacement, tons	160
Dimensions, feet	Length 114

Former buoy tender purchased from the US Coast Guard in 1955, commissioned in Jan 1956.

LA CRETE A PIERROT (ex-USCG 95315) GC 8 **VERTIÈRES** GC 9

Displacement, tons	100
Dimensions, feet	95 × 19 × 5
Gun	1—40 mm AA
Main engines	4 diesels; 2 shafts; 2 200 bhp = 21 knots
Range, miles	1 500
Complement	15

Former US Coast Guard steel cutters. Built at US Coast Guard Yard, Curtiss Bay, Maryland. *La Crête a Pierrot* was acquired on 26 Feb 1956. *Vertières* was transferred to Haiti at Norfolk, Virginia in Oct 1956 and commissioned in Dec 1956.

16 AOUT 1946 (ex-*SC* 453) GC 2

Displacement, tons	110 standard; 138 full load
Dimensions, feet	110·5 × 18·8 × 6·5
Guns	2—40 mm; 2—20 mm
Main engines	Diesels; 2 shafts; 1 000 = 15 knots

Submarine chaser of the SC type acquired during 1947 from the US Navy. Launched in 1943. Laid up in reserve.

SAVANNAH GC 1

Displacement, tons	47
Dimensions, feet	83 × 16 × 4·2
Main engines	Diesels; 2 shafts; 200 bhp = 9 knots
Complement	12

Ex-USCG cutter 56200, built in the USA in 1944 and acquired in 1944.

ARTIBONITE (ex-US *LCT*) GC 5

Displacement, tons	134 standard; 285 full load
Dimensions, feet	120·3 oa × 32 × 4·2
Main engines	3 diesels; 675 bhp = 8 knots
Complement	12

Former US tank landing craft. Salvaged by Haitian Coast Guard after grounding and converted. Laid up in reserve having been damaged by grounding in Mar 1956.

SANS SOUCI (ex-*Captain James Taylor*)

Displacement, tons	161
Main engines	Diesels; 2 shafts; 300 bhp = 10 knots

Employed, when required, as the Presidential Yacht.

HONDURAS

Coast Guard

There are three small coastguard cutters.

Mercantile Marine

Lloyd's Register of Shipping: 58 vessels of 74 030 tons gross

HONDURAS, BRITISH

2 PATROL CRAFT

BELIZE PBM 01 **BELMOPAN** PBM 02

Displacement, tons	15
Dimensions, feet	40 × 12 × 2
Guns	3 MG
Main engines	2 Diesels; 370 hp = 22 knots

Built by Brooke Marine, Lowestoft.

HONG KONG

Mercantile Marine

Lloyds' Register of Shipping: 98 vessels of 342 529 tons gross

7-78 FT VOSPER THORNYCROFT PATROL CRAFT

Displacement, tons	80
Dimensions, feet	78·5 oa × 17·2 × 5·5
Guns	1—·50 cal MG
Main engines	Two Cummins diesels; 1 500 hp = 20 knots
Range, miles	700 at 15 knots
Complement	16

Steel hulled craft built by Vosper Thornycroft Private Ltd, Singapore. Delivered May 1972 to May 1973 to the Royal Hong Kong Police.

Note. There are also about 40 smaller patrol boats manned by the Police.

HUNGARY

Diplomatic Representation

Military and Air Attaché London: Lieut Colonel Károly Mészáros

Personnel

(a) 1974: 500 officers and men
(b) 2 years national service

Mercantile Marine

Lloyd's Register of Shipping: 21 vessels of 53 580 tons gross

The Navy was dissolved by 1969 but a maritime wing of the Army is still very active on the Danube.

10 100 ton PATROL CRAFT

5 LCU's

No. 542-007 *1972, Hungarian River Guard*

ICELAND

Duties

The Coast Guard Service (Landhelgisgaezlan) deals with fishery protection, salvage, rescue, hydrographic research, surveying and lighthouse duties.

Strength of the Coast Guard

5 Patrol Vessels; colour: dark grey
2 Whalecatchers
1 Patrol Aircraft and helicopter

Personnel

1974: 120 officers and men

Mercantile Marine

Lloyd's Register of Shipping:
325 vessels of 142 777 tons gross

COAST GUARD PATROL VESSELS

ÆGIR

Displacement, tons	1 150
Dimensions, feet	204 × 33 × 13
Guns	1—57 mm
Main engines	2 diesels; 2 shafts; 8 000 bhp = 19 knots
Complement	22

The first new construction patrol vessel for the Icelandic Coast Guard Service for about eight years. Projected in Feb 1965. Built by Aalborg Vaerft, Denmark. Laid down in May 1967. Completed in 1968.

ÆGIR *1969, Icelandic Coast Guard Service*

ODINN

Measurement, tons	1 000
Dimensions, feet	187 pp × 33 × 13
Guns	1—57 mm
Main Engines	2 diesels; 2 shafts; 5 000 bhp = 18 knots
Complement	22

Designed as a coast guard vessel. Built at Aalborg Vaerft A/S, Denmark. Laid down in Jan 1959. Launched in Sep 1959. Completed in Jan 1960. To be refitted with a new tripod mast in 1972.

ODINN *1967, Icelandic Coast Guard Service*

ALBERT

Measurement, tons	200 gross
Dimensions, feet	Length: 111·2
Guns	1—47 mm
Main engines	1 Nohab diesel; 650 bhp = 12·5 knots
Complement	15

Launched in 1956. Completed and commissioned for service in Apr 1957. To be refitted in 1972.

THOR

Displacement, tons	920
Dimensions, feet	183·3 pp; 206 oa × 31·2 × 13
Guns	2—57 mm
Main engines	2 diesels; 3 200 bhp = 17 knots
Complement	22

Built at Aalborg, Denmark. Launched in 1951. Completed and commissioned in late 1951. Rated as coastal inspection and salvage vessel. Fitted with helicopter platform during refit in 1972.

THOR *1969, Icelandic Coast Guard Service*

ARVAKUR

Displacement, tons	716
Dimensions, feet	106 × 33 × 13
Guns	1 small to be mounted
Main engines	1 diesel; 1 000 bhp = 12 knots
Complement	12

Built as a lighthouse tender in the Netherlands in 1962. Acquired by Iceland for duty in the Coast Guard Service in 1969.

ARVAKUR *1969, Icelandic Coast Guard Service*

NEW CONSTRUCTION

A new patrol vessel is under construction for delivery, possibly in 1974. Order from Aarhus and Aalborg, Denmark 29 Aug 1973.

NOTE. Two 20 knot whale-catchers requisitioned in 1972.

INDIA

Administration

Chief of the Naval Staff:
Admiral S. N. Kohli

Flag Officer C in C, Western Naval Command:
Vice-Admiral J. Cursetji

Flag Officer Commanding Western Fleet:
Rear-Admiral S. Parkash

Flag Officer C in C, Eastern Naval Command:
Vice-Admiral K. L. Kulkarni

Flag Officer Commanding Eastern Fleet:
Rear-Admiral R. L. Pereira

Flag Officer, Southern Naval Area:
Rear-Admiral S. H. Sarma

Diplomatic Representation

Naval Adviser in London:
Rear Admiral R. K. S. Ghandi

Naval Attaché in Bonn:
Captain L. Ramdas

Naval Attaché in Moscow:
Captain I. J. S. Khurana

Naval Adviser, Dacca:
Captain R. B. Mukherjee

Personnel

(a) 1974: 30 000 officers and ratings (including Naval Air Arm)
(b) Voluntary service

Strength of the Fleet

Type	*Active*	*Building*
Attack Carrier (Medium)	1	—
Cruisers	2	—
Destroyers	3	—
Frigates	23	4
Patrol Submarines	4	4
Fast Attack Craft—Missile	8	?4
Large Patrol Craft	3	—
Coastal Patrol Craft	14	—
Landing Ships	1	—
Landing Craft	4	—
Minesweepers—Coastal	4	—
Minesweepers—Inshore	4	—
Survey Ships	4	—
Submarine Tenders	1	—
Submarine Rescue Ships	1	—
Replenishment Tanker	1	—
Support Tankers	2	—
Harbour Tankers	2	—
Repair Ship	1	—
Ocean Tug	1	—

Prefix to Ships Names

IS (Indian Ship)

Naval Air Arm

Squadron No.	*Aircraft*	*Role*
300	Seahawk FGA6	Strike
310	Alize 1050	ASW
321	Alouette III	SAR
330	Sea Kings	ASW
331	Alouette III	ASW
550	Alize, Alouette	Training
561	HTZ16, Devon Hughes 300, Alouette III	Training

Naval Bases and Establishments

Bombay (C in C Western Fleet, barracks and main Dockyard);
Vishakapatnam (C in C Eastern Command, submarine base, dockyard and barracks);
Cochin (FO Southern Area Naval Air Station, barracks and professional schools);
Lonavala and Jamnagar (professional schools);
Calcutta, Goa, and Port Blair small bases only.

Mercantile Marine

Lloyd's Register of Shipping:
430 vessels of 2 886 595 tons gross

AIRCRAFT CARRIER (*Attack Medium*)

Name	*No.*	*Builders*	*Engineers*	*Laid down*	*Launched*	*Completed*
VIKRANT (ex-HMS *Hercules*)	R 11	Vickers-Armstrong Ltd, Tyne	Parsons Marine Steam Turbine Co	14 Oct 1943	22 Sep 1945	4 Mar 1961

1 Ex-BRITISH "MAJESTIC" CLASS

Displacement, tons	16 000 standard; 19 500 full load
Length, feet (*metres*)	630 (*192·0*) pp; 700 (*213·4*) oa
Beam, feet (*metres*)	80 (*24·4*) hull
Width, feet (*metres*)	128 (*39·0*)
Draught, feet (*metres*)	24 (*7·3*)
Aircraft	21 capacity
Guns, AA	15—40 mm; 4 twin, 7 single
Boilers	4 Admiralty 3-drum; 400 psi; 700°F
Main engines	Parsons single reduction geared turbines; 40 000 shp; 2 shafts
Speed, knots	24·5 designed
Complement	1 343, designed accommodation

Acquired from Great Britain in Jan 1957 after having been suspended in May 1946 when structurally almost complete and 75% fitted out. Taken in hand by Harland & Wolff Ltd, Belfast, in Apr 1957 for completion in 1961 Commissioned on 4 Mar 1961 and renamed *Vikrant*.

AIRCRAFT. Still equipped with Seahawks although re-equipment is planned. Harrier trials in mid-1972 showed promise, but subsequently the IN is understood to have preferred Soviet Yakovlev VTOL aircraft due to problems in purchasing the Harrier.

ENGINEERING. Engines and boilers are arranged *en echelon*, one set of turbines and two boilers being installed side by side in each of the two propelling machinery spaces, on the unit system, so that the starboard propeller shaft is longer than the port.

FLIGHT DECK. The aircraft including strike and anti-submarine aircraft, operate from an angled deck with steam catapult, landing sights and two electrically operated lifts.

HABITABILITY. Partially air-conditioned and insulated for tropical service, the ship's sides being sprayed with asbestos cement instead of being lagged. Separate messes and dining halls.

RADAR. Search: Type 960, Type 277. Tactical: Type 293. Miscellaneous: Type 963 Carrier Controlled Approach.

DRAWING. Scale:
115 feet = 1 inch

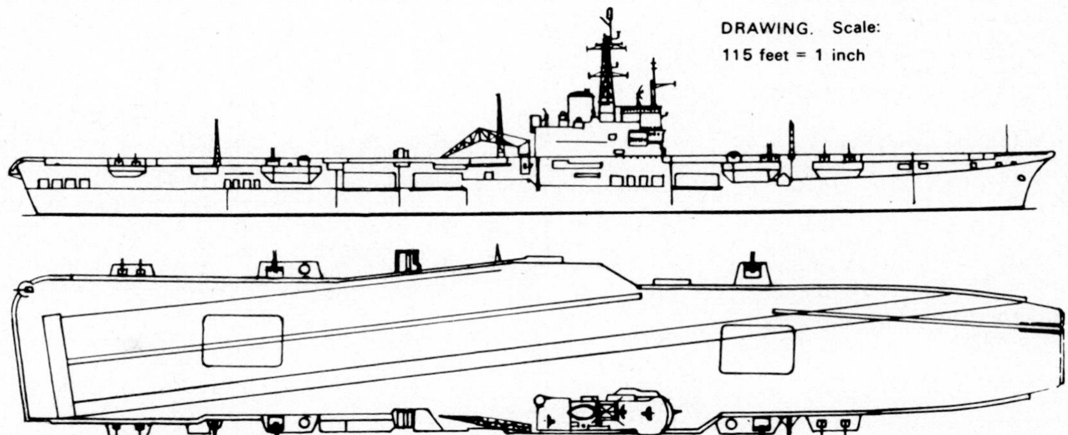

VIKRANT — *1971, John G. C. llis*

CRUISERS

Name	No.	Builders	Engineers	Laid down	Launched	Completed
MYSORE (ex- HMS *Nigeria*)	C 60	Vickers-Armstrongs, Ltd, Tyne	Parsons	8 Feb 1938	18 July 1939	23 Sep 1940

Displacement, tons	8 700 standard; 11 040 full load
Length, feet (*metres*)	538·0 (*164·0*)pp; 549·0 (*167·3*)wl 555·5 (*169·3*) oa
Beam, feet (*metres*)	62·0 (*18·9*)
Draught, feet (*metres*)	21·0 (*6·4*) max
Guns	9—6 in (*152 mm*), 3 triple; 8—4 in (*102 mm*) LP, 4 twin; 12—40 mm AA; 5 twin, 2 single
Armour	Side 4½ in—3 in (*114—76 mm*); Deck 2 in (*51 mm*); Conning tower 4 in (102 *mm*); Turrets 2 in (*51 mm*)
Main engines	Parsons geared turbines; 4 shafts; 72 500 shp
Speed, knots	31·5
Boilers	4 Admiralty 3-drum type
Complement	800

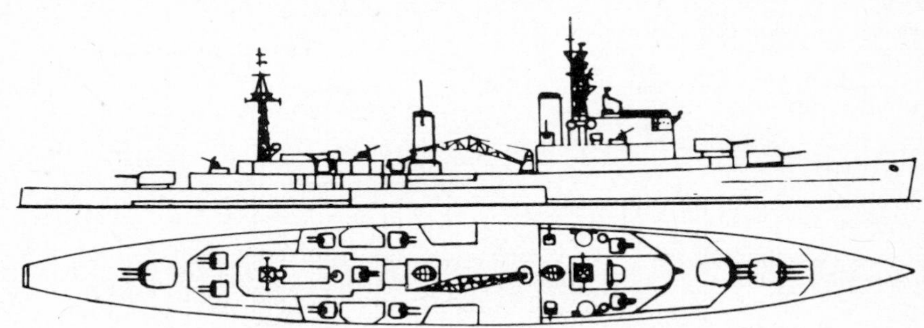

GENERAL
Formerly a "Colony" class cruiser in the Royal Navy. Purchased from Great Britain on 8 Apr 1954 for £300 000. Extensively refitted and reconstructed by Cammell Laird & Co Ltd, Birkenhead, before commissioning. Formally handed over to the Indian Navy at Birkenhead and renamed *Mysore* on 29 Aug 1957. Involved in two serious collisions, the second in late 1972 with *Beas*, resulting in two months of repairs.

RADAR. Search: Type 960, Type 277. Tactical: Type 293. Fire Control: X Band.

RECONSTRUCTION. Ship formerly had tripod masts. During reconstruction the triple 6 inch turret in "X" position and the 6—21 inch torpedo tubes (tripled) were removed, the bridge was modified, two lattice masts were stepped, all electrical equipment was replaced and the engine room and other parts of the ship were refitted.

DRAWING. Starboard elevation and plan. Drawn in 1971. Scale: 125 feet = 1 inch

MYSORE — *1971, Roland Rodwell*

Name	No.	Builders	Laid down	Launched	Completed
DELHI (ex HMS *Achilles*)	C 74	Cammell Laird & Co Ltd, Birkenhead	11 June 1931	1 Sep 1932	5 Oct 1933

Displacement, tons	7 114 standard; 9 740 full load
Length, feet (*metres*)	522·0 (*159·1*)pp; 544·5 (*166·0*)oa
Beam, feet (*metres*)	55·2 (*16·8*)
Draught, feet (*metres*)	20·0 (*6·1*) max
Guns	6—6 in (*152 mm*); 8—4 in (*102 mm*) AA; 14—40 mm AA; 4—3 pdr saluting
Armour	4 in-2 in side; 1 in gunhouses; 1 in bridge; 2 in deck
Main engines	Parsons geared turbines; 4 shafts 72 000 shp
Speed, knots	32
Boilers	4 Admiralty 3-drum type
Oil fuel, tons	1 800
Complement	800

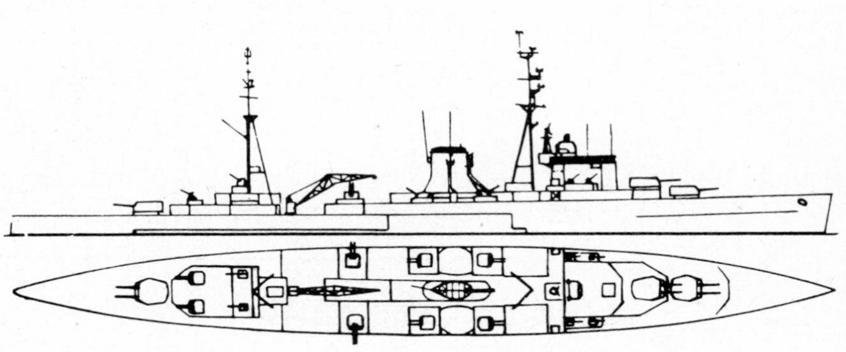

Formerly a "Leander" class light cruiser in the Royal Navy. Purchased from Great Britain and delivered on 5 July 1948. Refitted in 1955. Now used for training.

RADAR. Search: Type 960, Type 277. Tactical: Type 293. Fire Control: Early design.

TORPEDO TUBES. In 1958 the original eight 21 inch torpedo tubes, in two quadruple banks, were removed, and the forecastle deck plating was consequently extended aft to the twin 40 mm AA gun mounting abreast the boat stowage.

HISTORICAL. As HMS *Achilles*, then lent to the Royal New Zealand Navy, this ship, with HMS *Ajax* and HMS *Exeter*, defeated the German battleship *Admiral Graf Spee* in the Battle of the River Plate on 13 Dec 1939.

DRAWING. Starboard elevation and plan. Drawn in 1971. Scale: 122 feet = 1 inch

DELHI

DESTROYERS

3 Ex-BRITISH "R" CLASS

Name	No.	Builders	Begun	Launched	Completed	Transferred
RANA (ex-HMS *Raider*)	D 115	Cammell Laird & Co Ltd. Birkenhead	16 Apr 1941	1 Apr 1942	16 Nov 1942	9 Sep 1949
RAJPUT (ex-HMS *Rotherham*)	D 209	John Brown & Co Ltd, Clydebank	10 Apr 1941	21 Mar 1942	27 Aug 1942	29 July 1949
RANJIT (ex-HMS *Redoubt*)	D 141	John Brown & Co Ltd, Clydebank	19 June 1941	2 May 1942	1 Oct 1942	4 July 1949

Displacement, tons 1 725 standard; 2 424 full load
Length, feet (*metres*) 339·5 (*103·5*)wl; 362·0 (*110·3*)oa
Beam, feet (*metres*) 35·7 (*10·9*)
Draught, feet (*metres*) 17·1 (*5·2*)
Guns 4—4·7 in (*120 mm*); 4—40 mm AA
A/S weapons 4 DCT
Torpedo tubes 8—21 in (2 quadruple) in *Rana*
Main engines Parsons geared turbines; 2 shafts 40 000 shp
Speed, knots 32
Boilers 2 Admiralty 3-drum type
Oil fuel, tons 490
Range, miles 2 500 at 20 knots
Complement 240

First British destroyers with officers accommodation forward instead of aft. Refitted and modernised before transfer. Arrived in Indian waters in Jan 1950. Constitute 11th Destroyer Squadron of which *Rajput* is Leader.

RADAR. Search: Type 293. Fire Control: Early design.

RAJPUT

FRIGATES

6 NEW CONSTRUCTION "LEANDER" CLASS

HIMGIRI F 234 **NILGIRI** F 233 + 4

Displacement, tons 2 450 standard; 2 800 full load
Length, feet (*metres*) 360 (*109·7*) wl; 372 (*113·4*) oa
Beam, feet (*metres*) 43 (*13·1*)
Draught, feet (*metres*) 18 (*5·5*)
Aircraft 1 Wasp helicopter
Missiles, AA 2 "Seacat" quadruple launchers
Guns, dual purpose 2—4·5 in (*115 mm*) 1 twin 2—40 mm
A/S weapons 1 "Limbo" 3 barrelled DC mortar
Boilers 2
Main engines 2 geared turbines; 30 000 shp
Speed, knots 30 max
Oil fuel, tons 460
Range, miles 4 500 at 12 knots
Complement 263

First major warships built in Indian yards. Of similar design to later (broad beam) "Leander" class general purpose frigates in the Royal Navy. All ordered from Mazagon Docks Ltd, Bombay. *Nilgiri* was laid down in Oct 1966, launched on 23 Oct 1968 and was commissioned on 3 June 1972. *Himgiri* was launched on 6 May 1970. The third ship was laid down on 14 Sep 1970. Three further ships of the class are projected to complete at yearly intervals.

Note: In February 1974 India concluded an agreement with France for the construction of A69 Avisos (see French section) at Mazgaon Dockyard, Bombay. The first is expected to be laid down in 1975.

LEANDER *Class*

8 "PETYA" CLASS

ANDROTH
ANJADIP P 173
ARNALA
KADMATT P 178
KAMORTA P 177
KATCHAL P 181
KAVARATTI P 180
KILTAN P 179

Displacement, tons 950 standard; 1 150 full load
Length, feet (*metres*) 250·0 (*76·2*) wl; 270 (*82·3*) oa
Beam, feet (*metres*) 29·9 (*9·1*)
Draught, feet (*metres*) 10·5 (*3·2*)
Guns 4—3 in (*76 mm*) dp, 2 twin
A/S weapons 4 MBU 2 500; 16 barrelled rocket launchers
Torpedo tubes 5—16 in ("K" Series); 3—21 in ("A" Series)
Main engines 2 gas turbines; 30 000 hp; 2 diesels; 2 shafts; 6 000 hp
Speed, knots 34

Transferred to the Indian Navy since 1969. Pennant numbers of two units are reported to be P 179 and P 181.

RADAR. "K" series, Head Net A. "A" series, Slim Net.

"PETYA" CLASS *Ex-Soviet*

KADMATT

2 "WHITBY" CLASS

Name	No.	Builders	Launched	Completed
TALWAR	F 140	Cammell Laird & Co Ltd, Birkenhead	18 July 1958	1960
TRISHUL (*Leader*)	F 143	Harland & Wolff Ltd, Belfast	18 June 1959	1960

Displacement, tons 2 144 standard; 2 545 full load (*Talwar*), 2 557 (*Trishul*)
Length, feet (*metres*) 360 (*109·7*) pp 369·8 (*112·7*) oa
Beam, feet (*metres*) 41 (*12·5*)
Draught, feet (*metres*) 17·8 (*5·4*)
Guns, surface 2—4·5 in (*115 mm*)
Guns, AA 4—40 mm (1 twin before "Limbos", 2 singles abaft funnel)
A/S weapons 2 "Limbo" 3-barrelled DC mortars
Boilers 2 Babcock & Wilcox
Main engines 2 sets geared turbines; 30 000 shp; 2 shafts
Speed, knots 30 max
Oil fuel, tons 400
Range, miles 4 500 at 12 knots
Complement 231 (11 officers, 220 men)

GENERAL
Built in Great Britain and generally similar to the British frigates of the "Whitby" class, but slightly modified to suit Indian conditions.

RADAR. Tactical: Type 293. Fire Control: X Band.

TALWAR, TRISHUL

TALWAR *A. & J. Pavia*

Frigates—*continued*

3 "LEOPARD" CLASS

Name	No.	Builders	Launched	Completed
BEAS	F 137	Vickers-Armstrongs Ltd, Newcastle-on-Tyne	9 Oct 1958	24 May 1960
BETWA	F 139	Vickers-Armstrongs Ltd, Newcastle-on-Tyne	15 Sep 1959	8 Dec 1960
BRAHMAPUTRA (ex-*Panther*)	F 31	John Brown & Co Ltd, Clydebank	15 Mar 1957	28 Mar 1958

BRAHMAPUTRA — *1971, Indian Navy,*

Displacement, tons	2 251 standard; 2 515 full load
Length, feet (*metres*)	320·0 (*97·5*) pp; 330·0 (*100·6*)wl; 339·8 (*103·6*) oa
Beam, feet (*metres*)	40·0 (*12·2*)
Draught, feet (*metres*)	16·0 (*4·9*) max
Guns	4—4·5 in (*114 mm*), 2 twin; 4—40 mm AA
A/S weapons	1 Squid 3-barrelled DC mortar
Main engines	Admiralty standard range diesels 2 shafts; 12 380 bhp
Speed, knots	25
Range, miles	7 500 at 16 knots
Complement	210

BEAS, BETWA, BRAHMAPUTRA

Brahmaputra (Leader), originally ordered as *Panther* for the Royal Navy on 28 June 1951, was the first major warship to be built in Great Britain for the Indian Navy since India became independent. All three ships are generally similar to the British frigates of the "Leopard" class, but modified to suit Indian conditions.

RADAR. Search: Type 960. Tactical: Type 293. Fire Control: X Band forward and aft.

2 "BLACKWOOD" CLASS

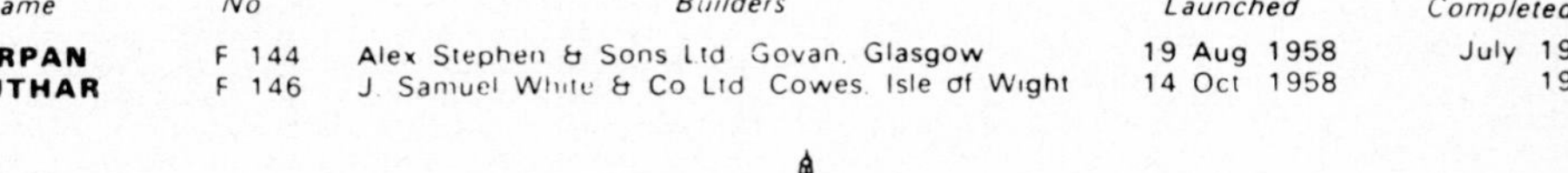

Name	No	Builders	Launched	Completed
KIRPAN	F 144	Alex Stephen & Sons Ltd Govan, Glasgow	19 Aug 1958	July 1959
KUTHAR	F 146	J. Samuel White & Co Ltd Cowes, Isle of Wight	14 Oct 1958	1959

Displacement, tons	1 180 standard; 1 456 full load
Length, feet (*metres*)	300 (*91·4*) pp; 310 (*94·5*) oa
Beam, feet (*metres*)	33 (*10·0*)
Draught, feet (*metres*)	15·5 (*4·7*)
Guns, AA	3—40 mm (single)
A/S weapons	2 "Limbo" 3-barrelled DC mortars
Boilers	Babcock & Wilcox
Main engines	1 set geared turbines; 15 000 shp; 1 shaft
Speed, knots	27·8 max; 24·5 sustained sea
Range, miles	4 000 at 12 knots
Oil fuel, tons	300
Complement	150

KIRPAN, KUTHAR

KHUKRI (others similar) — *A. & J. Pavia*

Built in Great Britain, and generally similar to the British frigates of the "Blackwood" class, but slightly modified to suit Indian requirements. *Kirpan* means sword. *Khukri* was sunk in the Pakistan war on 9 Dec 1971.

RADAR. Fitted with S band air and surface surveillance radar.

3 "HUNT" CLASS TYPE II

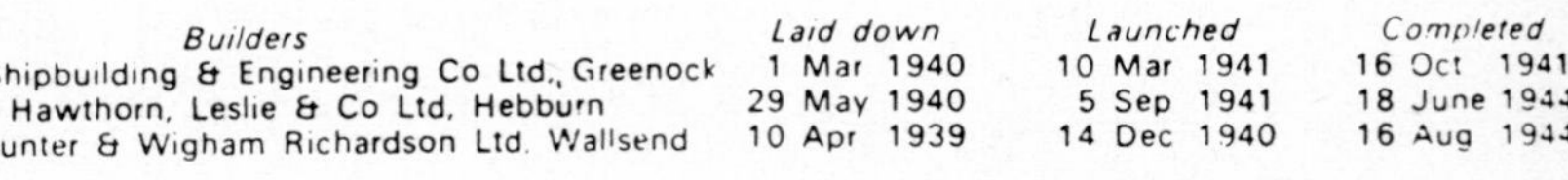

Name	No.	Builders	Laid down	Launched	Completed
GANGA (ex-HMS *Chiddingfold*)	D 94	Scott's Shipbuilding & Engineering Co Ltd, Greenock	1 Mar 1940	10 Mar 1941	16 Oct 1941
GODAVARI (ex-HMS *Bedale*, ex-*Slazak*, ex-*Bedale*)	D 92	R. & W. Hawthorn, Leslie & Co Ltd, Hebburn	29 May 1940	5 Sep 1941	18 June 1944
GOMATI (ex-HMS *Lamerton*)	D 93	Swan, Hunter & Wigham Richardson Ltd, Wallsend	10 Apr 1939	14 Dec 1940	16 Aug 1944

Displacement, tons	1 050 standard; 1 610 full load
Length, feet (*metres*)	264·2 (*80·5*) pp; 280·0 (*85·3*) oa
Beam, feet (*metres*)	31·5 (*9·6*)
Draught feet (*metres*)	14·0 (*4·3*)
Guns	6—4 in (*102 mm*) dp; 4—20 mm AA
Main engines	Parsons geared turbines; 2 shafts; 19 000 shp
Speed, knots	25
Boilers	2 Admiralty 3-drum
Oil fuel, tons	280
Range, miles	3 700 at 14 knots
Complement	150

GANGA, GODAVARI, GOMATI

GANGA — *Added 1971, A. & J. Pavia*

Former "Hunt" class, Type II frigates F 131, F 126 and F 88, respectively, (ex-Escort Destroyers). Transferred from Great Britain in Apr/May 1953. Lent to the Indian Navy for three years, subject to extension by agreement. Officially rated as destroyers with D pennant Nos. Constitute the 22nd Destroyer Squadron of which *Godavari* is leader. Now used for training.

Frigates—*continued*

2 "KISTNA" CLASS

Name	No.	Builders	Laid down	Launched	Completed
KAVERI	F 110	Yarrow & Co. Ltd, Scotstoun Glasgow	28 Oct 1942	15 June 1943	21 Oct 1943
KISTNA	F 46	Yarrow & Co Ltd Scotstoun Glasgow	14 July 1942	22 Apr 1943	23 Aug 1943

Displacement, tons	1 470 standard; 1 925 full load
Length, feet (*metres*)	283·0 (*86·3*) pp; 295·5 (*90·1*) wl 299·5 (*91·3*) oa
Beam, feet (*metres*)	38·5 (*11·7*)
Draught, feet (*metres*)	11·2 (*3·4*)
Guns	4—4 in (*102 mm*); 4—40 mm AA
A/S weapons	2 DCT
Main engines	Parsons geared turbines; 2 shafts; 4 300 shp
Speed, knots	19
Boilers	2 three-drum type
Range, miles	4 500 at 12 knots
Oil fuel, tons	370
Complement	210

Former sloops of the British "Black Swan" class built for India and modified to suit Indian conditions. *Cauvery* was renamed *Kaveri* in 1968.

RADAR. Fitted with S band air and surface surveillance radar and ranging radar for the gunfire control system.

1 "RIVER" CLASS

TIR F 256 (ex-HMS *Bann*)

Displacement, tons	1 463 standard; 1 934 full load
Length, feet (*metres*)	283·0 (*86·3*) pp; 303 (*92·4*) oa
Beam, feet (*metres*)	36·7 (*11·2*)
Draught, feet (*metres*)	14·5 (*4·4*)
Guns	1—4 in (*102 mm*); 1—40 mm AA; 2—20 mm AA
Main engines	Triple expansion; 2 shafts; 5 500 ihp
Speed, knots	18
Boilers	2 Admiralty 3-drum type
Range, miles	4 200 at 12 knots
Oil fuel, tons	385
Complement	120

Former "River" class frigate in the Royal Navy. Built by Charles Hill & Sons Ltd, Bristol. Laid down on 18 June 1942, launched on 29 Dec 1942, completed on 7 May 1942 and transferred on 3 Dec 1945. Converted to a Midshipman's Training Frigate by Bombay Dockyard in 1948. Originally the sister ship of *Investigator*, see under Survey Ships.

SUBMARINES

4 + 4 Ex-SOVIET "FOXTROT" CLASS

KALVARI S 123 **KARANJ** S 121
KANDERI S 122 **KURSURA** S 120

Displacement, tons	2 000 surface; 2 300 dived
Length, feet (*metres*)	296·8 (*90·5*)
Beam, feet (*metres*)	42·1 (*7·3*)
Draught, feet (*metres*)	19·0 (*5·8*)
Tubes	10—21 in (20 torpedoes carried)
Main machinery	3 diesels; 3 shafts; 6 000 bhp; 3 electric motors; 6 000 hp
Speed, knots	20 surface; 15 dived
Complement	70

Kalvari arrived in India on 16 July 1968 and *Kanderi* in May 1969. *Karanj* in Jan 1970 and *Kursura* in Apr 1970.

NEW CONSTRUCTION
Four more were ordered in 1973, two for delivery in 1974 and two later.

KANDERI — *1971, Dr. Louis Th. Berge*

Note: India is now making plans to build her own Submarines though no details have been released.

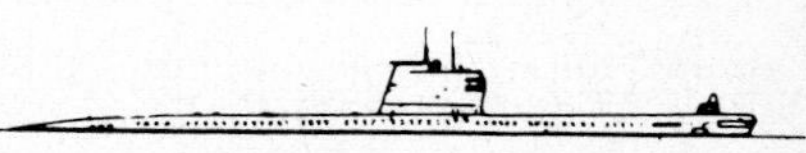

"Foxtrot" *Class*

LIGHT FORCES

8 Ex-SOVIET "OSA" CLASS (FAST ATTACK CRAFT—MISSILE)

NASHAK P 684 **VEER** P 686
NIPAT P 691 **VIDYUT** P 694
NIRBHIK P 685 **VIJETA** P 693
NIRGHAT P 690 **VINASH** P 692

Displacement, tons	165 standard; 200 full load
Dimensions, feet	128·7 × 25·1 × 5·9
Guns	4—30 mm (2 twin)
Main engines	3 diesels; 3 shafts; 13 000 bhp = 32 knots
Missile launchers	4 in two pairs for SSN 2A (Styx)

Some of these craft took part in a night attack with Styx off Karachi on 4-5 Dec 1971. They sank the PNS *Khaibar*, damaged *Badr* and a CMS as well as one Panamanian m/s without damage to themselves. Four more may be supplied to India.

RADAR. Square Tie. IFF—Ski Pole.

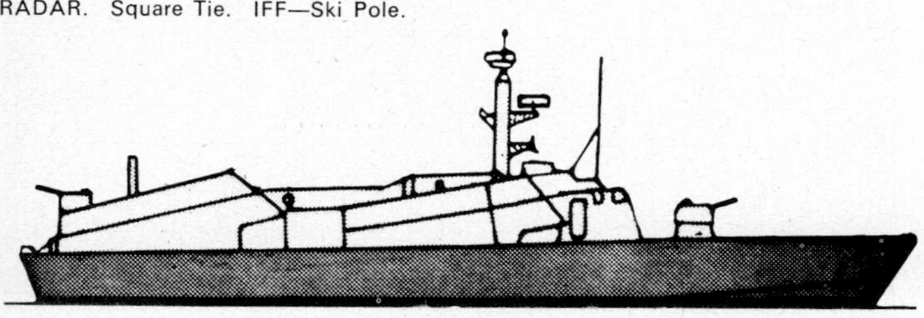

OSA *Class*

3 "AJAY" CLASS (LARGE PATROL CRAFT)

ABHAY P3135 **AJAY** P 3134 **AKHAY** P 3136

Displacement, tons	120 standard; 151 full load (*Ajay* 146)
Dimensions, feet	110 pp; 117·2 oa × 20 × 5
Guns	1—40 mm AA
Main engines	2 diesels; speed = 18 knots

Generally similar to the "Ford" class in the Royal Navy. *Ajay* was built by Garden Reach Workshop, Calcutta and commissioned on 21 Sep 1969. *Abhay* and *Akhay* were both built by Hoogly Docking and Engineering Company Ltd. Calcutta and commissioned on 13 Nov 1961 and 8 Jan 1962 respectively.

AJAY — *1964, Indian Navy*

5 Ex-USSR "POLUCHAT" CLASS (COASTAL PATROL CRAFT)

PAMBAN P 247 **PANVEL** P 246 **PURI** P 248
PANAJI P 249 **PULICAT** P 250

Displacement, tons	86 standard; 91 full load
Dimensions, feet	98 × 15 × 4·8
Guns	2—14·5 mm (twin)
Main engines	2 Diesels; 2 shafts; 1 200 bhp = 18 knots
Range, miles	460 at 17 knots
Complement	16

Six originally supplied—one transferred to Bangladesh.

1 "SHARADA" CLASS (COASTAL PATROL CRAFT)

SHARADA SPB 3133

Displacement, tons	86
Dimensions, feet	103·2 length
Guns	Small arms
Main engines	Diesels

Built in Yugoslavia. Commissioned on 5 Dec 1959.

4 HDML TYPE (COASTAL PATROL CRAFT)

SPC 3110 (ex-*HDML* 1110) **SPC 3117** (ex-*HDML* 1117)
SPC 3112 (ex-*HDML* 1112) **SPC 3118** (ex-*HDML* 1118)

Displacement, tons	48 standard; 54 full load
Dimensions, feet	72 oa × 16 × 4·7
Guns	2—20 mm AA
Main engines	Diesel; 2 shafts; 320 bhp = 12 knots
Complement	14

Former British Harbour Defence Motor Launches. These boats constitute the 321st Sea/Land Patrol Craft Squadron.

4 "SAVITRI" CLASS (COASTAL PATROL CRAFT)

SAVITRI SPB 3128 **SHARAYU** SPB 3129 **SUBHADRA** SPB 3130
SUVARNA SPB 3131

Displacement, tons	63
Dimensions, feet	85·3 pp; 90·2 oa × 20 × 5
Guns	Small Arms
Main Engines	2 diesels; 2 shafts; 1 900 bhp = 21 knots

Built in Italy. Commissioned on 6 Feb 1958, 28 Oct 1957, 20 Aug 1957 and 28 Aug 1957, respectively. Constitute the 322nd SDB Squadron. *Sharayu* is Leader.

AMPHIBIOUS FORCES

4 Ex-SOVIET "POLNOCNY" CLASS

GHARIAL L 3032
GULDAR L 3033

Displacement, tons	780 standard; 1 000 full load
Dimensions, ft (*m*)	246 × 29·5 × 9·8 (*75 × 9 × 3*)
Guns	2—30 mm
A/S weapons	2 18 barrelled MBU
Main engines	2 diesels; 5 000 bhp = 18 knots

First pair transferred from USSR in 1966.

POLNOCNY *Class*

MAGAR (ex-HMS *Avenger*, LST (3) 3011)

Displacement, tons	2 256 light; 4 980 full load
Dimensions, feet	347·5 oa × 55·2 × 11·2
Guns	2—40 mm AA; 6—20 mm AA; (2 twin, 2 single)
Main engines	Triple expansion; 2 shafts; 5 500 ihp = 13 knots

Former British tank landing ship of the LST (3) type transferred in 1949. There is also LCT 4294 (ex-1294), yard craft of 200 tons, 187·2 × 38·8 × 3·5 feet, speed 9·5 knots.

MAGAR *1964, A. & J. Pavia*

MINE WARFARE FORCES

4 Ex-BRITISH "TON" CLASS (MINESWEEPERS—COASTAL)

CANNANORE (ex-*Whitton*) M 1191
KUDDALORE (ex-*Wennington*) M 1190
KAKINADA (ex-*Durweston*) M 1201
KARWAR (ex-*Overton*) Leader M 1197

Displacement, tons	360 standard; 425 full load
Dimensions, feet	140·0 pp; 153·0 oa × 28·8 × 8·2
Guns	2—20 mm AA
Main engines	Napier Deltic diesels; 2 shafts; 1 250 bhp = 15 knots
Oil fuel, tons	45
Range, miles	3 000 at 8 knots
Complement	40

"Ton" class coastal minesweepers of wooden construction built for the Royal Navy, but transferred from Great Britain to the Indian Navy in 1956. *Cannanore* was built by Fleetlands Shipyard, Ltd Gosport and launched 30 Jan 1956, *Karwar* was built by Camper & Nicholson, Ltd, Gosport, and launched 30 Jan 1956. *Kuddalore*, built by J. S. Doig Ltd, Grimsby, and *Kakinada*, built by Dorset Yacht Co Ltd, Hamworthy were taken over in Aug 1956, and sailed for India in Nov-Dec 1956. Named after minor ports in India. Constitute the 18th Mine Counter Measures Squadron, together with the inshore minesweepers.

4 Ex-BRITISH "HAM" CLASS (IMS)

BASSEIN (ex-*Littleham*) M 2707
BHATKAL M 89
BIMLIPITAN (ex-*Hildersham*) M 2705
BULSAR

Displacement, tons	120 standard; 170 full load
Dimensions, feet	98·0 pp; 107·0 oa × 22·0 × 6·7
Gun	1—20 mm AA
Main engines	2 Paxman diesels; 550 bhp = 14 knots (9 knots sweeping)
Oil fuel, tons	15
Complement	16

"Ham" class inshore minesweepers of wooden construction two of which were built for the Royal Navy but transferred from Great Britain to the Indian Navy in 1955. *Bassein* was built by Brooke Marine Ltd, Oulton Broad, Lowestoft, and launched on 4 May 1954; *Bimlipitan* was built by Vosper Ltd, Portsmouth, and launched on 5 Feb 1954. Two further units were built at Magazon Dockyard Bombay. *Bhaktal* was launched in Apr 1967, and *Bulsar* on 17 May 1969.

Barq (ex-*MMS* 132), *MMS* 130 and *MMS* 154, former British motor minesweepers of the "105 ft" type of wooden construction, transferred from Great Britain, are employed as yard craft. *MMS* 1632 and *MMS* 1654 are yard craft in Bombay.

KARWAR 1971, *Wright & Logan*

BASSEIN *1971, A. & J. Pavia*

SURVEY SHIPS

DARSHAK

Displacement, tons	2 790
Length, feet (*metres*)	319 (*97·2*) oa
Beam, feet (*metres*)	49 (*14·9*)
Draught, feet (*metres*)	28·8 (*8·8*)
Main engines	2 diesel-electric units, 3 000 bhp
Speed, knots	16
Complement	150

DARSHAK *1967*

DARSHAK

First ship built by Hindustan Shipyard, Vishakapatnam for the Navy. Launched on 2 Nov 1959 and commissioned on 28 Dec 1964. Provision was made to operate a helicopter. The ship is all welded.

Survey Ships—*continued*

1 "RIVER" CLASS (Ex-FRIGATE)

INVESTIGATOR F 243 (ex-*Khukri*, ex-HMS *Trent*)

Displacement, tons	1 460 standard; 1 930 full load
Length, feet (*metres*)	283 (*86·3*) pp; 303 (*92·4*) oa
Beam, feet (*metres*)	36·7 (*11·2*)
Draught, feet (*metres*)	14 (*4·3*)
Boilers	2 Admiralty 3-drum
Main engines	Triple expansion 5 500 shp; 2 shafts
Speed, knots	18 max
Range, miles	5 000 at 10 knots
Oil fuel, tons	400
Complement	172

INVESTIGATOR

INVESTIGATOR 1965, *Indian Navy*

Former "River" class frigate in the Royal Navy. Built by Charles Hill & Sons Ltd, Bristol. Laid down on 31 Jan 1942, launched on 10 Oct 1942, completed on 15 Feb 1943, and transferred in April 1946. Converted to a survey ship and renamed *Investigator* in 1951. Originally the sister ship of the training frigate *Tir*.

2 "SUTLEJ" CLASS

(Ex-FRIGATES. Ex-SLOOPS)

JUMNA F 11 **SUTLEJ** F 95

Displacement, tons	1 300 standard; 1 750 full load
Length, feet (*metres*)	276 (*84·1*) wl; 292·5 (*89·2*) oa
Beam, feet (*metres*)	37·5 (*11·4*)
Draught, feet (*metres*)	11·5 (*3·5*)
Boilers	2 Admiralty 3-drum
Main engines	Parsons geared turbines 3 600 shp; 2 shafts
Speed, knots	18
Range, miles	5 600 at 12 knots
Oil fuel, tons	370
Complement	150

JUMNA

JUMNA 1971, *Indian Navy*

Former frigates employed as survey ships since 1957 and 1955 respectively. Both ships are generally similar to the former British frigates of the "Egret" class. *Jumna* and *Sutlej* together with *Kaveri* and *Kistna* (see previous page) formerly constituted the 12th Frigate Squadron.

CONSTRUCTION. Both built by Wm. Denny & Bros Ltd, Dumbarton. *Jumna* was laid down on 20 Feb 1940, launched on 16 Nov 1940 and completed on 13 May 1941. *Sutlej* was laid down on 4 Jan 1940, launched on 10 Oct 1940 and completed on 23 Apr 1941.

SERVICE FORCES

AMBA A 14 (SUBMARINE TENDER)

Displacement, tons	6 000 light; 9 000 full load
Dimensions, feet	370 pp; 420 oa × 65 × 20
Guns, dual purpose	4—3 in (*76 mm*) (Twins)
Main engines	Diesels; 2 shafts; 7 000 bhp = 17 knots

Modified "Ugra" type acquired from the USSR in 1968. Provision for helicopter.

RADAR. Slim Net.

AMBA

NISTAR (SUBMARINE RESCUE SHIP)

Displacement, tons	790 standard; 900 full load
Dimensions, feet	220·0 × 29·5 × 7·9
Main engines	2 diesels; 2 shafts; 5 000 bhp = 18 knots

Converted from a fleet minesweeper of the Soviet "T 58" type to a submarine rescue ship and transferred from USSR late-1971.

DHARINI A 306 (ex-*Hermine*) (REPAIR SHIP)

Displacement, tons	4 625
Dimensions, feet	328 × 46 × 19
Main engines	Triple expansion
Oil fuel (tons)	621

Cargo ship converted to a tender. Commissioned in May 1960.

DHARINI 1964, *Indian Navy*

DEEPAK A 1750 (REPLENISHMENT TANKER)

On charter to Indian Navy from Mogul Lines. Fleet replenishment tanker. Fitted with a helicopter landing platform aft, but no hangar.

SHAKTI A 136 (SUPPORT TANKER)

Displacement, tons	3 500
Dimensions, feet	323 × 44 × 20
Main engines	Diesel; speed = 13 knots

Rated as Fleet Replenishment Group Tanker. Acquired from Italy in Nov 1953.

HOOGHLY (SUPPORT TANKER)

Formerly "*Baqir*" of Gulf Shipping Corp. Ltd. Acquired in 1972.

CHILKA **SAMBHAR** (HARBOUR TANKERS)

Displacemrnt. tons	1 530 (oil capacity 1 000)
Dimensions, feet	202 × 30·7 × 13
Main engines	Triple expansion; 809 ihp = 9 knots

Chilka built by Blythwood Shipbuilding Co, Scotstoun. *Sambhar* by A. & J. Inglis, Ltd, Glasgow, launched 1942. Both acquired in 1948. Engined by David Rowan & Co. Two steam dynamos, two steam pumps, ballast pump. Rated as yard craft.

HATHI (TUG—OCEAN)

Displacement, tons	668
Dimensions, feet	147·5 × 23·7 × 15
Main engines	Triple expansion; speed = 13 knots

Built by the Taikoo Dock & Engineering Company, Hong Kong. Launched in 1932.

INDONESIA

Administration

Commander-in-Chief of the Navy and Chief of the Naval Staff:
Admiral R. Subono

Depury Chief of the Naval Staff Operations:
Rear-Admiral Wulujo Sugito

Inspector General of the Navy:
Commodore M. Wibowo

Chief for Naval Material:
Rear Admiral Sudiono

Chief for Naval Personnel:
Commodore R. Saheran

Commander of Navy Marine Corps:
Major General Moch, Anwar

Commander-in-Chief Indonesian Fleet:
Rear-Admiral Rudy Purwana

Diplomatic Representation

Naval Attaché and Naval Attaché for Air in London:
Colonel D. U. Martojo

Naval Attaché and Naval Attaché for Air in Washington:
Colonel Kko. Santoso

Personnel

(a) 1974: 39 000 including 5 000 Marine Commando Corps and Naval Air Arm
(b) Selective National Service

Strength of the Fleet

Note. This is a formidable total of ships but the number truly operational is probably a fairly small proportion of that total.

Type	*Active*	*Building*
Frigates	9	—
Corvettes	18	—
Patrol Submarines (ineffective)	10	—
Fast Attack Craft—Missile	12	—
Fast Attack Craft—Torpedo	21	—
Large Patrol Craft	30	—
Coastal Patrol Craft	35	—
LST's	8	—
LCT's	9	—
Minesweepers—Ocean	6	—
Minesweepers—Coastal	20	—
Survey Ships	4	—
Submarine Tenders	3	—
Destroyer Depot Ship	1	—
Repair Ship	1	—
Support Tankers	5	—
Harbour Rankers	2	—
Transports	2	—
Salvage Vessel	1	—
Cable Ship	1	—
Tugs	5	—
Auxiliary Patrol Craft	48	—
Training Ship	1	—

Ex-Soviet Ships

Indonesia obtained 104 ships from the USSR. Of these half have now been deleted and all will have gone by end 1976.

Future Plans

It is planned, over the next 20 years, to provide a Navy of some 25 000 seamen and 5 000 marines to man a Fleet of 4 fast A/S Frigates, some Submarines, Light Forces of Fast Attack Craft—Missile and —Torpedo, Minelayers, Minesweepers, a fast HQ ship and a fast Supply Ship. It is reported that enquiries for frigate construction have already been made in Europe.

Naval Air Arm

6—C 47 and 3 Alouette III helicopters.

Disposals

Cruiser

1972 *Irian*

Destroyers

1973 *Brawidjaja, Sandjaja, Sultan Babarudin*

Frigates

1973 *Lambung Mangkurat, Slamet Rijadi*

Light Forces

1970 *310, 314, 315, 316* (Kraljevica), *Dorang, Lajang, Rubara*

Survey Ships

1972 *Hidral*

FRIGATES

1 Ex-US "CLAUD JONES" CLASS

SAMADIKUN (ex-USS *John R. Perry* DE 1034)

Displacement, tons	1 450 standard; 1 750 full load
Length, feet (*metres*)	310 (*95*) oa
Beam, feet (*metres*)	37 (*11·3*)
Draught, feet (*metres*)	18 (*5·5*)
Guns	1—3 in 50 cal
A/S weapons	2 triple Torpedo Tubes (Mk 32)
Main engines	4 diesels; 9 200 hp; 1 shaft
Speed, knots	22
Complement	175

Purchased from USN 20 Feb 1973

RADAR. SPS 6 and 10.

SONAR. SQS 29.

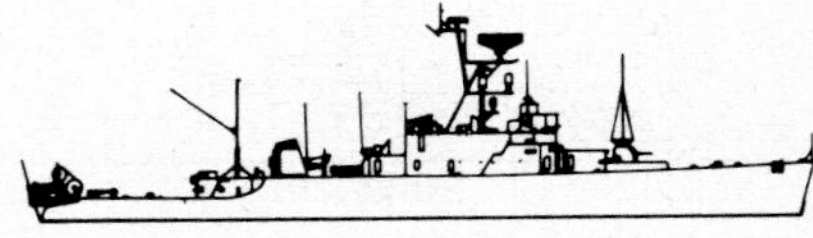

SAMADIKUN

4 Ex-USSR "RIGA" CLASS

JOS SUDARSO 351 **NGURAH RAI** 353
KAKIALI 359 **NUKU** 360

Displacement, tons	1 200 standard; 1 600 full load
Length, feet (*metres*)	298·8 (*91*)
Beam, feet (*metres*)	33·7 (*10·2*)
Draught, feet (*metres*)	11 (*3·4*)
Guns, dual purpose	3—3·9 in (*100 mm*) single mounts
Guns, AA	4—37 mm
A/S weapons	4 DC projectors
Torpedo tubes	3—21 in (*533 mm*)
Mines	Fitted with mine rails
Boilers	2
Main engines	Geared steam turbines; 2 shafts, 25 000 shp
Speed, knots	28
Range, miles	2 500 at 15 knots
Complement	150

RIGA Class *Sergei Romanov*

Transferred in 1964.

RADAR. Slim Net search and warning; fire control Sun Visor A with Wasp Head director; navigation Neptun; IFF, High Pole A.

2 "SURAPATI" CLASS

SURAPATI 251 **IMAN BONDJOL** 250

	6—20 mm (3 twin)
A/S weapons	2 hedgehogs; 4 DCT
Torpedo tubes	3—21 in (*533 mm*)
Boilers	2 Foster Wheeler
Main engines	2 sets Parsons geared turbines; 2 shafts; 24 000 shp
Speed, knots	32
Range, miles	2 800 at 22 knots
Oil fuel, tons	350
Complement	200

Both completed in May 1958 by Ansaldo, Genoa
Near sisters of the *Almirante Clemente* class of Venezuela

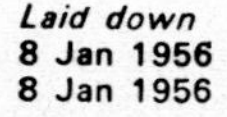

Name	*No.*	*Builders*	*Laid down*	*Launched*	*Completed*
IMAN BONDJOL	250	Ansaldo, Leghorn	8 Jan 1956	5 May 1956	19 May 1958
SURAPATI	251	Ansaldo, Leghorn	8 Jan 1956	5 May 1956	28 May 1958

IMAN BONDJOL *courtesy Dr Ing Luigi Accorsi*

Frigates—*continued*

2 "PATTIMURA" CLASS

	Launched	*Completed*
PATTIMURA 252	1 July 1956	28 Jan 1958
SULTAN HASANUDIN 253	24 Mar 1957	8 Mar 1958

Displacement, tons	950 standard; 1 200 full load
Length, feet (*metres*)	246 (*75·0*) pp; 270·2 (*82·4*) oa
Beam, feet (*metres*)	34 (*10·4*)
Draught, feet (*metres*)	9 (*2·7*)
Guns, AA	2—3 in (*76 mm*) 40 cal. 2—30 mm 70 cal twin
A/S weapons	2 hedgehogs; 4 DCT
Main engines	3 Ansaldo-Fiat diesels; 3 shafts; 6 900 bhp
Speed, knots	22
Range, miles	2 400 at 18 knots
Oil fuel, tons	100
Complement	110

Both laid down on 8 Jan 1956 by Ansaldo, Leghorn. Similar to Italian *Albatros* class.

PATTIMURA *Dr Ing Luigi Accorsi*

CORVETTES

14 Ex-USSR "KRONSTADT" CLASS

BARAKUDA 817
KAKAP 816
KATULA 811
LANDJURU
LAPAI
LUMBA LUMBA
MADIDIHANG
MOMARE
PALU 818
PANDRONG 814
SURA 815
TOHOK 829
TONGKOL
TJUTJUT

Displacement, tons	310 standard; 380 full load
Dimensions, ft (*m*)	170·6 × 21·5 × 9 (*52·0 × 6·5 × 2·7*)
Guns	1—3·5 in; 2—37 mm AA; 4—25 mm AA
A/S weapons	Depth charge projectors
Mines	2 mine rails for 10 mines
Main engines	3 Diesels; 3 shafts; 3 300 bhp = 24 knots
Oil fuel, tons	20
Range, miles	1 500 at 12 knots
Complement	65

Built in 1951-54. Transferred to the Indonesian Navy on 30 Dec 1958.

RADAR. Ball Gun or Don 2; IFF, High Pole A

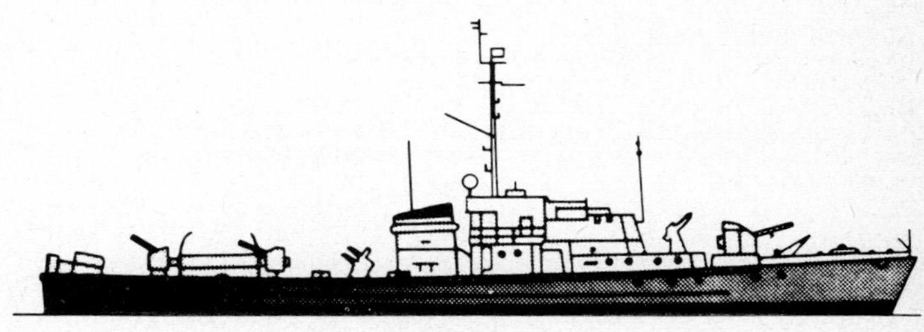

KRONSTADT *Class*

4 Ex-US PC TYPE

HUI (ex-USS *Malvern, PC* 580) 318
TENGGIRI (ex-USS *PC* 1183) 309
TJAKALANG (ex-USS *Pierre, PC* 1141) 313
TORANI (ex-USS *Manville, PC* 581) 317

Displacement, tons	280 standard; 450 full load
Dimensions, feet	170 wl; 173·7 oa × 23 × 10·8 max
Guns	1—3 in; 1—40 mm AA; 2—20 mm AA; 4 DCT
Main engines	2 GM diesels; 2 shafts; 2 880 bhp = 20 knots
Oil fuel, tons	60
Range, miles	5 000 at 10 knots
Complement	54 (4 officers, 50 men)

Built in 1942-43. *Pierre* transferred from the US Navy at Pearl Harbour, Hawaii in Oct 1958 and *Malvern* and *Manville* in Mar 1960.

TENGGIRI *1966, Indonesian Navy*

SUBMARINES

POSSIBLY 10 Ex-USSR "WHISKY" CLASS

ALUGORO 406
BRAMASTRA 412
HENDRADJALA 405
NAGABANDA 403
NAGARANGSANG 404
PASOPATI 410
TJANDRASA 408
TJUNDMANI 411
TRISULA 402
WIDJAJADANU 409

Displacement, tons	1 030 surface; 1 180 submerged
Length, feet (*metres*)	240 (*73·2*)
Beam feet (*metres*)	22 (*6·7*)
Draught, feet (*metres*)	15 (*4·6*) max
Torpedo tubes	6—21 in (*533 mm*) 4 forward, 2 aft; 18 torpedoes carried
Mines	40 in lieu of torpedoes
Main machinery	4 000 bhp diesels; 2 500 hp electric motors, diesel-electric drive; 2 shafts
Speed, knots	17 on surface; 15 dived
Range, miles	13 000 at 8 knots surfaced
Complement	60

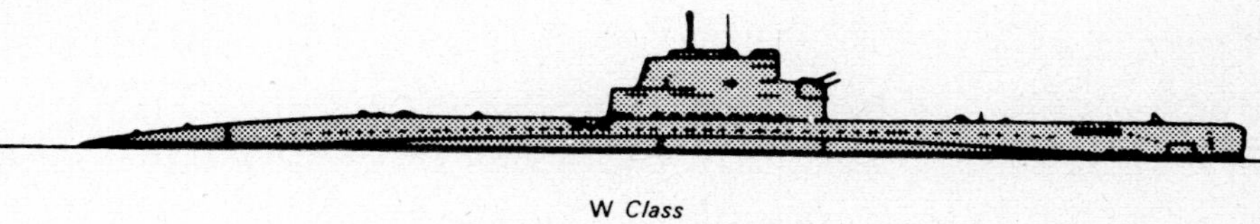

W *Class*

The four Soviet submarines of the "W" class, which arrived in Indonesia on 28 June 1962, brought the total number of this class transferred to Indonesia to 14 units, but it was reported that only six would be maintained operational, while six would be kept in reserve and two used for spare parts. It is unlikely that any of these submarines is fully operational and what remain are used only for surface training.

LIGHT FORCES

12 Ex-USSR "KOMAR" CLASS

(FAST ATTACK CRAFT—MISSILE)

GRIWIDJAJA **HARDADALI** **KALAMISANI** **KALANADA** **KATJABOLA** **KOLAPLINTAH** **PULANGGENI** **NAGAPASA** **SAROTAMA** **SARPAMINA** **SARPAWISESA** **TRITUSTA**

Displacement, tons	70 standard; 80 full load
Dimensions, ft (*m*)	83·7 × 19·8 × 5 (*25·5* × *6·0* × *1·8*)
Guns	2—35 mm AA (1 twin)
Guided weapons	2 launchers for SSN2A (Styx)
Main engines	4 diesels; 4 800 hp = 40 knots
Range, miles	400 at 30 knots

Six were transferred to Indonesia in 1961-63, four more in Sep 1964 and two in 1965.

7 GERMAN-BUILT "JAGUAR" CLASS

(FAST ATTACK CRAFT—TORPEDO)

ADJAK **ANOA** **BIRUANG** **HARIMAU** **MADJAN KUMBANG** **SERIGALA** **SINGA**

Displacement, tons	160 standard; 190 full load
Dimensions, feet	131 pp; 138 oa × 22 × 7·5
Guns	2—40 mm AA (single)
Torpedo tubes	4—21 in
Main engines	4 Daimler-Benz diesels; 4 shafts; 12 000 bhp = 42 knots
Complement	39

Built by Lürssen, Bremen-Vegesack in 1959-60. The first four boats had wooden hulls, but the second four were built of steel. Pennant Nos. 601, 602, 603, 604, 605, 607, and 608.

HARIMAU *Indonesia*

14 Ex-USSR "P6" CLASS (FAST ATTACK CRAFT—TORPEDO)

ANGIN BADAI **ANGIN BOHOROK** **ANGIN BRUBU** **ANGIN GENDING** **ANGIN GRENGGONG** **ANGIN KUMBANG** **ANGIN PASAT** **ANGIN PRAHARA** **ANGIN PUJUH** **ANGIN RIBUT** **ANGIN TAUFAN** **ANGIN TONGGI** **ANGIN WAMANDAIS** **ANGIN WAMBRAU**

Displacement, tons	66 standard; 75 full load
Dimensions, ft (*m*)	84·2 × 20 × 6 (*25·7* × *6·1* × *1·8*)
Guns	4—25 mm AA (2 twin)
Tubes	2—21 in (single)
Main engines	4 Diesels; 4 800 bhp; 4 shafts = 43 knots
Range, miles	450 at 30 knots
Complement	25

A total of 14 were reported delivered since 1961, including eight in 1961, and six in 1962. Fitted with *Skinhead* target detection radar.

ANGIN KUMBANG *1968, Indonesian Navy*

18 Ex-USSR "BK" CLASS (LARGE PATROL CRAFT)

Displacement, tons	120
Dimensions, feet	124·7 × 19 × 4·6
Guns	1—85 mm; 4—25 mm AA
Main engines	Diesels; speed 20 knots

First of class transferred from the USSR to Indonesia in 1962. Ten were reported to have been transferred to Indonesia at Djakarta 11 Oct 1961.

3 Ex-USN PGM TYPE (LARGE PATROL CRAFT)

SILUNGKANG (ex-*PGM 55*) 572
WAITATIRE (ex-*PGM 65*) 571
KALAKUANG (ex-*PGM 57*) 570

Displacement, tons	122 full load
Dimensions, feet	100 × 21 × 8·5
Guns	2—20 mm AA 2 MG
Main engines	2 diesels, 2 shafts = 17 knots
Transferred 1965.	

Transferred 1965. Used as Amphibious Control Craft.

2 Ex-AUSTRALIAN "ACUTE" CLASS
(LARGE PATROL CRAFT)

ex-**BANDOLIER** ex-**ARCHER**

Displacement, tons	146 full load
Dimensions, feet	107·5 × 20 × 7·3
Guns	1—40 mm; 2 medium MG's
Main engines	2 Paxman diesels; 2 shafts = 21 knots
Complement	19 (3 officers 16 men)

Transferred from RAN after refit—*Bandolier* in 1973, *Archer* in 1974.

6 Ex-YUGOSLAVIAN "KRALJEVICA" CLASS

(LARGE PATROL CRAFT)

BUBARA **DORANG** **KRAPU** **LAJANG** **LEMADANG** **TODAK**

Displacement, tons	190 standard; 245 full load
Dimensions, feet	134·5 × 20·8 × 7
Guns	1—3 in; 1—40 mm AA; 6—20 mm AA
A/S weapons	DC
Main Engines	2 MAN diesels; 2 shafts; 3 300 bhp = 20 knots
Oil fuel (tons)	15
Radius, miles	1 500 at 12 knots
Complement	54

Former Yugoslavian craft of the "Kraljevica" class. Purchased and transferred on 27th Dec 1958.

DORANG *1968, Indonesian Navy*

3 "MAWAR" CLASS (LARGE PATROL CRAFT)

KALAHITAM **KELABANG** **KOMPAS**

Displacement, tons	147
Guns	40 mm AA
Main engines	2 diesels; speed 21 knots

Indonesian built.

KALAHITAM *1968, Indonesian Navy*

25 Ex-HDML PATROL BOAT TYPES

(COASTAL PATROL CRAFT)

PP 01 **PP 02** **PP 03** **PP 04** **PP 05** **PP 06** **PP 07** **PP 08** **PP 09** **PP 10** **PP 011** **PP 012** **PP 013** **PP 014** **PP 015** **PP 016** **PP 017** **PP 018** **PP 019** **PP 020** **PP 021** **PP 022** **PP 023** **PP 024** **PP 025**

Displacement, tons	46 standard; 54 full load
Dimensions, feet	72 × 16 × 5·5
Guns	1—37 mm; 2—20 mm Oerlikon MG
Main Engines	2 diesels; 2 shafts; 300 bhp = 11 knots
Complement	10

All ex-Netherlands patrol boats. Built in 1943-46. Formerly Britiah HDML type *RP* 109, *RP* 111, *RP* 112, *RP* 114, and *RP* 118 (ex-*HDML* 1451, *HDML* 1472, *HDML* 1473, *HDML* 1454 and *HDML* 1449).

Light Forces—*continued*

9 Ex-US MOTOR LAUNCHES

Displacement, tons	44 standard, 56 full load
Dimensions, feet	62 oa × 18·3 × 4
Guns	1—20 mm AA; 1 MG
Main Engines	1 diesel; 165 bhp = 10 knots
Complement	10

Built in 1945-46. Former American Higgins type motor launches, later Netherlands *RP* 120, *RP* 121, *RP* 122, *RP* 125, *RP* 127, *RP* 128, *RP* 130, *RP* 134, and *RP* 136. Transferred to Indonesia in 1950.

1 Ex-DUTCH MOTOR LAUNCH

Displacement, tons	54
Guns	1—40 mm AA; 2—20 mm AA
A/S weapons	3 DCT
Main Engines	Speed = 11 knots
Complement	10

Former Netherlands motor launch *RP* 138, transferred by the Royal Netherlands Navy in 1950.

AMPHIBIOUS VESSELS

TANDJUNG NUSANIVE	(ex-USS *Lawrence City* LST 889)	887
TELUK BAJUR	(ex-USS *LST 616*)	502
TELUK KAU	(ex-USS *LST 652*)	504
TELUK SALEH	(ex-USS *Clarke County LST* 601)	510
TELUK MANADO	(ex-USS *LST 657*)	505
TELUK BONE	(ex-USS *Iredell County LST 839*)	511
TELUK LANGSA	(ex-USS *LST 1128*)	501

Displacement, tons	1 653 standard; 4 080 full load
Dimensions, feet	316 wl; 328 oa × 50 × 14
Guns	7—40 mm AA; 2—20 mm AA
Main engines	GM diesels; 2 shafts; 1 700 bhp = 11·6 knots
Oil fuel (tons)	600
Range, miles	7 200 at 10 knots
Cargo capacity	2 100 tons
Complement	119 (accommodation for 266)

TRANSFERS:
505 in Mar 1960, 887 in Dec 1960, 502, 510 and 511 in June 1961, 504 and 501 in July 1970.

1 JAPANESE TYPE

TELUK AMBOINA LST 869

Displacement, tons	2 200 standard; 4 800 full load
Dimensions, feet	327 × 50 × 15
Guns	2—85 mm; 4—40 mm
Main Engines	MAN diesels; 2 shafts; 3 000 bhp = 13·1 knots
Oil fuel (tons)	1 200
Radius, miles	4 000 at 13·1 knots
Complement	88 (accommodation for 300)

Built in Japan. Launched on 17 Mar 1961 and transferred in June 1961.

3 Ex-US LCT TYPE

AMAHAI (ex-*Tropenvogel, LCI* 467) 864
MARICH (ex-*Zeemeeuw*) 866
PIRU (ex-*Zeearend, LCI* 420) 868

Displacement, tons	250 standard; 381 full load
Dimensions, feet	158 × 23 × 7
Guns	1—37 mm; 2 Vickers MG
Main engines	GM diesels; 1 800 bhp = 15 knots
Complement	60

Former US infantry landing craft. Turned over from Netherlands East Indies Government on formation of Indonesian Navy in 1950. Sister ship *Baruna* (ex-*Ijsvogel* LCI 948) and *Namlea* (ex-*Stormvogel* LCI 588) were rerated as pilot ship and light ship in 1961.

3 Ex-YUGOSLAV LCT TYPE

TELUK KATURAI 862 **TELUK WEDA** 861 **TELUK WORI** 863

Displacement, tons	110 standard; 250 full load
Dimensions, feet	166 × 21·5 × 5·5
Guns	1—40 mm; 2—20 mm
Main engines	2 diesels; 2 shafts; 375 bhp = 7 knots
Oil fuel (tons)	6
Complement	15

Transferred from Yugoslavia on 1 Nov 1958. In non-operational reserve.

2 Ex- "LCVT" TYPE

DORE **AMURANG**

Displacement, tons	182 standard; 275 full load
Dimensions, feet	125·7 × 32·8 × 5·9
Main engines	Diesels; 210 hp = 8 knots
Complement	17

1 Ex-USSR LCT TYPE

TELUK PARIGI

Displacement, tons	600 standard; 800 full load
Dimensions, feet	246·0 × 39·3 × 9·8
Main engines	Diesels; 2 shafts; 2 200 hp = 10 knots

MINE WARFARE FORCES

6 Ex-USSR "T43" CLASS (MINESWEEPERS—OCEAN)

PULAU RANI **PULAU RATENO** **PULAU ROON**
PULAU RADJA **PULAU RONDO** **PULAU RORBAS**

Displacement, tons	500 standard; 610 full load
Dimensions, ft (*m*)	190·2 × 28·2 × 6·9 (*58 × 8·6 × 2·1*)
Guns	4—37 mm AA; 4—25 mm AA
Main engines	2 diesels; 2 shafts; 2 000 bhp = 17 knots
Range, miles	1 600 at 10 knots
Complement	40

Transferred to Indonesia by the USSR, four in 1962 and two in 1964. *Pulau Rondo* is in reserve.

T 43 *Class*

4 Ex-DUTCH (MINESWEEPERS—COASTAL)

DJAMPEA **DJOMBANG** **ENGGANO** (ex-*Hino Maru*) **FLORES**

Displacement, tons	175
Dimensions, feet	106·7 pp; 113·7 (*Flores*) 114·1 oa × 18·8 × 6·2
Main Engines	1 Enterprise diesel; 360 bhp = 12·5 knots

First three were commissioned in 1941. *Flores* was completed by the Japanese during the occupation of Java. First two were built at Droogdok, Maatschappij, Soerabaya and the other two at Droogdok Mij, Tandjong Priok. Used as auxiliary minesweepers by the Royal Netherlands Navy. *Enggano* was re-named by Japanese. These ships were recovered after the war. *Enggano* in reserve since 1969.

10 "R" CLASS (MINESWEEPERS—COASTAL)

PULAU RAAS **PULAU REMPANG** **PULAU ROMA**
PULAU RANGSANG **PULAU RENGAT** **PULAU ROTI**
PULAU RAU **PULAU RINDJA** **PULAU RUPAT**
PULAU RUSA

Displacement, tons	139·4 standard
Dimensions, feet	129 × 18·7 × 5
Guns	1—40 mm AA; 2—20 mm AA
Main engines	2 MAN diesels; 12 cyl; 2 800 bhp = 24·6 knots
Complement	26

Built by Abeking & Rasmussen Jacht-und Bootswerft, Lemwerder in 1945-57. These boats have a framework of light metal covered with wood. *Pulau Raas, Pulau Rempang* and *Pulau Roti* in reserve.

PULAU ROTI *Indonesian Navy*

6 Ex-US "BLUEBIRD" CLASS (MINESWEEPERS—COASTAL)

PULAU ALOR (ex-*Meadowlark*)	717
PULAU ANJER (ex-*Limpkin*)	719
PULAU ANTANG (ex-*Frigate Bird*)	721
PULAU ARU (ex-*Falcon*)	722
PULAU ARUAN (ex-*Jacana*)	718
PULAU IMPALASA (ex-*Humming Bird*)	720

Displacement, tons	320 light; 370 full load
Dimensions, feet	138·0 pp; 144·0 oa × 28·0 × 8·2
Guns	2—20 mm AA (1 twin)
Main engines	Packard diesels; 2 shafts; 1 200 bhp = 12·5 knots
Complement	39

Transferred from the USN in 1971; *Falcon* (24 June), *Frigate Bird* (11 Aug), *Humming Bird* (12 July), *Jacana* (12 July), *Limpkin* (24 June), *Meadowlark* (11 Aug). All have wooden hulls with low magnetic signature.

SURVEY SHIPS

BURUDJULASAD 1006

Displacement, tons	2 150 full load
Dimensions, feet	269·5 × 37·4 × 11·5
Machinery	4 MAN diesels; 2 shafts; 6 850 bhp = 19·1 knots
Complement	113

Burudjulasad was launched in 1966; her equipment includes laboratories for oceanic and meteorological research, a cartographic room, and a helicopter.

BURUDJULASAD *1968, Indonesian Navy*

BURDIAMHAL

Displacement, tons	1 500 full load
Dimensions, feet	211·7 oa; 192 pp × 33·2 × 10
Main engines	2 Werkspoor diesels; 1 160 bhp = 10 knots
Complement	90

Built by Schweepserf De Waal, Zaltbommel. Launched on 6 Sep 1952. Completed on 6 July 1953.

JALANIDHI

Displacement, tons	985
Complement	58

Launched in 1962.

ARIES (ex-*Samudera*)

Measurement, tons	200 gross
Dimensions, feet	125·2 × 21·5 × 9·8
Main engines	Werkspoor diesel engines; 450 bhp

Built by Ferus Smit, Foxol. Launched on 28 May 1952. Completed on 28 Aug 1952. Same type as "Bango" class motor patrol vessels. Equipped as a laboratory ship, used for deep sea exploration in Indonesian waters. Another survey ship, *Dewa Kembar*, was laid up in reserve in Feb 1972.

SERVICE FORCES

MULTATULI 476 (SUBMARINE TENDER)

Displacement, tons	3 220
Dimensions, feet	338 pp; 365·3 oa × 52·5 × 23
Guns	1—85 mm; 4—40 mm (single mountings)
Main engines	B & W diesel; 5 500 bhp = 18·5 knots max
Oil fuel (tons)	1 400
Range, miles	6 000 at 16 knots cruising speed
Complement	134

Built in Japan by Ishikawajima-Harima Heavy Industries Co. Ltd, as a submarine tender. Launched on 15 May 1961. Delivered to Indonesia Aug 1961. Flush decker. Capacity for replenishment at sea (fuel oil, fresh water, provisions, ammunition, naval stores and personnel). Medical and hospital facilities. Equipment for supplying compressed air, electric power and distilled water to submarines. Air conditioning and mechanical ventilation arrangements for all living and working quarters.

1 Ex-USSR "ATREK" CLASS (SUBMARINE TENDER)

THAMRIN

Displacement, tons	3 500 standard; 6 700 full load
Measurement, tons	3 258 gross
Dimensions, feet	336 × 49 × 20
Main engines	Steam expansion and exhaust turbine; 2 450 ihp = 13 knots
Boilers	2
Range, miles	3 500 at 13 knots

Built in 1955-57 and converted to naval use from a mercantile freighter. Arrived in Indonesia on 28 June 1962.

Service Forces—*continued*

1 Ex-USSR "DON" CLASS (SUBMARINE TENDER)

RATULANGI

Displacement, tons	6 700 standard; 9 000 full load
Dimensions, feet	458·9 × 57·7 × 22·3
Guns	4—3·9 in; 8—57 mm AA
Main engines	Diesels; 14 000 bhp = 21 knots approx
Complement	300

A submarine support ship, escort vessel and maintenance tender transferred from the USSR to Indonesia in 1962, arriving in Indonesia in July. Fitted with SLIM NET search and warning radar and with fire control radar.

RATULANGI *1968, Indonesian Navy*

DJAJA WIDJAJA (ex-USS *Askari* 9109, ex-*ARL* 30, ex-*LST* 1131) 9017 (REPAIR SHIP)

Displacement, tons	1 625 light; 4 100 full load
Dimensions, feet	316·0 wl; 328·0 oa × 50·0 × 11·0
Guns	8—40 mm AA (2 quadruple)
Main engines	General Motors diesels; 2 shafts; 1 800 bhp = 11·6 knots
Complement	280

Of wartime construction, this ship was in reserve from 1956-66. She was recommissioned and reached Vietnam in 1967 to support River Assault Flotilla One. She was used by the USN and Vietnamese Navy working up the Mekong in support of the Cambodian operations in May 1970. Transferred on lease to Indonesia at **Guam** on 31 Aug 1971.

DUMAI (ex-USS *Tidewater*) AD 31 (DESTROYER DEPOT SHIP)

Displacement, tons	8 165 standard; 16 635 full load
Dimensions, feet	465 wl; 492 oa × 69·5 × 27·2
Guns	1—5 in; 38 cal dp
Main engines	Geared turbines; 1 shaft; 8 500 shp = 18·4 knots
Boilers	2 Babcock & Wilcox
Complement	778

Transferred Feb 1971, as destroyer depot ship. Also used to maintain off-shore drilling rigs.

2 Ex-USSR TYPE (SUPPORT TANKERS)

BUNJU 904 **SAMBU** 903

Displacement, tons	2 170 standard; 6 170 full load
Dimensions, feet	350·5 × 49·2 × 20·2
Guns	2—20 mm
Main engines	Polar diesel; 1 shaft; 2 650 bhp = 10 knots
Oil fuel (tons)	390
Cargo capacity	4 739 tons
Complement	71

Transferred to the Indonesian Navy on 19 June 1959. Both laid up in 1969.

TJEPU (ex-*Scandus*, ex-*Nordhem*) 901 (SUPPORT TANKER)

Displacement, tons	1 372
Measurement, tons	1 042 gross
Dimensions, feet	226·5 × 34 × 14·2
Main engines	Polar diesel; 1 shaft; 850 bhp = 11 knots

Built in Sweden in 1949. Acquired in 1951. Laid up in 1969.

5 Ex-USSR "UDA" CLASS (SUPPORT TANKERS)

BALIKPAPAN **PANGKALAN BRANDAN** +3

Displacement, tons	5 500 standard; 7 200 full load
Dimensions, feet	400·3 × 51·8 × 20·3
Main engines	Diesels; 2 shafts; 8 000 bhp = 17 knots

TARAKAN BULA (HARBOUR TANKER)

Displacement, tons	1 340 full load
Dimensions, feet	352·0 × 37·7 × 14·8
Main engines	Diesels; 1 shaft; 1 500 bhp = 13 knots

PAKAN BARU (HARBOUR TANKER)

Displacement, tons	1 500 full load
Dimensions, feet	63 × 11·5 × 4·5
Main engines	Diesels; 2 shafts; 800 bhp = 11 knots

TRANSPORTS

2 "BANGGAI" TYPE

BANGGAI (ex-*Biscaya*) 925 **NUSA TELU** (ex-*Casa Blanca*) 924

Measurement, tons 750
Dimensions, feet 168 × 27·9 × 7·8

Dual purpose troop and cargo ships. Renamed in 1961.

SALVAGE VESSEL

TRITON (ex-*Mutsunoura Maru*) 926

Displacement, tons 384
Measurement, tons 383 gross
Dimensions, feet 182·5 × 30 × 15
Main engines Triple expansion reciprocating; 700 ihp = 7 knots
Complement 43

Former Japanese vessel renamed. Launched in 1941. Laid up in reserve in 1969.

CABLE SHIP

BIDUK

Displacement, tons 1 250 standard
Dimensions, feet 213·2 oa × 39·5 × 11·5
Main engines 1 Triple expansion engine; 1 600 ihp = 12 knots
Complement 66

Cable Layer, Lighthouse Tender, and multi-purpose naval auxiliary. Built by J. & K. Smit, Kinderijk. Launched on 30 Oct 1951. Completed on 30 July 1952.

TUGS

RAKATA (ex-USS *Menominee, ATF* 73) 928

Displacement, tons 1 235 standard; 1 675 full load
Dimensions, feet 195 wl; 205 oa × 38·5 × 15·5 max
Guns 1—3 in; 4—40 mm AA; 2—20 mm AA
Main engines 4 diesels with electric drive; 3 000 bhp = 16·5 knots
Complement 85

Former American fleet ocean tug of the "Apache" class. Launched on 14 Feb 1942. Transferred from the United States Navy to the Indonesian Navy at San Diego in Mar 1961.

LAMPO BATANG 934

Displacement, tons 250
Dimensions, feet 92·3 oa; 86·7 pp × 23·2 × 11·3
Main engines 2 diesels; 1 200 bhp = 11 knots
Oil fuel (tons) 18
Range, miles 1 000 at 11 knots
Complement 43

Ocean tug. Built in Japan. Launched in April 1961. Delivered in Nov 1961.

GANDENG

Measurement, tons 610 gross
Main engines Speed = 7·5 knots

Launched in 1940. Reported to have been given a new Indonesian name.

BROMO 936 **TAMBORA** 935

Displacement, tons 150
Dimensions, feet 71·7 wl; 79 oa × 21·7 × 9·7
Main engines MAN diesel; 2 shafts; 600 bhp = 10·5 knots
Oil fuel (tons) 9
Range, miles 690 at 10·5 knots
Complement 15

Harbour tugs. Built in Japan. Launched in June 1961. Delivered in Aug 1961.

AUXILIARY PATROL CRAFT

5 DKN TYPE

DKN 901 **DKN 902** **DKN 903** **DKN 904** **DKN 905**

Displacement, tons 140
Dimensions, feet 128 × 19 × 5·2
Guns 4—20 mm AA
Main engines Maybach diesels; 2 shafts; 3 000 bhp = 24·5 knots

Patrol craft and police boats. Projected as a class of ten units. 901, 902 and 904 were built by Lürssen, Vegesack, 903 and 905 by Abeking & Rasmussen Lemwerder.

6 "PAT" CLASS

PAT 01 **PAT 02** **PAT 03** **PAT 04** **PAT 05** **PAT 06**

Dimensions, feet 91·9 pp; 100 oa × 17 × 6
Main engines 2 Caterpillar diesels; 340 bhp

Auxiliary Patrol Craft—*continued*

6 "BALAM" CLASS

BALAM **BARAU** **BEKAKA** **BELATIK** **BENDALU** **BOGA**

Measurmeent, tons 200 gross
Dimensions, feet 125·2 oa × 21·3 × 6·5
Main engines Werkspoor diesel engine; 400-430 bhp = 11 knots

All launched in 1953. *Balam* and others were commissioned for service in 1953.

7 "BANGO" CLASS

BANGO **BABUT** **BEO** **BETTET** **BIDO** **BLEKOK** **BLIBIS**

Measurement, tons 194 gross
Dimensions, feet 120·5 pp; 125·2 oa × 21·3 × 6·6
Main engines Werkspoor diesel engine; 430 bhp = 11 knots

All launched in 1952.

7 "DURIAN" CLASS

DAIK **DAGONG** **DAMARA** **DATA** **DUATA** **DUKU** **DURIAN**

Displacement, tons 90
Dimensions, feet 78·2 × 16 × 6·8
Main engines Caterpillar diesel; 190 bhp

All launched in 1951.

12 "ALKAI" CLASS

ALKAI **ALULU** **AMPIS** **ANKANG** **ANTANG** **ARYAT**
ALLAP **AMPOK** **ANDIS** **ANKLOENG** **AROKWES** **ATTAT**

Displacement, tons 143; 247 full load
Dimensions, feet 124·3 × 18·5 × 5·5
Guns 1—37 mm AA; 4 MG
Main engines Enterprise diesel; 400-450 = 12 knots
Complement 20

Built in the Netherlands. *Ampok* and *Alkai* were shipped to Indonesia on 17 Mar 1950. *Ampis in reserve* in 1969.

3 Ex-US SC TYPE

BHAYAMKARA I **BHAYAMKARA II** **BHAYAMKARA III**

Displacement, tons 116 (trials); 148 full load
Dimensions, feet 107·5 wl; 110·8 oa 17 × 6·5
Main engines Diesel; 800 bhp = 15·5 knots

Former US submarine chasers of the 110 SC type. Operated by Indonesian Marine Police.

2"MERABU"CLASS

MERABU (ex-*Merbaboe*) **RINDJANI**

Displacement, tons 80
Dimensions, feet 74·5 × 14·5 × 5
Main engines Diesel; 135 bhp = 10 knots
Complement 20

Merabu is laid up in reserve.

TRAINING SHIP

DEWARUTJI

Displacement, tons 810 standard; 1 500 full load
Dimensions, feet 191·2 oa; 136·2 pp × 31·2 × 13·9
Main engines MAN diesels; 600 bhp = 10·5 knots
Complement 110 (32 + 78 midshipmen)

Built in Germany by H. C. Stülcken & Sohn, Hamburg. Launched on 24 Jan 1953. Completed on 9 July 1953. Barquentine of iron construction. Sail area, 1 305 sq yds (*1 091 sq metres*). Speed with sails 12·8 knots.

DEWARUTJI *Indonesia*

IRAN

Administration

Commander-in-Chief Imperial Iranian Navy:
Rear Admiral R. A. Attaie

Diplomatic Representation

Naval Attaché in London:
Captain Ali Ashgar Bahram

Naval Attaché in Washington:
Captain Movaghari

Personnel

(a) 1974: 13 000 officers and men
(b) 2 years National Service

Note. A Naval Infantry Division is being formed

Strength of the Fleet

Type	*Active*	*Building/ (Planned)*
Destroyers	3	(?8)
Frigates	4	(?4)
Corvettes	4	—
Large Patrol Craft	7	(?12)
Coastal Patrol Craft	9	—
Hovercraft	12	2
Landing Craft	2	—
Minesweepers—Coastal	4	—
Minesweepers—Inshore	2	—
Supply Ships	—	2
Repair Ships	2	—
Harbour Tanker	1	—
Water Boat	1	—
Tug	1	—
Yachts	2	—

New Construction

Interest is being shown by Iranian authorities in the building of both frigates and submarines. No details or orders have yet been released but there are reports of a possible building programme of 8 destroyers, 4 frigates, 12 gunboats and 14 hovercraft. There are other reports of interest in an "Invincible" class command-cruiser

Bases

Persian Gulf	Bandar Abbas (MHQ)
	Khorramshar (Light Forces)
	Kharg Island
Indian Ocean	Chah Bar (under construction)
Caspian Sea	Bandar—Pahlavi (Training)

Mercantile Marine

Lloyd's Register of Shipping:
93 vessels of 192 386 tons

DESTROYERS

1 Ex-BRITISH "BATTLE" CLASS

Name	*No.*	*Builders*	*Laid down*	*Launched*	*Completed*
ARTEMIZ (ex-HMS *Sluys*, D 60)	D 5	Cammell Laird & Co Ltd, Birkenhead	24 Nov 1943	28 Feb 1945	30 Sep 1946

Displacement, tons	2 325 standard; 3 360 full load
Length, feet (*metres*)	355·0 (*108·2*) pp; 379·0 (*115·5*) oa
Beam, feet (*metres*)	40·5 (*12·3*)
Draught, feet (*metres*)	17·5 (*5·2*) max
Guns	4—4·5 in (*115 mm*) 2 twin forward
Guns	8—40 mm Bofors AA
Missile launchers	1 quadruple "Seacat" AA aft
A/S weapons	1 "Squid" 3-barrelled DC mortar
Main engines	Parsons geared turbines; 2 shafts; 50 000 shp
Speed, knots	35·5 max; 31 sustained sea
Boilers	2 Admiralty 3-drum type
Oil fuel, tons	680
Range, miles	3 000 at 20 knots
Complement	270

ARTEMIZ 1971

Transferred to Iran at Southampton on 26 Jan 1967, and handed over to the Imperial Iranian Navy after a 3-year modernisation refit by the Vosper Thornycroft Group.

RADAR. Search: Plessey AWS 1. Air surveillance with on-mounted IFF; Contraves Sea-Hunter fire control; Decca RDL 1 radar intercept; Racal DF equipment.

ARTEMIZ

2 Ex-US ALLEN M. SUMNER CLASS

Name	*No.*	*Builders*	*Launched*	*Commissioned*
BABR (ex-USS *Zellars*, DD 777)	DDG 7	Todd Pacific Shipyards	19 July 1944	25 Oct 1944
PALANG (ex-USS *Stormes*, DD 780)	DDG 9	Todd Pacific Shipyards	4 Nov 1944	27 Jan 1945

Displacement, tons	2 200 standard; 3 320 full load
Length, feet (*metres*)	376·5 (*114·8*) oa
Beam, feet (*metres*)	40·9 (*12·4*)
Draft, feet (*metres*)	19 (*5·8*)
Missiles	4 Standard launchers with 7 reloads each
Guns	6—5 inch (*127 mm*) 38 calibre dual-purpose (twin)
ASW weapons	2 fixed Hedgehogs; depth charges 2 triple torpedo launchers (Mk 32) 2 fixed torpedo launchers (Mk 25) 2 Drone A/S helicopters
Main engines	2 geared turbines; 60 000 shp; 2 shafts
Boilers	4
Speed, knots	34
Complement	274 (14 officers, 260 ratings) (designed wartime 345)

Two "FRAM II" conversion destroyers of the "Allen M. Sumner" class nominally transferred to Iran from the USN in March 1971 for delivery in 1972. Renamed on transfer with names previously used for the ex-British "Loch" class (*Babr*) and the ex-British "Algerine" class (*Palang*) paid off on 30 Oct 1969 and Dec 1966

USS *Gainard* (DD 706) was taken over in Mar 1971, but, being beyond repair, was used for spares and training; being replaced by USS *Stormes* (DD 780).

RADAR. SPS 10 search; SPS 37 air-surveillance with on-mounted IFF; Gun fire control system Mk 56 with radar on director.

SONAR. SQS 23 or SQS 29 Sonar; VDS.

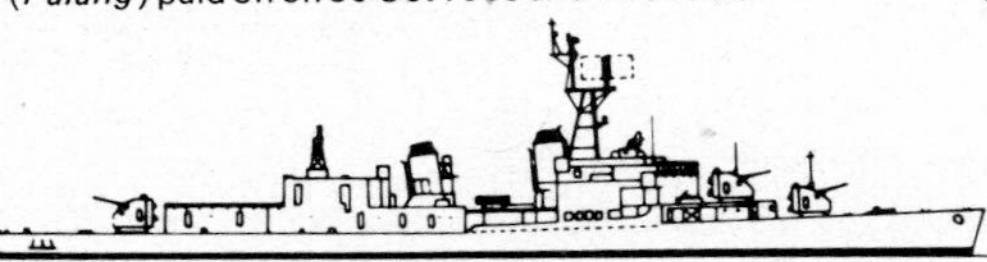

BABR and PALANG

BABR (as ZELLARS) *United States Navy*

FRIGATES

4 "SAAM" CLASS

Name	No.	Builders	Laid down	Launched	Completed
FARAMAZ	DE 18	Vosper Thornycroft, Woolston	25 July 1968	30 July 1969	28 Feb 1972
ROSTAM	DE 16	Vickers, Newcastle & Barrow	10 Dec 1967	4 Mar 1969	June 1972
SAAM	DE 12	Vosper Thornycroft, Woolston	22 May 1967	25 July 1968	20 May 1971
ZAAL	DE 14	Vickers, Barrow	3 Mar 1968	4 Mar 1969	1 Mar 1971

Displacement, tons: 1 110 standard; 1 290 full load
Length, feet (*metres*): 310·0 (*94·4*) oa
Beam, feet (*metres*): 34·0 (*10·4*)
Draught, feet (*metres*): 11·2 (*3·4*)
Missile launchers: 1 quintuple "Seakiller" surface-to-surface; 1 triple "Seacat" surface-to-air
Guns: 1—4·5 in (*115 mm*) Mk 8 (Mk 5 in *Saam, Zaal*); 2—35 mm Oerlikon (1 twin) AA
A/S weapons: 1 "Limbo" 3-barrelled DC mortar
Main engines: 2 Rolls-Royce "Olympus" gas turbines; 2 Paxman diesels; 2 shafts; 46 000 + 3 800 shp
Speed, knots: 40
Complement: 125 (accommodation for 146)

GENERAL
It was announced on 25 Aug 1966 that Vosper Ltd, Portsmouth had received an order for four vessels for the Iranian Navy. Air conditioned throughout. Fitted with Vosper stabilisers. *Rostam* was towed to Barrow for completion.

RADAR. Plessey AWS 1 air surveillance with on-mounted IFF. Two Contraves Seahunter systems for control of 35 mm, Seakillers and Seacats. Decca RDL 1 passive DF equipment.

FARAMAZ — *1972, C. & S. Taylor*

CORVETTES

4 US PF TYPE

Name	No.	Builders	Laid down	Launched	Completed
BAYANDOR	F 25 (ex-USS *PF* 103)	Levingstone Shipbuilding Co, Orange, Texas	20 Aug 1962	7 July 1963	18 May 1964
KAHNAMUIE	F 28 (ex-USS *PF* 106)	Levingstone Shipbuilding Co, Orange, Texas	12 June 1967	4 Apr 1968	13 Feb 1969
MILANIAN	F 27 (ex-USS *PF* 105)	Levingstone Shipbuilding Co, Orange, Texas	1 May 1967	4 Jan 1968	13 Feb 1969
NAGHDI	F 26 (ex-USS *PF* 104)	Levingstone Shipbuilding Co, Orange, Texas	12 Sep 1962	10 Oct 1963	22 July 1964

Displacement, tons: 900 standard; 1 135 full load
Length, feet (*metres*): 275·0 (*83·8*) oa
Beam, feet (*metres*): 33·0 (*10·0*)
Draught, feet (*metres*): 10·2 (*3·1*)
Guns: 2—3 in (*76 mm*); 2—40 mm AA
A/S weapons: 1 Hedgehog, 4 DCT
Main engines: F-M diesels; 2 shafts; 6 000 bhp
Speed, knots: 20 max
Complement: 140

BAYANDOR *Class*

MILANIAN — *1972, Imperial Iranian Navy*

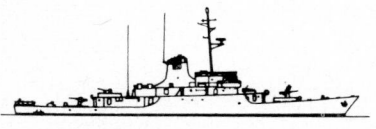

Built as two pairs, five years apart. Transferred from the USA to Iran under the Mutual Assistance Programme in 1964 (*Bayandor* and *Naghdi*) and 1969 (*Kahnamuie* and *Milanian*). SPS 12 Search radar and navigation radar.

LIGHT FORCES

3 IMPROVED PGM TYPE (LARGE PATROL CRAFT)

BATTRAAM (ex-US PGM 112) PGM 66
NAHID (ex-US PGM 122) PGM 67
PARVIN (ex-US PGM 103) PGM 65

Displacement, tons: 105 standard; 146 full load
Dimensions, feet: 100 × 22 × 10
Guns: 1—40 mm; 2—20 mm, 2—50 cal MG
Main engines: 8 MG diesels; 2 000 bhp = 15 knots

Motor gunboats of an enlarged design, compared with the "Kayvan" class below. Built in USA by Tacoma Boatbuilding Co of Tacoma and Petersen Builders Inc of Sturgeon Bay, Wisconsin, and transferred to Iran under MAP in 1967-70.

Note: In February 1974 Iran concluded an agreement with France for the construction of 6 La Combattante II Class Fast Attack Craft armed with Exocet missiles.

4 PGM TYPE (LARGE PATROL CRAFT)

KAYVAN (MDA1) **MAHAN** 64 **MEHRAN** **TIRAN**

Displacement, tons: 85 standard; 107 full load
Dimensions, feet: 90 pp; 95 oa × 20·2 × 6·8 max
Gun: 1—40 mm AA
A/S weapons: 8-barrelled 7·2 in projector, 8—300 lb depth charges
Main engines: 4 Cummins diesels; 2 shafts; 2 200 bhp = 20 knots
Range, miles: 1 500 cruising
Complement: 15

Kayvan, built in USA in 1955, was delivered to Iran on 14 Jan 1956. *Tiran* was built by the US Coast Guard at Curtis Bay, Maryland, and transferred to Iran in 1957. *Mahan* and *Mehran* were delivered to Iran in 1959.

PARVIN — *1971*

MAHAN — *1969, Imperial Iranian Navy*

AT LEAST 6 40ft TYPE (COASTAL PATROL CRAFT)

MAHNAVI-HAMRAZ **MAHNAVI-VAHEDI** **MORVARID**
MAHNAVI-TAHERI **MARDJAN** **SADAF**

Displacement, tons: 10 standard
Dimensions, feet: 40·0 × 11·0 × 3·7
Guns: Light MG
Main engines: 2 General Motors diesels = 30 knots

Small launches for port duties of Sewart (USA) standard 40 ft type. Pennant numbers 5001 and above. Some serve in the Caspian Sea.

3 PATROL BOATS (COASTAL PATROL CRAFT)

GOHAR **SHAHPAR** **No. 3**

Displacement, tons: 70
Dimensions, feet: 75·2 × 16·5 × 6
Main engines: 2 diesels; 1 100 hp; 2 shafts = 27 knots

Built by Abeking and Rasmussen. *Gohar* launched 22 Jan 1970, *Shahpar* on 19 Mar 1970.

Light Forces—*continued*

6 "WELLINGTON" (BH.7) CLASS (HOVERCRAFT)

101 **102** 103 104

Displacement, tons	50 max weight, 33 empty
Dimensions, feet	76 × 45 × 42 (height inflated)
Guns	2 Browning MG
Main engines	1 Proteus 15 M/541 gas turbine = 60 knots max
Oil fuel tons	10 max

First pair are BH 7 Mk 4 (delivered Nov 70 and Mar 71) and the next four are Mk 5 craft (two in 1973, one in late 1974 and one in early 1975).

101 *1971*

8 "WINCHESTER" (SR.N6) CLASS (HOVERCRAFT)

01 **02** **03** **04** **05** **06** **07** **08**

Displacement, tons	10 normal gross weight (basic weight 14 200 lbs; disposable load 8 200 lbs)
Dimensions, feet	48·4 × 25·3 × 15·9 (height)
Main engines	1 Gnome Model 1050 gas turbine = 58 knots max. 1 Peters diesel as auxiliary power unit.

The Imperial Iranian Navy has the world's largest fully operational hovercraft squadron, which is used for coastal defence and logistic duties.

03 *1971*

LANDING CRAFT

QUESHM (ex-USS *LCU* 1431) LCU 47

Displacement, tons	160 light; 320 full load
Dimensions, feet	119 × 32 × 5·7
Guns	2—20 mm AA
Main engines	Diesels; 675 bhp = 10 knots
Complement	14

LCU 1431 was transferred to Iran by US in 1964 under the Military Aid Programme.

QUESM *1971*

LARAK (ex-US *LSIL* 710) LSIL 42

Transferred Dec 1958.

MINE WARFARE FORCES

4 MSC TYPE (MINESWEEPERS—COASTAL)

KARKAS (ex-USS *MSC* 292) 34
SHAHBAZ (ex-USS *MSC* 275) 32
SHAHROKH (ex-USS *MSC* 276) 31
SIMORGH (ex-USS *MSC* 291) 33

Displacement, tons	320 light; 378 full load
Dimensions, feet	138 pp; 145·8 oa × 28 × 8·3
Gun	1—20 mm
Main engines	2 GM diesels; 2 shafts; 890 bhp = 12·8 knots
Oil fuel (tons)	27
Range, miles	2 400 at 11 knots
Complement	40 (4 officers, 2 midshipmen, 34 men)

Built by Bellingham Shipyards Co (*Shahbaz* and *Shahrokh*), Petersen Builders Inc. (*Karkas*) and Tacoma Boatbuilding Co, (*Simorgh*). Of wooden construction. Launched in 1958-61 and transferred from US to Iran under MAP in 1959-62. *Shahrokh* now in the Caspian Sea.

SHAHROKH *1971, John G. Callis*

2 US MSI TYPE (MINESWEEPERS—INSHORE)

HARISCHI (ex-*Kahnamuie*) 301 (ex-*MSI* 14) **RIAZI** 302 (ex-*MSI* 13)

Displacement, tons	180 standard; 235 full load
Dimensions, feet	111 × 23 × 6
Guns	MG
Main engines	diesels; 650 bhp = 13 knots
Oil fuel, tons	20
Radius, miles	1 000 at 9 knots
Complement	23 (5 officers, 18 men)

Built in USA by Tacoma Boatbuilding Co and delivered to Iran under MAP. Laid down on 22 June 1962 and 1 Feb 1963, and transferred at Seattle, Washington, on 3 Sep 1964 and 15 Oct 1964, respectively. In Aug 1967 *Kahnamuie* was renamed *Harischi* as the name was required for one of the new US PFs, see above.

RIAZI *1971.*

SERVICE FORCES

2 STORE SHIPS

HENGAM + 1

2 ships of 300 feet, 2 500 tons twin-screw diesel, ordered from Yarrow in 1972. *Hengam* launched 24 Sept 1973.

1 Ex-US ARL (Ex-LST) TYPE (REPAIR SHIP)

SOHRAB (ex-USS *Gordlus*, *ARL* 36, ex-*LST* 1145)

Displacement, tons	1 625 light; 4 100 full load
Dimensions, feet	316 wl; 328 oa × 50 × 11·2
Guns	8—40 mm AA
Main engines	GM diesels; 2 shafts; 1 800 bhp = 11·6 knots

Former US repair ship for landing craft. Built by Chicago Bridge & Iron Co, Seneca Ill. Laid down on 5 Feb 1945. Launched on 7 May 1945. Completed on 18 May 1945. Transferred by the USA under the Military Aid Programme in Sep 1961.

SOHRAB 1971

1 Ex-US AR TYPE (REPAIR SHIP)

CHAHBAHAR (ex-USS *Amphion*) AR 13

Displacement, tons	7 826 standard; 14 490 full load
Dimensions, feet	456·0 wl; 492·0 oa × 70·0 × 27·5
Guns	2—3 in 50 cal AA
Main engines	Westinghouse turbines; 1 shaft; 8 500 shp = 16·5 knots
Boilers	2 Foster-Wheeler
Complement	Accommodation for 921.

Built by Tampa Shipbuilding Co. Launched on 15 May 1945. Commissioned on 30 Jan 1946. Transferred to IIN on 1 Oct 1971. Based at Bandar Abbas.

CHAHBAHAR 1972, *Imperial Iranian Navy*

HORMUZ (ex-*YO* 247) 43 (HARBOUR TANKER)

Displacement, tons	1 250 standard; 1 700 full load
Dimensions, feet	171·2 wl; 178·3 oa × 32·2 × 14
Main engines	1 Ansaldo Q 370, 4 cycle diesel
Oil fuel, tons	25

Hormuz was built by Cantiere Castellamare di Stabia. Own oil fuel: 25 tons. Cargo oil capacity: 5 000 to 6 000 barrels.

HORMUZ 1970, *Imperial Iranian Navy*

Service Forces—*cont.*

LENGEN (ex-USS *YW* 88) 46 (WATER BOAT)

Displacement, tons	1 250 standard
Dimensions, feet	178 × 32 × 14
Main engines	Diesels; speed = 10 knots

Transferred to Iran by US in 1964. Similar to oiler *Hormuz* above.

BAHMANSHIR 45 (TUG)

Harbour tug (ex-US Army ST 1002), 150 tons, transferred in 1962.

IMPERIAL YACHTS

KISH

Displacenemt, tons	178
Dimensions, feet	122 × 25 × 7
Main engines	2 sets by Motor und Turbinen Union Friedrichshafen GMBH MAN-Maybach-Mercedes-Benz; 2 920 hp

A smaller and more modern Imperial Yacht built by Yacht und Bootswerft, Burmester, Germany. Commissioned in 1970. In the Persion Gulf.

KISH 1971

SHAHSAVAR

Displacement, tons	530
Dimensions, feet	176 × 25·3 × 10·5
Main engines	2 sets diesels; 1 300 bhp

Built by N. V. Boele's Scheepwerven, Bolnes, Netherlands. Engined by Gebr Stork of Hengelo. Launched in 1936. In the Caspian Sea.

SHAHSAVAR 1971, *Imperial Iranian Navy*

IRAQ

Personnel

(a) 1974: 2 000 officers and men
(b) 2 years National Service

Mercantile Marine

Lloyd's Register of Shipping: 46 vessels of 228 274 tons gross

SOVIET-IRAQI TREATY

Under this treaty, signed in April 1972, the Soviet fleet will have access to the Iraqi base of UMM QASR. In return Soviet assistance will be given to strengthen Iraq's defences. From the naval aspect, taking into account the small number of personnel, this is most "SO 1's".

CORVETTES

3 Ex-USSR "SO-I" TYPE

Displacement, tons	215 light; 250 full load
Dimensions, feet	138·6 × 20 × 9·2
Guns	4—25 mm AA
A/S weapons	4 five-barrelled ahead-throwing rocket launchers.
Main engines	3 diesels; 6 000 bhp = 29 knots
Complement	30

Former Soviet submarine chasers delivered by the USSR to Iraq in 1962.

LIGHT FORCES

5 Ex-USSR "OSA" CLASS (FAST ATTACK CRAFT—MISSILE)

Displacement, tons	165 standard; 200 full load
Dimensions, ft (*m*)	128·7 × 25·1 × 5·9 (*39·3 × 7·7 × 1·8*)
Missiles	4 launchers for SS-N-2 (Styx)
Guns	4—30 mm (twin)
Main engines	3 Diesels; 13 000 hp = 32 knots
Range, miles	800 at 25 knots
Complement	25

This increase in the Iraqui navy, foretold as a probability last year, must make a major impact on naval affairs in the Persian Gulf. Other navies have shown the effectiveness of the Styx missiles, even in comparatively untrained hands, against unalerted forces. It will be a surprise if this Soviet incursion does not accelerate the build up of high-effectiveness forces in this area.

12 Ex-USSR "P 6" TYPE

Displacement, tons	66 standard; 75 full load
Dimensions, feet	84·2 × 20 × 6
Guns	4—25 mm
Tubes	2—21 in
Main engines	Diesels; 4 800 bhp = 45 knots
Complement	25

Transferred from the USSR. Two were received in 1959, four in Nov 1960, and six in Jan 1961. Some remain non-operational.

No. 1 **No. 2** **No. 3** **No. 4**

Displacement, tons	67
Dimensions, feet	100 × 17 × 3 mean
Guns	1—3·7 in howitzer; 2—3 in mortars; 4 MG
Main engines	2 Thornycroft diesels; 2 shafts; 280 bhp = 12 knots

Protected by bullet-proof plating. All built by John I. Thornycroft & Co Ltd, Woolston Southampton. All launched, completed and delivered in 1937.

No. 1 *John I. Thornycroft & Co. Ltd*

6 Ex-USSR PATROL TYPE

Six small patrol boats supplied by the USSR.

8 PORTS ADMINISTRATION TYPE

Length, feet	36
Main engines	1 diesel; 125 bhp

Patrol boats built by John I. Thornycroft & Co for the Iraqi Ports Administration.

4 PILOT DESPATCH TYPE

Length, feet	21
Main engines	1 diesel; 40 bhp

Pilot despatch launches built by John Thornycroft & Co for the Iraqi Ports Administration.

TUG

ALARM (ex-*St. Ewe*)

Displacement, tons	570 standard; 820 full load
Dimensions, feet	135 × 30 × 14·5
Main engines	Triple expansion; 1 shaft; 1 200 ihp = 12 knots
Boilers	2 oil-fired

Former British Rescue type tug of the "Saint" class. Built by Murdock & Murray. Launched in 1919.

LIGHTHOUSE TENDER

— (ex-*Sans Peur*, ex-*Restless*)

Displacement, tons	1 025
Dimensions, feet	186 × 29·5 × 14·5
Main engines	Triple expansion; 2 shafts; 850 ihp = 13 knots
Boilers	1 oil-fired

Former Royal Yacht. Designed by G. L. Watson Ltd. Built by John Brown & Co Ltd. Clydebank. Launched in 1923.

PRESIDENTIAL YACHT

AL THAWRA (ex-*Melike Aliye*)

Displacement, tons	746
Main engines	Diesels; 2 shafts; 1 800 shp = 14 knots

Royal Yacht before assassination of King Faisal II in 1958, after which she was renamed *Al Thawra* (*The Revolution*) instead of *Malike Aliye* (*Queen Aliyah*).

AL THAWRA ***Added 1966, Aldo Fraccaroli***

IRELAND (REPUBLIC OF)

Minister for Defence: Mr. J. Cronin, TD

Commanding Officer and Director Naval Service: Captain T. McKenna

The Irish Naval Service is administered from Naval Headquarters, Department of Defence, Dublin, by the Commanding Officer and Director of the Service. The naval base and dockyard are on Haulbowline Island in Cork Harbour.

Personnel

DISPOSALS
Cliona (ex-HMS *Bellwort*) and *Macha* (ex-HMS *Borage*), both built by George Brown, & Co (Marine) Ltd, Greenock, were sold for breaking up in 1970-71. *Maev* (ex-HMS *Oxlip*) deleted 1972. Tender *Wyndham* sold in 1968 and *General McHardy* in 1971,

Mercantile Marine

Lloyd's Register of Shipping: 97 vessels of 229 349 tons gross

FISHERY PROTECTION VESSEL

DEIRDRE FP 20

Displacement, tons	972
Dimensions, feet	184·5 pp × 34·0 × 14·5
Guns	1—40 mm Bofors
Main engines	2 British Polar diesels coupled to 1 shaft; 4 200 bhp = approx 18 knots
Oil fuel	170 bunker capacity
Complement	42

Designed as an all weather ship. Built by Verolme, Cork. Controllable pitch propelle stabilisers and sonar. The first vessel ever built for the Naval Service in the Republi of Ireland. Launched on 29 Dec 1971. Completed May 1972.

COASTAL MINESWEEPERS

3 Ex-BRITISH "TON" CLASS

BANBA CM 11 (ex-HMS *Alverton*, M 1104)
FÓLA CM 12 (ex-HMS *Blaxton* M 1132)
GRAINNE CM 10 (ex-HMS *Oulston*, M 1129)

Displacement, tons	360 standard; 425 full load
Dimensions, feet	140·0 pp; 153·0 oa × 28·8 × 8·2
Guns	1—40 mm AA; 2—20 mm AA
Main engines	2 diesels; 2 shafts; 3 000 bhp = 15 knots max
Oil fuel, tons	45
Range, miles	2 300 at 13 knots
Complement	30 average

Former British "Ton" class coastal minesweepers. Built in 1954-59. Double mahogany hulls and otherwise constructed of aluminium alloy and other materials with the lowest possible magnetic attraction to attain the greatest possible safety factor when sweeping. Purchased from Great Britain in 1971. See fuller particulars of the numerous "Ton" class in the United Kingdom section on later page. Acquired for fishery protection duties as replacements for the old corvettes. Arrived in Irish Republican waters in Spring 1971.

FOLA *1972, Irish Naval Service*

JOHN ADAMS

Measurement ,tons	94 gross
Dimensions, feet	85 × 18·5 × 7
Main engines	diesel; 125 bhp = 8 knots

Built by Richard Dunston, Ltd, Thorne, Doncaster, Yorks. Launched in 1934.

ISRAEL

Administration

Commander in Chief of the Israeli Navy:
Rear Admiral Benjamin Telem

Diplomatic Representation

Naval, Military and Air Attaché in London and Paris:
Commodore H. Kimchy

Personnel

(a) 4 500 (350 officers and 4 150 men, including a Naval Commando)
(b) 3 years National Service for Jews and Druses.
Note (An additional 5 000 Reserves available on mobilization).

Strength of the Fleet

Type	*Active*	*Building*
Patrol Submarines	2	3
Fast Attack Craft (Missile)	18	—
Fast Attack Craft (Torpedo)	3	—
Large Patrol Craft	2	—
Coastal Patrol Craft	28	—
"Firefish"	1	?
LCT's	7	—
LCM's	3	—
Transports	2	—

Prefix to Ship's Names

INS (Israeli Naval Ship)

Bases

Haifa, Ashdod, Sharm-el-Sheikh
A repair base is being built at Eilat where a synchro-lift is being installed.

Mercantile Marine

Lloyd's Register of Shipping:
90 vessels of 645 391 tons gross

SUBMARINES

3 IKL/VICKERS 500-ton CLASS

(PATROL SUBMARINES)

Displacement, tons	420 surfaced; 600 dived
Dimensions, ft (*m*)	156 × 15 × 12 (*47·6 × 4·6 × 3·7*)
Torpedo tubes	8—21 in bow
Main machinery	Diesels; 2 000 hp; Electric motor; 1 800 hp; 1 shaft
Speed, knots	11 surfaced; 17 dived
Complement	22

A contract was signed for the building of these boats by Vickers in April 1972. They will, presumably, be operational from 1975 onwards.

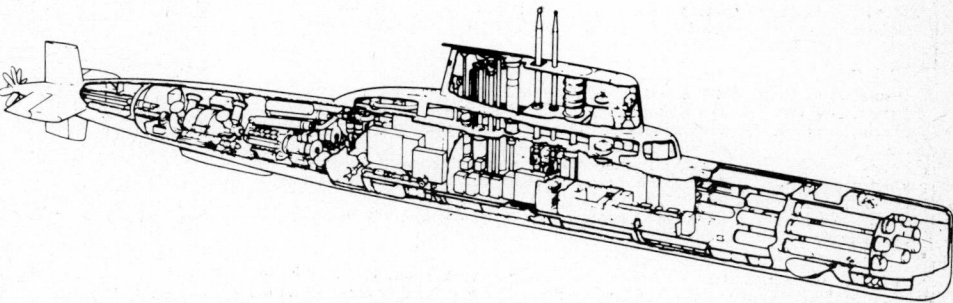

Cutaway impression of the Vickers/IKL 500-ton oceangoing submarine *1972, Vickers Limited*

2 Ex-BRITISH "T" CLASS

(PATROL SUBMARINES)

Name	*No.*	*Builders*	*Laid down*	*Launched*	*Completed*
LEVIATHAN (ex-HMS *Turpin*)	75	HM Dockyard, Chatham	24 May 1943	5 Aug 1944	18 Dec 1944
DOLPHIN (ex-HMS *Truncheon*)	77	HM Dockyard, Devonport	5 Nov 1942	22 Feb 1944	25 May 1945

Displacement, tons	*Dolphin:* 1 310 standard; 1 535 surface; 1 740 submerged *Leviathan:* 1 280 standard; 1 505 surface; 1 700 submerged
Length, feet (*metres*)	*Dolphin:* 293·5 (*89·5*) oa *Leviathan:* 285·5 (*87·0*) oa
Beam, feet (*metres*)	26·5 (*8·1*)
Draught, feet (*metres*)	14·8 (*4·5*)
Torpedo tubes	6—21 m (*533 mm*) 4 bow, 2 stern
Main machinery	Diesels; 2 500 bhp (surface); Electric Motors: 2 900 hp (submerged)
Speed, knots	15·25 on surface; 15 to 18 submerged
Complement	*Dolphin:* 65 *Leviathan:* 69

Both aged T class who were lengthened and modernised during conversion (*Leviathan* plus 12 feet *Dolphin* plus 20 feet). Handed over after extensive refit. *Leviathan* on 19 May 1967, *Dolphin* on 9 Jan 1968.

LOSS. Original sister ship *Dakar* (ex-HMS *Totem*), handed over to Israel on 10 Nov 1967, was lost in the Eastern Mediterranean on 25 Jan 1968.

LEVIATHAN *1972, Israeli Navy*

LIGHT FORCES

6 "SAAR IV" CLASS (FAST ATTACK CRAFT—MISSILE)

RESHEF **KESHET** + 4

Displacement, tons	415 standard
Dimensions, feet	190·6 × 25 × 8 (*58 × 7·8 × 2·4*)
Missile launchers	7 Gabriel
Guns	2—76 mm Oto Melara. 2 MGs
A/S weapons	4 DC
Engines	4 Mayback diesels; 2 670 hp each; 2 screws
Speed, knots	32 knots
Range, miles	approx 1 500 at 30 knots
Complement	45

Built in Israel these steel-hulled boats carry Israeli-made missiles and electronics. The first was launched on 19 Feb 1973 for service in April 1973. Craft of this, *Reshef*, class were engaged successfully in the Arab-Israeli war Oct 1973. The new Gabriel missile, with a range of 22 miles, will presumably be mounted in these vessels.

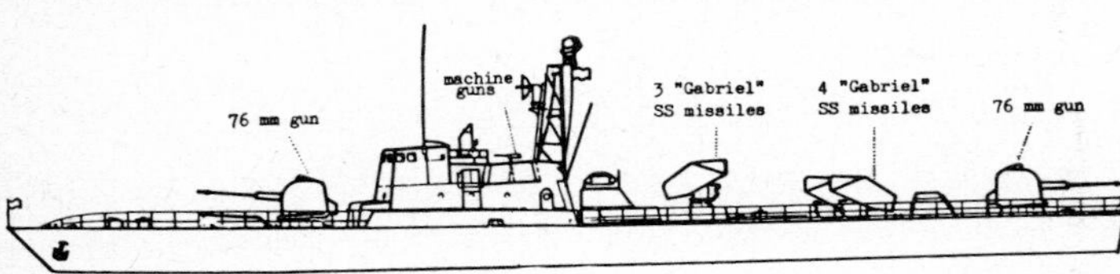

RESHEF *1973, Israeli Navy*

RESHEF *1973, Israeli Navy*

12 "SAAR" CLASS (FAST ATTACK CRAFT—MISSILE)

***ACCO**	***HAIFA**	**HETZ**	***MIZNAK**
***EILAT**	**HANIT**	***MISGAV**	**SAAR**
GAASH	**HEREV**	***MIVTACH**	**SOUFA**

*Group A

Displacement, tons	220 standard; 250 full load
Dimensions, feet	147·6 *oa* × 23·0 × 5·9 (8·2) max
Missile launchers	Gabriel surface to surface (see notes)
Guns, AA	40 mm or 76 mm (see notes)
Tubes	2 side launchers for 21 in torpedoes (surface or A/S)
Main engines	4 Maybach diesels; 13 500 bhp 4 shafts = 40+ knots
Oil fuel, tons	30
Range, miles	2 500 at 15 knots; 1 600 at 20 knots; 1 000 at 30 knots
Complement	35 to 40

Built by Ch de Normandie, Cherbourg, from designs by Lürssen Werft of Bremen. Political problems caused their building in France instead of Germany—a political embargo kept the last five in France until their journey to Israel began on Christmas Eve 1969. Two batches were built, the first six (Group A—*Acco, Eilat, Haifa, Misgav, Mivtach, Miznak*) being fitted originally with three 40 mm AA guns and ordered in 1965. The second six (*Gaash, Hanit, Herev, Hetz, Saar, Soufa*) were ordered in 1966 and fitted with 76 mm O.T.O. Melara AA guns. Five of these ships were delivered to Israel and two (*Acco* and *Saar*) made the journey on completion of local trials after the 1969 French arms embargo. The last five arrived off Haifa in January 1970 after a much-publicised passage which proved the remarkable endurance of this class.
The first batch was fitted for sonar but this was omitted from the 76 mm gun fitted group. Since their arrival in Israel provision of Gabriel surface to surface missiles has progressed. The first group can mount an armament varying from one 40 mm gun and eight Gabriel missiles (two single fixed mounts forward and two triple trainable mounts amidships) to three 40 mm guns and two twin 21 inch torpedo launchers. The second group can mount the two triple Gabriel launchers amidships as well as the 76 mm Oto Melara gun forward.
The Gabriel missile system is controlled by radar and optical sights and launches a low-altitude missile with a 150 lb HE head to a range of 12·5 miles in the first configuration and 22 miles in the later versions.

HANIT *1971, Israeli Navy*

3 "OPHIR" CLASS (FAST ATTACK CRAFT—TORPEDO)

OPHIR T 150 **SHVA** T 151 **TARSHISH** T 152

Displacement, tons	40
Dimensions, feet	70 × 17 × 5
Guns,	1—40 mm AA; 2—20 mm AA
Torpedoes	2—17·7 in
Main engines	High octane petrol engines; 4 000 bhp = 40 knots.

Motor torpedo Boats/Gunboats built for the Israeli Navy by Cantieri Baglieto, Varraze Italy, in 1956-57. In reserve.

SHVA *1964, Israeli Navy*

2 "YAR" CLASS (LARGE PATROL CRAFT)

YARDEN 42 **YARKON** 44

Displacement, tons	96 standard; 109 full load
Dimensions, feet	100 × 20 × 6
Guns,	2—20 mm AA
Main engines	Diesels; 2 shafts; speed 22 knots
Complement	16

Both built by Yacht & Bootswerft, Burmester Bremen-Burg Germany. *Yarkon* was launched on 25 July 1956 and *Yarden* in 1957.

YARDEN *Israeli Navy*

4 "KEDMA" CLASS (COASTAL PATROL CRAFT)

KEDMA 46 **NEGBA** 52 **YAMA** 48 **ZAFONA** 60

Displacement, tons	32
Dimensions, feet	67·0 × 15·0 × 4·8
Guns	2—20 mm
Main engines	2 diesels; 2 shafts; 1 540 bhp = 25 knots
Complement	10

Built in Japan during 1968. Handy boats of the small seaward defence type. Used for coastguard and police work in peace time.

KEDMA *1970, Israeli Navy*

Light Forces—*continued*

10 "DABUR" CLASS (COASTAL PATROL CRAFT)

Displacement, tons	35 full load
Dimensions, ft (*m*)	64·9 × 19 × 2·6 (*19·8 × 5·8 × 0·8*)
Guns	2 Twin ·5 MGs on bridge wings; 2—20 mm
A/S weapons	DC launchers
Main engines	2 geared diesels; 960 shp; 2 shafts = 25 knots
Complement	6

Built to the general design of the US "Swift" class but with 16·5 feet greater length and 4 ft greater beam. There are several variations in their armament. Deployed in the Mediterranean and Red Seas. Good rough weather performance.

DABUR *1972, Dr. Giorgio Arra*

12 "PBR" TYPE (COASTAL PATROL CRAFT)

Displacement, tons	7·5
Length, feet	30·2 oa
Guns	1—0·5 MG
Main engines	Diesels; speed = 24 knots
Complement	5

Joined the fleet in 1971.

PBR *Israeli Navy*

2 "HDML" TYPE (COASTAL PATROL CRAFT)

DROR 21 **TIRTSA** 25

Displacement, tons	46 standard; 54 full load
Dimensions, feet	72 oa × 16 × 5·5
Guns	2—20 mm AA
A/S	8 DC
Main engines	2 diesels; 2 shafts; 320 bhp = 12 knots
Complement	12

Former British harbour defence motor launches. Built in Great Britain in 1943. Used for coastguard and police work in peacetime.

FIREFISH MODEL III

Displacement, tons	6
Dimensions, feet	28 × 7·5
Main engines	2 Mercruiser V-8; 430 hp
Speed, knots	52 max
Range, miles	250 cruising; 150 max speed

Under construction by Sandaire, San Diego. Glass fibre craft, can carry five men. Capable of being radio-controlled for attack missions or minesweeping under ship or aircraft control.

FIREFISH Model III *1972, Courtesy Sandaire*

AMPHIBIOUS FORCES

BEIT SHAFEI (LCT)

Dimensions, feet	225·0 × 38·9 × 5·0
Capacity	16 tanks
Speed	12·5 knots

3 "ASH" CLASS (LCT)

ASHDOD 61 **ASHKELON** 63 **ACHZIV** 65

Displacement, tons	400 standard; 730 full load
Dimensions, feet	180·5 pp; 205·5 oa × 32·8 × 5·8
Guns	2—20 mm AA
Main engines	3 MWM diesels; 3 shafts; 1 900 bhp = 10·5 knots
Oil fuel, tons	37
Complement	20

These three landing craft were completed during 1966-67 by Israel Shipyards, Haifa.

ASHDOD *Israeli Navy*

3 "LC" TYPE (LCT)

ETZION GUEBER 51 **SHIKOMONA** 53 **LC 55**

Displacement, tons	182 standard; 230 full load
Dimensions, feet	120·0 × 23·2 × 4·7
Guns, AA	2—20 mm
Main engines	2 diesels; 2 shafts; 1 280 bhp = 10 knots
Complement	12

Built by Israeli shipyards, Haifa.

SHIKOMONA *Israeli Navy*

3 "LCM" TYPE

LCM

Displacement, tons	22 tons standard; 60 full load
Dimensions, feet	50 × 14 × 3·2
Main engines	2 diesels; 450 bhp = 11 knots

Former United States vessels of the LCM (Landing Craft Mechanised) type.

TRANSPORTS

1 "BAT SHEVA" TYPE

BAT SHEVA

Displacement, tons	900
Dimensions, feet	311·7 × 36·7 × 26·9
Guns	4—20 mm AA
Main engines	diesels; speed = 10 knots
Complement	26

BAT SHEVA *1971, Israeli Navy*

1 "BAT YAM" TYPE

BAT YAM

A small armed merchant ship used as a transport.

ITALY

Administration

Chief of Naval Staff:
Ammiraglio di Squadra G. De. Giorgi

Commander, Allied Naval Forces, Southern Europe (Naples):
Ammiraglio di Squadra Giuseppe Pighini

Commander-in-Chief of Fleet (and Comedcent):
Ammiraglio di Squadra L. Bucalossi

Director General Navy Personnel:
Ammiraglio di Squadra Mario Gambetta

Chief of Naval Staff:
Ammiraglio di Squadra Giuseppe Roselli Lorenzini

Diplomatic Representation

Naval Attaché in London:
Captain F. Mottolese

Naval Attaché in Washington:
Captain Mario Porta

Naval Attaché in Moscow:
Captain Ubaldo Garagnani

Naval Attaché in Paris:
Captain P. Della Croce di Dojola

Personnel

(a) 1974: 44 900 (including Naval Air Arm and an expanding Force of Marines)
(b) 2 years National Service

Strength of the Fleet

Type	*Active*	*Building*
Cruisers	3	—
Destroyers	9	—
Frigates	11	—
Corvettes	12	—
Submarines, Patrol	11	2
Hydrofoil—Missile	1	—
Fast Attack Craft—Torpedo	8	—
Fast Attack Craft (Convertible)	4	—
LST's	2	—
LCT's	2	—
Minesweepers—Ocean	4	—
Minesweepers—Coastal	36	—
Minesweepers—Inshore	20	—
Survey Vessels	(2)	1
Replenishment Tanker	1	—
Transports	2	—
Fleet Support Ship	1	—
Coastal Transports	10	—
Transports (LCM)	23	—
Transports (LCVP)	39	—
Sail Training Ships	4	—
Netlayers	2	—
Trials Ship	1	—
Lighthouse Tenders	4	—
Salvage Ship	1	—
Repair Craft	7	—
Water Carriers	23	—
Tugs—Large	37	—
Tugs—Small	42	—

Disposals

Cruiser
1972 *Giuseppe Garibaldi*

Destroyers
1971 *San Marco, Artigliere*

Corvettes
1970-72 12 *Ape* Class

Submarines
1972 *Pietro Calvi*
1973 *Leonardo da Vinci, Enrico Tazzoli*

Minesweepers (Coastal)
1966-67 17 ships of *Azalea* and *Anemone* classes

Naval Air Arm

3 LRMP Squadrons. Originally with S-2 Trackers. Re-equipping with 18 Breguet Atlantics (first delivered 27 June 1972).

Helicopters. 24 SH-3D, 30 AB-204B Bell 47, HU-16A.

Mercantile Marine

Lloyd's Register of Shipping:
1 726 vessels of 8 867 205 tons gross

CRUISERS

1 HELICOPTER CRUISER

Name	*No.*	*Builders*	*Laid down*	*Launched*	*Completed*
VITTORIO VENETO	C 550	Navalmeccanica Castellammare di Stabia	10 June 1965	5 Feb 1967	30 Apr 1969

Displacement, tons	7 500 standard; 8 850 full load
Length, feet (*metres*)	589 (*179·6*) oa
Beam, feet (*metres*)	63·6 (*19·4*)
Draught, feet (*metres*)	19·7 (*6*)
Aircraft	9 A/B 240B ASW helicopters
Missiles, AA	1 "Terrier"/"Asroc" twin launcher forward
Guns, AA	8—3 in (*76 mm*) 62 cal.
Torpedo tubes	2 triple for A/S torpedoes
Boilers	4 Foster-Wheeler; 711 psi (*50 kg/cm²*); 842°F (*450°C*)
Main engines	2 Tosi double reduction geared turbines; 73 000 shp; 2 shafts
Speed, knots	32 designed
Range, miles	6 000 at 20 knots
Oil fuel, tons	1 200
Complement	530 (60 officers, 470 men)

GENERAL
Developed from the "Doria" class but with much larger helicopter squadron and improved facilities for anti-submarine operations. Projected under the 1959-60 New Construction Programme, but her design was recast several times. She was commissioned for service on 12 July 1969. Flagship of C-in-C Fleet.

RADAR. SBS 48 3-dimensional air search and target designator on fore funnel SPS 29 long range search set on after funnel. One SMA/SPQ-2 combined search and navigation set-X band. 2 SPG-55A fire control groups forward for Terrier. 4 Orion fire-control sets for guns.

VITTORIO VENETO — *1973, Italian Navy*

VITTORIO VENETO — *1971, Commander Aldo Fraccaroli*

Cruisers—*continued*

DRAWING. Scale 125 feet = 1 inch (1 : 1 500)

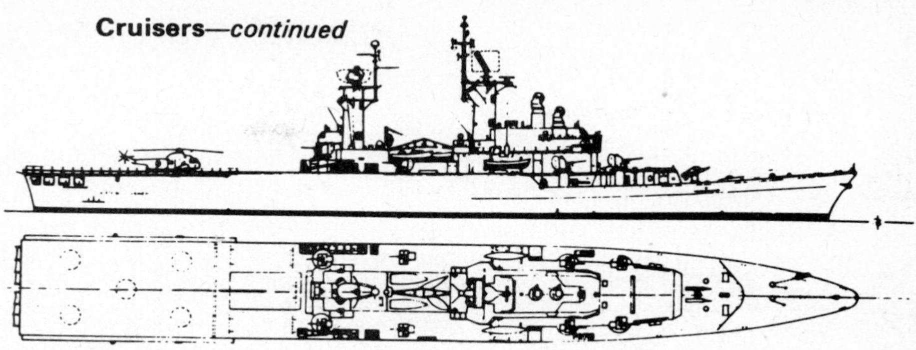

2 "ANDREA DORIA" CLASS

Name	*No.*	*Builders*	*Laid down*	*Launched*	*Completed*
ANDREA DORIA	553	Cantieri del Tirreno, Riva Trigoso	11 May 1958	27 Feb 1963	23 Feb 1964
CAIO DUILIO	554	Navalmeccanica Castellammare di Stabia	16 May 1958	22 Dec 1962	30 Nov 1964

Displacement, tons	5 000 standard; 6 500 full load
Length, feet (*metres*)	489·8 (*149·3*) oa
Beam, feet (*metres*)	56·4 (*17·2*)
Draught, feet (*metres*)	16·4 (*5·0*)
Aircraft	4 A/B 204B ASW helicopters
Missiles, AA	1 "Terrier" twin launcher forward
Guns, AA	8—3 in (*76 mm*) 62 cal.
Torpedo tubes	2 triple for 12 in (*305 mm*) A/S torpedoes
Main engines	2 double reduction geared turbines 60 000 shp; 2 shafts
Boilers	4 Foster-Wheeler; 711 psi (*50 kg/cm²*); 842°F (*450°C*)
Speed, knots	31 (*31·6* on trials)
Range, miles	6 000 at 20 knots
Oil fuel, tons	1 100
Complement	478 (53 offficers, 425 men)

Escort cruisers of novel design and generous beam with a good helicopter capacity in relation to their size. *Enrico Dandolo* was the name originally allocated to *Andrea Doria*.

GUNNERY. The anti-aircraft battery includes eight 3-inch fully automatic guns of a new pattern, disposed in single turrets, four on each side amidships abreast the funnels and the bridge.

HELICOPTER PLATFORM. Helicopters operate from a platform aft measuring 98·5 feet by 52·5 feet (*30* by *16 metres*). The Harrier, designed and built by Hawker Siddeley, demonstrated its capabilities of operating from shipborne platforms when it completed a two-day demonstration with a vertical landing on the comparatively small helicopter flight deck of the *Andrea Doria*.

ROLL DAMPING. Both ships have Gyrofin-Salmoiraghi stabilisers.

RADAR. SPS 39 three dimensional air surveillance and target designator on main mast. SPS-12 search set forward. Nav radar. Two SPG-55 control groups for Terrier. Four Orion fire control radars for guns. LSAG NA-9 gun fire control system. ECM and DF. Tacan beacon.

CAIO DUILIO *1972, Commander Aldo Fraccaroli*

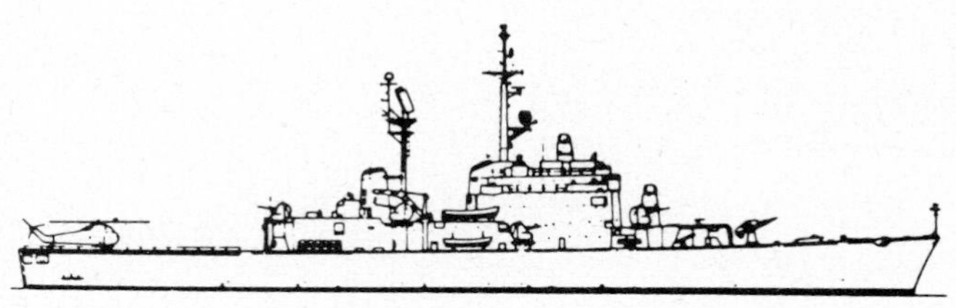

ANDREA DORIA, CAIO DUILIO

CAIO DUILIO *1971, Commander Aldo Fraccaroli*

DESTROYERS *(DDG)*

2 "AUDACE" CLASS (DDG)

Name	*No.*	*Builders*	*Laid Down*	*Launched*	*Completed*
ARDITO	D 550	Navalmeccanica Castellamare	19 July 1968	27 Nov 1971	Mar 1973
AUDACE	D 551	Cantieri del Tirreno, Riva Trigoso	27 April 1968	2 Oct 1971	16 Nov 1972

Displacement, tons	3 600 standard; 4 400 full load
Length, feet (*metres*)	446·4 (*136·6*)
Beam, feet (*metres*)	47·1 (*14·5*)
Draught, feet (*metres*)	15 (*4·6*)
Aircraft	2 A/S helicopters (AB204B)
Missile launchers	1 RIM-66A Standard
Guns, dual purpose	2—5 in (*127 mm*) 54 cal single
Guns, AA	4—3 in (*76 mm*) 62 cal
Torpedo tubes	6 A/S (two tripled) 4 fixed tubes
Main engines	2 geared turbines; 73 000 shp; 2 shafts
Boilers	4 Foster Wheeler type
Speed, knots	33
Complement	395

AUDACE *1973*

GENERAL
It was announced in Apr 1966 that two new guided missile destroyers would be built. They are basically similar to, but an improvement in design on that of the "Impavido" class.

AIRCRAFT. Originally planned to carry two AB 204 AS helicopters carrying two A/S torpedoes. These may be replaced by two Sea King SH3Ds.

ELECTRONICS. Fitted with SCLAR control and launch units for 105 mm rockets which can be fitted with chaff dispensers, flares or HE heads having a range of 7 miles.

RADAR. SPS-52 three dimensional air surveillance on after funnel; two SPG 51 tracking and missile guidance; three Orion RTN 10X for Argo NA 10 fire control system. SPS 12 nav radar Elsag NA 10 fire control system.

TORPEDO TUBES. The two triple Mk 32 launchers for Mk 44 torpedoes are on either beam amidships. The four fixed torpedo tubes (Canguro System) for A/S or anti ship torpedoes are built into the transom, a pair being fitted high on either quarter.

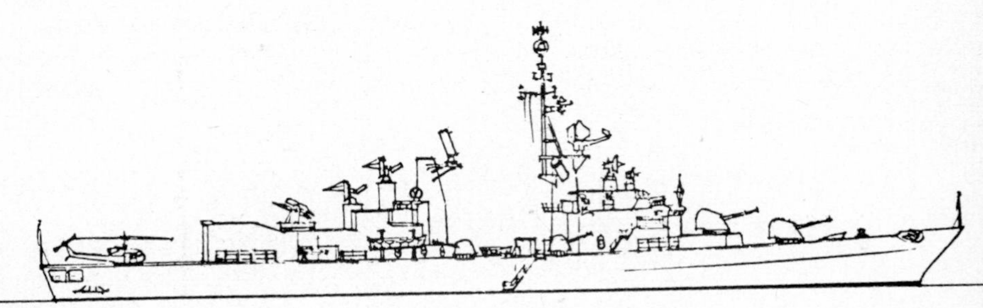

AUDACE *Class*

AUDACE *1972, Aviazione e Marina Genova*

FRIGATES

2 "ALPINO" CLASS

Name	No.	Builders	Laid down	Launched	Completed
ALPINO (ex-*Circe*)	F 580	Cantiere Navali del Tirreno, Riva Trigoso	27 Feb 1963	10 June 1967	14 Jan 1968
CARABINIERE (ex-*Climene*)	F 581	Cantiere Navali del Tirreno, Riva Trigoso	9 Jan 1965	30 Sep 1967	28 Apr 1968

Displacement, tons: 2 700 full load
Length, feet (*metres*): 349·0 (*106·4*) pp; 352·0 (*107·3*) wl; 371·7 (*113·3*) oa
Beam, feet (*metres*): 43·6 (*13·3*)
Draught, feet (*metres*): 12·7 (*3·9*)
Aircraft: 2 A/B 204B ASW helicopters
Guns: 6—3 in (*76 mm*) dp 62 cal single
A/S weapons: 1 single depth charge mortar
Tubes: 6 (2 triple) 12 in (*305 mm*) for A/S torpedoes
Main engines: 4 Tosi diesels = 16 800 hp; 2 Tosi Metrovick gas turbines = 15 000 hp; 2 shafts; 31 800 hp
Speed, knots: 22 (diesel), 29 (diesel and gas)
Range, miles: 4 200 at 18 knots
Oil fuel, tons: 275
Complement: 254 (21 officers, 233 men)

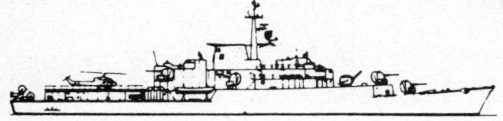

CARABINIERE — *1972, Italian Navy*

ALPINO CARABINIERE

Circe and *Climene* were provided for under the 1959-60 programme. The original "Circe" class project was modified in 1962, in respect of both machinery and armament. The originally allocated names *Circe* and *Climene* were changed to *Alpino* and *Carabiniere*, respectively in June 1965. The new design is an improved version of that of the "Centauro" class combined with that of the "Bergamini" class. They have similar basic characteristics but increased engine power.

RADAR. Search: SPS 12. SMA/SPQ-2 combined air/surface search/nav radar-X band. MM/SPR-A radar intercept. 3 Orion fire-control radars in ELSAG Argo "O" fire control system.

SONAR. Possibly SQS-4, SQS-30, SQS-36 with ELSAG fire control system DLB-1.

4 "BERGAMINI" CLASS

Name	No.	Builders	Laid down	Launched	Completed
CARLO BERGAMINI	F 593	San Marco, CRDA Trieste	19 May 1957	16 June 1960	23 June 1962
CARLO MARGOTTINI	F 595	Navalmeccanica, Castellammare	26 May 1957	12 June 1960	5 May 1962
LUIGI RIZZO	F 596	Navalmeccanica, Castellammare	26 May 1957	6 Mar 1957	15 Dec 1961
VIRGINIO FASAN	F 594	Navalmeccanica, Castellammare	6 Mar 1960	9 Oct 1960	10 Oct 1962

Displacement, tons: 1 650 full load
Length, feet (*mteres*): 311·7 (*95·0*) oa
Beam, feet (*metres*): 37·4 (*11·4*)
Draught, feet (*metres*): 10·5 (*3·2*)
Aircraft: 1 A/B-204B helicopter
Guns: 2—3 in (*76 mm*) dp 62 cal single
A/S weapons: 1 single depth charge mortar
Tubes: 6 (2 triple) 12 in (*305 mm*) for A/S torpedoes
Main engines: 4 diesels (Fiat in *Fasan* and *Margottini*, Tosi in others); 2 shafts; 15 000 bhp
Speed, knots: 24·5
Range, miles: 4 000 at 18 knots
Complement: 160

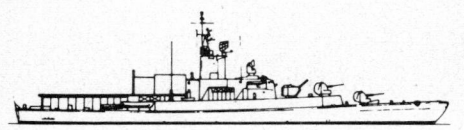

VIRGINIO FASAN (after conversion) — *1972, Dr. Giorgio Arra*

BERGAMINI *Class*

RADAR. Search: SPS 12. Fire Control: X Band. Single ARGO NA2 fire control system and radar. MM/SPR-A radar intercept. Nav-Surface warning.

MODIFICATION. The anti-submarine capability was augmented in *Carlo Margottini* in 1968, *Virginio Fasan* in 1969, *Carlo Bergamini* in 1970 and *Luigi Rizzo* in 1971 by the allocation of an AB-204 A/S helicopter for the operation of which the enlargement of the flight deck was necessary together with the removal of the 3-inch gun aft.

ANTI-SUBMARINE. The single-barrelled automatic depth charge mortars have a range of 1 000 yards. Rate of fire is 15 DC per minute. The 12-inch torpedoes have a life of six minutes at 30 knots. ELSAG DLB-1 fire control system.

ROLL DAMPING. Two Denny-Brown stabilisers reduce inclination in heavy seas from 20 to 5 degrees.

4 "CENTAURO" CLASS

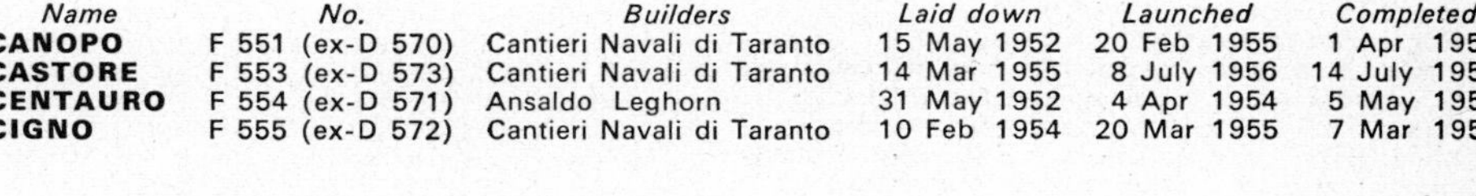

Name	No.	Builders	Laid down	Launched	Completed
CANOPO	F 551 (ex-D 570)	Cantieri Navali di Taranto	15 May 1952	20 Feb 1955	1 Apr 1958
CASTORE	F 553 (ex-D 573)	Cantieri Navali di Taranto	14 Mar 1955	8 July 1956	14 July 1957
CENTAURO	F 554 (ex-D 571)	Ansaldo Leghorn	31 May 1952	4 Apr 1954	5 May 1957
CIGNO	F 555 (ex-D 572)	Cantieri Navali di Taranto	10 Feb 1954	20 Mar 1955	7 Mar 1957

Displacement, tons: 1 807 standard; 2 250 full load
Length, feet (*metres*): 308·4 (*94*) pp; 338·4 (*103·1*) oa
Beam, feet (*metres*): 39·5 (*12*)
Draught, feet (*metres*): 12·6 (*3·8*)
Guns, AA: 3—3 in (*76 mm*) 62 cal single
A/S weapons: 1 three-barrelled depth charge mortar
Tubes: 6 (2 triple) 12 in (*305 mm*) for A/S torpedoes
Main engines: 2 double reduction geared turbines; 2 shafts; 22 000 shp
Speed, knots: 25
Boilers: 2 Foster Wheeler; 626 psi (*44 kg/cm²*) working pressure; 842°F (*450°C*) superheat temperature
Oil fuel, tons: 400
Range, miles: 3 660 at 20 knots
Complement: 255 (16 officers, 239 men)

CENTAURO *Class* as converted

CIGNO (CENTAURO *Class* original)

Frigates—*continued*

Cigno and *Castore* were built to Italian plans and specifications under the US off-shore programme.

CANOPO 1973, *Commander Aldo Fraccaroli*

RADAR. Search: SPS 6. Fire Control: X Band. SMA/SPQ-2 combined surface and air search-navigation—X band. MM/SPR-A intercept.

SONAR. SQS-11.

CONVERSION. Carried out as follows: *Castore*—1966-67, *Canopo*—1968-69, *Centauro*—1970-71, *Cigno*—1972-73. This provided the new 3 in (*76 mm*) armament.

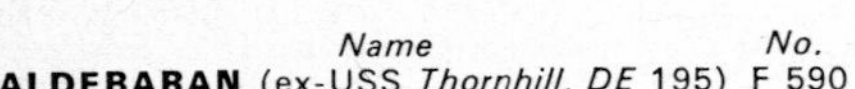

Name	*No.*	*Builders*	*Laid down*	*Launched*	*Completed*
ALDEBARAN (ex-USS *Thornhill, DE* 195)	F 590	Federal SB & DD Co. P. Newark	7 Oct 1943	30 Dec 1943	1 Feb 1944

Displacement, tons	1 900 full load
Length, feet (*metres*)	306 (*93·3*) oa
Beam, feet (*metres*)	36·7 (*11·2*)
Draught, feet (*metres*)	14 (*4·3*)
Guns, surface	3—3 in (*76 mm*) 50 cal.
Guns, AA	6—40 mm; 18—20 mm
A/S weapons	1 Hedgehog; 8 DCT; 2 DC racks
Main engines	GM diesel-electric; 2 shafts; 6 000 hp
Speed, knots	21 designed; 16·5 actual sea
Range, miles	11 500 at 11 knots
Oil fuel, tons	300
Complement	160

ALDEBARAN 1973, *Italian Navy*

Ex-US destroyer escort of the "Bostwick" class. Transferred on 10 Jan 1951. In 1956 a pentapod foremast was stepped in place of the former polemast.

RADAR. Search: SPS 6. Fire Control: X Band.

CORVETTES

4 "DE CRISTOFARO" CLASS

Name	*No.*	*Builders*	*Laid down*	*Launched*	*Completed*
LICIO VISINTINI	F 546	CRDA Monfalcone	30 Sep 1963	30 May 1965	25 Aug 1966
PIETRO DE CRISTOFARO	F 540	Cantiere Navali de Tirreho, Riva Tregoso	30 Apr 1963	29 May 1965	19 Dec 1965
SALVATORE TODARO	F 550	Cantiere Ansaldo, Leghorn	21 Oct 1962	24 Oct 1964	25 Apr 1966
UMBERTO GROSSO	F 541	Cantiere Ansaldo, Leghorn	21 Oct 1962	12 Dec 1964	25 Apr 1966

Displacement, tons	850 standard; 1 020 full load
Length, feet (*metres*)	246 (*75·0*) pp; 263·2 (*80·2*) oa
Beam, feet (*metres*)	33·7 (*10·3*)
Draught, feet (*metres*)	9 (*2·7*)
Guns, dual purpose	2—3 in (*76 mm*), 62 cal, single
A/S weapons	1 single-barrelled DC mortar
Tubes	2 triple for A/S torpedoes
Main engines	2 diesels = 8 400 bhp; 2 sha/ts
Speed, knots	23·5 max; 21·5 sustained sea
Range, miles	4 000 at 18 knots
Oil fuel, tons	100
Complement	131 (8 officers, 123 men)

The design is an improved version of the "Albatros" class.

LICIO VISINTINI 1972, *Italian Navy*

RADAR. Air and surface surveillance radar with antenna mounted at top of foremast. Gunfire control system has director mounted aft, above compass platform, with X band tracker radar.

SONAR. SQS-36. ELSAG DLB-1 fire control system.

DE CRISTOFARO *Class*

Corvettes—*continued*

3 "APE" CLASS

BOMBARDA F 549 **SFINGE** F 579
GABBIANO F 571

Displacement, tons	670 standard; 771 full load
Length, feet (*metres*)	192.8 (*58·8*) wl; 212·6 (*64·8*) oa
Beam, feet (*metres*)	28·5 (*8·7*)
Draught, feet (*metres*)	8·9 (*2·7*)
Guns, AA	4—40 mm 56 cal in *Chimera* and *Sfinge*; 2—40 mm 56 cal and 2—20 mm 70 cal in *Bombarda*
A/S weapons	1 Hedgehog Mk 10
Main engines	2 Fiat diesels; 2 shafts; 3 500 bhp
Speed, knots	15
Range, miles	2 450 at 15 knots
Oil fuel, tons	64
Complement	100 to 108

Completed in 1942 (*Gabbiano*), 1943 (*Sfinge*), 1951 (*Bombarda*). Originally fitted for minesweeping. Modified with navigating bridge. *Ape* is now support ship (*nave appoggio*) for frogmen and commandos.

CHIMERA *1972, Dr Giorgio Arra*

RADAR. Search: SPS 6 in *Sfinge* (see photograph in the 1968-69 to 1971-72 editions).

VEDETTA (ex-*Belay Deress*, ex-USS *PC* 1616) F 597

Displacement, tons	325 standard; 450 full load
Dimensions, feet	170 pp; 174 oa × 23 × 10
Guns	2—40 mm 56 cal Bofors AA; 2—20 mm AA
Main engines	4 diesels; 2 shafts; 3 240 bhp = 19 knots
A/S weapons	1 Hedgehog; 4 DCT; 2 DC racks
Range, miles	3 000 at 12 knots
Complement	60

She was sold to Italy, being transferred on 3 Feb 1959. Air-conditioning equipment is installed Refitted in La Spezia Navy Yard in 1959. Employed as a Fishery Protection Vessel.

VEDETTA *1969, Italian Navy*

SUBMARINES

2 "SAURO" CLASS

Displacement, tons	1 300 surface; 1 450 dived
Length, feet (*metres*)	210 (*64*)
Beam, feet (*metres*)	22·5 (*6·8*)
Draught, feet (*metres*)	15 (*4·5*)
Torpedo tubes	6—21 in (bow)
Main machinery	2 Diesels; 2 electric motors; 1 shaft
Speed, knots	11 surfaced; 19 dived
Complement	45

Two of this class were originally ordered in 1967 but were cancelled in the following year. Reinstated in the building programme in 1972. To be fitted with Selenia passive and active Sonars, search/navigation radar and ECM.

4 "TOTI" CLASS

Name	*No.*	*Builders*	*Laid down*	*Launched*	*Completed*
ATTILIO BAGNOLINI	S 505	CRDA Monfalcone	15 Apr 1965	26 Aug 1967	16 June 1968
ENRICO DANDOLO	S 513	CRDA Monfalcone	10 Mar 1967	16 Dec 1967	25 Sep 1968
LAZZARO MOCENIGO	S 514	CRDA Monfalcone	12 June 1967	20 Apr 1968	11 Jan 1969
ENRICO TOTI	S 506	CRDA Monfalcone	15 Apr 1965	12 Mar 1967	22 Jan 1968

Displacement, tons	460 standard; 524 surface; 582 submerged
Length, feet (*metres*)	151·5 (*46·2*)
Beam, feet (*metres*)	15·4 (*4·7*)
Draught, feet (*metres*)	13·1 (*4·0*)
Torpedo tubes	4—21 in
Main machinery	2 Fiat MB 820 N/I diesels, 1 electric motor, Diesel-electric drive; 2 200 hp; 1 shaft
Speed, knots	14 on surface; 15 dived
Range, miles	3 000 at 5 knots (surfaced)
Complement	24

Italy's first indigenously-built submarines since the Second World War. The design was recast several times, being finalised as coastal submarines of the hunter-killer type.

ELECTRONICS. WT, HF, UHF and VLF equipment. Computer based fire control.

RADAR. Search/nav set. IFF, ECM.

TOTI with new hydroplanes *1972, Dr Giorgio Arra*

SONAR. Passive set in stem. Active set in bow dome. Passive range finding. Ray path analyzer.

3 Ex-US "BALAO" CLASS

Name	*No.*	*Builders*	*Launched*	*Completed*	*Transferred*
ALFREDO CAPPELLINI (ex-USS *Capitaine, SS* 336)	S 507	Electric Boat Div, General Dynamics Corpn	1 Oct 1944	26 Jan 1945	5 Mar 1966
EVANGELISTA TORRICELLI (ex-USS *Lizardfish, SS* 373)	S 512	Manitowoc SB Co, Manitowoc, Wisconsin	16 July 1944	30 Dec 1944	9 Jan 1960
FRANCESCO MOROSINI (ex-USS *Besugo, SS* 321)	S 508	Electric Boat Div, General Dynamics Corpn	27 Feb 1944	19 June 1944	31 Mar 1966

Displacement, tons	1 600 standard; 1 855 surface; 2 455 submerged
Length, feet (*metres*)	311·5 (*95·0*)
Beam, feet (*metres*)	27 (*8·2*)
Draught, feet (*metres*)	17 (*5·2*)
Torpedo tubes	10—21 in (*533 mm*) 6 bow and 4 stern
Main engines	4 GM 16/278 diesels, 6 000 hp; 4 electric motors; 2 750 hp
Speed, knots	18 on surface; 10 submerged
Range, miles	14 000 at 10 knots
Oil fuel, (tons)	300
Complement	85

Lizardfish was originally to have been renamed *Luigi Torelli*.

FRANCESCO MOROSINI *1971, Commander Aldo Fraccaroli*

Submarines—*continued*

2 Ex-US GUPPY III TYPE

Name	*Builders*	*Laid down*	*Launched*	*Completed*	*Transferred*
GIANFRANCO GAZZANA PRIAROGGIA (ex-USS *Volador* SS 490)	Portsmouth Navy Yard	15 June 1945	17 Jan 1946	10 Jan 1948	18 Aug 1972
PRIMO LONGOBARDO (ex-USS *Pickerel* SS 524)	Boston Navy Yard	8 Feb 1944	15 Dec 1944	4 Apr 1949	18 Aug 1972

Displacement, tons	1 975 standard; 2 450 dived
Length, feet (*metres*)	326·5 (*99·4*) oa
Beam, feet (*metres*)	27 (*8·2*)
Draught, feet (*metres*)	17 (*5·2*)
Torpedo tubes	10—21 in; 6 bow, 4 stern
Main engines	4 diesels; 6 400 bhp—2 electric motors; 5 400 shp; 2 shafts
Speed, knots	20 surface; 15 dived
Range, miles	12 000 at 10 knots (surfaced)
Oil fuel, tons	300
Complement	85

Arrived in Taranto 19 Oct 1972.

GIANFRANCO GAZZANIA PRIAROGGIA — *1973, Italian Navy*

2 Ex-US "TANG" CLASS

	Builder	*Laid down*	*Launched*	*Completed*	*Transferred*
ROMEO ROMEI (ex-USS *Trigger* SS 564)	Electric Boat Co. Groton	24 Feb 1949	14 June 1951	31 Mar 1952	10 July 1973
LIVIO PIOMARTA					

Displacement, tons	2 100 surface; 2 700 dived
Length, feet (*metres*)	287 (*87·4*)
Beam, feet (*metres*)	27·3 (*8·3*)
Draught, feet (*metres*)	19 (*6·2*)
Torpedo tubes	8—21 in, 6 bow, 2 stern
Main machinery	3 Diesels 4 500 shp; 2 electric motors 5 600 hp
Speed, knots	20 surface; 18 dived
Complement	83 (8 officers, 75 men)

LIGHT FORCES

1 "P-420 SWORDFISH" (HYDROFOIL—MISSILE)

Displacement, tons	62·5
Dimensions, feet	75 × 36·5 × 14·4 (length and beam foils extended, draught hullborne)
Missile launchers	2 fixed for "Otomat" ship-to-ship missiles
Guns	1 Oto Melara 76 mm automatic anti-aircraft
Main engines	Rolls Royce "Proteus" gas turbine driving waterjet pump; 4 500 bhp; diesel and retractable propeller unit for hullborne propulsion
Range, miles	400 at 45 knots; 1 200 at 8 knots
Speed, knots	50 max, 42 cruising (sea state 4)
Complement	10

Completed for trials 9 May 1973 by Oto Melara, La Spezia. Missiles made by Oto Melara Matra. Fitted with Elsag NA-10 Mod 1 fire control system with Orion RTN-10X radar.

SWORDFISH — *1973, Italian Navy*

2 "FRECCIA" CLASS (FAST ATTACK CRAFT—CONVERTIBLE)

FRECCIA (ex-*MC* 590) P 493 — **SAETTA** (ex-*MC* 591) P 494

Displacement, tons	188 standard; 205 full load
Dimensions, feet	150 × 23·8 × 5·5
Guns	*As Gunboat*: 3—40 mm, 70 cal or 2—40 mm, 70 cal *As Fast Minelayer*: 1—40 mm AA with 8 mines *As Torpedo Boat*: 1—40 mm, 70 cal
Tubes	*As Torpedo Boat*: 2—21 in
Main engines	2 diesels; 7 600 bhp; 1 Bristol Siddeley Proteus gas turbine. 4 250 shp; Total hp 11 850 = 40 knots
Complement	36

Freccia was laid down by Cantiere del Tirreno, Riva Trigoso on 30 Apr 1963, launched on 9 Jan 1965 and commissioned on 6 July 1965. *Saetta* was laid down by CRDA, Monfalcone on 11 June 1963, launched on 11 Apr 1965, and completed in 1966. Special convertible version designed to carry mines or depth charges. Can be converted in 24 hours to gunboat, torpedo boat, fast minelayer, or missile boat. Fitted with S band navigation and tactical radar employing a slotted waveguide antenna. The gunfire control system has a director with X band tracker radar. *Saetta* has been armed with Sea Killer Mk I system with 5 round trainable launcher. Contraves fire control including target-tracking radar with TV camera mounted on top. It is planned to fit *Freccia* with Otomat, Selina radar, and Ecograph sonar.

SAETTA experimentally armed with 5 short range missiles — *1970*

FRECCIA — *1972, Dr. Giorgio Arra*

2 "LAMPO" CLASS (FAST ATTACK CRAFT—CONVERTIBLE)

BALENO (ex-*MC* 492) P 492 — **LAMPO** (ex-*MC* 491) P 491

Displacement, tons	170 standard; 196 full load
Dimensions, feet	131·5 × 21 × 5
Guns	*As Gunboat*: 3—40 mm, 70 cal or 2—40 mm, 70 cal *As Fast Minelayer*: 1—40 mm, 70 cal
Tubes	*As Torpedo Boat*: 2—21 in
Main engines	2 Fiat diesels, 1 Metrovick gas turbine; 3 shafts; total 11 700 hp = 39 knots.
Complement	36

Light Forces—*continued*

Convertible gunboats, improved versions of the *Folgore* prototype. Both built by Arsenale MM Taranto. *Lampo* was laid down on 4 Jan 1958, launched on 22 Nov 1960 and commissioned in July 1963. *Baleno* was laid-down on the same slip on 22 Nov 1960, launched on 10 May 1964 and commissioned on 16 July 1965. She has been converted to an improved design.

LAMPO with modified funnel *1972, Dr. Giorgio Arra*

BALENO *1972, Dr. Giorgio Arra*

FOLGORE (ex-*MC* 490) P 490 (FAST ATTACK CRAFT—TORPEDO)

Displacement, tons	160 standard; 190 full load
Dimensions, feet	129·5 × 19·7 × 5
Guns	2—40 mm AA
Tubes	2—21 in
Main engines	4 diesels; 4 shafts; 10 000 bhp = 38 knots (accelerating from 20 knots to full speed very rapidly)
Complement	38

Authorised in Nov 1950, launched on 21 Jan 1954 from CRDA Monfalcone Yard, and commissioned on 21 July 1955. Two rudders.

FOLGORE *1972, Dr. Giorgio Arra*

MS 441 (ex-841) **MS 443** (ex-843) **MS 453** (ex-853)

(FAST ATTACK CRAFT—TORPEDO)

Displacement tons	64 full load
Dimensions, feet	78 × 20 × 6
Guns	1—40 mm, 56 cal; 2 or 3—20 mm, 70 cal
Torpedoes	2—17·7 in (no tubes)
Main engines	3 petrol motors; 3 shafts; 4 500 bhp = 34 knots
Range, miles	1 000 at 20 knots
Complement	28

Light Forces—*continued*

MS 453 *1969, Italian Navy*

MS 441 converted into a fast transport for commandos & frogmen. Former US PT boats of Higgins type. Refitted in Italy in 1949-53. New radar installed. MS 442 (ex-842). MS 451 (ex-851) and MS 452 (ex-852) transferred to Customs in 1966

MS 472 (ex-612) **MS 473** (ex-813) **MS 474** (ex-614) **MS 481** (ex-615)

(FAST ATTACK CRAFT—TORPEDO)

Displacement, tons	72 full load
Dimensions, feet	92 × 15 × 5
Guns	1 or 2—40 mm, 56 cal
Torpedoes	2—17·7 in
Main engines	Petrol motors; 3 shafts; 3 450 bhp = 27 knots
Range, miles	600 at 16 knots
Complement	20

Built in 1942-43 at CRDA Monfalcone yard; converted as MV (motovedette) with no tubes under the Peace Treaty. Reconverted in 1951-53. MS 472 and MS 473 were refitted as convertible boats in 1960 and MS 474 and MS 481 in 1961.

MS 481 *1971, Dr. Giorgio Arra*

The British MTBs *Dark Avenger*, *Dark Biter*, *Dark Hunter* and *Dark Invader* were taken over in 1967 for the Guardia di Finanza (Customs House Guard).

5 "ALANO" CLASS

(Ex-US LANDING SHIPS, SUPPORT/LARGE)

BRACCO (ex-*LSSL* 38) **MASTINO** (ex-*LSSL* 62) **MOLOSSO** (ex-*LSSL* 63) **SEGUGIO** (ex-*LSSL* 64) **SPINONE** (ex-*LSSL* 118)

Displacement, tons	246 standard; 430 full load
Dimensions, feet	153 wl; 158·5 oa × 32·7 × 5·7
Guns	5—40 mm 56 cal; 4—20 mm, 70 cal.; 4—12·7 mm
Main engines	8 Gray Marine diesels; 2 shafts; 1 800 bhp = 12 knots
Oil fuel, tons	87
Range, miles	4 660 at 10 knots

Transferred from the USN on 25 July 1951, under the Mutual Defense Assistance Program.

MOLOSSO *1970, Italian Navy*

AMPHIBIOUS FORCES

2 Ex-US "COUNTY" CLASS (LST's)

GRADO L 9890 (ex-USS *De Soto County*, LST 1171)
CAORLE L 9891 (ex-USS *York County*, LST 1175)

Displacement, tons	4 164 light; 8 000 full load
Dimensions, ft (*m*)	444 × 62 × 16·5 (*133·4 × 18·9 × 5*)
Guns	6—3 inch (*76 mm*)
Main engines	Diesels; 1 440 shp; 2 shafts; (CP propellers) = 17·5 knots
Complement	184 (10 officers, 174 men)
Troops	Approx 575

Both completed 1957 and transferred 17 July 1972.

CAORLE *1972, Commander Aldo Fraccaroli*

Amphibious Forces—*continued*

1 Ex-US "COUNTY" CLASS (LCT)

ANTEO (ex-USS *Alameda County*, AVB 1, ex-*LST* 32) A 5306

Displacement, tons	1 625 light; 2 366 beaching; 4 080 full load
Dimensions, feet	316 wl; 328 oa × 50 × 14 max
Guns	7—40 mm AA; 2—20 mm AA
Main engines	GM diesels; 2 shafts; 1 700 bhp = 11·6 knots max
Range, miles	15 900 at 9 knots

Former US tank landing ship. Built by Dravo Corp. Neville Island, Pa. Laid down on 17 Feb 1943. Launched on 23 May 1943. Completed on 12 July 1943. Reclassified from LST 32 to AVB 1 (Advanced Aviation Base ship) on 28 Sep 1957 Transferred to the Italian Navy in Nov 1962 as a transport.

ANTEO — *1972, Dr. Giorgio Arra*

QUARTO L 9881 (LCT)

Displacement, tons	764 standard; 980 full load
Dimensions, feet	226·4 × 31·3 × 6
Guns	4—40 mm AA (2 twin)
Main engines	3 diesels; 2 300 bhp = 13 knots
Range, miles	1 300 at 13 knots

Quarto was laid down on 19 Mar 1966 at Taranto Naval Shipyard and launched on 18 Mar 1967. The design is intermediate between that of LSM and LCT.

QUARTO — *1972, Commander Aldo Fraccaroli*

MINE WARFARE FORCES

4 "SALMONE" CLASS (Ex-US MSO TYPE)

(MINESWEEPERS—OCEAN)

SALMONE (ex-*MSO* 507) M 5430
SGOMBRO (ex-*MSO* 517) M 5432
SQUALO (ex-*MSO* 518) M 5433
STORIONE (ex-*MSO* 506) M 5431

Displacement, tons	665 standard; 750 full load
Dimensions, feet	165 wl; 173 oa × 35 × 13·6 (*52·7 × 10·7 × 4*)
Guns	1—40 mm 56 cal AA
Main engines	2 diesels; 2 shafts; 1 600 bhp = 14 knots
Oil fuel, tons	46
Range, miles	3 000 at 10 knots

Former US "Agile" class. Wooden hulls and non-magnetic diesels of stainless steel alloy. Controllable pitch propellers. *Storione*, launched on 13 Nov 1954, was built by Martinolich SB Company, San Diego, and transferred on 23 Feb, 1956. *Salmone*, launched on 19 Feb 1955 was built by Martinolich SB Co, and transferred at San Diego, on 17 June 1956. *Sgombro* and *Squalo* were delivered in June 1957.

SGOMBRO — *1972, Commander Aldo Fraccaroli*

17 "ABETE" CLASS (MINESWEEPERS—COASTAL)

ABETE	M 5501	**FAGGIO**	M 5507	**OLMO**	M 5512
ACACIA	M 5502	**FRASSINO**	M 5508	**ONTANO**	M 5513
BETULLA	M 5503	**GELSO**	M 5509	**PINO**	M 5514
CASTAGNO	M 5504	**LARICE**	M 5510	**PIOPPO**	M 5515
CEDRO	M 5505	**NOCE**	M 5511	**PLATANO**	M 5516
CILIEGIO	M 5506			**QUERCIA**	M 5517

Displacement, tons	378 standard; 405 full load (*Mandorlo* 360)
Dimensions, feet	138 pp; 144 oa × 26·5 × 8·5
Guns	2—20 mm, 70 cal AA
Main engines	2 diesels; 2 shafts; 1 200 bhp = 13·5 knots
Oil fuel (tons)	25
Range, miles	2 500 at 10 knots

Wooden hulled *Dragomine Costieri* constructed throughout of anti-magnetic materials All transferred by the US in 1953-54. *Pioppo* used for surveying.

ONTANO — *1972, Dr. Giorgio Arra*

19 "AGAVE" CLASS (MINESWEEPERS—COASTAL)

AGAVE	M 5531	**GLICINE**	M 5537	**BAMBÙ**	*M 5521
ALLORO	M 5532	**LOTO**	M 5538	**EBANO**	*M 5522
EDERA	M 5533	**MIRTO**	M 5539	**MANGO**	*M 5523
GAGGIA	M 5534	**TIMO**	M 5540	**MOGANO**	*M 5524
GELSOMINO	M 5535	**TRIFOGLIO**	M 5541	**PALMA**	*M 5526
GIAGGIOLO	M 5536	**VISCHIO**	M 5542	**ROVERE**	*M 5526
				SANDALO	*M 5527

Displacement, tons	375 standard; 405 full load
Dimensions, ft (*m*)	144 oa × 25·6 × 8·5 (*43 × 8 × 2·6*)
Guns	2—20 mm 70 cal AA
Main engines	2 diesels; 2 shafts; 1 200 bhp = 13·5 knots
Oil fuel (tons)	25
Range, miles	2 500 at 10 knots
Complement	38

Non-magnetic minesweepers of composite wooden and alloy construction similar to those transferred from the US but built in Italian yards. *Last 7 were built by CRDA, Monfalcone, and launched in 1956. *Mirto* used for surveying.

TRIFOGLIO — *1972 Dr. Giorgio Arra*

Minewarfare Forces—*continued*

20 "ARAGOSTA" CLASS (MINESWEEPERS—INSHORE)

ARAGOSTA	M 5450	**GAMBERO**	M 5457	**POLIPO**	M 5463
ARSELLA	M 5451	**GRANCHIO**	M 5458	**PORPORA**	M 5464
ASTICE	M 5452	**MITILO**	M 5459	**RICCIO**	M 5465
ATTINIA	M 5453	**OSTRICA**	M 5460	**SCAMPO**	M 5466
CALAMARO	M 5454	**PAGURO**	M 5461	**SEPPIA**	M 5467
CONCHIGLIA	M 5455	**PINNA**	M 5462	**TELLINA**	M 5468
DROMIA	M 5456			**TOTANO**	M 5469

Displacement, tons	188 full load
Dimensions, ft (*m*)	106 × 21 × 6 (*32·5 × 6·4 × 1·8*)
Main engines	2 diesels; 1 000 bhp = 14 knots
Oil fuel (tons)	15
Range, miles	2 000 at 9 knots
Complement	14

Similar to the British "Ham" class. All constructed in Italian yards to the order of NATO in 1955-57. All names of small sea creatures. Designed armament of one 20 mm gun not mounted.

POLIPO *1971, Italian Navy*

SURVEY VESSEL

AMMIRAGLIO MANAGHI

Displacement, tons 1 582 full load

Building under the 1972 new construction programme. NOTE. In addition *Pioppo* and *Mirto* minesweepers are used for surveying.

SERVICE FORCES

1 Ex-US "T2" TYPE (REPLENISHMENT TANKER)

STEROPE (ex-*Enrico Insom*) A 5368

Displacement, tons	5 350 light; 21 800 full load
Dimensions, ft (*m*)	523·5 oa × 68 × 30·8 (*159·5 × 20·7 × 9*)
Main engines	Turbo-electric; 6 000 shp = 15 knots
Boilers	2 Babcock & Wilcox

Former United States built oiler of the T 2 type acquired by the Italian Navy in 1959 and refitted at La Spezia Navy Yard in April 1959.

STEROPE *1972, Dr. Giorgio Arra*

1 AV TYPE (TRANSPORT)

ANDREA BAFILE (ex-USS *St. George*, AV 16, ex-A 5314) L 9871

Displacement, tons	8 510 standard; 14 000 full load
Dimensions, ft (*m*)	492 oa × 69·5 × 26 max (*163 × 23 × 8·5*)
Aircraft	1 or 2 helicopters
Guns	2—5 in 38 cal
Main engines	Allis-Chalmers geared turbines; 1 shaft; 8 500 shp = 17 knots
Boilers	2 Foster-Wheeler
Range, miles	13 400 at 13 knots

Former USN seaplane carrier, launched on 14 Feb 1944. Purchased and commissioned in the Italian Navy on 17 May 1969 and modified. Troop transport and command ship. Serves as a depot ship for "Special Forces" (frogmen etc.).

ANDREA BAFILE *1971, Commander Aldo Fraccaroli*

1 AVP TYPE

PIETRO CAVEZZALE (ex-USS *Oyster Bay*, *AVP* 28, ex-*AGP* 6) A 5301

Displacement, tons	1 766 standard; 2 800 full load
Dimensions, ft (*m*)	300 wl; 311·8 oa × 41 × 13·5 max (*95 × 12·5 × 3·7*)
Guns	1—76 mm; 2—40 mm, 56 cal AA
Main engines	2 sets diesels; 2 shafts; 6 080 bhp = 16 knots
Oil fuel (tons)	400
Range, miles	10 000 at 11 knots
Complement	200

Former United States seaplane tender (previously motor torpedo boat tender) of the "Barnegat" class, built at Lake Washington Shipyard and launched on 7 Sep 1942. Transferred to the Italian Navy on 23 Oct 1957 and renamed.

PIETRO CAVEZZALE *1971, Commander Aldo Fraccaroli*

10 Ex-GERMAN MFP TYPE (COASTAL TRANSPORTS)

MTC 1001	**MTC 1005**	**MTC 1007**	**MTC 1009**	**MTC 1101**
MTC 1004	**MTC 1006**	**MTC 1008**	**MTC 1010**	**MTC 1102**

Displacement, tons	240 standard
Dimensions, feet	164 × 21·3 × 5·7
Guns	2 or 3—20 or 37 mm
Main engines	2 or 3 diesels; 500 bhp = 10 knots

Moto-Trasporti Costieri, MTC 1001 to 1010 are Italian MZ (*Motozattere*). MTC 1102 and 1103 are ex-German built in Italy. MTC 1002 was removed from the effective list in 1964, MTC 1101 and MTC 1104 in 1970, and MTC 1103 in 1971.

MTC 1010 *1971, Dr. Giorgio Arra*

Service Forces—*continued*

23 Ex-US LCM TYPE

MTM 9901	**MTM 9905**	**MTM 9911**	**MTM 9916**	**MTM 9921**
MTM 9902	**MTM 9906**	**MTM 9912**	**MTM 9917**	**MTM 9922**
MTM 9903	**MTM 9908**	**MTM 9913**	**MTM 9918**	**MTM 9923**
MTM 9904	**MTM 9909**	**MTM 9914**	**MTM 9919**	**MTM 9924**
		MTM 9915	**MTM 9920**	**MTM 9925**

Displacement, tons	20 standard
Dimensions, feet	49·5 × 14·8 × 4·2
Guns	2—20 mm AA
Main engines	diesels; speed 10 knots

Rated as *Moto-Trasporti Medi*. Former US landing craft of the LCM type. MTM 9907 was removed from the effective list in 1967, and MTM 9910 in 1971.

39 Ex-US LCVP TYPE

MTP 9701	**MTP 9709**	**MTP 9717**	**MTP 9726**	**MTP 9734**
MTP 9702	**MYP 9710**	**MTP 9718**	**MTP 9727**	**MTP 9735**
MTP 9703	**MTP 9711**	**MTP 9719**	**MTP 9728**	**MTP 9736**
MTP 9704	**MTP 9712**	**MTP 9720**	**MTP 9729**	**MTP 9737**
MTP 9705	**MTP 9713**	**MTP 9721**	**MTE 9730**	**MTP 9738**
MTP 9706	**MTP 9714**	**MTP 9722**	**MTP 9731**	**MTP 9739**
MTP 9707	**MTP 9715**	**MTP 9723**	**MTP 9732**	**MTP 9740**
MTP 9708		**MTP 9724**	**MTP 9733**	**MTP 9741**

Displacement, tons	8 to 10 standard
Dimensions, feet	36·5 × 10·8 × 3
Guns	2 MG
Main engines	Diesels; Speed: 10 knots

Rated as *Moto-Trasporti Piccoli*. MTP 9701 to 9724 are former US landing craft of the LCVP type. MTP 9726 of 10 tons displacement and similar characteristics is of Italian construction. MTP 9725 was officially removed from the effective list in 1963, and MTP 9716 in 1971.

1 AKA TYPE (TRANSPORT)

ETNA (ex-USS *Whitley, AKA* 91, ex-A 5328) L 9870

Displacement, tons	7 430 light; 14 200 full load
Measurement, tons	5 145 gross; 7 700 deadweight
Dimensions, ft (*m*)	435·0 wl; 459·2 oa × 63·0 × 26·3 max (*140* × *19·2* × *7·8*)
Guns	4—40 mm
Main engines	GE geared turbines; 1 shaft; 6 000 shp = 15 knots
Boilers	2 Combustion Engineering
Range, miles	18 900 at 12 knots

Former US Navy attack cargo ship of the "Andromeda" class. Built by Moore DD Co, Oakland, California. Launched on 22 June 1944. Completed on 21 Sep 1944. C2—S—B 1 type. Transferred to Italy in Feb 1962.

ETNA *1970, Italian Navy*

Name	*No.*	*Builders*	*Laid down*	*Launched*	*Completed*
AVIERE (ex-USS *Nicholson, DD* 442)	D 554	Boston Navy Yard	1 Nov 1939	31 May 1940	3 June 1941

Displacement, tons	1 700 standard; 2 580 full load
Length, feet (*metres*)	341 (*103·9*) wl; 348·3 (*106·1*) oa
Beam, feet (*metres*)	36·0 (*11·0*)
Draught, feet (*metres*)	11·5 (*3·5*)
Guns	1—5 in (*127 mm*) 2—3 in (76 *mm*) Oto Melara
A/S weapons	4 DC throwers; 2 DC racks
Main engines	GE geared turbines; 2 shafts; 50 000 shp
Boilers	4 Babcock & Wilcox
Speed, knots	30
Oil fuel, tons	600
Range, miles	6 000 at 12 knots
Complement	240

Former US "Gleaves" class destroyer. Transferred from USA and commissioned on 25 May 1951. Officially turned over to Italy on 11 June 1951. The 5—21 in torpedo tubes were removed.

GUNNERY. In 1970 she was fitted with Oto Melara 127/54 (5-inch) gun mounting in "B" position and new Oto Melara 76/62 (3-inch) gun mounting in "X" position.

AVIERE *1972, Italian Navy*

RADAR. Search: SPS 6. Fire Control US Mk 57.

STATUS. Classification changed from Fleet Destroyer to Experimental Ship in 1971.

TRAINING SHIPS

AMERIGO VESPUCCI A 5312

Displacement, tons	3 543 standard; 4 146 full load
Dimensions feet (*m*)	229·5 pp; 270 oa hull; 330 oa bowsprit × 51 × 22 (*82·4* × *15·5* × 7)
Guns	4—3 in, 50 cal; 1—20 mm
Main engines	Two Fiat diesels with electric drive to 2 Marelli motors, 1 shaft; 2 000 hp = 10 knots
Sail area	22 604 square feet
Endurance	5 450 miles at 6·5 knots
Complement,	400 + 150 midshipmen

Built at Castellammare. Launched on 22 March 1930 and completed in 1931. Hull, masts and yards are of steel. Extensively refitted at La Spezia Naval Dockyard in 1964.

AMERIGO VESPUCCI *1973, Italian Navy*

Training Ships—*continued*

PALINURO (ex-*Commandant Louis Richard*) A 5311.

Displacement, tons	1 042 standard; 1 450 full load
Measurement, tons	858 gross
Dimensions, ft (*m*)	204 pp; 226·3 oa × 32 × 18·7 (*59 × 10 × 4·8*)
Main engines	1 diesel; 1 shaft; 450 bhp = 7·5 knots
Endurance, miles	5 390 at 7·5 knots
Sail area, square feet	1 152

Barquentine, ex-French, launched in 1920. Purchased in 1950. Rebuilt and commissioned in Italian Navy on 16 July 1955.

PALINURO *1968, Italian Navy*

CORSARO II

Measurement, tons	41
Dimensions, ft (*m*)	68·6 × 15·4 × 9·5 (*20·9 × 4·7 × 2·9*)
Auxiliary engines	1 Mercedes-Benz diesel, 96 bhp
Sail area	2 117 square feet

Special yacht for sail training and oceanic navigation. RORC class. Built by Costaguta Yard, Voltri, in 1959-60.

STELLA POLARE

Measurement, tons	47
Dimensions, feet	6·9 × 15·4 × 9·8
Sail area, square feet	2 200
Complement	14

Yawl. Buiit by Sangermani. Chiavari in 1964-65 as a sail training vessel for the Italian Navy.

2 "ALICUDI" CLASS (NETLAYERS)

ALICUDI A 5304 (ex-USS AN 99)
FILICUDI A 5305 (ex-USS AN 100)

Displacement, tons	680 standard; 834 full load
Dimensions, ft (*m*)	151·8 pp; 165·3 oa × 33·5 × 10·5 (*46·3 × 10·2 × 3·2*)
Guns	1—40 mm, 70 cal AA; 4—20 mm, 70 cal AA
Main engines	Diesel-electric: 1 200; hp = 12 knots

Built to the order of NATO. Laid down on 22 Apr 1954 and 19 July 1954, respectively, by Ansaldo, Leghorn, launched on 11 July 1954 and 26 Sep 1954.

FILICUDI *1972, Dr. Giorgio Arra*

LIGHTHOUSE TENDERS

RAMPINO A 5309

Displacement, tons	350 standard; 645 full load
Dimensions, feet	158·8 × 24·2 × 13
Main engines	Triple expansion = 7 knots

Buoy tender. Of netlayer type. Built at Osaka. Classed as *Nave Ausiliarie*.

Lighthouse Tenders—*continued*

3 Ex-BRITISH LCT(3) TYPE

MTF 1301 **MTF 1302** **MTF 1303**

Displacement, tons	296 light; 700 full load
Dimensions, feet	192 × 31 × 7
Guns	1—40 mm, 56 cal AA; 2—20 mm, 70 cal AA
Main engines	diesel; 1 shaft; speed = 8 knots

Converted landing craft of the British LCT (3) type. Lighthouse motor transports (Moto-Trasporti Fari). NATO Pennant Nos.: A 5361, A 5362 and A 5363.

MFT 1301 *1968, Italian Navy*

SALVAGE SHIP

PROTEO (ex-*Perseo*). A 5310

Displacement, tons	1 865 standard; 2 147 full load
Dimensions, feet	220·5 pp; 248 oa × 38 × 21 max
Main engines	2 diesels; 4 800 bhp = 16 knots
Range, miles	7 500 at 13 knots

Laid down at Cantieri Navali Riuniti, Ancona, in 1943. Suspended in 1944. Seized by Germans and transferred to Trieste. Construction recommenced at Cantieri Navali Riuniti, Ancona, in 1949. Diesels at 250 rpm drive a single propeller through hydraulic couplings and reduction gearing. Formerly mounted one 3·9 inch AA gun and two 20 mm, 70 cal AA guns.

PROTEO *1969, Italian Navy*

REPAIR CRAFT

MOC 1201 **MOC 1202** **MOC 1203** **MOC 1204** **MOC 1205** **MOC 1207** **MOC 1208**

Displacement, tons	350 standard; 640 full load
Dimensions, feet	192 × 31 × 7
Guns	2—40 mm; 2—20 mm (2 ships have 2—40 mm and 1 ship has 3—20 mm)
Main engines	Diesel = 8 knots

Former British LCT (3) type landing craft converted to repair craft. MOC 1207 and 1208 are ammunition transports. NATO Nos.: A 5331 to 5338, respectively.

WATER CARRIERS

PIAVE **TEVERE**

4 973 tons full load—built 1971-73.

BASENTO A 5256 **BRADANO** A 5357 **BRENTA** A 5358

1 914 tons. Built by Inma di La Spezia. Laid down in 1969-70 and launched and completed in 1970-72.

ADIGE (ex-*YW* 92) A 5369
FLEGETONTE (ex-*YW* 95) A 5371
ISONZO (ex-*YW* 77) A 5372
TICINO (ex-*YW* 79) A 5376
TANARO (ex-*YW* 99) A 5377

Ex-US Army YW type. 1 470 tons full load.

PO A 5365 **VOLTURNO** A 5366

6 000 tons full load. Built 1936-37.

SESIA A 5375

1 050 tons. Launched in 1933.

METAURO A 5373

592 tons. Launched in 1933.

ARNO A 5370

634 tons. Launched in 1929.

MINCIO A 5374

645 tons. Launched in 1929.

Water Carriers—*continued*

TIMAVO
645 tons. Built by COMI, Venezia, 1926.

FRIGIDO (ex-*Fukuiu Maru*)
398 tons Launched in 1912.

OFANTO
250 tons. Built 1913-14.

LENO **SIMETO** **SPRUGOLA** **STURA**
Small water carriers of 270, 167, 212 and 126 tons displacement, respectively.

TUGS

PORTO D'ISCHIA **RIVA TRIGOSO**

Displacement, tons	296 full load
Dimensions, feet	83·7 × 23·3 × 10·8
Main engines	Diesel; 1 shaft; 850 bhp = 12·1 knots

Both launched in Sep 1969. Controllable pitch propeller.

ARSACHENA
BOEO
CABONARA
CIRCEO
GORGONA
LISCOSIA ABAZIA
MESCO
NISIDA
SAN ANTIOCO
SAN ANTONIO
SAN BENEDETTO
SAN DANIELE
TAVOLARA
TEULADA

Completed in 1955. Small tugs for local and general purposes.

AUSONIA **PANARIA**

Displacement, tons	240

Both launched in 1948. Coastal tugs for general utility duties.

CICLOPE A 5319 **TITANO** A 5320

Displacement, tons	1 200
Dimensions, feet	157·5 × 32·5 × 13
Main engines	Triple expansion; 1 shaft; 1 000 ihp = 8 knots

Both were launched in 1948.

MISENO **MONTE CRISTO**

Displacement, tons	285

Former United States Navy harbour tugs.

GAGLIARDO A 5322 **ROBUSTO** A 5323

Displacement, tons	389 standard; 506 full load
Main engines	1 000 ihp = 8 knots

Both launched in 1939.

SAN GIUSTO

Displacement, tons	486 standard
Main engines	900 hp = 12 knots

PORTO FOSSONE
PORTO PISANO
PORTO RECANATI
PORTO TORRES
PORTO VECCHIO
SALVORE
TINO

Displacement, tons	226 to 270
Dimensions, feet	88·8 × 22 × 10
Main engines	600 ihp = 9 knots

All launched in 1936-37, except *Tino*, 1931. Principally employed as harbour tugs.

ATLETA (ex-*LT* 152) A 5318
COLOSSO (ex-*LT* 214) A 5320
FORTE (ex-*LT* 159) A 5321
TENACE (ex-*LT* 154) A 5324

Displacement, tons	525 standard; 835 full load
Dimensions, feet	142·8 × 32·8 × 11
Main engines	2 diesel-electric; 690 hp = 11 knots

Ex-US Army.

VENTIMIGLIA

Displacement, tons	230 standard
Dimensions, feet	108·2 × 23 × 7·2
Main engines	550 hp = 10 knots

Note. There are also 42 harbour tugs, ferry tugs, lagoon tugs, and minor tugs.

IVORY COAST

Personnel

1974: 120 officers and men

Mercantile Marine

Lloyd's Register of Shipping: 39 vessels of 88 749 tons gross

PATROL BOATS

1 FRANCO-BELGE TYPE

VIGILANT

Displacement, tons	240 normal
Dimensions, feet	149·3 pp; 155·8 oa × 23·6 × 8·2
Guns	2—40 mm AA
Missiles	8 SS12
Main engines	2 diesels; 2 shafts; 2 400 bhp = 18·5 knots
Range, miles	2 000 at 15 knots
Complement	25 (3 officers and 22 men)

Built by Franco-Belge. Laid down in Feb 1967. Launched on 23 May 1967. Completed in 1968. Sister ship to *Malaika* of Madagascan Navy.

1 Ex-FRENCH VC TYPE

PERSEVERANCE (ex-*VC* 9, *P* 759)

Displacement, tons	75 standard; 82 full load
Dimensions, feet	104·5 × 15·5 × 5·5
Guns	2—20 mm AA
Main engines	2 Mercedes-Benz diesels; 2 shafts; 2 700 bhp = 28 knots
Oil fuel, tons	10
Range, miles	1 100 at 16·5 knots; 800 at 21 knots
Complement	15

Patrolboats—*continued*

Former French seaward defence motor launch. Built by Constructions Mecaniques de Normandie, Cherbourg. Completed in 1958. Transferred from France to Ivory Coast 26 April 1963.

PERSEVERANCE *1964, Ivory Coast Armed Forces*

8 PATROL BOATS

These are 30 ft craft for coastal and river patrols.

LOKODJO

1 TRAWLER TYPE

LANDING CRAFT

There are six landing craft of the LCVP type, 7 tons, 2 machine guns and Mercedes diesels 200 hp, 9 knots. 2 were built in Abidjan in 1970.

JAMAICA

Defence Force Coast Guard

Jamaica, which became independent within the Commonwealth, on 6 Aug 1962, formed the Coast Guard as the Maritime Arm of the Defence Force. This is based at HMJS Cagway, Port Royal.
The Jamaican Government signed an agreement with the USA for the transfer of a small number of coastguard vessels for the new navy.
Great Britain lent several RN petty officers for technical assistance. The British Mission included a technical team to survey sites for the establishment of local naval bases.

Administration

Officer Commanding Jamaican Defence Force Coast Guard:
Captain J. E Farnol D.S.C., RN.(Retd)

Personnel

1974: 12 officers, 70 Petty officers and ratings (*Coast Guard Reserve:* 8 officers, 27 men)

Mercantile Marine

Lloyd's Register of Shipping: 6 vessels of 12 899 tons gross

PATROL BOATS

DISCOVERY BAY P 4 **HOLLAND BAY** P 5 **MANATEE BAY** P 6

Displacement, tons	60
Dimensions, feet	85 × 18·8 × 5·9
Guns	3—·50 cal Browning
Main engines	3 GM 12 V71 TI diesels; 3 shafts; 2 000 shp = 26·5 knots
Oil fuel, tons	13
Range, miles	1 000 at 20 knots
Complement	10

Built by Teledyne Sewart Seacraft Inc, Berwick, La, USA. All aluminium construction. *Discovery Bay*, the prototype was launched in Aug 1966 and commissioned on 3 Nov 1966. *Holland Bay*, commissioned 4 Apr 1967, and *Manatee Bay*, commissioned 9 Aug 1967, were supplied under the US Military Assistance Programme. All three boats were extensively refitted and modified in 1972-73 by the builders with GM 12V 71 Turbo-injected engines to give greater range, speed and operational flexibility.

DISCOVERY BAY *1973, Jamaica C G*

NEW CONSTRUCTION

Displacement, tons	
Dimensions, feet	105 × 19 × 7
Guns	2—20 mm; 3—·50 cal MG; 1—81 mm mortar
Main engines	2 Maybach MB 16V 538 TB90; 6 000 shp = 32 knots
Complement	15

Designed by Teledyne Sewart Inc, Berwick, La USA. First boat to be delivered in 1974. Boats will have accommodation for 24 soldiers and may be used as mobile hospitals in an emergency.

AVR TYPE
The former 3 ex-US AVR type patrol boats have been disposed of.

JORDAN

Coastal Guard

It was officially stated in 1969 that Jordan had no naval force known as such, but the Jordan Coastal Guard, sometimes called the Jordan Sea Force, took orders direct from the Director of Operations at General Headquarters.
The force of two Bertram fibre glass patrol boats, two Polson aluminium motor boats and four wooden motor boats is based at Aqaba. There is no flotilla in the Dead Sea.

JAPAN

Naval Board

Chief of the Maritime Staff, Defence Agency:
Admiral Hiroichi Samejima

Commander-in-Chief, Self-Defence Fleet:
Vice Admiral Tetsuro Motomura

Chief Administration Division Maritime Staff Office:
Rear Admiral Yasunori Yonemura

Diplomatic Representation

Defence (Naval) Attaché in London:
Captain Hideo Sato

Defence (Naval) Attaché in Washington:
Captain Yasuhiro Tamagawa

Defence Attaché in Moscow:
Colonel Tadao Miyezaki

Defence Attaché in Paris:
Colonel Ryuzo Yabunaka

Five Year Defence Plan

The tourth 5-year defence programme (1973-77) announced 9 October 1972 provides for the building of the following.

2 Haruna class DDH of 5 200 tons
1 SAM DDG of 3 900 tons
1 SSM DDG of 3 600 tons
3 DDs of 2 500 tons
3 Frigates of 1 450 tons
3 Frigates of 1 500 tons,
3 Isoshio class submarines of 1 800 tons.
2 Submarines of 2 200 tons
19 Minesweepers
3 Missile Boats of 200 tons
3 Torpedo Boats of 100 tons
2 LSTs of 1 500 tons
3 LSTs of 2 000 tons
1 Supply Ship of 5 000 tons
1 Submarine Tender of 2 700 tons
1 Oceanographic Research Ship of 2 000 tons
18 Patrol Boats
Plus miscellaneous craft

At the end of this programme (1977) the fleet should consist of 170 modern ships totalling 214 000 tons.

New Construction Programmes

1973 1 Destroyer, 1 Frigate, 1 S/M, 2 MSC, 2 MSB, 1 PT, 3 LST
1974 1 DDH, 1 Destroyer, 1 Frigate, 1 S/M, 4 MSC, 1 PT, 1 LST

NUCLEAR POWER STUDY. The Director of the Japanese Defence Agency stated on 5 May 1955 that Japan was studying the possibility of building a nuclear powered submarine. In the meantime, conventional submarines would be ordered.

Strength of the Fleet

Type	*Active*	*Building*	*Projected*
Destroyers	29	2	3
Frigates	16	3	2
Corvettes	20	—	—
Submarines—Patrol	14	2	2
Fast Attack Craft—Torpedo	5	—	2
Patrol Craft—Coastal	13	—	—
LST's	5	2	2
LCU's	6	—	—
LCM's	42	—	—
LCVP's	20	—	—
Minelayers	2	—	—
M/S Support Ships	2	—	—
Minesweepers—Coastal	36	2	4
Auxiliary M/S	4	—	—
MSB's	8	—	2
Training Ships	2	—	—
S/M Rescue Vessels	2	—	—
Salvage Vessel	1	—	—
Support Tanker	1	—	—
Icebreaker	1	—	—
Tugs	7 (6 small)	—	—
Auxiliaries	8	—	—

Personnel

1974: 46 000 (8 000 officers, 33 000 men, 5 000 civil)

Names

The practice of painting the ship's names on the broadsides of the hulls was discontinued in 1970.

Bases

Naval—Yokosuka, Kure, Sasebo, Maizuru, Oominato
Fleet Air—Atsugi, Hachinohe, Iwakuni, Kanoya, Okinawa Oominato, Oomura, Shimofusa, Tateyama.

Fleet Air Arm

12 Air ASW Sqns. P2-J, P2V-7, PS-1, S2F-1, UF-2, HSS-2, HSS-1N.
5 Air Training Sqns. P2-J, P2V-7, YS-11, B-65, KM-2, Mentor, Bell-47, OH-6, HSS-2.
1 Transport Sqn. YS-11.
Miscellaneous V-107.

Deletions and Transfers

Destroyers

1974 *Ariake, Yugure*

Frigates

1970 *Kiri, Keyaki, Nire, Sugi, Shii* to US.
1972 *Kaya, Bura, Kashi, Moni, Tochi, Ume, Maki, Kusu, Matsu, Nata, Sakura* (All ex-US PFs). *Wakaba.*

Submarines

1971 *Kuroshio* to US.

Light Forces

1972 PT 2, 3, 4 and 9. *Kosoku* 1, 22-28, 30.
1973 PT 7 and 8, *Kosoku* 3.

LST

1972 *Hayatomo.*

LSM

1973 3001

Maritime Safety Agency (Coast Guard)

9 Large Patrol Vessels
41 Medium Patrol Vessels
37 Small Patrol Vessels
3 Fire Fighting Craft
42 Patrol Craft
6 Surveying Vessels
5 Tenders
1 Underwater Research Vessel
150 Coastal Patrol Craft
33 Harbour Patrol Craft

Mercantile Marine

Lloyd's Register of Shipping:
9 469 vessels of 36 785 094 tons gross

List of Pennant Numbers

Destroyers

DD
101 Harukaze
102 Yukikaze
103 Ayanami
104 Isonami
105 Uranami
106 Shikinami
107 Murasame
108 Yuudachi
109 Harusame
110 Takanami
111 Oonami
112 Makinami
113 Yamagumo
114 Makigumo
115 Asagumo
116 Minegumo
117 Natsugumo
118 Murakumo
119 Aokumo
120 Yuugumo
121 Akigumo
141 Haruna
142 Hiei
161 Akizuki
162 Teruzuki
163 Amatsukaze
164 Takatsuki
165 Kikuzuki
166 Mochizuki
167 Nagatsuki
168 Tachikaze
183 Ariake
184 Yuugure

Frigates

DE
201 Akebono
202 Ikazuchi
203 Inazuma
211 Isuzu
212 Mogami
213 Kitakami
214 Ooi
215 Chikugo
216 Ayase
217 Mikuma
218 Tokachi
219 Iwase
220 Chitose
221 Niyodo
222 Teshio
223 Yoshino
224 Kumano
262 Ashai
263 Hatsuhi

Corvettes

PC
301 Kari
302 Kiji
303 Taka
304 Washi
305 Kamome
306 Tsubame
307 Misago
308 Hayabusa
309 Umitaka
310 Ootaka
311 Mizutori
312 Yamadori
313 Ootori
314 Kasasagi
315 Hatsukari
316 Umidori
317 Wakataka
318 Kumataka
319 Shiratori
320 Hiyodori

Submarines—Patrol

SS
511 Oyashio
521 Hayashic
522 Wakashio
523 Natsushio
524 Huyushio
561 Ooshio
562 Asashio
563 Harushio
564 Michishio
565 Arashio
566 Uzushio
567 Makishio
568 Isoshio
569 Narushio
570 Kuroshio
571 Takashio

Minesweepers—Coastal

MSC
604 Kasado
605 Shisaka
606 Kanawa
607 Sakito
608 Habushi
610 Tatara
611 Tsukumi
612 Mikura
613 Shikine
614 Hirado
615 Koshiki
616 Hotaka
617 Karato
618 Hario
619 Mutsure
620 Chiburi
621 Ootsu
622 Kudako
623 Rishiri
624 Rebun
625 Amami
626 Urume
627 Minase
628 Ibuki
629 Katsura
630 Takami
631 Iou
632 Miyake
633 Utone
634 Awaji
635 Toushi
636 Teuri
637 Murotsu
638 Tashiro
639 Miyato
640 Takane
641 Muzuki
642 Yokose
643 Sakate

Minesweeper Tenders

MST
462 Hayase
473 Koozu

Mine Layers

MMC 951 Sooya
AMC 491 Erimo

Landing Ships

LST
4001 Oosumi
4002 Shimokita
4003 Shiretoko
4101 Atsumi
4102 Motobu
4103 Nemuro
4151 Miura
4152 Ozika

Submarine Rescue Ships

ASR
401 Chihaya
402 Fushimi

Tanker

AO 411 Hamana

Training Ship

TV 3501 Katori

Training Support Ship

ATS 4201 Azuma

Cable Layer

ARC 481 Tsugaru

Icebreaker

AGB 5001 Fuji

Surveying Ship

AGS 5101 Akashi

DESTROYERS

2 NEW CONSTRUCTION DDG

TACHIKAZE DD 168 — DD 169

Displacement, tons	3 850
Dimensions, feet	443 × 47 × 15
Missiles	Standard RIM 60A SAM
Guns	2—5 in (singles)
A/S weapons	ASROC and 2 triple A/S torpedo tubes
Main engines	2 turbines; 60 000 hp
Speed	32 knots

Building by Mitsubishi, Nagasaki. Laid down 19 June 1973. To be fitted with VDS for launch in Dec 1974 and completion Mar 1976. Second to complete in 1977.

1 + 2 "HARUNA" CLASS

Name	No.	Builders	Laid down	Launched	Completion
HARUNA	141	Mitsubishi (Nagasaki)	19 Mar 1970	1 Feb 1972	Feb 1973
HIEI	142	Ishikawajima (Tokyo)	8 Mar 1972	13 Aug 1973	(Nov 1974)
—	143	—		—	1977(?)

Displacement, tons	4 700
Length, feet (*metres*)	502·0 (*153·0*)
Beam, feet (*metres*)	57·4 (*17·5*)
Draught, feet (*metres*)	16·7 (*5·1*)
Aircraft	3 anti-submarine helicopters
A/S weapons	Asroc multiple launcher
Guns	2—5 in (*127 mm*) single, rapid fire
Torpedo tubes	6—21 in (*533 mm*) 2 triple
Main engines	70 000 shp
Speed, knots	32
Range, miles	7 000 at 20 knots
Complement	364

Ordered under the third five-year defence programme (from 1968 to 1972). The third of class projected under the 1974 programme.

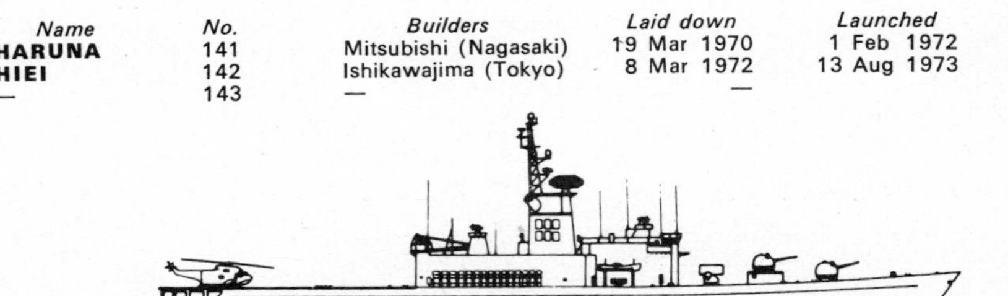

HARUNA (DDH Helocarrier)

HARUNA — *1973, Japanese Maritime Self-Defence Force*

4 ''TAKATSUKI'' CLASS

Name	No.	Builders	Laid down	Launched	Completed
KIKUZUKI	DD 165	Mitsubishi Jyuko Co, Nagasaki	15 Mar 1966	25 Mar 1967	27 Mar 1968
MOCHIZUKI	DD 166	Ishikawajima Jyuko Co, Tokyo	25 Nov 1966	15 Mar 1968	25 Mar 1969
NAGATSUKI	DD 167	Mitsubishi Jyuko Co, Nagasaki	2 Mar 1968	19 Mar 1969	12 Feb 1970
TAKATSUKI	DD 164	Ishikawajima Jyuko Com Tokyo	8 Oct 1964	7 Jan 1966	15 Mar 1967

Displacement, tons	3 050 (official figure)
Length, feet (*metres*)	446·2 (*136·0*) oa
Beam, feet (*metres*)	44·0 (*13·4*)
Draught, feet (*metres*)	14·5 (*4·4*)
Aircraft	1 helicopter
A/S weapons	Octuple Asroc; 1 four barrelled rocket launcher
Guns, dual purpose	2—5 in (*127 mm*) 54 cal. single
Torpedo launchers	2 triple for A/S homing torpedoes
Boilers	2 Mitsubishi CE
Main engines	2 Mitsubishi WH geared turbines 60 000 shp; 2 shafts
Speed, knots	32
Range, miles	7 000 at 20 knots
Complement	270

Anti-submarine type. *Takatsuki* (High Moon) was provided under the 1963 programme. Equipped with drone anti-submarine helicopter and hangar.

RADAR. Search: Metric wavelength. Tactical: Probably C Band. Fire Control: GFCS 56 with X Band.

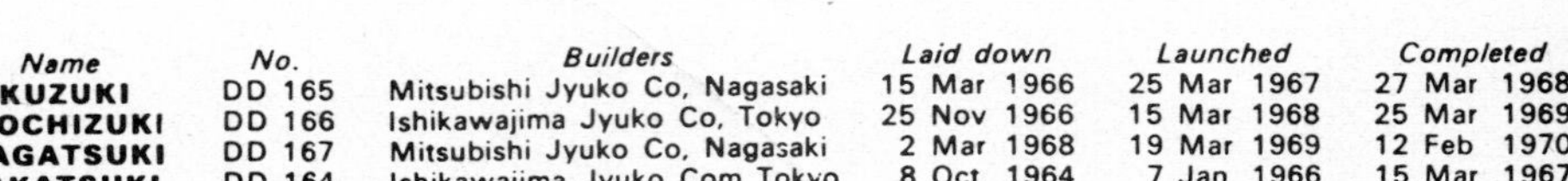

TAKATSUKI *Class*

KIKUZUKI — *1971, S. Woodrifle*

Destroyers—*continued*

5 "YAMAGUMO" CLASS

Name	No.	Builders	Laid down	Launched	Completion
AKIGUMO	DD 121	Sumitomo Uraga	7 July 1972	23 Oct 1973	31 July 1974
AOKUMO	DD 119	Sumitomo Uraga	2 Oct 1970	30 Mar 1972	25 Nov 1972
ASAGUMO	DD 115	Maizuru	24 June 1965	25 Nov 1966	29 Aug 1967
MAKIGUMO	DD 114	Uraga Yokosuka	10 June 1964	26 July 1965	19 Mar 1966
YAMAGUMO	DD 113	Mitsui, Tamano	23 Mar 1964	27 Feb 1965	29 Jan 1966

Displacement, tons 2 150
Length, feet (*metres*) 377 (*115*)
Beam, feet (*metres*) 38 7 (*11·8*)
Draught, feet (*metres*) 13·1 (*4*)
Guns 4—3 in; 50 cal (2 twin)
A/S weapons 1 Asroc; 1 four barrelled rocket launcher
Torpedo tubes 2 triple mountings for A/S torpedoes
Main engines 6 Diesels; 26 500 bhp; 2 shafts
Speed, knots 27
Range, miles 7 000 at 20 knots
Complement 210

RADAR. Search; Metric Tactical; C Band-Fire Control; GFCS 56 with X Band.

SONAR. *Yamagumo* and *Makigumo* fitted with VDS.

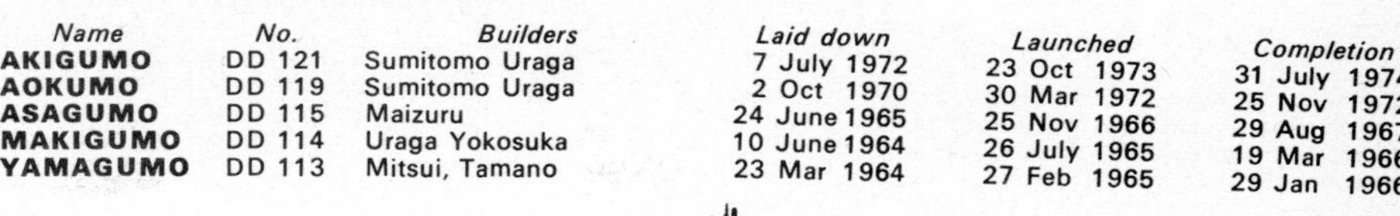

YAMAGUMO *Class*

YAMAGUMO *1972, Toshio Tamura*

4 + 1 "MINEGUMO" CLASS

Name	No.	Builders	Laid down	Launched	Completed
MINEGUMO	DD 116	Mitsui, Tamano	14 Mar 1967	16 Dec 1967	21 Aug 1968
MURAKUMO	DD 118	Maizuru	19 Oct 1968	15 Nov 1969	21 Aug 1970
NATSUGUMO	DD 117	Uraga, Yokosuka	26 June 1967	25 July 1968	25 Apr 1969
YUUGUMO	DD 120	Sumitimo, Uraga	1 Nov 1972	1 Sep 1973	June 1974
—	DD 122	—	—	—	? 1976

All details as for *Yamagumo* class except:

A/S weapons 1 Dash helicopter in place of ASROC

Note difference in silhouettes between this and the *Yamagumo* class. One extra projected in 1974 programme.

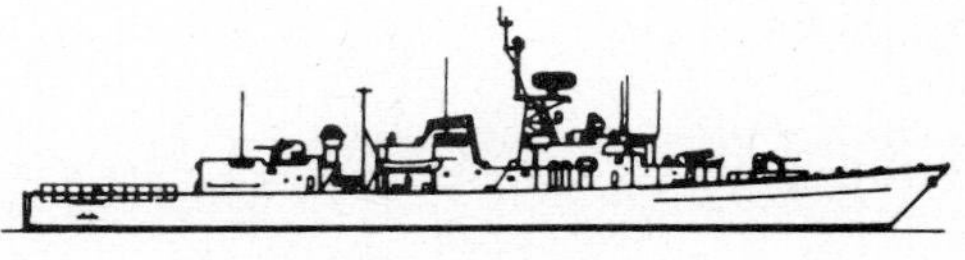

MINEGUMO *Class*

NATSUGUMO *1972, Japanese Maritime Self-Defence Force*

1 "AMATSUKAZE" CLASS (DDG)

AMATSUKAZE DD 163

Displacement, tons 3 050 standard; 4 000 full load
Length, feet (*metres*) 429·8 (*131·0*)
Beam, feet (*metres*) 44 (*13·4*)
Draught, feet (*metres*) 13·8 (*4·2*)
Aircraft Can operate Helicopter
Missile launchers 1 single "Tartar" (US)
Guns 4—3 in (*76 mm*) 50 cal, 2 twin
A/S weapons ASROC; 2 Hedgehogs
Torpedo mountings 1 each side for A/S short torpedoes
Main engines 2 Ishikawajima GE geared turbines 2 shafts; 60 000 shp
Speed, knots 33
Boilers 2 Ishikawajima Foster Wheeler
Oil fuel, tons 900
Range, miles 7 000 at 18 knots
Complement 290

Ordered under the 1960 programme. Built by Mitsubishi, Nagasaki. Laid down on 29 Nov 1962, launched on 5 Oct 1963 and completed on 15 Feb 1965.

RADAR. Search: SPS 37 and SPS 39 3 D. Fire Control: SPS 51 for "Tartar", X Band for guns.

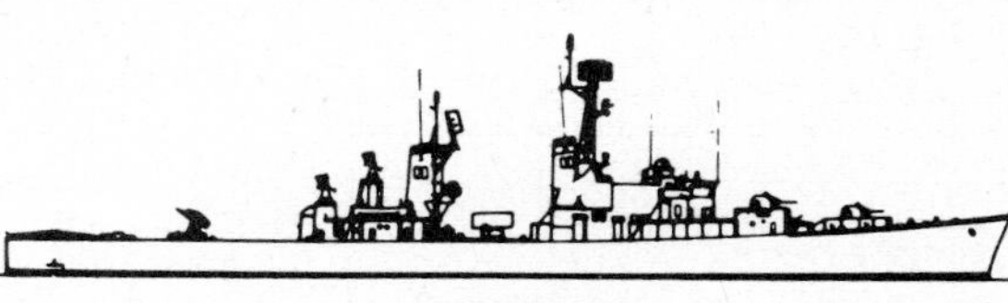

AMATSUKAZE

AMATSUKAZE *1969, Japanese Maritime Self-Defence Force*

Destroyers—*continued*

2 "AKIZUKI" CLASS

Name	No.	Builders	Laid down	Launched	Completed
AKIZUKI	DD 161	Mitsubishi Zosen Co, Nagasaki	31 July 1958	26 June 1959	13 Feb 1960
TERUZUKI	DD 162	Shin Mitsubishi Jyuko Co, Kobe	15 Aug 1958	24 June 1959	29 Feb 1960

Displacement, tons 2 350 standard; 2 890 full load
Length, feet (*metres*) 387·2 (*118·0*) oa
Beam, feet (*metres*) 39·4 (*12·0*)
Draught, feet (*metres*) 13·1 (*4·0*)
Guns, dual purpose 3—5 in (*127 mm*) 54 cal. single
Guns, AA 4—3 in (*76 mm*) 50 cal., 2 twin
Torpedo tubes 4—21 in (*533 mm*) quadrupled
A/S 1—US model Mk 108 rocket launcher; 2 hedgehogs; 2 Y-mortars; 2 DCT
Boilers 2 Mitsubishi CE type
Main engines 2 geared turbines:— *Akizuki:* Mitsubishi Escher-Weiss *Teruzuki:* Westinghouse 45 000 shp, 2 shafts
Speed, knots 32
Complement 330

Destroyers of unusual design with long forecastle hull. Built in Japan under the 1957 Military Aid Programme.

RADAR
Search: SPS 6. Tactical: SPS 10. Fire Control: X Band

AKIZUKI, TERUZUKI

TERUZUKI *1971, courtesy Mr. Michael D. J. Lennon*

3 "MURASAME" CLASS

Name	No.	Builders	Laid down	Launched	Completed
HARUSAME	DD 109	Urage Dock Co, Yokosuka	17 June 1958	18 June 1959	15 Dec 1959
MURASAME	DD 107	Mitsubishi Zosen Co, Nagasaki	17 Dec 1957	31 July 1958	28 Feb 1959
YUDACHI	DD 108	Ishakawajima Jyuko Co, Tokyo	16 Dec 1957	29 July 1958	25 Mar 1959

Displacement, tons 1 800 standard; 2 500 full load
Length, feet (*metres*) 354·3 (*108·0*) oa
Beam, feet (*metres*) 36 (*11·0*) oa
Draught, feet (*metres*) 12·2 (*3·7*)
Guns, dual purpose 3—5 in (*127 mm*) 54 cal
Guns, AA 4—3 in (*76 mm*) 50 cal, 2 twin
A/S 8 short torpedoes; 1 Hedgehog 1 DC rack; 1 Y-gun
Boilers 2 (see *Engineering* notes)
Main engines 2 sets geared turbines 30 000 shp; 2 shafts
Speed, knots 30
Range, miles 6 000 at 18 knots
Complement 250

Murasame and *Yudachi* were built under the 1956 Programme, *Harusame* 1957 Programme.

ENGINEERING. *Murusame* has *Mitsubishi* Jyuko turbines and Mitsubishi CE boilers; and the other two have Ishikawajima Harima Jyuko turbines and Ishikawajima FW-D boilers.

RADAR. Search: SPS 6. Tactical: SPS 10. Fire Control: X Band.

MURASAME *Class*

MURASAME *1972, Japanese Maritime Self-Defence Force*

7 "AYANAMI" CLASS

Name	No.	Builders	Laid down	Launched	Completed
AYANAMI	DD 103	Mitsubishi Zosen Co, Nagasaki	20 Nov 1956	1 June 1957	12 Feb 1958
ISONAMI	DD 104	Shin Mitsubishi Jyuko Co, Kobe	14 Dec 1956	30 Sep 1957	14 Mar 1958
MAKINAMI	DD 112	Iino Jyuko Co, Maizuru	20 Mar 1959	25 Apr 1960	30 Oct 1960
ONAMI	DD 111	Ishikawajima Jyuko Co, Tokyo	20 Mar 1959	13 Feb 1960	29 Aug 1960
SHIKINAMI	DD 106	Mitsui Zosen Co, Tamano	24 Dec 1956	25 Sep 1957	15 Mar 1958
TAKANAMI	DD 110	Mitsui Zosen Co, Tamano	8 Nov 1958	8 Aug 1959	30 Jan 1960
URANAMI	DD 105	Kawasaki Jyuko Co, Tokyo	1 Feb 1957	29 Aug 1957	27 Feb 1958

Displacement, tons 1 700 standard; 2 500 full load
Length, feet (*metres*) 357·6 (*109·0*) oa
Beam, feet (*metres*) 35·1 (*10·7*)
Draught, feet (*metres*) 12 (*3·7*)
Guns 6—3 in (*76 mm*) 50 cal (3 twin)
A/S weapons 2 US Model Mk 15 Hedgehogs; 2 Y-guns; 2 DC racks
Torpedo tubes 4—21 in (*533 mm*) quadruple
Torpedo launchers 4 fixed, for A/S homing torpedoes
Main engines 2 Mitsubishi Escher-Weiss geared turbines; 2 shafts; 35 000 shp
Speed, knots 32
Boilers 2 (see *Engineering*)
Range, miles 6 000 at 18 knots
Complement 230

ANTI-SUBMARINE. Trainable Hedgehogs forward of the bridge. Originally all ships fitted with A/S torpedo launchers on quarter-deck but in *Shikinami* (1972) *Isonami* (1971) *Uranami* (1970) and *Ayanami* (1969) these were removed and two triple A/S torpedo tubes were fitted.

RADAR. Search: SPS 12 Tactical: SPS 10. Fire Control: X Band.

ENGINEERING. Types of boilers installed are as follows. Mitsubishi CE in *Ayanami, Isonami* and *Uranami*; Hitachi Babcock & Wilcox in *Ōnami, Shikinami* and *Takanami*; Kawasaki Jyuko BD in *Makinami*.

AYANAMI *Class*

MAKINAMI *1972, Japanese Maritime Self-Defence Force*

Destroyers—*continued*

2 "HARUKAZE" CLASS

Name	No.	Builders	Laid down	Launched	Completed
HARUKAZE	DD 101	Mitsubishi Zosen Co, Nagasaki	15 Dec 1954	20 Sep 1955	26 Apr 1956
YUKIKAZE	DD 102	Mitsubishi Jyuko Co, Kobe	17 Dec 1954	20 Aug 1955	31 July 1956

Displacement, tons	1 700 standard; 2 340 full load
Length, feet (*metres*)	347·8 (*106·0*) wl; 358·5 (*109·3*) oa
Beam, feet (*metres*)	34·5 (*10·5*)
Draught, feet (*metres*)	12·0 (*3·7*)
Guns	3—5 in (*127 mm*) 38 cal dp 8—40 mm (2 quadruple) AA
A/S weapons	Tubes for short homing torpedoes; 2 Hedgehogs; 1 DC rack; 4 K-guns
Main engines	2 sets geared turbines; *Harukaze:* 2 Mitsubishi Escher Weiss; *Yukikaze:* 2 Westinghouse; 2 shafts; 30 000 shp
Speed, knots	30
Boilers	*Harukaze:* 2 Hitachi-Babcock; *Yukikaze:* 2 Combustion Engineering
Range, miles	6 000 at 18 knots
Oil fuel, tons	557
Complement	240

HARUKAZE — *1972, Japanese Maritime Self-Defence Force*

HARUKAZE, YUKIKAZE

Authorised under the 1953 programme. First destroyer hulled vessels built in Japan after the Second World War. Electric welding was extensively used in hull construction; development of weldable high tension steel in main hull and light alloy in superstructure were also novel.

RADAR. Search: L Band. Tactical: SPS 10. Fire Controls: X Band.

YUKIKAZE — *1972, Toshio Tamura*

ANTI-SUBMARINE. Armament was modified in Mar. 1969 when homing torpedo tubes were mounted and depth charge equipment correspondingly reduced.

Nearly all the armament was supplied from the USA under the MSA clause.

FRIGATES

7 + 5 "CHIKUGO" CLASS

Name	No.	Builder	Laid down	Launched	Completion
AYASE	DE 216	—	5 Dec 1969	16 Sep 1970	20 May 1971
CHIKUGO	DE 215	Mitsui Zoosen	9 Dec 1968	13 Jan 1970	31 July 1970
CHITOSE	DE 220	Hitachi, Maizuru	7 Oct 1971	25 Jan 1973	31 Aug 1973
IWASE	DE 219	Mitsui Zoosen	6 Aug 1971	29 June 1972	12 Dec 1972
MIKUMA	DE 217	—	17 Mar 1970	16 Feb 1971	26 Aug 1971
NIYODO	DE 221	Mitsui Zoosen	20 Sep 1972	28 Aug 1973	Mar 1974
TOKACHI	DE 218	Mitsui Zoosen	11 Dec 1970	25 Nov 1971	17 May 1972
TESHIO	DE 222	Hitachi, Maizuru	1973	May 1974	Feb 1975
YOSHINO	DE 223	Mitsui, Tamano	1973	Aug 1974	Feb 1975
KUMANO	DE 224	Hitachi, Maizuru	May 1974	Mar 1975	Nov 1975
—	DE 225	Mitsui, Tamano	—	—	1976
—	DE 226	—	—	—	1977

Displacement, tons	1 470 standard; 1 750 full load
Length, feet (*metres*)	305·5 (*93·0*) oa
Beam, feet (*metres*)	35·5 (*10·8*)
Draught, feet (*metres*)	11·5 (*3·5*)
Guns, dual purpose	2—3 in (*76 mm*) 50 cal, (1 twin)
Guns, AA	2—40 mm (1 twin)
A/S weapons	Octuple ASROC
Torpedo launchers	2 triple 12·7 in (*324 mm*)
Main engines	4 Mitsui B & W diesels; 2 shafts; 16 000 shp
Speed, knots	25
Complement	165

RADAR. Search: L Band. Tactical: SPS 10. Fire Control: X Band.

SONAR. Fitted with VDS.

MIKUMA — *1972. Toshio Tamura*

CHIKUGO *Class.*

4 "ISUZU" CLASS

Name	No.	Builders	Laid down	Launched	Completed
ISUZU	DE 211	Mitsui Zosen Co, Tamano	16 Apr 1960	17 Jan 1961	29 July 1961
KITAKAMI	DE 213	Ishikawajima-Harima Co, Tokyo	7 June 1962	21 June 1963	27 Feb 1964
MOGAMI	DE 212	Mitsubishi Zosen Co, Nagasaki	4 Aug 1960	7 Mar 1961	28 Oct 1961
OOI	DE 214	Maizuru (former Iino) Co, Maizuru	10 June 1962	15 June 1963	22 Jan 1964

Displacement, tons	1 490 standard; 1 700 full load
Length, feet (*metres*)	308·5 (*94·0*) oa
Beam, feet (*metres*)	34·2 (*10·4*)
Draught, feet (*metres*)	11·5 (*3·5*)
Guns, dual purpose	4—3 in (*76 mm*) 50 cal, 2 twin
A/S weapons	1 4-barrelled rocket launcher; 1 DCT; 1 DC rack *Isuzu* Mk 108 rocket launcher (Weapon A)
Torpedo tubes	4—21 in (*533 mm*) quadrupled
Torpedo launchers	2 triple for A/S homing torpedoes
Main engines	4 diesels, Mitsui in *Ooi*, *Isuzu*, Mitsubishi in *Kitakami*, *Mogami*, 16 000 hp; 2 shafts
Speed, knots	25
Complement	180

ISUZU, MOGAMI

ISUZU — *1970, courtesy, Toshio Tamura*

Frigates—*continued*

RADAR. Search: SPS 6. Tactical: SPS 10.

CLASS VARIATION. The second pair of this type, *Kitakami* and *Ooi*, have a number of improvements in armament and equipment and are of slightly different dimensions.

KITAKAMI, OOI

KITAKAMI *1972, Japanese Maritime Self-Defence Force*

2 "IKAZUCHI" CLASS

Name	*No.*	*Builders*	*Laid down*	*Launched*	*Completed*
IKAZUCHI	DE 202	Kawasaki Jyuko Co, Kobe	18 Dec 1954	6 Sep 1955	29 May 1956
INAZUMA	DE 203	Mitsui Zosen Co, Tamano	25 Dec 1954	4 Aug 1955	5 Mar 1956

Displacement, tons	1 070 standard; 1 300 full load
Length, feet (*metres*)	287 (*87·5*) wl; 288·7 (*88·0*) oa
Beam, feet (*metres*)	28·5 (*8·7*)
Draught, feet (*metres*)	10·2 (*3·1*)
Guns	2—3 in (*76 mm*) 50 cal. dp; 2—40 mm AA
A/S weapons	1 Hedgehog; 8 K-guns; 2 DC racks
Main engines	12 000 hp diesels; Mitsubishi in *Ikazuchi:* Mitsui B & W in *Inazuma:* 2 shafts
Range, miles	5 500 at 15 knots
Speed, knots	25
Complement	160

IKAZUCHI, INAZUMA

INAZUMA *1967, Japanese Maritime Self-Defence Force*

GUNNERY. The original 2—3 inch guns and 4—40 mm guns were removed in Mar. 1959 and replaced by 2—3 inch quick firing guns and 2—40 mm guns.

RADAR. Search: SPS 6. Tactical: SPS 10. Fire Control: X Band.

1 "AKEBONO" CLASS

Name	*No.*	*Builders*	*Laid down*	*Launched*	*Completed*
AKEBONO	DE 201	Ishikawajima Jyuko, Co, Tokyo	10 Dec 1954	15 Oct 1955	20 Mar 1956

Displacement, tons	1 060 standard; 1 350 full load
Length, feet (*metres*)	295 (*90·0*) oa
Beam, feet (*metres*)	28·5 (*8·7*)
Draught, feet (*metres*)	11 (*3·4*)
Guns, AA	2—3 in (*76 mm*) 50 cal; 1—40 mm
A/S weapons	4 K-guns; 1 Hedgehog; 1 DC rack
Main engines	Ishikawajima geared turbines; 2 shafts; 18 000 shp
Speed, knots	28
Boilers	2 Ishikawajima-Foster Wheeler
Range, miles	4 000 at 16 knots
Complement	190

AKEBONO

AKEBONO *1972, Japanese Maritime Self-Defence Force*

GUNNERY. The original 2—3 inch guns and 4—40 mm guns were removed in March 1959 when 2—3 inch quick firing guns were mounted.

RADAR. Search: SPS 6. Tactical: SPS 10. Fire Control: X Band.

2 "ASAHI" CLASS

Name	*No.*	*Builders*	*Laid down*	*Launched*	*Completed*
ASAHI (ex-USS *Amick, DE* 168)	DE 262	Federal Port, Newark	30 Nov 1942	27 May 1943	26 July 1943
HATSUHI (ex-USS *Atherton, DE* 169)	DE 263	Federal Port, Newark	14 Jan 1943	27 May 1943	29 Aug 1943

Displacement, tons	1 250 standard; 1 900 full load
Length, feet (*metres*)	306 (*93·3*) oa
Beam, feet (*metres*)	36·1 (*11·0*)
Draught, feet (*metres*)	12 (*3·7*)
Guns	3—3 in (*76 mm*) 50 cal, dp
A/S weapons	8 K-guns; 1 DCT
Main engines	GM diesels; electric drive; 2 shafts; 6 000 hp
Range, miles	11 500 at 11 knots 5 500 at 18 knots
Speed, knots	20
Complement	220

ASAHI, HATSUHI

Former US "Bostwick" class destroyer escorts. Taken over from the US Navy on 14 June 1955.

ASAHI *1972, Toshio Tamura*

CORVETTES

8 "MIZUTORI" CLASS (PC)

Name	No.	Builders	Laid down	Launched	Completed
HATSUKARI	315	Sasebo Shipyard	25 Jan 1960	24 June 1960	15 Nov 1960
HIYODORI	320	Sasebo Shipyard	26 Feb 1965	25 Sep 1965	28 Feb 1966
KASASAGI	314	Fujinagata, Osaka	18 Dec 1959	31 May 1960	31 Oct 1960
MIZUTORI	311	Kawasaki, Kobe	13 Mar 1959	22 Sep 1959	27 Feb 1960
OTORI	313	Kure Shipyard	16 Dec 1959	27 May 1960	13 Oct 1960
SHIRATORI	319	Sasebo Shipyard	29 Feb 1964	8 Oct 1964	26 Feb 1965
UMIDORI	316	Sasebo Shipyard	15 Feb 1962	15 Oct 1962	30 Mar 1963
YAMADORI	312	Fujinagata, Osaka	14 Mar 1959	22 Oct 1959	15 Mar 1960

Displacement, tons	420 to 450 standard
Dimensions, feet	197·0 × 23·3 × 7·5
Guns	2—40 mm (1 twin) AA
A/S weapons	1 hedgehog; 1 DC rack; 6 homing torpedo launchers (Triple)
Main engines	2 MAN diesels; 2 shafts; 3 800 bhp = 20 knots
Complement	80
Range, miles	2 000 at 12 knots

OTORI 1972, *Toshio Tamura*

***Mizutori* and *Yamadori* built under 1958 programme, *Ōtori, Kasasagi* and *Hatsukari* 1959, *Umidori* (Sea Bird) and *Wakataka* (Young Hawk) 1961, *Kumataka* 1962, *Shirâtori* (White Bird) 1963, *Hiyodori* 1964.**

4 "UMITAKA" CLASS (PC)

Name	No.	Builders	Laid down	Launched	Completed
ŌTAKA	310	Kure Shipyard	18 Mar 1959	3 Sep 1959	14 Jan 1960
UMITAKA	309	Kawasaki, Kobe	13 Mar 1959	25 July 1959	30 Nov 1959
KUMATAKA	318	Fujinagata, Osaka	20 Mar 1963	21 Oct 1963	25 Mar 1964
WAKATAKA	317	Kure Shipyard	5 Mar 1962	13 Nov 1962	30 Mar 1963

Displacement, tons	440 to 480 standard
Dimensions, feet	197·0 × 23·3 × 8·0
Guns	2—40 mm (1 twin) AA
A/S weapons	1 Hedgehog, 1 DC rack; 2 triple A/S torpedo launchers
Main engines	2 B & W diesels; 2 shafts; 4 000 bhp = 20 knots
Complement	80

OTAKA 1967, *Hajime Fukaya*

KUMATAKA 1972, *Japanese Maritime Self-Defence Force*

1 "HAYABUSA" CLASS (PC)

HAYABUSA 308

Displacement, tons	360 standard
Dimensions, feet	190·2 × 25·7 × 7
Guns	2—40 mm AA (1 twin)
A/S weapons	1 hedgehog; 2 Y Guns; 2 DC racks
Main engines	2 diesels; 4 000 bhp; 2 shafts = 20 knots
Complement	75

Built under the 1954 fiscal year programme by Mitsubishi Shipbuilding & Engineering Co Ltd, Nagasaki. Laid down on 23 May 1956. Launched on 20 Nov 1956. Completed on 10 June 1957. A gas turbine was installed in Mar 1962 and removed in 1969.

HAYABUSA 1972, *Japanese Maritime Self-Defence Force*

7 "KARI" and "KAMOME" CLASS (PC)

Name	No.	Builders	Laid down	Launched	Completed
KAMOME	305	Uraga	27 Jan 1956	3 Sep 1956	14 Jan 1957
KARI	301	Fujimagata, Osaka	18 Jan 1956	26 Sep 1956	8 Feb 1957
KIJI	302	Iino, Maizuru	14 Dec 1955	11 Sep 1956	29 Jan 1957
MISAGO	307	Uraga	27 Jan 1956	1 Nov 1956	11 Feb 1957
TAKA	303	Fujimagata, Osaka	18 Jan 1956	17 Nov 1956	11 Mar 1957
TSUBAME	306	Kure Shipyard	15 Mar 1956	10 Oct 1956	31 Jan 1957
WASHI	304	Iino, Maizuru	14 Dec 1955	12 Nov 1956	20 Mar 1957

Displacement, tons	330 standard; (*Kari, Kiji, Taka, Washi,* 310)
Dimensions, feet	173·3 oa × 21·8 × 6·8
Guns	2—40 mm (1 twin)
A/S weapons	1 Hedgehog; 2-Y guns; 2 DC racks
Main engines	2 diesels (*Kari, Kiji, Taka,* and *Washi* Kawasaki-MAN; others Mitsui-Burmeister & Wain). 2 shafts; 4 000 bhp = 20 knots
Oil fuel (tons)	21·5
Range, miles	2 000 at 12 knots
Complement	70

MISAGO 1970, *Japanese Maritime Self Defence Force*

Authorised under the 1954 programme. At the time they were an entirely new type of fast patrol vessels, reminiscent of the United States PC type but modified and improved in many ways. *Kari* class (301-304). *Kamome* class (305-307).

SUBMARINES

4 + 4 "UZUSHIO" CLASS

Name	No.	Builders	Laid down	Launched	Completion
UZUSHIO	SS 566	Kawasaki	25 Sep 1968	11 Mar 1970	21 Jan 1971
MAKISHIO	SS 567	Mitsubishi	21 June 1969	27 Jan 1971	2 Feb 1972
ISOSHIO	SS 568	Kawasaki	9 July 1970	18 Mar 1972	25 Nov 1972
NARUSHIO	SS 569	Mitsubishi	8 May 1971	22 Nov 1972	28 Sep 1973
KUROSHIO	SS 570	Kawasaki	5 July 1972	Mar 1974	Feb 1975
TAKASHIO	SS 571	Mitsubishi	6 July 1973	July 1974	Nov 1975
—	SS 572	Kawasaki	—	—	1976
—	SS 573	—	—	—	1977

Displacement, tons: 1 850 standard
Length, feet (*metres*): 236·2 (*72·0*)
Beam, feet (*metres*): 32·5 (*9·9*)
Draught, feet (*metres*): 24·6 (*7·5*)
Torpedo tubes: 6—21 in (*533 mm*); bow
Main Machinery: 2 diesels; 3 400 bhp; 1 shaft; 1 electric motor; 7 200 hp
Speed, knots: 12 on surface; 20 submerged
Complement: 80

Of double-hull construction and "tear-drop" form.

NARUSHIO — *1973, Japanese Maritime Self-Defence Force*

5 "OOSHIO" CLASS

Name	No.	Builders	Laid down	Launched	Completed
ARASHIO	SS 565	Mitsubishi Jyuko, Kobe	5 July 1967	24 Oct 1968	25 July 1969
ASASHIO	SS 562	Kawasaki Jyuko Co, Kobe	10 Oct 1964	27 Nov 1965	13 Oct 1966
HARUSHIO	SS 563	Mitsubishi Jyuko Co, Kobe	12 Oct 1965	25 Feb 1967	1 Dec 1967
MICHISHIO	SS 564	Kawasaki Jyuko, Kobe	26 July 1966	5 Dec 1967	29 Aug 1968
OOSHIO	SS 561	Mitsubishi Jyuko Co, Kobe	29 June 1963	30 Apr 1964	31 Mar 1965

Displacement, tons: 1 650 standard; *Ooshio* 1 600
Length, feet (*metres*): 288·7 (*88·0*)
Beam, feet (*metres*): 26·9 (*8·2*)
Draught, feet (*metres*): 16·2 (*4·9*). *Ooshio* 15·4 (*4·7*)
Torpedo tubes: 8—21 in (*533 mm*); 6 bow 2 stern
Main Machinery: 2 diesels; 2 900 bhp; 2 shafts; 2 electric motors; 6 300 hp
Speed, knots: 14 on surface; 18 submerged
Complement: 80

Double-hulled boats. This class is the first ever built in Japanese yards with a deep-diving capability. A bigger design to obtain improved seaworthiness, a larger torpedo capacity and more comprehensive sonar and electronic devices. *Ooshio* was built under the 1961 programme, *Asashio* 1963. Cost $5 600 000.

MICHISHIO — *1972, Japanese Maritime Self-Defence Force*

4 "HAYASHIO" and "NATSUSHIO" CLASS

Name	No.	Builders	Laid down	Launched	Completed
FUYUSHIO	SS 524	Kawasaki Jyuko Co, Kobe	6 Dec 1961	14 Dec 1962	17 Sep 1963
HAYASHIO	SS 521	Shin Mitsubishi Jyuko Co, Kobe	6 June 1960	31 July 1961	30 June 1962
NATSUSHIO	SS 523	Shin Mitsubishi Jyuko Co, Kobe	5 Dec 1961	18 Sep 1962	29 June 1963
WAKASHIO	SS 522	Kawasaki Jyuko Co, Kobe	7 June 1960	28 Aug 1961	17 Aug 1962

Displacement, tons: 750 standard (SS 521, 522); 780 standard (SS 523, 524)
Length, feet (*metres*): 193·6 (*59·0*) oa (SS 521, 522); 200·1 (*61·0*) oa (SS 523, 524)
Beam, feet (*metres*): 21·3 (*6·5*)
Draught, feet (*metres*): 13·5 (*4·1*)
Torpedo tubes: 3—21 in (*533 mm*); bow
Main engines: 2 diesels, total 1 350 hp; 2 shafts; 2 electric motors, total 1 700 hp
Speed, knots: 11 on surface; 14 submerged
Complement: 40

Medium submarines of improved type, with more efficient sonar devices, giving them slightly increased displacement. Very handy and successful boats, with a large safety factor, complete air-conditioning and good habitability.

Hayashio class: SS 521-522.
Natsushio class: SS 523-524.

NATSUSHIO — *1973, Japanese Maritime Self-Defence Force*

1 "OYASHIO" CLASS

OYASHIO SS 511

Displacement, tons: 1 130 surface; 1 420 submerged
Length, feet (*metres*): 258·5 (*78·8*)
Beam, feet (*metres*): 23 (*7·0*)
Draught, feet (*metres*): 15·2 (*4·6*)
Torpedo tubes: 4—21 in (*533 mm*); 10 torpedoes
Main engines: 2 diesels, total 2 700 hp; 2 electric motors, total 5 960 hp
Speed, knots: 13 on surface; 19 submerged
Range, miles: 5 000 at 10 knots
Complement: 65

OYASHIO — *1972, Japanese Maritime Self-Defence Force*

Ordered under the 1956 Programme. Built by Kawasaki Jyuko Co Kobe. Laid down on 25 Dec 1957, launched on 25 May 1959 and completed on 30 June 1960. The first submarine built in a Japanese shipyard after the Second World War, *Oyashio* is the name of a tide stream in the Pacific off Honshu. First estimated to cost £2 718 000, but this figure was exceeded. Of double-hull construction.

LIGHT FORCES

PT 11 PT 12 PT 13 PT 14 PT 15 (FAST ATTACK CRAFT—TORPEDO)

Displacement, tons	100
Dimensions, feet	116·4 × 30·2 × 3·9
Guns	2—40 mm AA
Tubes	4—21 inch
Main engines	2 Mitsubishi diesels; 2 IHI gas turbines; 3 shafts; 11 200 hp (PT 11 10 500 hp) = 40 knots
Complement	28

Built by Mitsubishi, Shimonoseki. PT 11 laid down 11 Mar 1970, completed 27 Mar 1971. PT 12 laid down 22 April 1971, completed 28 Mar 1972. PT 13 laid down 28 Mar 1972, completed 16 Dec 1972. PT 14 laid down 23 Mar 1973, completed 15 Feb 1974. PT 15 launched July 1974. One more projected.

PT 13 *1972, Ships of the World*

PT 10 (FAST ATTACK CRAFT—TORPEDO)

Displacement, tons	90 standard; 120 full load
Dimensions, feet	105 × 27·8 × 3·7
Guns	2—40 mm AA (1 forward, 1 aft)
Tubes	4—21 in (single, amidships)
Main engines	3 Napier Deltic diesels; 9 400 bhp = 40 knots
Complement	26

1960 programme. Built by Mitsubishi, Shimonoseki. Laid down on 30 Jan 1961 Launched on 28 July 1961. Completed on 25 May 1962. Light metal hull.

PT 10 *1971, Japanese Maritime Self-Defence Force*

HAYATE (HYDROFOIL)

Displacement, tons	78
Dimensions, feet	78·8 × 18 × 8·5
Main engines	2 Gas Turbines; 1 Diesel; 6 500 bhp = 50 knots
Complement	19

Completed March 1970. Belongs to Technical Research and Development Institute.

PB 19, 20, 21, 22, 23, 24, 25, 26, 27 (PATROL CRAFT—COASTAL)

Displacement, tons	18
Dimensions, feet	55·8 × 14·1 × 2·7
Gun	1—20 mm
Main engines	2 diesels; 760 hp = 20 knots
Complement	6

19-22 completed 31 Mar 1971, 23-24 31 Mar 1972, 25-27 Mar 1973. All built by Ishikawajima Yokohama. GRP hulls.

KOSOKU 4 ASH 04 **KOSOKU 5** ASH 05 **KOSOKU 6**

(PATROL CRAFT—COASTAL)

Displacement, tons	30
Dimensions, feet	75·5 × 18 × 2·5
Main engines	2 Packard engines; 1 600 bhp = 30 knots

Of aluminium construction. Laid down on 10 Oct 1958 and 11 Dec 1958 at Mitsubishi, Shimonoseki Works under the 1957 and 1958 Programme, launched on 11 Dec 1958 and 2 Mar 1959, and completed on 11 May ,1959 and 12 June 1959. respectively.

KOSOKU 5 *1972, Toshio Tamura*

KOSOKU 2 (PATROL CRAFT—COASTAL)

Displacement, tons	30
Dimensions, feet	65·7 × 17 × 2·7
Main engines	2 Packard petrol engines; 3 000 bhp = 42 knots

ASH category. Of wooden construction. All are Maritime Self-Defence Force Auxiliaries.

AMPHIBIOUS SHIPS

4 2000 TON CLASS (LST)

MIUR 4151 **OZIKA 4152** **4153** **4154**

Displacement, tons	2 000
Guns	2—3 in (singles)
Main engines	6 000 hp = 17 knots or 4 400 hp = 13·5 knots

Fitted with bow doors. First laid down Nov 1973 for completion August 1975. Two more under 1973 programme and one more under 1974 programme.

3 "ATSUMI" CLASS (LST)

ATSUMI 4101 **MOTOBU** 4102 **NEMURO** 4103

Displacement, tons	1 480
Dimensions, feet	291·9 × 42·6 × 8·5
Guns	4—40 mm AA (twins)
Main engines	2 diesels; 4 400 hp = 14 knots
Complement	100

Atsumi completed 27 Nov 1972 at Sasebo Jyuko Co, Sasebo. *Motobu* laid down at Sasebo 23 April 1973, launched 3 Aug 1973. Completion 21 Dec 1973. Nemuro to complete in 1975.

ATSUMI *1972, Toshio Tamura*

2 "OOSUMI" CLASS

SHIMOKITA 4002 **SHIRETOKO** 4003

Displacement, tons	1 650 standard; 4 080 full load
Dimensions, feet	316·0 wl; 328·0 oa × 50·0 × 14·0
Guns	4—40 mm single; 2—40 mm twin; 12—20 mm AA single
Main engines	GM diesels; 2 shafts; 1 700 bhp = 11 knots
Range, miles	9 500 at 9 knots
Complement	100

Former *Hillsdale County, LST* 835, and *Nansemond County, LST* 1064, built by American Bridge Co. Ambridge; Pa; and Bethlehem Steel Co, Hingham, Mass. respectively, in 1954-55. Commissioned in the Japanese MSDF on 1 Apr 1961.

SHIMOKITA *1972, Japanese Maritime Self-Defence Force*

OOSUMI *1972, Toshio Tamura*

Amphibious Ships—*continued*

LCU 2001 LCU 2002 LCU 2003 LCU 2004 LCU 2005 LCU 2006

Ex-US LCU 1602 to 1607 of 187 tons transferred on 2 June 1955.

LCM 1001—1042

29 LCMs of 22 tons and 20 LCVPs of 8 tons were transferred from USA on 2 June 1955 and 13 LCMs, Nos 1030—1042 in 1961.

MINE WARFARE FORCES

1 "SOOYA" CLASS MINELAYER

SOOYA 951

Displacement, tons	1 950 standard; 2 500 full load
Length, feet (*metres*)	324·8 (*99·0*)
Beam, feet (*metres*)	42·7 (*13·0*)
Draught, feet (*metres*)	12·5 (*3·8*)
Guns	2—3 in (*76 mm*) 50 cal. (1 twin); 2—20 mm
Torpedo tubes	6 anti-submarine type (2 triple)
Main engines	2 diesels; 4 000 bhp; 2 shafts
Speed, knots	18
Complement	185

Laid down by Hitachi Zosen, Maizuru on 9 July 1970, launched 31 Mar 1971 and completed 30 Sept 1971. With twin rails can carry 200 buoyant mines. Has helicopter platform aft and acts at times as command ship for MCM forces.

SOOYA *1972, Maizuru Jukogyo*

ERIMO 491 (MINELAYER)

Displacement, tons	630 standard
Dimensions, feet	210 × 26 × 8
Guns	2—40 mm AA; 2—20 mm AA
A/S weapons	1 Hedgehog; 2 K-guns; 2 DC racks
Main engines	Diesel; 2 shafts; 2 500 bhp = 18 knots
Complement	80

Authorised under 1953 fiscal programme. Built by Uraga Dock Co. Laid down on 10 Dec 1954. Launched on 12 July 1955. Completed on 28 Dec 1955.

ERIMO *1970, Japanese Maritime Self-Defence Force*

HAYASE 462 (MINESWEEPER SUPPORT SHIP)

Displacement, tons	2 150 standard
Dimensions, feet	324·8 × 49·2 × 13·8
Guns	2—3 in (*76 mm*); 2—20 mm
Main engines	4 diesels; 6 400 bhp; 2 screws = 18 knots
Torpedo tubes	6 anti-submarine
Complement	185

Laid down by Ishikawajima Haruna 16 Sep 1970, launched 21 June 1971, completed 6 Nov 1971. Has helicopter platform aft.

HAYASE *1972, Japanese Maritime Self Defence Force*

24 "KASADO" CLASS (MINESWEEPERS—COASTAL)

Name	*No.*	*Laid down*	*Launched*	*Completed*
AMAMI	MSC 625	1 Mar 1966	31 Oct 1966	6 Mar 1967
CHIBURI	MSC 620	27 Mar 1963	29 Nov 1963	25 Mar 1964
HABUSHI	MSC 608	25 Aug 1958	19 June 1959	22 Sep 1959
HARIO	MSC 618	19 Mar 1962	10 Dec 1962	23 Mar 1963
HIRADO	MSC 614	14 Mar 1960	3 Oct 1960	17 Dec 1960
HOTAKA	MSC 616	22 Mar 1961	23 Oct 1961	24 Feb 1962
IBUKI	MSC 628	27 Feb 1967	2 Dec 1967	27 Feb 1968
KANAWA	MSC 606	25 Aug 1958	22 Apr 1959	24 July 1959
KARATO	MSC 617	15 Mar 1962	11 Dec 1962	23 Mar 1963
KASADO	MSC 604	9 July 1957	19 Mar 1958	26 June 1958
KATSURA	MSC 629	10 Feb 1967	18 Sep 1967	15 Feb 1968
KOSHIKI	MSC 615	20 Mar 1961	9 Nov 1961	29 Jan 1962
KUDAKO	MSC 622	17 Mar 1964	8 Dec 1964	24 Mar 1965
MIKURA	MSC 612	30 Mar 1959	14 Mar 1960	27 May 1960
MINASE	MSC 627	1 Feb 1966	10 Jan 1967	25 Mar 1967
MUTSURE	MSC 619	28 Mar 1963	16 Dec 1963	24 Mar 1964
OOTSU	MSC 621	25 Mar 1964	6 Nov 1964	24 Feb 1965
REBUN	MSC 624	17 Feb 1964	18 Dec 1964	25 Mar 1965
RISHIRI	MSC 623	9 Mar 1964	22 Nov 1965	5 Mar 1966
SAKITO	MSC 607	16 Aug 1958	22 Apr 1959	25 Aug 1959
SHIKINE	MSC 613	12 Jan 1960	22 July 1960	15 Nov 1960
TATARA	MSC 610	30 Mar 1959	14 Jan 1960	26 Mar 1960
TSUKUMI	MSC 611	24 Mar 1959	12 Jan 1960	27 Apr 1960
URUME	MSC 626	1 Feb 1966	12 Nov 1966	30 Jan 1967

Displacement, tons	340 standard
Dimensions, feet	150·9 × 27·6 × 7·5; 170·6 × 28·9 × 7·9 later ships
Guns	1—20 mm AA
Main engines	2 diesels; 2 shafts; 1 200 bhp, 1 440 later ships= 14 knots

Hull is of wooden construction. Otherwise built of non-magnetic materials. *Habushi, Kanawa, Kasado* were built by Hitachi, Kanawaga Works, *Sakito* by Nippon Steel Tube Co, Tsurumi. *Shisaka* now acts as an auxiliary—YAS62.

SHIKINE *1972, Toshio Tamura*

Minewarfare Forces—*continued*

12 + 5 "TAKAMI" CLASS (MINESWEEPERS—COASTAL)

Name	*No.*	*Laid down*	*Launched*	*Completed*
AWAJI	MSC 634	20 Apr 1970	11 Dec 1970	29 Mar 1971
IOU	MSC 631	21 Sep 1968	12 Aug 1969	22 Jan 1970
MIYAKE	MSC 632	14 Aug 1969	3 June 1970	19 Nov 1970
MIYATO	MSC 639	22 Apr 1972	3 Apr 1973	24 July 1973
MUROTSU	MSC 637	16 Apr 1971	16 Dec 1971	31 Mar 1972
TAKAMI	MSC 630	25 Sep 1968	15 July 1969	15 Dec 1969
TASHIRO	MSC 638	26 May 1972	2 Apr 1973	30 July 1973
TEURI	MSC 636	12 Apr 1971	19 Oct 1971	14 Mar 1972
TOUSHI	MSC 635	14 May 1970	12 Oct 1970	18 Mar 1971
UTONE	MSC 633	6 Aug 1969	6 Apr 1970	3 Sep 1970
TAKANE	MSC 640	26 Apr 1973	May 1974	Aug 1974
MUZUKI	MSC 641	7 June 1973	Apr 1974	Aug 1974
YOKOSE	MSC 642	—	Feb 1975	1975
SAKATE	MSC 643	—	Feb 1975	1975
—	MSC 644	—	—	1976?
—	MSC 645	—	—	1976?
—	MSC 646	—	—	1977?
—	MSC 647	—	—	1977?

Of similar dimensions to "Kasado" class but of slightly different construction and with a displacement of 380 tons. Same builders as "Kasado" class.

TAKAMI *1972, Japanese Maritime Self-Defence Force*

1 "KOOZU" CLASS

KOOZU MST 473

Similar to "Kasado" class but has had minesweeping gear removed and was fitted as MCM Command Ship in July 1972.

4 "YASHIMA" CLASS

HASHIMA (ex-USS *AMS* 95) YAS 47
TOSHIMA (ex-USS *MSC* 258) YAS 61
TSUSHIMA (ex-USS *MSC*, ex-*AMS* 255) YAS 60
YASHIMA (ex-USS *AMS* 144) YAS 46

Displacement, tons	335 standard; 375 full load
Dimensions, feet	138 pp; 144 oa × 26·5 × 8·3
Guns	1—20 mm AA
Main engines	2 GM diesels; 880 bhp = 13 knots
Range, miles	2 500 at 10 knots

Former US auxiliary minesweepers *Hashima* and *Yashima* now used as accommodation ships. *Tsushima* and *Toshima* now act as auxiliaries.

10 "ICHIGO" CLASS (MSBs)

01 02 05 06 07 08 09 10 11 12

Displacement, tons	40 (53 for 07-12)
Dimensions, feet	62·3 oa × 16 × 4 (07-12 73·8 × 17·7 × 3·3)
Main engines	2 diesels; 2 shafts; 320 bhp = 10 knots (07-12 480 hp = 11 knots)
Complement	10

05-6 were laid down in Aug 1958 and completed in Feb-Mar 1959. 07 and 10 were built by Hitachi, Kanagawa; and the others by Nippon Steel Tube Co, Tsurumi. No. 07 laid down 26 May 1972 and completed 29 Mar 1973. No. 08 laid down 3 Aug 1972 and completed 29 Mar 1973. No. 09 laid down 5 July 1973, completed 30 Mar 1974. No 10 laid down 7 June 1973, completion March 1974. No. 11 and 12 launched July-Aug 1974 respectively.

MB 5 ***1963***

SERVICE FORCES

AZUMA 4201 (TRAINING SHIP)

Displacement, tons	1 950 standard; 2 500 full load
Length, feet (*metres*)	325 (*99·0*)
Beam, feet (*metres*)	42·7 (*13·0*)
Draught, feet (*metres*)	12·5 (*3·8*)
Aircraft	1 helicopter
Guns	2—3 in (*76 mm*) 50 cal. 2—20 mm
A/S weapons	2 triple torpedo launchers
Main engines	2 diesels; 2 shafts; 4 000 bhp
Speed, knots	18
Complement	185

Built by Maizuru Jyuko Co, Maizuru as a training support ship. Laid down on 30 July 1968, launched on 14 Apr 1969 and completed 26 Nov 1969. Has helicopter hangar amidships. Acts as drone carrier.

AZUMA

KATORI 3501 (TRAINING SHIP)

Displacement, tons	3 372 standard; 4 000 full load
Length, feet (*metres*)	418·5 (*127·0*)
Beam, feet (*metres*)	49·3 (*14·6*)
Draught, feet (*metres*)	14·6 (*4·3*)
Aircraft	1 helicopter
Guns, dual purpose	4—3 in (*76 mm*) 50 cal
A/S weapons	1 four barrelled rocket launcher
Torpedo launchers	6 (2 triple mounts) for homing torpedoes
Main engines	geared turbines; 2 shafts; 20 000 shp
Range, miles	7 000 at 18 knots
Speed, knots	25
Complement	460 including trainees

Built by Ishikawajima Harima, Tokyo. Laid down 8 Dec 1967, launched on 19 Nov 1968 and completed on 10 Sep 1969. Provided with a landing deck aft for a helicopter and amidships hangar.

RADAR Search: SPS 12. Tactical: SPS 10.

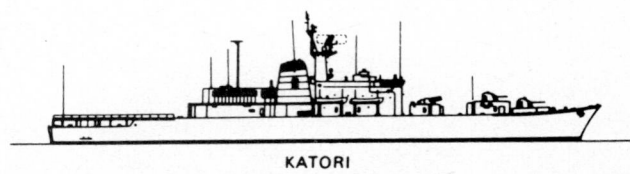

KATORI

KATORI *1970, Courtesy, Toshio Tamura*

Service Forces—*continued*

FUSIMI ASR 402 (SUBMARINE RESCUE)

Displacement, tons	1 430 standard
Dimensions, feet	249·5 × 41 × 12
Main engines	2 diesels; 1 shaft; 3 000 bhp = 16 knots
Complement	100

Built by Sumnitomo SB & Machinery Co, laid down on 5 Nov 1968, launched 10 Sep 1969, completed 10 Feb 1970. Has a rescue chamber and two decompression chambers.

FUSIMI *1972, Japanese Maritime Self-Defence Force*

CHIHAYA ASR 401 (SUBMARINE RESCUE)

Displacement, tons	1 340 standard
Dimensions, feet	239·5 × 39·3 × 12·7
Main engines	Diesels; 2 700 bhp = 15 knots
Complement	90

Authorised under the 1959 programme. The first vessel of her kind to be built in Japan. Laid down on 15 Mar 1960. Launched by Mitsubishi Nippon Heavy Industries Co, Yokohama on 4 Oct 1960. Completed on 15 Mar 1961 Has rescue chamber, 2 decompression chambers, four-point mooring equipment and a 12 ton derrick.

CHIHAYA *1972, Japanese Maritime Self-Defence Force*

SHOBO 41 (SALVAGE VESSEL)

Displacement, tons	45
Dimensions, feet	75 × 18 × 3·3
Main engines	4 diesels; Speed = 19 knots

A fire defence boat. Built by Azumo Zosen, Yokosuka. Completed 28 Feb 1964.

TSUGARU ARC 481 (CABLE LAYER)

Displacement, tons	2 150 standard
Dimensions, feet	337·8 × 40·7 × 16
Guns	2—20 mm AA
Main engines	Diesel; 2 shafts; 3 200 bhp = 13 knots
Complement	100

Dual purpose cable layer and coastal minelayer. Built under the 1953 programme by Yokohama Shipyard & Engine Works, Mitsubishi Nippon-Heavy Industries Ltd. Laid down on 18 Dec 1954. Launched on 19 July 1955. Completed on 15 Dec 1955. Converted to cable-layer 10 July 1969-30 April 1970 by Nippon Steel Tube Co.

TSUGARU *1972, Toshio Tamura*

HAMANA (SUPPORT TANKER)

Displacement, tons	2 900 light; 7 550 full load
Dimensions, feet	420 × 51·5 × 20·5
Guns	2—40 mm AA
Main engines	Diesel; 5 000 bhp = 16 knots

Built by Uraga Dock Co under the 1960 programme. Laid down on 17 Apr 1961 launched on 24 Oct 1961, and completed on 10 Mar 1962. Named after the lake.

MISCELLANEOUS

2 "NASAMI" CLASS

MIHO (ex-USS *FS* 524) YAS 59 **NASAMI** (ex-USS *FS* 408) YAS 51

Displacement, tons	706
Dimensions, feet	177 × 30 × 10
Main engines	Diesels; 2 shafts; 1 000 bhp = 11 knots

Transferred from the United States in 1955. *Nasami* is rated as a minesweeper tender (MST), *Miho*, formerly rated as ASS, was refitted as an inshore minesweeper depot ship in August 1959.

NASAMI *1972, Toshio Tamura*

YAS 48 (ex-PT 1) **YAS 54** (ex-PT 5) **YAS 55** (ex-PT 6)

Displacement, tons	75
Dimensions, feet	82 × 20 × 6
Main engines	diesel engines; 13 knots

PTs converted to Harbour auxiliaries.

2 "ATADA" CLASS

Name	*No.*	*Laid down*	*Launched*	*Completed*
ATADA	YAS 56	20 June 1955	12 Mar 1956	30 Apr 1956
ITSUKI	YAS 57	22 June 1955	12 Mar 1956	20 June 1956

Displacement, tons	240 standard; 260 full load
Dimensions, feet	118 pp; 123·3 oa × 21 × 6·8
Guns	1—20 mm AA
Main engines	Diesel; 2 shafts; 1 200 bhp = 13 knots

Former minesweepers of wood and light metal construction. Authorised under the 1953 programme. Built by the Hitachi Zosen Co. Now used as auxiliaries.

ATADA *1972, Toshio Tamura*

1 "YASHIRO" CLASS

YASHIRO YAS 58

Displacement, tons	230 standard; 255 full load
Dimensions, feet	118 pp × 22·7 × 6·2
Guns	1—20 mm AA
Main engines	diesel; 2 shafts; 1 200 bhp = 13 knots

Built under the 1963 Programme by the Nippon Steel Tube Co, Tsurumi. Laid down on 22 June 1955, launched on 26 Mar 1956 and completed on 10 July 1956. Former minesweeper, now used as auxiliary.

YASHIRO *1970, Japanese Maritime Self-Defence Force*

ICEBREAKER

FUJI 5001

Displacement, tons	5 250 standard; 7 760 normal; 8 566 full load
Dimensions, feet	328 × 72·2 × 29
Aircraft	3 helicopters
Main engines	4 diesel-electric; 2 shafts; 12 000 shp = 16 knots
Radius, miles	5 000 at 15 knots
Complement	200 plus 35 scientists and observers

Antarctic Support Ship. Built by Tsurumi Shipyard, Yokohama, Nippon Kokan Kabushiki Kaisha. Laid down on 28 Aug 1964, launched on 18 Mar 1965, delivered on 15 July 1965. Hangar and flight deck aft. Named after the mountain.

FUJI 1968, *Japanese Maritime Self-Defence Force*

TUGS

SUMA YAS 45

Displacement, tons	115
Dimensions, feet	70·5 × 19 × 5
Main engines	1 diesel; 600 bhp = 12 knots

ATR category. Steel construction. Former name YTL 749. The small harbour tugs 72, 167, 203, 244, 749 and 750 were transferred by the USA.

MARITIME SAFETY AGENCY

Established in May 1948 — *Commandant:* Toru Sahara — Personnel 1974: 11 236

LARGE PATROL VESSELS

2 "IZU" CLASS

IZU PL 31 — **MIURA** PL 32

Displacement, tons	2 080 normal
Dimensions, feet	295·3 wl × 38 × 12·8
Main engines	diesel; 2 shafts; 10 400 bhp = 21·6 knots
Range, miles	14 500 at 12·7 knots; 5 000 at 21 knots
Complement	72

Izu was laid down in Aug 1966, launched in Jan 1967 and completed in July 1967. *Miura*, built by Maizuru Jukogyo Ltd, was laid down in May 1968, launched in Oct 1968 and completed in Mar 1969. Employed in long range rescue and patrol and weather observation duties. Equipped with weather observation radar, various types of marine instruments. Ice proof hull for winter work.

3 "ERIMO" CLASS

DAIO PL 15 — **ERIMO** PL 13 — **SATSUMA** PL 14

Displacement, tons	1 009 normal (1 206 *Daio*)
Dimensions, feet	239·5 wl × 30·2 × 9·9 (31·5 × 10·7 *Daio*)
Guns	1—3 in 50 cal; 1—20 mm AA (1—40 mm; 1—20 mm *Daio*)
Main engines	Diesels; 2 shafts; 4 800 bhp = 19·78 knots (7 000 bhp = 20 knots, *Daio*)
Range, miles	5 000 at 17 knots

First pair built by Hitachi Zosen Co Ltd. *Erimo* was laid down on 29 Mar 1965, launched on 14 Aug 1965 and completed on 30 Nov 1965. Her structure is strengthened against ice. Employed as a patrol vessel off northern Japan. *Satsuma*, completed on 30 July 1966, is assigned to guard and rescue south of Japan. *Daio* built by Hitachi Maizuru—laid down 18 Oct 1972, launched 19 June 1973, completed 28 Sep 1973 (cp propellers).

KOJIMA PL 21

Displacement, tons	1 100
Dimensions, feet	228·3 × 33·8 × 10·5
Guns	1—3 in; 1—40 mm AA; 1—20 mm AA
Main engines	Diesels; 2 600 hp = 17 knots
Range, miles	6 000 at 13 knots
Complement	17 officers, 42 men, 47 cadets

Maritime Safety Agency training ship. Completed on 21 May 1964 at Kure Zosen.

2 "NOJIMA" CLASS

NOJIMA PL 11 — **OJIKA** PL 12

Displacement, tons	950 standard; 980 normal; 1 100 full load
Dimensions, feet	208·8 pp; 226·5 oa × 30·2 × 10·5
Main engines	2 sets diesels; 3 000 bhp = 17·5 knots
Complement	51

Nojima was built by Uraga Dock Co Ltd. Laid down on 27 Oct 1961, launched on 12 Feb 1962, and completed on 30 Apr 1962. *Ojika* was completed on 10 June 1963. Both employed as patrol vessels and weather ships.

Large Patrol Craft—*continued*

MIURA 1970, *Japanese Maritime Safety Agency*

DAIO 1973, *Japanese Maritime Safety Agency*

KOJIMA 1965, *Japanese Maritime Safety Agency*

OJIKA 1972, *Japanese Maritime Safety Agency*

Large Patrol Vessels—*continued*

1 "MUROTO" CLASS

MUROTO PL 01

Displacement, tons	750 standard; 840 normal
Dimensions, feet	182 pp; 200 oa × 30·5 × 10·2
Guns	1—3 in, 50 cal; 2—20 mm AA
Main engines	2—4 cycle single acting diesels; 1 500 bhp = 15·37 knots

Muroto, built by Uraga Dock Company Ltd, Tokyo, was laid down on 16 Aug 1949, launched on 5 Dec 1949, and delivered on 20 Mar 1950.

MUROTO 1970, *Japanese Maritime Safety Agency*

SOYA PL 107

Displacement, tons	4 364 normal; 4 818 full load
Dimensions, feet	259·2 wl × 51·9 (*including bulge*) × 18·9
Aircraft	4 helicopters (see *notes*)
Main engines	2 sets diesels; 4 800 bhp = 12·5 knots on trials
Range, miles	10 000 at 12 knots
Complement	96

Assigned to guard and rescue service as a patrol vessel.

SOYA 1970, *Japanese Maritime Safety Agency*

MEDIUM PATROL VESSELS

3 "MIYAKE" CLASS

AWAJI PM 71 **MIYAKE** PM 70 **YAEYAMA** PM 72

Displacement, tons	530 standard; 574 full load
Dimensions, feet	190·4 oa × 24·2 × 8·2
Gun	1—20 mm
Main engines	Diesels; 2 shafts; 3 200 hp = 17·8 knots
Range, miles	3 580 at 16 knots
Complement	40

Miyake and *Awaji* completed on 25 Jan 1973, *Yaeyama* 20 Dec 1972. Of similar hull design to "Kunashiri" class. CP propellers.

MIYAKE 1973, *Japanese Maritime Safety Agency*

4 "KUNASHIRI" CLASS

SAROBETSO PM 67 **KAMISHIMA** PM 68 **SADO** PM 03

Displacement, tons	498 normal
Dimensions, feet	190·4 oa × 24·2 × 7·9
Gun	1—20 mm AA
Main engines	2 sets diesels; 2 600 bhp = 17·6 knots
Range, miles	3 000 at 16·9 knots
Complement	40

Kunashiri was built by Maizuru Jukogyo Ltd. Laid down in Oct 1968, launched in Dec 1968 and completed in Mar 1969. *Minabe*, laid down in Oct 1969, and completed in Mar 1970.

Medium Patrol Vessels—*continued*

KUNASHIRI 1970, *Japanese Maritime Safety Agency*

5 "CHIFURI" CLASS

CHIFURI PM 18 **KOZU** PM 20 **SHIKINE** PM 21
DAITO PM 22 **KUROKAMI** PM 19

Displacement, tons	465 standard; 483 normal
Dimensions, feet	169 pp; 177 wl × 25·2 × 8·5 (normal)
Guns	1—3 in 50 cal; 1—20 mm AA
Main engines	2 sets diesels; 1 300 bhp = 15·8 knots
Range, miles	3 000 at 12 knots

DAITO 1970, *Japanese Maritime Safety Agency*

14 "REBUN" CLASS

AMAKUSA	PM 09	**HIRADO**	PM 17	**NOTO**	PM 13
GENKAI	PM 07	**IKI**	PM 05	**OKI**	PM 06
HACHIJO	PM 08	**KOSHIKI**	PM 16	**OKUSHIRI**	PM 10
HEKURA	PM 14	**KUSAKAKI**	PM 11	**REBUN**	PM 04
		MIKURA	PM 15	**RISHIRI**	PM 12

Displacement, tons	450 standard; 488 trials; 495 normal
Dimensions, feet	155·2 pp; 164 wl; 170 oa × 26·5 × 8·5
Guns	1—3 in 50 cal; 1—20 mm AA
Main engines	2 sets diesels; 1 300 bhp = 15 knots
Range, miles	3 000 at 12 knots

A development of the original "Awaji" class medium patrol vessel design. All completed in 1951.

HIRADO 1972, *Japanese Maritime Safety Agency*

SADO PM 03

Displacement, tons	510 standard; 550 full load
Dimensions, feet	172 oa × 26·7 × 9·2
Guns	1—3 in 50 cal; 1—20 mm AA
Main engines	2 sets diesels; 1 300 bhp = 15 knots
Range, miles	6 000 at 12 knots

Of a design resembling United States Coast Guard Cutters. All completed in 1950.

TESHIO PM 53

Displacement, tons	421·5 normal
Dimensions, feet	149·4 pp; 159 wl × 23 × 8·2
Gun	1—40 mm AA
Main engines	2 sets diesels; 1 400 bhp = 15·71 knots
Range, miles	3 800 at 12 knots
Complement	37

Built by Uraga Dock Co Ltd. Laid down on 15 Sep 1954, launched on 12 Jan 1955, completed on 19 Mar 1955.

5 "MATSUURA" CLASS

AMAMI PM 62 **MATSUURA** PM 60 **SENDAI** PM 61
KARATSU PM 64 **NATORI** PM 63

Displacement, tons	420 standard; 425 normal
Dimensions, feet	163·3 pp; 181·5 oa × 23 × 7·5
Gun	1—20 mm AA
Main engines	2 sets diesels; 1 400 bhp = 16·5 knots (*Matsuura, Sendai*); 1 800 bhp = 16·8 knots (*Amami, Natori*); 2 600 bhp (*Karatsu*)
Range, miles	3 500 at 12 knots
Complement	37

Matsuura and *Sendai* were built by Osaka Shipbuilding Co Ltd. *Matsuura* was laid down on 16 Oct 1960, launched on 24 Dec 1960 and completed on 18 Mar 1961. *Sendai* was laid down on 23 Aug 1961, launched on 18 Jan 1962 and completed on 21 Apr 1962. *Amami* completed on 29 Mar 1965, *Natori*, completed in 1966, and *Karatsu*, delivered to MSA on 31 Mar 1967, were built by Hitachi Zosen Co Ltd.

MATSUURA *1970, Japanese Maritime Safety Agency*

6 "YAHAGI" CLASS

CHITOSE PM 56 **SORACHI** PM 57 **YAHAGI** PM 54
HORONAI PM 59 **SUMIDA** PM 55 **YUBARI** PM 58

Displacemment, tons	333·15 standard; 375·7 normal
Dimensions, feet	147·3 pp; 157·2 wl × 24 × 7·4 (normal)
Gun	1—40 mm AA
Main engines	2 sets diesels; 1 400 bhp = 15·5 knots
Range, miles	3 500 at 12 knots
Complement	37

All built by Niigata Engineering Co Ltd, *Yahagi* was laid down on 9 Dec 1955, launched on 19 May 1956 and completed on 31 July 1956. *Sumida* was completed on 30 June 1957. *Chitose* was laid down on 20 Sep 1957, launched on 24 Feb 1958 and completed on 30 Apr 1958. *Sorachi* was completed in Mar 1959, *Yubari* on 15 Mar 1960 *Horonai* on 4 Feb 1961.

SORACHI *1972, Japanese Maritime Safety Agency*

2 "TOKACHI" CLASS

TATSUTA PM 52 **TOKACHI** PM 51

Displacement, tons	336 standard; 381 normal (*Tokachi*) 324 standard; 369 normal (*Tatsuta*)
Dimensions, feet	157·5 pp; 164 wl; 170 oa × 21·9 × 11·2
Gun	1—40 mm AA
Main engines	2 sets of 4 cycle single acting diesels 1 500 bhp = 16 knots (max); 12 knots (service) (*Tokachi*) 1 400 bhp = 15 knots (max); 12 knots (service) (*Tatsuta*)
Range, miles	3 800 at 12 knots
Complement	37

Tokachi was built by Harima Dockyard, Kure. Laid down on 14 Nov 1953, launched on 8 May 1954 and completed on 31 July 1954. *Tatsuta* was completed on 10 Sep 1954.

TOKACHI *1972, Japanese Maritime Safety Agency*

SMALL PATROL VESSELS

5 SPECIAL RESCUE TYPE

AKAGI PS 40

Displacement, tons	42
Dimensions, feet	78·8 oa × 17·8 × 3·2
Main engines	2 Mercedes Benz diesels; 2 200 bhp = 28 knots
Range, miles	350 at 21 knots

Completed by Hitachi Zosen Kanagawa in 1965.

Small Patrol Vessels—*continued*

3 "NAGARA" CLASS

KITAKAMI PS 20 **NAGARA** PS 18 **TONE** PS 19

Displacement, tons	260
Dimensions, feet	131·2 × 23 × 7·2
Gun	1—40 mm AA
Main engines	2 diesels; 2 shafts; 800 bhp = 13·5 knots
Range, miles	2 000 at 12 knots
Complement	35

Improved versions of the "Fuji" class. All launched and completed in 1952.

NAGARA *1970 Japanese Maritime Safety Agency*

16 "FUJI" CLASS

ABUKUMA PS 08 **KIKUCHI** PS 10 **NOSHIRO** PS 13
CHIKUGO PS 16 **KISO** PS 14 **OYODO** PS 07
FUJI PS 02 **KUMANO** PS 17 **SAGAMI** PS 06
ISHIKARI PS 05 **KUZURYU** PS 09 **SHINANO** PS 15
ISUZU PS 04 **MOGAMI** PS 11 **TENRYU** PS 03
YOSHINO PS 12

Displacement, tons	258 standard; 275 normal
Dimensions, feet	122 pp; 126·3 wl; 132·2 oa × 23 × 7·5
Gun	1—40 mm AA
Main engines	2 sets diesels; 800 bhp = 13·6 knots
Range, miles	2 000 at 12 knots
Complement	35

Built in the early 1950's.

MOGAMI *1970, Japanese Maritime Safety Agency*

13 "HIDAKA" CLASS

ASHITAKA PS 43 **IBUKI** PS 45 **ROKKO** PS 35
AKIYOSHI PS 37 **KAMUI** PS 41 **TAKANAWA** PS 36
HIDAKA PS 32 **KUNIMI** PS 38 **TAKATSUKI** PS 39
HIYAMA PS 33 **KURAMA** PS 44 **TOUMI** PS 46
TSURUGI PS 34

Displacement, tons	166·2 to 164·4 standard; 169·4 normal
Dimensions, feet	100 pp; 111 oa × 20·8 × 5·5
Main engines	1 set diesels; 1 shaft; 690 to 700 bhp = 13·5 knots
Range, miles	1 200 at 12 knots

Hidaka was built by Azuma Shipbuilding Co. Laid down on 4 Oct 1961. launched on 2 Mar 1962 and completed on 23 Apr 1962. Both *Hiyama* and *Tsurugi* were completed in Mar 1963 by Hitachi Shipbuilding Co. *Kunimi* was built under the 1964 fiscal year programme by Hayashikane Shipbuilding & Engineering Co, Shimoneseki, laid down on 15 Nov 1964, launched on 19 Dec 1964 and completed on 15 Feb 1965. Three more local patrol ships were completed in 1965, two in 1966, two in 1967 and two in 1968.

ASHITAKA *1972, Japanese Maritime Safety Agency*

Small patrol vessels—*continued*

TSUKUBA PS 31

Displacement, tons	65
Dimensions, feet	80·5 × 21·5 × 3·7
Main engines	2 Niigata diesels; 1 800 bhp = 18·4 knots trials
Range, miles	230 at 15 knots

Built by Hitachi Zosen, Kanagawa and completed on 30 May 1962.

ASAMA PS 47 **BIZAN** PS 42 **SHIRAMINE** PS 48

Displacement, tons	40 normal; *Shiramine* 48 normal
Dimensions, feet	80·5 × 18·3 × 2·8
Guns	1 MG aft
Main engines	2 Mitsubishi diesels; 1 140 bhp = 21·6 knots; *Shiramine*, 2 Benz diesels; 2 200 bhp = 25 knots
Range, miles	400 at 18 knots; *Shiramine* 250 at 25 knots

Bizan and *Asama* were built by Shimonoseki Shipyard & Engine Works, Mitsubishi Heavy Industries Ltd. Completed in Mar 1966 and in Feb 1969 respectively. *Shiramine* was built by the same shipyard and completed in Dec 1969. Of light metal construction.

SHIRAMINE *1972, Japanese Maritime Safety Agency*

FIRE FIGHTING CRAFT

3 "HIRYU" CLASS

HIRYU FL 01 **NANRYU** FL 03 **SHYORYU** FL 02

Displacement, tons	251 normal
Dimensions, feet	90·2 oa × 34·1 × 7·2
Main engines	2 sets diesels; 2 200 bhp = 13·5 knots
Range, miles	395 at 13·4 knots
Complements	14

Hiryu, a catamaran type fire boat, was built by Nippon Kokan Kabushiki Kaisha, Asano Dockyard. Laid down in Oct 1968, launched in Feb 1969 and completed in Mar 1969 Designed and built for fire fighting services to large tankers. Seven water nozzles (6 000 l/min × 2, 3 000 l/min × 4 and 1 800 l/min × 1) are installed and fire extinguishing foamy liquid of 14·5 cubic metres is carried and to be discharged from these nozzles. *Shyoryu* was completed in Mar 1970, and *Nanryu*, in Mar 1971, both at the same Asano Dockyard.

HIRYU *1970, Japanese Maritime Safety Agency*

PATROL CRAFT

2 "HATSUNAMI" CLASS

SUZUNAMI PC 08 **HAYANAMI** PC 10

6 "MAKIGUMO" CLASS

HATAGUMO	PC 31	**YAEGUMO**	PC 33	**NATSUGUMO**	PC 35
MAKIGUMO	PC 32	**ASAGUMO**	PC 34	**TATSUGUMO**	PC 36

3 "HANAYUKI" CLASS

HANAYUKI PC 37 **MINEYUKI** PC 38 **ISOYUKI** PC 39

Displacement, tons	42 to 46 normal
Dimensions, feet	69 oa × 17·2 × 3·2 (Makigumo Class) 72 oa × 17·6 × 3·2 (Hanayuki Class)

Patrol craft—*continued*

Main engines	2 diesels; 700 bhp = 13·9 knots (*Hatsunami*) 2 diesels; 1 400 bhp = 20·5 knots (*Makigumo*) 3 diesels; 1 500 bhp = 20·7 knots (*Hanayuki*) 2 diesels; 1 800 bhp = 21·3 knots (*Isoyuki*)

Isoyuki was completed in Feb 1960, *Hanayuki* and *Mineyuki* in Mar 1959, *Asagumo Natsugumo* and *Tatsugumo* in Apr 1955 and the others before 1954. Of light wooden hulls.

13 "MATSUYUKI" CLASS

MATSUYUKI	PC 40	**SHIMAYUKI**	PC 41	**TAMAYUKI**	PC 42
HAMAYUKI	PC 43	**YAMAYUKI**	PC 44	**KOMAYUKI**	PC 45
UMIGIRI	PC 46	**ASAGIRI**	PC 47	**HAMAGIRI**	PC 48
SAGIRI	PC 49	**SETOGIRI**	PC 50	**HAYAGIRI**	PC 51
HAMANAMI	PC 52	**MATSUNAMI**	PC 53		

Displacement, tons	39 for 40, 40 for 41-43, 41 for 44-45, 42 for 46-47 and 49-51, 51 for 48, 60 for 52
Dimensions, feet	69 oa × 16·6 × 3·2
Gun	1—13 mm
Main engines	2 Mercedes Benz diesels; 2 200 bhp = 26·3 knots; PC 48 1 140 bhp = 14·6 knots; PC 52 = 21.8 knots; PC 53 = 20·8
Range, miles	About 300 miles at near maximum speed
Complement	10

Since 1964 two or three craft of this type have been built per year by Hitachi Kanagawa Dockyard; PC's 40-47 and 49-51 were built of light alloy frames with wooden hulls. PC's 48 and 52 were built of steel; PC 53 was built completely of light alloy.

18 "SHIKINAMI" CLASS

SHIKINAMI	PC 54	**TOMONAMI**	PC 55	**WAKANAMI**	PC 56
ISENAMI	PC 57	**TAKANAMI**	PC 58	**MUTSUKI**	PC 59
MOCHIZUKI	PC 61	**KIYOZUKI**	PC 62	**URAZUKI**	PC 63
AKIZUKI	PC 64	**SHINONOME**	PC 65	**URANAMI**	PC 66
TAMANAMI	PC 67	**MINEFUMO**	PC 68	**KIYONAMI**	PC 69
OKINAMI	PC 70	**WAKAGUMO**	PC 71		

Displacement, tons	44 for 54-63 and 66-71, 55 for 64-65
Dimensions, feet	69 oa × 17·4 × 3·2 (81·9 oa × 19·0 × 4·3 for PC 64-65)
Main engines	2 Mercedes Benz Diesels, 2 200 bhp = 26·5 knots
Range, miles	280 miles at near maximum speed
Complement	10

Since 1971 four or five craft of this type have been built per year by Hitach Kanagawa Dockyard and Mitsubishi Shimonoseki Factory. They were built completely of light alloy.

KIYONAMI *1973, Japanese Maritime Safety Agency*

SURVEYING VESSELS

SHOYO HL 01

Displacement, tons	2 000
Dimensions, feet	262·4 × 40·3 × 13·8
Main engines	2 Fuji V-12; 4 800 hp; 1 shaft = 17·4 knots
Complement	73

Built by Hitachi Zosen, Maizuru. Completed March 1972. Fully equipped for all types of hydrographic and oceanographic work.

SHOYO *1973, Japanese Maritime Safety Agency*

TENYO HM 05

Displacement, tons	181
Dimensions, feet	95 × 19·2 × 9·2
Main engines	Diesels; 230 bhp = 10 knots
Range, miles	3 160 at 10 knots

Corvettes—*continued*

2 EX-US LSIL TYPE

P 111 (ex-*LSIL 9039*, ex-*LSIL 875*)

Displacement, tons	230 standard; 387 full load
Dimensions, feet	169 × 23·7 × 5·7
Guns	1—3 in; 1—40 mm AA; 2—20 mm AA
Main engines	2 GM diesels; 2 shafts; 1 000 bhp = 15 knots
Oil fuel (tons)	100
Range, miles	8 000 at 12 knots
Complement	58

Former US infantry landing ship of the LSIL type. Transferred from the US Navy to the French Navy, on 2 Mar 1951 and stationed in Indo-China; and again transferred to the MNK in 1957.

P 112 (ex-*Medecin Capitaine Le Gall*)

Displacement, tons	230 standard; 350 full load
Dimensions, feet	160 × 23 × 6
Guns	1—3 in; 5—20 mm AA
Main engines	2 GM diesels; 2 shafts; 1 800 bhp = 15 knots
Oil fuel	120 tons
Range, miles	8 000 at 12 knots
Complement	40

2 Ex-YUGOSLAV 108 TYPE (FAST ATTACK CRAFT—TORPEDO)

VR 1 **VR 2**

Displacement, tons	55 standard; 60 full load
Dimensions, feet	69 pp; 78 oa × 21·3 × 7·8
Guns	1—40 mm AA; 4—12·7 mm MG
Tubes	2—21 in
Main engines	3 Packard petrol motors; 5 000 bhp = 36 knots
Complement	14

Torpedo boats presented by Yugoslavia in 1965 and numbered by the MNK. Similar to US "Higgins" class.

6 Ex-US "SWIFT" CLASS (COASTAL PATROL CRAFT)

Displacement, tons	22·5
Dimensions, feet	50 × 13 × 3·5
Guns	1—81 mm mortar; 3—50 cal MG
Main engines	2 diesels; 960 hp; 2 shafts = 28 knots
Complement	6

Transferred in 1972.

2 Ex-US AVR TYPE (COASTAL PATROL CRAFT)

VR 3 **VR 4**

Displacement, tons	30
Dimensions, feet	63 × 13 × 4·6
Guns	4—12·7 mm MG
Main engines	GM Diesel 500 bhp = 15 knots
Complement	12

3 Ex-CHINESE CPB TYPE (COASTAL PATROL CRAFT)

VP 1 **VP 2** **VP 3**

Displacement, tons	7·7 standard; 9·7 full load
Dimensions, feet	42 × 9 × 3·9
Guns	2—12·7 mm MG
Main engines	Diesel, 300 bhp = 20 knots
Complement	10

Coastal patrol boats transferred from the People's Republic of China in Jan 1968.

Light Forces—*continued*

1 Ex-HDML TYPE (COASTAL PATROL CRAFT)

VP 212 (*ex-VP 748*, ex-*HDML 1223*)

Displacement, tons	46 standard; 54 full load
Dimensions, feet	72 oa × 16 × 5·5
Guns	2—20 mm AA; 4—7·5 mm MG
Main engines	2 diesels; 2 shafts; 300 bhp = 10 knots
Complement	8

Former British harbour defence motor launch of the HDML type. Transferred from the British Navy to the French Navy in 1950 and again transferred from the French Navy to the MNK in 1956.

AMPHIBIOUS VESSELS

1 EDIC TYPE

T 916 (ex-*EDIC 606*)

Displacement, tons	292 standard; 650 full load
Dimensions, feet	193·5 × 39·2 × 4·5
Guns	1—81 mm mortar; 2—12·7 mm MG
Main engines	2 MGO diesels; 2 shafts; 1 000 bhp = 10 knots
Complement	16 (1 officer, 15 men)

Completed and transferred from the French Government in Aug 1969.

2 Ex-US LCU TYPE

T 914 (ex-USS *LCU 783*) **T 915** (ex-USS *LCU 1421*)

Displacement, tons	180 standard, 360 full load
Dimensions, feet	115 wl; 119 oa × 34 × 6
Guns	2—20 mm AA
Main engines	3 diesels; 3 shafts; 675 bhp = 8 knots
Complement	12

Former US utility landing craft of the LCU type. LCU 783 and LCU 1421 were transferred on 31 May 1962. T 919 (ex-USS *LCU* 1577) was sunk by a mine on 5 May 1970. Former LCT(6)s 9085 (ex-622) and 9091 (ex-720) were deleted from the list in 1969, with ex-LCU 9073 (ex-USS *LCU* 1420). All now believed deleted.

T 913 *1969, Marine Nat. Khmere*

TUG

PINGOUIE R 911 (ex-USS *YTL* 556)

KOREA (North)

Administration

Commander of the Navy: Rear Admiral Yu Chang Kwon

Personnel

1974: 12 000 officers and men

Strength of the Fleet
(new construction not known)

Type	*Active*
Submarines—Patrol	4
Corvettes	19
Fast Attack Craft—Missile	18
Fast Attack Craft—Torpedo	90
Fast Attack Craft—Gun	54

Mercantile Marine

Lloyd's Register of Shipping: 13 vessels of 60 347 tons gross

SUBMARINES

4 Ex-SOVIET "WHISKY" CLASS

Displacement, tons	1 030 surface; 1180 submerged
Dimensions, ft (*m*)	240 × 22 × 15 (*73·2 × 6·7 × 4·6*)
Tubes	6—21 in (4 bow, 2 stern); 18 torpedoes carried normally (or up to 40 mines)
Main Machinery	2 diesels; 4 000 bhp; 2 Electric motors: 2 500 hp; 2 shafts
Range, miles	13 000 at 8 knots
Speed, knots	17 surfaced; 15 dived
Complement	60

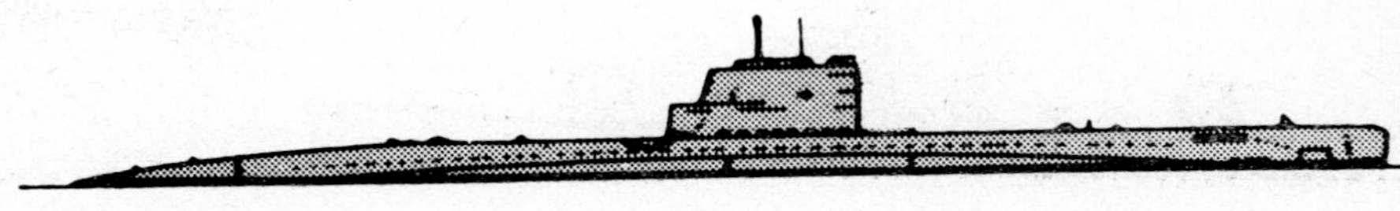

W *Class*

CORVETTES

15 SOVIET "SO 1" CLASS

Displacement, tons	215 light; 250 normal
Dimensions, ft (*m*)	138·6 × 20·9 × 9·2 (*42·3 × 6·1 × 2·8*)
Guns	4—25 mm (2 twin)
A/S weapons	4 five barrelled launchers
Main engines	3 diesels; 6 000 bhp = 29 knots
Range, miles	1 100 at 13 knots
Complement	30

"SO 1" Class *1972*

4 PATROL CRAFT

Displacement, tons	500
Length, feet	200

LIGHT FORCES

8 Ex-SOVIET "OSA" CLASS (FAST ATTACK CRAFT—MISSILE)

Displacement, tons	165 standard, 200 full load
Dimensions, ft (*m*)	128·7 × 25·1 × 5·9 (*39·3 × 7·7 × 1·8*)
Missile launchers	4 in two pairs abreast for *Styx* missiles
Guns	4—30 mm (1 twin forward, and aft)
Main engines	3 diesels; 13 000 bhp = 32 knots
Range, miles	800 at 25
Complement	25

The combination of the "Osa" flotilla and the "Komar" units (below), both armed with the very potent 15 mile range "Styx" missiles, provides a powerful striking force on the South Korean border and within 250 miles of Japan.

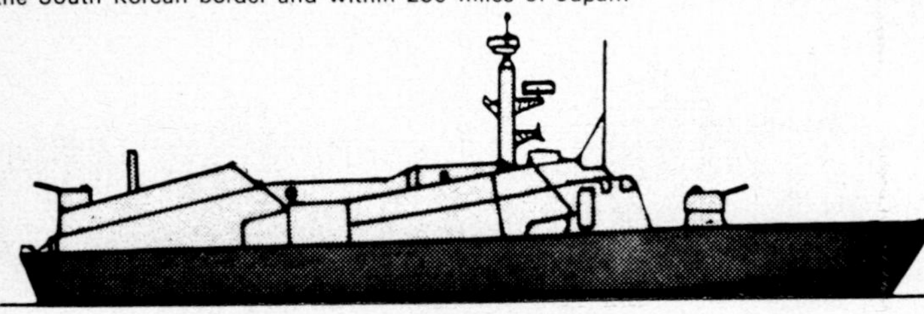
OSA *Class*

10 Ex-SOVIET "KOMAR" CLASS (FAST ATTACK CRAFT—MISSILE)

Displacement, tons	70 standard; 80 full load
Dimensions, ft (*m*)	83·7 × 19·8 × 5·0 (*25·5 × 6·0 × 1·8*)
Missile launchers	2 for "Styx" missiles
Guns	2—25 mm AA (1 twin forward)
Main engines	4 diesels; 4 shafts; 4 800 bhp = 40 knots
Range, miles	400 at 30 knots

See note under "Osa" type above.

15 "SHANGHAI II" CLASS (FAST ATTACK CRAFT—GUN)

Displacement, tons	120 standard; 155 full load
Dimensions, ft (*m*)	128 × 18 × 5·6 (*39 × 5·5 × 1·7*)
Guns	1—56 mm fwd; 2—37 mm (twin aft); 2—25 mm (twin abaft bridge)
Main engines	4 diesels; 4 800 bhp = 30 knots
A/S weapons	8 DC
Mines	Rails can be fitted for 10 mines
Range, miles	800 at 17 knots
Complement	25

Fast patrol boats or motor gunboats reported acquired from China since 1967. Skinhead radar.

SHANGHAI II *Class*

Light Forces—*continued*

8 "SWATOW" CLASS (FAST ATTACK CRAFT—GUN)

Displacement, tons	80
Dimensions, ft (*m*)	83·5 × 19 × 6·5 (*25·5 × 5·8 × 2*)
Guns	4—37 mm; 2—12·7 mm
A/S weapons	8 DC
Main engines	4 diesels; 4 800 bhp = 42 knots
Range, miles	500 at 30 knots
Complement	17

Transferred from China in 1968.

7 MGB TYPE

Reported to have been incorporated into the North Korean Navy since 1 Jan 1967. Probably locally built.

4 PTG TYPE

Larger vessels of the patrol gunboat type reported to have been built in 1967-68.

20 LIGHT GUNBOATS

Believed to be for inshore patrols. Locally built.

15 PTF TYPE (FAST ATTACK CRAFT—TORPEDO)

Displacement, tons	160 approx
Dimensions, feet	120 approx length
Guns	4
Tubes	2—21 in

Commissioned 1967-68.

30 Ex-SOVIET "P 6" CLASS (FAST ATTACK CRAFT—TORPEDO)

Displacement, tons	66 standard; 75 full load
Dimensions, ft (*m*)	84·2 × 20 × 6 (*25·7 × 6·1 × 1·8*)
Guns	4—25 mm
Torpedo tubes	2—21 in (or mines or DC)
Main engines	4 Diesels; 4 800 hp; 4 shafts = 43 knots
Range, miles	450 at 30 knots

There is a growing number of these craft in N. Korea. A local building programme is believed to be the reason. Pothead or Skinhead radar.

P 6. *Class*

45 Ex-SOVIET "P 4" CLASS (FAST ATTACK CRAFT—TORPEDO)

Displacement, tons	25
Dimensions, ft (*m*)	62·7 × 11·6 × 5·6 (*19·1 × 3·5 × 1·7*)
Guns	2—MG
Tubes	2—18 in
Main engines	2 diesels; 2 200 bhp = 50 knots

Built in 1951-57. Aluminium hulls.

"P-4" Type *1971*

ESCORT TRANSPORTS

6 Ex-US APD TYPE

Name	No.	Launched	US Comm.	Transferred
KYONG NAM (ex-USS *Cavallaro*, APD 128)	APD 81	15 June 1944	13 Mar 1945	Oct 1959
AH SAN (ex-USS *Harry L. Corl*, APD 108)	APD 82	1 Mar 1944	5 June 1945	June 1966
UNG PO (ex-*Julius A. Raven*, APD 110)	APD 83	3 Mar 1944	28 June 1945	June 1966
KYONG PUK (ex-USS *Kephart*, APD 61)	APD 85	6 Sep 1943	7 Jan 1944	Aug 1967
JONNAM (ex-USS *Hayter*, APD 80)	APD 86	11 Nov 1943	16 Mar 1944	Aug 1967
CHR JU (ex-*William M. Hobby*, APD 95)	APD 87	11 Feb 1944	4 Apr 1945	Aug 1967

Displacement, tons	1 400 standard; 2 130 full load
Length, feet (*metres*)	300 (*91·4*) wl; 306 (*93·3*) oa
Beam, feet (*metres*)	37 (*11·3*)
Draught, feet (*metres*)	12·6 (*3·2*)
Guns	1—5 inch (*127 mm*) 38 cal DP 6—40 mm AA (twin)
A/S weapons	depth charges
Main engines	Turbo-electric (General Electric turbines); 12 000 shp; 2 shafts
Boilers	2 (Foster Wheeler "D" Express)
Speed, knots	23·6
Complement	approx 200
Troop capacity	approx 160

All begun as destroyers escorts (DE), but converted during construction or after completion to high-speed transports (APD). APD 81 built by Defoe Shipbuilding Co. Bay City, Michigan; APD 82 and APD 83 by Bethlehem Shipbuilding Co. Hingham, Massachusetts; APD 85-87 by Charleston Navy Yard, South Carolina.
In Korean service four latter ships originally rated as gunboats (PG); changed in 1972 to APD. All are fitted to carry approximately 160 troops.

PHOTOGRAPHS. Note davits aft of funnel for carrying four LCVP-type landing craft or other small boats. Two different configurations: ex-APD 37 class with high bridge and lattice mast supporting 10-ton capacity boom; ex-APD 87 class with low bridge and tripod mast supporting 10-ton capacity boom.
One twin 40 mm gun mount is forward of bridge; two others aft; on either side of boom.

KYONG NAM

PATROL VESSELS

1 Ex-US "ASHEVILLE" CLASS

PAEK KU (ex-USS *Benicia*, PG 96) PGM 11 20 Dec 1969

Displacement, tons	225 standard; 245 full load
Dimensions, feet	164·5 oa × 23·8 × 9·5
Guns	1—3 inch (*76 mm*) 50 cal AA (forward); 1—40 mm AA (aft); 4—·50 cal MG (twin)
Main engines	CODAG: 2 diesels (Cummins); 1 450 bhp; 2 shafts = 16 knots; 1 gas turbine (General Electric); 13 300 shp; 2 shafts = 40+ knots
Complement	approx 25

Former US "Asheville" class patrol gunboat Built by Tacoma Boatbuilding Co, Tacoma, Washington; launch date above; commissioned in US Navy on 25 Apr 1970; transferred to ROK Navy on 15 Oct 1971 and arrived in Korea in January 1972. This is the first ship of the class to be transferred to a foreign navy by the United States. See United States section for design, engineering, and gunnery notes. No anti-submarine sensors or weapons are fitted.

MISSILES. During 1971, while in US Navy service, this ship was fitted experimentally with one launcher for the standard surface-to-surface missile. The box-like container/launcher held two missiles. See 1971-1972 edition for additional photo of *Benicia* in missile configuration (page 706).

PAEK KU

SHIN SONG

3 Ex-US "AUK" CLASS MSF TYPE

SHIN SONG (ex-USS *Ptarmigan*, MSF 376)	PCE 1001	15 July 1944
SUNCHON (ex-USS *Speed*, MSF 116)	PCE 1002	18 Apr 1942
KOJE (ex-USS *Dextrous*, MSF 341)	PCE 1003	17 Jan 1943

Displacement, tons	890 standard; 1 250 full load
Dimensions, feet	215 wl; 221·2 oa × 32·2 × 10·8
Guns	2—3 inch (*76 mm*) 50 cal AA (single); 4—40 mm AA (twin), 4—20 mm AA (twin)
A/S weapons	3—12·75 inch (*324 mm*) torpedo tubes (Mk 32 triple); 1 hedgehog; depth charges
Main engines	Diesel-electric (General Motors diesels); 3 532 bhp; 2 shafts = 18 knots
Complement	approx 110

Former US Navy minesweepers (originally designated AM). Built by Savannai Machine & Foundry Co, Savannah, Georgia; American SB Co, Lorain, Ohio; ano Gulf SB Corp. Madisonville, Texas, respectively. Launch dates above; PCE 1001 commissioned in US Navy on 15 Jan 1944, PCE 1002 on 15 Oct 1942, and PCE 1003 on 8 Sep 1943; PCE 1001 transferred to ROK Navy in July 1963, PCE 1002 in Nov 1967, and PCE 1003 in Dec 1967.
The minesweeping gear was removed prior to transfer and a second 3 inch gun fitted aft; additional anti-submarine weapons also fitted. See 1973-1974 edition for broadside views.

8 Ex-US 185-ft PCE TYPE

KO JIN (ex-USS *Report*, MSF 289)	PCE 50	8 Aug 1944
RO RYANG (ex-USS PCEC 882)	PCEC 51	3 Dec 1943
MYONG RYANG (ex-USS PCEC 896)	PCEC 52	22 May 1943
HAN SAN (ex-USS PCEC 873)	PCEC 53	5 May 1943
OK PO (ex-USS PCEC 898)	PCEC 55	3 Aug 1943
PYOK PA (ex-USS *Dania*, PCE 870)	PCE 57	27 Feb 1943
RYUL PO (ex-USS *Somerset*, PCE 892)	PCE 58	1 May 1943
SA CHON (ex-USS *Batesburg*, PCE 903)	PCE 59	6 Sep 1943

Displacement, tons	640 standard; 950 full load
Dimensions, feet	180 wl; 184·5 oa × 33 × 9·5
Guns	1—3 inch (*76 mm*) 50 cal AA; 6—40 mm AA (twin) except *Ko Jin* only 4—40 mm; 4 or 8—20 mm AA (single or twin)
A/S weapons	1 hedgehog (except *Ko Jin*); depth charges
Main engines	Diesels (General Motors); 2 000 bhp; 2 shafts = 15 knots
Complement	approx 100

OK PO 1969

Patrol Vessels—*continued*

Ex-US 185-ft PCE TYPE—*continued*

Former US Navy patrol craft. Launch dates above. Four units had been modified in US service as "control" ships (PCEC) for operation with landing craft, being fitted with additional communications equipment in an enlarged bridge area.
The USS *Report* was transferred to the US Army after World War II for experimental work; refitted with additional electronic equipment and subsequently transferred to South Korea as *Ko Jin* (designated PCE).
Ro Ryang and *Myong Ryang* transferred to South Korea in Feb 1955; *Han San* and *Ok Po* in Sep 1955; *Pyok Pa, Ryul Po,* and *Sa Chon* in Dec 1961.
Tang Po (PCE 56, ex-USS *Maria*, PCE 842) was sunk by North Korean coastal guns on 19 Jan 1967.

O TAE SAN *1961*

3 Ex-US 173-ft PC TYPE

O TAE SAN (ex-USS *Winnemuca*, PC 1145)	PC 707	27 Oct 1943
KUM CHONG SAN (ex-USS *Grosse Point*, PC 1546)	PC 708	30 Jan 1944
SOL AK (ex-USS *Chadron*, PC 564)	PC 709	12 Apr 1942

Displacement, tons	280 standard; 450 full load
Dimensions, feet	170 wl; 173·66 oa × 23 × 10·8
Guns	1—3 inch (*76 mm*) 50 cal AA; 1—40 mm AA; 4—20 mm AA (single) reduced or removed from some units
A/S weapons	1 mousetrap; depth charges
Main engines	Diesels (General Motors in PC 707 and 708; Fairbanks Morse in PC 709); 2 880 bhp; 2 shafts = 20 knots
Complement	approx 70

Former US Navy patrol craft. Launch dates above. *Kum Chong San* and *Sol Ak* transferred to South Korea in Nov 1960; *O Tae San* in Jan 1964.
Pak Tu San PC 701 (ex-US Merchant Marine Academy *Ensign Whitehead*, ex-USS PC 823), *Kum Kang San* PC 702 (ex-USS PC 810), and *Sam Kak San* PC 703 (ex-USS PC 802) decommissioned in 1960 and scrapped; *Han Ra San* PC 705 (ex-USS PC 485) sunk in typhoon off Guam in Nov 1962, subsequently raised but scrapped in 1964; *Myo Hyang San* PC 706 (ex-USS PC 600) decommissioned in 1968 and scrapped.

Ex-US 136-ft PCS TYPE

The former US wood-hulled PCS type submarine chasers loaned to South Korea in 1952 have been returned to US custody and discarded: *Hwa Song* PCS 201 (ex-USS PCS 1426), *Kum Song* PCS 202 (ex-USS PCS 1445), *Mok Song* PCS 203 (ex-USS PCS 1446), and *Su Song* PCS 205 (ex-USS PCS 1448).

8 Ex-US COAST GUARD 95-ft TYPE

PB 3 (ex-USCGC *Cape Rosier*, WPB 95333)
PB 5 (ex-USCGC *Cape Sable*, WPB 95334)
PB 6 (ex-USCGC *Cape Providence*, WPB 95335)
PB 8 (ex-USCGC *Cape Porpoise*, WPB 95327)
PB 9 (ex-USCGC *Cape Falcon*, WPB 95330)
PB 10 (ex-USCGC *Cape Trinity*, WPB 95331)
PB 11 (ex-USCGC *Cape Darby*, WPB 95323)
PB 12 (ex-USCGC *Cape Kiwanda*, WPB 95329)

Displacement, tons	98 full load
Dimensions, feet	95 oa × 19 × 6
Guns	1—50 cal MG/1—81 mm mortar ;several ·30 cal MG
Main engines	4 diesels (General Motors); 2 200 bhp; 2 shafts=20 knots max
Complement	13

Former US Coast Guard steel-hulled patrol craft. Built in 1958-1959. Nine units transferred to South Korea in Sep 1968. PB 7 (ex-USCGC *Cape Florida*, WPB 95325) stricken after grounding in May 1971.
Combination machinegun/mortar mount is forward; single light machineguns are aft. See US Coast Guard listings for additional details.

PB 11

1 COASTAL PATROL AND INTERDICTION CRAFT

Displacement, tons	approx 70 full load
Dimensions, feet	99·1 oa × 18 × 6
Guns	light cannon and machine guns planned; see notes
Main engines	3 gas turbines (Avco Lycoming TF 35); 5 400 hp; 3 shafts = 40+ knots maximum; 2 diesels (300 bhp) with outboard drive for low-speed cruising

The prototype Coastal Patrol and Interdiction Craft (CPIC) sponsored by the US Navy was constructed by Tacoma Boatbuilding, Tacoma, Washington; after completion in mid-1973 the craft was to undergo brief trials for the US Navy and then transfer to South Korea.

The CPIC was designed to intercept infiltration attempts into South Korea and other nations with long and vulnerable coastlines. Plans for additional craft for US and foreign use are under study. See United States section for CPIC illustration. Twin 30 mm rapid-fire gun mount planned for these craft reportedly is encountering development problems.

9 65-ft SEWART TYPE

FB 1 **FB 2** **FB 3** **FB 5** **FB 6** **FB 7** **FB 8** **FB 9** **FB 10**

Displacement, tons	33 full load
Dimensions, feet	65 oa × 16
Guns	2—20 mm (single)
Main engines	3 diesels (General Motors 12V71); 1 590 bhp; 3 shafts = 25 knots
Complement	5

These craft were built in the United States by Sewart. The design is adapted from a commercial 65-foot craft. Referred to as "Toksuuri" No. 1 through 10 by the South Koreans (with the No. 4 being considered unlucky and not assigned). Transferred to South Korea in August 1967.

FB 10 on marine railway

4 US 40-ft SEWART TYPE

SB 1 **SB 2** **SB 3** **SB 5**

Displacement, tons	9·25 full load
Dimensions, feet	40 oa × 12 × 3
Guns	1—·50 cal MG; 2—·30 cal MG
Main engines	2 diesels (General Motors); 500 bhp; 2 shafts = 31 knots
Complement	7

These are aluminium-hulled craft built in the United States by Sewart. Transferred to South Korea in 1964. No. 4 not assigned.

MOTOR TORPEDO BOATS

Ol Pe Mi (ex-USS PT 812) stricken in 1969; *Kal Mae Ki* (ex-USS PT 616) stricken in 1969. Latter craft returned to United States for use as a memorial.

KO CHANG —see following page *Korean Navy*

COASTAL MINESWEEPERS

8 Ex-US MSC TYPE

KUM SAN (ex-US MSC 284) MSC 522
KO HUNG (ex-US MSC 285) MSC 523
KUM KOK (ex-US MSC 286) MSC 525
NAM YANG (ex-US MSC 295) MSC 526
NA DONG (ex-US MSC 296) MSC 527
SAM CHOK (ex-US MSC 316) MSC 528
YONG DONG (ex-US MSC 320) MSC 529 (under construction)
OKCHEON (ex-US MSC 321) MSC 530 (under construction)

Displacement, tons	320 light; 370 full load
Dimensions, feet	144 oa × 28 × 8·2
Guns	2—20 mm AA
Main engines	2 diesels; 1 200 bhp; 2 shafts = 14 knots
Complement	approx 40

"Bluebird" class coastal minesweepers built by the United States specifically for transfer under the Military Aid Programme. Wood hulled with non-magnetic metal fittings.

Kum San transferred to South Korea in June 1959, *Ko Hung* in Sep 1959, *Kum Kok* in Nov 1959, *Nam Yang* in Sep 1963, *Ha Dong* in Nov 1963, and *Sam Chok* in July 1968.

Two additional units MSC 230 and MSC 3219 under construction at Peterson Builders, Sturgeon Bay, Wisconsin, both launched in 1974 and scheduled for delivery in mid-1975.

KUM KOK

4 Ex-US YMS TYPE

KWANG CHU (ex-USS YMS 413) MSC 503
KUM HWA (ex-USS *Curlew*, MSCO 8, ex-AMS 8, ex-YMS 218) MSC 519
KIM PO (ex-USS *Kite*, MSCO 22, ex-AMS 22, ex-YMS 375) MSC 520
KO CHANG (ex-USS *Mockingbird*, MSCO 27, ex-AMS 27, ex-YMS 419) MSC 521

Displacement, tons	270 standard; 350 full load
Dimensions, feet	136 oa × 24·5 × 8
Guns	1—40 mm AA; 2—20 mm AA
Main engines	diesels; 1 000 bhp = 15 knots
Complement	approx 50

Former US Navy auxiliary motor minesweepers built 1941-1942. Wood hulled. *Kum Hwa*, *Kim Po*, and *Ko Chang* transferred to South Korea in Jan 1956.

Yong Kung MSC 518 (ex-US BYMS 8) scrapped in 1955, *Kil Chu* MSC 514 (ex-US BYMS 5) scrapped in 1959, *Kang Wha* MSC 508 (ex-USS YMS 245) lost in 1959, *Kim Chon* MSC 513 (ex-USS YMS 258) scrapped in 1968, *Ka Pyong* MSC 509 (ex-USS YMS 210) sunk in 1950, *Kupo* MSC 512 (ex-USS YMS 323) scrapped in 1956, *Kang Kyong* MSC 510 (ex-USS YMS 330) scrapped in 1963, *Ko Yung* MSC 515 (ex-USS BYMS 55) scrapped in 1959; *Kang Jim* MSC 501 (ex-USS YMS 354) scrapped in 1959, *Kyoung Chu* MSC 502 (ex-USS YMS 358) scrapped in 1962, *Ka Ya San* MSC 511 (ex-USS YMS 423) lost in 1949, *Kang Nung* MSC 507 (ex-YMS 463) scrapped in 1959, *Ko Won* MSC 517 (ex-US YMS type unnumbered) lost in 1948 *Kong City* MSC 516 (ex-US BYMS 6) sunk in 1950.

MINESWEEPING BOAT

MSB 1 (ex-US MSB 2)

Displacement, tons	30 light; 39 full load
Dimensions, feet	57·2 oa × 15·3 × 4
Guns	machineguns
Main engines	2 geared diesels (Packard); 600 bhp; 2 shafts = 12 knots

Former US Navy Minesweeping boat transferred on 1 Dec 1961. Wood hulled.

LANDING SHIPS

8 Ex-US LST TYPE

UN PONG	(ex-USS LST 1010)	LST 807	29 Mar 1944
DUK BONG	(ex-USS LST 227)	LST 808	21 Sep 1943
BI BONG	(ex-USS LST 218)	LST 809	20 July 1943
KAE BONG	(ex-USS *Berkshire County*, LST 288)	LST 810	7 Nov 1943
WEE BONG	(ex-USS *Johnson County*, LST 849)	LST 812	30 Dec 1944
SU YONG	(ex-USS *Kane County*, LST 853)	LST 813	17 Nov 1944
BUK HAN	(ex-USS *Lynn County*, LST 900)	LST 815	9 Dec 1944
HWA SAN	(ex-USS *Pender County*, LST 1080)	LST 816	2 May 1945

Displacement, tons	1 653 standard; 2 366 beaching; 4 080 full load
Dimensions, feet	316 wl; 328 oa × 50 × 14
Guns	10 or 8—40 mm AA
Main engines	diesels; 1 700 bhp; 2 shafts = 11·6 knots
Complement	approx 110

Ex-US LST Type—*continued*

Former US Navy tank landing ships. Cargo capacity 2 100 tons. Launch dates above. *Un Bong* transferred to South Korea in Feb 1955, *Duk Bong* in Mar 1955, *Bi Bong* in May 1955, *Kae Bong* in Mar 1956, *Wee Bong* in Jan 1959, *Su Yong* and *Buk Han* in Dec 1958, and *Hwa San* in Oct 1958.

LSTs previously operated by South Korea and stricken were: ex-USS LST 120, ex-USS LST 213, *Dan Yang* ex-USS LST 343, ex-USS LST 378, ex-USS LST 380, *Ryong Pi* LST 806 ex-USS LST 388, *An Tong* LST 803 ex-USS LST 491 sunk in 1952, ex-USS LST 536, ex-USS LST 594, *Chon Po* LST 805 ex-USS LST 595, ex-USS LST 624 *Ryong Hwa* LST 801 ex-USS LST 659, *Lyung Wha* ex-USS LST 805.

HWA SAN

1 Ex-US LSMR TYPE

SI HUNG (ex-USS *St Joseph River*, LSMR 527) LSMR 311

Displacement, tons	944 standard; 1 084 full load
Dimensions, feet	204·5 wl; 206·2 oa × 34·5 × 10
Guns	1—5 inch (*127 mm*) 38 cal DP; 2—40 mm AA; 4—20 mm AA
Rocket launchers	8 twin rapid-fire launchers for 5 inch rockets
Main engines	2 diesels (General Motors); 2 800 bhp; 2 shafts = 12·6 knots
Complement	approx 140

Former US Navy landing ship completed as a rocket-firing ship to support amphibious landing operations. Transferred to South Korea on 15 Sep 1960. Configuration differs from conventional LSM type with "island" bridge structure and 5 inch gun aft; no bow doors.

SI HUNG — *1967, Korean Navy*

11 Ex-US LSM TYPE

TAE CHO (ex-USS LSM 546) LSM 601
TYO TO (ex-USS LSM 268) LSM 602
KA TOK (ex-USS LSM 462) LSM 605
KO MUN (ex-USS LSM 30) LSM 606
PIAN (ex-USS LSM 96) LSM 607
PUNG TO (ex-USS LSM 54) LSML 608
WOL MI (ex-USS LSM 57) LSM 609
KI RIN (ex-USS LSM 19) LSM 610
NUNG RA (ex-USS LSM 84) LSM 611
SIN MI (ex-USS LSM 316) LSM 612
UL RUNG (ex-USS LSM 17) LSM 613

Displacement, tons	743 beaching; 1 095 full load
Dimensions, feet	196·5 wl; 203·5 oa × 34·6 × 8·5
Guns	2—40 mm AA (twin); several 20 mm AA
Main engines	2 diesels (direct drive; Fairbanks Morse except *Tyo To* General Motors); 2 800 bhp; 2 shafts = 12·5 knots
Complement	approx 60

Former US Navy medium landing ships. Built 1944-1945. LSM 601, 602, and 605 transferred to South Korea in 1955; others in 1956. *Sin Mi* served in Indochina as French L 9014 and *Ul Rung* as French L 9017 during 1954-1955; returned to United States in Oct 1955 and retransferred to South Korea in fall 1956.

Pung To serves as mine force flagship fitted with mine-laying rails and designated LSML.

Arrangement of 20 mm guns differs; some ships have two single mounts adjacent to forward 40 mm mount on forecastle; other 20 mm guns along sides of cargo well.

Tok To LSM 603 (ex-USS LSM 419) scrapped in 1963.

Po Song Man LSSL 109 (ex-USS LSSL 54), *Yung Hung Man* LSSL 107 (ex-USS LSSL 77), *Yong Il Man* LSSL 110 (ex-USS LSSL 84), and *Kang Hwa Man* LSSL 108 (ex-USS LSSL 91) have been scrapped.

TYO TO — *1969*

Landing Ships—*continued*

1 Ex-US LCU TYPE

LCU 1 (ex-USS LCU 531)

Displacement, tons	309 full load
Dimensions, feet	105 wl; 119·1 oa × 32·66 × 5
Main engines	diesels (Gray Marine); 675 bhp; 3 shafts = 10 knots

Former US Navy utility landing craft. Built in 1943 as LCT(6) 531. Transferred to South Korea in Dec 1960. No name assigned.

AUXILIARY SHIPS

1 REPAIR SHIP: Ex-US ARL TYPE

TUK SU (ex-USS *Minotaur*, ARL 15, ex-LST 645) ARL 1

Displacement, tons	2 366 standard; 4 100 full load
Dimensions, feet	316 wl; 328 oa × 50 × 11·2
Guns	8—40 mm AA; 12—20 mm AA
Main engines	diesels (General Motors); 1 800 bhp; 2 shafts = 11·6 knots
Complement	approx 250

Former US Navy landing craft repair ship. Converted during construction from an LST. Launched on 20 Sep 1944 and commissioned in US Navy on 30 Sep 1944. Transferred to South Korea in Oct 1955.

TUK SU

6 SUPPLY SHIPS: Ex-US FREIGHT SUPPLY TYPE

IN CHON	(ex-US Army FS 198)	AKL 902
CHIN NAM PO	(ex-US Army FS 356)	AKL 905
MOK PO	(ex-USCGC *Trillium*, WAK 170, ex-US Army FS 397)	AKL 907
KUN SAN	(ex-USS *Sharps*, AKL 10, ex-AG 139, ex-US Army FS 385)	AKL 908
MA SAN	(ex-USS AKL 35, ex-US Army FS 383)	AKL 909
UL SAN	(ex-USS *Brule*, AKL 28, ex-US Army FS 370)	AKL 910

Displacement, tons	approx 700
Dimensions, feet	176·5 oa × 32·8 × 10
Guns	2—20 mm AA (single) in most ships
Main engines	diesel; 1 000 bhp; 1 shaft = 10 knots
Complement	approx 20

Originally US Army freight and supply ships built in World War II for coastal operation. *In Chon* built by Higgins Industries, *Chin Nam Po* by J. K. Welding, *Ul San* by Sturgeon Bay, others by Ingalls (Dectaur, Alabama).
Many subsequently served in US Navy and Military Sea Transportation Service (now Military Sealift Command). Details and configurations differ.
In Chon and *Chin Nam Po* transferred to South Korea in 1951; *Mok Po*, *Kin San*, and *Ma San* in 1956; *Ul San* on 1 Nov 1971.
Pusan AKL 901 (ex-US Army FS 162), *Wonsan* AKL 903 (ex-US Army FS 254), *Song Chin* AKL 906 (ex-US Army FS 285) scrapped in 1958.

MA SAN 1957

1 OILER NORWEGIAN TYPE:

CHUN JI (ex-*Birk*) AO 2

Displacement, tons	1 400 standard; 4 160 full load
Dimensions, feet	297·5 oa × 44·5 × 18·2
Guns	1—40 mm AA; several 20 mm AA
Main engines	2 diesels; 1 800 bhp; 1 shaft = 12 knots
Complement	approx 70

Former Norwegian tankers built by A/S Berken Mek Verks, Bergen, Norway, in 1951. Transferred to South Korea in Sep 1953. Sister ship *Pujon* AO 3 (ex-*Hassel*) ran aground and was lost on 24 May 1971.

CHUN JI 1969

1 OILER: Ex-US 235-ft YO TYPE

HWA CHON (ex-*Paek Yeon* AO 5, ex-USS *Derrick* YO 59) AO 5

Displacement, tons	890 standard; 2 700 full load
Dimensions, feet	236 oa × 37·9 × 15
Guns	several 20 mm AA
Main engines	diesel (Fairbanks Morse); 1 150 bhp; 1 shaft = 10·5 knots
Complement	approx 45

Former US Navy self-propelled fuel barge. Transferred to South Korea on 14 Oct 1955. Capacity 10 000 barrels petroleum. Reportedly, the ship has been laid up in reserve.

HWA CHON 1969

2 OILERS: Ex-US 174-ft YO TYPE

KU YONG (ex-USS YO 118) YO 1 — (ex-USS YO 179) YO 6

Displacement, tons	1 400 full load
Dimensions, feet	174 oa × 32
Guns	several 20 mm AA
Main engines	diesel (Union); 500 bhp; 1 shaft = 7 knots
Complement	approx 35

Former US Navy self-propelled fuel barges. Transferred to South Korea on 3 Dec 1946 and 13 Sep 1971, respectively. Cargo capacity 6 570 barrels.

2 AUXILIARY TUGS: Ex-US ATA TYPE

YONG MUN	(ex-USS *Keosanqua*, ATA 198)	ATA 2	17 Jan 1945
DO BONG	(ex-USS *Pinola*, ATA 206)	ATA (S) 3	14 Dec 1944

Displacement, tons	538 standard; 835 full load
Dimensions, feet	133·66 wl; 143 oa × 33·8
Guns	1—3 inch (*76 mm*) 50 cal AA; 4—20 mm AA
Main engines	diesel (General Motors); 1 500 bhp; 1 shaft = 13 knots
Complement	approx 45

Former US Navy auxiliary ocean tugs. Launch dates above. Both transferred to South Korea in February 1962. *Do Bong* modified for salvage work.

The South Korean Navy also operates nine small harbour tugs (designated YTL). These are one ex-US Navy craft (YTL 550) and five ex-US Army craft.

SERVICE CRAFT

The South Korean Navy operates approximately 35 small service craft in addition to the YO-type oilers listed above and the harbour tugs noted above. These craft include open lighters, floating cranes, diving tenders, dredges, ferries, non-self-propelled fuel barges, pontoon barges, and sludge removal barges. Most are former US Navy craft.

HYDROGRAPHIC SERVICE

The following craft are operated by the Korean Hydrographic Service and are not rated as Navy. All are engaged in surveying operations.

1 Ex-US ATA TYPE

TAN YUNG (ex-USS *Tillamook*, ATA 192) 15 Nov 1944

Characteristics similar to the two ex-US ocean tugs listed previously. Launch date above. Transferred to South Korea on 25 July 1971 for use as surveying ship.

2 Ex-BELGIAN MSI TYPE

SURO 5 (ex-Belgian *Temse*) — **SURO 6** (ex-Belgian *Tournai*, ex-US MSI 93)

Displacement, tons	160 light; 190 full load
Dimensions, feet	113·2 oa × 22·3 × 6
Main engines	Diesels; 1 260 bhp; 2 shafts = 15 knots

Former Belgian inshore minesweepers. Built in Belgium, the *Tournai* being financed by United States. Launched on 6 Aug 1956 and 18 May 1957, respectively. Transferred to South Korea in March 1970

1 Ex-US YMS TYPE

SURO 3 (ex-USC & GS *Hodgson*)

Displacement, tons	289 full load
Dimensions, feet	136 oa × 24·5 × 9·25
Main engines	2 diesels; 1 000 bhp; 2 shafts = 15 knots

YMS type transferred to South Korea from US Coast & Geodetic Survey in 1968.

COAST GUARD

The Korean Coast Guard operates about 25 small ships and craft including several tugs and small rescue craft.

KUWAIT

Personnel

1974: 200 (Coastguard)

Mercantile Marine

Lloyd's Register of Shipping: 162 vessels of 676 879 tons gross

PATROL BOATS

10 "78 ft" TYPE

AL SALEMI	**AMAN**	**MASHHOOR**	**MURSHED**
AL SHURTI	**INTISAR**	**MAYMOON**	**WATHAH**
AL MUBARAKI	**MARZOOK**		

Displacement, tons	40
Dimensions, feet	78 oa × 15·5 × 4·5 mean
Main engines	2 Rolls Royce 8-cylinder 90° V form marine diesels; 1 340 shp at 1 800 rpm, 1 116 shp at 1 700 rpm = 20 knots
Guns	1 MG
Range, miles	700 at 15 knots
Complement	12 (5 officers, 7 men)

INTISAR 1972, *Vosper Thornycroft*

Two were built by Thornycroft before the merger and six by Vosper afterwards. *Al-Salemi* and *Al Mubaraki* were shipped to Kuwait on 8 Sep 1966. Hulls are of welded steel construction, with superstructures of aluminium alloy. Twin hydraulically operated rudders, Decca type D 202 radar. The later boats are slightly different in appearance with modified superstructure and no funnel, see photograph of *Intisar*.

2 "56 ft" TYPE

Displacement, tons	25
Length, feet	56
Main engines	2 MTU MB6 V.331 diesels; 1 350 hp = 26 knots
Guns	1—20 mm, 2 MG
Range, miles	320 at 20 knots
Complement	8 (2 officers, 6 men)

Ordered from Vosper Thornycroft, Private Ltd, Singapore September 1973. Completion June 1974.

Vosper Thornycroft "56 ft" Type 1973, *Vosper Thornycroft*

PATROL LAUNCHES

7 "50 ft" TYPE

Built by the Singapore Yard of Thornycroft (Malaysia) Limited, now the Tanjong Rhu, Singapore, Yard of Vosper Thornycroft Private Ltd. Known as 50-foot patrol craft. Completed in 1962.

8 "35 ft" TYPE

Built by Vosper Thornycroft Private Ltd, Singapore. Of double-skinned teak construction with twin turbo-charged Perkins diesels they are capable of 24 knots. Ordered July 1972. All delivered by May 1973.

"35 ft" type 1972, *Vosper Thornycroft*

LANDING CRAFT

WAHEED **FAREED**

Two 88-ft landing craft built for the Ministry of the Interior, Kuwait by Vosper Thornycroft Private Ltd, Singapore. Ordered 1970 and handed over May 1971. Used for storing parties working on Kuwait's off-shore islands.

LAOS

Administration

Commander, Royal Lao Navy and Chief of Naval Staff: Colonel Prince Sinthanavong Kindavong

Personnel

1974: 550 officers and men

RIVER PATROL CRAFT

7	LCM (6) Type	28 tons	4 in commission, 3 in reserve
6	Cabin Type	21 tons	2 in commission, 4 in reserve
2	Chris Craft Type	15 tons	2 in commission
12	11 metre Type	10 tons	5 in commission, 7 in reserve
8	8 metre Type	6 tons	8 in reserve
7	Cargo Transport	50 tons	1 in commission, 6 in reserve

It was stated in 1972 that the above craft are formed into four squadrons.

LEBANON

Diplomatic Representation

Naval Military and Air Attaché in London: Brigadier Antoine Raphael

Personnel

1974: 250 officers and men

Mercantile Marine

Lloyd's Register of Shipping: 81 vessels of 119 468 tons gross

PATROL BOATS

TARABLOUS 31

Displacement, tons	105 standard
Dimensions, feet	124·7 × 18 × 5·8
Guns	2—40 mm
Main engines	2 Mercedes-Benz diesels; 2 shafts; 2 700 bhp = 27 knots
Radius, miles	1 500
Complement	19 (3 officers, 16 men)

Tarablous was built by Ch. Navals de l'Estérel. Laid down in June 1958. Launched in June 1959. Completed in 1959.

TARABLOUS 1968 *Lebanese Navy*

3 "BYBLOS" CLASS

BYBLOS 11 **SIDON** 12 **BEYROUTH** (ex-*TIR*) 13

Displacement, tons	28 standard
Dimensions, feet	66 × 13·5 × 4
Guns	1—20 mm AA; 2 MG
Main engines	General Motors diesels; 2 shafts; 530 bhp = 18·5 knots

French built ML type craft. Built by Ch. Navals de l'Estérel. Launched in 1954-55

DJOUNIEH 41

Displacement, tons	82 standard; 130 full load
Dimensions, feet	112 × 18 × 7·5
Guns	1—20 mm; 2—12·7 mm MG
Main engines	2 GM diesels; 2 shafts = 16 knots
Complement	16

Ex-Fairmile "B" motor launch of the Royal Navy built in 1940-41.

DJOUNIEH 1970, *Lebanese Navy*

LANDING CRAFT

SOUR (ex-LCU 1474)

Displacement, tons	180 standard; 360 full load
Dimensions, feet	115 × 34 × 6
Guns	2—20 mm AA
Main engines	3 diesels; 3 shafts; 675 bhp = 10 knots

Former United States utility landing craft built in 1957, transferred in Nov 1958.

SOUR 1968, *Lebanese Navy*

LIBERIA

Personnel

1974: about 200 officers and men

Mercantile Marine

Lloyd's Register of Shipping: 2 289 vessels of 49 904 744 tons gross

MOTOR GUNBOAT

ALERT (ex-USN *PGM* 102) — (ex-USN *PGM* 69)

Displacement, tons	100
Dimensions, feet	95 oa × 19 × 5
Guns	1—40 mm AA
Main engines	4 diesels; 2 shafts; 2 200 bhp = 21 knots
Complement	15

PGM 102 (US number) was built in the United States for transfer under the Military Aid Programme in 1967.

PRESIDENTIAL YACHT

LIBERIAN (ex-*Virginia*)

Measurement, tons	692·27 gross; 341·6 net
Dimensions, feet	173 wl; 209 oa × 29·7 × 13·1

Motor yacht of 742 tons (yacht measurement) built in 1930 by William Beardmore & Co Ltd, Dalmuir. Purchased by Liberia for use as the Presidential Yacht in 1957. Extensively refitted by Cammell Laird & Co Ltd, Birkenhead, at the end of 1962.

PATROL BOATS

ML 4001 **ML 4002**

Displacement, tons	11·5
Dimensions, feet	40·5 oa × 11·5 × 3·5
Guns	2 MG
Main engines	2 GM diesels; 2 shafts; 380 bhp = 23 knots max

Coastguard cutters built at the United States Coast Guard Yard, Curtis Bay, Maryland, presented by the USA and transferred during 1957.

ML 4002 *Dr Giorgio Arra*

LANDING CRAFT

Landing craft reported to be used for transport and general utility purposes.

LIBYA

Establishment

The Libyan Navy was established in Nov 1962 when a British Naval Mission was formed and first recruits were trained at HMS *St. Angelo*, Malta. Cadets were also trained at the Britannia Royal Naval College, Dartmouth, and technical ratings at HMS *Sultan*, Gosport, and HMS *Collingwood*, Fareham, England.

Personnel

(a) 1974: Total 2 000 officers and ratings, including Coast Guard
(b) Voluntary service

Administration

Senior Officer, Libyan Navy: Captain A. Shaksuki

Strength of the Fleet
(no new construction in hand)

Type	*Active*
Frigate	1
LSD	1
Corvette	1
Fast Attack Craft—Missile	3
Large Patrol craft	10
Coastal Patrol Craft	1
Minesweepers—Inshore	2
MRC	1

Mercantile Marine

Lloyd's Register of Shipping: 13 vessels of 5 932 tons gross

FRIGATE

1 VOSPER THORNYCROFT MARK 7

DAT ASSAWARI F 01

Displacement, tons	1 325 standard; 1 625 full load
Length, feet (*metres*)	310·0 (*94·5*) pp; 330·0 (*100·6*) oa
Beam, feet (*metres*)	36·0 (*11·0*)
Draught, feet (*metres*)	11·2 (*3·4*)
A/S weapons	1 Mortar Mark 10
Missile launchers	6 (2 triple) "Seacat" close range ship-to-air
Guns	1—4·5 in; 2—40 mm (twin); 2—35 mm (twin)
Main engines	CODOG arrangement; 2 shafts; 2 Rolls Royce gas turbines; 23 200 shp = 37·5 knots max; 2 Paxman diesels; 3 500 bhp = 17 knots economical cruising speed
Range, miles	5 700 at 17 knots

DAT ASSAWARI *1973, John G. Callis*

Mark 7 Fast Frigate ordered from Vosper Thornycroft on 6 Feb 1968. Generally similar in design to the two Iranian ships built by this firm, but larger and with different armament. Laid down 27 Sep 1968, was launched without ceremony in Sep 1969 and completed 1 Feb 1973. After trials she carried out work-up at Portland, England, reaching Tripoli autumn 1973.

RADAR. AWS-1 air surveillance set; fire control radar and RDL-1 radar direction finder.

LOGISTIC SUPPORT SHIP

1 DOCK TYPE

ZELTIN

Displacement, tons	2 200 standard; 2 470 full load
Ship:	
Length, feet (*metres*)	300·0 (*91·4*) wl; 324·0 (*98·8*) oa
Beam, feet (*metres*)	48·0 (*14·6*)
Draught, feet (*metres*)	10·2 (*3·1*); 19·0 (*5·8*) aft when flooded
Dock:	
Length, feet (*metres*)	135·0 (*41·1*)
Width, feet (*metres*)	40·0 (*12·2*)
Guns	2—40 mm AA
Main engines	2 Paxman 16 cyl diesels; 3 500 bhp; 2 shafts
Speed, knots	15
Range, miles	3 000 at 14 knots
Complement	As Senior Officer Ship: 101 (15 officers and 86 ratings)

ZELTIN *1969*

The ship provides full logistic support, including mobile docking maintenance and repair facilities for the Libyan fleet. Craft up to 120 ft can be docked.

The Vosper-Thornycroft Group received the order for this ship in Jan 1967 for delivery in late 1968. She was designed and built at the Group's Woolston Shipyard. Launched on 29 Feb 1968. Commissioned (with *Sirte* and *Susa*) on 23 Jan 1969.

Fitted with accommodation for a flag officer or a senior officer and staff. Operational and administrative base of the squadron. Workshops with a total area of approx 4 500 sq ft are situated amidships with ready access to the dock, and there is a 3-ton travelling gantry fitted with outriggers to cover ships berthed alongside up to 200 feet long.

CORVETTE

TOBRUK

Displacement, tons	440 standard; 500 full load
Dimensions, feet	162 wl; 177 oa × 28·5 × 10 mean (13 props)
Guns	1—4 in; 4—40 mm AA (single)
Main engines	2 Paxman Ventura 16 YJCM diesels; 2 shafts; 3 800 bhp = 18 knots
Range, miles	2 900 at 14 knots
Complement	63 (5 officers and 58 ratings)

Designed and built by Vosper Limited, Portsmouth, in association with Vickers Limited. Launched on 29 July 1965, completed on 30 Mar 1966, commissioned for service at Portsmouth on 20 Apr 1966, and arrived in Tripoli on 15 June 1966. Fitted with surface warning radar, Vosper roll damping fins and air-conditioning. A suite of State apartments is included in the accommodation.

TOBRUK *1971, A. & J. Pavia*

LIGHT FORCES

3 "SUSA" CLASS (FAST ATTACK CRAFT—MISSILE)

SEBHA (ex-*Sokna*) **SIRTE** **SUSA**

Displacement, tons	95 standard; 114 full load
Dimensions, feet	90·0 pp; 96·0 wl; 100·0 oa × 25·5 × 7·0
Missiles	8—SS 12
Guns	2—40 mm AA (single)
Main engines	3 Bristol Siddeley "Proteus" gas turbines; 3 shafts; 12 750 bhp = 54 knots
Complement	20

The order for these three fast patrol boats from Vosper Limited, Portsmouth, England, was announced on 12 Oct 1966. They are generally similar to the motor torpedo boats designed and built by Vosper for the Royal Danish Navy. Built at the Vosper-Thornycroft Group's Portchester shipyard. Fitted with air conditioning and modern radar and radio equipment. *Susa* was launched on 31 Aug 1967, *Sirte* on 10 Jan 1968 and *Sokna* (renamed *Sebha*) on 29 Feb 1968. First operational vessels in the world to be armed with Nord-Aviation SS 12(M) guided weapons with sighting turret installation and other equipment developed jointly by Vosper and Nord. These weapons, of which eight can be fired by each boat without reloading, have a destructive power equivalent to a six-inch shell.

SEBHA *1969, Wright & Logan*

4 "GARIAN" CLASS (LARGE PATROL CRAFT)

GARIAN **KHAWLAN** **MERAWA** **SABRATHA**

Displacement, tons	120 standard; 159 full load
Dimensions, feet	100 pp; 106 oa × 21·2 × 5·5
Guns	1—20 mm AA
Main engines	2 Paxman diesels; 1 100 bhp = 14 knots
Range, miles	1 500 at 12 knots
Complement	15 to 22

Built by Brooke Marine, Lowestoft. Launched on 21 Apr, 29 May, 25 Oct and 30 Sep 1969, respectively, and completed on 30 Aug 1969 (*Garian* and *Khawlan*) and early 1970 (other two).

KHAWLAN *1970, Brooke Marine*

Light Forces—*continued*

6 THORNYCROFT TYPE (LARGE PATROL CRAFT)

AKRAMA **BENINA** **HOMS**
AR RAKIB **FARWA** **MISURATA**

Displacement, tons	100
Dimensions, feet	100 × 21 × 5·5
Gun	1—20 mm
Main engines	3 Rolls-Royce DV8TLM Diesels; 1 740 bhp = 18 knots
Range, miles	1 800 at 14 knots

Welded steel construction. *Ar Rakib* and *Farwa* completed 4 May 1967 by John I. Thornycroft, Woolston; *Benina* and *Misurata*, 29 Aug 1968 and last pair in early 1969, all by Vosper-Thornycroft.

FARWA *1969, Thornycroft*

1 THORNYCROFT TYPE (COASTAL PATROL CRAFT)

Dimensions, feet	78 × 15 × 4·5
Gun	1 MG
Main engines	3 Rolls-Royce diesels; 3 shafts; 945 bhp = 22·5 knots
Range, miles	400 at 15 knots

Built by John I. Thornycroft, Singapore in 1962. Two similar but smaller boats transferred to Malta in 1974.

INSHORE MINESWEEPERS

2 BRITISH "HAM" TYPE

BRAK (ex-HMS *Harpham*) **ZUARA** (ex-HMS *Greetham*)

Displacement, tons	100
Dimensions, feet	102·0 × 20·0 × 5·0
Guns	1—40 mm; 1—20 mm
Main engines	2 Paxman 12 YJCM diesels; 3 600 bhp = 24 knots
Range, miles	1 800 at 13 knots
Complement	20

Lent by Great Britain in 1963 to form the nucleus of a navy for Libya, and given outright to the Royal Libyan Navy in 1966. Given Libyan names in Sep 1966.

BRAK *A. & J. Pavia*

MAINTENANCE REPAIR CRAFT

ZLEITEN (ex-*MRC* 1013, ex-LCT)

Displacement, tons	657 standard; 900 approx full load
Dimensions, feet	225·0 pp, 231·3 oa × 39·0 × 3·3 forward, 5·0 aft
Main engines	4 Paxman diesels; 2 shafts; 1 840 bhp = 9 knots cruising

Built in 1944-45. Purchased from Great Britain on 5 Sep 1966. Depot ship for minesweepers.

MALAWI

Three small patrol-boats are deployed on Lake Nyasa; the first was bought in 1968.

MALAYSIA

SEE ALSO SABAM

Administration

Chief of the Naval Staff:
Rear-Admiral Dato K. Thanabalasingam, DPMT JMN, SMJ

Deputy to the Chief of the Naval Staff:
Captain Mohd Zain bin Mohd Salleh, KMN

Commander Naval Forces West Malaysia:
Captain P. K. Nettur, AMN

Commander Naval Forces East Malaysia:
Captain Cheah Leong Voon, AMN

Diplomatic Representation

Services Adviser in London:
Colonel Michael Peh Tek Foo

Strength of the Fleet

(No new construction known—3 Fast Attack Craft reportedly ordered from France)

Type	*Active*
Frigates	2
Fast Attack Craft—Missile	8
Large Patrol Craft	24
Minesweepers—Coastal	6
Diving Tender	1
Survey Vessel	1
Support Ship	1
Police Launches	24

Personnel

(a) 1974: 4 900 (430 officers and 4 470 ratings)
(b) Voluntary service

Prefix to Ships' Names

The names of Malaysian warships are prefixed by KD, (Kapal Diraja) meaning Royal Ship

Mercantile Marine

Lloyd's Register of Shipping:
117 vessels of 226 350 tons gross

FRIGATES

1 YARROW TYPE

RAHMAT (ex-*Hang Jebat*) F 24

Displacement, tons	1 250 standard; 1 600 full load
Length, feet (*metres*)	300·0 (*91·44*)pp; 308 (*93·9*) oa
Beam, feet (*metres*)	34·1 (*10·4*)
Draught, feet (*metres*)	14·8 (*4·5*)
Aircraft	1 helicopter
Missile launchers	1 quadruple "Seacat" surface-to-air
Guns, dual purpose	1—4·5 in (*114 mm*)
Guns, AA	2—40 mm
A/S weapons	1 "Limbo" three-barrelled mortar
Main engines	1 Bristol Siddeley Olympus gas turbine; 19 500 shp; Crossley Pielstick diesel; 3 850 bhp; 2 shafts
Speed, knots	26 boosted by gas turbine; 16 on diesel alone
Range, miles	6 000 at 16 knots 1 000 at 26 knots
Complement	140

General purpose frigate of new design developed by Yarrow. Fully automatic with saving in complement. Delivered mid-1971.

RAHMAT — *1972, Wright & Logan*

Ordered from Yarrow & Co Ltd, Scotstoun, on 11 Feb 1966. Launched on 18 Dec 1967. Delivered 13 Sep 1972.

RADAR. Air Surveillance: HSA LW 02. Fire control; M 20 with radar in spherical radome for guns; M 44 for Seacat.

1 Ex-BRITISH "LOCH" CLASS

HANG TUAH (ex-HMS *Loch Insh*) F 433

Displacement, tons	1 575 standard; 2 400 full load
Length, feet (*metres*)	297·2 (*90·6*) wl; 307·0 (*93·6*) oa
Beam, feet (*metres*)	38·5 (*11·7*)
Draught, feet (*metres*)	14·8 (*4·5*)
Guns, AA	6—40 mm
Boilers	2 Admiralty 3-drum
Main engines	2 triple expansion; 5 500 ihp; 2 shafts
Speed, knots	19·5 designed
Range, miles	6 400 at 10 knots
Complement	140

HANG TUAH — *1972, Royal Malaysian Navy*

Built by Henry Robb Ltd, Leith. Laid down on 17 Nov 1943, launched on 10 May 1944 and completed on 20 Oct 1944. On transfer, refitted (in Portsmouth Dockyard) with helicopter deck, air-conditioning, modern radar and extra accommodation. Re-commissioned on 12 Oct 1964. Sailed on 12 Nov 1964. Converted into a training ship in Apr 1971, the two 4-inch guns and the two "Squid" mortars having been removed. *Hang Tuah* was the name of a Malay Admiral of the 15th century.

RADAR. Search: Type 227.

LIGHT FORCES

4 "PERDANA" CLASS (FAST ATTACK CRAFT—MISSILE)

PERDANA **GANAS** **SERANG** **GANYANG**

Displacement, tons	234 standard; 265 full load
Dimensions, ft (*m*)	154·2 × 23·1 × 12·8 (*16·5 × 7·0 × 3·7*)
Missile launchers	2 MM38 ("Exocet") surface-to-surface
Guns	1—57 mm Bofors; 1—40 mm 70 cal Bofors
Main engines	4 MTU diesels; 4 shafts; 14 000 bhp = 36·5 knots
Range, miles	800 at 25 knots

First pair built by Constructions Mécaniques de Normandie, *Perdana* launched 31 May 1972 completed December 1972 and *Ganas* launched 26 Oct 1972 for completion 28 Feb 1973. Second pair built by Société Francaise de Constructions Navales (ex-Franco-Belge), *Serang* launched 22 Dec 1971, completed 31 Jan 1973 and *Ganyang* launched 16 March 1972, completed 20 March 1973. All of basic "La Combattante II" design. Left Cherbourg for Malaysia 2 May 1973.

GANAS — *1973, John G. Callis*

Light Forces—*continued*

4 "PERKASA" CLASS (FAST ATTACK CRAFT—MISSILE)

GEMPITA P 152 **HANDALAN** P 151 **PENDEKAR** P 153 **PERKASA** P 150

Displacement, tons	95 standard; 114 full load
Dimensions, feet	90 pp; 96 wl; 99 oa × 25·5 × 7
Guns	1—40 mm AA; 1—20 mm AA
Missiles	8—SS 12(M) in 2 quadruple launchers
Main engines	3 Rolls Royce Proteus gas turbines; 3 shafts; 12 750 bhp = 54 knots GM diesels on wing shafts for cruising = 10 knots

The design is a combination of the "Brave" class hull form and "Ferocity" type construction. Ordered from Vosper Limited, Portsmouth, England, on 22 Oct 1964. Generally similar to the motor torpedo boats built by Vosper for the Royal Danish Navy. They can also operate in the gunboat role or a minelaying role. *Perkasa* (Valiant) was launched on 26 Oct 1965, *Handalan* (Reliant) on 18 Jan 1966, *Gempita* (Thunderer) on 6 Apr 1966 and *Pendekar* (Champion) on 24 June 1966. The hull is entirely of glued laminated wooden construction, with upperworks of aluminium alloy. Equipment includes Rover gas turbine generating sets, full air conditioning, Decca radar, and comprehensive navigation and communications system. The craft were shipped to Malaysia in mid-1967. They were re-armed with eight SS.12 missiles in place of four 21-inch torpedoes in 1971.

GEMPITA (Firing SS 12 missile) *1972, Royal Malaysian Navy*

3 "LA COMBATTANTE II" TYPE (FAST ATTACK CRAFT—GUN)

It was reported in October 1972 that the Malaysian Government intended to order these craft which would be fitted with additional guns in place of missiles. No further news.

6 "KEDAH" CLASS (LARGE PATROL CRAFT)

SRI KEDAH P 3138 **SRI PAHANG** P 3141 **SRI SELANGOR** P 3139
SRI KELANTAN P 3142 **SRI PERAK** P 3140 **SRI TRENGGANU** P 3143

4 "SABAH" CLASS (LARGE PATROL CRAFT)

SRI MELAKA P 3147 **SRI SABAH** P 3144
SRI NEGRI SEMBILAN P 3146 **SRI SARAWAK** P 3145

14 "KRIS" CLASS (LARGE PATROL CRAFT)

		KRIS	P 34	**SERAMPANG**	P 41
BADEK	P 37	**LEMBING**	P 40	**SRI JOHOR**	P 49
BELEDAU	P 44	**PANAH**	P 42	**SRI PERLIS**	P 47
KELEWANG	P 45	**RENCHONG**	P 38	**SUNDANG**	P 36
KERAMBIT	P 43	**RENTAKA**	P 46	**TOMBAK**	P 39

Displacement, tons	96 standard; 109 full load
Dimensions, feet	95 wl; 103 oa × 19·8 × 5·5
Guns	2—40 mm; 70 cal AA
Main engines	2 Bristol Siddeley/Maybach MD 655/18 diesels; 3 500 bhp = 27 knots max
Range, miles	1 400 (*Sabah* class 1 660) at 14 knots
Complement	22 (3 officers, 19 ratings)

All 24 craft were built by Vosper Limited, Portsmouth. The first six boats, constituting the "Kedah" class were ordered in 1961 for delivery in 1963. The four boats of the "Sabah" class were ordered in 1963 for delivery in 1964. The remaining 14 boats of the "Kris" class were ordered in 1965 for delivery between 1966 and 1968. All are of prefabricated steel construction and are fitted with Decca radar, air conditioning and Vosper roll damping equipment. The difference between the three classes are minor, the later ones having improved radar, communications, evaporators and engines of Maybach, as opposed to Bristol Siddeley construction. *Sri Johor*, the last of the 14 boats of the "Kris" class, was launched on 22 June 1967.

BADEK ("Kris" Class) *1972, Royal Malaysian Navy*

MINE WARFARE FORCES

6 Ex-BRITISH "TON" CLASS (MINESWEEPERS—COASTAL)

BRINCHANG (ex-*Thankerton*) M 1172 **LEDANG** (ex-*Hexton*) M 1143
JERAI (ex-*Dilston*) M 1168 **MAHAMIRU** (ex-*Darlaston*) M 1127
KINABALU (ex-*Essington*) M 1134 **TAHAN** (ex-*Lullington*) M 1163

Displacement, tons	360 standard; 425 full load
Dimensions, feet	140 pp; 152 oa × 28·8 × 8·2
Guns	1—40 mm AA forward; 2—20 mm AA aft
Main engines	Diesels; 2 shafts; 2 500 bhp = 15 knots max
Oil fuel, tons	45
Range, miles	2 300 at 13 knots
Complement	39

Mahamiru transferred from the Royal Navy on 24 May 1960. *Ledang*, refitted at Chatham Dockyard before transfer, commissioned for Malaysia in Oct 1963. *Jerai* and *Kinabalu*, refitted in Great Britain, arrived in Malaysia summer 1964. *Brinchang* and *Tahan*, refitted in Singapore, transferred to Malaysian Navy in May and Apr 1966, respectively. All six have been programmed for a 9-month refit by Vosper-Thornycroft Singapore which will extend their availability by some years.

MAHAMIRU *1972, Royal Malaysian Navy*

DIVING TENDER

DUYONG

Displacement, tons	120 standard; 140 full load
Dimensions, feet	99·5 wl; 110·0 oa × 21·0 × 5·8
Guns	1—20 mm
Main engines	2 Cummins diesels, 1 900 rpm; 500 bhp = 10 knots
Complement	23

Built by Kall Teck (Pte) Ltd, Singapore. Launched on 18 Aug 1970. Commissioned on 5 Jan 1971.

Royal Malaysian Police

18 PX CLASS

Mahkota, Temenggong, Hulubalang, Maharajasetia, Maharajalela, Pahlawan, Bentara, Perwira, Pertanda, Shahbandar, Sangsetia, Laksamana, Pekan, Kelang, Kuala Kangsar, Arau, Sri Gumantong, Sri Labuan, (Numbered PX 1-18).

Displacement, tons	85
Dimensions, feet	87·5 oa × 19 × 4·8
Guns	2—20 mm
Main engines	2 Mercedes Benz diesels; 2 shafts; 2 700 hp = 25 knots
Range, miles	700 at 15 knots
Complement	15

6 IMPROVED PX CLASS

Alor Star, Kota Bahru, Kuala Trengganu, Johore Bahru, Sri Menanti, Kuching (Numbered PX 19-24).

Displacement, tons	92
Dimensions, feet	91 oa
Guns	2—20 mm
Main engines	2 diesels; 2 460 hp = 25 knots
Range, miles	750 at 15 knots
Complement	18

All 24 boats built by Vosper Thornycroft Private, Singapore, PX class between 1963 and 1970, Improved PX class 1972-73. *Sri Gumantong* and *Sri Labuan* operated by Sabah Government, remainder by Royal Malaysian Police.

SRI MENANTI *1972, Yam Photos, Singapore*

SURVEY VESSEL

1 Ex-BRITISH "TON" CLASS

PERANTAU (ex-HMS *Myrmidon*, ex-HMS *Edderton*) A 151

Displacement, tons	360 standard; 420 full load
Dimensions, feet	153 oa × 28·8 × 8·5
Main engines	Diesels; 2 shafts; 3 000 bhp = 15 knots
Range, miles	2 300 at 13 knots
Complement	35

A former coastal minesweeper of the "Ton" type, converted by the Royal Navy into a survey ship, renamed *Myrmidon* in Apr 1964, and commissioned for service on 20 July 1964. Paid off in 1968 and purchased by Malaysia in 1969. Service in Malaysian waters since 1970. *Perantau* means "a rover".

PERANTAU *1972, Royal Malaysian Navy*

SUPPORT SHIP

SRI LANGKAWI (ex-USS *Hunterdon County* LST 838, AGP 838) A 1500

Displacement, tons	1 653 standard; 2 366 beaching; 4 080 full load
Dimensions, feet	316·0 wl; 328·0 oa × 50·0 × 14·0
Guns	8—40 mm (2 twin, 4 single)
Main engines	GM diesels; 2 shafts; 1 700 bhp = 11·6 knots
Complement	138 (11 officers, 127 ratings)

An LST of the 511-1152 series built in 1945. Transferred from the US Navy and commissioned in the Royal Malaysian Navy on 1 July 1971.

SRI LANGKAWI *1972, Royal Malaysian Navy*

MALAGASY

Personnel

1974: 250 officers and men (including Marine Coy)

Mercantile Marine

Lloyd's Register of Shipping: 50 vessels of 63 919 tons gross

PATROL VESSELS

MALAIKA

Displacement, tons	235 light
Dimensions, feet	149·3 pp; 155·8 oa × 23·6 × 8·2
Guns	2—40 mm AA
Main engines	2 MGO diesels; 2 shafts; 2 400 bhp = 18·5 knots
Range, miles	4 000 at 18 knots
Complement	25

Ordered by the French Navy to be built by Chantiers Navals Franco-Belges for delivery to Madagascar. Laid down in Nov 1966, launched on 22 Mar 1967 and completed in Dec 1967. A second unit is planned.

FANANTENANA (ex-*Richelieu*)

Displacement, tons	1 040 standard; 1 200 full load
Dimensions, feet	183·7 pp; 206·4 oa × 30 × 14·8
Guns	2—40 mm AA
Main engines	2 Deutz diesels; 1 shaft; 1 060 + 500 bhp = 12 knots

Trawler purchased and converted in 1966-67 to Coast Guard and training ship. 691 tons gross. Built in 1959 by A. G. Weser, Bremen, Germany.

JASMINE (ex-*D* 385, ex-*D* 211, ex-*YMS* 31)

Displacement, tons	280 standard; 325 full load
Dimensions, feet	134·5 × 24·5 × 12
Main engines	2 diesels; 2 shafts; 1 000 bhp = 12 knots
Oil fuel, tons	22

Former coastal minesweeper of the YMS type launched on 10 Apr 1942 and acquired by France in 1954. Acquired by Madagascar on 19 Aug 1965 as a light tender. Same type originally as *Tanamasoandro* (ex-*Marjolaine*, ex-*D* 337, ex-*YMS* 69) which was discarded on delivery of *Malaika* (ex-*P* 758, *VC* 8) and returned to the French Navy in 1967.

5 PATROL BOATS

Displacement, tons	46
Guns	1—40 mm
Main engines	2 diesels = 22 knots

Used by the Maritime Police. Built by Küstenwache.

1 TRANSPORT

DIEGO SUAREZ

Displacement, tons	810
Dimensions, ft (*m*)	208·9 × 41 × 6·2 (*63·7 × 12·5 × 1·9*)
Guns	1—3 in; 2—20 mm; 1—81 mm mortar
Main engines	2 diesels = 13 knots
Complement	27
Troops	120 with Transport

Completed at Diego Suarez in 1973.

MALI

Personnel

50 officers and men

Patrol Craft

A small river patrol service with 3 craft

MALTA

A coastal patrol force of small craft was formed in 1973. It is manned by the Maltese Regiment and primarily employed as a coastguard.

2 Ex-USN "SWIFT" CLASS

Displacement, tons	22·5
Dimensions, feet	50 × 13 × 3·5
Guns	3 MG
Main engines	2 Diesels = 28 knots
Complement	6

3 Ex-GERMAN CUSTOMS LAUNCHES

2 Ex-LIBYAN CUSTOMS LAUNCHES

Built by Thornycroft in 1962—the first was transferred on 16 Jan 1974.

MAURITANIA

Personnel

(a) 1974: 200 officers and men
(b) Voluntary service

Mercantile Marine

Lloyd's Register of Shipping: 4 vessels of 2 249 tons gross

PATROL BOATS

DAR EL BARKA **TICHITT**

Displacement, tons	75 standard; 82 full load
Dimensions, feet	105 × 18·9 × 5·5
Guns	1—20 mm AA 1 MG
Main engines	2 Mercedes Maybach diesels; 2 shafts; 2 700 bhp = 28 knots
Range, miles	1 500 at 15 knots
Complement	19

Built by Ch Navales de L'Estérel, in service June and April 1969 respectively.

IM RAQ NI **SLOUGHI**

Displacement, tons	20
Dimensions, feet	59 × 13·5 × 3·8
Guns	1—12·7 mm
Main engines	2 GM diesels; 512 bhp = 21 knots
Range, miles	860 at 12 knots

Built by Ch. Navales de L'Estérel in 1965 and 1968, respectively

MEXICO

Administration

Secretary of the Navy:
Admiral C. G. Demn. Luis M. Bravo Carrera

Under-Secretary of the Navy:
Rear-Admiral Ing. M. N. Ricardo Chazaro Lara

Commander-in-Chief of the Navy:
Vice-Admiral C. G. Demn. Humberto Uribe Escandon

Chief of the Naval Staff:
Rear-Admiral C. G. Demn. Miguel A. Gomez Ortega

Director of Services:
Rear-Admiral C. G. Demn. Mario Artigas Fernandez

Diplomatic Representation

Naval Attaché in London:
Rear-Admiral J. Blanco Peyrefitte

Naval Attaché in Washington:
Vice-Admiral Miguel Manzarraga

Personnel

(a) 1974: Total 11 500 officers and men (including Naval Air Force and Marines)
(b) Voluntary Service

Strength of the Fleet

Type	*Active*	*Building*
Destroyers	2	—
Frigates	10	—
Minesweepers (Ocean) (some as escorts)	34	—
Fishery protection vessels	—	21
Oceanographic Ship	1	—
Survey Ships	1	—
Coastal Patrol Craft	10	—
LST's (1 repair ship)	3	—
Tankers-Harbour	2	—
Tugs	5	—
Floating Cranes	6	—

Naval Air Force

5 PBY Catalinas
4 Bell 47G Helicopters
1 Bell 47J Helicopter
4 Alouette III helicopters.

Mercantile Marine

Lloyd's Register of Shipping:
248 vessels of 453 024 tons gross

DESTROYERS

2 Ex-US "FLETCHER" CLASS

Name	*Builders*	*Laid down*	*Launched*	*Completed*
CUAUTHEMOC F 1 (ex-*Harrison* DD 574)	Consolidated Steel	25 Jan 41	7 May 43	25 Jan 43
CUITLAHUAC F 2 (ex-*John Rodgers* DD 573)	Consolidated Steel	25 July 41	7 May 43	9 Feb 43

Displacement, tons	2 100 standard; 3 050 full load
Length, feet (*metres*)	376·5 (*114·7*) oa
Beam, feet (*metres*)	39·5 (*12·0*)
Draught, feet (*metres*)	18·0 (*5·5*)
Guns (*original*)	5—5 in (*127 mm*); 14—40 mm
Torpedo tubes	5—21 in (*533 mm*) quintupled
A/S weapons	8 DCT, 2 Hedgehogs
Main engines	2 geared turbines; 2 shafts; 60 000 shp
Boilers	4
Speed, knots	34
Oil fuel, tons	650
Range, miles	5 000 at 15 knots
Complement	250

Former US destroyers of the original "Fletcher" class. Transferred to the Mexican Navy in Aug 1970.

CUAUTHEMOC *1972, Mexican Navy*

FRIGATES

1 Ex-US "EDSALL" CLASS

	Builders	*Launched*	*Completed*	*Transferred*
MANUEL AZUETA (ex-USS *Swasey*, DE 248)	Brown SB Co, Houston	18 Mar 1943	31 Aug 1943	1 Oct 1973

Displacement, tons	1 200 standard; 1 850 full load
Dimensions, ft (*m*)	306 × 36·6 × 11 (*93·3* × 11·3 × *3·4*)
Guns	3—3 in (*76 mm*), 50 cal AA
AS weapons	2 Hedgehogs; DC racks
Main engines	4 diesels; 6 000 shp; 2 shafts
Speed, knots	21
Complement	149

Transferred to Mexico 1 Oct 1973.

"EDSALL" Class *Skyphotos*

Frigates—*continued*

5 Ex-US "APD" TYPE

Name		No.	Builders	Laid down	Launched	Completed
CHIHUAHUA	(ex-USS *Rednour*, APD 102, ex-DE 592)	B 8	Bethlehem SB Co, Hingham	9 Jan 1944	1 Mar 1944	15 Mar 1945
COAHUILA	(ex-USS *Barber*, LPR, ex-APD 57, ex-*DE* 161)	B 7	Norfolk Navy Yard, Norfolk, Va	27 Apr 1943	20 May 1943	10 Oct 1943
PAPALOAPAN	(ex-USS *Earhart*, APD 113, ex-*DE* 603)	B 4 (ex-H 4)	Bethlehem SB Co, Hingham	20 Mar 1945	12 May 1945	26 July 1945
TEHUANTEPEC	(ex-USS *Joseph M. Auman*, APD 117, ex-DE 674)	B 5 (ex-H 5)	Consolidated Steel Corp, Orange	8 Nov 1943	5 Feb 1944	25 Apr 1945
USUMACINTA	(ex-USS *Don O. Woods*, APD 118, ex-DE 721)	B 6 (ex-H 6)	Consolidated Steel Corp, Orange	1 Dec 1943	19 Feb 1944	28 May 1945

Displacement, tons	1 400 standard; 2 130 full load
Length, feet (*metres*)	300·0 (*91·5*) wl; 306·0 (*93·3*) oa
Beam, feet (*metres*)	37·0 (*11·3*)
Draught, feet (*metres*)	12·7 (*3·9*)
Guns	1—5 in (*127 mm*) 38 cal. dp; 6—40 mm AA (3 twin)
Main engines	GE turbo-electric; 2 shafts; 12 000 shp
Speed, knots	23·6 full; 13 economical sea
Boilers	2 Foster Wheeler "D" with superheater; 475 psi (*33·4 kg/cm²*) 750°F (*399°C*)
Range, miles	5 000 at 15 knots
Oil fuel, tons	350
Complement	204 plus 162 troops

B 4-6 were purchased by Mexico in December 1963 and B 7 and 8 on 17 Feb 1969. The first four replaced the four ex-US "Tacoma" type frigates bearing the same names, which were deleted in June and Aug 1964. *California* stranded and lost 16 Jan 1972 on Bahia Peninsula.

PAPALOAPAN 1972, Mexican Navy

1 "DURANGO" TYPE

Name	No.	Builders	Launched	Completed
DURANGO	B—1 (ex-128)	Union Naval de Levante, Valencia	28 June 1935	1936

Displacement, tons	1 600 standard; 2 000 full load
Length, feet (*metres*)	256·5 (*78·2*) oa
Beam, feet (*metres*)	36·6 (*11·2*)
Draught, feet (*metres*)	10·5 (*3·1*)
Guns	2—4 in (*102 mm*); 2—2·24 in (*57 mm*); 4—20 mm
Main engines	2 Enterprise DMR-38 diesels, electric drive; 2 shafts; 5 000 bhp
Speed, knots	18 max, 12 sea (cruising)
Range, miles	3 000 at 12 knots
Oil fuel, tons	140
Complement	149 (24 officer and 125 men)

Originally designed primarily as an armed transport with accommodation for 20 officers and 450 men. The two Yarrow boilers and Parsons geared turbines of 6 500 shp installed when first built were replaced with two 2 500 bhp diesels in 1967 when the ship was re-rigged with remodelled funnel. Carries a lighter armament than the "Guanajuato" class (see next page) which besides troop carrying and transport capacity are equivalent to frigates in many ways. *Durango* replaced *Zaragoza* as training ship in Mar 1964.

DURANGO 1972. Mexican Navy

3 "GUANAJUATO" CLASS

Name	No.	Builders	Launched
GUANAJUATO	C-7	Sociedad Espanol de Construction Naval, Ferrol	29 May 1934
POTOSI	C-9	Sociedad Espanol de Construction Naval, Motagorda, Cadiz	24 Aug 1934
QUERETARO	C-8	Sociedad Espanol de Construction Naval, Ferrol	29 June 1934

Displacement, tons	1 300 standard: 1 950; full load
Length, feet (*metres*)	264·0 (*80·5*)
Beam, feet (*metres*)	37·8 (*11·5*)
Draught, feet (*metres*)	11·5 (*3·5*)
Guns	3—4 in (*102 mm*) single; 4—20 mm, single
Main engines	2 Enterprise DMR-38 diesels; 2 shafts; 5 000 bhp
Speed, knots	14
Oil fuel, tons	140
Complement	140 (20 officers and 120 men)

Officially classified as gunboats (*canoneros*), but can be used as transports with berths for 120 troops. The Parsons geared turbines (2 shafts; 5 000 shp=19 knots, and Yarrow boilers installed when originally built in 1934 were replaced with two diesels each of 2 500 bhp: *Querétaro* in 1958, *Potosi* in 1961, and *Guanajuato* in 1964.

GUANAJUATO 1970, Wright & Logan

ESCORT MINESWEEPERS

Ex-US "AUK" CLASS

Name	No.
FRANCISCO ZARCO (ex-*Threat*, MSF 124)	IG 13
GUILLERMO PRIETO (ex-*Symbol*, MSF 123)	IG 02
HERMENEGILDO GALEANA (ex-*Sage*, MSF 111)	IG 19
IGNACIO ALTAMIRANO (ex-*Sway*, MSF 120)	IG 12
IGNACIO L. VALLARTA (ex-*Velocity*, MSF 128)	IG 14
IGNACIO DE LA LLAVE (ex-*Spear*, MSF 322)	IG 08
JESUS G. ORTEGA (ex-*Chief*, MSF 315)	IG 15
JUAN ALDARMA (ex-*Pilot*, MSF 104)	IG 18
JUAN N. ALVARES (ex-*Ardent*, MSF 340)	IG 09
LEANDRO VALLE (ex-*Pioneer*, MSF 105)	IG 01
MANUAL G. ZAMORA (ex-*Scoter*, MSF 381)	IG 16
MANUAL DOBLADO (ex-*Defense*, MSF 317)	IG 05
MARIANO ESCOBEDO (ex-*Champion*, MSF 314)	IG 03
MARIANO MATAMOROS (ex-*Herald*, MSF 101)	IG 17
MELCHOR OCAMPO (ex-*Roselle*, MSF 379)	IG 10
PONCIANO ARRIAGA (ex-*Competent*, MSF 316)	IG 04
SANTOS DEGOLLADO (ex-*Gladiator*, MSF 319)	IG 07
SEBASTIAN L. DE TEJADA (ex-*Devastator*, MSF 318)	IG 06
VALENTIN G. FARIAS (ex-*Starling*, MSF 64)	IG 11

JUAN ALDARMA (ex Pilot) USN

Displacement, tons	890 standard; 1 250 full load
Dimensions, feet	215 wl; 221·2 oa × 32·2 × 10·8
Guns	1—3 in 50 cal; 2 or 4—40 mm
Main engines	Diesel electric; 2 shafts; 3 500 bhp = 18 knots
Complement	9 officers and 96 ratings

Transferred—6 in Feb 1973, 4 in Apr 1973, 9 in Sept 1973.

Escort Minesweepers—*continued*

15 Ex-US "ADMIRABLE" CLASS

Name	No.	Ex-US Name & No.		Name	No.	Ex-US Name & No.	
DM-01	ID-1	*Jubilant*	255	**DM-13**	IE-3	*Knave*	256
DM-02	ID-2	*Hilarity*	241	**DM-14**	IE-4	*Rebel*	284
DM-03	ID-3	*Execute*	232	**DM-15**	IE-5	*Crag*	214
DM-04	ID-4	*Specter*	306	**DM-16**	IE-6	*Dour*	223
DM-05	ID-5	*Scuffle*	298	**DM-17**	IE-7	*Diploma*	221
DM-06	ID-6	*Eager*	224	**DM-18**	IE-8	*Invade*	254
DM-10	ID-0	*Instill*	252	**DM-19**	IE-9	*Intrigue*	253
DM-12	IE-2	*Ransom*	283	**DM-20**	IE-0	*Harlequin*	365

Displacement, tons 650 standard; 945 full load
Dimensions, feet 180 wl; 184·5 oa × 33 × 10
Guns 1—3 in, 50 cal dp; 2—40 mm AA; 4—6 20 mm
Main engines 2 diesels; 2 shafts; 1 710 bhp = 15 knots
Range, miles 4 300 at 10 knots
Complement 104

Former US steel-hulled "180-ft" fleet minesweepers of the "Admirable" class. MSF, ex-AM type. All completed in 1943-44. Of the twenty vessels transferred at Orange, Texas, on 2 Oct 1962 ten were designated *dragaminas* for minesweeping duties, with D pennant numbers, and ten *escoltas* for escort and general purpose duties with E pennant numbers. (5 previous members of this class deleted and to be used for spare parts.)

DM 17 — *1970, Mexican Navy*

FISHERY PROTECTION VESSELS

21 "AZTECA" CLASS

Displacement, tons 130
Dimensions, ft (*m*) 108 × 20 × 5 (*33 × 6·1 × 1·5*)
Guns 2—20 mm
Main engines 2—12 cyl. Paxman Ventura diesels = approx 20 knots

Ordered by Mexico on 27 Mar 1973 from Association of British Tool Manufacturers Ltd. To be built by Ailsa Shipbuilding Co (11), J. Lamont & Co Ltd (5), and Scott & Sons, Bowling (5) for completion 1974-75.

OCEANOGRAPHIC SHIP

1 Ex-US PCE TYPE

VIRGILIO URIBE (ex-*Tomas Marin*, ex-PCE 875) **C 1** (ex-C 3)

Displacement, tons 600 standard; 903 full load
Dimensions, feet 180 wl; 184·5 oa × 33·1 × 9·5
Guns 1—3 in, 50 cal; 6—40 mm AA (3 twin); 4—20 mm AA (single)
A/S weapons 2 DCT
Main engines GM diesels; 2 shafts; 1 800 bhp = 15 knots
Range, miles 4 300 at 10 knots
Complement 80

Sole survivor of five former US patrol vessels of the PCE type, all completed in 1943-44 and purchased from US Navy in 1947. Formerly rated as *Corbeta*. Now employed on oceanographic research.

VIRGILIO URIBE — *1972, Mexican Navy*

SURVEY SHIP

SOTAVENTO 1 A

Displacement, tons 300 standard; 400 full load
Dimensions, feet 165·5 × 28 × 10
Main engines Diesels; 1 800 bhp = 17 knots
Complement 30

Built by Higgins, New Orleans. Launched in 1947. Handsome, streamlined, with truncated funnel, air conditioned and equipped with radar. Formerly the Presidential Yacht, but officially reclassified as *Buque Hidrografico* in 1966.

SOTAVENTO — *1967, Mexican Navy*

PATROL BOATS

2 "AZUETA" CLASS

AZUETA G 9 **VILLAPANDO** G 6

Displacement, tons 80 standard; 85 full load
Dimensions, feet 85·3 × 16·4 × 7·0
Guns 2—13·2 mm AA (1 twin)
Main engines Superior diesels; 600 bhp = 12 knots

Of all steel construction. Built at Astilleros de Tampico in 1959 and 1960 respectively.

AZUETA — *Mexican Navy*

5 RIVER TYPE

AM 4 **AM 5** **AM 6** **AM 7** **AM 8**

Displacement, tons 35
Main engines Diesel; speed = 10 knots

River patrol craft of steel construction. Built in Tampico and Veracruz. Entered service from 1960 to 1962.

POLIMAR 1 G 1 **POLIMAR 2** G 2 **POLIMAR 3** G 3

Displacement, tons 37 standard; 57 full load
Dimensions, feet 60·1 × 15·1 × 4·0
Main engines 2 diesels; 456 bhp = 16 knots

Small patrol craft of steel construction. *Polimar 1* was built at Astilleros de Tampico in 1961 and entered service on 1 Oct 1962. *Polimar 2* and *Polimar 3* were built at Icacas Shipyard, Guerrero and entered service in 1966.

POLIMAR III — *1972, Mexican Navy*

TRANSPORT

ZACATECAS B 2

Displacement, tons 780 standard
Dimensions, feet 158 × 27·2 × 9
Guns 1—40 mm AA; 2—20 mm AA (single)
Main engines 1 MAN diesel; 560 hp = 10 knots
Complement 50 (13 officers and 37 men)

Built at Ulua Shipyard, Veracruz. Launched in 1959. Cargo ship type. The hull is of welded steel construction.

LANDING SHIPS

2 Ex-US LST (511-1152 Series)

RIO PANUCO (ex-USS *Park County* LST 1077) IA 01
MANZILLO (ex-USS *Clearwater County* LST 602) IA 02

Displacement, tons	1 653 standard; 2 366 beaching; 4 080 full load
Dimensions, feet	316 wl; 328 oa × 50 × 14
Guns	6—40 mm (1 twin; 4 singles)
Main engines	GM diesels; 2 shafts; 1 700 bhp = 11·6 knots
Range, miles	6 000 at 11 knots
Complement	130
Troop capacity	147

Transferred to Mexico on 20 Sep 1971 and 25 May 1972 respectively. Both employed as rescue ships.

1 Ex-US ARV (ex-LST)

VICENTE GUERRERO (ex-USS *Megara* ARV A6)

Displacement, tons	1 625 light; 4 100 full load
Dimensions, feet	328 oa × 50 × 14
Guns	8—40 mm
Main engines	2 GM diesels; 2 shafts; 1 800 bhp = 11·6 knots
Complement	250

Ex-aircraft repair ship sold to Mexico 1 Oct 1973.

OILERS

2 Ex-US YO TYPE

AGUASCALIENTES (ex-YOG 6) A 5 **TLAXCALA** (ex-YO 107) A 6

Displacement, tons	440 light; 1 480 to 1 800 full load
Dimensions, feet	174·5 oa × 33·0 × 11·8 max
Main engines	Union diesel direct; 500 bhp = 8 knots
Capacity	6 570 barrels
Complement	26 (5 officers and 21 ratings)

Former US self-propelled fuel oil barges. Built by Geo. H. Mathis Co Ltd, Camden, N.J. and Geo. Lawley & Son, Neponset, Mass. respectively, in 1943. Purchased in 1964. Entered service in Nov 1964.

TUGS

R-1 (ex-*Farallon*) **R-3** (ex-*Point Vicente*) **R-5** (ex-*Burnt Island*)
R-2 (ex-*Montauk*) **R-4** (ex-*Moose Teak*)

Acquired by the Mexican Navy in 1968.

6 FLOATING CRANES

Ex-US YDs transferred 1964-1971.

MONTSERRAT

This small Crown Colony in the Leeward Islands purchased a single Brooke Marine 12 m Patrol Craft in 1971. This craft of 15 tons is powered by two 370 hp diesels, is capable of 22 knots and armed with 3 machine-guns.

MOROCCO

Personnel

(a) 1974: 2 000 officers and ratings (including 500 Marines)
(b) 18 months National Service

Mercantile Marine

Lloyd's Register of Shipping:
46 vessels of 56 125 tons gross

FRIGATE

Name	*Builders*	*Laid down*	*Launched*	*Completed*
AL MAOUNA (ex-*La Surprise*, ex-HMS *Torridge*) 31 (ex-033)	Blyth Dry Dock & Ship Building Co	17 Oct 1942	16 Aug 1943	6 Apr 1944

Displacement, tons	1 450 standard; 2 150 full load
Length, feet (*metres*)	283·0 (*86·3*) pp; 301·3 (*91·8*) oa
Beam, feet (*metres*)	36·5 (*11·1*)
Draught, feet (*metres*)	12·5 (*3·8*)
Aircraft	1 helicopter
Guns, surface	2—4·1 in (*105 mm*)
Guns, AA	3—40 mm; 2—20 mm
A/S weapons	1 "Hedgehog"; 4 DCT; 2 DC racks
Main engines	Triple expansion; 2 shafts; 5 500 ihp
Boilers	2 Admiralty 3-drum
Speed, knots	18
Oil fuel, tons	645
Range, miles	14 400 at 12 knots
Complement	123 (10 officers, 113 men)

Former British "River" class frigate purchased by France in 1944. Sold to Morocco in June 1964 and converted as flagship and Royal yacht by Chantiers Dubigeon at Brest. A helicopter landing deck and extra accommodation were provided aft. SPS 6 search radar. Accepted on 5 March 1965.

CORVETTES

2 PR 72 TYPE

Displacement, tons	370 standard; 440 full load
Dimensions, ft (*m*)	188·8 × 25 × — (*57·5 × 7·6 × —*)
Guns	1—76 mm Oto-Melara 1—40 mm L70 Bofors
Main engines	4 diesels; 11 040 hp = 28 knots

Ordered June 1973 from Soc. Française de Constructions Navales. This type can be fitted with Exocet—as the Vega control system will be installed this would be a simple operation.

PATROL VESSELS

AL BACHIR 22 (ex-12)

Displacement, tons	125 light; 154 full load
Dimensions, feet	124·7 pp; 133·2 oa × 20·8 × 4·7
Guns	2—40 mm AA and MG
Main engines	2 SEMT-Pielstick diesels; 2 shafts; 3 600 bhp = 25 knots
Oil fuel, tons	21
Range, miles	4 000 at 15 knots
Complement	23

Ordered in 1964 from Constructions Mécaniques de Normandie, Cherbourg, launched 25 Feb 1967, delivered 30 Mar 1967.

AL BACHIR *1967, Royal Moroccan Navy*

SEAWARD PATROL CRAFT

ES SABIQ (ex-*P 762, VC 12*) 11

Displacement, tons	60 standard; 82 full load
Dimensions, feet	104·5 × 15·5 × 5·5
Guns	2—20 mm AA
Main engines	Mercedes-Benz diesels; 2 shafts; 2 700 bhp = 28 knots
Range, miles	3 000 at 15 knots
Complement	17

Former French seaward defence motor launch of the VC type. Built by Chantiers Navals d'Estérel. Launched on 13 Aug 1957. Completed in 1958. Transferred from the French Navy to the Moroccan Navy on 15 Nov 1960 and renamed *Es Sabiq*.

LANDING CRAFT

LIEUTENANT MALGHAGH 21

Displacement, tons	292 standard; 642 full load
Dimensions, feet	193·6 × 39·2 × 4·3
Guns	2—20 mm AA
Main engines	MGO diesels; 2 shafts; 1 000 bhp = 8 knots
Complement	16 (1 officer, 15 men)

Ordered early in 1963 from Chantiers Navals Franco-Belges and completed in 1964. Similar to the French landing craft of the EDIC type built at the same yard.

There are also the yacht *Essaoira*, 60 tons, from Italy in 1967, used as a training vessel for watchkeepers; and twelve customs boats, four of 40 tons, 82 feet, diesels 940 bhp = 23 knots, and eight 42·7 feet; all built in 1963. The *Murene*, Coast Guard Cutter, has also been reported.

FRIGATES

6 "VAN SPEIJK" CLASS

Name	No.	Builders	Laid down	Launched	Completed
TJERK HIDDES	F 804	Nederlandse Dok en Scheepsbouw Mij, Amsterdam	1 June 1964	17 Dec 1965	16 Aug 1967
VAN GALEN	F 803	Koninklijke Maatschappij De Schelde, Flushing	25 July 1963	19 June 1965	1 Mar 1967
VAN NES	F 805	Koninklijke Maatschappij De Schelde, Flushing	25 July 1963	26 Mar 1966	9 Aug 1967
VAN SPEIJK	F 802	Nederlandse Dok en Scheepsbouw Mij, Amsterdam	1 Oct 1963	5 Mar 1965	14 Feb 1967
EVERTSEN	F 815	Koninklijke Maatschappij De Schelde, Flushing	6 July 1965	18 June 1966	21 Dec 1967
ISAAC SWEERS	F 814	Nederlandse Dok en Scheepsbouw Mij, Amsterdam	5 May 1965	10 Mar 1967	15 May 1968

Displacement, tons	2 200 standard; 2 850 full load
Dimensions, feet	360 wl, 372 oa × 41 × 18
Guns	2—4·5 in (twin turret)
Missile launchers	2 quadruple "Seacat" anti-aircraft
A/S weapons	1 "Limbo" three-barrelled depth charge mortar
Aircraft	1 lightweight helicopter armed with homing torpedoes
Boilers	2 Babcock & Wilcox
Main engines	2 double reduction geared turbines; 2 shafts; 30 000 shp
Speed, knots	28·5 sea, 30 max
Complement	254

GENERAL. Four ships were ordered in Oct 1962 and two later. Have ECM and VDS. Ships of this class will undergo mid-life conversion from 1976 to 1980.

VAN SPEIJK class

DESIGN. Although in general these ships are based on the design of the British Improved Type 12 ("Leander" class), there are a number of modifications to suit the requirements of the Royal Netherlands Navy. As far as possible equipment of Netherlands manufacture was installed. This resulted in a number of changes in the ship's superstructure compared with the British "Leander" class. To avoid delay these ships were in some cases fitted with equipment already available, instead of going through long development stages.

RADAR. LW 02 air surveillance on mainmast; DA 05 target indicator on foremast; surface-warning/nav set on foremast; 1-M45 for 4·5 in guns; 2-M44 for Seacat.

EVERTSEN — *1973, Wright & Logan*

8 "FRIESLAND" CLASS

Name	No.	Builders	Laid down	Launched	Completed
FRIESLAND	D 812	Nederlandse Dok en Scheepsbouw Mij, Amsterdam	17 Dec 1951	21 Feb 1953	22 Mar 1956
GRONINGEN	D 813	Nederlandse Dok en Scheepsbouw, Mij, Amsterdam	21 Feb 1952	9 Jan 1954	12 Sep 1956
LIMBURG	D 814	Koninklijke Maatschappij De Schelde, Flushing	28 Nov 1953	5 Sep 1955	31 Oct 1956
OVERIJSSEL	D 815	Dok-en-Werfmaatschappij Wilton-Fijenoord	15 Oct 1953	8 Aug 1955	4 Oct 1957
DRENTHE	D 816	Nederlandse Dok en Scheepsbouw Mij, Amsterdam	9 Jan 1954	26 Mar 1955	1 Aug 1957
UTRECHT	D 817	Koninklijke Maatschappij De Schelde, Flushing	15 Feb 1954	2 June 1956	1 Oct 1957
ROTTERDAM	D 818	Rotterdamse Droogdok Mij, Rotterdam	7 Jan 1954	26 Jan 1956	28 Feb 1957
AMSTERDAM	D 819	Nederlandse Dok en Scheepsbouw Mij, Amsterdam	26 Mar 1955	25 Aug 1956	10 Aug 1958

FRIESLAND — ***1971, Royal Netherlands Navy***

Displacement, tons	2 497 standard; 3 070 full load
Length, feet (*metres*)	370 (*112·8*) pp; 380·5 (*116·0*) oa
Beam, feet (*metres*)	38·5 (*11·7*)
Draught, feet (*metres*)	17 (*5·2*)
Guns, surface	4—4·7 in (*120 mm*) twin turrets
Guns, AA	4—40 mm (2 removed during recent refits)
A/S weapons	2 four-barrelled depth charge mortars. Bofors rocket launchers
Boilers	4 Babcock
Main engines	2 Werkspoor geared turbines, 60 000 shp; 2 shafts
Speed, knots	36
Complement	284

GENERAL
These ships have side armour as well as deck protection. "Limbo" type anti-submarine rocket throwers. Twin rudders. Propellers 370 rpm. Named after provinces of the Netherlands, and the two principal cities. To be replaced by a new class of frigates as from 1975.

RADAR. Search: LW 03. Tactical: DA 05. Fire Control HSA M 45 for 4·7 in. HSA fire control for 40 mm and A/S rockets.

GUNNERY. The 4·7 inch guns are fully automatic with a rate of fire of 50 rounds per minute. All guns are radar controlled. Originally six 40 mm guns were mounted.

TORPEDO TUBES. *Utrecht* was equipped with eight 21 inch A/S torpedo tubes (single, four on each side) in 1960 and *Overijssel* in 1961, and the others were to have been, but the project was dropped and tubes already fitted were removed.

FRIESLAND *Class*

Frigates—*continued*

2 "HOLLAND" CLASS

Name	*No.*	*Builders*	*Laid down*	*Launched*	*Completed*
HOLLAND	D 808	Rotterdamse Droogdok Mij, Rotterdam	21 Apr 1950	11 Apr 1953	31 Dec 1954
ZEELAND	D 809	Koninklijke Maatschappji De Schelde, Flushing	12 Jan 1951	27 June 1953	1 Mar 1955

Displacement, tons	**2 215 standard; 2 765 full load**
Length, feet (*metres*)	**360·5 (*109·9*) pp; 371·1 (*113·1*) oa**
Beam, feet (*metres*)	**37·5 (*11·4*)**
Draught, feet (*metres*)	**16·8 (*5·1*)**
Guns	**4—4·7 in (*120 mm*); 1—40 mm**
A/S weapons	2 four-barrelled DC mortars. Bofors rocket launchers
Main engines	Werkspoor Parsons geared turbines; 2 shafts; 45 000 shp
Speed, knots	32
Boilers	4 Babcock
Complement	247

HOLLAND *Class*

GENERAL
The two ships of this class are equipped with engines of the pre-war "Callenburgh" class design. (The four "Callenburgh" class destroyers were being built in 1940. *Isaac Sweers* was towed to England and completed there. *Tjerk Hiddes* was completed by the Germans as ZH 1. The other two, *Callenburgh* and *Van Almonde*, were too severely damaged for further use and were scrapped, the engines being installed in the "Holland" class).

Gelderland now a harbour-training hulk in Amsterdam. *Noord Brabant* too severely damaged in collision 9 Jan 1974 for repair.

RADAR. Search: LW 03. Tactical: DA 02. Fire Control: HSA M 45 for 4·7 in. HSA fire control for A/S rocket launcher.

GUNNERY. The 4·7 inch guns are fully automatic with a rate of fire of 50 rounds per minute. All guns are radar controlled.

HOLLAND *1973, Royal Netherlands Navy*

4 "S" CLASS (NEW CONSTRUCTION)

Displacement, tons	3 600
Dimensions, ft (*m*)	419·8 × 47·2 × —(*128 × 14·4 × —*)
Aircraft	1 or 2 helicopters
Missiles	Surface-to-surface system; NATO Seasparrow surface-to-air
Gun	1—76 mm
Torpedo tubes	Two triple mountings for Mk 46 A/S torpedoes
Main engines	2 Rolls-Royce Olympus gas turbines—50 000 shp; 2 Rolls-Royce Tyne gas turbines—8 000 shp; 2 variable pitch propelers
Speed	30 knots
Range, miles	4 000 on Tyne cruising turbines
Complement	185

Contract to De Schelde Shipyard announced on 13 Dec 1973. Order Spring 1974. Completion targets—Oct 1978, July 1979, Jan 1980, July 1980. With a high degree of automation, these ships, planned to replace the 4 "*Friesland*" class, are costed at 208 million guilders at 1974 prices. Four more to be ordered in 1974.

CORVETTES

6 "WOLF" CLASS

Name	*No.*	*Builders*	*Laid down*	*Launched*	*Completed*
FRET (ex-*PCE* 1604)	F 818	General Shipbuilding and Engineering Works, Boston	18 Dec 1952	30 July 1953	4 May 1954
HERMELIJN (ex-*PCE* 1605)	F 819	General Shipbuilding and Engineering Works, Boston	2 Mar 1953	6 Mar 1954	5 Aug 1954
JAGUAR (ex-*PCE* 1609)	F 822	Avondale Marine Ways, Inc. New Orleans, Louisiana	10 Dec 1952	20 Mar 1954	11 June 1954
PANTER (ex-*PCE* 1608)	F 821	Avondale Marine Ways, Inc, New Orleans, Louisiana	1 Dec 1952	30 Jan 1954	11 June 1954
VOS (ex-*PCE* 1606)	F 820	General Shipbuilding and Engineering Works, Boston	3 Aug 1952	1 May 1954	2 Dec 1954
WOLF (ex-*PCE* 1607)	F 817	Avondale Marine Ways, Inc, New Orleans, Louisiana	15 Nov 1952	2 Jan 1954	26 Mar 1954

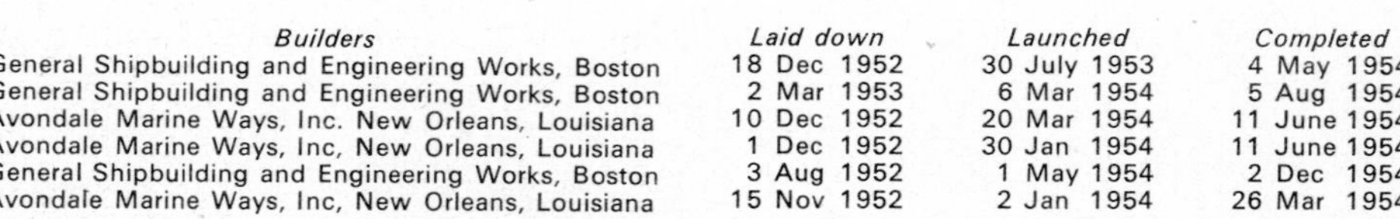

Displacement, tons	**808 standard; 975 full load**
Length, feet (*metres*)	**180 (*54·9*) pp; 184·5 (*56·2*) oa**
Beam, feet (*metres*)	**33 (*10·0*)**
Draught, feet (*metres*)	**9·5 (*2·9*) mean; 14·5 (*4·4*) max**
Guns, dual purpose	**1—3 in (*76 mm*)**
Guns, AA	**6—40 mm (*Jaguar, Panter*: 4—40 mm); 8—20 mm**
A/S	**1 Hedgehog; 2 DCT (*Jaguar, Panter*: 4); 2 DC racks**
Main engines	**2 GM diesels; 1 600 bhp; 2 shafts**
Range, miles	**4 300 at 10 knots**
Speed, knots	**15**
Complement	**96**

20 mm guns not fitted in peacetime.

PANTER *1972, Wright & Logan*

WOLF *Class*

Corvettes—*continued*

5 "BALDER" CLASS

Name	*No.*	*Laid down*	*Launched*	*Completed*
BALDER	P 802	12 Sep 1953	24 Feb 1954	6 Aug 1954
BULGIA	P 803	10 Oct 1953	24 Apr 1954	9 Aug 1954
FREYR	P 804	24 Feb 1954	21 July 1954	1 Dec 1954
HADDA	P 805	24 Apr 1954	2 Oct 1954	3 Feb 1955
HEFRING	P 806	21 July 1954	1 Dec 1954	23 Mar 1955

Displacement, tons 149 standard; 225 full load
Dimensions, feet 114·9 pp; 119·1 oa × 20·2 × 5·9
Guns 1—40 mm; 3—20 mm
A/S weapons 2 DGT, Mousetrap
Main engines Diesels; 2 shafts; 1 050 shp = 15·5 knots
Range, miles 1 000 at 13 knots
Complement 27

Built in the Netherlands by Rijkswerf Willemsoord on US account. US submarine chaser type, SC Nos 1627-1631.

HEFRING *1971, Royal Netherlands Navy*

SUBMARINES

2 "ZWAARDVIS" CLASS

Name	*No.*	*Builders*	*Laid down*	*Launched*	*Completed*
TIJGERHAAI	S 807	Rotterdamse Droogdok Mij, Rotterdam	14 July 1966	25 May 1971	20 Oct 1972
ZWAARDVIS	S 806	Rotterdamse Droogdok Mij, Rotterdam	14 July 1966	2 July 1970	18 Aug 1972

Displacement, tons 2 350 surface; 2 640 submerged
Length, feet (*metres*) 213·3 (*65·0*)
Beam, feet (*metres*) 27·5 (*8·4*)
Draught, feet (*metres*) 23·3 (*7·1*)
Torpedo tubes 6—21 in (*533 mm*)
Main engines Diesel-electric; 3 diesel generators; 1 shaft
Speed, knots 13 on surface; 20 submerged
Complement 67

In the 1964 Navy Estimates a first instalment was approved for the construction of two conventionally powered submarines. HSA M8 Fire Control.

ZWAARDVIS *1972, Royal Netherlands Navy*

2 "POTVIS" CLASS
2 "DOLFIJN" CLASS

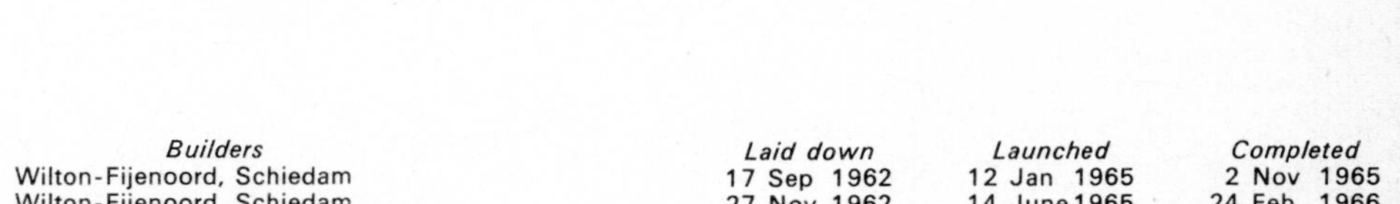

Name	*No.*	*Builders*	*Laid down*	*Launched*	*Completed*
POTVIS	S 804	Wilton-Fijenoord, Schiedam	17 Sep 1962	12 Jan 1965	2 Nov 1965
TONIJN	S 805	Wilton-Fijenoord, Schiedam	27 Nov 1962	14 June 1965	24 Feb 1966
DOLFIJN	S 808	Rotterdamse Droogdok Mij, Rotterdam	30 Dec 1954	20 May 1959	16 Dec 1960
ZEEHOND	S 809	Rotterdamse Droogdok Mij, Rotterdam	30 Dec 1954	20 Feb 1960	16 Mar 1961

Displacement, tons 1 140 standard; 1 494 surface 1 826 submerged
Length, feet (*metres*) 260·9 (*79·5*)
Beam, feet (*metres*) 25·8 (*7·8*)
Draught, feet (*metres*) 15·8 (*4·8*)
Torpedo tubes 8—21 in (*533 mm*)
Main engines 2 MAN diesels; total 3 100 bhp Electric motors, 4 200 hp; 2 shafts
Speed, knots 14·5 on surface; 17 submerged
Complement 64

These submarines are of a triple-hulled design, giving a diving depth 980 feet (*300 metres*). *Potvis* and *Tonijn*, originally voted for in 1949 with the other pair, but suspended for some years, had several modifications compared with *Dolfijn* and *Zeehond* and were officially considered to be a separate class; but modernisation of both classes has been completed, and all four boats are now almost identical. HSA M8 Fire Control.

CONSTRUCTION. The hull consists of three cylinders arranged in a triangular shape. The upper cylinder accommodates the crew, navigational equipment and armament. The lower two cylinders house the propulsion machinery comprising diesel engines, batteries and electric motors.

TONIJN *1973. Royal Netherlands Navy*

MINE WARFARE FORCES

5 "ONVERSAAGD" CLASS (MCM SUPPORT SHIPS and ESCORTS)

Name	No.	Laid down	Completed
ONVERSAAGD (ex-AM 480)	A 854 (ex-M 884)	1952	27 May 1954
ONBEVREESD (ex-AM 481)	A 855 (ex-M 885)	1952	21 Sep 1954
ONVERVAARD (ex-AM 482)	A 858 (ex-M 888)	1952	31 Mar 1955
ONVERDROTEN (ex-AM 485)	A 859 (ex-M 889)	1952	22 Nov 1954
MERCUUR (ex-*Onverschrokken*)		1952	22 July 1954

Displacement, tons	735 standard; 790 full load
Dimensions, feet	165·0 pp; 172·0 oa × 36·0 × 10·6
Guns	1—40 mm AA
A/S weapons	2 DC
Main engines	Diesels; 1 600 bhp = 15·5 knots
Oil fuel, tons	46
Range, miles	2 400 at 12 knots
Complement	70

Built in USA for the Netherlands, *Onversaagd*, *Onbevreesd* and *Onvervaard* by Astoria Marine Construction Co and the remaining two by Peterson Builders, Wisconsin. Of wooden and non-magnetic construction. Originally designed as Minesweepers—Ocean—reclassified in 1966 and in 1972. *Onbevreesd*, *Onverdroten* and *Onvervaard* are MCM Command/Support Ships. *Mercuur* (ex-*Onverschrokken*) was converted into a Torpedo Trials Ship in 1972. *Onversaagd* has been converted for temporary duty as survey ship until the new construction Oceanographic Ship is delivered in 1976.

ONVERVAARD (Escort type) *1972, Royal Netherlands Navy*

18 "DOKKUM" CLASS (CMS and MINEHUNTERS)

ABCOUDE	M 810	**HOOGEZAND**	M 802	**ROERMOND**	M 806 D
DOKKUM	M 801 H	**HOOGEVEEN**	M 827	**SITTARD**	M 830
DRACHTEN	M 812	**NAALDWIJK**	M 809	**STAPHORST**	M 828 H
DRUNEN	M 818 H	**NAARDEN**	M 823	**VEERE**	M 842 H
GEMERT	M 841	**OMMEN**	M 813	**VENLO**	M 817
GIETHOORN	M 815	**RHENEN**	M 844 D	**WOERDEN**	M 820 D

2 "WILDERVANK" CLASS (MINESWEEPERS—COASTAL)

LEERSUM M 822 D **WAALWIJK** M 807 D

Displacement, tons	373 standard; 417 full load
Dimensions, feet	149·8 oa × 28 × 6·5
Guns	2—40 mm
Main engines	2 diesels; Fyenoord MAN or Werkspoor; 2 500 bhp = 16 knots
Range, miles	2 500 at 10 knots
Complement	38

Of 32 Western Union type non-magnetic coastal minesweepers built in the Netherlands (*Kustmynenvegers*), 18 were under offshore procurement as the "Dokkum" class, with MAN engines, and 14 on Netherlands account as the "Wildervank" class, with Werkspoor diesels. All launched in 1954-56 and completed in 1955-56. Named after small towns in the Netherlands. The remaining eleven minesweepers are subject to a fleet rehabilitation and modernisation programme during 1973-77. One ship was sold to Ethiopia in 1972. Five ships were converted to diving vessels (D) (1962-68) and four to minehunters (H) (1968-73). Eleven ships have been deleted.

DOKKUM (Hunter) *1971, Royal Netherlands Navy*

GEMERT (sweeper) *1973, C. and S. Taylor*

9 "BEEMSTER" CLASS (MINESWEEPERS—COASTAL)

BEEMSTER (ex-*AMS* 105)	M 845	**BLARICUM** (ex-*AMS* 112)	M 853
BEDUM (ex-*Beerta* ex-*AMS* 106)	M 847	**BRIELLE** (ex-*AMS* 167)	M 854
BEILEN (ex-*AMS* 110)	M 848	**BRESKENS** (ex-*AMS* 148)	M 855
BORCULO (ex-*AMS* 107)	M 849	**BOXTEL** (ex-*AMS* 149)	M 857
BORNE (ex-*AMS* 108)	M 850		

Displacement, tons	330 standard; 384 full load
Dimensions, feet	138 pp; 144·7 oa × 27·9 × 7·5
Guns	2—20 mm AA
Main engines	2 diesels; 880 bhp = 13·6 knots
Range, miles	2 500 at 10 knots
Complement	37

All completed and transferred from USA in 1953-54. Of non-magnetic construction. Named after small towns in the Netherlands. Five have been returned to USA and remainder will be returned during period 1973-77 as "Dokkum" class conversions complete.

BORCULO *1973, Royal Netherlanda Nsvy*

16 "VAN STRAELEN" CLASS (MINESWEEPERS—INSHORE)

ALBLAS	M 868	**MAHU**	M 880	**VAN MOPPES**	M 873
BUSSEMAKER	M 869	**SCHUILING**	M 876	**VAN STRAELEN**	M 872
CHÖMPFF	M 874	**STAVERMAN**	M 881	**VAN VERSENDAAL**	M 877
HOUTEPEN	M 882	**VAN DER WEL**	M 878	**VAN WELL GROENVELD**	M 875
LACOMBLÉ	M 870	**VAN HAMEL**	M 871		
		VAN 'T HOFF	M 879	**ZOMER**	M 883

Displacement, tons	151 light; 169 full load
Dimensions, feet	90 pp; 99·3 oa × 18·2 × 5·2
Gun	1—20 mm AA
Main engines	Werkspoor diesels; 2 shafts; 1 100 bhp = 13 knots
Complement	12

Built, 6 by Werf de Noord at Albasserdam; 5 by N.V. de Arnhemse Scheepsbouw Maatschappij at Arnhem; and 5 by Amsterdamsche Scheepswerft G. de Vries Lentsch Jr at Amsterdam. Eight were built under the offshore procurement programme, with MDAP funds, and the remaining eight were paid for by Netherlands. All ordered in mid-1957. Built of non-magnetic materials. *Alblas*, the first, was laid down at Werf de Noord N.V. at Albasserdam on 26 Feb 1958, launched on 29 June 1959, started trials on 15 Jan 1960 and completed on 12 Mar 1960. All the others were laid down in 1958-61, launched in 1958-61 and commissioned in 1960-62.

VAN WELL GROENVELD *1972, Wright & Logan*

AMPHIBIOUS FORCES

L 9521 **L 9526**

Displacement, tons	20
Dimensions, feet	50 × 11·8 × 5·8
Main engines	2 Kromhout diesels; 75 bhp = 8 knots
Complement	3

Now officially rated as LCA Type,

L 9510 **L 9511** **L 9512** **L 9513** **L 9514** **L 9515** **L 9517** **L 9518** **L 9520** **L 9522**

Displacement, tons	13·6
Dimensions, feet	46·2 × 11·5 × 6
Main engines	Rolls Royce diesel; Schottel propeller; 200 bhp = 12 knots
Complement	3

New landing craft made of plastic (polyester), all commissioned in 1962-63, except L 9520 in 1964.

SURVEY SHIPS

1 NEW CONSTRUCTION

HYDROGRAPHIC OCEANOGRAPHIC TYPE

Displacement, tons	2 950
Dimensions, ft (*m*)	295 × 47·2 × 15·7 (*90 × 14·4 × 4·8*)
Speed, knots	15
Complement	64 plus 15 scientists

This ship is to replace *Luymes*. Ordered in 1974. Until she is completed in 1976 the converted Minesweeper—Ocean *Onversaagd* will serve in her place.

2 "BUYSKES" CLASS

BLOMMENDAL A 905 **BUYSKES** A 904

Displacement, tons	967 standard; 1 033 full load
Dimensions, ft (*m*)	196·6 oa × 36·4 × 12 (*60 × 11·1 × 3·7*)
Main engines	Diesel electric; 2 100 hp (3 × 700) = 13·5 knots
Complement	43

Built by Boele's Scheepswerven en Machinefabriek BV. Bolne to replace the survey ships *Snellius* and *Zeefakkel*. Both designed primarily for hydrographic work but have also limited oceanographic and meteorological capability. They will operate mainly in the North Sea. A data logging system is installed as part of the automatic handling of hydrographic data. They carry two 22 ft survey launches capable of 15 knots and two work-boats normally used for sweeping. Both ships can operate two floats, each housing an echo-sounding transducer, one streaming on each beam. This will enable the running of three simultaneous sounding lines 100 m. apart. *Buyskes* commissioned on 9 Mar 1973 and *Blommendal* on 22 May 1973.

BLOMMENDAL *1973, Royal Netherlands Navy*

DREG IV A 920

Displacement, tons	46 standard; 48 full load
Dimensions, feet	65·7 × 15·1 × 4·9
Main engines	120 hp = 9·5 knots
Complement	10

SERVICE FORCES

2 "POOLSTER" CLASS (FAST COMBAT SUPPORT SHIPS)

POOLSTER A 835 **ZUIDERKRUIS**

Displacement, tons	16 800 full load; 16 900 (*Zuiderkruis*)
Measurement, tons	10 000 deadweight
Dimensions, feet	515 pp; 556 oa × 66·7 × 27 (*Zuiderkruis* 561 oa)
Guns	2—40 mm AA
Aircraft	Capacity: 5 helicopters (official complement 3 SH-34 J)
Main engines	22 500 shp turbines = 21 knots (18 service); 2 Werkspoor 16TM410 diesels of 21 000 hp = 21 knots in *Zuiderkruis*
Complement	200

Fast fleet replenishment ships. *Poolster* built by Rotterdam se Droogdok Mij. Laid down on 18 Sep 1962. Launched on 16 Oct 1963. Trials mid-1964. Commissioned on 10 Sep 1964. Helicopter deck aft. Funnel heightened by 4·5 m. *Zuiderkruis* built by Verolme ship yards Alblasserdam. Ordered Oct 1972. Laid down 16 July 1973 for launching in mid 1974 and completion 1975.

POOLSTER (note modified funnel) *1972, Wright & Logan*

Service Forces —*continued*

ZUIDERKRUIS *1973, Royal Netherlands Navy*

TRAINING SHIPS

ZEEFAKKEL A 903

Displacement, tons	355 standard; 384 full load
Dimensions, ft (*m*)	149 oa × 24·7 × 6·9 (*45·4 × 7·6 × 2·1*)
Guns	1—3 in AA; 1—40 mm AA
Main engines	2 Smit/MAN 8 cyl diesels; 2 shafts; 640 bhp = 12 knots
Complement	29

Built by J. & K Smit, Kinderdijk. Laid down Sept 1949, launched 21 July 1950 and completed 22 May 1951. Now used as local Training ship at Den Helder.

Note. Gelderland (ex-destroyer) and *Grijpskerk* (ex-minesweeper) are used at Amsterdam as harbour training and accommodation ships.

URANIA (ex-*Tromp*) Y 8050

Displacement, tons	38
Dimensions, feet	72 × 16·3 × 10
Main engines	Diesel; 65 hp
Complement	15

Schooner used for training in seamanship. Commissioned on 23 Apr 1938.

TUGS

WESTGAT A 872 **WIELINGEN** A 873

Displacement, tons	185
Dimensions, feet	90·6 × 22·7 × 7·7
Guns	2—20 mm AA
Main engines	Bolnes diesel; 720 bhp = 12 knots

Built by Rijkswerf, Willemsoord. Launched on 22 Aug 1967 and 6 Jan 1968 and completed on 10 Jan 1968 and 4 Apr 1968, respectively. Equipped with salvage pumps and fire fighting equipment. Stationed at Den Helder.

WAMANDAI A 870 (ex-Y 8035)

Displacement, tons	159 standard; 185 full load
Dimensions, feet	89·2 × 21·3 × 7·5
Guns	2—20 mm AA
Main engines	Diesel; 500 bhp = 11 knots

Built by Rijkswerf, Willemsoord, Den Helder. Launched on 28 May 1960. Equipped with salvage pumps and fire fighting equipment. In the Netherlands Antilles since 1964.

WAMBRAU A 871

Displacement, tons	154 standard; 184 full load
Dimensions, feet	86·5 oa × 20·7 × 7·5
Guns	2—20 mm AA
Main engines	Werkspoor diesel and Kort nozzle; 500 bhp = 10·8 knots

Built by Rijkswerf Willemsoord. Launched on 27 Aug 1956. Completed on 8 Jan 1957. Equipped with salvage pumps and fire fighting equipment. Stationed at Den Helder.

BERKEL Y 8037 **DINTEL** Y 8038 **DOMMEL** Y 8039 **IJSSEL** Y 8040

Displacement, tons	139 standard; 163 full load
Dimensions, feet	82 oa × 20·5 × 7·3
Main engines	Werkspoor diesel and Kort nozzle; 500 bhp

Harbour tugs built by H. H. Bodewes, Millingen. Specially designed for use at Den Helder. Completed in 1956-57.
There are also five small harbour tugs — Y 8014, Y 8016, Y 8017, Y 8022, Y 8028.

TENDERS

VAN BOCHOVE A 923

Displacement, tons	150
Dimensions, feet	97·2 × 18·2 × 6
Main engines	Kromhout diesel; Schottel propeller; 140 bhp = 8 knots
Complement	8

Torpedo recovery vessel. Built by Zaanlandse Scheepsbouw Mij, Zaandam. Ordered Oct 1961. launched on 20 July 1962 and completed in Aug 1962.

ACCOMMODATION SHIPS

(See note under Training Ships)

Cornelis Drebbel is the name of the new "Boatel"—775 tons, length 206·7 feet, beam 38·7 feet, draught 3·6 feet, complement 200, cost 3m guilders. Ordered in 1969 from Scheepswerft Voorwaarts at Hoogezand, launched on 19 Nov 1970 and completed in 1971. Serves as accommodation vessel for crews of ships refitting at private yards in the Rotterdam area. *Luymes* (ex-survey ship) also used for accommodation. *Snellius* (ex-survey ship) is used for accommodation for R. Neth. N. personnel at the RN Submarine Base, Faslane.

NEW ZEALAND

Defence Headquarters Naval Staff

Chief of Naval Staff:
Rear Admiral E. C. Thorne, CBE

Deputy Chief of Naval Staff:
Commodore R. H. L. Humby

The three New Zealand Service Boards were formally abolished in 1971 as part of the Defence Headquarters reorganization. The former three Service Headquarters and Defence Office have been reorganised into functional branches and offices.
On 1 June 1970 the command and control of the three New Zealand Services was vested in the Chief of Defence Staff who exercises this authority through the three Service Chiefs of Staff.

Diplomatic Representation

Head of New Zealand Defence Liaison Staff, London and Senior Naval Liason Officer:
Commodore M. J. McDowell

Deputy Head of New Zealand Defence Staff, Washington and Naval Attaché:
Captain K. M. Saul

Personnel

January 1971: 2 870 officers and ratings

January 1972: 2 993 officers and ratings

January 1973: 2 966 officers and ratings

January 1974: 2 730 officers and ratings

Strength of the Fleet

Type	*Active*	*Building*
Frigates	4	—
Corvettes	2	—
Patrol Craft	11	4
Survey Ship	1	—
Research Vessel	1	—
Tenders	2	—

Naval Base

Auckland

Mercantile Marine

Lloyd's Register of Shipping:
113 vessels of 156 503 tons gross

Disposals

Cruiser

Dec 1971 *Black Prince*

Frigate

April 1971 *Blackpool* returned to Royal Navy

Miscellaneous

June 1971 *Endeavour* (ex-USS *Namakagon*) returned to USN for transfer to Taiwan. (now *Lung Chuan*)

PENNANT LIST

Frigates

F 55 Waikato
F 111 Otago
F 148 Taranaki
F 421 Canterbury

Minesweepers

M 233 Inverell
M 353 Kiama

Survey Ship

M 364 Lachlan

Patrol Craft

P 3551 Mako
P 3552 Paea
P 3553 Kahawai
P 3555 Tamure
P 3556 Takapu
P 3562 Parore
P 3563 Kuparu
P 3564 Koura
P 3565 Haku
P 3566 Tarapunga
P 3567 Manga
P 3568 Pukaki
P 3569 Rotoiti
P 3570 Taupo
P 3571 Hawea

Research Vessel

AGOR 5 Tui

FRIGATES

2 "LEANDER" CLASS

Displacement, tons	2 450 standard; 2 860 full load *Waikato:* 2 470 standard; 2990 full load *Canterbury*
Length, feet (*metres*)	360·0 (*109·7*) pp; 372·0 (*113·4*) oa *Waikato*; 370·0 (*112·8*) pp *Canterbury*
Beam, feet (*metres*)	41·0 (*12·5*) *Waikato*; 43·0 (*13·1*) *Canterbury*
Draught, feet (*metres*)	18 (*5·5*)
Aircraft	1 Wasp helicopter armed with homing torpedo
Missile launchers	1 quadruple "Seacat"
Guns	2—4·5 in (*155 mm*) in twin turret; 2—20 mm AA
A/S weapons	1 Limbo 3-barrelled DC mortar *Waikato*; 2—TF Mk 32 Mod 5 torpedo tubes *Canterbury*
Main engines	2 sets d.r. geared turbines; 2 shafts; 30 000 shp

Name	*No.*	*Builders*	*Laid down*	*Launched*	*Completed*
CANTERBURY	F 421	Yarrow Ltd, Clyde	12 Apr 1969	6 May 1970	22 Oct 1971
WAIKATO	F 55	Harland & Wolff Ltd, Belfast	10 Jan 1964	18 Feb 1965	19 Sep 1966

Speed, knots	30 *Waikato*; 28 *Canterbury*
Boilers	2 Babcock & Wilcox
Complement	248 (14 officers, 234 ratings) *Waikato*; 243 (14 officers 229 ratings) *Canterbury*

Waikato, ordered on 14 June 1963. Commissioned on 16 Sep 1966, trials in the United Kingdom until spring 1967, arrived in New Zealand waters in May 1967. *Canterbury* was ordered in Aug 1968, arrived in New Zealand in Aug 1972.

RADAR. Search: Type 965. Tactical 993. Fire Control MRS 3 System and X Band.

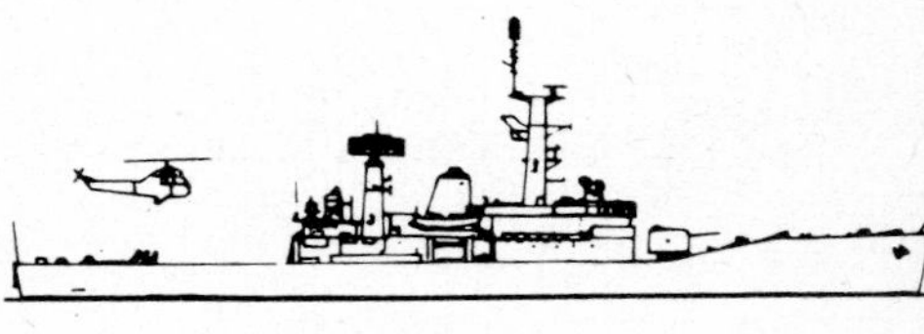

WAIKATO

CANTERBURY — *1972, Wright & Logan*

Frigates—*continued*

2 "ROTHESAY" CLASS TYPE 12

Name	*No.*	*Builders*	*Launched*	*Completed*
OTAGO (ex-*Hastings*)	F 111	John I. Thornycroft & Co, Ltd, Woolston, Southampton	11 Dec 1958	22 June 1960
TARANAKI	F 148	J. Samuel White & Co, Ltd, Cowes, Isle of Wight	19 Aug 1959	28 Mar 1961

Displacement, tons	2 144 standard; 2 557 full load
Length, feet (*metres*)	360·0 (*109·7*) pp; 370·0 (*112·8*) oa
Beam, feet (*metres*)	41·0 (*12·5*)
Draught, feet (*metres*)	17·3 (*5·3*) max (props)
Missile launchers	1 quadruple "Seacat"
Guns	2—4·5 in (*115 mm*) in twin turret; 2—40 mm (*Taranaki* only)
A/S weapons	2 Limbo 3-barrelled DC mortars
Main engines	2 sets d.r. geared turbines; 2 shafts; 30 000 shp
Speed, knots	30
Boilers	2 Babcock & Wilcox
Complement	240 (13 officers, 227 ratings)

Scale: 150 feet = 1 inch (1 : 1 800)

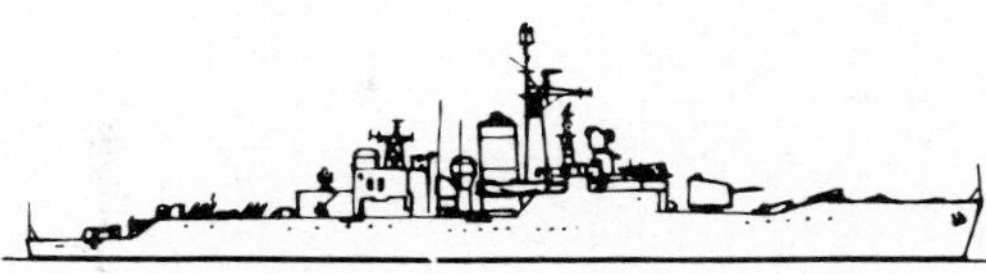

OTAGO, TARANAKI

Anti-submarine frigates. *Taranaki* was ordered direct (announced by J. Samuel White & Co on 22 Feb 1957). For *Otago* New Zealand took over the contract (officially stated on 26 Feb 1957) for *Hastings* originally ordered from John I. Thornycroft & Co in Feb 1956 for the Royal Navy. Both vessels are generally similar to those in the Royal Navy, but were modified to suit New Zealand conditions. *Otago* has had enclosed foremast since 1967 refit; *Taranaki* was similarly fitted during 1969.

RADAR. Search Type 993 and Type 277. Fire Control X Band

TUBES. The original twelve 21 in (*533 mm*) A/S torpedo tubes (8 single and 2 twin) were suppressed.

TARANAKI — *1971, Royal New Zealand Navy*

CORVETTES

2 "BATHURST" CLASS

Name	*No*	*Builders*	*Laid down*	*Launched*	*Completed*
INVERELL	M 233	Mort's Dock, Sydney	7 Dec 1941	2 May 1942	2 May 1943
KIAMA	M 353	Evans Deakins, Brisbane	2 Nov 1942	3 July 1943	26 Jan 1944

Displacement, tons	790 standard; 1 025 full load
Length, feet (*metres*)	162·0 (*49·4*) pp; 186·0 (*56·7*) oa
Beam, feet (*metres*)	31·0 (*9·4*)
Draught, feet (*metres*)	9·5 (*2·9*)
Guns	2—40 mm AA
Main engines	Triple expansion; 2 shafts; 1 800 ihp
Speed, knots	15
Boilers	2 Admiralty 3-drum small tube
Complement	71

Originally four vessels of this class were given to New Zealand by Australia in 1952 (see disposal note below).

Kiama was recommissioned on 15 Mar 1966 for training and fishery protection duties, her 4-inch gun being replaced by a 40 mm AA gun, and a deckhouse being built aft.

Inverell was recommissioned on 15 Aug 1965 as a training ship for new entry ratings, replacing the frigate *Rotoiti*. Her sweeping gear was removed and her deckhouse extended further aft. 4-inch gun replaced by 40 mm.

DISPOSALS
Echuca was scrapped at Auckland in April 1968, and *Stawell* in Aug 1968.

KIAMA — *1972, Royal New Zealand Navy*

SURVEY SHIPS

LACHLAN F 364

Displacement, tons	1 420 standard; 2 220 full load
Length, feet (*metres*)	301·2 (*91·8*)
Beam, feet (*metres*)	36·7 (*11·2*)
Draught, feet (*metres*)	16·0 (*4·9*)
Main engines	Triple expansion; 2 shafts; 5 500 ihp
Speed, knots	20
Boilers	2 Admiralty 3-drum type
Complement	143

Former Australian "River" class frigate. Built by Mort's Dock, Sydney, NSW, launched on 25 Mar 1944, transferred on loan from RAN in 1948 and purchased outright in 1962. Her forecastle deck was subsequently extended aft from the shelter deck to the quarter deck. Guns were removed on conversion for survey duties. A helicopter platform 50 feet by 30 feet, 7 feet above the quarter deck, was laid in 1966. An enclosed bridge was fitted during 1970 refit. Due to end her service in 1975 and consideration for a replacement is now being given.

LACHLAN — *1972, Royal New Zealand Navy*

Note. Lachlan is due for replacement during 1974 by *Moana Roa*, a converted inter-island ship built in 1960.

PATROL CRAFT

4 "LAKE" CLASS

Displacement, tons	105 standard; 138 full load
Dimensions, ft (*m*)	107·7 oa × 20 × 11·8 (*32·8 × 6·1 × 3·6*)
Guns	Possibly 2—40 mm
Main engines	2 Paxman 12YJCM Diesels; 2 400 hp = 28 knots
Complement	3 officers, 16 ratings

Under construction by Brooke Marine, Lowestoft, England, the first to complete Autumn 1974 and the remainder by end of 1974.

107ft fast patrol craft by Brooke Marine Ltd Lowestoft Suffolk U.K. for the R.N.Z.N.

"LAKE" Class 1973, Brooke Marine

11 HDML TYPE

HAKU P 3565 (ex-*Wakefield* ex-Q 1197)
KAHAWAI P3553 (ex-*Tamaki*)
KOURA P 3564 (ex-*Toroa* ex-Q 1350)
KUPARU P 3563 (ex-*Pegasus* ex-Q 1349)
MAKO P3551 (ex-Q 1183)
MANGA P3567 (ex-Q 1185)
PAEA P3552 (ex-Q 1184)
PARORE P3562 (ex-Q 1190 ex *Olphert*)
TAKAPU P3556 (ex-Q 1188)
TAMURE P3555 (ex-*Ngapona* ex-Q 1193)
TARAPUNGA (P 3566 ex-Q 1387)

Displacement, tons	46 standard; 54 full load
Dimensions, feet	72 × 16 × 5·5
Guns	Armament temporarily removed
Main engines	Diesel; 2 shafts; 320 bhp = 12 knots
Complement	9

Originally known as Harbour Defence Motor Launches. All built in various yards in the United States and Canada and shipped to New Zealand.

Patrol Craft—*continued*

Takapu and *Tarapunga* are commissioned as surveying MLs and operate with *Lachlan*. All others have been converted with lattice masts surmounted by a radar serial, *Mako*, *Paea*, *Kahawai* and *Haku* are employed on Fishery Protection duties, others are attached to RNZNVR Divisions. *Maroro* was disposed of in 1972. From 1974 onwards some of these will be phased-out to provide the manpower for the "Lake" class.

HAKU 1973, Royal New Zealand Navy

RESEARCH VESSEL

TUI A 2 (ex-USS *Charles H. Davis*, T-AGOR 5)

Displacement, tons	1 200 standard; 1 380 full load
Dimensions, feet	208·9 × 37·4 × 15·3
Main engines	Diesel-electric; 1 shaft; 10 000 hp = 12 knots
Complement	8 officers, 16 ratings, 15 scientists

Oceanographic research ship built by Christy Corp, Sturgeon Bay, Wis. Laid down on 15 June 1961, launched on 30 June 1962 and completed on 25 Jan 1963. On loan from US since 28 July 1970 for 5 years. Commissioned in the Royal New Zealand Navy on 11 Sep 1970. Bow propeller 175 hp.

TUI 1971, Royal New Zealand Navy

TENDERS

ARATAKI **MANAWANUI**

Dimensions, feet	Length: 75
Main engines	Diesel

Steel tugs. *Arataki* is used as a dockyard tug and *Manawanui* as a diving tender.

NICARAGUA

Mercantile Marine

Lloyd's Register of Shipping: 11 vessels of 21 845 tons gross

PATROL CRAFT

Personnel

200 officers and men

1 SEWART TYPE

Displacement, tons	60
Dimensions, ft (*m*)	85 × 18·8 × 5·9 (*25·9 × 5·6 × 1·8*)
Guns	3—50 cal MG
Main engines	3 GM diesels; 3 shafts; 2 000 shp = 26·5 knots
Range, miles	1 000 at 20 knots
Complement	10

Delivered July 1972.

RIO CRUTA

Dimensions, feet	Length: 85
Guns	1—20 mm automatic cannon in bow
Main engines	Diesels; speed = 9 knots maximum
Complement	11

A wooden *guardacosta* of the Marine Section of the Guardia Nacional of Nicaragua. Another *guardacosta* without name or number is a diesel launch of approx 26 ft with a 20 mm gun, a designed speed of 25 knots and a crew of 5 or 6. Also reported were six wooden patrol boats, four 90 ft and two about 80 ft, and a former patrol boat, 75 ft, wooden, built in 1925, used for training.

NIGERIA

Administration

Chief of the Naval Staff:
Rear-Admiral Joseph Etim Akinwole Wey, OFR

Naval Officer-in-Charge (Lagos):
Commodore Nelson Bossman Soroh

Chief of Staff:
Commander Mugibi Ayinde Adelanwa

Diplomatic Representation

Naval Attaché (Assistant Defence Adviser) in London:
Lieutenant Commander Emanuel Omotepinwa

Strength of the Fleet

Type	*Active*	*Building*
Frigate	1	—
Corvettes	2	—
Fast Attack Craft—Torpedo	3	—
Large Patrol Craft	6	2
Coastal Patrol Craft	8	—
Landing Craft	1	—
Survey Ships	2	1
Fishery Protection Ships	2	—
Tug	1	—

Personnel

(a) 1971: 180 Officers and 2 000 ratings
1972: 190 Officers and 2 000 ratings
1973: 200 Officers and 2 100 ratings
1974: 260 Officers and 2 600 ratings
(b) Voluntary Service

Mercantile Marine

Lloyd's Register of Shipping:
72 vessels of 110 015 tons gross

FRIGATE

Name	No.	Builders	Laid down	Launched	Completed
NIGERIA	F 87	Wilton, Fijenoord NV	9 Apr 1964	12 Apr 1965	16 Sep 1965

Displacement, tons	1 724 standard; 2 000 full load
Length, feet (*metres*)	341·2(*104·0*) pp; 360·2(*109·8*) oa
Beam, feet (*metres*)	37·0 (*11·3*)
Draught, feet (*metres*)	11·5 (*3·5*)
Guns	2—4 in (*102 mm*) dp (1 twin) 5—40 mm AA single
A/S weapons	1—triple-barrelled DC mortar
Main engines	4 MAN Diesels; 2 shafts; 16 000 bhp
Speed, knots	26
Range, miles	3 500 at 15 knots
Complement	216

Anti-aircraft and anti-submarine frigate built in the Netherlands by Wilton, Fijenoord. Cost £3 500 000. Commissioned in Sep 1965. Helicopter platform laid on aft.

NIGERIA *1970, Nigerian Navy*

CORVETTES

2 Mk 3 VOSPER THORNYCROFT TYPE

DORINA **OTOBO**

Displacement, tons	500 standard; 650 full load
Dimensions, feet	202 oa × 31 × 11·33 (over props)
Guns	2—4 in (1 twin); 2—40 mm Bofors (single) 2—20 mm cannons
Main engines	2 MAN diesels; = 23 knots max
Range, miles	3 500 at 14 knots
Complement	66 (7 officers and 59 ratings)

Ordered on 28 Mar 1968. *Dorina* laid down 26 Jan 1970, launched 16 Sep 1970, completed June 1972. *Otobo* laid down 28 Sep 1970, launched 25 May 1971, completed November 1972. Known as the "Hippopotamus" class as each name means "hippopotamus" in one of the principal Nigerian languages. Plessey AWS-1 air search radar; HSA M 20 fire control. Decca TM 626 navigation radar. Plessey M 26 Sonar. HSA M 22 Fire Control.

OTOBO *1972, Wright and Logan*

LIGHT FORCES

2 BROOKE-MARINE TYPE (LARGE PATROL CRAFT)

No details available from Nigerian sources. The following is approximately correct.

Displacement, tons	105 standard
Dimensions, feet	107 × 20 × 12
Guns	Possibly 2—40 or 20 mm
Main engines	2 Diesels = 28 knots
Complement	20

Building by Brooke Marine, Lowestoft, England. Ordered in 1971. Delivery 1974.

6 "FORD" CLASS

BENIN (ex-HMS *Hinksford*)
BONNY (ex-HMS *Difford*) P 3111
ENUGU P 3137
KADUNA (ex-HMS *Axford*) P 03
SAPELE (ex-HMS *Dubford*) P 3119
IBADAN II (ex-HMS *Bryansford*)

Displacement, tons	120 standard; 160 full load
Dimensions, feet	110 pp; 117·2 oa × 20 × 5
Guns	1—40 mm Bofors AA; 2—20 mm Oerlikon
A/S weapons	DC rails and DC
Main engines	Davey Paxman diesels; Foden engine on centre shaft; 1 100 bhp = 18 knots max; 15 knots sea speed
Complement	26

Enugu was the first warship built for the Nigerian Navy. Ordered from Camper and Nicholson's Gosport, in 1960. Completed on 14 Dec 1961. Sailed from Portsmouth for Nigeria on 10 Apr 1962. Fitted with Vosper roll damping fins. *Benin, Ibadan* and *Kaduna* were purchased from Great Britain on 1 July 1966 and transferred at Devonport on 9 Sep 1966. *Ibadan* was seized by the Eastern Region prior to its declaration of independence as the Republic of Biafra on 30 May 1967 and renamed *Vigilance* but was sunk at Port Harcourt on 10 Sep 1967 by Nigerian Navy, salved but later scrapped at Lagos. *Dubford* and *Gifford* were purchased from Great Britain during 1967-68 and *Bryansford* in 1968-69.

KADUNA *1970, Nigerian Navy*

Light Forces—*continued*

3 Ex-SOVIET "P 6" CLASS (FAST ATTACK CRAFT—TORPEDO)

EKPEN **EKUN** **ELOLE**

Displacement, tons	66 standard; 75 full load
Dimensions, ft (*m*)	84·2 × 20 × 6 (*25·7 × 6·1 × 1·8*)
Guns	4—25 mm (2 twin)
A/S weapons	2 DCT; 2 DC racks
Main engines	4 12 cyl diesels; 4 800 bhp = 43 knots
Complement	25
Range, miles	450 at 30 knots

Soviet built fast patrol boats of the small submarine chaser type purchased from the USSR in 1967. Torpedo tubes removed. POT HEAD search/navigation radar.

EKPEN *1969, Nigerian Navy*

8 VOSPER-THORNYCROFT TYPE (COASTAL PATROL CRAFT)

Displacement, tons	15
Dimensions, feet	34 oa × 10 × 2·8
Guns	1 machine gun
Main engines	2 Diesels; 290 hp = 19 knots
Complement	6

Ordered for Nigerian Police March 1971, completed 1971-72. GRP hulls.

LANDING CRAFT

LOKOJA (ex-*LCT* (4) 1213)

Displacement, tons	350 standard; 586 full load
Dimensions, feet	187·5 × 38·8 × 4·5
Guns	2—20 mm AA
Main engines	2 Paxman diesels; 920 bhp = 10 knots

Purchased from Great Britain in 1959. Allocated the name *Lokoja* in 1961. Underwent a major refit in 1966-67, including complete replating of the bottom.

SURVEY SHIPS

1 NEW CONSTRUCTION

Displacement, tons	800 standard; 1 100 full load
Dimensions, ft (*m*)	189 × 37·5 × 12 (*57·8 × 11·4 × 3·7*)
Main engines	4 Diesels; 2 shafts; 2 000 bhp = 15 knots
Range, miles	4 000 at 12 knots
Complement	38

Ordered from Brooke Marine, Lowestoft in late 1973 for delivery in 1976.

PATHFINDER P 06

Measurement, tons	544 gross
Dimensions, feet	154·2 × 27 × 11
Gun	1—40 mm AA
Main engines	2 triple expansion; 200 ihp = 8 knots

Built by J. Samuel White & Co Ltd, Cowes, Isle of Wight. Launched on 23 Oct 1953 and completed in 1954.

PENELOPE P 11

Measurement, tons	79 gross
Dimensions, feet	79·5 × 7·8 × 4·5
Main engines	2 Gardner diesels; speed 10 knots

Built by Aldous Successors, Brightlingsea in 1958. Used for local survey duties.

2 FISHERY PROTECTION SHIPS

YOLA **ARGUNGU**

Displacement, tons	90
Dimensions, ft (*m*)	95·1 × 18·0 × 5·2 (*29 × 5·5 × 1·6*)
Main engines	2 Paxman Diesels; 2 200 hp; 2 shafts = 20 knots
Complement	25

Completed in 1973 by Abeking and Rasmussen, Lemwerder.

RIBADU

Displacement, tons	147
Dimensions, ft (*m*)	93·5 × 23·6 × 12·1 (*28·5 × 7·2 × 3·7*)
Main engines	Diesel; 800 shp = 12 knots

Completed 19 May 1973 by Oelkers, Hamburg. Fitted for firefighting and salvage work.

NORWAY

Administration

Commander-in-Chief (Inspector-General):
Rear Admiral Hans Sigurd Skjong

Commander Naval Logistics Services:
Rear-Admiral Thorleif Petersen, KCVO, MBE

Commander Coastal Fleet:
Commadore Rolf Hellingsen

Diplomatic Representation

Defence Attaché in London:
Lieutenant-Colonel Ivar Kollbotn

Defence Attaché in Washington (for USA and Canada):
Rear Admiral Magne Braadland, CVO

Defence Attaché in Moscow:
Commodore Sjur Østervold, DSC

Personnel

1971: 9 000 officers and ratings
1972: 8 000 officers and ratings
1973: 8 500 officers and ratings
1974: 8 400 officers and ratings
(All above figures include the Coast Artillery)

Prefix to Ships' Names

The prefix KNM is used before ships' names.

Naval Bases

Haakonsvern, Ramsund, Orlogsstasjon, Ramfjordnes

Strength of the Fleet

(No building programme announced)

Type	*Active*
Frigates	5
Corvettes	2
Submarines—Coastal	15
Fast Attack Craft—Missile	26
Fast Attack Craft—Torpedo	20
Minelayers	5
Minesweeper—Coastal	10
LCTs	7
LCU	1
Depot Ship	1
Royal Yacht	1
Fishery Protection Ships (not under naval command)	6

FRIGATES

5 "OSLO" CLASS

Name	*No.*	*Builders*	*Laid down*	*Launched*	*Completed*
BERGEN	F 301	Marinens Hovedverft, Horten	1964	23 Aug 1965	15 June 1967
NARVIK	F 304	Marinens Hovedverft, Horten	1964	8 Jan 1965	30 Nov 1966
OSLO	F 300	Marinens Hovedverft, Horten	1963	17 Jan 1964	29 Jan 1966
STAVANGER	F 303	Marinens Hovedverft, Horten	1965	4 Feb 1966	1 Dec 1967
TRONDHEIM	F 302	Marinens Hovedverft, Horten	1963	4 Sep 1964	2 June 1966

Displacement, tons	1 450 standard; 1,745 full load
Length, feet (*metres*)	308 (*93·9*) pp; 317 (*96·6*) oa
Beam, feet (*metres*)	36·7 (*11·2*)
Draught, feet (*metres*)	17·4 (*5·3*)
Guns, dual purpose	4—3 in (*76 mm*) 2 twin mounts
Missile launchers	"Penguin"
A/S weapons	"Terne" system
Torpedo launchers	2
Boilers	2 Babcock & Wilcox
Main engines	1 set De Laval Ljungstron double reduction geared turbines; 1 shaft; 20 000 shp
Speed, knots	25
Complement	151 (11 officers, 140 ratings)

OSLO *Class*

Built under the five-year naval construction programme approved by the Norwegian "Storting" (Parliament) late in 1960. Although all the ships of this class were constructed in the Norwegian Naval Dockyard, half the cost was borne by Norway and the other half by the United States. The design of these ships is based on that of the "Dealey" class destroyer escorts in the United States Navy, but modified to suit Norwegian requirements. They have traditional Norwegian destroyer names or torpedo boat names.

RADAR. Search: DRBV 22. Tactical and Fire Control: HSA M 24 system.

ENGINEERING The main turbines and auxiliary machinery were all built by De Laval Ljungstrom, Sweden at the company's works in Stockholm-Nacka.

BERGEN *1971, Royal Norwegian Navy*

OSLO *1972, Royal Norwegian Navy*

CORVETTES

2 "SLEIPNER" CLASS

ÆGER F 311 **SLEIPNER** F 310

Displacement, tons	600 standard; 780 full load
Dimensions, feet	227·8 oa × 26·2
Guns	1—3 in; 1—40 mm
A/S weapons	"Terne" ASW system
Main engines	4 Maybach diesels; 2 shafts; 9 000 bhp = over 20 knots
Complement	62

Under the five-year programme only two instead of the originally planned five new patrol vessels were built. *Sleipner* was launched on 9 Nov 1963 at the Nylands Verksted shipyard, Oslo, and completed on 29 Apr 1956. *Aeger*, originally to have been named *Balder*, was launched on 24 Sep 1965, and completed on 31 Mar 1967. Temporarily employed as training ships until a relief is provided for KNM Haakon VII.

SLEIPNER *1972, Royal Norwegian Navy*

SUBMARINES

15 TYPE 207 *Commissioned*

Name	No.	Launched	Completed
KAURA	S 315	16 Oct 1964	5 Feb 1965
KINN	S 316	30 Nov 1963	8 Apr 1964
KOBBEN	S 318	25 Apr 1964	17 Aug 1964
KUNNA	S 319	16 July 1964	1 Oct 1964
KYA	S 317	20 Feb 1964	15 June 1964
SKLINNA	S 305	21 Jan 1966	27 May 1966
SKOLPEN	S 306	24 Mar 1966	17 Aug 1966
STADT	S 307	10 June 1966	15 Nov 1966
STORD	S 308	2 Sep 1966	9 Feb 1967
SVENNER	S 309	27 Jan 1967	1 July 1967
ULA	S 300	19 Dec 1964	7 May 1965
UTHAUG	S 304	8 Oct 1965	16 Feb 1966
UTSIRA	S 301	11 Mar 1965	1 July 1965
UTSTEIN	S 302	19 May 1965	9 Sep 1965
UTVAER	S 303	30 June 1965	1 Dec 1965

Displacement, tons	370 standard; 435 submerged
Length, feet (*metres*)	149 (*45·2*)
Beam, feet (*metres*)	15 (*4·6*)
Draught, feet (*metres*)	14 (*4·3*)
Tubes	8—21 in (*533 mm*) bow
Main machinery	2 MB 820 Maybach-Mercedes-Benz diesels; 1 200 bhp; electric drive; 1 200 hp; 1 shaft
Speed, knots	10 surface; 17 dived
Complement	18 (5 officers, 13 men)

GENERAL
It was announced in July 1959 that the USA and Norway would share equally the cost of these submarines. All were built by Rheinstahl-Nordseewerke in Emden, West Germany. These are a development of IKL Type 205 (West German U4-U8) with increased diving depth. *Svenner* has a second periscope for COs training operations.

NAMES. *Kobben* was the name of the first submarine in the Royal Norwegian Navy. Commissioned on 28 Nov 1909.

KINN — *1970, Royal Norwegian Navy*

SVENNER (with second periscope) — *1972, Royal Norwegian Navy*

LIGHT FORCES

(N.B Armament varies in all classes as Penguin SSM is installed)

6 "SNÖGG" CLASS (FAST ATTACK CRAFT—MISSILE)

KJAPP P 985 | **RAPP** P 981 | **SNAR** P 982
KVIKK P 984 | **RASK** P 983 | **SNOGG** (ex-Lyr) P 980

Displacement, tons	100 standard; 125 full load
Dimensions, feet	120·0 × 20·5 × 5·0
Missile launchers	4 "Penguin" SSM; range 20 km plus
Guns	1—40 mm
Tubes	4—21 in
Main engines	2 Maybach diesels; 2 shafts; 7 200 bhp = 32 knots
Complement	18

These steel hulled torpedo boats of a new design ordered from Batservice Werft, A/S, Mandal, Norway, started coming into service in 1970. Hulls are similar to those of the "Storm" class gunboats: see next column. Armed with missiles in addition to gun and tubes.

RAPP — *1973, Royal Norwegian Navy*

20 "STORM" CLASS (FAST ATTACK CRAFT—MISSILE)

ARG	P 968	**DJERV**	P 966	**ODD**	P 975	**STEIL**	P 969
BLINK	P 961	**GLIMT**	P 962	**PIL**	P 976	**STORM**	P 960
BRANN	P 970	**GNIST**	P 979	**ROKK**	P 978	**TRAUST**	P 973
BRASK	P 977	**HVASS**	P 972	**SKJOLD**	P 963	**TROSS**	P 971
BROTT	P 974	**KJEKK**	P 965	**SKUDD**	P 967	**TRYGG**	P 964

Displacement, tons	100 standard; 125 full load
Dimensions, feet	120·0 × 20·5 × 5·0
Missile launchers	6 "Penguin" SSM; range 20 km plus
Guns	1—3 in; 1—40 mm
A/S weapons	DC throwers
Main engines	2 Maybach diesels; 2 shafts; 7 200 bhp = 32 knots

The first of 20 (instead of the 23 originally planned) gunboats of a new design built under the five-year programme was *Storm*, launched on 8 Feb 1963, and completed on 31 May 1963, but this prototype was eventually scrapped and replaced by a new series construction boat as the last of the class. The first of the production boats was *Blink*, launched on 28 June 1965 and completed on 18 Dec 1965. The first was armed with "Penguin" surface-to-surface guided missile launchers in 1970, in addition to originally designed armament.

TRAUST with 6 Penguins fitted — *1971, A/S Kongsberg Vapenfabrikk*

Light Forces—*continued*

20 "TJELD" CLASS (FAST ATTACK CRAFT—TORPEDO)

DELFIN	P 386	**HAI**	P 381	**LAKS**	P 384	**SKARV**	P 344
ERLE	P 390	**HAUK**	P 349	**LOM**	P 347	**SKREI**	P 380
FALK	P 350	**HVAL**	P 383	**LYR**	P 387	**STEGG**	P 348
GEIR	P 389	**JO**	P 346	**RAVN**	P 357	**TEIST**	P 345
GRIBB	P 388	**KNURR**	P 385	**SEL**	P 382	**TJELD**	P 343

Displacement, tons	70 standard; 82 full load
Dimensions, feet	75·5 pp; 80·3 oa × 24·5 × 6·8 max
Guns	1—40 mm AA; 1—20 mm AA
Tubes	4—21 in
Main engines	2 Napier Deltic Turboblown diesels; 2 shafts; 6 200 bhp = 45 knots
Radius, miles	450 at 40 knots; 600 at 25 knots
Complement	18

SKARV *1973, Royal Norwegian Navy*

MINE WARFARE FORCES

10 "SAUDA" CLASS (MINESWEEPERS—COASTAL)

ALTA (ex-*Arlon* M 915, ex-*MSC* 104)	M 314
GLOMMA (ex-*Bastogne* M 916, ex-*MSC* 151)	M 317
KVINA	M 332
OGNA	M 315
SAUDA (ex-USS *AMS* 102)	M 311
SIRA (ex-USS *MSC* 132)	M 312
TANA (ex-*Roeselaere* M 914, ex-*MSC* 103)	M 313
TISTA	M 331
UTLA	M 334
VOSSO	M 316

Displacement, tons	333 standard; 384 full load
Dimensions, feet	144 × 28 × 8·5 max
Guns	2—20 mm AA
Main engines	GM diesels; 880 bhp = 13·5 knots
Oil fuel, tons	25
Complement	38

Sauda, built by Hodgeson Bros, Gowdy & Stevens, East Boothbay, Maine, was completed on 25 Aug 1953 and *Sira* on 28 Nov 1955. Hull of wooden construction. Five coastal minesweepers were built in Norway with US engines. Completed on 5 Mar 1955 (*Ogna*), 16 Mar 1955 (*Vosso*), 27 Apr 1955 (*Tista*), 12 July 1955 (*Kvina*) and 15 Nov 1955 (*Utla*). *Kvina*, *Ogna* and *Utla* were built by Båtservice Ltd, Mandal, *Tista* by Forende Batbyggeriex, Risör, and *Vosso* by Skaaluren Skibsbyggeri, Rosendal. *Alta*, *Glomma* and *Tana* were taken over from the Royal Belgian Navy in May, Sep and Mar 1966, respectively, having been exchanged for two Norwegian ocean minesweepers of the US MSO type, *Lagen* (ex-*MSO* 498) and *Nansen* (ex-*MSO* 499).

TISTA *1973, Royal Norwegian Navy*

BORGEN N 51 (CONTROLLED MINELAYER)

Displacement, tons	282 standard
Dimensions, feet	94·5 pp; 102·5 oa × 26·2 × 11
Main engines	2 GM diesels; 2 Voith-Schneider propellers; 330 bhp=9 knots

BORGEN *1972, Royal Norwegian Navy*

Minewarfare Forces—*continued*

BRAGE (ex-USS *Triumph*, MMC 3)	N 49
GOR (ex-USS *Strive*, MMC 1)	N 48
TYR (ex-USS *Sustain*, MMC 2)	N 47
ULLER (ex-USS *Seer*, MMC 5)	N 50

Displacement, tons	890 standard; 1 250 full load
Dimensions, feet	215 wl; 221·2 oa × 32·2 × 16
Guns	1—3 in, 50 cal; 4—20 mm AA (2 twin) (*Brage, Gor, Tyr*) 1—3 in, 50 cal; 1—40 mm AA (*Uller*)
A/S weapons	2 Hedgehogs; 3 DCT (*Brage, Gor, Tyr*) "Terne" ASW system; 1 DCT (*Uller*)
Main engines	GM diesels; electric drive; 2 shafts; 2 070 bhp = 16 knots
Complement	83

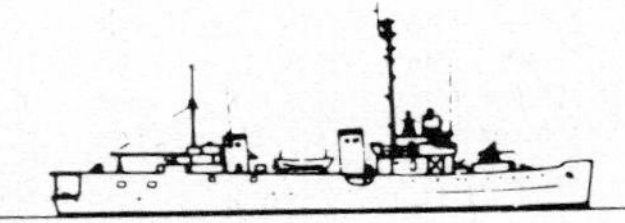

BRAGE, GOR, TYR, ULLER

Former US Coastal Minelayers (MMC). *Gor*, *Tyr* and *Uller* were built by American Shipbuilding Co in 1942 and *Brage* by Associated Shipbuilders in 1944. *Gor* and *Tyr* converted 1959 and *Brage* 1960 into coastal minelayers at Charleston Naval Shipyard, but *Uller* was converted in Norway. All transferred 1959-1960.

BRAGE *1972, Royal Norwegian Navy*

AMPHIBIOUS FORCES

2 "KVALSUND" CLASS (LCT)

KVALSUND A 31 — **RAFTSUND** A 32

5 "REINØYSUND" CLASS (LCT)

BORGSUND A 37 — **REINØYSUND** A 33 — **ROTSUND** A 36
MAURSUND A 35 — **SØRØYSUND** A 34

Displacement, tons	560
Dimensions, feet	167·3 × 33·5 × 5·9
Guns	2—20 mm
Speed, knots	11

Built by Mjellem and Karlsen, Bergen. First pair delivered in 1970 remainder in following two years.

REINØYSUND *1973, Royal Norwegian Navy*

1 Ex-US LCU

TJELDSUND (ex-US LCU 1478) A 30

Displacement, tons	180 light; 360 full load
Dimensions, feet	119 oa × 34 × 6
Guns	2—20 mm
Main engines	3 Diesels; 3 shafts; 6 758 bhp = 10 knots
Complement	14

Transferred from US on completion 1952.

DESTROYERS

1 Ex-BRITISH "BATTLE" CLASS

Name	No.	Builders	Laid down	Launched	Completed
BADR (ex-HMS *Gabbard*)	161 (ex-D 47)	Swan, Hunter & Wigham Richardson Ltd, Wallsend-on-Tyne	2 Feb 1944	16 Mar 1945	10 Dec 1946

Displacement, tons	2 325 standard; 3 361 full load
Length, feet (*metres*)	355·0(*108·2*) pp; 379·0(*115·5*) oa
Beam, feet (*metres*)	40·2 (*12·3*)
Draught, feet (*metres*)	17·0 (*5·2*)
Guns	4—4·5 in (*115 mm*); 10—40 mm AA
A/S weapons	"Squid" triple DC mortar
Torpedo tubes	8—21 in (*533 mm*) quadrupled
Main engines	Parsons geared turbines; 2 shafts; 50 000 shp
Speed, knots	35·75 designed; 31 sea
Boilers	2 Admiralty 3-drum type
Range, miles	6 000 at 20 knots
Oil fuel, tons	680
Complement	270

Purchased from Britain on 29 Feb 1956. Modernised with US funds under MDAP. Refitted at Palmers Hebburn, Yarrow, transferred to Pakistan on 24 Jan 1957 and sailed from Portsmouth for Karachi on 17 Feb 1957.

RADAR. Search: Type 277, Type 293. Fire Control: X Band.
PENNANT No. Changed from D 47 to 161 in 1963.

LOSS
Sister ship *Khaibar* (ex-HMS *Cadiz*) No. 163 (ex-D 79) was sunk during the Indo-Pakistan War in Dec 1971.

BADR — *1972, Pakistan Navy*

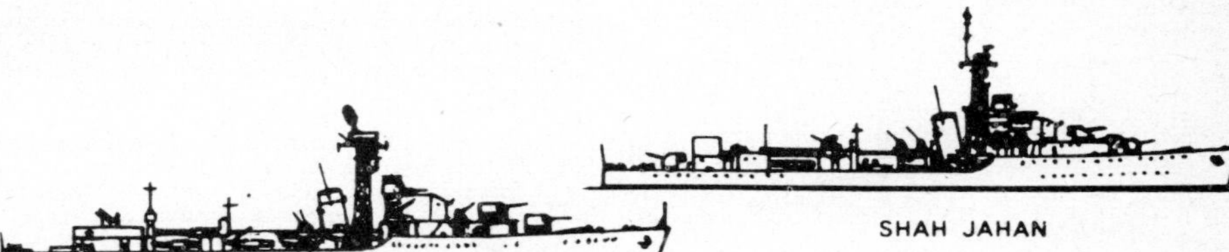
BADR, SHAH JAHAN

1 Ex-BRITISH "CH" CLASS

SHAH JAHAN (ex-HMS *Charity*) 164 (ex-D 29)

Displacement, tons	1 710 standard; 2 545 full load
Length, feet (*metres*)	350·0(*106·7*) wl; 362·7(*110·5*) oa
Beam, feet (*metres*)	35·7 (*10·9*)
Draught, feet (*metres*)	17·0 (*5·2*)
Guns	3—4·5 in (*115 mm*); 6—40 mm AA
A/S weapons	2 "Squid" triple DC mortars
Torpedo tubes	4—21 in (*533 mm*) quadrupled
Main engines	Parsons geared turbines; 2 shafts; 40 000 shp
Speed, knots	36·75 designed; 31·25 sea
Boilers	2 Admiralty 3-drum type
Range, miles	5 600 at 20 knots
Complement	200

Built by John I. Thornycroft, Co Ltd, Woolston, laid down on 9 July 1943, launched on 30 Nov 1944 and completed on 19 Nov 1945. Purchased by USA and handed over to Pakistan on 16 Dec 1958, under MDAP, at yard of J. Samuel White & Co Ltd, Cowes, who refitted her.

SHAH JAHAN — *1972, Pakistan Navy*

Sister ship *Taimur* (ex-HMS *Chivalrous*) was returned to the Royal Navy and scrapped in 1960-61.

RADAR. Search: Type 293. Fire Control: X Band.

2 Ex-BRITISH "CR" CLASS

Name	No.	Builders	Laid down	Launched	Completed
ALAMGIR (ex-HMS *Creole*)	160 (ex-D 82)	J. Samuel White & Co Ltd, Cowes	3 Aug 1944	22 Nov 1945	14 Oct 1946
JAHANGIR (ex-HMS *Crispin*, ex-*Craccher*)	162 (ex-D 168)	J. Samuel White & Co Ltd, Cowes	1 Feb 1944	23 June 1945	10 July 1946

Displacement, tons	1 730 standard; 2 560 full load
Length, feet (*metres*)	350·0(*106·7*) wl; 362·8(*110·5*) oa
Beam, feet (*metres*)	35·7 (*10·9*)
Draught, feet (*metres*)	17·0 (*5·2*)
Guns	3—4·5 in (*115 mm*); 6—40 mm AA
A/S weapons	2 "Squid" triple DC mortars
Torpedo tubes	4—21 in (*533 mm*) quadrupled
Main engines	Parsons geared turbines; 2 shafts 40 000 shp
Speed, knots	36·75 designed; 31·25 sea
Boilers	2 Admiralty 3-drum type
Range, miles	5 600 at 20 knots
Oil fuel, tons	580
Complement	200

ALAMGIR — *1973, Pakistan Navy*

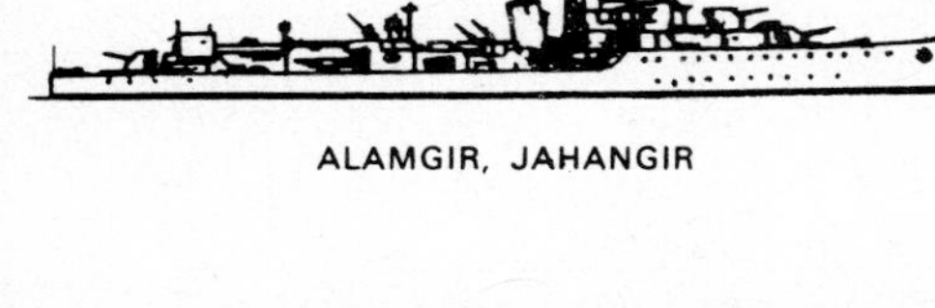
ALAMGIR, JAHANGIR

Purchased by Pakistan in Feb 1956. Refitted and modernised in Great Britain by John I. Thornycroft & Co Ltd, Woolston, Southampton, in 1957-58 with US funds under MDAP. Turned over to the Pakistan Navy at Southampton in 1958 (*Crispin* on 18 Mar and *Creole* 20 June) and renamed.

RADAR. Search: Type 293. Fire Control: X Band.

GUNNERY. "B" gun replaced in 1956-57 and "X" gun was replaced by two "Squids".

JAHANGIR — *1972, Pakistan Navy*

FRIGATES

Note. Pakistan has now acquired the two "Whitby" class frigates *Tenby* and *Scarborough* from the Royal Navy. These, after refit later in 1974, will join the fleet in 1975.

2 Ex-BRITISH TYPE 16

Name	*No.*	*Builders*	*Laid down*	*Launched*	*Completed*
TIPPU SULTAN (ex-HMS *Onslow*, ex-*Pakenham*)	260 (ex-F 249)	John Brown & Co Ltd, Clydebank	1 July 1940	31 Mar 1941	8 Oct 1941
TUGHRIL (ex-HMS *Onslaught*, ex-*Pathfinder*)	261 (ex-F 204)	Fairfield SB & Eng Co Ltd, Glasgow	14 Jan 1941	9 Oct 1941	19 June 1942

Displacement, tons	1 800 standard; 2 300 full load
Length, feet (*metres*)	328·7 (*100·2*) pp; 345·0 (*10·72*) oa
Beam, feet (*metres*)	35·0 (*10·7*)
Draught, feet (*metres*)	15·7 (*4·8*)
Guns	2—4 in (*102 mm*); 5—40 mm AA
A/S weapons	2 "Squid" triple DC mortars
Torpedo tubes	4—21 in (*533 mm*)
Main engines	Parsons geared turbines; 2 shafts; 40 000 shp
Speed, knots	34
Boilers	2 Admiralty 3-drum type
Complement	170

TUGHRIL — *1972, Pakistan Navy*

TIPPU SULTAN, TUGHRIL

Originally three "O" class destroyers were acquired from Great Britain, *Tippu Sultan* being handed over on 30 Sep 1949; *Tariq* on 3 Nov 1949; and *Tughril* on 6 Mar 1951. An agreement was signed in London between Great Britain and USA for refit and conversion in the United Kingdom of *Tippu Sultan* and *Tughril* (announced 29 Apr 1957) with US funds. All three ships were scheduled for conversion into fast anti-submarine frigates. *Tippu Sultan* and *Tughril* were converted at Liverpool by Grayson Rolls & Clover Docks Ltd, Birkenhead, and C. & H. Crighton Ltd, respectively. *Tariq* was not converted. She was handed back to Great Britain at Portsmouth on 10 July 1959 and broken up at Sunderland, arriving there in Oct 1959.

RADAR. Equipped with Type 293 search radar.

SUBMARINES

3 "HANGOR" CLASS (FRENCH "DAPHNE" TYPE)

Name	*Pennant No.*	*Builders*	*Laid Down*	*Launched*	*Completed*
HANGOR	S 131	Arsenal de Brest	1 Dec 1967	28 June 1969	12 Jan 1970
MANGRO	S 133	C. N. Ciotal (Le Trait)	8 July 1968	7 Feb 1970	8 Aug 1970
SHUSHUK	S 132	C. N. Ciotal (Le Trait)	1 Dec 1967	30 July 1969	12 Jan 1970

Displacement, tons	700 standard; 869 surface; 1 043 submerged
Length, feet (*metres*)	189·6 (*57·8*)
Beam, feet (*metres*)	22·3 (*6·8*)
Draught, feet (*metres*)	15·1 (*4·6*)
Torpedo tubes	12—21 in (*550 mm*) 8 bow, 4 stern (external)
Main engines	Diesel electric (SEMT-Pielstick); 1 300 bhp surface; electric motors 1 600 hp submerged; 2 shafts
Speed, knots	13 surface; 15·5 submerged
Complement	45

SHUSHUK — *1972*

MANGRO — *1971, Admiral M. J. Adam*

These are the first submarines built for the Pakistan Navy. They are basically of the French "Daphne" class design, but slightly modified internally to suit Pakistan requirements and naval conditions. They are broadly similar to the submarines built in France for Portugal and South Africa and the submarines being constructed to the "Daphne" design in Spain.

6 "SX 404" CLASS

Displacement, tons	40
Dimensions, ft (*m*)	52·4 × 6·6 × — (*16 × 2 × —*)
Speed, knots	11 surfaced; 6·5 dived
Range, miles	1 200 surfaced; 60 dived
Complement	4

Purchased 1972-73 from Cosmos, Livorno. With a diving depth of 330 ft and capable of carrying 12 passengers these submarines are valuable craft for clandestine raidings, reconnaissance and a multitude of shallow-water tasks. Only Colombia has submarines of a similat size.

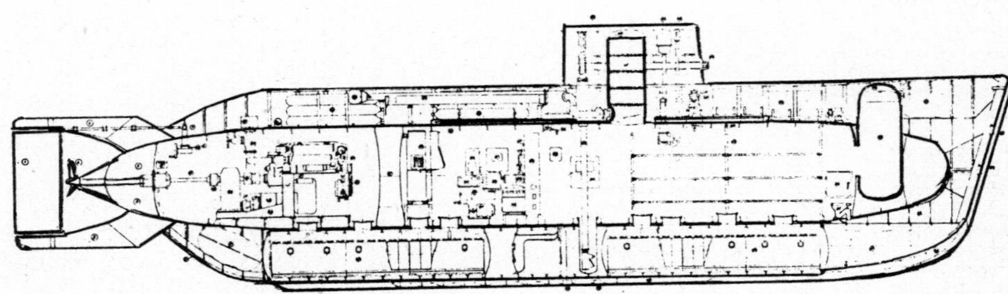

Drawing of "SX 404" Class — *1973*

LIGHT FORCES

8 Ex-Chinese "SHANGHAI II" CLASS

(FAST ATTACK CRAFT—GUN)

LAHORE **QUETTA** **MARDEN** **SUKKUR** + 4

Displacement, tons	120 full load
Dimensions, feet	130 × 18 × 5·6
Guns	4—37 mm; 4—25 mm
Main engines	4 Diesels; 5 000 bhp = 30 knots
Complement	25

Reportedly transferred early 1972. Discussions on fitting missiles have taken place, presumably referring to Styx-type.

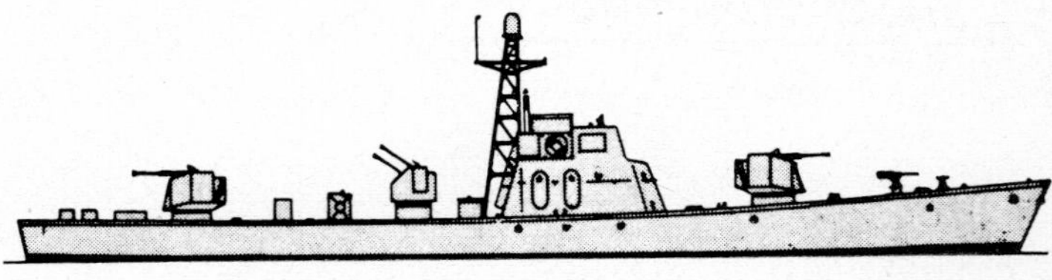

SHANGHAI II *Class*

Light Forces—*continued*

4 Ex-Chinese "HU CHWAN" CLASS

(FAST ATTACK CRAFT—TORPEDO)

Displacement, tons	45
Dimensions, ft (*m*)	70 × 16·5 × 3·1 (*21·4 × 5·0 × 0·9*)
Torpedo tubes	2—21 inch
Guns	4—12·7 mm (twins)
Main engines	2—12 cyl diesels; 2 shafts; 2 200 hp = 55 knots (calm)

Hydrofoil craft transferred by China in 1973.

Chinese "Hu Chwan" class

1 "TOWN" CLASS (LARGE PATROL CRAFT)

RAJSHAHI P 140

Displacement, tons	115 standard; 143 full load
Dimensions, feet	100 wl; 107 oa × 20 × 11
Guns	2—40 mm; 70 cal Bofors AA
Main engines	2 Maybach/Mercedes MD 655/18 diesels; 3 400 bhp (tropical) = 24 knots
Complement	19

The last survivor of a class of four built by Brooke Marine in 1965. Steel hull and aluminium superstructure.

RAJSHAHI 1973, *Pakistan Navy*

Light Forces—*continued*

2 Ex-BRITISH HDML (COASTAL PATROL CRAFT)

SDML 3517 (ex-*SDML* 1261) **SDML 3520** (ex-*SDML* 1266)

Displacement, tons	46 standard; 54 full load
Dimensions, feet	72 oa × 15·8 × 5·3
Guns	1—3 pdr; 1—20 mm AA
Main engines	Diesels; 2 shafts; 320 bhp = 12 knots
Complement	14

Former British Harbour Defence Motor Launches of wooden construction, built under the emergency programme during the Second World War, and re-designated Seaward Defence Motor Launches after the war.

SDML 3520 *1965, Pakistan Navy*

MINE WARFARE FORCES

7 MSC TYPE (MINESWEEPERS—COASTAL)

MAHMOOD (ex-*MSC* 267) M 160
MOMIN (ex-*MSC* 293) M 161
MOSHAL (ex-*MSC* 294) M 167
MURABAK (ex-*MSC* 262) M 162
MUJAHID (ex-*MSC* 261) M 164
MUKHTAR (ex-*MSC* 274) M 165
MUNSIF (ex-*MSC* 273) M 166

Displacement tons	335 light; 375 full load
Dimensions, feet	138 pp; 144 oa × 27 × 8·5
Guns	2—20 mm
Main engines	GM diesels; 2 shafts; 880 bhp = 14 knots
Complement	39

Transferred to Pakistan by the US under MAP. *Mukhtar* and *Munsif* on 25 June 1959, *Muhafiz* on 25 Feb 1955, *Mujahid* in Nov 1956, *Mahmood*, M 160, in May 1957, *Murabak* in 1957, *Momin* in Aug 1962 and *Moshal* M 167, on 13 July 1963. *Muhafiz* M 163 sunk during Indo-Pakistan War Dec 1971.

MUNSIF *1972, Pakistan Navy*

SURVEY SHIP

Name	*Builders*	*Laid down*	*Launched*	*Completed*
ZULFIQUAR (ex-*Dhanush*, ex-*Deveron*) 262 (ex-F 265)	Smith's Dock Co Ltd, South Bank-on-Tees	16 Apr 1942	12 Oct 1942	2 Mar 1943

Displacement, tons	1 370 standard; 2 100 full load
Length, feet (*metres*)	283·0 (*85·3*) pp; 301·5 (*91·9*) oa
Beam, feet (*metres*)	36·7 (*11·2*)
Draught, feet (*metres*)	12·5 (*3·8*)
Guns	1—4 in (*102 mm*); 2—40 mm AA
Main engines	Triple expansion; 5 500 ihp
Speed, knots	20
Boilers	2 Admiralty 3-drum type
Range, miles	6 000 at 12 knots
Oil fuel, tons	400
Complement	150

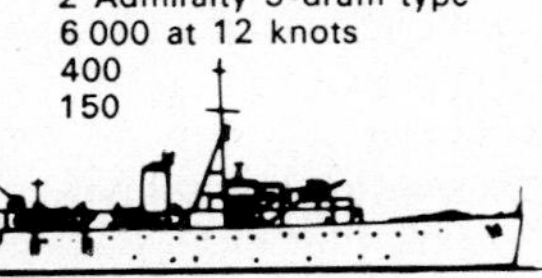

ZULFIQUAR

ZULFIQUAR *1972, Pakistan Navy*

Former British frigate of the "River" class converted into a survey ship, with additional charthouse aft. She has strengthened davits and carries survey motor boats. The after 4-inch gun was removed.

TANKERS

DACCA (ex-USNS *Mission Santa Cruz*, AO 132) A 41

Displacement, tons	5 730 light; 22 380 full load
Dimensions, feet	503 wl; 523·5 oa × 68 × 30·9
Main engines	Turbo-electric; 6 000 shp = 15 knots
Boilers	2 Babcock & Wilcox
Oil capacity	20 000 tons (official figure); 134 000 barrel capacity
Complement	160 (15 officers and 145 men)

Former US fleet tanker of the "T2-SE-A1" Type ("Mission" class). Transferred on loan to Pakistan under MDAP. Handed over from the US on 17 Jan 1963.

DACCA

Tankers—*continued*

ATTOCK (ex-USS YO 249) A 298

Displacement, tons	600 standard; 1 255 full load
Dimensions, feet	177·2 oa × 32 × 15
Main engines	Direct coupled diesel; speed 8·5 knots
Complement	26

A harbour oiler of 6 500 barrels capacity built in Trieste, Italy, in 1960 for the Pakistan Navy, under the Mutual Defence Assistance Programme of USA.

FLOATING DOCK

1 FLOATING DOCK

PESHAWAR (ex-USN ARD 6)

Transferred June 1961. 3 000 tons lift.

TUGS

MADADGAR (ex-USS *Yuma, ATF* 94) A 42

Displacement, tons	1 235 standard; 1 675 full load
Dimensions, feet	195 wl; 205 oa × 38·5 × 15·3 max
Main engines	4 GM diesels; electric drive; 1 shaft; 3 000 bhp = 16·5 knots
Complement	85

Ocean-going salvage tug. Built by Commercial Iron Works, Portland, Oregon. Laid down on 13 Feb 1943. Launched on 17 July 1943. Completed on 31 Aug 1943. Transferred from the US Navy to the Pakistan Navy on 25 Mar 1959 under MDAP. Fitted with powerful pumps and other salvage equipment.

Tugs—*continued*

RUSTOM

Dimensions, feet	105·0 × 30·0 × 11·0
Main engines	Crossley diesel; 1 000 bhp = 9·5 knots
Range, miles	3 000 at economic speed
Complement	21

General purpose tug for the Pakistan Navy originally ordered from Werf-Zeeland at Hansweert, Netherlands, in Aug 1952, but after the liquidation of this yard the order was transferred to Worst & Dutmer at Meppel. Launched on 29 Nov 1955.

BHOLU (ex-US YTL 755) **GAMA** (ex-US YTL 754)

These are small harbour tugs built under an "off-shore" order by Costaguta-Voltz.

WATER CARRIERS

ZUM ZUM YW 15

Built in Italy under MDA programme.

ZUM ZUM *1973, Pakistan Navy*

PARAGUAY

Strength of the Fleet

2 River Defence Vessels
3 Patrol vessels
2 Patrol launches
3 River Patrol Boats
1 Tug
3 Service Craft

Personnel

1973 1 900 officers and men including coastguard and marines.

Mercantile Marine

Lloyd's Register of Shipping: 26 vessels of 21 884 tons gross

RIVER DEFENCE VESSELS

2 "HUMAITA" CLASS

HUMAITA (ex-*Capitan Cabral*) C 2 **PARAGUAY** (ex-*Commodor Meza*) C 1

Displacement, tons	636 standard; 865 full load
Dimensions, feet	231 × 35 × 5·3
Guns	4—4·7 in; 3—3 in AA; 2—40 mm AA
Mines	6
Armour	·5 in side amidships; ·3 in deck; ·8 in CT
Main engines	Parsons geared turbines; 2 shafts; 3 800 shp = 17 knots
Boilers	2
Oil fuel, tons	150
Range, miles	3 400 at 16 knots
Complement	86

Rated as gunboats but also fitted for minelaying. The armour is of high tensile steel. Both built by Odero, Genoa, laid down in Apr 1929, launched in 1930, and completed in May 1931.

CORVETTES

3 "BOUCHARD" CLASS

CAPITAN MEZA (ex-*Parker*)
TENIENTE FARINA (ex-*Py*)
NANAVA (ex-*Bouchard*)

Displacement, tons	450 standard; 620 normal; 650 full load
Dimensions, feet	164 pp; 197 oa × 24 × 8·5
Guns	4—40 mm Bofors AA; 2 MG
Main engines	2 sets MAN 2-cycle diesels; 2 000 bhp = 16 knots
Oil fuel tons	50
Range, miles	6 000 at 12 knots
Complement	70

Former Argentinian minesweepers of the "Bouchard" class. Built at Sanchez Shipyard, San Fernando, Rio Santiago Naval Yard, and Hansen & Puccini, San Fernando, respectively. Laid down in 1936, 1935 and 1937. Launched on 2 May 1937, 20 Mar 1936 and 18 Aug 1938. Can carry mines. Transferred from the Argentinian Navy to the Paraguayan Navy in Apr 1964 onward.

CAPITAN MEZA

LIGHT FORCES

2 CG TYPE

P1 (ex-USCGC 20417) **P2** (ex-USCGC 20418)

Displacement, tons	16
Dimensions, feet	45·5 oa × 13·5 × 3·5
Guns	2—20 mm AA
Main engines	2 petrol motors; 2 shafts; 190 hp = 20 knots
Complement	10

Of wooden construction. Built in the United States in 1944. Acquired from the United States Coast Guard in 1944.

6 "701" CLASS (COASTAL PATROL CRAFT)

P 101 **102** **103** **104** **105** **106**

Patrol craft of 40 ft and 10 tons transferred by USA—2 in Dec 1967, 3 in Sept 1970 and 1 in Mar 1971.

CAPITAN CABRAL (ex-*Adolfo Riquelme*) A 1

Displacement, tons	180 standard; 206 full load
Dimensions, feet	98·5 pp; 107 ·2oa × 23·5 × 9·8
Guns	1—3 in Vickers; 2—37 mm Vickers; 4 MG
Main engines	Triple expansion; 1 shaft; 300 ihp = 9 knots
Complement	47

Former tug. Built by Werf-Conrad, Haarlem. Launched in 1907. Of wooden construction.

1 FLOATING DOCK

Ex-US AFDL 26

Transferred March 1965. Lift 1 000 tons.

1 FLOATING WORKSHOP

Ex-US YR 37

Transferred March 1965.

1 DREDGER

TENIENTE O CARRERAS SAGUIER

2 FERRIES

YFB 82 **YFB 86**

Leased by USA in June 1970.

TUG

YLT 559 A 4 (ex-USS YTL 211)

Dimensions, feet	66·2 × 17 × 5
Main engines	Diesel; 300 bhp

Small harbour tug transferred to Paraguay by the USA under the Military Aid Programme in March 1967. Built by Everett Pacific SB & DD Co, Wash.

PERU

Administration

Minister of Marine and Chief of Naval Operations:
Vice Admiral Luis E. Vargas Caballero

Chief of Naval Staff:
Vice Admiral Fernando Zapater Vantosse

Commander-in-Chief of the Fleet:
Rear Admiral Oscar Cuadros

Diplomatic Representation

Naval Attaché in London and Paris:
Rear Admiral Cesar Barandiaran

Naval Attaché in Washington:
Vice Admiral Jose Arce Larco

Personnel

(a) 1974: 8 000 (730 officers, 7 270 men)
(b) 2 years National Service

Strength of the Fleet

Type	*Active*	*Building*
Cruisers	3	—
Destroyers	4	—
Frigates	3	—
Corvettes	2	—
Submarines—Patrol	4	2
Large Patrol Craft	8	—
Coastal Patrol Craft	3	—
Lake Patrol Craft	11	—
River Gun Boats	5	—
Minesweepers—Coastal	2	—
Landing Ships	4	—
LCU's	3	—
LCA's	10	—
Transports	3	—
Tankers	6	—
Floating Docks	2	—
Survey Vessels	2	—
Tug	1	—
Water Boat	1	—

Prefix to Ship's Names

BAP (Baque Armada Peruana)

Mercantile Marine

Lloyd's Register of Shipping:
655 vessels of 446 374 tons gross

CRUISERS

1 Ex-NETHERLANDS

Name	*No.*	*Builders*	*Laid down*	*Launched*	*Completed*
ALMIRANTE GRAU (*ex-de Ruyter*)	81	Wilton-Fijenoord Schiedam	5 Sep 1939	24 Dec 1944	18 Nov 1953

Displacement, tons	9 529 standard; 11 850 full load
Dimensions, ft (*m*)	590·5 pp; 614·5 oa × 56·7 × 22 (*180* pp; *190·3* oa × *17·3* × *6·7*)
Guns	8—6 in (twin turrets); 8—57 mm AA (twins); 8—40 mm AA
Main engines	2 De Schelde-Parsons geared turbines; 85 000 shp; 2 shafts
Boilers	4 Werkspoor-Yarrow
Speed, knots	32
Complement	926

Transferred by purchase 7 March 1973.

RADAR. Search: LWO 1; SPS 39 (3D); SGR 104, Heightfinder; Tactical: DA 02; Fire Control: HSA M20 for 6 in guns and M45 for secondary battery.

ALMIRANTE GRAU *1973, Peruvian Navy*

Cruisers—*continued*

2 Ex-BRITISH "CEYLON" CLASS

Name	*No.*	*Builders*	*Laid down*	*Launched*	*Completed*
CAPITAN QUIÑONES (ex-HMS *Newfoundland*)	83	Swan, Hunter & Wigham Richardson, Ltd, Wallsend-on-Tyne	9 Nov 1939	19 Dec 1941	31 Dec 1942
CORONEL BOLOGNESI (ex-HMS *Ceylon*)	82	Alexander Stephen & Sons, Ltd, Govan, Glasgow	27 Apr 1939	30 July 1942	13 July 1943

Displacement, tons: *Almirante Grau:* 8 800 standard; 11 090 full load; *Col. Bolognesi:* 8 781 standard; 11 110 full load
Length, feet (*metres*): 538 (*164·0*) wl; 549 (*167·4*) wl; 555·5 (*169·3*) oa
Beam, feet (*metres*): 63·6 (*19·4*)
Draught, feet (*metres*): 16·5 (*5·0*) mean; 20·5 (*6·2*) max
Guns, surface: 9—6 in (*152 mm*) three triple
Guns, dual purpose: 8—4 in (4 twin)
Guns, AA: 12—40 mm *Almirante Grau*; 18—40 mm *Col. Bolognesi*
Armour: 4 in (*102 mm*) sides and CT; 2 in (*51 mm*) turrets and deck
Boilers: 4 Admiralty 3-drum; 400 psi (*28 kg/cm²*); 720°F (*382°C*)
Main engines: Parsons s.r. geared turbines 72 500 shp; 4 shafts
Speed, knots: 31·5
Range, miles: 6 000 at 13 knots; 2 800 at full power
Oil fuel (tons): 1 620
Complement: *Almirante Grau:* 743; *Col. Bolognesi:* 766

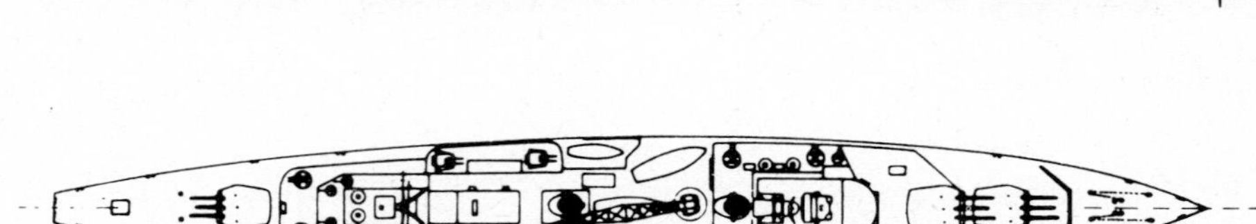

GENERAL
CL 83 was transferred as *Almirante Grau* in December 1959, being renamed *Capitán Quiñones* on 15 May 1973. CL 82 was transferred as *Coronel Bolognesi* on 9 Feb 1960.

RADAR. Search: Types 960, 277 and 293; Fire Control: S band surface, X band AA.

RECONSTRUCTION. CL 83 was reconstructed in 1951-53 at HM Dockyard, Devonport, with two lattice masts, new bridge and improved AA armament, her torpedo tubes being removed. CL 82 was similarly modified in 1955-56.

CAPITAN QUIÑONES (before pennant change) — *1971, Peruvian Navy*

DESTROYERS

2 Ex-BRITISH "DARING" CLASS

Name	*No.*	*Builders*	*Laid down*	*Launched*	*Completed*
FERRÉ (ex-HMS *Decoy*)	74	Yarrow, Co Ltd, Scotstoun	22 Sep 1946	29 Mar 1949	28 Apr 1953
PALACIOS (ex-HMS *Diane*)	73	Yarrow, Co Ltd, Scotstoun	3 Apr 1947	8 May 1952	29 Mar 1954

FERRÉ — *1973, C. & S. Taylor*

Displacement, tons: 2 800 standard; 3 600 full load
Length, feet (*metres*): 366 (*111·7*) pp; 375 (*114·3*) wl; 390 (*118·9*) oa
Beam, feet (*metres*): 43 (*13·1*)
Draught, feet (*metres*): 18 (*5·5*) max
Guns, surface: 6—4·5 in (*115 mm*); 2 twin fwd; 1 twin aft; Mk VI
Guns, AA: 2—40 mm
A/S weapons: 1 Squid 3 barrelled DC mortar
Torpedo tubes: 5—21 in (*533 mm*)
Boilers: 2 Foster Wheeler; Pressure 650 psi (*45·7 kg/cm²*); Superheat 850°F (454°C)
Main engines: English Electric dr geared turbines 2 shafts
Speed, knots: 34·75 designed; 31·5 deep
Range, miles: 3 000 at 20 knots
Oil fuel (tons): 580
Complement: 297

REFIT. The main points after the refit are the reconstructed and enclosed foremast carrying Plessey ASW-Z radar and the Exocet launcher positions in place of the Close Range Blind Fire Director forward of X Turret.

Commissioned after refit—*Palacios* Feb 1973, *Ferré* April 1973.
Purchased by Peru in 1969 and refitted by Cammel Laird (Ship repairers) Ltd, Birkenhead, for further service.

Destroyers—*continued*

2 Ex-US "FLETCHER" CLASS

Name	No.	Builders	Launched	Completed
GUISE (ex-USS *Isherwood, DD* 520)	72	Bethlehem Steel Co, Staten Island	24 Nov 1942	10 Apr 1943
VILLAR (ex-USS *Benham, DD* 796)	71	Bethlehem Steel Co, Staten Island	29 Aug 1943	20 Dec 1943

Displacement, tons	2 120 standard; 2 715 normal; 3 050 full load
Length, feet (*metres*)	360·2 (*109·8*) pp; 370 (*112·8*) wl; 376·2 (*114·7*) oa
Beam, feet (*metres*)	39·7 (*12·1*)
Draught, feet (*metres*)	12·2 (*3·7*) mean; 18 (*5·5*) max
Guns, dual purpose	4—5 in (*127 mm*) 38 cal (5—5 in *Guise*)
Guns, AA	6—3 in (*76 mm*) 50 cal, 3 twin
A/S weapons	2 fixed Hedgehogs; 1 DC rack
Torpedo tubes	5—21 in (*533 mm*) quintupled
Torpedo racks	2 side-launching for A/S torpedoes
Boilers	4 Babcock & Wilcox: 600 psi (*42 kg/cm²*); 850°F (*455°C*)
Main engines	2 GE impulse reaction geared turbines; 60 000 shp; 2 shafts
Speed, knots	34 max; 15 economical sea
Range, miles	5 000 at 15 knots; 900 at full power
Oil fuel (tons)	650
Complement	Allowance; 245 (15 officers and 230 men) Max accommodation: 275 (15 officers and 260 men)

VILLAR *1971, Peruvian Navy*

GUISE, VILLAR

Former United States destroyers of the later "Fletcher" class (*Villar*) and "Fletcher" class (*Guise*).

RADAR. Search: SPS 6, SPS 10. Fire Control: GFCS 68 system forward, GFCS 56 system aft.

TRANSFER. Transferred from the United States Navy to the Peruvian Navy at Boston, Massachusetts, on 15 Dec 1960, and at San Diego, California, on 8 Oct 1961 respectively.

FRIGATES

3 Ex-US "CANNON" CLASS

Name	No.	Launched	Completed
AGUIRRE (ex-USS *Waterman, DE* 740)	62	4 July 1943	31 Dec 1943
CASTILLA (ex-USS *Bangust, DE* 739)	61	6 June 1943	30 Oct 1943
RODRIQUEZ (ex-USS *Weaver, DE* 741)	63	20 June 1943	30 Nov 1943

Displacement, tons	1 240 standard; 1 900 full load
Length, feet (*metres*)	300 (*91·4*) pp; 302·2 (*92·1*) wl; 306 (*93·3*) oa
Beam, feet (*metres*)	36·9 (*11·2*)
Draught, feet (*metres*)	12 (*3·6*) mean; 14·1 (*4·3*) max
Guns, dual purpose	3—3 in (*76 mm*) 50 cal
Guns, AA	6—40 mm, 3 twin; 10—20 mm
A/S weapons	1 Mk 10 ahead-throwing mortar; 8 K mortars; 2 DC racks aft
Main engines	4 GM diesel-electric sets 60 000 hp; 2 shafts
Speed, knots	21 designed; 19 max continuous
Range, miles	10 500 at 12 knots; 3 000 at full power
Oil fuel (tons)	322
Complement	Allowance: 172 (12 officers and 160 men); Max accommodation: 212 (12 officers and 200 men)

CASTILLA *1970, Peruvian Navy*

AGUIRRE, CASTILLA, RODRIGUEZ

Former United States destroyer escorts, DE, of the "Cannon" class. All built by the Western Pipe & Steel Co, San Pedro, California, in 1943. Transferred to Peru on 26 Oct 1951, under the Mutual Defence Assistance Programme. Reconditioned and modernised at Green Cove Springs and Jacksonville, Flor. Actually arrived in Peru on 24 May 1952. Almost due for retirement.

TORPEDO TUBES. The original three 21 inch torpedo tubes in a triple mounting were removed.

CORVETTES

Ex-US MSF TYPE

Name	No.	Laid down	Launched	Completed
DIEZ CANSECO (ex-USS *Shoveler, MSF* 382)	69	1 Apr 1944	10 Dec 1944	28 June 1945
GALVEZ (ex-USS *Ruddy, MSF* 380)	68	24 Feb 1944	29 Oct 1944	28 Apr 1945

Displacement, tons	890 standard; 1 250 full load
Dimensions, feet	215 wl; 221·2 oa × 32·2 × 11 max
Guns	1—3 in, 50 cal dp; 2—40 mm AA
A/S weapons	1 Hedgehog
Main engines	Diesel electric; 2 shafts; 3 532 bhp = 18 knots
Range, miles	4 300 at 10 knots
Complement	100

Former US "Auk" class fleet minesweepers, MSF Both built by the Gulf Shipbuilding Corp. Activated at San Diego, California, and transferred to the Peruvian Navy under the Mutual Defence Assistance Programme on 1 Nov 1960. Sonar equipment was fitted so that they could be used as patrol vessels. The 3 inch gun director was removed.

DIEZ CANSECO, GALVEZ

GALVEZ *1970, Peruvian Navy*

SUBMARINES

2 TYPE 209

Displacement, tons	990 surfaced; 1 290 dived
Length, feet (*metres*)	177·1 (*54·0*)
Beam, feet (*metres*)	20·3 (*6·2*)
Torpedo tubes	8—21 in (with reloads)
Main machinery	Diesel Electric; 4 MTU Siemens diesel-generators; 1 Siemens electric motor; 1 shaft
Speed, knots	10 surfaced; 22 dived
Range	50 days
Complement	31

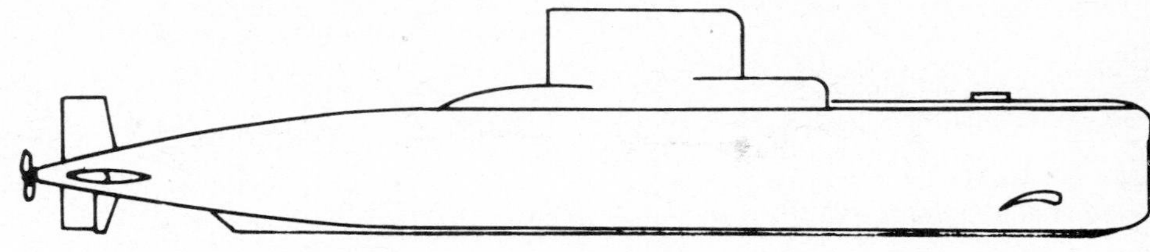

TYPE 209 — *1973, Howaldtswerke*

Designed by Ingenieurkontor, Lübeck for construction by Howaldtswerke, Kiel and sale by Ferrostaal Essen all acting as a consortium.
A single-hull design with two ballast tanks and forward and after trim tanks. Fitted with snort and remote machinery control. The single screw is slow revving, very high capacity batteries with GRP lead-acid cells and battery cooling—by Wilh. Hagen and VARTTA. Active and passive sonar, sonar detection equipment, sound ranging gear and underwater telephone. Fitted with two periscopes, radar and Omega receiver. Foreplanes retract.

4 "ABTAO" CLASS

Name	*No.*	*Laid down*	*Launched*	*Completed*
ABTAO (ex-*Tiburon*)	42	12 May 1952	27 Oct 1953	20 Feb 1954
ANGAMOS (ex-*Atun*)	43	27 Oct 1955	5 Feb 1957	1 July 1957
DOS DE MAYO (ex-*Lobo*)	41	12 May 1952	6 Feb 1954	14 June 1954
IQUIQUE (ex-*Merlin*)	44	27 Oct 1955	5 Feb 1957	1 Oct 1957

Displacement, tons	825 standard; 1 400 submerged
Length, feet (*metres*)	243 (*74·1*) oa
Beam, feet (*metres*)	22 (*6·7*)
Draught, feet (*metres*)	14 (*4·3*)
Guns, surface	1—5 in (*127 mm*) 25 cal (*Abtao* and *Dos de Mayo*)
Torpedo tubes	6—21 in (*533 mm*); 4 bow, 2 stern
Main machinery	2 GM 278A diesels; 2 400 bhp; Electric motors; 2 shafts
Speed, knots	16 on surface; 10 submerged
Range, miles	5 000 at 10 knots (surfaced)
Oil fuel (tons)	45
Complement	40

All built by Electric Boat Division—General Dynamics Corporation, Groton, Connecticut. They are of modified US "Mackerel" class.

DOS DE MAYO — *1970, Peruvian Navy*

LIGHT FORCES

6 VOSPER TYPE (LARGE PATROL CRAFT)

DE LOS HEROS	23	**LARREA**	25	**SANTILLANA**	22
HERRERA	24	**SANCHEZ CARRION**	26	**VELARDE**	21

Displacement, tons	100 standard; 130 full load
Dimensions, feet	103·7 wl; 109·7 oa × 21 × 5·7
Guns	2—20 mm AA
Main engines	2 Napier Deltic 18 cyl, turbocharged diesels; 6 200 bhp = 30 knots
Range, miles	1 100 at 15 knots
Complement	25 (4 officers and 21 ratings)

Designed and built by Vosper Ltd, Portsmouth, England, for the Peruvian Navy. Of all-welded steel construction with aluminium upperworks. Designed for coastal patrol, air-sea-rescue, and fishery protection. Equipped with Vosper roll damping fins, Decca Type 707 true motion radar, comprehensive radio, up-to-date navigation aids, sonar, depth charges in racks aft, and air-conditioning. The first boat, *Velarde*, was launched on 10 July 1964, the last, *Sanchez Carrion*, on 18 Feb 1965. Can be armed as gunboat, torpedo boat (four side-launched torpedoes) or minelayer. A twin rocket projector can be fitted forward instead of gun.

SANCHEZ CARRION — *1971, Peruvian Navy*

2 Ex-US PGM TYPE (LARGE PATROL

RIO SAMA PC 11 (ex-USS *PGM* 78)
RIO CHIRA PC 12 (ex-USS *PGM* 111)

Displacement, tons	130 standard; 147 full load
Dimensions, feet	101 × 21 × 6
Guns	2—40 mm, 4—20 mm, 2—0·5 cal MG
Main engines	2 Diesels; 2 shafts; 1 800 hp = 18·5 knots
Range, miles	1 500 at 10 knots
Complement	15

PC 11 transferred in Sep 1966 from the United States under the Military Aid Programme. PC 12 transferred 30 June 1972

RIO SAMA — *1971, Peruvian Navy*

3 "RIO" CLASS (COASTAL PATROL CRAFT)

RIO PIURA 04 **RIO TUMBES** 02 **RIO ZARUMILLA** 01

Displacement, tons	37 full load
Dimensions, feet	65·7 × 17 × 3·2
Guns	2—40 mm
Main engines	2 GM diesels; 2 shafts; 1 200 bhp = 18 knots

Built by Viareggio, Italy. Ordered in 1959, laid down on 15 July 1959, and entered service on 5 Sep 1960. *Rio el Salto*, 03, was deleted from the list in 1966.

RIO PIURA — *1973, Peruvian Navy*

Light Forces—*continued*

2 "MARANON" CLASS (RIVER GUNBOATS)

MARAÑÓN	13	John I. Thornycroft & Co	23 Apr 1951	July 1951
UCAYALI	14	Ltd. Southampton, England	7 Mar 1951	June 1951

Displacement, tons	365 full load
Dimensions, feet	154·8 wl × 32 × 4 max
Guns	2—3 in 50 cal dp; 7—20 mm AA (2 twin, 3 single)
Main engines	British Polar M 441 diesels; 800 bhp = 12 knots
Range, miles	6 000 at 10 knots
Complement	40

Ordered early in 1950. Employed on police duties in Upper Amazon. Very shallow draught. Superstructure of aluminium alloy. Based at Iquitos.

2 "LORETO" CLASS (RIVER GUNBOATS)

AMAZONAS 11 **LORETO** 12

Displacement, tons	250 standard
Dimensions, feet	145 × 22 × 4
Guns	1—3 in; 2—47 mm; 2—20 mm AA
Main engines	Diesel; 750 bhp = 15 knots
Range, miles	4 000 at 10 knots
Complement	35

Designed and built by the Electric Boat Co, Groton, Conn. Launched in 1934.

LORETO *1973, Peruvian Navy*

NAPO 301 (RIVER GUNBOAT)

Displacement, tons	98
Dimensions, feet	100 pp; 101·5 oa × 18 × 3
Main engines	Triple expansion; 250 ihp = 12 knots
Boilers	Yarrow
Complement	22

Built by Yarrow Co Ltd, Scotstoun, Glasgow. Launched in 1920. Built of steel. Converted from wood to oil fuel burning. In the Upper Amazon Flotilla. Converted to a Dispensary Vessel in 1968.

AMERICA 15 (RIVER GUNBOAT)

Displacement, tons	240
Dimensions, feet	133 × 19·5 × 4·5
Guns	2—3 pdr; 4—12·7 mm AA
Main engines	Triple expansion; 350 ihp = 14 knots
Complement	26

Built by Tranmere Bay Development Co Ltd, Birkenhead. Built of steel. Launched and completed in 1904. Converted from coal to oil fuel burning. In the Upper Amazon Flotilla. The river gunboat *Iquitos* was discarded in 1967 after 92 years service.

11 LAKE PATROL CRAFT

280-290

30 ft craft stationed on Lake Titicaca.

Patrol craft on Lake Titicaca *1973, Peruvian Navy*

MINE WARFARE FORCES

2 "BONDY" CLASS (MINESWEEPERS—COASTAL)

BONDY (ex-*YMS* 25) 137 **SAN MARTIN** (ex-*YMS* 35) 138

Displacement, tons	300 standard; 325 full load
Dimensions, feet	136 × 24·5 × 6
Guns	1—3 in; 2—20 mm AA
Main engines	2 GM diesels; 1 000 bhp = 13 knots (11 knots econ)
Range, miles	2 100 at 9·5 knots
Complement	30

Former US wooden motor minesweepers, YMS. *Bondy* was built by Greenport Basin & Construction Co, Long Island, NY, and launched on 28 Jan 1943, *San Martin* by C. Hilterbandt Drydock Co, Kingston, NY, and acquired from USA in 1947. Formerly known as *Alferez de Fragata Bondy* and *Guardiamarina San Martin*.

BONDY *1966, Peruvian Navy*

AMPHIBIOUS FORCES

CHIMBOTE (ex-M/S *Rawhiti*, ex-USS *LST* 283) 34

Displacement, tons	1 625 standard; 4 050 full load
Dimensions, feet	316 wl; 328 oa × 50 × 14·1
Guns	1—3 in
Main engines	GM diesels; 2 shafts; 1 700 bhp = 10 knots
Oil fuel, tons	600 oil tanks; 1 100 ballast tanks
Range, miles	9 500 at 9 knots
Complement	Accommodation for 16 officers and 130 men

Former US tank landing ship of the 1-510 Series. Built by American [illegible]ige Co Ambridge, Pennsylvania. Laid down on 2 Aug 1943, launched on 10 Oct [illegible]43 and completed on 18 Nov 1943. Sold to Peru by a British firm in 1951.

PAITA (ex-USS *Burnett County*, *LST* 512) 35 (ex-*AT* 4)

Displacement, tons	1 653 standard; 4 080 full load
Dimensions, feet	316 wl; 328 oa × 50 × 14·5 max
Guns	6—40 mm AA; 6—20 mm AA
Main engines	GM diesels; 2 shafts; 1 700 bhp = 10 knots
Range, miles	9 500 at 9 knots
Complement	13 officers, 106 men

Former US tank landing ship of the 511-1152 Series. Built by Chicago Bridge & Iron Co, Seneca, Illinois. Laid down on 29 July 1943. Launched on 10 Dec 1943 and completed on 8 Jan 1944. Purchased by Peru in 1957.

PAITA *1972, Peruvian Navy*

2 "LOMAS" CLASS

ATICO (ex-USS *LSM* 554) **LOMAS** (ex-USS *LSM* 396)

Displacement, tons	513 standard; 913 full load
Dimensions, feet	196·5 wl; 203·5 oa × 34·5 × 7
Guns	2—40 mm AA; 4—20 mm AA
Main engines	Diesels; 800 rpm; 2 shafts; 3 600 bhp = 12 knots
Range, miles	5 000 at 7 knots
Complement	Accommodation for 116 (10 officers and 106 men)

Former US medium landing ships of the LSM type. Both built by Charleston Navy Yard, Charleston, SC, USA. Purchased in 1959. A photograph of *Lomas* appears in the 1967-68 to 1971-72 editions.

Name	*No.*	*Laid down*	*Launched*	*Completed*
Atico	37	3 Mar 1945	22 Mar 1945	14 Sep 1945
Lomas	36	13 Dec 1944	2 Jan 1945	23 Mar 1945

ATICO *1972, Peruvian Navy*

Amphibious Forces—*continued*

3 Ex-US LCUs

PIRURA BT 4 (ex-US LCU 1161) **SALTO** BT 3 (ex-US LCU 855)
ZARUMILLA BT 1 (ex-US LCU 501)

Displacement, tons	160 light; 315 full load
Dimensions, feet	119 oa × 32·7 × 5
Guns	2—20 mm
Main engines	Gray Marine diesels; 3 shafts; 675 bhp = 10 knots
Complement	15

Sold to Peru Aug 1947.

10 LCAs

200-209

Employed on riverine operations.

SURVEY VESSELS

UNANUE

For details, see "Tug" Section.

CARDENAS

Of 19 tons, launched in 1950, with a complement of 4.

WATER CARRIER

MANTILLA (ex-US *YW* 122) 141

Displacement, tons	1 235 full load
Dimensions, feet	174 × 32
Gun	1 MG forward
Capacity gallons	200 000

Former US water barge. Built by Henry C. Grebe & Co Inc, Chicago, Ill. Lent to Peru in July 1963.

TRANSPORTS

INDEPENDENCIA (ex-USS *Bellatrix, AKA* 3, ex-*Raven, SKA* 20) 31 (ex-21)

Displacement, tons	6 194 light
Measurement, tons	Maritime Commission deadweight, 8 656
Guns	1—5 in 38 cal; 3—3 in 50 cal, 10—20 mm
Dimensions, feet	435 wl; 459 oa × 63 × 26·5
Main engines	1 Nordberg diesel; 1 shaft; 6 000 bhp = 16·5 knots

Former US attack cargo ship. Built by Tampa Shipbuilding Co, Tampa, Florida, in 1941. Transferred to Peru at Bremerton, Washington on 20 July 1963 under the Military Aid Program. Training ship for the Peruvian Naval Academy.

INDEPENDENCIA *1970, Peruvian Navy*

ILO 131 **RIMAC** 132

Displacement, tons	18 400 full load
Measurement, tons	13 000 deadweight
Dimensions, feet	507·7 × 67·3 × 27·2
Main engines	Diesels; Speed = 15·6 knots

The *Ilo* completed in Dec 1971 at Servicio Industrial de la Marina, Callao Her sister ship *Rimac* was launched at the same yard on 12 Dec 1971.

ILO *1972, Peruvian Navy*

FLOATING DOCK

The former US auxiliary floating dry dock *ARD* 8 was transferred to Peru in Feb 1961; displacement 5 200 tons; length 492 feet; beam 84 feet; draught 5·7 to 33·2 feet. The former US floating dock *AFDL* 33 launched in Oct 1964 was transferred to Peru in July 1969; displacement 1 900 tons; length 288 feet; beam 64 feet; draught 8·2 to 31·5 feet.

TANKERS

3 "PARINAS" CLASS

Name	*No.*	*Launched*	*Completed*
PARINAS	155	2 May 1967	13 June 1968
PIMENTAL	156	30 Dec 1967	27 June 1969
+1		Building	

Displacement, tons	3 434 light; 13 600 full load
Measurement, tons	10 000 deadweight
Dimensions, feet	410·9 × 63·1 × 26
Main engines	Burmeister and Wain Type 750 diesel; 5 400 bhp = 14·5 knots

Built by the Servicio Industrial de la Marina in the Naval Arsenal at Callao. In service 1969.

PARINAS *1970, Peruvian Navy*

2 "SECHURA" CLASS

LOBITOS 159 **ZORRITOS** 158

Displacement, tons	8 700 full load
Measurement, tons	4 300 gross; 6 000 deadweight
Dimensions, feet	360·0 wl; 385·0 oa × 52·0 × 21·2 max
Main engines	Burmeister & Wain diesels; 2 400 bhp = 12 knots (13·25 knots on trials)
Boilers	2 Scotch with Thornycroft oil burners for cargo tank cleaning

Both built by Servicio Industrial de la Marina, Callao. *Zorritos* launched 8 Oct 1958, *Lobitos* May 1965.

LOBITOS *1969, US Navy*

MOLLENDO (ex-*Amalienborg*) ATP 151

Displacement, tons	6 084 standard; 25 670 full load
Dimensions, feet	534·8 × 72·2 × 30
Main engines	674-VTFS-160 diesels; 7 500 bhp = 14·5 knots

This Japanese built tanker, completed Sep 1962, was acquired by Peru in Apr 1967.

TUGS

RIOS (ex-USS *Pinto ATF* 90) 123

Displacement, tons	1 235 standard; 1 675 full load
Measurement, tons	195 wl, 205 oa × 38·5 × 15·5 max
Main engines	4 GM diesel electric, 3 000 bhp = 16·5 knots

Former United States fleet ocean tug of the "Apache" class. Launched on 5 Jan 1943. Transferred to Peru in 1960 and delivered in Jan 1961. Fitted with powerful pumps and other salvage equipment.

UNANUE (ex-USS *Wateree, ATA* 174) 136

Displacement, tons	534 standard, 852 full load; official revised figure
Dimensions, feet	133·7 wl, 143 oa × 33·9 × 13·2
Main engines	GM diesel-electric; 1 500 bhp = 13 knots

Former United States auxiliary ocean tug of the "Maricopa" class. Built by Levingston SB Co, Orange, Texas. Laid down on 5 Oct 1943, launched on 18 Nov 1943 and completed on 20 July 1944. Purchased from the USA in Nov 1961 under MAP. Temporarily employed as a Survey Ship.

PHILIPPINES

Administration

Flag Officer in Command, Philippine Navy:
Commodore Hilario M. Ruiz

Commander, Naval Operating Forces:
Captain Simeon M. Alejandro

Diplomatic Representation

Naval, Military, and Air Attache in London:
Captain Jaime V. Francisco (Navy)

Personnel

1 200 officers and 13 000 men including Coast Guard

Strength of the Fleet

1 Frigate	18 Patrol Boats
6 Patrol Vessels	4 Minesweepers
9 Patrol Gunboats	2 Command Ships
4 Hydrofoil Patrol Boats	11 Landing Ships

DESTROYERS

The Philippine Navy can be expected to begin operating ships of destroyer size during the 1970s in view of the increasing level of competence of the Philippine Navy and the reduction of US naval forces in the Western Pacific.

Ships

Most names are those of geographical locations and are prefixed by RPS (Republic of Philippines Ship).

Coast Guard

Established Oct 1967 as a specialised branch within the Navy.
Commandant: Commodore Ernesto R. Ogbinar

Mercantile Marine

Lloyds' Register of Shipping:
327 vessels of 924 564 tons

FRIGATES

1 Ex-US "BOSTWICK" CLASS

Name	*No.*	*Launched*	*US Comm.*	*Transferred*
DATU KALANTIAW (ex-USS *Booth*, DE 170)	PS 76	21 June 1943	21 July 1943	15 Dec 1967

Displacement, tons: 1 220 standard; 1 620 full load
Length, feet (*metres*): 300 (*91·5*) wl; 306 (*93·2*) oa
Beam, feet (*metres*): 36·6 (*11·2*)
Draught, feet (*metres*): 14 (*4·3*)
Guns: 3—3 inch (*76 mm*) 50 cal AA; 6—40 mm AA (twin); 2—20 mm AA (single)
A/S weapons: 6—12·75 inch (*324 mm*) torpedo tubes (Mk 32 triple); depth charges
Main engines: Diesel-electric drive (General Motors diesels); 6 000 bhp; 2 shafts
Speed, knots: 21
Complement: Approx 165

Former US destroyer escort of the DET design. Built by Federal Shipbuilding & Dry Dock Co, Newark, New Jersey, and completed by the Norfolk Navy Yard. Triple 21 inch torpedo tube mount originally fitted has been removed. Equipped with SPS-5 and SPS-6 search radars.

DATU KALANTIAW

DISPOSALS
Rajah Soliman D 66 (ex-USS *Bowers*, APD 40), which had been transferred to the Philippines in 1961, was sunk in a typhoon in the Philippines in June 1962; raised but stricken on 3 Dec 1964.

PATROL VESSELS

2 Ex-US "AUK" CLASS MSF TYPE

RIZAL (ex-USS *Murrelet*, MSF 372)	PS 69	29 Dec 1944
QUEZON (ex-USS *Vigilance*, MSF 324)	PS 70	5 Apr 1943

Displacement, tons: 890 standard; 1 250 full load
Dimensions, feet: 215 wl; 221·2 oa × 32·2 × 10·8
Guns: 2—3 inch (*76 mm*) 50 cal AA (single); 4—40 mm AA (twin); 4—20 mm AA (twin)
A/S weapons: 3—12·75 inch (*324 mm*) torpedo tubes (Mk 32 triple); 1 hedgehog; depth charges
Main engines: Diesel-electric (General Motors diesels); 3 532 bhp; 2 shafts = 18 knots
Complement: approx 100

Former US Navy minesweepers (originally designated AM). Built by Savannah Machine & Foundry Co, Savannah, Georgia, and Associated Shipbuilders, Seattle, Washington, respectively. Launch dates above. PS 69 commissioned in US Navy on 21 Aug 1945 and PS 70 on 28 Feb 1944; PS 69 transferred to the Philippines on 18 June 1965 and PS 70 on 19 Aug 1967.
Upon transfer the minesweeping gear was removed and a second 3 inch gun fitted aft; additional anti-submarine weapons also fitted.

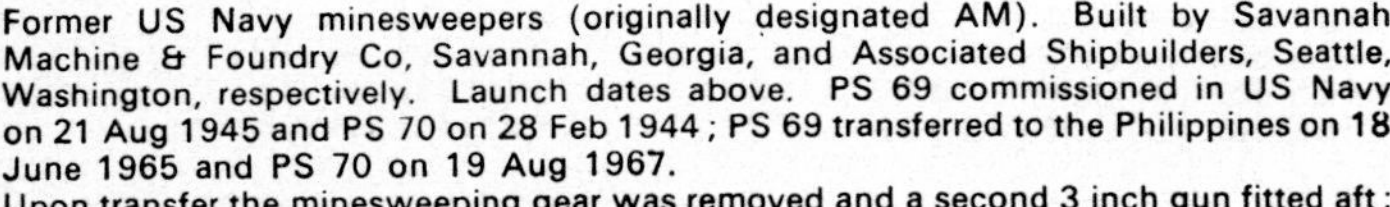

RIZAL

5 Ex-US 185-ft PCE TYPE

CEBU (ex-USS PCE 881)	PS 28	10 Nov 1943
NEGROS OCCIDENTAL (ex-USS PCE 884)	PS 29	24 Feb 1944
LEYTE (ex-USS PCE 885)	PS 30	30 Apr 1945
PANGASINAN (ex-USS PCE 891)	PS 31	15 June 1944
ILOILO (ex-USS PCE 897)	PS 32	3 Aug 1943

Displacement, tons: 640 standard; 850 full load
Dimensions, feet: 180 wl; 184·5 oa × 34 × 9·5
Guns: 1—3 inch (*76 mm*) 50 cal AA; 3 or 6—40 mm AA (single or twin); 4—20 mm AA (single)
A/S weapons: 2—12·75 inch (*324 mm*) torpedo tubes (Mk 32 single); depth charges; hedgehog in some
Main engines: Diesels (General Motors); 2 000 bhp; 2 shafts = 15 knots
Complement: approx 100

Former US Navy patrol craft. PS 28, 29, and 30 built by Albina Engineering & Machine Works, Portland, Oregon; PS 31 and 32 built by Willamette Iron & Steel Corp, Portland, Oregon. Launch dates above; completed 1944-1945. All five units transferred to the Philippines in July 1948.

CEBU *1971, Philippine Navy*

LEYTE *Philippine Navy*

Patrol Vessels—*continued*

4 Ex-US 173-ft PC TYPE

BATANGAS (ex-USS PC 1134)	PS 24	18 Jan 1943
NUEVA ECIJA (ex-USS PC 1241)	PS 25	24 Dec 1942
CAPIZ (ex-USS PC 1564)	PS 27	19 Apr 1944
NUEVA VISCAYA (ex-USAF *Altus*, ex-USS PC 568)	PS 80	25 Apr 1942

Displacement, tons	280 standard; 450 full load
Dimensions, feet	170 wl; 173·66 oa × 23 × 10·8
Guns	1—3 inch (*76 mm*) 50 cal AA; 1—40 mm AA; several—20 mm AA (single or twin)
A/S weapons	depth charges
Main engines	Diesels (General Motors); 2 880 bhp; 2 shafts = 20 knots
Complement	Approx 70

Former US Navy patrol craft. Launch dates above; completed 1942-1944. *Batangas* and *Capiz* transferred to the Philippines in July 1948; *Nueva Ecija* in Oct 1958; and *Nueva Viscaya* in Mar 1968. The *Nueva Viscaya* was stricken from the US Navy on 15 Mar 1963 and subsequently served with the US Air Force until transferred.

Bohol PS 22 (ex-USS PC 1131) scrapped in 1969, *Camarines Sur* C 21 (ex-USS PC 1121) stricken in 1953, *Negros Oriental* C 26 (ex-USS PC 1563) sunk in typhoon at Guam in Nov 1962 (raised and stricken in 1963).

Tatlac PG 11 (ex-USS PCS 1399, ex-YMS 450) and *Laguna* PG 12 (ex-USS PCS 1403) scrapped in 1969.

110ft SC TYPE

Cagayan R 14 (ex-USS SC 731), *Mountain Province* P 15 (ex-USS SC 736), *Liocus Sup* P 16 (ex-USS SC 739), *Surigao* P 17 (ex-USS SC 747), *Isabella* P 18 (ex-USS SC 750), *Cavite* P 19 (ex-USS SC 981) scrapped; *Alert* PY 54 (ex-USS SC 1267) sunk in 1956; *Malampay Sound* AF 20 (ex-USS SC 1274) stricken.

BOHOL—now stricken *1968, Philippine Navy*

4 100-ft PGM TYPE

AGUSAN	G 61	**ROMBLON**	G 63
CATANDUANES	G 62	**PALAWAN**	G 64

Displacement, tons	122 full load
Dimensions, feet	100·33 oa × 21·1 × 8·5
Guns	2—20 mm AA; 2—·50 cal MG
Main engines	Diesels (Mercedes Benz); 950 bhp; 2 shafts = 17 knots

Steel-hulled patrol gunboats built under US military assistance programme for the Philippines. Built by Tacoma Boatbuilding Co, Tacoma, Washington, and transferred to the Philippines upon completion, G 61 and 62 in Mar 1960, and G 63 and 64 in June 1960. Assigned US designations PGM 39-42 while under construction.
These craft are lengthened versions of the US Coast Guard 85-foot "Cape" class patrol boat design. *Catanduanes* is operated by the Philippine Coast Guard.

ROMBLON *1968, Philippine Navy*

110 -ft PGM TYPE

Camarines PG 48, *Sulu* PG 49, *La Union* PG 50, *Antique* PG 51 *Mismamis Occidental* PG 53 reportedly were decommissioned in 1973-1974 and cannibalised for parts. See 1973-1974 edition for characteristics. Assigned US designations PGM 33-36 and 38 while under construction. *Masbate* PG 52 (built as PGM 37) sunk in 1965.

HYDROFOIL PATROL BOATS

CAMIGUIN Type on foils *1965*

Hydrofoil Patrolboats—*continued*

2 ITALIAN DESIGN

CAMIGUIN H 72 **SIQUIJOR** H 73

Displacement, tons	36
Dimensions, feet	67·75 × 15·3 (24·1 overfoils) × 8·9 (3·8 foilborne)
Guns	1—20 mm AA
Main engines	Diesel (Mercedes Benz); 1 250 bhp; 2 shafts = 38 knots

Built by Cantiere Navale Leopaldo Rodriquez, Messina, Sicily. Laid down on 26 May and 28 Oct 1964. Completed in Apr 1965. For military and police patrol.

CAMIGUIN *1969, Philippine Navy*

2 JAPANESE DESIGN

BALER H 75 **BONTOC** H 74

Displacement, tons	32 full load
Dimensions, feet	68·9 × 15·7 × 24·6 over foils
Guns	MG fore and aft
Main engines	Ikegai-Mercedes Benz diesel; 3 200 bhp = 37·8 knots (32 cruising). Also auxiliary engine
Complement	15 (3 officers, 12 ratings)

Built by Hitachi Zosen, Kanagawa Japan. Completed in Dec 1966. For smuggling prevention. Also used as inter-island ferries.

INSHORE PATROL CRAFT

6 65-ft SEWART TYPE

Displacement, tons	33 full load
Dimensions, feet	65 oa × 16
Guns	6 machineguns
Main engines	3 diesels (General Motors 12V71); 1 590 bhp; 3 shafts = 25 knots

These craft were ordered in the United States from Sewart in 1971. The design is adopted from a commercial 65-foot boat. Similar to the FB 1-10 operated by the South Korean Navy.

18 "SWIFT" TYPE

PCF 300 (ex-USN PCF 6633)	**PCF 309** (ex-USN PCF 684)
PCF 301 (ex-USN PCF 6634)	**PCF 310** (ex-USN PCF 685)
PCF 302 (ex-USN PCF 35)	**PCF 311** (ex-USN PCF 686)
PCF 303 (ex-USN PCF 36)	**PCF 312** (ex-USN PCF 687)
PCF 304 (ex-USN PCF 37)	**PCF 313** (ex-USN PCF 688)
PCF 305 (ex-USN PCF 38)	**PCF 314** (ex-USN PCF 6911)
PCF 306 (ex-USN PCF 681)	**PCF 315** (ex-USN PCF 6912)
PCF 307 (ex-USN PCF 682)	**PCF 316** (ex-USN PCF 6913)
PCF 308 (ex-USN PCF 683)	**PCF 317** (built 1970)

Displacement, tons	22·5 full load
Dimensions, feet	51·3 × 13·6
Guns	2—50 cal MG
Main engines	2 geared diesels (General Motors); 860 bhp; 2 shafts = 28 knots

Inshore patrol craft of the "Swift" type built in the United States. PCF 302-305 served in US Navy prior to transfer to the Philippines; others built for US military assistance programmes. PCF 300 and 301 transferred to Philippines in Mar 1966, PCF 302-305 in Aug 1966, PCF 306-313 in Feb 1968, PCF 314-316 in July 1970. PCF 317 is Philippine built (ferro concrete).

PCF 310 *1969, Philippine Navy*

PATROL MINESWEEPERS

2 Ex-US MSO TYPE

DAVAO DEL NORTE (ex-USS *Energy*, MSO 436)	PM 91	13 Feb 1953
DAVAO DEL SUR (ex-USS *Firm*, MSO 444)	PM 92	15 Apr 1953

Displacement, tons	665 light; 750 full load
Dimensions, feet	165 wl; 172 oa × 36 × 13·6
Guns	2—20 mm AA
Main engines	4 diesels (Packard); 2 280 bhp; 2 shafts (controllable-pitch propellers) = 15·5 knots
Complement	approx 70

Former US Navy ocean minesweepers of the "Agile" class. Built by J. M. Martinac Shipbuilding Corp, Tacoma, Washington; launch dates above. Commissioned in US Navy on 16 July 1954 and 12 Oct 1954, respectively. Wood-hulled with non-magnetic engines and fittings.
Both ships transferred to the Philippine Navy on 5 July 1972; designated PM for patrol minesweepers.

DAVAO DEL NORTE (as USS *Energy*) *1968, US Navy*

2 Ex-US MSC TYPE

ZAMBALES (ex-USS MSC 218)	PM 55
ZAMBOANGA DEL NORTE (ex-USS MSC 219)	PM 56

Displacement, tons	320 light; 385 full load
Dimensions, feet	144 oa × 28 × 8·2
Guns	2—20 mm AA
Main engines	2 diesels; 880 bhp; 2 shafts = 12 knots
Complement	approx 40

"Bluebird" class coastal minesweepers built by the United States specifically for transfer under the military aid programme. Transferred on 7 Mar 1956 and 23 Apr 1956, respectively. Wood hulled with non-magnetic metal fittings.

ZAMBALES

ZAMBALES *1969, Philippine Navy*

COMMAND SHIPS

THE PRESIDENT (ex-*Roxas*, ex-*Lapu-Lapu*) TP 777

Dimensions, feet	275 oa × 42·6 × 21
Guns	2—20 mm AA
Main engines	Diesels; 5 000 bhp; 2 shafts = 18 knots
Complement	approx 90

Built at Ishikawajima, Japan, as war reparation; launched in 1958 and completed in 1959. Used as presidential yacht and command ship.
Originally named *Lapu-Lapu* after the chief who killed Magellan; renamed *Roxas* on 9 Oct 1962 after the late Manuel Roxas, the first President of the Philippines Republic renamed *The President* in 1967.

THE PRESIDENT *1968, Philippine Navy.*

MOUNT SAMAT (ex-*Pagasa*, ex-*Santa Maria* ex-*Pagasa*, ex-APO 21, ex-USS *Quest*, AM 281) TK 21 16 Mar 1944

Displacement, tons	650 standard; 945 full load
Dimensions, feet	184·5 wl; 180 oa × 33 × 9·8
Main engines	Diesels (Cooper Bessemer); 1 710 bhp; 2 shafts = 14·8 knots
Complement	approx 60

Former US Navy minesweeper (AM). Built by Gulf Shipbuilding Corp. Launch date above; commissioned on 25 Oct 1944. Transferred to the Philippines in July 1948. Used as presidential yacht and command ship. A sister ship serves as a surveying ship in the coast guard as the *Samar*.

MOUNT SAMAT *1971*

LANDING SHIPS

9 Ex-US LST TYPE

BULACAN (ex-USS LST 843)	LT 38	29 Nov 1944
ALBAY (ex-USS LST 865)	LT 39	22 Nov 1944
MISAMIS ORIENTAL (ex-USS LST 875)	LT 40	29 Nov 1944
BATAAN (ex-USS *Caddo Parish*, LST 515)	LT 85	31 Dec 1943
CAGAYAN (ex-USS *Hickman County*, LST 825)	LT 86	11 Nov 1944
ILCOS NORTE (ex-USS *Madera County*, LST 905)	LT 87	30 Dec 1944
MONDRO OCCIDENTAL (ex-USNS LST 222)	LT 93	17 Aug 1943
SURAGO DEL NORTE (es-USNS LST 546)	LT 94	16 Feb 1944
SURAGO DEL SUR (ex-USNS LST 488)	LT 95	5 Mar 1943

Displacement, tons	1 620 standard; 2 366 beaching; 4 080 full load
Dimensions, feet	316 wl; 328 oa × 50 × 14
Guns	7 or 8—40 mm AA (two twin, four single)
Main engines	Diesels (General Motors); 1 700 bhp; 2 shafts = 11·6 knots
Complement	approx 60

Former US Navy tank landing ships. Cargo capacity 2 100 tons. Launch dates above. Three ships transferred in July 1948; three ships on 29 Nov 1969; and three ships on 15 July 1972.

***Cutabato* T 36 ex-USS LST 75 and *Pampanga* T 37 ex-USS LST 842 have been scrapped.**

MISAMIS ORIENTAL *1968, Philippine Navy*

Landing Ships—*continued*

2 Ex-US LSM TYPE

ISABELA (ex-USS LSM 463) LP 41
ORIENTAL MINDORO (ex-USS LSM 320) LP 68

Displacement, tons	743 beaching; 1 095 full load
Dimensions, feet	196·5 wl; 203·5 oa × 34·6 × 8·5
Guns	2—40 mm AA (twin); several 20 mm AA
Main engines	Diesels (direct drive; General Motors except Fairbanks Morse in *Isabela*); 2 800 bhp; 2 shafts = 12·5 knots

Former US Navy medium landing ships. Built 1944-1945. Transferred to the Phillipines in Mar 1961, and Apr 1962, respectively. *Batanes* LP 65 ex-USS LSM 236 ran aground in June 1971 and stricken in 1972.

BATANES—now stricken *1962, Courtesy Mr W. H. Davis*

2 REPAIR SHIPS: Ex-US ARL TYPES

AKLAN (ex-USS *Romulus*, ARL 22, ex-LST 926) AR 67
NARRA (ex-USS *Krishna*, ARL 38, ex-LST 1149) AR 88

Displacement, tons	2 366 standard; 4 100 full load
Dimensions, feet	316 wl; 328 oa × 50 × 11·2
Guns	8—40 mm AA (quad); several 20 mm AA
Main engines	Diesels (General Motors); 1 800 bhp; 2 shafts = 11·6 knots
Complement	approx 220

Former US Navy landing craft repair ships. Converted during construction from LSTs; launched on 15 Nov 1944 and 25 May 1945, respectively. Transferred to the Philippines in Nov 1961 and on 30 Oct 1971, respectively.

AKLAN *1968, Philippine Navy*

2 OILERS: Ex-US YO and YOG TYPE

LAKE MAUJAN (ex-USS YO 173) YO 43
LAKE BOHI (ex-USS YOG 73) YO 78

Displacement, tons	520 standard; 1 400 full load
Dimensions, feet	174 oa × 32 × 13·2
Guns	2—20 mm AA (single)
Main engines	Diesel; 560 bhp; 1 shaft = 8 knots

Former US Navy self-propelled fuel oil barges. Built in 1943-1944. Cargo capacity 6 570 barrels. *Lake Maujan* carries fuel oil and *Lake Bohi* carries gasoline and diesel fuel. *Lake Lanao* of same design (see photo). Transferred to the Philippines in July 1948 and July 1967, respectively.

1 WATER CARRIER

LAKE LANAO (ex-USS YW 125) **YW 42**

Displacement, tons	1 235 full load
Dimensions, feet	174 oa × 32 × 15
Guns	2—20 mm AA
Main engines	Diesel; 560 bhp; 1 shaft = 8 knots

Former US Navy self-propelled water barge. Cargo capacity 200 000 gallons fresh water. Transferred to the Philippines in July 1948.

LAKE LANAO *1969, Philippine Navy*

1 TUG: Ex-US ATR TYPE

IFUGAO (ex-HMS *Emphatic*, ex-USS ATR 96) AQ 44

Displacement, tons	783 full load
Dimensions, feet	134·6 wl; 143 oa × 33·8 × 13·5
Guns	1—3 inch (*76 mm*) 50 cal AA; 2—20 mm AA
Main engines	Diesel; 1 500 bhp; 1 shaft = 13 knots

Rescue tug transferred to Royal Navy upon launching on 27 Jan 1944; subsequently returned to US Navy and retransferred to the Philippines in July 1948.

Landing Ships—*continued*

6 TUGS: Ex-US HARBOUR TYPE

MARANAO (ex-YTL 554)	YQ 221	**AETA** (ex-YTL 449)	YQ 224
IGOROT (ex-YTL 572)	YQ 222	**ILONGOT** ((ex-YTL 427)	YQ 225
TAGBANUA (ex-YTL 429)	YQ 223	**TASADAY** (ex-YTL 425)	YQ 226

Former US Navy 66-foot harbour tugs.

1 CARGO SHIP: Ex-US C1-M-AV1 TYPE

MACTAN (ex-USCGC *Kukui*, WAK 186, ex-USS *Colquitt*, AK 174) TK 90

Displacement, tons	4 900 light; 5 636 full load
Dimensions, feet	320 wl; 338·5 oa × 50 × 18
Guns	Unarmed
Main engines	Diesel (Nordberg); 1 750 bhp; 1 shaft = 11·5 knots

Cargo-ship built by Froemming Brothers, Milwaukee, Wisconsin, launched on 21 Jan 1945 and commissioned in US Navy on 22 Sep 1945 and transferred to the Coast Guard two days later. Subsequently served as Coast Guard supply ship in Pacific until transferred to Philippines on 1 Mar 1972. Used to supply military posts and lighthouses in the Philippine archipelago.

1 TENDER: Ex-US COAST GUARD TENDER

KALINGA (ex-USCGC *Redbud*, WLB 398, ex-USNS *Redbud*, T-AKL 398) TK 89

Displacement, tons	935 standard
Dimensions, feet	180 oa × 37 × 13
Guns	Unarmed
Main engines	Diesel-electric; 1 200 bhp; 1 shaft = 13 knots

Originally US Coast Guard buoy tender (WAGL 398) built by Marine Iron & Shipbuilding Co, Duluth, Minnesota; launched on 11 Sep 1943. Transferred to US Navy on 25 Mar 1949 as AG 398; redesignated AKL 398 on 31 Mar 1949; transferred to Military Sea Transportation Service on 20 Feb 1952 (T-AKL 398); reacquired by Coast Guard on 20 Nov 1970 and transferred to Philippines on 1 Mar 1972. (Corrected from previous edition.)

3 TENDERS: Ex-US ARMY FS TYPE

BOJEADOE (ex-US Army FS 203) TK 46
LAUIS LEDGE (ex-US Army FS 185) TK 45
LIMASAWA (ex-USCGC *Nettle* WAK 169, ex-US Army FS 169) TK 79

Displacement, tons	470 standard; 811 full load
Dimensions, feet	180 oa × 23 × 10
Main engines	Diesels; 1 000 shp; 1 shaft = 11 knots

Former US Army freight and supply ships. Employed as tenders for buoys and light houses.

LAUIS LEDGE *1969, Philippine Navy*

1 TENDER: Ex-AUSTRALIAN TYPE

PEARL BANK (ex-US Army LO 4, ex-Australian MSL)

Displacement, tons	160 standard; 300 full load
Dimensions, feet	120 oa × 24·5 × 8
Main engines	Diesels (Fairbanks Morse); 240 bhp; 2 shafts = 7 knots

Originally an Australian motor stores lighter; subsequently transferred to the US Army and then to the Philippines. Employed as a lighthouse tender.

COAST AND GEODETIC SERVICE

SAMAR (ex-USS *Project*, AM 278) M 33 20 Nov 1943

Former US Navy minesweeper, similar to the *Mount Samat*. Built by Gulf Shipbuilding Corp. Transferred to the Philippines in July 1948. Subsequently adapted for surveying and now operated by the Coast & Geodetic Service.

COAST GUARD

2 PATROL BOATS

ABRA FB 83 **BUKIDNON** FB 84

Displacement, tons	40 standard
Dimensions, feet	87·5 oa × 19 × 4·75
Guns	2—20 mm AA
Main engines	Diesels (Mercedes-Benz); 2 460 bhp; 2 shafts = approx 25 knots
Complement	15 (3 officers, 12 enlisted men)

One acquired from Singapore in late 1969. *Bukidnon* built at Cavite in 1970-1971. Wood hulls and aluminium superstructure.

The Coast Guard also has 14 40-foot utility boats, all transferred from the US Coast Guard except for the *CGC 127*, a 40-foot, 11-ton craft built in the Philippines with a ferro-concrete hull.

POLAND

Administration

Commander-in-Chief of the Polish Navy:
Vice-Admiral Ludwik Janczyszyn

Chief of the Naval Staff:
Rear-Admiral Henryk Pietraszkiewicz

Diplomatic Representation

Naval, Military and Air Attaché in London:
Colonel Henryk Krzeszowski

Naval, Military and Air Attaché in Washington:
Colonel Henryk Nowaczyk

Naval, Military and Air Attaché in Moscow:
Brigadier General Waclaw Jagas

Naval, Miliatry and Air Attaché in Paris:
Colonel Marian Bugaj

Strength of the Fleet
(No details of a building programme are known)

Type	*Active*
Destroyers	4
Corvettes	2
Submarines—Patrol	4
Fast Attack Craft—Missile	12
Fast Attack Craft—Torpedo	25
Large Patrol Craft	26
Coastal Patrol Craft	20
Minesweepers—Ocean	24
Minesweeping Boats	20
LSM	23
Surveying Vessels	2
Training Ships	2
Tankers	6
TRV's	Several
Tugs	20
Icebreaker	1
TCV's	2

Prefix to Ships' Names

Polish warships are referred with the prefix ORP, for *Okrety Polska Rzeczpospolita*

Naval Aviation

There is a Fleet Air Arm of about 50 fixed-wing aircraft (mainly MiG-17 and IL-28) and helicopters.

Personnel

(a) 1974: 25 000 (2 800 officers and 22 200 men)
(b) 3 years National Service

Mercantile Marine

Lloyd's Register of Shipping:
631 vessels of 2 072 531 tons gross

Disposals

Corvettes

1973 *Czuiny, Wytrwaly, Zawziety, Zrezczny, Zwinny, Zwrotny*

Fast Attack Craft—Torpedo

1973 3 P6 class

DESTROYERS

1 Ex-SOVIET "SAM KOTLIN" CLASS

WARSZAWA 275

Displacement, tons	2 850 standard; 3 885 full load
Length, feet (*metres*)	415·0 (*126·5*) oa
Beam, feet (*metres*)	42·3 (*12·9*)
Draught, feet (*metres*)	16·1 (*4·9*)
Missile launchers	1 twin SAN-1 (Goa) aft for surface-to-air missiles
Guns	2—5·1 in dp (1 twin); 4—45 mm (quad); 4—30 mm (twin)
A/S weapons	2—16 barrelled MBU; 4 side launch DC projectors
Main engines	Geared turbines; 2 shafts; 72 000 shp
Oil fuel, tons	800
Range, miles	5 500 at 16 knots
Speed, knots	36,
Complement	285

WARSZAWA *1973, Contre Amiral M. Adam*

Transferred from the USSR to the Polish Navy in 1970.

RADAR. Air Search: Head Net C. Fire Control: Peel Group (SAN-1), Wasp Head/Sun Visor B (main armament), Egg Cup (45 mm), 2 Drum Tilt (30 mm); IFF: High Pole B.

2 Ex-SOVIET "SKORY" CLASS

GROM (ex-*Smetlivy*) 273 **WICHER** (ex-*Skory*) 274

Displacement, tons	2 600 standard; 3 500 full load
Length, feet (*metres*)	395·2 (*120·5*)
Beam, feet (*metres*)	38·9 (*11·8*)
Draught, feet (*metres*)	15·1 (*5·6*)
Guns, surface	4—5·1 in (*130 mm*), 2 twin mounts
Guns, AA	2—3·4 in (*85 mm*); 8—37 mm
A/S weapons	4 DCT
Torpedo tubes	10—21 in (*533 mm*) 2 quintuple
Mines	80 capacity
Boilers	4 high pressure
Main engines	Geared turbines; 2 shafts; 60 000 shp
Speed, knots	33
Range, miles	3 900 at 13 knots
Oil fuel, tons	700
Complement	260

Former Soviet destroyers of the first "Skory" type. *Wicher* was in fact the prototype of the class. To Poland on 15 Dec 1957 (*Grom*) and 28 June 1958 (*Wicher*).

RADAR. Air Search: Cross Bird; Surface Search: High Sieve; Fire Control: Post Lamp; Navigation: Neptune; IFF: Ski Pole.

GROM *1968*

1 BRITISH BUILT

BLYSKAWICA 271

Displacement, tons	2 144 standard; 3 383 full load
Length, feet (*metres*)	357 (*108·8*) pp; 374 (*114·0*) oa
Beam, feet (*metres*)	37 (*11·3*)
Draught, feet (*metres*)	10·2 (*3·1*)
Guns, dual purpose	8—3·9 in (*100 mm*)
Guns, AA	10—37 mm
A/S weapons	4 DCT; 22 DC and racks
Torpedo tubes	3—21 in (*533 mm*) tripled
Boilers	4 three-drum type
Main engines	Parsons geared turbines; 2 shafts; 54 000 shp
Speed, knots	39
Complement	180

BLYSKAWICA *1965, Polish Navy*

Built by J. Samuel White & Co Ltd, Cowes, Isle of Wight. Laid down on 1 Oct 1935, launched on 1 Oct 1936 and completed on 1 Oct 1937. Bows strengthened for ice navigation. Possibly now non-operational

ARMAMENT. The original armament was 7—4·7 mm AA, 4 MG, 6—21 inch tubes (tripled), 2 DCT.

RECONSTRUCTION. The ship was completely dismantled in 1958 down to the hull, and superstructure was entirely rebuilt and armament modified in 1959-60.

CORVETTES

2 Ex-SOVIET "KRONSTADT" CLASS

GROZNY 362 **NIEUGIETY** 361

Displacement, tons	310 standard; 380 full load
Dimensions, feet	170·6 × 21·5 × 9
Guns	1—3·4 in; 2—37 mm AA; 4—13 mm MG AA
Main engines	3 diesels; 3 screws; 3 300 bhp = 27 knots
Complement	65

Delivered Dec 1957.

RADAR. Surface/Navigation-Don 2; IFF: High Pole A.

ZAWZIETY (others similar) *1968*

SUBMARINES

4 Ex-USSR "WHISKY" CLASS

BIELIK 295 **ORZEL** 292
KONDOR 294 **SOKOL** 293

Displacement, tons	1 030 surface; 1 180 dived
Length, feet (*metres*)	240 (*73·2*)
Beam, feet (*metres*)	22 (*6·7*)
Draught, feet (*metres*)	15 (*4·6*)
Torpedo tubes	6—21 in (*533 mm*), 4 bow, 2 stern 18 torpedoes carried
Mines	40 mines in lieu of torpedoes
Main machinery	2 Diesels; 4 000 hp; 2 shafts Electric motors; 2 500 hp
Speed, knots	17 on surface; 15 dived
Range, miles	13 000 at 8 knots (surfaced)
Complement	60

Built in the USSR and transferred to the Polish Navy.

RADAR. Snoop Plate.

SOKOL *1971, Polish Navy*

KONDOR *1972*

LIGHT FORCES

12 SOVIET "OSA" CLASS (FAST ATTACK CRAFT—MISSILE)

Displacement, tons	165 standard; 200 full load
Dimensions, ft (*m*)	128·7 × 25·1 × 5·9 (*39·3 × 7·7 × 1·8*)
Missiles	4 launchers for SSN-2A
Guns	4—30 mm (2 twin, 1 forward, 1 aft)
Main engines	3 diesels; 13 000 bhp = 32 knots
Range, miles	800 at 25 knots
Complement	25

All pennant numbers are in the low 100 series and are carried on side-boards on the bridge.

RADAR. Search: Square Tie and Strut Curve. Fire Control: Drum Tilt.

"Osa" class No. 164 *1969*

16 Ex-SOVIET "P 6" CLASS (FAST ATTACK CRAFT—TORPEDO)

401-419 (with three gaps)

Displacement, tons	66 standard; 75 full load
Dimensions, ft (*m*)	84·2 × 20 × 6 (*25·7 × 6·1 × 1·8*)
Guns	4—25 mm AA; 8 DC
Tubes	2—21 in
Main engines	4 diesels; 4 800 bhp = 45 knots
Complement	25

Acquired from the USSR in 1957-58. Torpedo tubes removed in some. SKIN HEAD surface search and navigation radar. At least two have been converted to target craft.

No. 410 *1971, Polish Navy*

9 "WISLA" CLASS (FAST ATTACK CRAFT—TORPEDO)

Displacement, tons	70 full load
Dimensions, ft (*m*)	82·0 × 18·0 × 6·0 (*25 × 5·5 × 1·8*)
A/S weapons	4 DC
Guns	2—30 mm AA Twin
Tubes	4—21 in (*533 mm*)
Main engines	Diesels; speed 30 knots

Polish built in a continuing programme. Pennant numbers in 490 series.

WISLA *1973*

Light Forces—*continued*

4 "OKSYWIE" CLASS (LARGE PATROL CRAFT)

301 **302** **303** **304**

Displacement, tons	170 standard
Dimensions, feet	134·5 × 19·0 × 6·9
Guns	4—37 mm (2 twin)
Main engines	Diesels; speed = 20 knots

Improved versions of earlier patrol boats of the type. Depth charge racks fitted.

OKSYWIE *1972*

8 "MODIFIED OBLUZE" CLASS (LARGE PATROL CRAFT)

351 **352** **353** **354** **355** **356** **357** **358**

"OBLUZE" Class *1972, S. Breyer*

5 "OBLUZE" CLASS (LARGE PATROL CRAFT)

321 **322** **323** **324** **325**

Displacement, tons	170
Dimensions, feet	143·0 × 19·0 × 7·0
Guns	4—30 mm AA (2 twins)

Built since 1965 at Oksywie Shipyard. 351 to 355 are slightly different. Belong to WOP (coastguard).

OBLUZE (old number) *1969*

9 "GDANSK" CLASS (LARGE PATROL CRAFT)

311 **312** **313** **314** **315** **316** **317** **318** **319**

Displacement, tons	120
Dimensions, feet	124·7 × 19·2 × 5·0
Guns	2—37 mm AA
Main engines	Diesels; speed 20 knots

Built in 1960. Depth charges carried. Belong to WOP (coastguard).

GDANSK *1970*

Light Forces—*continued*

20 "K8" CLASS (COASTAL PATROL CRAFT)

KP 118 **KP 119** **KP 120** **KP 121** **KP 122** **KP 123** **KP 124** **KP 125** **KP 126** **+ 11**

Displacement, tons	60
Guns	2 MG AA (in twin mounting)
Main engines	3 motors; speed 15 knots

Small patrol boats under the jurisdiction of the WOP (coastguard). Now obsolescent.

MINE WARFARE FORCES

12 "KROGULEC" CLASS (MINESWEEPERS—OCEAN)

ORLIK 613	**KORMORAN** 616		**619**	**622**
KROGULEC 614	**CZAPLA** 617	**TUKAN** 620		**623**
JASTRAB 615	**ALABATROS** 618		**621**	**624**

Displacement, tons	500
Dimensions, feet	190·3 × 24·6 × 8·2
Guns	6—25 mm AA
Main engines	Diesels; speed = 16 knots

Flushdecked minesweepers of a new type built at the Stocznia Yard from 1963 onwards. *Jastrab* and *Orlik* commissioned in 1964.

KROGULEC *1972, S. Breyer*

12 SOVIET "T 43" CLASS (MINESWEEPERS—OCEAN)

BIZON 605	**DZIK** 604	**MORS** 610	**TUR** 602
BOBR 606	**FOKA** 609	**ROSOMAK** 607	**ZBIK** 612
DELFIN 608	**LOS** 603	**RYS** 611	**ZUBR** 601

Displacement, tons	500 standard; 610 full load
Dimensions, feet	190·2 × 28·2 × 6·9
Guns	4—37 mm AA; 4—25 mm
Main engines	2 diesels; 2 shafts; 2 000 hp = 17 knots
Complement	40

Soviet "T43" class but built in Poland at Stocznia Gdynia in 1957-62.

DELFIN *1969, Polish Navy*

20 "K 8" CLASS (MSBs)

Displacement, tons	20 approx
Dimensions, feet	54·1 × 19·0 × 5·0

Minesweeping boats built in Poland. Pennant numbers run in 800 and 900 series.

AMPHIBIOUS FORCES

23 "POLNOCNY" CLASS (LSM)

801-811 **888-899**

Displacement tons	780 standard; 1 000 full load
Dimensions, feet	225 × 27·7 × 9·8
Armament	2—18 barrelled rocket projectors 1—30 mm
Main engines	2 diesels; 5 000 bhp = 18 knots

Polish built, in Gdansk, but same as the Soviet "Polnocny" class—can carry six tanks. Of various types including Polish variations.

POLNOCNY 806 *1971*

SURVEYING VESSELS

"MOMA CLASS"

KOPERNIK

Of 1 580 tons, launched in 1971.

BALTYK

Displacement, tons	1 200
Measurements, tons	658 gross; 450 deadweight
Dimensions, feet	194·3 oa; 175·3 pp × 29·5 × 14
Main engines	Steam; 1 000 hp = 11 knots

Trawler of B-10 type. Built in 1954 in Gdansk. Converted and structure altered.

BALTYK *1968*

TRAINING SHIPS

GRYF (ex-*Zetempowiec*, ex-*Opplem*, ex-*Omsk*, ex-*Empire Contees*, ex-*Irene Oldendorf*)

Measurement, tons	1 959 gross
Dimensions, feet	282·2 × 44·2 × 18·8
Guns	2—3·9 in; 4—37 mm AA
Main engines	Steam; 1 200 hp = 10 knots

Former German "Hansa" class ship. Built by Burmeister & Wain. Launched in 1944. Taken over in 1947. Transferred to the Navy in 1949. The name was changed from *Zetempowiec* to *Gryf* in 1957. Used as a cadet training ship.

GRYF *1969*

Training Ships—*continued*

ISKRA (ex-*Pigmy*, ex-*Iskra*, ex-*St Blanc*, ex-*Vlissingen*)

Displacement, tons	560
Dimensions, feet	128 × 25 × 10
Main engines	Diesels; 250 bhp = 7·5 knots
Complement	30, plus 40 cadets

A three masted schooner with auxiliary engines. Built by Muller, Foxhol, Holland. Launched in 1917. Cadet training ship.

ISKRA *1969*

TANKERS

Z 3 **Z 8** **Z 9**

Displacement, tons approx 700

Z 5 **Z 6** **Z 7**

Lighters of 300 tons gross with diesels, converted into tankers for coastal service.

TORPEDO RECOVERY VESSELS

Some of a new class, including K 11, have been reported.

Some 20 of various classes with H pennant numbers.

ICEBREAKER

PERKUN

Displacement, tons	800
Main engines	Diesel-electric; 2 shafts; 3 500 bhp = 12 knots

Icebreaker built in 1962 by P. K. Harris & Sons, Appledore, Devon, England. Not a naval vessel but can be employed with and for the Navy.

PERKUN *1972*

DEGAUSSING VESSELS

URAN **URANIA**

Displacement, tons	254
Main engines	Speed = 8 knots

Degaussing vessel of the British MMS minesweeper 11 type, classed as auxiliaries.

Being replaced by a more modern class of which SD 12 is a member

PORTUGAL

Administration

Chief of Naval Staff:
Admiral J. B. Pinheiro de Azevedo

Diplomatic Representation

Naval Attaché in London:
Captain C. A. Salgueiro Rego

Naval Attaché in Washington:
Captain Jose L. Ferreira Lamas

Naval Attaché in Paris:
Commander Silvano J. Freitas-Braneo

Personnel

(a) 1971: 18 300 (1 700 officers and 16 600 men) including marines
1972: 19 000 (1 800 officers and 17 200 men) including marines
1973: 19 000 (1 800 officers and 17 200 men) including marines
1974: 19 000 (1 800 officers and 17 200 men) including marines
(b) 4 years National Service

Strength of the Fleet

Type	*Active*	*Building*
Frigates	14	4
Corvettes	15	—
Submarines-Patrol	4	—
Large Patrol Craft	11	—
Coastal Patrol Craft	25	—
Minesweepers-Coastal	9	—
LCT	6	—
LCM	36	—
LCA	22	—
Survey Ships	7	—
Replenishment Tanker	1	—
Supply Ship	1	—
Sail Training Ship	1	—
Depot Ship	1	—
Fishery Protection Vessels	4	—
Ocean Tug	1	—
Harbour Tugs	2	—

Prefix to Ships' Names

NRP

Disposals

Frigates

1970 *Francisco de Almeida, Pacheco Pereira*
1971 *Alvares Cabral, Vasco da Gama*

Corvette

1971 *Cacheu*

Naval Bases

Main Base: Lisbon.
Dockyard: Arsenal do Alfeite.

Maritime Reconnaissance Aircraft

Whilst there are no aircraft belonging to the Navy, P2V Neptunes of the Portuguese Air Force are placed under naval operational control for specific maritime operations.

Mercantile Marine

Lloyd's Register of Shipping:
438 vessels of 1 271 815 tons gross

FRIGATES

4 "COMANDANTE JOÃO BELO" CLASS

Name	*No.*	*Builders*	*Laid down*	*Launched*	*Completed*
COMANDANTE HERMENEGILDO CAPELO	F 481	At et Ch de Nantes	13 May 1966	29 Nov 1966	26 Apr 1968
COMANDANTE JOÃO BELO	F 480	At et Ch de Nantes	6 Sep 1965	22 Mar 1966	1 July 1967
COMANDANTE ROBERTO IVENS	F 482	At et Ch de Nantes	13 Dec 1966	8 Aug 1967	23 Nov 1968
COMANDANTE SACADURA CABRAL	F 483	At et Ch de Nantes	18 Aug 1967	15 Mar 1968	25 July 1969

Displacement, tons	1 990 standard; 2 230 full load
Length, feet (*metres*)	321·5 (*98*) pp; 338 (*103·0*) oa
Beam, feet (*metresa*)	37·7 (*11·5*)
Draught, feet (*metres*)	14·5 (*4·42*)
Guns	3—3·9 in (*100 mm*) AA single; 2—40 mm AA
A/S weapons	1—12 in quadruple mortar
Torpedo tubes	6—21·7 in (*550 mm*) ASM, 2 triple
Main engines	SEMT-Pielstick diesels; 2 shafts; 18 760 bhp
Speed, knots	25
Range, miles	4 500 at 15 knots; 2 300 at 25 knots
Complement	200 (14 officers, 186 men)

COMANDANTE ROBERTO IVENS *1970, Portuguese Navy*

CONSTRUCTION. The prefabricated construction of these frigates was begun on 1 Oct 1964 at the Ateliers et Chantiers de Nantes, France.

DESIGN. They are similar to the French "Commandant Riviere" type except for the 30 mm AA guns which were replaced by 40 mm AA guns.

RADAR. Search: DRBV 22. Tactical: Probably S Band. Fire Control: DRBC 32 radar director.

COMANDANTE JOAO BELO *Class*

COMANDANTE SACADURA CABRAL *1972, Portuguese Navy*

Frigates—*continued*

3 "ALMIRANTE PEREIRA DA SILVA" CLASS

Name	*No.*	*Builders*	*Laid down*	*Launched*	*Completed*
ALMIRANTE GAGO COUTINHO	F 473 (ex-US DE 1042)	Estaleiros Navais Lisnave, Lisbon	2 Dec 1963	13 Aug 1965	29 Nov 1967
ALMIRANTE MAGALHÃES CORREA	F 474 (ex-US DE 1046)	Estaleiros Navais de Viana do Castelo	30 Aug 1965	26 Apr 1966	4 Nov 1968
ALMIRANTE PEREIRA DA SILVA	F 472 (ex-US DE 1039)	Estaleiros Navais Lisnave, Lisbon	14 June 1962	2 Dec 1963	20 Dec 1966

Displacement, tons	1 450 standard; 1 914 full load
Length, feet (*metres*)	314·6 (*95·9*)
Beam, feet (*metres*)	36·68 (*11·18*)
Draught, feet (*metres*)	14 (*4·3*) hull; 17·5 (*5·33*) max
Guns	4—3 in (*76 mm*) 50 cal. dp;
A/S weapons	2 Bofors 4-barrelled mortars 2 DC throwers
Torpedo tubes	6 (2 triple) for A/S torpedoes
Main engines	De Laval dr geared turbines; 1 shaft; 20 000 shp
Speed, knots	27 designed
Boilers	2 Foster Wheeler, 300 psi, 850°F
Range, miles	3 220 at 15 knots
Oil fuel, tons	400
Complement	166 (12 officers, 154 men)

CONSTRUCTION. The prefabrication of *Almirante Pereira da Silva* and *Almirante Gago Coutinho* was begun in 1961 at Lisnave (formerly Navalis Shipyard, Lisbon) and of *Almirante Magalhães Correa* in 1962.

RADAR. Search: SPS 6. Tactical: X Band. Surface warning and navigation Air surveillance: S band. Extensive EW.

DESIGN. Similar to the United States destroyer escorts of the "Dealey" class, but modified to suit Portuguese requirements.

SONAR. Probably DUBV-43.

ALMIRANTE GAGO COUTINHO *1973, Portuguese Navy*

ALMIRANTE PEREIRA DA SILVA *Class*

6+4 "JOAO COUTINHO" CLASS

Name		*Builders*	*Launched*	*Completed*
ANTONIO ENES	F 471	Empresa Nacional Bazan, Spain	16 Aug 1969	18 June 1971
AUGUSTO DE CASTILHO	F 484	Empresa Nacional Bazan, Spain	4 July 1969	14 Nov 1970
GENERAL PEREIRA D'ECA	F 477	Blohm and Voss A.G., Hamburg, Germany	26 July 1969	10 Oct 1970
HONORIO BARRETO	F 485	Empresa Nacional Bazan, Spain	11 Apr 1970	15 Apr 1971
JACINTO CANDIDO	F 476	Blohm and Voss A.G., Hamburg, Germany	16 June 1969	16 June 1970
JOÃO COUTINHO	F 475	Blohm and Voss A.G., Hamburg, Germany	2 May 1969	7 Mar 1970
JOÃO ROBY		Empresa Nacional Bazan, Spain	—	—
OLIVEIRA E CARMO		Empresa Nacional Bazan, Spain	—	—
AFONSO CERQUEIRA		Empresa Nacional Bazan, Spain	—	—
BAPTISTA DE ANDRADE		Empresa Nacional Bazan, Spain	—	—

Displacement, tons	1 203 standard; 1 380 full load
Length, feet (*metres*)	227·5 (*84·6*)
Beam, feet (*metres*)	33·8 (*10·3*)
Draught, feet (*metres*)	10·0 (*3·07*); 11·8 (*3·6*) deep
Guns	2—3 in (*76 mm*) dp; 2—40 mm AA
A/S weapons	1 Hedgehog; 2 DC throwers; 2 DC tracks
Main engines	2 OEW 12 cyl. Pielstick diesels; 10 560 bhp
Speed, knots	24·4
Range, miles	5 900 at 18 knots
Complement	100 (9 officers, 91 men) plus 34 marine detachment

JOÃO COUTINHO *1971, Portuguese Navy*

RADAR. Equipped with SPS 10 search radar. S-Band air surveillance and X-band surface warning and navigation.

NEW CONSTRUCTION. The four corvettes under construction at Empresa Nacional Bazan, Spain, will carry one French 3·9 inch gun in place of the two 3 inch above and will have Plessey AWS-2 air surveillance radar.

JOÃO COUTINHO *Class*

Frigates—*continued*

PERO ESCOBAR F 335

Displacement, tons	1 270 standard; 1 390 full load
Length, feet (*metres*)	306·7 (*93·5*) wl; 321·5 (*98·0*) oa
Beam, feet (*metres*)	35·5 (*10·8*)
Draught, feet (*metres*)	10 (*3·0*); 12·2 (*3·7*) deep
Guns	4—3 in (*76 mm*) 50 cal. dp
A/S weapons	2 "Squid" triple DC mortars
Torpedo tubes	6 (2 triple) for A/S torpedoes
Main engines	2 Ansaldo-Genova sr geared turbines; 2 shafts; 24 000 shp
Speed, knots	32·6 max
Boilers	2 Ansoldo-Foster Wheeler "D" 32 *kg/cm²*, 400°C
Complement	165 (10 officers, 155 men)

Built for the Portuguese Navy by Navalmeccanica, Castellammare di Stabia, Italy. Laid down on 9 Jan 1955. Launched on 25 Sep 1955. Completed on 30 June 1957.

RADAR. Search S Band air surveillance. Fire Control: Elsag X Band.

PEDRO ESCOBAR *1973, Portuguese Navy*

MODERNISATION in 1970-71 included new guns, sonar and A/S torpedo tubes similar to those in the "Almirante Pereira da Silva" class. Armament before modernisation: 2 single 3 inch guns, 1 twin 40 mm AA, 2 twin 20 mm AA, 3—21 inch torpedo tubes.

PERO ESCOBAR

CORVETTES

3 PORTUGUESE BUILT "MAIO" CLASS

Name	*No.*	*Builders*	*Launched*	*Completed*
BOAVISTA	P 592	Est Nav do Mondego	10 July 1956	17 May 1957
BRAVA	P 590	EN de Viana do Castelo	2 May 1956	27 Dec 1956
SANTA LUZIA	P 594	Arsenal do Alfeite	17 Jan 1957	24 Oct 1958

Displacement, tons	366 standard; 400 full load
Dimensions, feet	170 pp; 173·8 oa × 23 × 10
Guns	2—40 mm AA; 2—20 mm AA
A/S weapons	1 Hedgehog, 4 DCT; 2 depth charge racks
Main engines	4 SEMT-Pielstick diesels (4-stroke, 14 cylinder V); 2 shafts; 3 500 bhp = 19 knots
Oil fuel, tons	45
Range, miles	4 500 at 18 knots
Complement	62 (5 officers, 57 men)

Built in Portugal under the US off-shore procurement programme in 1956-57. Of all-welded construction.

FOGO (Maio class similar) *1972, Portuguese Navy*

2 FRENCH BUILT "MAIO" CLASS

Name	*No.*	*Builders*	*Launched*
MAIO (ex-*Funchal*, ex-P 4)	P 587	Dubigeon, Nantes	27 Sep 1954
S NICOLAU (ex-P 8)	P 589	Normand (Le Havre)	7 June 1955

Displacement, tons	366 standard; 400 full load
Dimensions, feet	170 pp; 173·7 oa × 23 × 10
Guns	2—40 mm AA; 2—20 mm AA
A/S weapons	1 Hedgehog; 4 DCT; 2 depth charge racks
Main engines	4 SEMT-Pielstick diesels; 2 shafts; 3 240 bhp = 18 knots
Range, miles	4 500 at 18 knots
Complement	62 (5 officers, 57 men)

Of PC design, but built in France as a US offshore procurement order under the Mutual Defense Assistance Program in 1954-55. Fitted with two mine rails.

S. NICOLAU *1973, Portuguese Navy*

10 "CACINE" CLASS

CACINE	P 1140	**GEBA**	P 1145	**ROVUMA**	P 1143
CUNENE	P 1141	**LIMPOPO**	P 1160	**SAVE**	P 1161
CUANZA	P 1144	**MANDOVI**	P 1142	**ZAIRE**	P 1146
				ZAMBEZE	P 1147

Displacement, tons	292·5 standard; 310 full load
Dimensions, feet	144·0 oa × 25·2 × 7·1
Guns	2—40 mm AA 1—32 barrelled rocket launcher 37 mm
Main engines	2 Maybach diesels; 2 000 bhp = 20 knots
Range, miles	4 400 at 12 knots
Complement	33 (3 officers, 30 men)

Cacine, Cunene Mandovi, Rovuma, Limpopo and *Save* were built in Arsenal do Alfeita, the other four in Estaleiros Navais do Mendogo in 1969-72.

CACINE *1973, Portuguese Navy*

SUBMARINES

4 "ALBACORA" CLASS (FRENCH "DAPHNE" CLASS)

Name	No.	Builders	Laid down	Launched	Completed
ALBACORA	S 163	Dubigeon-Normandie	6 Sep 1965	13 Oct 1966	1 Oct 1967
BARRACUDA	S 164	Dubigeon-Normandie	19 Oct 1965	24 Apr 1967	4 May 1968
CACHALOTE	S 165	Dubigeon-Normandie	27 Oct 1966	16 Feb 1968	25 Jan 1969
DELFIN	S 166	Dubigeon-Normandie	14 May 1967	23 Sep 1968	1 Oct 1969

BARRACUDA *1970, Captain Aluino Martins da Silva*

Displacement, tons	700 standard; 869 surface; 1 043 submerged
Length, feet (*metres*)	189·6 (*57·8*)
Beam, feet (*metres*)	22·3 (*6·8*)
Draught, feet (*metres*)	15·1 (*4·6*)
Torpedo tubes	12—21·7 in (*550 mm*); 8 bow, 4 stern
Main machinery	SEMT-Pielstick diesels, 1 300 bhp Electric motors; 450 kW, 1 600 hp; 2 shafts
Speed, knots	13·2 on surface and 16 submerged
Range, miles	2 710 at 12·5 knots on surface; 2 130 at 10 knots snorting
Oil fuel, tons	90
Complement	50 (5 officers; 45 men)

DELFIN *1972, Portuguese Navy*

The prefabricated construction of these submarines was begun during 1 Oct 1964 to 6 Sep 1965 at the Dubigeon-Normandie Shipyard, Nantes, France. They are basically similar to the French "Daphne" type, but slightly modified to suit Portuguese requirements.

LIGHT FORCES

10 "ARGOS" CLASS (LARGE PATROL CRAFT)

ARGOS	P 372	**DRAGÃO**	P 374	**LIRA**	P 361
CASSIOPEIA	P 373	**ESCORPIÃO**	P 375	**ORION**	P 362
CENTAURO	P 1130	**HIDRA**	P 376	**PEGASO**	P 379
				SAGITARIO	P 1131

Displacement, tons	180 standard; 210 full load
Dimensions, feet	131·2 pp; 136·8 oa × 20·5 × 7
Guns	2—40 mm AA
Main engines	2 Maybach diesels; 1 200 bhp = 17 knots
Oil fuel, tons	16
Complement	24 (2 officers, 22 men)

Six built by Arsenal do Alfeite, Lisbon, and four by Estaleiros Navais de Viana do Castelo. All completed June 1963 to Sep 1965. Named after constellations.

DRAGÃO *1973, Portuguese Navy*

2 "DOM ALEIXO" CLASS (COASTAL PATROL CRAFT)

DOM ALEIXO P 1148 **DOM JEREMIAS** P 1149

Displacement, tons	62·6 standard; 67·7 full load
Dimensions, feet	82·1 oa × 17·0 × 5·2
Gun	1—120 mm AA
Main engines	2 Cummins diesels; 1 270 bhp = 16 knots
Complement	10 (2 officers, 8 men)

Dom Aleixo was commissioned on 7 Dec 1967 and *Dom Jeremias* on 22 Dec 1967.

DOM JEREMIAS *1973, Portuguese Navy*

3 "ALVOR" CLASS (COASTAL PATROL CRAFT)

ALBUFEIRA P 1157 **ALJEZUR** P 1158 **ALVOR** P 1156

Displacement, tons	35·7 full load
Dimensions, feet	68 oa × 18 × 5·1
Gun	1—20 mm AA
Main engines	2 Cummins diesels; 235 bhp = 12·3 knots
Complement	7

They were all built at Arsenal do Alfeite and commissioned in 1967-86.

ALVOR *1973, Portuguese Navy*

SABRE P 1138 (RIVER PATROL CRAFT)

Displacement, tons	122 standard; 140 full load
Dimensions, feet (*metres*)	99·9 × 21·6 × 2·6 (27·7 × 6·6 × 0·8)
Guns	2—20 mm Oerlikon
Main engines	2 Daimler Benz Schottel; 244 hp = 10 knots
Complement	7 (1 officer, 6 men)

Light Forces—*continued*

11 "BELLATRIX" CLASS (COASTAL PATROL CRAFT)

ALDEBARAN	P 1152	**ESPIGA**	P 366	**PROCION**	P 1153
ALTAIR	P 377	**FOMALHAUT**	P 367	**RIGEL**	P 378
ARCTURUS	P 1151	**POLLUX**	P 368	**SIRIUS**	P 1154
BELLATRIX	P 363			**VEGA**	P 1155

Displacement, tons	23 light; 27·6 full load
Dimensions, feet	62·8 wl; 68·0 oa × 15·2 × 4·0
Gun	1—20 mm Oerlikon AA
Main engines	2 Cummins diesels; 450 bhp = 15 knots
Complement	7 (1 officer, 6 men)

The first batch was completed in 1961-62 in Germany by Beyerische Schiffbaugesellschaft and the last five (*Arcturus, Aldebaran* and *Procion*, commissioned on 17 May 1968, *Sirius* and *Vega*) were built in Arsenal do Alfeite, Lisbon.

ARCTURUS *1972, Portuguese Navy*

6 "JUPITER" CLASS (COASTAL PATROL CRAFT)

JUPITER	P 1132	**MERCURIO**	P 1135	**URANO**	P 1137
MARTE	P 1134	**SATURNO**	P 1136	**VENUS**	P 1133

Displacement, tons	32 standard; 43·5 full load
Dimensions, feet	69·0 oa × 16·5 × 4·3
Guns	1—20 mm Oerlikon AA
Main engines	2 Cummins diesels; 1 270 bhp = 20 knots
Complement	8 (1 officer, 7 men)

Built during 1964-65. All commissioned between 10 Mar 1965 and 12 Aug 1965.

JUPITER *Portuguese Navy*

CASTOR P 580 (COASTAL PATROL CRAFT)

Displacement, tons	22
Dimensions, feet	53·5 wl; 58 oa × 13·1 × 3·3
Gun	1—20 mm Oerlikon AA
Main engines	2 Cummins diesels; 500 bhp = 15 knots
Complement	7

Built at the Estalerios Navais do Mondego and commissioned on 3 Feb 1964.

ANTARES P 360 REGULUS P 369 (COASTAL PATROL CRAFT)

Displacement, tons	18
Dimensions, feet	56 oa; 51·5 wl × 15·2 × 4
Gun	1—20 mm Oerlikon
Main engines	2 Cummins diesels; 2 shafts; 460 bhp = 18·2 knots
Complement	7

Antares was built in 1959 by James Taylor (Shipbuilders) Ltd, Shoreham, Sussex, England. The hull is of Deborine resinglass fibre moulding. *Regulus* was built in Portugal by Navalis Shipyard, the hull being imported from England. Completed on 27 Jan 1962.

RIO MINHO P 370 (COASTAL PATROL CRAFT)

Displacement, tons	14
Dimensions, feet	49·2 × 10·5 × 2·3
Guns	2 light MG
Main engines	2 Alfa Romeo; 130 bhp = 9 knots
Complement	7

Built at Arsenal do Alfeite in 1955-57 for the River Minho on the Spanish border.

MINE WARFARE FORCES

4 "S. ROQUE" CLASS (MINESWEEPERS—COASTAL)

Name	*No.*	*Launched*	*Completed*
LAGOA	M 403	15 Sep 1955	10 Aug 1956
RIBEIRA GRANDE	M 402	14 Oct 1955	8 Feb 1957
ROSARIO	M 404	29 Nov 1955	8 Feb 1956
S ROQUE	M 401	15 Sep 1955	6 June 1956

Displacement, tons	394·4 standard; 451·9 full load
Dimensions, feet	140·0 pp; 152·0 oa × 28·8 × 7·0
Guns	2—20 mm AA (twin mount)
Main engines	2 Mirrlees diesels; 2 shafts; 2 500 bhp = 15 knots
Complement	47 (4 officers, 43 men)

Similar to British "Ton" class coastal minesweepers, but built in Portugal. All laid down at CUF Shipyard, Lisbon, on 7 Sep 1954, under the OSP-MAP. *Lagoa* and *S Roque* were financed by USA and the other two by Portugal.
40 mm AA gun removed 1972.

LAGOA (Before change of armament) *1972, Portuguese Navy*

5 "PONTA DELGADA" CLASS (MINESWEEPERS—COASTAL)

HORTA	(ex-*AMS* 61)	M 406
LAJES	(ex-*AMS* 146)	M 411
SANTA CRUZ	(ex-*AMS* 92)	M 409
VELAS	(ex-*AMS* 145)	M 410
VILA DO PORTO	(ex-*AMS* 91)	M 408

Displacement, tons	338 standard; 370 full load
Dimensions, feet	138·0 pp; 144·0 oa × 27·0 × 8·0
Guns	2—20 mm AA (twin mount)
Main engines	GM diesels; 900 bhp = 13 knots
Range, miles	1 800 at 13 knots
Complement	40 (4 officers, 36 men)

Of wooden and non-magnetic construction. Transferred by USA in 1954-55.

HORTA *1971, Portuguese Navy*

FISHERY PROTECTION VESSELS

4 "AZEVIA" CLASS

AZEVIA P595 **BICUDA** P596 **CORVINA** P 597 **DOURADA** P598

Displacement, tons	230 standard; 275 full load
Dimensions, feet	134·5 pp; 139·8 oa × 21·3 × 7·0
Guns	2—20 mm AA
Main engines	2 Sulzer 7-cyl 2-stroke diesels except first pair; 2 MAN 10-cyl 4-stroke diesels; 2 shafts; 2 400 bhp = 17 knots
Oil fuel, tons	25
Range, miles	2 250 at 12·8 knots; 1 080 at 17·3 knots
Complement	30 (2 officers, 28 men)

All launched in 1942-42.

AZEVIA ***1968, Portuguese Navy***

AMPHIBIOUS FORCES

2 "BOMBARDA" CLASS LGD (LCT)

ALABARDA LDG 202 **BOMBARDA** LDG 201 (ex-105)

Displacement, tons 510 standard; 652 full load
Dimensions, feet 184·3 × 38·7 × 6·2
(*metres*) (*56·2* × *11·8* × *1·9*)
Main engines 2 Maybach-Mercedes Benz diesels; 910 hp = 9·5 knots
Complement 20 (2 officers, 18 men)

BOMBARDA *1970, Portuguese Navy*

4 "ALFANGE" CLASS LDG (LCT)

ALFANGE LDG 101 **CIMITARRA** LDG 103
ARIETE LDG 102 **MONTANEE** LDG 104

Displacement, tons 500
Dimensions, feet Length: 187
Main engines 2 diesels; 1 000 bhp
Complement 20

Landing craft similar to the LCT (4) type built at the Estalerios Navias do Mondego and commissioned during 1965.

ALFANGE *1968· Portuguese Navy*

17 LDM 400 CLASS (LCM)

LDM 401	**LDM 404**	**LDM 407**	**LDM 410**	**LDM 413**
LDM 402	**LDM 405**	**LDM 408**	**LDM 411**	**LDM 414**
LDM 403	**LDM 406**	**LDM 409**	**LDM 412**	**LDM 415**
				LDM 416
				LDM 417

Last of class commissioned 17 Aug 1973.

2 LDM 300 CLASS (LCM)

LDM 304 **LDM 309**

1 LDM 200 CLASS (LCM)

LDM 204

16 LDM 100 CLASS (LCM)

LDM 101	**LDM 105**	**LDM 108**	**LDM 111**	**LDM 115**
LDM 102	**LDM 106**	**LDM 109**	**LDM 112**	**LDM 116**
	LDM 107	**LDM 110**	**LDM 113**	**LDM 117**
			LDM 114	**LDM 118**

Displacement, tons 50 full load
Dimensions, feet Length: 50 feet
Main engines 2 diesels; 450 bhp

The above LCM type landing craft were commissioned in 1964 to 1966 setting up four classes in LDM 100, 200, 300 and 400 series as above. All built at the Estaleiros Navias do Mondego.

3 LDP 300 (Ex-LD) CLASS (LCA)

LDP 301 **LDP 302** **LDP 303**

16 LDP 200 CLASS (LCA)

LDP 201	**LDP 203**	**LDP 206**	**LDP 209**	**LDP 212**	**LDP 215**
	LDP 204	**LDP 207**	**LDP 210**	**LDP 213**	**LDP 216**
	LDP 205	**LDP 208**	**LDP 211**	**LDP 214**	**LDP 217**

Thirteen LDP 200 class were commissioned in 1965-67, four in Jan-Feb 1969.

3 LDP 100 (Ex-LD) CLASS (LCA)

LDP 105 **LDP 107** **LDP 108**

Displacement, tons 12 light; 18 full load
Dimensions, feet Length: 46 oa
Main engines 2 diesels; 180 bhp

Built at the Estaleiros Navais do Mondego and commissioned on 22 Feb 1963 (LDP 105), 1964 (LDP 107, 108).

SURVEY SHIPS

AFONSO DE ALBUQUERQUE A 526
(ex-HMS *Dalrymple*, ex-*Luce Bay*, ex-*Loch Class*)

Displacement, tons 1 590 standard; 2 230 full load
Length, feet (*metres*) 286·0 (*87·2*) pp; 307·0 (*93·6*) oa
Beam, feet (*metres*) 38·5 (*11·7*)
Draught, feet (*metres*) 14·2 (*4·3*)
Main engines 4-cylinder triple expansion; 2 shafts; 5 500 ihp
Speed, knots 19·5
Boilers 2 Admiralty 3-drum type
Range, miles 7 055 at 9·1 knots
Complement 109 (9 officers, 100 men)

Modified "Bay" class frigate. Built by Wm. Pickersgill & Sons Ltd, Sunderland, but completed at HM Dockyard Devonport. Laid down on 29 Apr 1944. Launched on 12 Apr 1945, completed on 10 Feb 1949. Equipped with radar and sonar. Purchased from Great Britain in Apr 1966. Main machinery by George Clark Ltd. Sunderland. Power at 220 volts DC from two 120 kw turbogenerators and two 150 kw diesel generators.

AFONSO DE ALBUQUERQUE *1970, Portuguese Navy*

AFONSO DE ALBUQUERQUE

1 Ex-US "KELLAR" CLASS

ALMEIDA CARVALHO (ex-USNS *Kellar*, T-AGS 25)

Displacement, tons 1 200 standard; 1 400 full load
Dimensions, feet 191·5 wl; 109·0 oa × 39·0 × 15·0
Main engines Diesel-electric; 1 shaft; 1 200 bp = 15 knots
Complement 30 (5 officers, 25 men)

Laid down on 20 Nov 1962, launched on 30 July 1964 and completed on 31 Jan 1969. On loan from the US Navy since 21 Jan 1972.

1 Ex-BRITISH "BANGOR" CLASS FLEET MINESWEEPER

ALMIRANTE LACERDA (ex-*Caraquet*) A 525

Displacement, tons 672 standard; 830 full load
Dimensions, feet 171·5 pp; 180·0 oa × 28·5 × 9·5 max
Guns 1—3 in; 2—20 mm AA
Main engines Triple expansion; 2 shafts; 2 400 ihp = 16 knots
Boilers 2, of 3-drum small-tube type
Oil fuel, tons 160
Complement 49 (7 officers, 42 men)

Former British fleet minesweeper of the "Bangor" class, steam type. Built in Canada, launched on 2 June 1941, and purchased from Great Britain in 1946. Working off Mozambique.

Survey Ships—*continued*

1 "PEDRO NUNES" CLASS

PEDRO NUNES A 528

Displacement, tons	1 162 standard; 1 217 full load
Dimensions, feet	223·0 pp; 234·3 oa × 32·8 × 10·2
Guns	1—4·7 in, 50 cal; 4—20 mm AA (see Notes)
Main engines	2 sets MAN 8 cyl diesels; 2 400 bhp = 16·5 knots
Oil fuel, tons	110 normal; 126 max
Range, miles	6 400 at 13·4 knots
Complement	48 (7 officers, 41 men)

Built as a second class sloop (*aviso de segundo classe*) at Lisbon Naval Yard. Laid down on 5 Nov 1931, launched on 17 Mar 1934 and completed on 11 Apr 1935. Converted into a survey ship (*navio hidrografico*) in 1956, when the forward 4·7 inch gun was removed. Working off Guinea. Sister ship *Joao de Lisboa* (ex-*Infante D. Henrique*), A 5200, was discarded on 17 Aug 1966.

PEDRO NUNES *1968, Portuguese Navy*

1 Ex-BRITISH "FLOWER" CLASS CORVETTE

CARVALHO ARAUJO (ex-*Terje Ten* ex-*Commandant Drogou*, ex-*Chrysanthemum*) A524

Displacement, tons	1 020 standard; 1 340 full load
Dimensions, feet	190 pp; 205 oa × 33 × 16·5
Guns	1—3 inch; 4—20 mm AA
Main engines	Triple expansion; 2 750 ihp = 16 knots
Boilers	2 cylindrical
Oil fuel, tons	288
Complement	49 (7 officers, 42 men)

Former British "Flower" class corvette. Built by Harland & Wolff Ltd, Belfast. Laid down on 17 Feb 1940, launched on 11 Apr 1941, completed on 26 Jan 1942. Served in the French Navy during the Second World War. Sold out of the service after hostilities. Purchased by Portugal from the Hector Whaling Company, at Capetown, in Mar 1959, and equipped as a survey ship to replace the former *Carvalho Araujo* (ex-British "Flower" class minesweeping sloop *Jonquil*). Working off Angola and Sao Tomé.

CRUZEIRO DO SUL (ex-*Giroflée*)

Displacement, tons	100 standard
Dimensions, feet	93·2 × 17·8 × 8
Main engines	2 Gleenifer diesels; 320 bhp = 12 knots max
Range, miles	2 000 at 10 knots (economical speed)
Complement	8 (1 officer, 7 men)

Launched 1935.

MIRA (ex-*Formalhaut*, ex-*Arrabida*)

Displacement, tons	30 standard
Dimensions, feet	62·9 × 15·2 × 4
Main engines	3 Perkins diesels; 300 bhp = 15 knots max
Range, miles	650 at 8 knots (economical speed)
Complement	6 men

Launched 1961.

SERVICE FORCES

SAO GABRIEL A 5206 (REPLENISHMENT TANKER)

Displacement, tons	9 000 standard; 14 200 full load
Measurement, tons	9 854 gross; 9 000 deadweight
Dimensions, feet	452·8 pp 479·0; oa × 59·8 × 26·2
Main engines	1 Pametrada-geared turbine; 1 shaft; 9 500 shp= 17 knots
Boilers	2
Range, miles	6 000 at 15 knots
Complement	98 (10 officers, 88 men)

Built at Estaleiros de Viana do Castelo. Commissioned on 27 Mar 1963.

SAO GABRIEL *1973, Portuguese Navy*

SAM BRAS A 523 (FLEET SUPPLY SHIP)

Displacement, tons	5 766 standard; 6 374 full load
Dimensions, feet	333·1 pp; 356·8 oa × 47·3 × 16·5
Guns	1—3 in (*76 mm*); 2—40 mm; 2—20 mm
Main engines	B & W 2-stroke diesel; 1 shaft; 2,820 bhp = 12 knots
Oil fuel, tons	568
Range, miles	11 000 at 12 knots
Complement	100 (10 officers, 90 men)

Built at Arsenal do Alfeite. Laid down on 22 Feb 1941. Launched on 17 Mar 1942. Former fleet oiler converted to logistic ship and armed as above in Arsenal do Alfeite.

SAM BRAS *1971, Portuguese Navy*

SAGRES (ex-*Guanabara*, ex-*Albert Leo Schlageter*) A 520 (TRAINING SHIP)

Displacement, tons	1 725 standard; 1 869 full load
Dimensions, feet	293·5 oa × 39·3 × 17·0
Main engines	2 MAN auxiliary diesels; 1 shaft; 750 bhp = 10 knots
Oil fuel, tons	52
Range, miles	3 500 at 6·5 knots
Complement	153 (10 officers, 143 men)

Former German sail training ship. Built by Blohm & Voss, Hamburg. Launched in June 1937 and completed on 1 Feb 1938. Sister of US Coast Guard training ship *Eagle* (ex-German *Horst Wessel*). Taken by USA as a reparation after the Second World War in 1945 and sold to Brazil in 1948. Purchased from Brazil and commissioned in the Portuguese Navy on 2 Feb 1972 at Rio de Janeiro and renamed *Sagres*. Sail area 20 793 sq ft. Height of mast 142 ft.

SAGRES *1973, Portuguese Navy*

DEPOT SHIP

SANTO ANDRÉ (ex-*Sagres*, ex-*Flores*, ex-*Max*, ex-*Rickmer Rickmers*) A 5207

Displacement, tons	3 385 standard; 3 866 full load (officially revised figures)
Dimensions, feet	263·5 × 40·3 × 19·0
Guns	4—47 mm saluting
Main engines	2 Krupp diesels; 2 shafts; 700 bhp = 8 knots

Former German sailing vessel. Built at Bremerhaven. Launched in 1896. Captured during the First World War. Re-rigged as a barque and adapted as a naval training ship during 1924-27. Auxiliary motors were fitted in 1931. Reclassified as a depot ship and renamed *Santo André* 31 Jan 1962. Replaced on 8 Feb 1962 by the *Sagres*.

TUGS

SCHULTZ XAVIER (OCEAN TUG)

Displacement, tons	900
Main engines	2 Diesels; 2 shafts; 2 400 hp = 14·5 knots
Range, miles	3 000 at 12·5 knots

A dual purpose ocean tug and buoy tender ordered late in 1968 from the Alfeite Naval Yard. Commissioned 14 July 1972.

2 HARBOUR TUGS

RB 1 (ex-ST 1994) **RB 2** (ex-ST 1996)

Transferred from US Army 1961/62.

QATAR

Now possesses an expanding Naval Force, generally described as "Coastguard". The geographical position of the state, dividing the Persian Gulf and covering Bahrein, gives this force added importance.

Mercantile Marine

Lloyd's Register of Shipping:
3 vessels of 803 tons gross

6 VOSPER-THORNYCROFT 103ft TYPE

(LARGE PATROL CRAFT)

Displacement, tons	120
Dimensions, feet	103·7 pp; 109·7 oa × 21 × 5·5
Guns	2—40 mm
Main engines	2 Diesels; 4 000 hp = 27 knots
Complement	25

Ordered in 1972-73. Completion probably 1975-76.

2 75ft (COASTAL PATROL CRAFT)

Length, feet	75
Guns	2—20 mm
Main engines	2 Diesels; 1 420 hp

Built by Whittingham and Mitchell, Chertsey 1969.

3 45 ft (COASTAL PATROL CRAFT)

STANDARD VOSPER/KEITH NELSON TYPE

ROMANIA

Commander in Chief of the Navy:
Rear Admiral Sebastian Ulmeanu

Diplomatic Representation

Naval Attaché in London:
Captain 1st Rank A. A. Dusa

Naval, Military and Air Attaché in Washington:
Colonel Nicolae Gheorghe Plesa

Strength of the Fleet

(No building programme known).

Type	*Active*
Corvettes	6
Fast Attack Craft (Missile)	6
Fast Attack Craft (Torpedo)	12
Coastal Patrol Craft	10
Minesweepers Coastal	4
Minesweepers Inshore (many non-operational)	22
MSBs	8
Training Ships	2
Tugs	4

(other unconfirmed vessels listed at end of section).

Personnel

(a) 1974: 7 500 officers and ratings
(b) 2 years National Service

Mercantile Marine

Lloyd's Register of Shipping:
96 vessels of 474 497 tons gross

CORVETTES

3 Ex-USSR "POTI" CLASS

V 31 **V 32** **V 33**

Displacement, tons	550 standard; 650 full load
Dimensions, feet (*m*)	195·2 × 26·2 × 9·2 (*59·5 × 8 × 2·8*)
Guns	2—57 mm AA (1 twin mounting)
Tubes	4—16 in anti-submarine
A/S weapons	2—12 barrelled rocket launchers
Main engines	2 gas turbines; 2 diesels; 4 shafts; total 20 000 hp = 28 knots

Transferred from the USSR in 1970.

3 Ex-USSR "KRONSTADT" CLASS

V-1 **V-2** **V-3**

Displacement, tons	310 standard; 380 full load
Dimensions, ft (*m*)	170·6 × 21·5 × 9 (*52 × 6·5 × 2·7*)
Guns	1—3·4 in dual purpose forward; 2—37 mm AA single aft; 4—25 mm in twin mounts
A/S weapons	2 DC throwers; 2 depth charge racks
Main engines	3 diesels; 3 shafts; 3 300 bhp = 24 knots
Range, miles	1 500 at 12 knots
Complement	65

Built in USSR in 1950.

LIGHT FORCES

6 Ex-USSR "OSA" CLASS (FAST ATTACK CRAFT—MISSILE)

PENNANTS 194 to 199

Displacement, tons	165 standard; 200 full load
Dimensions, feet (*m*)	128·7 × 25·1 × 5·9 (*39·3 × 7·7 × 1·8*)
Missile launchers	4 for SSN 2A
Guns, AA	4—30 mm (2 twin, 1 forward, 1 aft)
Main engines	3 diesels; 13 000 bhp = 32 knots
Range, miles	800 at 25 knots
Complement	25

Built since 1961.

12 Ex-USSR "P 4" CLASS (FAST ATTACK CRAFT—TORPEDO)

PENNANTS 87 to 92.

Displacement, tons	25
Dimensions, feet	62·7 × 11·6 × 5·6
Guns	2 MG
Tubes	2—18 in
Main engines	2 diesels; 2 200 bhp = 50 knots

Built in 1955-56.

10 "VG" CLASS (COASTAL PATROL CRAFT)

Displacement, tons	40
Dimensions, feet	52·5 × 14·4 × 4
Gun	1—20 mm
Main engines	2 Diesels; 600 hp = 18 knots
Complement	10

Steel-hulled craft built at Galata in 1954.

MINE WARFARE FORCES

4 Ex-GERMAN TYPE (MINESWEEPERS—COASTAL)

DESCATUSARIA DB 13 **DEMOCRATIA** DB 15
DESROBIREA DB 14 **DREPTATEA** DB 16

Displacements, ton	543 standard; 775 full load
Dimensions, feet	188 pp; 203·5 oa × 28 × 7·5
Guns	2—3·4 in; 2—37 mm (twin) 3—20 mm (singles)
A/S weapons	2 DCT
Main engines	Triple expansion; 2 shafts; 2 400 ihp = 17 knots
Boilers	2 three-drum water tube
Range, miles	1 200 at 17 knots
Complement	80

German designed coal-burning minesweepers. Built in Romania from German materials 1943. Converted to oil in 1951.

DEMOCRATIA and DREPTATEA *1968*

22 Ex-USSR "T 301" CLASS (MINESWEEPERS—INSHORE)

Displacement, tons	130
Dimensions, feet	100 × 16 × 4·5
Guns	2—45 mm AA; 4—12·7 mm MG
Main engines	Diesel; 480 bhp = 10 knots
Complement	30

Former Soviet minesweepers transferred to Romania by the USSR in 1956-60 Probably half of these are non-operational.

8 Ex-POLISH "TR-40" CLASS (MSB's)

VD-241 VD-242 VD-243 VD-244 VD-245 VD-246 VD-247 VD-248

Displacement, tons	50 standard; 70 full load
Dimensions, feet	91·1 × 13·4 × 2·3
Guns	2—25 mm (twin)
Main engines	2 Diesels; 2 shafts; 600 hp = 16 knots
Complement	18

Eight "TR-40" Class minesweeping boats are employed on shallow water and river duties. These were originally a Polish class begun in 1955 but completed in Romania in late 1950's.

TUGS

4 USSR "ROSLAVL" CLASS

Displacement, tons	450
Dimensions, feet	135 × 29·3 × 11·8
Main engines	Diesels; 1 250 hp = 12·5 knots
Complement	28

Built in Galata ship-yard 1953-54.

TRAINING SHIPS

MIRCEA

Displacement, tons	1 604
Dimensions, feet	239·5 oa; 267·3 (with bowsprit) × 39·3 × 16·5
Sail area	18 830 sq ft
Main engines	Auxiliary MAN 6-cylinder Diesel; 500 bhp = 9·5 knots
Complement	83 + 140 midshipmen for training

Built by Blohm & Voss, Hamburg. Laid down on 30 Apr 1938. Launched on 22 Sep 1938. Completed on 29 Mar 1939. Refitted at Hamburg in 1966.

MIRCEA *1970, Michael D. J. Lennon*

RASARITUL (ex-*Taifun*)

Measurement, tons	34 (*Thames* measurement)
Dimensions, feet	54·0 × 12·5 × 3·0
Main engines	2 petrol motors; 2 shafts

Built by J. Samuel White & Co Ltd, Cowes, Isle of Wight, England. Launched in 1938. Of wooden construction. Yacht used as sail training ship.

MISCELLANEOUS

Although details are not available the following have been reported — two survey craft, three tankers, ten transports and twelve landing craft.

SABAH

In addition to two PX-class 87 ft patrol boats on detachment from the Royal Malaysian Police the following have been provided direct to Sabah by Vosper Thornycroft Private Ltd, Singapore.

2 55 ft PATROL BOATS

SRI SEMPORNA **SRI BANGJI**

Displacement, tons	50
Dimensions, feet	55 × 15 × 30
Guns	1—MG
Main engines	Diesels; 1 200 hp = 20 knots
Range, miles	300 at 15 knots
Complement	11

2 91 ft PATROL BOATS

SRI GUMANTONG **SRI LABUAN**

Delivered in 1973.

1 YACHT

PUTRI SABAH

Displacement, tons	117
Dimensions, feet	91 × 19 × 5·5
Main engines	1 Diesel = 12 knots
Complement	22

ST. LUCIA

Mercantile Marine

Lloyd's Register of Shipping: 2 vessels of 904 tons gross

1 BROOKE MARINE PATROL CRAFT

CHATOYER

Displacement, tons	15
Dimensions, feet	40 × 12 × 2
Guns	3 MG
Main engines	2 Diesels; 370 hp = 22 knots

ST. VINCENT

Mercantile Marine

Lloyd's Register of Shipping: 6 vessels of 2,247 tons gross

1 BROOKE MARINE PATROL CRAFT

HELEN

Details as *Chatoyer*, St Lucia.

SAUDI ARABIA

Personnel

(a) 1974. 950 officers and men
(b) Voluntary Service

Diplomatic Representation

Defence Attaché in London:
Brigadier Abdullah Al-Saheal

Mercantile Marine

Lolyd's Register of Shipping: 43 vessels of 58 530 tons gross

LIGHT FORCES

3 JAGUAR CLASS (FAST ATTACK CRAFT—TORPEDO)

RIFAQAT **SADAQAT** +1

Displacement, tons	160 standard; 190 full load
Dimensions, feet	138 oa × 23 × 5
Guns	2—40 mm
Torpedo tubes	4—21 in
Main engines	4 diesels; 12 000 bhp = 42 knots
Complement	33 (3 officers, 30 men)

Built in Germany and delivered in 1969.

RYADH (LARGE PATROL CRAFT)

Displacement, tons	100 standard
Dimensions, feet	95·0 × 19·0 × 6·0
Gun	1—40 mm AA
Main engines	4 diesels; 2 shafts; 2 200 bhp = 21 knots

Steel-hulled patrol boat of US CG design transferred to Saudi Arabia in 1960.

2 Ex-US 40 ft UTILITY BOATS

Transferred late 1960's.

NOTE. All the following craft with the exception of ASR1 and 2 belong to the Saudi Coastguard.

20 45 ft PATROL BOATS

Built by Whittingham and Mitchell, Chertsey, England. Armed with one ·5 cal MG and powered with two 362 hp diesels.

10 23 ft HUNTRESS PATROL BOATS

Built by Fairey Marine, Hamble, England. Capable of 20 knots with a cruising range of 150 miles and a complement of four.

20 ft PATROL BOATS

Smaller editions of the 45 ft craft above. By the same builder.

8 SRN-6 HOVERCRAFT

Displacement, tons	10 normal (load 8 200 lbs)
Dimensions, feet	48·4 × 25·3 × 15·9 (height)
Main machinery	1 Gnome model 1050 gas turbine
Speed, knots	58

Acquired from British Hovercraft Corporation Ltd, between Feb and Dec 1970.

2 AIR SEA-RESCUE LAUNCHES

ASR 1 **ASR 2**

With two diesels of 1 230 hp and capable of 25 knots. Belong to Ministry of Transportation.

SENEGAL

Personnel

1974 approx 350 officers and men

Mercantile Marine

Lloyds Register of Shipping:
43 vessels of 17 032 tons gross

PATROL VESSELS

SAINT LOUIS

Displacement, tons	235 standard
Dimensions, feet	149·3 pp; 155·8 oa × 23·6 × 8·2
Guns	2—40 mm AA
Missiles	8—SS12 SSM
Main engines	2 MGO diesels; 2 shafts; 2 400 bhp = 18·5 knots
Range, miles	2 000 at 15 knots

Ordered from Ch Navales Franco-Belges. Laid down on 20 Apr 1970, launched on 5 Aug 1970 and commissioned on 1 Mar 1971. Sister to *Malaika* of Malagasy, *Vigilant* of Ivory Coast and *Bizerte* of Tunisian Navy.

1 Ex-US "SC" TYPE

SÉNÉGAL (ex-*P* 700, ex-*CH* 62, ex-US *SC* 1344)

Displacement, tons	110 standard; 138 full load
Dimensions, feet	107·5 wl; 110·9 × 17 × 6·5
Guns	1—40 mm AA; 3—20 mm AA
Main engines	2 GM diesels; 2 shafts; 1 000 bhp = 13 knots max
Complement	25

Former US submarine chaser transferred to France on 19 Nov 1943, and from France to Senegal on 12 July 1961. First ship of Senegalese naval force.

12 VOSPER PATROL BOATS

Built by Vosper Thornycroft, Singapore. 45 ft boats of standard pattern.

2 Ex-FRENCH VC TYPE

CASAMANCE (ex-*VC* 5, *P* 755)
SINE-SALOUM (ex-*Reine N'Galifourou*, ex-*VC* 4, *P* 754)

Displacement, tons	75 standard; 82 full load
Dimensions, feet	104·5 × 15·5 × 5·5
Guns	2—20 mm AA
Main engines	2 Mercedes-Benz diesels; 2 shafts; 2 700 bhp = 28 knots
Complement	15

Former French patrol craft (Vedettes de Surveillance Côtière). Built by the Constructions Mécaniques de Normandie, Cherbourg. Completed in 1958. *Casamance* was transferred from France to Senegal in 1963. *Sine-Saloum* was given to Senegal on 24 Aug 1965 after having been returned to France by the Congo in Feb 1965.

SINE-SALOUM *1967, Senegalese Navy*

2 Ex-US LCM 6

DIOU LOULOU **DIOMBOS**

Transferred July 1968.

SINGAPORE

Personnel

(a) 1974: 1 100 officers and men
(b) 2-3 years National Service

Mercantile Marine

Lloyd's Register of Shipping: 387 vessels of 2 004 269 tons gross

Prefix to Ship's Names

RSS

LIGHT FORCES

4+2 LÜRSSEN VEGESACK DESIGN

(FAST ATTACK CRAFT—MISSILE)

SEA WOLF **SEA LION** **SEA SERPENT** **SEA DRAGON** +2

Displacement, tons	230
Dimensions, ft (*m*)	147·6 × 23 × 7·5 (*45 × 7 × 2·3*)
Missiles	5 Gabriel
Guns	1—57 mm; 1—40 mm
Main engines	4 diesels; 4 shafts; 14 400 hp = 40 knots
Complement	40

Designed by Lurssen Werft who built the first pair which arrived Autumn 1972. *Sea Serpent* built by Singapore Shipbuilding and Engineering Co launched 16 November 1972. *Sea Dragon* also built in Singapore.

6 VOSPER THORNYCROFT DESIGN

3 "TYPE A" (FAST ATTACK CRAFT—GUN)

INDEPENDENCE P 69 **FREEDOM** P 70 **JUSTICE** P 72

Displacement, tons	100 standard
Dimensions, feet	103·6 wl; 109·6 × 21·0 × 5·6
Guns	1—40 mm AA (forward); 1—20 mm AA aft
Main engines	2 Maybach diesels; 2 × 3 600 bhp = 32 knots (max)
Range, miles	1 100 at 15 knots
Complement	19 to 22

On 21 May 1968 the Vosper Thornycroft Group announced the receipt of an order for six of their 110-foot fast patrol boats for the Republic of Singapore. In design these vessels are of a hybrid type between that of the fast patrol craft built for the Malaysian Navy and those built for the Peruvian Navy. Two sub types, the first of each (*Independence* and *Sovereignty*) built in UK, the remainder in Singapore. Second type have more advanced armament. *Independence* was completed in 1970. *Freedom* and *Justice* in 1971.

INDEPENDENCE *1971, Vosper Thornycroft*

3 "TYPE B" (FAST ATTACK CRAFT—GUN)

SOVEREIGNTY P 71 **DARING** P 73 **DAUNTLESS** P 74

Displacement, tons	100 standard; 130 full load
Dimensions, feet	103·6 wl; 109·6 × 21·0 × 5·6
Guns	1—76 mm Bofors; 1—20 mm Oerlikon
Main engines	2 Maybach MD 872 diesels; 2 × 3 600 bhp = 32 knots max; continuous sea speed over 25 knots
Range, miles	1 100 at 15 knots
Complement	19 (3 officers, 16 ratings)

Sovereignty was built by Vosper Thornycroft Ltd, Portsmouth, England. *Daring* and *Dauntless* built by Vosper Thornycroft Private Ltd (formerly Uniteers Yard) in Singapore. All completed 1971. Steel hulls of round bilge form with spray strake and spray deflecting knuckle extending for more than half the length. Aluminium alloy superstructure.

SOVEREIGNTY *1971, Vosper Thornycroft*

Light Forces—*continued*

1 "FORD" CLASS (LARGE PATROL CRAFT)

PANGLIMA P 48

Displacement, tons	119 standard; 134 full load
Dimensions, feet	117·0 × 20·0 × 6·0
Guns	1—40 mm; 60 cal AA forward
Main engines	Paxman YHAXM supercharged B 12 diesels = 14 knots
Oil fuel, tons	15
Complement	15 officers and men

Built by United Engineers, Singapore. Laid down in 1954. Launched on 14 Jan 1956. Accepted by the Singapore Government in May 1956. Similar to the British seaward defence boats of the "Ford" class. Transferred to the Royal Malaysian Navy on the formation of Malaysia. Transferred to the Singapore Government (independent Republic of Singapore) in 1967.

PANGLIMA *1964*

4 VOSPER THORNYCROFT TYPE (COASTAL PATROL CRAFT)

PX 10 **PX 11** **PX 12** **PX 13**

Displacement, tons	40 standard
Length, feet	87·0
Guns	2—20 mm

Built by Vosper Thornycroft Group, Portsmouth, England for marine police duties. There is also the former Netherlands boat *Endeavor*, built in 1955.

AMPHIBIOUS FORCES

4 Ex-US LST TYPE

ENDURANCE A 81 (ex-USS *Holmes County*, LST 836)
—— (ex-USS *LST* 276)
—— (ex-USS *LST* 532)
—— (ex-USS *LST* 117)

Displacement, tons	1 653 light; 4 080 full load
Dimensions, feet	316·0 wl; 328·0 oa × 50·0 × 14·0
Guns	8—40 mm (4 twin)
Main engines	GM diesels; 2 shafts; 1 700 bhp = 11·6 knots
Complement	120

Endurance transferred from the United States Navy on 1 July 1971, remainder in 1973. There are also six small landing craft.

SIERRA LEONE

Mercantile Marine

Lloyd's Register of Shipping: 10 vessels of 3 047 tons gross

2 Ex-CHINESE "SHANGHAI II" CLASS

(FAST ATTACK CRAFT—GUN)

Displacement, tons	120 standard; 155 full load
Dimensions, feet	128 × 18 × 5·6
Guns	4—37 mm; 4—25 mm
A/S weapons	8 DC
Mines	Mine rails can be fitted
Main engines	4 Diesels; 4,800 hp = 30 knots
Complement	25

Transferred by China June 1973.

SHANGHAI II *Class*

SOMALI REPUBLIC

Mercantile Marine

Lloyd's Register of Shipping: 239 vessels of 1 612 656 tons gross

6 Ex-USSR "P4" CLASS (FAST ATTACK CRAFT—TORPEDO)

Displacement, tons	100 standard, 120 full load
Dimensions, feet	98·4 × 20·0 × 5·9
Guns	2—25 mm AA
Main engines	Diesels = 15 knots

4 Ex-USSR "P6" CLASS (FAST ATTACK CRAFT—TORPEDO)

Displacement, tons	66 standard 75 full load
Dimensions, feet	84·2 × 20·0 × 6·0
Guns	4—25 mm
Torpedo tubes	2—21 inch
Main engines	4 diesels; 4 shafts; 4 800 hp = 43 knots
Range, miles	450 at 30 knots
Complement	25

SOUTH AFRICA

Administration

Chief of South African Defence Force:
Admiral H. H. Biermann SSA, OBE

Chief of the Navy:
Vice-Admiral J. Johnson, SM, DSC

Chief of Naval Staff:
Rear-Admiral S. C. Biermann, SM

Diplomatic Representation

Armed Forces Attaché in London:
Maj Gen H. R. Meintjes, SM

Naval Attaché in London:
Commander C. H. Bennett

Defence and Armed Forces Attaché in Washington:
Brigadier F. A. Beeton, SM

Naval Attaché in Washington:
Commander R. L. Shelves

Naval Attaché in Paris:
Captain P. H. Wijnberg, SM

Strength of the Fleet

Type	*Active*	*Building (Planned)*
Destroyers	2	—
Frigates	7	—
Corvettes	—	(6)
Submarines Patrol	3	—
Large Patrol Craft	5	—
Minesweepers Coastal	10	—
Survey Ship	1	—
Fleet Replenishment Ship	1	—
BDV	1	—
TRV	1	—
Training Ships	2	—
Tugs	2	—
SAR Launches	4	—

Naval Base

HM Dockyard at Simonstown was transferred to the Republic of South Africa on 2 Apr 1957. The new submarine base at Simonstown, SAS *Drommedaris*, incorporating offices, accommodation and operations centre alongside a Synchrolift marine elevator, capable of docking all South African ships except the *Tafelberg*, was opened in July 1972.
A new Maritime Headquarters was opened in March 1973 at Silvermine on the Cape Peninsula.

New Construction

The construction of six new corvettes is being discussed—the building yard is as yet undecided but, almost certainly, will not be in UK.

Prefix to Ships' Names

SAS (Suid Afrikaanse Skip)

Personnel

(a) 1973: Total 4 665 (427 officers, 3 038 ratings and 1 200 National Service ratings)
1974: Total 4 204 (475 officers, 2 329 ratings and 1 400 National Service ratings)
(b) Voluntary plus 9-12 months National Service

Air Sea Rescue Base

The SAAF Maritime Group base at Langebaan was transferred to the South African Navy on 1 Nov 1969, becoming SAN Sea Rescue Base (SAS *Flamingo*). The ASR launches were given Naval Coastal Forces numbers to replace SAAF "R" numbers.

Mercantile Marine

Lloyd's Register of Shipping:
252 vessels of 490 751 tons gross

DESTROYERS

2 Ex-BRITISH "W" CLASS

Name	*No.*	*Builders*	*Laid down*	*Launched*	*Completed*
JAN VAN RIEBEECK (ex-HMS *Wessex*, ex-*Zenith*)	D 278	Fairfield SB & Eng Co Ltd, Govan, Glasgow	20 Oct 1942	2 Sep 1943	11 May 1944
SIMON VAN DER STEL (ex-HMS *Whelp*)	D 237	R. & W. Hawthorn Leslie & Co Ltd	1 May 1942	3 June 1943	25 Apr 1944

Displacement, tons	2 205 standard; 2 850 full load
Length, feet (*metres*)	339·5 (*103·6*)pp; 362·8 (*110·6*)oa
Beam, feet (*metres*)	35·7 (*10·9*)
Draught, feet (*metres*)	17·1 (*5·2*) max (props)
Aircraft	2 Westland "Wasp" helicopters
Guns, surface	4—4 in (*102 mm*) 2 twin
Guns, AA	2—40 mm (single)
Guns, saluting	4—3 pdr.
Torpedo tubes	4—21 in (quadruple)
Torpedo tubes, A/S	6 (2 triple)
A/S weapons	2 DCT; 2 DC racks
Boilers	2 Admiralty 3-drum type; 300 psi; 670°F
Main engines	2 Parsons sr geared turbines; 2 shafts; 40 000 shp
Speed, knots	36·75 designed; 31·25 sea
Range, miles	3 260 at 14 knots; 1 000 at 30 knots
Oil fuel, tons	579 (95%)
Complement	192 (11 officers, 181 men)

Purchased from Great Britain, *Jan van Riebeeck* was transferred to South Africa on 29 Mar 1950, and *Simon van der Stel* early in 1952.

GUNNERY. The main armament formerly comprised four 4·7 inch guns.

MODERNISATION. *Simon van der Stel* was modernised in 1962-64 and *Jan van Riebeeck* in 1964-66.

RADAR. Search: Type 293. Fire Control: X Band (NSG NA 9 system)

JAN VAN RIEBEECK — 1973 *South African Navy*

JAN VAN RIEBEECK & SIMON VAN DER STEL

FRIGATES

3 "PRESIDENT" CLASS

Name	*No*	*Builders*	*Laid down*	*Launched*	*Completed*
PRESIDENT KRUGER	F 150	Yarrow & Co. Scotstoun	6 Apr 1959	20 Oct 1960	1 Oct 1962
PRESIDENT PRETORIUS	F 145	Yarrow & Co. Scotstoun	21 Nov 1960	28 Sep 1962	4 Mar 1964
PRESIDENT STEYN	F 147	Alex Stephen & Sons, Govan	20 May 1960	23 Nov 1961	25 Apr 1963

Displacement, tons	2 250 standard; 2 800 full load
Length, feet (*metres*)	360 (*109·7*) wl; 370 (*112·8*) oa
Beam, feet (*metres*)	41·0 (*12·5*)
Draught, feet (*metres*)	17·1 (*5·2*) max (props)
Guns, surface	2—4·5 in (*115 mm*) 1 twin
Guns, AA	2—40 mm Bofors
Guns, saluting	4—3 pdr.
Aircraft	1 "Wasp" helicopter
A/S weapons	1 "Limbo" 3-barrel DC mortar
Boilers	2 Babcock & Wilcox; 550 psi; 850°F
Main engines	2 sets double reduction geared turbines; 2 shafts; 30 000 shp
Speed, knots	over 30 max, 28 sustained sea
Range, miles	4 500 at 12 knots
Oil fuel, tons	430
Complement	203 (13 officers, 190 men)

Originally "Whitby" Type 12 frigates. *President Kruger* arrived in South Africa on 27 Mar 1963.

PRESIDENT KRUGER — *1973, South African Navy*

Frigates—*continued*

MODERNISATION. Refitted to carry a "Wasp" A/S helicopter, with hangar and landing deck. To accommodate this, one "Limbo" A/S mortar was removed and the two single 40 mm remounted on the hangar roof. *President Kruger* completed refit and recommissioned on 5 Aug 1969, *President Steyn* completed refit in 1971, when *President Pretorius* was taken in hand although delayed to take advantage gained from the previous conversions. The refits were carried out at S.A. Naval Dockyard, Simonstown and included replacement of the lattice foremast by a truncated pyramid tower. *Kruger* retained her original GDS5 director but will later be brought into line with the other pair. Small differences exist between all three ships.

RADAR. Thomson CSF Jupiter 23 cm surveillance; Type 293 air/surface warning; nav set. Elsag NA9C fire control (Kruger with original fire control radar) ECM and DF.

PRESIDENT KRUGER 1973

PRESIDENT STEYN 1973, *South African Navy*

1 FORMER BRITISH TYPE 15

VRYSTAAT (ex-HMS *Wrangler*) F 157

Displacement, tons	2 240 standard; 2 880 full load
Length, feet (*metres*)	339·5 (*103·5*) pp; 362·8 (*110·6*) oa
Beam, feet (*metres*)	35·7 (*10·9*)
Draught, feet (*metres*)	17·1 (*5·2*) max props
Guns, surface	2—4 in (*102 mm*) 1 twin
Guns, AA	2—40 mm Bofors
Guns, saluting	4—3 pdr
A/S weapons	2 Squid DC mortars
Boilers	2 Admiralty 3-drum; 300 psi; 675°F
Main engines	Parsons single reduction geared turbines; 2 shafts; 40 000 shp
Speed, knots	36·75 designed; 31·25 sea
Range, miles	3 200 at 14 knots 1 300 at full power
Oil fuel, tons	505
Complement	195 (13 officers, 182 men)

Built by Vickers-Armstrongs, Barrow. Laid down on 23 Sep 1942, launched on 30 Dec 1943, completed on 14 June 1944. Fully converted into a Type 15 fast anti-submarine frigate from a fleet destroyer of the "W" class in 1951-52 by Harland & Wolf Ltd, Belfast. Refitted by the Mount Stewart Dry Dock Ltd, Cardiff, and taken over from the Royal Navy on 29 Nov 1956 as a unit of the South African Navy and renamed *Vrystaat*. Sailed for South Africa at the end of Jan 1957.

RADAR. Search: Type 277, Type 293. ECM and DF.

VRYSTAAT 1970, *South African Navy*

VRYSTAAT 1973

2 FORMER BRITISH "LOCH" CLASS

Name	No.	Builders	Laid down	Launched	Completed
GOOD HOPE (ex-HMS *Loch Boisdale*)	F 432	Blyth Dry Docks & SB Co Ltd	8 Nov 1943	5 July 1944	1 Dec 1944
TRANSVAAL (ex-HMS *Loch Ard*)	F 602	Harland & Wolff, Ltd. Belfast	20 Jan 1944	2 Aug 1944	21 May 1945

Displacement, tons	1 610 standard; 2 450 full load
Length, feet (*metres*)	286 (*87·2*) pp; 307 (*93·6*) oa
Beam, feet (*metres*)	38·5 (*11·7*)
Draught, feet (*metres*)	15·1 (*4·6*)
Guns, surface	2—4 in (*102 mm*) 1 twin
Guns, AA	*Transvaal:* 6—40 mm Bofors *Good Hope:* 2—40 mm Bofors
Guns, saluting	*Good Hope:* 4—3 pdr
A/S weapons	2 "Squid" triple DC mortars
Boilers	2 Admiralty 3-drum; 225 psi
Main engines	2 sets triple expansion; 2 shafts; 5 500 ihp
Speed, knots	19
Range, miles	9 500 at 12 knots
Oil fuel, tons	720
Complement	165 (10 officers, 155 men)

These two frigates, and a sister ship, *Natal*, were presented to South Africa by Great Britain in 1944-45.

CONSTRUCTION. ***Transvaal*** **was completed by Lobnitz & Co Ltd, Renfrew.**

MODIFICATION. When ***Transvaal*** **was modernised she had her forecastle deck extended aft to provide extra accommodation (see photograph).**

TRANSVAAL ***1971, South African Navy***

CONVERSION. *Good Hope* was converted into a despatch vessel in 1955 as Administrative Flagship of the South African Navy. She has deckhouse superstructure for extra cabins, and reception platform above built on aft, and mainmast. Refitted in 1961. Sister ship *Natal* (survey ship).

RADAR. Equipment includes Type 277 search radar.

Frigates—*continued*

1 FORMER BRITISH "ALGERINE" CLASS

PIETERMARITZBURG (ex-HMS *Pelorus*) M 291

Displacement, tons	1 040 standard; 1 330 full load
Length, feet (*metres*)	212·5 (*64·8*) pp; 225 (*68·6*) oa
Beam, feet (*metres*)	35·5 (*10·8*)
Draught feet (*metres*)	11·5 (*3·5*)
Guns, surface	2—4 in (*102 mm*) 1 twin
Guns, AA	2—40 mm Bofors
A/S weapons	4 DCT
Boilers	2 three-drum type; 250 psi
Main engines	2 sets triple expansion; 2 shafts; 2 400 ihp
Speed, knots	16
Range, miles	5 500 at 10 knots
Oil fuel, tons	270
Complement	115 (8 officers, 107 men)

Built as ocean minesweeper by Lobnitz & Co Ltd. Renfrew. Laid down on 8 Oct 1942, launched on 18 June 1943, completed on 7 Oct 1943. Purchased from Great Britain in 1947 Re-commissioned as midshipmen's training ship on 30 Aug 1962. Refitted in 1971.

PIETERMARITZBURG *1969, South African Navy*

SUBMARINES

3 "FRENCH" "DAPHNE" CLASS

Name	*No.*	*Builders*	*Laid down*	*Launched*	*Completed*
EMILY HOBHOUSE	S 98	Dubigeon—Normandie (Nantes-Chantenay	18 Nov 1968	24 Oct 1969	25 Jan 1971
JOHANNA VAN DER MERWE	S 99	Dubigeon—Normandie (Nantes-Chantenay)	24 Apr 1969	21 July 1970	21 July 1971
MARIA VAN RIEBEECK	S 97	Dubigeon—Normandie (Nantes-Chantenay)	14 Mar 1968	18 Mar 1969	22 June 1970

Displacement, tons	850 surface; 1 040 submerged
Length, feet (*metres*)	190·3 (*58*)
Beam, feet (*metres*)	22·3 (*6·8*)
Draught, feet (*metres*)	15·4 (*4·7*)
Torpedo tubes	12—21·7 in (*550 mm*) (8 bow, 4 stern)
Main engines	SEMT-Pielstick diesel electric; 1 300 bhp surface; 1 600 hp submerged; 2 shafts
Speed, knots	16 surface and submerged
Range, miles	4 500 at 5 knots (snorting)
Complement	47 (6 officers, 41 men)

First submarines ordered for the South African Navy. They are of the French "Daphne" design, similar to those built in France for Pakistan and Portugal.

EMILY HOBHOUSE *1973, South African Navy*

LIGHT FORCES

4 BRITISH "FORD" CLASS (LARGE PATROL CRAFT)

GELDERLAND (ex-*Brayford*) P 3105
HAERLEM P 3126
NAUTILUS (ex-*Glassford*) P 3120
OOSTERLAND P 3127
REIJGER P 3125

Displacement, tons	120 standard; 160 full load
Dimensions, feet	110·0 wl; 117·2 oa × 20·0 × 4·5
Guns	1—40 mm AA
A/S weapons	2 DCT in *Haerlem, Oosterland* and *Rijger*
Main engines	2 Davey Paxman diesels; Foden engine on centre shaft; 1 100 bhp = 18 knots max; sea speed 15 knots

Gelderland built by A. & J. Inglis Ltd, Glasgow, was purchased from Britain, and handed over to South Africa at Portsmouth on 30 Aug 1954, Second ship, *Nautilus* was purchased in 1955, *Reijger* was launched on 6 Feb 1958, *Haerlem* on 18 June 1958, *Oosterland* on 27 Jan 1959. All three of these later ships, built by Vosper Ltd. Portsmouth, are fitted with Vosper roll damping fins, *Haerlem* had a charthouse added aft (see photograph in the 1966-67 to 1970-71 editions) as an inshore survey boat.

REIJGER *1971*

MINE WARFARE FORCES

10 BRITISH "TON" CLASS (MINESWEEPERS COASTAL)

DURBAN M 1499
EAST LONDON (ex-*Chilton*) M 1215
JOHANNESBURG (*Castleton*) M 1207
KAAPSTAD (ex-*Hazleton*) M 1142
KIMBERLEY (ex-*Stratton*) M 1210
MOSSELBAAI (ex-*Oakington*) M 1213
PORT ELIZABETH (*Dumbleton*) M 1212
PRETORIA (ex-*Dunkerton*) M 1144
WALVISBAAI (ex-*Packington*) M 1214
WINDHOEK M 1498

Displacement, tons	360 standard; 425 full load
Dimensions, feet	140·0 pp; 152·0 oa × 28·8 × 8·2
Guns	1—40 mm Bofors AA; 2—20 mm AA
Main engines	Mirrlees diesels in *Kaapstad* and *Pretoria*, 2 500 bhp; Deltic diesels in remainder; 3 000 bhp = 15 knots
Range, miles	2 300 at 13 knots

Kaapstad and *Pretoria*, open bridge and lattice mast, were purchased in 1955. *Windhoek*, frigate bridge and tripod mast, was launched by Thornycroft, Southampton, on 27 June 1957. *Durban*, covered bridge and tripod mast, was launched at Camper & Nicholson, Gosport, on 12 June 1957. *East London* and *Port Elizabeth*, transferred from the Royal Navy at Hythe on 27 Oct 1958, sailed for South Africa in Nov 1958. *Johannesburg, Kimberley* and *Mosselbaai* were delivered in 1959. *Walvisbaai* was launched by Harland & Wolff, Belfast on 10 Dec 1958 and delivered in 1959.

DURBAN *1971*

SURVEY SHIP

PROTEA

Displacement, tons	1 930 standard; 2 750 full load
Length, feet (*metres*)	235 (*71·6*); 260·1 (*79·3*)
Beam, feet (*metres*)	49·1 (*15·0*)
Draught, feet (*metres*)	15·1 (*4·6*)
Aircraft	1 helicopter
Main engines	4 Paxman/Ventura diesels geared to 1 shaft and controllable pitch propeller; 4 880 bhp
Speed, knots	16
Range, miles	12 000 at 11 knots
Oil fuel, tons	560
Complement	Total 123 (12 officers, 104 ratings plus 7 scientists)

An order was placed with Yarrow (Shipbuilders) Ltd, for a "Hecla" class survey ship on 7 Nov 1969. Equipped for hydrographic survey with limited facilities for the collection of oceanographical data and for this purpose fitted with special communications equipment, naval surveying gear, survey launches and facilities for helicopter operations. Hull strengthened for navigation in ice and fitted with a transverse bow thrust unit and passive roll stabilisation system. Capable of undertaking long ocean passages in any part of the world including winter pasasges in the North Atlantic. Laid down 20 July 1970. launched 14 July 1971. Commissioned 23 May 1972.

PROTEA — *1973, South African Navy*

FLEET REPLENISHMENT SHIP

TAFELBERG (ex-*Annam*) A 243

Measurement, tons	12 500 gross; 18 430 deadweight
Main engines	B & W diesels; 8 420 bhp = 15·5 knots
Complement	100 as naval vessel (40 as tanker)

Built by Nakskovs Skibsvaert as Danish East Asiatic Co tanker. Launched on 20 June 1958. Purchased by the Navy in 1965. Accommodation rehabilitated by Barens Shipbuilding & Engineering Co, Durban with extra accommodation, air conditioning, re-wiring for additional equipment, new upper RAS (replenishment at sea) deck to contain gantries, re-fuelling pipes. Provision for helicopters. Remainder of conversion by Jowies, Brown & Hamer, Durban.

TAFELBERG — *1973, South African Navy*

TAFELBERG — *1973*

TORPEDO RECOVERY VESSEL

FLEUR P 3148

Displacement, tons	220 standard; 257 full load
Dimensions, feet	115·0 wl; 121·5 oa × 27·5 × 11·1
Main engines	2 Paxman Ventura diesels; 1 400 bhp

Built by Dorman Long (Africa) Ltd at Durban and completed on 28 Nov 1969. Commissioned 3 Dec 1969. Combined Torpedo Recovery Vessel and Diving Tender.

FLEUR — *1973, South African Navy*

TRAINING VESSELS

HDML 1204

Displacement, tons	45 standard; 54 full load (revised official figures)
Dimensions, feet	72·0 × 15·5 × 5·3
Main engines	2 Gardner 8-cylinder diesels; 300 bhp = 11 knots

Sole survivor of the former British Admiralty type HDMLs (Harbour Defence Motor Launches) later designated Seaward Defence Motor Launches. Built in South Africa 1941-42. Guns removed. Attached to Military Academy, Saldanha, as Midshipmen's training vessel. SDML 1202 was converted to a gunnery target. SDML 1330 and 1331 were scrapped in 1953, SDML 1199 and 1201 in 1955, SDML 1198 in 1956, SDML 1332 in 1958 and SDMLs 1197, 1200, 1202 and 1203 in 1968.

NAVIGATOR

Navigational Training Vessel. 75 tons displacement; 63 × 20 feet; 2 Foden diesels, 200 bhp = 9·5 knots. Based at Naval College, Gordon's Bay. Round bilge fishing boat wooden hull. Built by Fred Nicholls (Pty) Ltd, Durban in 1964.

BOOM DEFENCE VESSEL

SOMERSET (ex-HMS *Barcross*) P 285

Displacement, tons	750 standard; 960 full load
Dimensions, feet	150·0pp; 182·0 oa × 32·2 × 11·5
Main engines	Triple expansion; 850 hp = 11 knots
Boilers	2 single ended
Oil fuel, tons	186

Built by Blyth Dry Dock & SB Co Ltd. Laid down on 15 Apr 1941, launched on 21 Oct 1941, completed on 14 Apr 1942. Engined by Swan, Hunter & Wigham Richardson Ltd, Tyne. Renamed in 1951 after Dick King's horse. Sister ship *Fleur* (ex-HMS *Barbrake*) P 273 was sunk as a target in False Bay on 8th Oct 1965.

NAVAL TUGS

DE NEYS **DE NOORDE**

Displacement, tons	180 and 170, respectively
Dimensions, feet	94·0 × 26·5 × 15·75 and 104·5 × 25·0 × 15·0
Main engines	2 Lister Blackstone diesels; 2 shafts; 608 bhp = 9 knots
Complement	10

Both built by Globe Engineering Works Ltd, CapeTown. Completed on 23 July 1969 and Dec 1961.

AIR SEA RESCUE LAUNCHES

P 1551 (ex-*R* 31) **P 1552** (ex-*R* 30) **P 1554** **P 1555**

P 1554 and 1555: 26 tons, 64 × 16 × 5 feet, 2 diesels, 1 120 bhp = 28 kts. Built by Groves and Gutteridge, Cowes. P 1551 & 1552: 87 tons, 96 × 19 × 4 feet, 2 diesels, 4 480 bhp = 30 kts. (1962, 1961). There are also 2 ex-seaplane tenders, 41 ft, and 2 ex-marine tenders, 24 ft.

P1554 — *1973, South African Navy*

SPAIN

Administration

Minister of Marine:
Admiral Excmo Sr Don Adolfo Baturone Colombo

Chief of Naval Staff:
Admiral Excmo Sr Don Enrique Barbudo Duarte

Deputy Chief of Naval Staff:
Vice-Admiral Excmo Sr Don José R. González López

Commander-in-Chief of the Fleet:
Vice-Admiral Excmo Sr Don Gabriel Pita de Veiga y Sanz

Diplomatic Representation

Naval Attaché in London:
Captain Don Jesus Diaz del Rio

Naval Attaché in Washington:
Captain Sr Don Angel Liberal Lucini

Strength of the Fleet

Type	*Active*	*Building*	*Proposed*
Helicopter Carrier	1	—	—
Cruiser	1	—	1 (light cruiser
Destroyers	13	—	3 (DDG)
Frigates	16	3	—
Corvettes	4	3	7
Submarines Patrol	8	—	2
Submarines Small	2	—	—
Fast Attack Craft—Missile	—	—	12 (?)
Fast Attack Craft—Torpedo	3	—	—
Large Patrol Craft	1	3	10
Coastal Patrol Craft	9	—	10
LSD	1	—	—
Attack Transports	2	—	—
LST	3	—	—
LSM	3	—	—
LCT	8	—	—
Minor Landing Craft	99	—	—
Minesweepers—Ocean	11	—	—
Minesweepers—Coastal	12	—	—
Survey Ships	6	2	—
Transports	1	—	1
Fleet Logistic Ship	—	—	1
Submarine Tender	—	—	1
Replenishment Tanker	1	—	—
Harbour Tankers	15	—	—
Training Ships	3	—	—
Auxiliary Patrol Craft	21	—	—
Tugs (Ocean, Coastal and Harbour)	31	—	—
Miscellaneous	58	—	—

Mercantile Marine

Lloyd's Register of Shipping:
2 420 vessels of 4 833 048 tons gross

Personnel

(a) 1974: Total 52 000 (4 350 officers, 36 650 ratings 4 600 civil branch, 6 400 marines)
(b) 18 months National Service

Naval Air Service

12 Bell 47G
4 AB 204B
12 Sikorsky SH 3D
12 Hughes 369 HM
7 Bell AH-1G "Hueycobra"
4 Bell 212

NOTE. Harrier AV-8 aircraft ordered from US marines in 1973. Initial order of 8 with possible follow-up of 12 and an additional 4.

Replacement Programme

In January 1973 the following new construction programme was announced; 1 light Cruiser, 3 DDG's, 10 Corvettes, 2 "Agosta" class Submarines, a number of PF Type, 6 Large Patrol Craft, 6 Coastal Patrol Craft, (the last two types for fishery protection), 1 Fleet Logistic Ship, 1 Submarine Tender, 1 Light Transport, 2 Oceanographic Ships, 2 Coastal Survey Ships and a number of landing craft.

(Later plans propose 13 Large Patrol Craft and 10 Coastal Patrol Craft.)

New Construction

Of the above the following are under construction;
3 Corvettes
2 Oceanographic Ships
3 Large Patrol Craft

US Agreement

Under an Agreement of 6 Aug 1970 the USA agreed to supply 2 submarines, 5 destroyers, 4 MSO's, 3 LST's, 1 AE and 1 AO. Of this list an LDS was substituted for the AE and the AO was in too poor condition for further service. Otherwise all but 3 DD's were received by end-1972.

Disposals

Destroyers

1970 *Am. Miranda*
1971 *Magallanes, Vasco Nunez de Balbao, Hernan Cortes*

Frigates

1971 *Mate*
1972 *Neptune, Eolo, Triton*
1973 *Osado*

Corvettes

1971 *Descubierta*
1973 *Diana*

Submarines

1971 D 2 (S 21), D 3 (S 22), G 7 (ex-U573 VII C)
Midget submarines SA 41 (F 1), SA 42 (F 2)

Minesweepers

1971 *Lerez*
1972 *Bidasoa, Nervion, Segura, Tambre, Ter*

Patrol Vessels

1970 *Arcila, Xanen*
1971 *Javier Quiroga*
1973 *Cies*

Survey Ships

1971 *Mataspina*

HELICOPTER CARRIER

1 Ex-US CVL

Name	*No*	*Builders*	*Laid down*	*Launched*	*Completed*
DÉDALO (ex-USS *Cabot,* AVT 3, ex-CVL 28, ex-*Wilmington,* CL 79)	PH 01	New York Shipbuilding Corporation	16 Aug 1942	4 Apr 1943	24 July 1943

Displacement, tons 13 000 standard; 16 416 full load
Length, feet (*metres*) 600·0 (*182·8*)wl; 623·0(*189·9*) oa
Beam, feet (*metres*) 71·5 (*21·8*) hull
Width, feet (*metres*) 109·0 (*33·2*)
Draught, feet (*metres*) 26·0 (*7·9*)
Aircraft 20 helicopters (ASW/Sea Kings—Combat/Huey Cobras—Landings/specially embarked S55's or Bell 212's)
Guns 26—40 mm AA (2 quadruple, 9 twin)
Armour 2 to 5 in sides; 2 to 3 in deck
Main armour GE geared turbines 4 shafts; 100 000 shp
Speed, knots 32
Boilers 4 Babcock & Wilcox
Range, miles 7 200 at 15 knots
Oil fuel, tons 1 800
Complement 1 112 (without Air Groups)

DEDALO *1969 Spanish Navy*

Helicopter Carriers—*cont.*

Completed as an aircraft carrier from the hull of a "Cleveland" class cruiser. Originally carried over 40 aircraft. Converted with strengthened flight and hangar decks, large port side catapult, revised magazine arrangements, new electronic gear, corrected stability to counter Flight deck: 545 × 108 feet (*166·1 × 32·9 metres*)

Reactivated and modernised at Philadelphia Naval Shipyard, where she was transferred to Spain on 30 Aug 1967, on loan for five years. Purchased 1973.

RADAR. SPS 6 and SPS 40 air search; SPS 10 tactical; SPS 8 heightfinder; four fire control radars; Tacan.

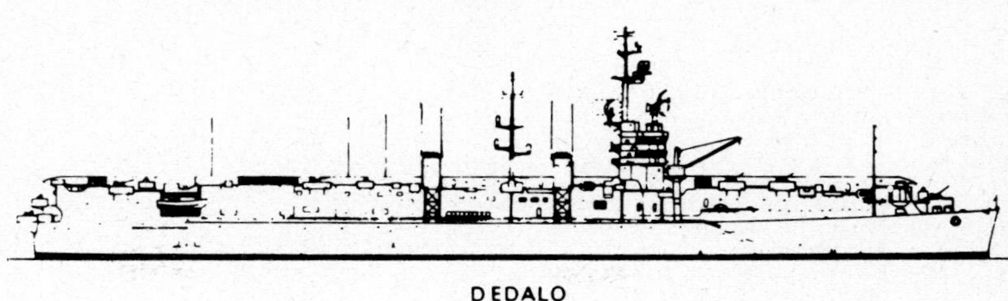

DEDALO

CRUISER

Name	*No.*	*Builders*	*Laid down*	*Launched*	*Completed*
CANARIAS	C 21	Sociedad Española de Construcción Naval El Ferrol	15 Aug 1928	28 May 1931	1 Oct 1936

Displacement, tons	10 282 standard; 13 969 full load
Length, feet, (*metres*)	636·5 (*194·0*)
Beam, feet (*metres*)	64·0 (*19·5*)
Draught, feet (*metres*)	21·3 (*6·5*)
Guns	8—8 in (*203 mm*) 50 cal (4 twin); 8—4·7 in (*120 mm*) 45 cal. single; 4—1·5 in (*38 mm*) 80 cal (2 twin); 4—40 mm AA; 2—20 mm 70 cal AA
Armour	sides 1·5—2 in (*38—50 mm*); turrets and deck 1 in (*25 mm*); magazines 4 in (*100 mm*)
Main engines	Parsons geared turbines; 2 shafts; 92 000 shp
Speed, knots	31
Boilers	8 Yarrow type
Range, miles	8 000 at 15 knots
Oil fuel, tons	2 794
Complement	1 000 (40 officers, 960 men)

CANARIAS *1970, Spanish Navy*

This ship was designed by the late Sir Philip Watts on the basic pattern of the contemporary British heavy cruisers of the later "County" classes. From initial completion until 1952 she had trunked funnels, but she emerged from refit in 1953 with two separate funnels, this being a reversion to the original design which had never been carried out.

RADAR. MLA-IB air search; Marconi surface warning/navigation sets.

TORPEDO TUBES. The twelve 21 inch torpedo tubes in four triple mountings were removed in 1960.

GUNNERY. Elevation of the 8 inch guns is 70 degrees.

CLASS. Only sister ship *Baleares* was torpedoed and sunk on 6 Mar 1938 during the Spanish Civil War.

DRAWING. Starboard elevation and plan. Scale 125 feet = 1 inch (1 : 1 500).

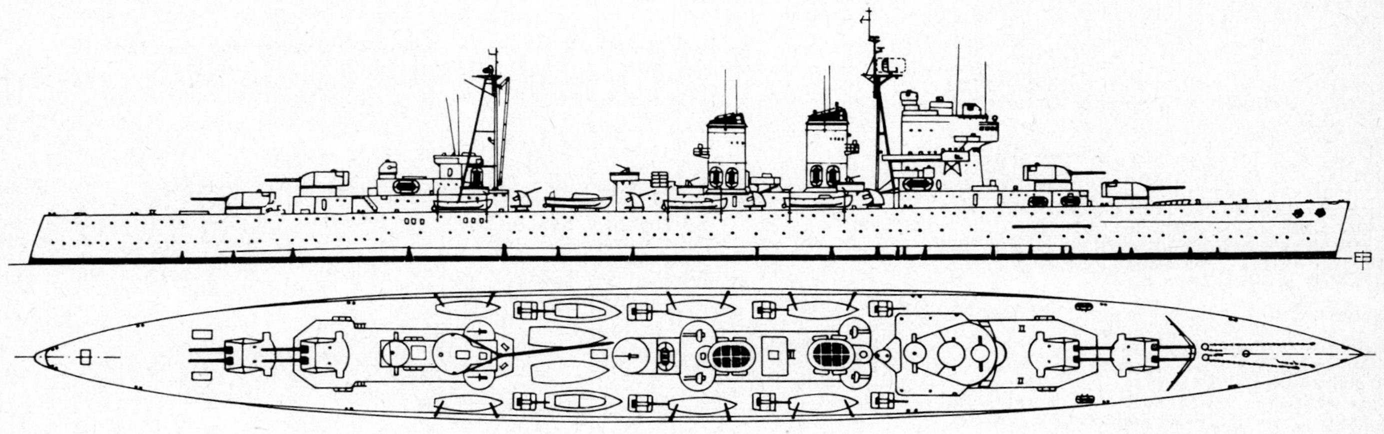

DESTROYERS

NOTE. 3 DDG's are in an advanced state of planning, to be laid down possibly in 1974. Likely details are—Surface to surface and surface-to-air missiles, 5 inch Oto Melara guns, A/S helicopters, COGOG propulsion giving a speed of 34 knots.

5 Ex-US "GEARING FRAM I" CLASS

Displacement, tons	2 425 standard; 3 480 full load
Length, feet (*metres*)	390·5 (*119·0*) oa
Beam, feet (*metres*)	40·9 (*12·4*)
Draught, feet (*metres*)	19 (*5·8*)
Guns	4—5 in (*127 mm*) 38 cal DP twin
A/S weapons	1 Asroc launcher; 2 Triple Mk 32 tubes; Facilities for Hughes 369 HM helicopter
Main engines	2 geared turbines (GE or Westinghouse) 60 000 shp; 2 shafts
Boilers	4 Babcock and Wilcox
Speed, knots	34
Fuel, tons	650
Range, miles	4 800 at 15 knots
Complement	274

Name	*No.*	*Completed*	*Transferred*
CHURRUCA (ex-USS *Eugene A. Greene* DD 711)	D 61	8 June 1945	31 Aug 1972
GRAVINA (ex-USS *Furse* DD 882)	D 62	10 July 1945	31 Aug 1972
MENDEZ NUÑEZ (ex-USS *O'Hare* DD 889)	D 63	29 Nov 1945	31 Oct 1973
LANGARA (ex-USS *Leary* DD 879)	D 64	7 May 1945	31 Oct 1973
BLAS DE LEZO (ex-USS *Noa* DD 841)	D 65	2 Nov 1945	31 Oct 1973

RADAR. D61 and 62—Air Search, SPS 40; Surface search, SPS 10; Fire control Mk 37.

SONAR. D 61 and 62—SQS 23 (hull mounted).

TRANSFERS. D61 and 62 have undergone major refits at El Ferrol since transfer. The next three ships offered by the USN were rejected due to their material state and the current trio was substituted.

Destroyers—*continued*

2 MODIFIED "OQUENDO" TYPE

Name	*No.*	*Laid down*	*Launched*	*Commissioned*
MARQUÉS DE LA ENSENADA	D43	4 Sep 1951	15 July 1959	10 Sep 1970
ROGER DE LAURIA	D42	4 Sep 1951	12 Nov 1958	30 May 1969

Displacement, tons	3 370 standard; 3 785 full load
Length, feet (*metres*)	391·5 (*119·3*)
Beam, feet (*metres*)	42·7 (*13·0*)
Draught, feet (*metres*)	18·4 (*5·6*)
Aircraft	1 Hughes 369 HM ASW helo
Guns	6—5 in (*127 mm*) 38 cal (3 twin)
A/S weapons	2 triple Mk 32 tubes for Mk 44 A/S torpedoes
Torpedo, tubes	2—21 in (*533 mm*) fixed single Mk 25 tubes for Mk 37 torpedoes
Main engines	2 Rateau-Bretagne geared turbines; 2 shafts; 60 000 shp
Speed, knots	31
Boilers	3 three-drum type
Oil fuel, tons	673
Range, miles	4 500 at 15 knots
Complement	318 (20 officers, 298 men)

MARQUÉS DE LA ENSENADA, ROGER DE LAURIA

ROGER DE LAURIA — *1970, Spanish Navy*

Ordered at Ferrol in 1948. Originally of the same design as *Oquendo*. Towed to Cartegena for reconstruction to a new design. *Roger de Lauria* was re-launched after being lengthened and widened on 29 Aug 1967 and *Marqués de la Ensenada* on 2 Mar 1968. Weapons and electronics identical to Gearing Fram II.

RADAR. Search: SPS 40. Tactical: SPS 10. Fire Control: One Mk 37 and one Mk 56.

SONAR. One hull mounted, probably SQS 29; one VDS, probably SQA 10.

1 "OQUENDO" CLASS

Name	*No.*	*Laid down*	*Launched*	*Completed*
OQUENDO	D 41	15 June 1951	5 Sep 1956	13 Sep 1960

Displacement, tons	2 582 standard; 3 005 full load
Length, feet (*metres*)	382 (*116·4*)
Beam, feet (*metres*)	36·5 (*11·1*)
Draught, feet (*metres*)	12·5 (*3·8*)
Guns	4—4·7 (*120 mm*) 50 cal (2 twin); 6—40 mm, 70 cal. single
A/S weapons	2 Hedgehogs
Torpedo tubes	2 Mk 4 with 3 Mk 32 homing torpedoes each
Main engines	2 Rateau-Bretagne geared turbines; 2 shafts; 60 000 shp
Speed, knots	32·4
Boilers	3 three-drum type
Oil fuel, tons	659
Range, miles	5 000 at 15 knots
Complement	250 (17 officers, 233 men)

OQUENDO — *Spanish Navy*

Ordered at Ferrol in 1947. Initially completed on 13 Sep 1960. Completed modernisation on 22 April 1963.

CONSTRUCTION. Designed as a conventional destroyer but modified during construction. Seven 21-inch torpedo tubes and two depth charge throwers were replaced by modern anti-submarine weapons. The 4·7 inch guns may soon be replaced by 5 inch.

RADAR. Search: British 293 type. Fire Control: Mk 8 and close range blind fire British types.

5 Ex-US "FLETCHER" CLASS

Name	*No.*	*Builders*	*Laid down*	*Launched*	*Completed*
ALCALA GALIANO (ex-USS *Jarvis*, DD 799)	D 24	Todd Pacific Shipyards	—	14 Feb 1944	3 June 1944
ALMIRANTE FERRANDIZ (ex-USS *David W. Taylor*, DD 551)	D 22	Gulf SB Corpn, Chickasaw, Ala	12 June 1941	4 July 1942	18 Sep 1943
ALMIRANTE VALDES (ex-USS *Converse*, DD 509)	D 23	Bath Iron Works Corp, Maine	23 Feb 1942	30 Aug 1942	8 June 1943
JORGE JUAN (ex-USS *McGowan*, DD 678)	D 25	Federal SB & DD Co	—	14 Nov 1943	20 Dec 1943
LEPANTO (ex-USS *Capps*, DD 550)	D 21	Gulf SB Corpn, Chickasaw, Ala	12 June 1941	31 May 1942	23 June 1943

Displacement, tons	2 080 standard; 2 750 normal; 3 050 full load
Length, feet (*metres*)	376·5 (*114·8*) oa
Beam, feet (*metres*)	39·5 (*12·0*)
Draught, feet (*metres*)	18·0 (*5·5*)
Guns, surface	*D21, D22:* 5—5 in (*127 mm*) 38 cal; *Others:* 4—5 in (*127 mm*) single
Guns, AA	*D21, D22:* 6—40 mm, 60 cal, 3 twin; 6—20 mm, 70 cal, single *Others:* 6—3 in (*76 mm*) 50 cal, 3 twin
A/S weapons	2 "Hedgehogs"; 6 DCT in D21, D22, 4 in D23; 2 DC racks in D21, D22, 1 in others
Torpedo tubes	3—21 in (*533 mm*) in D 24 and 25 only
Torpedo racks	2 side launching Mk 4 each with 3 Mk 32 A/S torpedoes
Main engines	Geared turbines; Westinghouse in D21, D22, GE in others; 2 shafts; 60 000 shp
Speed, knots	35 max, 16 economical sea
Boilers	4 Babcock & Wilcox
Range, miles	5 000 at 15 knots
Oil fuel, tons	650
Complement	290 (17 officers, 273 men)

JORGE JUAN (four 5 inch) — *1972, Spanish Navy*

ALMIRANTE FERRANDIZ, LEPANTO

ALCALA GALIANO, JORGE JUAN, VALDES

Lepanto, and *Almirante Ferrandiz*, were reconditioned at San Francisco, Cal, and there turned over to the Spanish Navy on 15 May 1957, sailing for Spain on 1 July 1957. *Valdes* was transferred at Philadelphia on 1 July 1959, *Jorge Juan*, was transferred at Barcelona on 1 Dec 1960 and *Alcala Galiano*, at Philadelphia on 3 Nov 1960, both being of the later "Fletcher" class. Modernisation of A/S equipment is planned. All purchased from US on 1 Oct 1972.

RADAR. Search: SPS 6C. Tactical: SPS 10. Fire Control: D 23, 24 and 25—Mk 37 and Mk 56, 2 Mk 63 for 3 inch guns; D 21 and 22—Mk 37.

SONAR. One hull mounted set.

FRIGATES

5 "BALEARES" CLASS

Name	No.	Laid down	Launched	Completion
ANDALUCIA	F 72	2 July 1969	30 Mar 1971	May 1974
ASTURIAS	F 74	30 Mar 1971	13 May 1972	1974-75
BALEARES	F 71	31 Oct 1968	20 Aug 1970	24 Sep 1973
CATALUÑA	F 73	20 Aug 1970	3 Nov 1971	1974-75
EXTREMADURA	F 75	3 Nov 1971	21 Nov 1972	1975-76

Displacement, tons	3 000 standard; 4 177 full load
Length, feet (*metres*)	415·0 (*126·5*) pp; 438·0 (*133·5*) oa
Beam, feet (*metres*)	46·9 (*14·3*)
Draught, feet (*metres*)	25·9 (*7·9*)
Missile launchers	1 single for "Standard" missiles
Guns	1—5 in (*127 mm*) 54 cal dp
A/S weapons	1 eight-tube ASROC launcher
Torpedo tubes	4 Mk 32 for Mk 44 torpedoes; 2 Mk 25 for Mk 37 torpedoes (stern)
Main engines	1 set geared turbines; 1 shaft; 35 000 shp
Boilers	2 high pressure V2M type; 1 200 psi (84·4 *kg/cm²*)
Speed, knots	28
Range	Over 4 000 miles at 20 knots
Complement	256 (15 officers, 241 men)
A/S System	8 Reloads carried for ASROC
Gunnery	600 5 inch rounds carried
Missile system	Mk 22 launcher with stowage for 16 missiles. Single director with two lines of fire against different targets

BALEARES — *1973, J. Talbo*

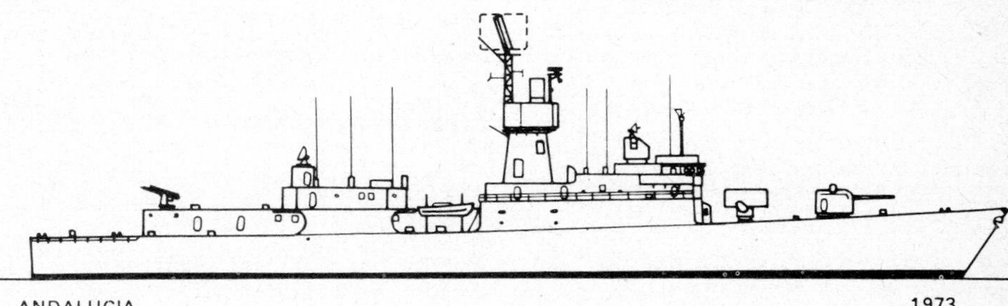
ANDALUCIA — 1973

In June 1966 Spain and USA signed an agreement for the construction of five frigates by Empresa Nacional Bazán at El Ferrol with technical and material assistance by USA. Generally similar in appearance to the US escort ships of the "Brooke" class but with modified weapons system and other characteristics to meet the requirements of the Spanish Navy. Equipped with weapons and electronic equipment furnished by USA.

RADAR. Search: SPS 52 (3D). Tactical: SPS 10. Fire Control: SPS 51 continuous wave for missiles; Mk 68 for guns with continuous wave injection for limited use with missiles.

TORPEDOES AND TUBES. All are fitted internally. Total of 41 torpedoes carried.

SONAR. SQS 23 bow mounted; SQA 13 VDS.

5+2 "AUDAZ" CLASS

Name	No.	Laid down	Launched	Completed
AUDAZ	D 31	26 Sep 1945	24 Jan 1951	30 June 1953
FUROR	D 34	3 Aug 1945	24 Feb 1955	7 Sep 1960
INTRÉPIDO	D 38	14 July 1945	15 Feb 1961	25 Mar 1965
METEORO (*ex-Atravido*)	D 33	3 Aug 1945	4 Sep 1951	30 Nov 1955
RAYO	D 35	3 Aug 1945	4 Sep 1951	20 May 1958
RELÁMPAGO	D 39	14 July 1945	26 Sep 1961	7 July 1965
TEMERARIO	D 37	14 July 1945	29 Mar 1960	16 Mar 1964

Displacement, tons	1 227 standard; 1 550 full load
Length, feet (*metres*)	295·2 (*90·0*) pp; 308·2 (*94·0*) oa
Beam, feet (*metres*)	30·5 (*9·3*)
Draught, feet (*metres*)	17·1 (*5·2*)
Guns (except D 31 and D 33)	2—3 in (*76 mm*) 50 cal dp; 2—40 mm 70 cal AA
A/S weapons	2 Hedgehogs; 8 mortars; 2 DC racks
Torpedo tubes	2 side launching for Mk 32 A/S torpedoes (6 torpedoes)
Main engines	Rateau-Bretagne geared turbines; 2 shafts; 28 000 shp
Speed, knots	32
Boilers	2 La Seine 3-drum type
Range, miles	3 800 at 15 knots, 900 at 32 knots
Oil fuel, tons	290
Complement	199 (13 officers, 186 men) except D31 and 33—106 (8 officers, 98 men)

Based on the French "Le Fier" design. All built at Ferrol. Allocated D Pennant numbers in 1961, D 31 and 33 now training ships with only one 40 mm and Marconi navigational radar.

AUDAZ *Class*

INTRÉPIDO — *1969, Spanish Navy*

ENGINEERING. The boilers are in two compartments separated by the engine rooms.

MODERNISATION. Delivery dates after modernisation: *Audaz* 28 June 1961, *Furor* 9 Sep 1960, *Meteoro* 21 Feb 1963, *Rayo* 21 Feb 1963.

RADAR. (except D 31 and 33) Surface search, SPS 5B; Air search, MLA-1B; Fire control, one Mk 63.

SONAR. One hull mounted-set

2 "ALAVA" CLASS

Name	No.	Builders	Laid down	Launched	Completed	Modernised
ALAVA	D 52 (ex-23)	Cartagena	21 Dec 1944	19 May 1947	21 Dec 1950	17 Jan 1962
LINIERS	D 51 (ex-21)	Cartagena	1 Jan 1945	1 May 1946	27 Jan 1951	18 Sep 1962

Displacement, tons	1 842 standard; 2 287 full load
Length, feet (*metres*)	336·3 (*102·5*)
Beam, feet (*metres*)	31·5 (*9·6*)
Draught, feet (*metres*)	19·7 (*6·0*)
Guns	3—3 in (*76 mm*) 50 cal, Mk 22; 3—40 mm, 70 cal AA
A/S weapons	2 "Hedgehogs"; 8 DC mortars; 2 DC racks
Torpedo racks	2 side launching for Mk 32 torpedoes, 6 A/S torpedoes
Main engines	Parsons geared turbines; 2 shafts; 31 500 shp
Speed, knots	29
Boilers	4 Yarrow 3-drum type
Range, miles	4 100 at 15 knots
Oil fuel, tons	370
Complememt	222 (15 officers, 207 men)

ALAVA, LINIERS

LINIERS — *1972, Admiral M. Adam*

Ordered in 1936, but construction was held up by the Civil War. After being resumed, was again suspended in 1940, but restarted at Empresa Nacional Bazan in 1944.

RADAR. Air search; MLA IB. One surface-search set. Fire Control: 2-Mk 63.

SONAR. One hull-mounted set, probably SQS-4.

Frigates—*continued*

2 MODERNISED "PIZARRO" CLASS

Name	No.	Launched	Completed
LEGAZPI	F 42	8 Aug 1944	8 Aug 1951
VICENTE YAÑEZ PINZON	F 41	3 Aug 1944	5 Aug 1949

Displacement, tons	1 924 standard; 2 228 full load
Length, feet (*metres*)	279·0 (*85·0*) pp; 312·5 (*95·3*) oa
Beam, feet (*metres*)	39·5 (*12·0*)
Draught, feet (*metres*)	17·7 (*5·4*)
Guns, surface	2—5 in (*127 mm*) 38 cal.
Guns, AA	4—40 mm, 70 cal.
A/S weapons	2 "Hedgehogs"; 8 mortars; 2 racks
Torpedo racks	2 side launching for Mk 32 torpedoes
Main engines	2 sets Parsons geared turbines; 2 shafts; 6 000 shp
Speed, knots	18·5
Boilers	2 Yarrow type
Range, miles	3 000 at 15 knots
Oil fuel, tons	390
Complement	255 (16 officers 239 men)

LEGAZPI, VICENTE YANEZ PINZON

VICENTE YAÑEZ PINZON *1971, Spanish Navy*

All built at Ferrol. Originally designed to carry 30 mines *Legazpi* and *Vicente Yañez Pinzon* completed modernisation on 14 Jan and 25 Mar 1960 respectively.

RADAR. Surface search; SP 5B; Air search, MLA-1B; Fire Control: Mk 52.

1 "PIZARRO" CLASS

Name	No.	Launched	Completed
SARMIENTO DE GAMBOA	F 36	8 Aug 1944	2 May 1950

Main particulars are the same as the "Modernised Pizarro" class with the exception of her armament.

Guns	6—4·7 in (*120 mm*); 8—37 mm; 6—20 mm
A/S weapons	Probably now removed

This ship was due for disposal in 1971 but has been retained.

SARMIENTO DE GAMBOA *1971, Spanish Navy, Official*

2 "JUPITER" CLASS

Name	No.	Launched	Completed
JUPITER	F 11	14 Sep 1935	1937
VULCANO	F 12	12 Oct 1935	1937

Displacement, tons	2 103 standard; 2 360 full load
Length, feet (*metres*)	302·8 (*92·3*) pp; 328·1 (*100·0*) oa
Beam, feet (*metres*)	41·5 (*12·6*)
Draught, feet (*metres*)	11·5 (*3·5*)
Guns	4—3 in (*76 mm*) Mk 26, single; 4—40 mm, 70 cal AA
A/S weapons	2 "Hedgehogs"; 8 mortars; 2 DC racks
Mines	*Jupiter* 254, *Vulcano* 238
Main engines	2 sets Parsons geared turbines; 2 shafts; 5 000 shp
Speed, knots	17·4 max, 10 economical sea
Boilers	2 Yarrow type
Range, miles	5 700 at 12 knots
Oil fuel, tons	340
Complement	255 (16 officers, 239 men)

VULCANO *1971, Spanish Navy*

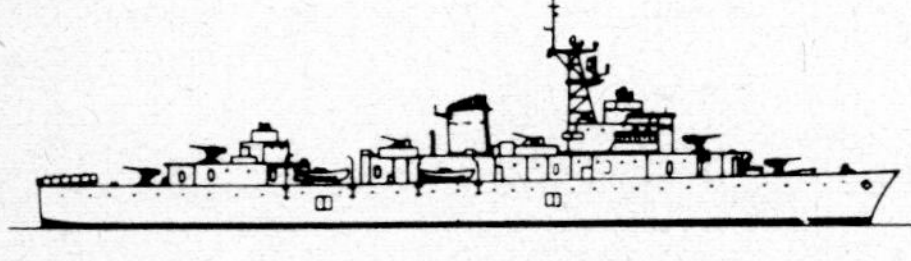
JUPITER, VULCANO

Both built by the Sociedad Española de Construccion Naval, Ferrol. The modernisation of *Jupiter* with lattice mast and four 3-inch guns was completed on 28 Oct 1960, and of *Vulcano* on 28 Feb 1961. Both allocated F pennant numbers in 1961.

RADAR. Air search, MLA-IB; Fire Control: MK 51.

CORVETTES

The new corvertes, first of a class probably of 10 and apparently of an improved "João Coutinho" class, were laid down at El Ferrol in late 1973.

4 "ATREVIDA" CLASS

Name	No.	Laid down	Launched	Completion of Modernization
ATREVIDA	F 61	26 June 1950	2 Dec 1952	14 June 1960
NAUTILUS	F 64	27 July 1953	23 Aug 1956	15 Dec 1959
PRINCESA	F 62	18 Mar 1953	31 Mar 1956	3 Oct 1959
VILLA DE BILBAO	F 65	18 Mar 1953	19 Feb 1958	2 July 1960

Displacement, tons	1 031 standard; 1 135 full load
Length, feet (*metres*)	247·8 (*75·5*) oa
Beam, feet (*metres*)	33·5 (*10·2*)
Draught, feet (*metres*)	9·8 (*3·0*)
Guns	1—3 in (*76 mm*) 50 cal dp; 3—40 mm, 70 cal AA
A/S weapons	2 Hedgehogs; 8 mortars; 2 DC racks
Mines	20 can be carried
Main engines	Sulzer diesels; 2 shafts; 3 000 bhp
Speed, knots	18·5 max
Range, miles	8 000 at 10 knots
Oil fuel, tons	100
Complement	132 (9 officers. 123 men)

ATREVIDA *Class*

Corvettes—*cont.*

Atrevida commissioned on 19 Aug 1954. All have been modernised since 1959. No funnel, the diesel exhaust being on the starboard side waterline. Allocated F pennant numbers in 1961. SPS 10 radar.

RADAR. Modified SPS-5B combined air/surface search.

ATREVIDA — *1971, Michael D. J. Lennon*

SUBMARINES

NOTE. It is reported that two French "Agosta" class are to be laid down at Cartagena in 1974.

4 FRENCH "DAPHNÉ" CLASS

Name	*No.*	*Builders*	*Laid down*	*Launched*	*Commission*
DELFIN	S 61	E. N. Bazan, Cartegena	13 Aug 1968	25 Mar 1972	3 May 1973
TONINA	S 62	E. N. Bazan, Cartagena	1969	3 Oct 1972	10 July 1973
MARSOPA	S 63	E. N. Bazan, Cartagena	1971	1973	1974
NARVAL	S 64	E. N. Bazan, Cartagena	1971	1973	1974

NOTE. It is reported that two French "Agosta" class are to be laid down at Cartagena in 1974.

Displacement, tons	870 surface; 1 040 submerged
Length, feet (*metres*)	189·6 (*57·8*)
Beam, feet (*metres*)	22·3 (*6·8*)
Draught, feet (*metres*)	15·1 (*4·6*)
Tubes	12—21·7 in (*550 mm*) (8 bow, 4 stern)
Main machinery	SEMT- Pielstick diesel-electric; 1 300 bhp surface; 1 600 hp submerged; 2 shafts

Basically similar to the French "Daphne" class and being built with extensive French assistance in the Cartagena Yard.

RADAR. Thompson CSF "Calypso II" plus ECM.

SONAR. Active, DUUA 1; Passive with rangefinding DSUV.

DELFIN — *1973, J. Taibo*

ALMIRANTE GARCIA DE LOS REYES S31
(ex-USS *Kraken, SS* 370)

Displacement, tons	1 880 surface; 2 060 submerged
Length, feet (*metres*)	311·5 (*95·0*)
Beam, feet (*metres*)	27·2 (*8·3*)
Draught, feet (*metres*)	17·2 (*5·2*)
Torpedo tubes	6—21 in (*533 mm*), and 4 for acoustic torpedoes
Main machinery	4 GMC 278D, V-16 Diesels, total 6 400 bhp; 2 shafts; 2 GE electric motors, 5 400 shp
Speed, knots	20 on surface; 10 submerged
Oil fuel, tons	300
Range, miles	12 000 at 10 knots
Complement	89 (10 officers, 79 men)

ALMIRANTE GARCIA DE LOS REYES — *1969, Spanish Navy*

Former US Navy submarine of the "Balao" class. Built by Manitowoc SB Co. Launched on 30 Apr 1944 and completed on 8 Sep 1944. Transferred on 24 Oct 1959 after modernisation and overhaul at Pearl Harbour.

3 Ex-US GUPPY IIA TYPE

Name	*No.*	*Laid down*	*Launched*	*Completed*
ISAAC PERAL (ex-USS *Ronquil,* SS 396)	S 32	9 Sep 1943	27 June 1944	23 Apr 1944
NARCISO MONTURIOL (ex-USS *Picuda,* SS 382	S 33	15 Mar 1943	12 July 1943	16 Oct 1943
COSME GARCIA (ex-USS *Bang.* SS 385)	S 34	30 Apr 1943	30 Aug 1943	4 Dec 1943

Displacement, tons	1 840 surface; 2 445 submerged
Length, feet (*metres*)	306·0 (*93·3*); ao
Beam, feet (*metres*)	27·0 (*8·2*)
Draught, feet (*metres*)	17·0 (*5·2*)
Torpedo tubes	10—21 in (*533 mm*), 6 bow, 4 stern
Main machinery	3 Fairbanks-Morse diesels; total 4 800 bhp; 2 shafts; 2 Elliot electric motors; 5 400 shp
Speed, knots	18 on surface; 15 submerged
Range, miles	12 000 at 10 knots
Complement	84

Built by Portsmouth Navy Yard. Transferred to Spain on 1 July 1971 (*Ronquil*) 1 Oct 1972 (*Bang* and *Picuda*).

NARCISO MONTURIOL — *1972, Dr. Giorgio Arra*

COSME GARCIA (PERAL similar) — *1973, J. Taibo*

Submarines—*continued*

2 "TIBURON" CLASS

SA 51 **SA 52**

Displacement, tons	78 surface; 81 submerged
Length, feet (*metres*)	70·5 (*21·5*)
Beam, feet (*metres*)	9 (*2·7*)
Draught, feet (*metres*)	9 (*2·7*)
Torpedo tubes	2—21 in (*533 mm*)
Main engines	Pegaso diesels; 400 hp Electric motors; 400 hp
Speed, knots	10 on surface; 14·5 submerged
Range, miles	2 000 at 6 knots (surfaced) 150 at 7 knots (dived)
Complement	8

Launched in 1958. Originally rated as *Submarinos Experimentales*, but in 1963 designated Assault Submarines with "SA" numbers.

ENGINEERING. The diesels were built by ENASA formerly Hispano-Suiza) Barcelona, 200 hp each at 2 000 rpm, with reduction gear on the single screw disposed in a nozzle in continuation of the conic after hull.

LIGHT FORCES

LA COMBATTANTE II TYPE (FAST ATTACK CRAFT—MISSILE)

It is reported that several of these missile boats (probably up to 12) are to be built by France for Spain under an agreement signed between M. Debré and Sr. Lopez Bravo on 15 Feb 1973. Will probably mount Otomat SSMs and have MTU 956 diesels. No further information available.

3 LÜRSSEN TYPE (FAST ATTACK CRAFT—TORPEDO)

LT 30 **LT 31** **LT 32**

Displacement, tons	100 standard; 116 full load
Dimensions, feet	114 × 16·8 × 5
Gun	1—20 mm AA
Tubes	2—21 in
Main engines	3 diesel; 3 shafts; 7 500 bhp = 41 knots
Oil fuel, tons	20
Range, miles	650 at 30 knots
Complement	26

Built at La Carraca, Cadiz, to the design of Lurssens of Bremen. LT 31 was commissioned on 21 July 1956. L 32 was launched in 1956. Decca Radar in LT 32 only.

LT 31 *1970, Spanish Navy*

3 NEW CONSTRUCTION 300 TON TYPE (LARGE PATROL CRAFT)

Displacement, tons	300-400
Guns	3 in and 40 mm
Main engines	8 000 bhp
Speed, knots	18 cruising; 25 max
Range, miles	4 000 at 15 knots

These vessels, which could be equipped with A/S gear, were ordered from Bazán's La Carraca yard in early 1973. They are primarily required for Fishery Protection. A further 3 are due to be ordered and 7 more are included in the III Development Programme (1972-75) and could be transferred to the IV Development Programme (1976-79).

RADAR. Surface search with helicopter control capability.

100 TON TYPE (LARGE PATROL CRAFT)

Displacement, tons	100
Guns	40 mm
Speed, knots	20 cruising; 40 max
Range, miles	1 200 at 20 knots

Although ten of this type are included in the III Development Programme only six are to be built in the near future, the remaining four presumably being slipped to the next programme.

CANDIDO PEREZ (ex-*SC* 679) W11 (LARGE PATROL CRAFT)

Displacement, tons	108 standard; 138 full load
Dimensions, feet	107·5 wl; 111·0 oa × 19·0 × 7·0
Guns	1—40 mm AA; 3—20 mm AA
A/S weapons	2 DCT; 2 Mouse Trap Mk 20
Main engines	GM diesels; 2 shafts; 1 000 bhp = 15·6 knots
Range, miles	2 300 at 10 knots

Built by Walter E. Abrams Shipyard, Inc. Laid down on 4 Mar 1942. Launched on 29 Aug 1942. Completed on 19 Dec 1942. Transferred to Spain on 24 Oct 1956 by USA. Frogmen tender.

CANDIDO PEREZ *Spanish Navy*

Light Forces—*continued*

CABO FRADERA (COASTAL PATROL CRAFT)

Displacement, tons	25 standard; 28 full load
Dimensions, feet	58·5 × 14 × 5·2
Main engines	2 diesels; 760 bhp = 12 knots
Complement	9

Built at La Carraca, in 1963.

5 "LP1" CLASS (COASTAL PATROL CRAFT)

LP 1 **LP 2** **LP 3** **LP 4** **LP 5**

Displacement, tons	25
Dimensions, feet	46 × 15·4 × —
Guns	2—7·62 mm

3 USCG 83ft TYPE (COASTAL PATROL CRAFT)

LAS 10 (ex-LAS 1) **LAS 20** (ex-LAS 2) **LAS 30** (ex-LAS 3)

Displacement, tons	49 standard; 63 full load
Dimensions, feet	78·0 pp; 83·3 oa × 16·1 × 6·6
Guns	1—20 mm AA; 2—7 mm (single)
A/S launchers	2 Mousetrap Mk 20 (4 rockets each)
Main engines	800 bhp = 15 knots
Complement	15

Of wooden hull construction. First units were built by E. N. Bazán, Cadiz in 1963-64.

LAS 10 *1971*

AMPHIBIOUS FORCES

1 Ex-US "CASA GRANDE" CLASS (LSD)

GALICIA TA 31 (ex-USS *San Marcos*, LSD 25)

Displacement, tons	4 790 standard; 9 375 full load
Dimensions, feet	475·4 oa × 76·2 × 18·0 max
Guns	12—40 mm, 60 cal AA (2 quadruple, 2 twin)
Main engines	Geared turbines; 2 shafts; 7 000 shp = 15·4 knots
Boilers	2
Range, miles	8 000 at 15 knots
Complement	265 (15 officers, 250 men)

Transferred to Spain on 1 July 1971. Fitted with helicopter platform. Can carry 3 LCUs or 18 LCMs. 1 347 tons of cargo or 100 2½ ton trucks or 27 M-48 tanks or 11 heavy helicopters. Accommodation for 137 troops (overnight) or 500 for short haul.

GALICIA (as *San Marcos*) *A. & J. Pavia*

1 Ex-US "HASKELL" CLASS

ARAGON (ex-USS *Noble*, APA 218) TA 11

Displacement, tons	6 720 light; 12 450 full load
Dimensions, feet	436·5 wl; 455 oa × 63·5 × 24
Guns	12—40 mm 60 cal (1 quad, 4 twin)
Main engines	Geared turbines; 8 500 shp = 17 knots
Boilers	2 Babcock & Wilcox
Range, miles	14 700 at 16 knots

Amphibious Forces—*continued*

Former US Attack Transport, transferred at San Francisco on 19 Dec 1964. Can carry 1 190 men and 680 tons cargo (or 11 2½ ton trucks and 49 ¾ ton trucks). 24 landing craft.

RADAR. Air search SPS 6; surface search.

ARAGON *1971, Michael D. J. Lennon*

1 Ex-US "ANDROMEDA" CLASS

CASTILLA (ex-USS *Achernar*, AKA 53) TA 21

Displacement, tons	7 430 light; 11 416 full load
Dimensions, feet	435 wl; 457·8 oa × 63 × 24
Guns	1—5 in 38 cal; 8—40 mm 60 cal (twins)
Main engines	2 GE geared turbines; 12 000 shp = 16 knots
Boilers	2 Foster-Wheeler

Former US Attack Cargo Ship transferred at New York on 2 Feb 1965. Can carry 98 men, 6 M-48 tanks, 36 2½ ton trucks and 267 jeeps. 24 landing craft.

CASTILLA *1970, Spanish Navy*

3 Ex-US LST

CONDE DE VENADITO L 13 (ex-USS *Tom Green County*, LST 1159)
MARTIN ALVAREZ L 12 (ex-USS *Wexford County*, LST 1168)
VELASCO L 11 (ex-USS *Terrebonne Parish*, LST 1156)

Displacement, tons	2 590 standard; 5 800 full load
Dimensions, feet	384·0 oa × 55·0 × 17·0
Guns	6—3 in, 50 cal (3 twin, 2 forward, 1 aft)
Main engines	4 GM diesels; 2 shafts; 6 000 bhp = 15 knots
Range, miles	15 000 at 9 knots
Complement	116 (troops 395)

LST 1156 and 1168 transferred on 29 Oct 1971, LST 1159 on 5 Jan 1972. Can carry 395 men, 10 M-48 tanks or 17 LVTP. 4 landing craft.

VELASCO (as *Terrebonne Parish*) *A. & J. Pavia*

LSM 1 (ex-USS *LSM* 329) L 01
LSM 2 (ex-USS *LSM* 331) L 02
LSM 3 (ex-USS *LSM* 343) L 03

Displacement, tons	930 standard; 1 094 full load
Dimensions, feet	196·5 wl × 203·5 oa × 34·5 × 8·3
Guns	2—40 mm AA
Main engines	2 diesels; 2 shafts; 3 600 bhp = 12·5 knots

Medium landing ships transferred at Bremerton, Washington, on 25 Mar 1960. Can carry 49 men overnight or 400 for short haul. As transport can lift 306 tons of vehicles or 160 tons for landing.

LSM 3 *1969*

Amphibious Forces—*continued*

2 Ex-BRITISH LCT (4)

BDK 1 K 1 **BDK 2** K 2

Displacement, tons	440 standard; 868 full load
Dimensions, ft m	185·3 × 38·7 × 6·2 (*56·5 × 11·8 × 1·9*)
Guns	2—20 mm (single)
Main engines	2 Paxman diesels; 2 shafts; 920 bhp = 10 knots
Range, miles	1 100 at 8 knots

Can carry 350 tons or 500 men.

3 SPANISH BUILT LCT's

BDK 3 K 3 **BDK 4** K 4 **BDK 5** K 5

Displacement, tons	902 full load
Dimensions, ft (m)	186 × 38·4 × 6 (*56·6 × 11·6 × 1·7*)
Guns	2—20 mm singles
Main engines	2 M60 V8 AS diesels; 2 shafts; 1 000 hp = 8½ knots
Range, miles	1 000 at 7 knots
Complement	20 (1 officer, 19 men)

All commissioned 15 June 1959. Can carry 300 tons or 400 men.

BDK 5 *1971, Spanish Navy*

BDK 6 K 6 **BDK 7** K 7 **BDK 8** K 8

Displacement, tons	315 standard; 665 full load
Dimensions, feet	193·5 × 39·0 × 5·0
Guns	1—20 mm AA; 2—12·7 mm AA MG
Main engines	2 diesels; 2 shafts; 1 040 bhp = 9·5 knots
Range, miles	1 500 at 9 knots

Landing craft of the French EDIC type built at La Carraca. Completed in Dec 1966.

NOTE. Total of landing craft (including those attached to Aragón, Castilla, Galicia and LST's): 27 LCM, 43 LCVP, 16 LCP (L), 1 LCP (R), 12 LCU. All of US origin except 4 LCP (L) built at Cartagena.

MINEWARFARE FORCES

4 Ex-US "AGILE" CLASS (MINESWEEPERS—OCEAN)

Name	No.	Ex-Name & No.		Launched	Completed
GUADALETE	M 41	*Dynamic*	MSO 432	17 Dec 1952	15 Dec 1953
GUADALMEDINA	M 42	*Pivot*	MSO 463	9 Jan 1954	12 July 1954
GUADALQUIVIR	M 43	*Persistant*	MSO 491	23 Apr 1955	3 Feb 1956
GUADIANA	M 44	*Vigor*	MSO 473	24 June 1953	8 Nov 1954

Displacement, tons	665 standard; 750 full load
Dimensions, feet	165·0 wl; 172·0 oa × 36·0 × 13·6
Guns	2—20 mm AA (Twin)
Main engines	4 Packard diesels; 2 shafts; controllable pitch propellers; 2 280 bhp = 15·5 knots
Range, miles	3 000 at 10 knots
Complement	71 (6 officers, 65 men)

The first three were transferred and commissioned on 1 July 1971. The fourth unit was delivered 4 April 1972. Surface search radar. VDS SQQ 14 with mine classification capability.

GUADALETE *1973, J. Taibo*

Minewarfare Forces—*continued*

7 "GUADIARO" CLASS (MINESWEEPERS—OCEAN)

Name	No.	Builders	Launched	Completed	Modernised
ALMANZORA	M 14	Cartagena	27 July 1953	Nov 1954	20 May 1960
EO	M 17	Cadiz	22 Sep 1953	Mar 1955	22 Mar 1961
EUME	M 13	Cartagena	27 July 1953	Dec 1953	20 July 1960
GUADALHORCE	M 16	Cartagena	18 Feb 1953	Dec 1953	18 Feb 1960
GUADIARO	M 11	Cartagena	26 June 1950	Apr 1953	14 Dec 1959
NAVIA	M 15	Cadiz	28 July 1953	Mar 1955	22 Nov 1960
TINTO	M 12	Cartagena	26 June 1950	May 1953	28 July 1959

Displacement, tons: 671 standard; 770 full load
Dimensions, feet: 243·8 × 33·5 × 12·3 max
Guns: 2—20 mm AA
Main engines: Triple expansion and exhaust turbines; 2 shafts; 2 400 hp = 13 knots after modernisation
Boilers: 2 Yarrow
Oil fuel, tons: 90
Range, miles: 1 000 at 6 knots
Complement: 79

ALMANZORA — *1971, Cdr Aldo Fraccaroli*

12 Ex-US AMS TYPE (MINESWEEPERS—COASTAL)

DUERO (ex-*Spoonbill, MSC* 202) M 28
EBRO (ex-*MSC* 269) M 26
GENIL (ex-*MSC* 279) M 31
JUCAR (ex-*AMS* 220) M 23
LLOBREGAT (ex-*AMS* 143) M 22
MIÑO (ex-*AMS* 266) M 22
NALÓN (ex-*AMS* 139) M 21
ODIEL (ex-*MSC* 288) M 32
SIL (ex-*Redwing, MSC* 200) M 29
TAJO (ex-*MSC* 287) M 30
TURIA (ex-*AMS* 130) M 27
ULLA (ex *AMS* 265) M 24

Displacement, tons: 355 standard; 384 full load
Dimensions, feet: 138·0 pp; 144·0 oa × 27·2 × 8·0
Guns: 2—20 mm AA (1 twin)
A/S weapons: 2 Mouse Trap Mk 20 rocket launchers
Main engines: 2 diesels; 2 shafts; 900 bhp = 14 knots
Oil fuel, tons: 30
Range, miles: 2 700 at 10 knots
Complement: 39

EBRO, Class A, small crane — *1970, Spanish Navy*

Transferred from the USA, *Nalón* on 16 Feb 1954, *Llobregat* on 5 Nov 1954, *Turia* on 1 June 1955, *Jucar* on 22 June 1956, *Ulla* on 24 July 1956, *Miño* on 25 Oct 1956, *Sil* and *Duero* on 16 June 1959, *Ebro* on 19 Dec 1958, *Genil* on 11 Sep 1959, *Tajo* on 9 July 1959 and *Odiel* on 9 Oct 1959.

Two sub-types: (a) with derrick on mainmast: M 21, 22, 23, 24, 25, 27, 28, 29 (b) with no mainmast but crane abreast the funnel: M 26, 30, 31, 32. Tactical radar of various types. AN/UQS-1 sonar.

ULLA, Class B, with mainmast — *1971, Spanish Navy*

Minewarfare Forces—*cont.*

JUAN DE LA COSA (ex-*Artabro*)

Displacement, tons: 770 standard; 1 100 full load
Dimensions, feet: 188· × 35·5 × 8·8
Guns: 2—20 mm
Main engines: B & W diesels; electric drive; 500 bhp = 9 knots
Complement: 51

Launched by UNL, Valence in 1935. Early disposal expected.

SURVEY SHIPS

CASTOR H 4 **POLLUX** H 5 **ANTARES RIGEL**

Displacement, tons: 327 standard; 383 full load
Dimensions, feet: 111 pp; 125·9 oa × 24·9 × 8·9
Main engines: 1 Sulzer 4TD-36 diesel; 720 hp = 11·7 knots
Range, miles: 3 620 at 8 knots
Complement: 39

Built by E. N. Bazán, La Carraca. First pair completed on 10 Nov 1966 and 6 Dec 1966, second pair late 1973, being improved ships of the same class. *Antares* and *Rigel* fitted with Raydist, Omega and digital presentation of data.

CASTOR — *1970, Spanish Navy*

TOFIÑO

Displacement, tons: 998 standard; 1 255 full load
Dimensions, feet: 224·5 × 35 × 11
Gun: 1—37 mm
Main engines: Triple expansion; 2 shafts; 810 ihp = 12·5 knots
Boilers: 2 Yarrow
Complement: 88

Built at Ferrol. Launched on 21 Aug 1933. Early disposal expected.

2 NEW CONSTRUCTION OCEANOGRAPHIC SHIPS

MALASPINA A 31 ———— A 32

Displacement, tons: 1 090 full load
Length, ft (m): 189·3 (*57·7*) oa
Guns: Some light MG
Main engines: 2 diesels; 2 700 bhp
Complement: 63 (9 officers, 54 men)

Building by E. N. Bazán, La Carraca. A 31 laid down early 1973, launched 15 Aug 1973. A 32 laid down 15 Aug 1973 for launch mid 1974.

SERVICE FORCES

ALMIRANTE LOBO (ex-*Torrelaguna*) (TRANSPORT)

Displacement, tons: 5 662 standard; 8 038 full load
Dimensions, feet: 362·5 × 48·2 × 25·7
Guns: 1—1·5 in, 85 cal
Main engines: 1 triple expansion; 2 000 ihp = 12 knots

Ex-cargo vessel. Built at Astilleros Echevarrieta, Cadiz. Commissioned 4 Oct 1954.

ALMIRANTE LOBO

Service Forces—*cont.*

TEIDE BP 11 (REPLENISHMENT TANKER)

Displacement, tons	**2 747 light; 8 030 full load**
Oil capacity, tons	**5 350**
Dimensions, feet	**385·5 × 48·5 × 20·3**
Guns	**1—4·1 in, not mounted, but provision for AA**
Main engines	**2 diesels; 3 360 bhp = 12 knots**

Ordered from Factoria de Bazan, Cartagena, in December 1952. Laid down on 11 Nov 1954. Launched on 20 June 1955. In service October 1956. Rated as *Petrolero de Escuadra*. Modernised in 1962 with refuelling at sea equipment.

TEIDE *1968, Spanish Navy*

PP 1, PP 2 (HARBOUR TANKERS)

Displacement, tons	470
Dimensions, feet	138 pp; 147·5 oa × 25 × 9·5
Main engines	Deutz diesel; 220 bhp = 10 knots
Complement	12

Both built at Santander and launched in 1939.

PP 3 PP 4 PP 5 (HARBOUR TANKERS)

Follow on class of harbour tankers.

PB 1, 2, 3, 4, 5, 6, 17, 20, 21, 22 (HARBOUR TANKERS)

Small harbour tankers with capacity between 100 and 300 tons. Except for the veteran PB 17 all built by Bazán between 1960 and 1965.

PG 12 and 14 (OIL LIGHTERS)

Dumb lighters of 100 and 300 tons capacity.

PEGASO W 21 **PROCYON** W 22 (TRAINING SHIPS)

Displacement, tons	**436 standard; 498 full load**
Dimensions, feet	**137·8 × 27·0 × 9·5**
Guns	**2—20 mm AA**
Main engines	**Reciprocating; 1 shaft; 532 bhp = 12 knots**
Fuel, tons	**200 coal**
Range, miles	**3 500 at 9 knots**
Complement	**39**

Both were commissioned at Cartegena in Jan 1951. Attached to the Naval School.

PROCYON (3 inch gun now removed) *Spanish Navy*

JUAN SEBASTIAN DE ELCANO (TRAINING SHIP)

Displacement, tons	3 420 standard; 3754 full load
Dimensions, feet	269·2 pp; 308·5 oa × 43 × 23
Guns	2—37 mm
Main engines	1 Sulzer diesel; 1 shaft; 1 500 bhp = 9·5 knots
Oil fuel, tons	230
Endurance, miles	10 000 at 9·5 knots
Complement	224 + 80 cadets

Four masted top sail schooner. Named after the first circumnavigator of the world (1519-26) who succeeded to the command of the expedition led by Magallanes after the latter's death. Built by Echevarrieta Yard, Cadiz. Launched on 5 Mar 1927. Completed in 1928.

JUAN SEBASTIAN DE ELCANO *1972 US Navy*

CENTINELA W 33 **SERVIOLA** W 34 (FISHERY PROTECTION VESSELS)

Displacement, tons	255 standard; 282 full load
Dimensions, feet	117·5 × 22·5 × 9·8
Guns	2—37 mm
Main engines	1 diesel; 430 bhp = 12 knots

Completed at Ferrol, in 1953. Given pennant numbers as above in 1972.

SERVIOLA ***1969, Spanish Navy***

SALVORA W 32 (FISHERY PROTECTION VESSEL)

Displacement, tons	**180 standard; 275 full load**
Dimensions, feet	**107·0 × 20·5 × 9·0**
Guns	**1—20 mm MG**
Main engines	**1 Sulzer diesel; 400 bhp = 12 knots**
Complement	**24**

Purchased in Dec 1952.

SALVORA ***1969, Spanish Navy***

AZOR (CHIEF OF STATE'S YACHT)

Displacement, tons	**442 standard; 486 full load**
Dimensions, feet	**153·0 × 25·2 × 12·5**
Main engines	**2 diesels; 1 200 bhp = 12 knots**
Range, miles	**4 000**

Service Forces—*cont.*

Built as the Caudillo's yacht by E. N. Bazan at El Ferrol. Launched on 9 June 1949. Commissioned on 20 July 1949. Underwent an extensive refit, her hull being cut to admit an extension in length.

AZOR *1969, Spanish Navy*

CALAHEDES (ex-*G 6*) **I** CR (BOOM DEFENCE VESSEL)

Displacement, tons	630 standard; 831 full load
Dimensions, feet	165·5 × 34 × 10·5
Guns	1—40 mm AA; 4—20 mm AA single
Main engines	2 diesels; electric drive; 1 shaft; 1 500 bhp = 12 knots
Range, miles	5 200 at 12 knots

Built by Penhoët, France, as a US off-shore order. Launched on 28 Sep 1954. Transferred from the US in 1955 under MDAP.

PBP 1, 2 and 3

Gate Vessels.

PRA 1-8

Tugs for PBPs and PRs.

PR 1-5

Net laying barges.

6 OCEAN TUGS

RA 3 (ex-*Metinda III*)

Displacement, tons	762 standard; 1 080 full load
Dimensions, feet	137 × 33·1 × 15·5
Main engines	Triple expansion; 12 knots

RA 1 **RA 2**

Displacement, tons	757 standard; 1 039 full load
Dimensions, feet	184 × 33·5 × 12
Guns	2 MG
Main engines	2 Sulzer diesels; 3 200 bhp = 15 knots

Ordered in 1949. Built at Factoria de Bazán, Cartagena. Launched on 2 Sep 1954 and 5 Oct 1954, commissioned on 9 July 1955 and 12 Sep 1955, respectively.

RA 2

BS 1 (ex-RA 6) **RA 4** **RA 5**

Displacement, tons	951 standard; 1 069 full load
Dimensions, feet	183·5 × 32·8 × 15·8
Main engines	2 Sulzer diesels; 3 200 bhp = 15 knots

All built at La Carraca, in 1963. RA 6 was renumbered BS 1 when she became a frogman support ship.

8 COASTAL TUGS

RR 15

Displacement, tons	434
Dimensions, feet	124 × 27·5 × 10
Main engines	800 ihp = 11·5 knots

Built in England in 1918.

RR 16

Built at EN Bazán La Carraca in 1962. Length 88·6 feet

RR 50 **RR 51** **RR 52** **RR 53** **RR 54** **RR 55**

Displacement, tons	205 standard; 227 full load
Dimensions, feet	91·2 × 23 × 11
Main engines	Diesels; 1 shaft; 1 400 bhp (53 to 55), 800 bhp (50 to 52)

All built at Cartagena for naval service, first three in 1963, last three in 1967.

17 HARBOUR TUGS

RP 1-12

Of 65 tons and 200 bhp (Diesel). Commissioned 1965-67.

RP 18, RP 30

Of 160 tons and 300 ihp (coal-burning). Built in 1946 and 1952.

RP 25, RP 38
Of 160 tons and 280 ihp (coal burning).

RP 40

Of 150 tons and 600 bhp (diesel). Commissioned 1961.

Service Forces—*cont.*

NOTE. 5 tug-launches of less than 50 tons:— LR 47, 51, 67, 68, 69.

WATER CARRIERS

A 1 **A 2** **A 6**

A 1 and A2 built in 1936, A 6 in 1949. Of 1 785 tons full load with 1 000 tons capacity. Ocean going.

A 7-A 11

5 ships built 1949-52. Of 610 tons full load with 350 tons capacity. A 9-11 completed in 1963 have radar. All oceangoing.

AB 1, 2, 3, 10, 17, 18

All of less than 400 tons. Harbour water boats with 200 tons or less capacity.

TORPEDO RECOVERY CRAFT

BTM 1-6

Built by Bazán 1961-63 of 100-300 tons. To carry torpedoes and mines and, in emergency can act as minelayers.

L 51

Minelaying experimental craft.

ST 5

TRV based at Poligone.

LRT 3 and 4

TRVs built in 1956. Can carry 6 torpedoes. Have stern ramp and crane.

DIVING CRAFT

BZL 1, 2, 3, 9 and 10

Small self-propelled craft of less than 50 tons.

BL 10 and 13

Dumb barges for diving.

FLOATING CRANES

SANSÓN GRI (100 tons lift)
GR 3, 4 and 5 (30 tons lift)
GR 6, 7, 8 and 9 (15 tons lift)

MISCELLANEOUS

5 PATROL VESSELS

RR 10 **RR 19** **RR 20** **RR 28** **R 29**

Displacement, tons	364 standard; 498 full load
Dimensions, feet	124·0 × 29·0 × 10·0
Guns	1—1·5 in, 85 cal or 1—47 mm; 1—20 mm AA
Main engines	Triple expansion; 1 shaft; 800 ihp = 11·5 knots
Boilers	1 cylindrical, 13 kg/cm
Fuel, tons	200 coal
Range, miles	620 at 10 knots

Former tugs. All launched in 1941-42. All classed as *Patrulleros* except RR 28, classed as *remolcador de rada*, some have navigation radar. Some to be discarded shortly.

16 PATROL LAUNCHES

V 2	Displacement: 22 tons	Gun: 1—7 mm	Speed: 6·7 knots
V 4	Displacement: 65 tons	Gun: 1—7 mm	Speed: 9 knots
V 5	Displacement: 4·5 tons	Gun: 1—7 mm	Speed: 5 knots
V 6	Displacement: 42 tons	Guns: 2—20 mm	Speed: 19·2 knots
V 7	Displacement: 20 tons	Gun: 1—7 mm	Speed: 8·5 knots
V 8	Displacement: 26·5 tons	Gun: 1—7 mm	Speed: 7·8 knots
V 9	Displacement: 15·6 tons	Gun: 1—7 mm	Speed: 9 knots
V 10	Displacement: 11·6 tons	Gun: 1—7 mm	Speed: 9·5 knots
V 11	Displacement: 11·6 tons	Gun: 1—7 mm	Speed: 9·5 knots
V 12	Displacement: 28 tons	Gun: 1—7 mm	Speed: 7·8 knots
V 13	Displacement: 45·1 tons	Gun: 1—7 mm	Speed: 7·8 knots
V 17	Displacement: 110·9 tons	Gun: 1—20 mm	Speed: 10·5 knots
V 18	Displacement: 116 tons	Gun: 1—13 mm	Speed: 6 knots
V 21	Displacement: 16 tons	Gun: 1—13 mm	Speed: 17·6 knots

There are also V 1, yacht, ex-*Azor*, and launch *Gaviota*. Coastal launches employed on surveillance and fishery protection duties, *Lanchos guardapescas*, except V 17 and V 21, rated as *patrulleros*. V 4 is named *Alcatraz:* V 12 *Esturión* and V 18 *Lanzón*.

LANZON (V 18) *1969, Spanish Navy*

SRI LANKA (CEYLON)

Administration

The Royal Ceylon Navy was formed on 9 Dec 1950 when the Navy Act was proclaimed.

Captain of the Navy:
Commodore D. V. Hunter

Diplomatic Representation

Services Attaché in London:
Withdrawn from 1 November 1970

Naval Base

The Naval Base is established at Trincomalee, which was a British base from 1795 until 1957.

Strength of the Fleet

1 Frigate	27 Coastal Patrol Craft
5 Fast Gunboats	1 Tug
1 Hydrofoil Craft	

Personnel

(a) 1974: 2 300 (200 officers and 2 100 sailors)
(b) Voluntary Service

Mercantile Marine

Lloyd's Register of Shipping:
33 vessels of 43 754 tons gross

Defence Expenditure and Policy

Since the Indo-Pakistan war visits by US, British and Russian ships have taken place. It is reported that Defence spending has been doubled and that "20 small police and gunboats" have been acquired.

FRIGATES

1 Ex-CANADIAN "RIVER" CLASS

Name	No.	Builders	Launched
GAJABAHU (ex-*Misnak*, ex-HMCS *Hallowell*)	F 232	Canadian Vickers Ltd, Montreal	8 Aug 1944

Displacement, tons	1 445 standard; 2 360 full load
Lenght, feet (*metres*)	283 (*86·3*) pp; 295·5 (*90·1*) wl; 310·5 (*91·9*) oa
Beam, feet (*metres*)	36·5 (*11·1*)
Draught, feet (*metres*)	13·8 (*4·2*)
Guns, surface	1—4 in (*102 mm*)
Guns, AA	3—40 mm
Main engines	Triple expansion; 5 500 ihp; 2 shafts
Boilers	2 three-drum type
Speed, knots	20
Range, miles	4 200 at 12 knots
Oil fuel, tons	585
Complement	160

GENERAL
Acquired from Canada by Israel in 1950 and sold by Israel to Ceylon in 1959. Guns above replaced 3—4·7 inch, 8—20 mm in 1965. Reportedly now non-operational.

GAJABAHU *1971, Royal Ceylon Navy*

LIGHT FORCES

5 Ex-CHINESE "SHANGHAI IV" CLASS (FAC—GUN)

SURAYA WEERAYA +3

Displacement, tons	120 full load
Dimensions, feet	130 × 18 × 5·6
Guns	4—37 mm (2 twin) 4—25 mm (2 twin abaft the bridge) 1—small mortar forward
Main engines	4 Diesels; 5 000 bhp = 30 knots
Complement	25

Shanghai *Class*

GENERAL
The first pair was transferred by China in Feb 1972, the second pair in July 1972 and the last in December 1972. In monsoonal conditions off the Ceylonese coast these boats will be lively and uncomfortable. Skinhead Radar.

21 THORNYCROFT TYPE (COASTAL PATROL CRAFT)

101-110, 202-209 + 3

Displacement, tons	15
Dimensions, feet	45·5 × 12 × 3
Main engines	2 boats: Thornycroft K6SMI engines; 500 bhp = 25 knots 7 boats: General Motors 6 71-Series; 560 bhp = 25 knots

GENERAL
Fast twin screw motor launches built by Thornycroft (Malasyia) Limited in Singapore The hulls are of hard chine type with double skin teak planking. Equipped with radar, radio, searchlight etc. Two ordered in 1965 and completed in 1966. Seven ordered in 1966 and completed in 1967. 12 more assembled in Ceylon and completed by Sep 1968.

PC 102 *1970, Royal Ceylon Navy*

2 ITALIAN TYPE (COASTAL PATROL CRAFT)

HANSAYA LIHINIYA

Displacement, tons	36
Dimensions, feet	63·5 pp; 66 oa × 14 × 4
Main engines	3 General Motors diesels; 450 bhp = 16 knots

Built at Venice by the Korody Marine Corporation.

DIYAKAWA KORAWAKKA SERUWA TARAWA

Displacement, tons	13
Dimensions, feet	46 pp; 48 oa × 12 × 3
Main engines	2 Foden FD.6 diesels; 240 bhp = 15 knots

Diyakawa and *Korawakka* were rated as harbour launches in June 1970. *Seruwa* and *Tarawa* were rated as hydrographic vessels. Built in Italy.

1 SHORT HYDROFOIL TYPE

Dimensions, feet	22·2 × 9·9 hull; 10·2 oa. Depth over side moulded; 3; Draught at anchor, 3·7, Draught at speed, 1·7 official figures.
Main engines	2 Volvo Penta Aquamatic 100 hp engines. Total 200 hp = 40 knots

A Short type of hydrofoil craft added to the Royal Ceylon Navy List in 1964.

HYDROFOIL CRAFT *1964, Royal Ceylon Navy*

TUG

ALIYA (ex-*Adept*, ex-*Empire Barbara*)

Displacement, tons	503 full load
Dimensions, feet	105 × 26·5 × 12·8
Main engines	Triple expansion; 850 ihp = 10 knots

Built by Cochrane & Sons Ltd., Selby, Yorks, England. Transferred from Great Britain Decommissioned in 1964 to be sold, but this intention was rescinded. She was re-commisioned in 1966, and underwent major refit in 1967.

BOOM DEFENCE VESSEL. *Baron* was purchased from Great Britain by the Colombo Port Commission.

SWEDEN

Administration

Commander-in-Chief:
Vice-Admiral Bengt Lundvall

Chief of Naval Material Department:
Rear Admiral Gunnar Grandin

Commander-in-Chief of Coastal Fleet:
Rear-Admiral Christer Kierkegaard

Chief of Naval Staff:
Major-General Bo Varenius

Chief of Staff Coastal Fleet (Acting):
Captain S. Hakanson

Diplomatic Representation

Naval Attaché in London:
Captain N. U. Rydström

Naval Attaché in Washington:
Captain N. L. Lindgren

Personnel

(a) 1974: 14 500 officers and men of Navy and Coast Artillery made up of 4 500 regulars, 2 500 Reservists and 7 500 National Servicemen. In addition 12 000 conscripts receive annual training.
(b) 15 months.

Strength of the Fleet

Type	*Active*	*Building (Planned)*
Destroyers	8	—
Frigates	5	—
Submarines—Patrol	22	5
Corvettes—Light Forces	—	(2)
Fast Attack Craft—Missile	1	(16)
Fast Attack Craft—Torpedo	39	9
Large Patrol Craft	1	—
Coastal Patrol Craft	22	—
Minelayers	2	1+(1)
Minelayers—Coastal	9	(1)
Minelayers—Small	37	1
Minehunters	—	(6?)
Minesweepers—Coastal	18	—
Minesweepers-Inshore—	18	2
LCM's	9	—
LCU's	63	(16)
LCA's	54	—
Mine Transports	2	—
Survey Ships	5	—
Tankers—Support	2	—
Supply Ship	1	—
Command Ship	1	—
Tugs	8	—
Salvage Vessel	1	—
Sail Training Ships	2	—
Ice Breakers	6	2
TRV's	2	—
Tenders	4	—
Water Boats	2	—

Naval Air Arm

7 Alouette II helicopters
10 Jet Ranger helicopters
7 Kawasaki-Vertol 107 ((Hkp-4C)
3 Vertol 107 (Hkp-4B)

Future Plans

In June 1972 the Swedish Parliament approved the Government's Defence Plan for the next 5 years. The proposals of the Defence Minister, Mr Andersson, reduced the service vote by a tenth below the minimum requirement of General Stig Synnergren, the Supreme Commander. The effects of this reduction on the Navy may be the scrapping of all frigates without replacement by 1978, leaving only helicopters in the A/S role and a reduction of submarines from 22 to 11.

Composition of the Navy

In addition to seagoing personnel the Navy includes the Coastal Artillery, manning 20 mobile and 45 coastal batteries of both major guns and SSMs.

Disposals and Transfers

Cruisers

1971 *Göta Lejon* to Chile (*Latorre*)

Depot Ships

1972 *Patricia*

Surveying Vessels

1972 *Johen Nordenankar, Petter Gedda*

Mercantile Marine

Lloyd's Register of Shipping:
875 vessels of 5 632 336 tons gross

DESTROYERS

4 "ÖSTERGÖTLAND" CLASS

Name	*No.*	*Builders*	*Laid down*	*Launched*	*Completed*
GÄSTRIKLAND	J 22	Götaverken, Göteborg	1 Oct 1955	6 June 1956	14 Jan 1959
HÄLSINGLAND	J 23	Kockums Mek Verkstads A/B	1 Oct 1955	14 Jan 1957	17 June 1959
ÖSTERGÖTLAND	J 20	Götaverken, Göteborg	1 Sep 1955	8 May 1956	3 Mar 1958
SÖDERMANLAND	J 21	Eriksberg Mekaniska Verkstad	1 June 1955	28 May 1956	27 June 1958

Displacement, tons	2 150 standard; 2 600 full load
Length, feet (*metres*)	367·5 (*112·0*) oa
Beam, feet (*metres*)	36·8 (*11·2*)
Draught, feet (*metres*)	12·0 (*3·7*)
Missile launchers	1 quadruple "Seacat" surface-to-air
Guns	4—4·7 in (*120 mm*), 2 twin; 4—40 mm AA single
A/S weapons	Triple barrelled mortar
Torpedo tubes	6—21 in (*533 mm*), 2 triple
Mines	60 can be carried
Main engines	De Laval turbines; 2 shafts; 40 000 shp
Speed, knots	35
Boilers	2 Babcock & Wilcox
Range, miles	2 200 at 20 knots
Oil fuel, tons	330
Complement	244 (18 officers, 226 men)

ÖSTERGÖTLAND *Class*

These ships have improved anti-aircraft defence and anti-submarine weapons of the Bofors type.

MODERNISATION. *Gästrikland* in 1965, *Södermanland* in 1967, *Hälsingland* in 1968, *Östergötland* in 1969.

RADAR. Thomson CSF Saturn S-band long-range search and target designator; HSA M 44 series for Seacat; M 45 series for guns.

HÄLSINGLAND *1972, Royal Swedish Navy*

Destroyers—*continued*

2 "HALLAND" CLASS

Name	No.	Builders	Laid down	Launched	Completed
HALLAND	J 18	Götaverken, Göteborg	1951	16 July 1952	8 June 1955
SMÅLAND	J 19	Eriksberg Mekaniska Verkstad, Göteborg	1951	23 Oct 1952	12 Jan 1956

Displacement, tons	2 800 standard; 3 400 full load
Length, feet (*metres*)	380·5 (*116·0*)wl; 397·2 (*121·0*)oa
Beam, feet (*metres*)	41·3 (*12·6*)
Draught, feet (*metres*)	14·8 (*4·5*)
Launcher	1 rocket launcher RB 8
Guns	4—4·7 in (*120 mm*) dp (2 twin) 2—57 mm AA; 6—4 mm AA
A/S weapons	2 four-barrelled mortars
Torpedo tubes	8—21 in (*533 mm*) 2 quadruple
Mines	Can be fitted for minelaying
Main engines	De Laval double reduction geared turbines; 2 shafts; 58 000 shp
Speed, knots	35
Boilers	2 Penhöet
Range, miles	3 000 at 20 knots
Oil fuel, tons	500
Complement	290 (18 officers, 272 men)

HALLAND *Class*

Both ordered in 1948. The first Swedish destroyers of post-war design and construction. Fully automatic gun turrets forward and aft, ahead throwing anti-submarine weapons of the Bofors type forward, and rocket launcher abaft the after funnel.

RADAR. Thomson CSF Saturn S-band long-range search and target designator on foremast; LW 02/03 air warning radar on main mast M 22 series with co-mounted search and tracking radars in radome. ECM.

HALLAND — *1968, Royal Swedish Navy*

2 "ÖLAND" CLASS

Name	No.	Builders	Laid down	Launched	Completed	Modernised
ÖLAND	J 16	Kockums Mek Verkstads A/B, Malmö	1943	15 Dec 1945	5 Dec 1947	1960, 1969
UPPLAND	J 17	Karlskrona Dockyard	1943	5 Nov 1946	31 Jan 1949	1963

Displacement, tons	2 000 standard; 2 400 full load
Length, feet (*metres*)	351 (*107·0*) pp; 367·5 (*112·0*) oa
Beam, feet (*metres*)	36·8 (*11·2*)
Draught, feet (*metres*)	11·2 (*3·4*)
Guns	4—4·7 in (*120 mm*) dp (2 twin); 6—40 mm AA single
A/S weapons	1 triple-barrelled DC mortar
Torpedo tubes	6—21 in (*533 mm*) 2 triple
Mines	60 capacity, fitted for laying
Main engines	De Laval geared turbines; 2 shafts; 44 000 shp
Speed, knots	35
Boilers	2 Penhöet
Range, miles	2 500 at 20 knots
Oil fuel, tons	300
Complement	210

ÖLAND

Superstructure and machinery spaces lightly armoured.

RADAR. Thomson CSF Saturn S-band long-range search and target-designator; Two M 45 series fire control radars for guns; navigation set.

GUNNERY. 4·7 inch guns semi-automatic with 80° elevation. 40 mm AA gun near jackstaff was removed in 1962, and eight 20 mm AA guns in 1964.

RECONSTRUCTION. *Öland* was modernised with new bridge in 1960 and again in 1969; and *Uppland* with new bridge and helicopter platform in 1963.

ÖLAND — *1970, Royal Swedish Navy*

FRIGATES

4 "VISBY" CLASS

Name	No.	Builders	Launched	Completed
HÄLSINGBORG	13	Götaverken	23 Mar 43	30 Nov 43
KALMAR	14	Eriksberg	20 July 43	3 Feb 44
SUNDSVALL	F 12	Eriksberg	20 Oct 42	17 Sep 43
VISBY	F 11	Götaverken	16 Oct 42	10 Aug 43

Displacement, tons	1 150 standard; 1 320 full load
Length, feet (*metres*)	310·0 (*94·5*) wl; 321·5 (*98·0*) oa
Beam, feet (*metres*)	30 (*9·1*)
Draught, feet (*metres*)	12·5 (*3·8*)
Aircraft	1 helicopter (F 11 and F 12)
Guns	3—4·7 in (*120 mm*); 3—40 mm AA (2—57 mm only in F 11 and F 12)
A/S weapons	1 four-barrelled DC mortar
Torpedo tubes	5—21 in (*533 mm*) F 11 F 12
Main engines	De Laval geared turbines; 2 shafts; 36 000 shp
Speed, knots	39
Boilers	3 three-drum type
Range, miles	1 600 at 20 knots
Oil fuel, tons	150
Complement	140

SUNDSVALL *1972, Royal Swedish Navy*

Kalmar was laid down on 16 Nov 1942, and *Visby* on 29 Apr 1942. All were originally fitted for minelaying. All four will be paid off for disposal in the near future.

RADAR. Thomson CSF Saturn S-band long-range search and target designator; M 24 fire control systems with co-mounted radars for search and tracking for guns.

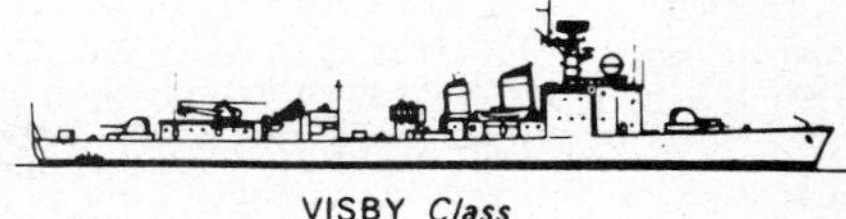
VISBY *Class*

KARLSKRONA F 79

Displacement, tons	1 200 standard; 1 400 full load
Length, feet (*metres*)	304·1 (*92·7*) wl; 310·5 (*94·6*) oa
Beam, feet (*metres*)	31·8 (*9·7*)
Draught, feet (*metres*)	12·5 (*3·8*)
Guns	3—4·7 in (*120 mm*) dp single; 4—40 mm AA single
A/S weapons	2 triple-barrelled DC mortars
Main engines	De Laval geared turbines; 2 shafts; 32 000 shp
Speed, knots	39
Boilers	3 Penhöet
Range, miles	1 200 at 20 knots
Oil fuel, tons	150
Complement	130

Last of a class of six. Built at Karlskrona Dockyard. Launched on 16 June 1939 and completed on 12 Sep 1940. Originally carried up to 60 mines. Refitted for anti-submarine warfare and reclassified as frigate on 1 Jan 1961. Converted in 1963.

RADAR. Equipped with Type 293 search installation.

KARLSKRONA *1970, Stefan Terzibaschitsch*

SUBMARINES

NEW CONSTRUCTION PATROL TYPE

5 "NÄCKEN (A14) CLASS

NÄCKEN **NEPTUN**
NAJAD +2

Displacement, tons	980 surfaced; 1 125 submerged
Length, feet (*metres*)	167·3 (*51·0*)
Beam, feet (*metres*)	20·0 (*6·1*)
Draught, feet (*metres*)	16·7 (*5·1*)
Torpedo tubes	4—21 in (*533 mm*) (8 reloads)
Main engines	Diesels, electric motors; 1 shaft
Speed, knots	*circa* 20 surface and submerged
Complement	25

Building at Karlskrona and Kockums, Malmö for completion in 1977-78.

SJÖBJÖRNEN *1971, Royal Swedish Navy, Official*

5 "SJÖORMEN" CLASS (A11B)

Name	Builders	Launched	Completed
SJÖORMEN	Kockums	25 Jan 67	31 July 67
SJÖLEJONET	Kockums	29 June 67	16 Dec 68
SJÖHUNDEN	Kockums	21 Mar 68	25 June 69
SJÖHÄSTEN	Karlskrona	6 Aug 68	15 Sep 69
SJÖBJÖRNEN	Karlskrona	9 Jan 68	28 Feb 69

Displacement, tons	11 25 standard; 1 400 submeged
Length, feet (*metres*)	167·3 (*51·0*)
Beam, feet (*metres*)	20·0 (*6·1*)
Draught, feet (*metres*)	16·7 (*5·1*)
Torpedo tubes	4—21 in (*533 mm*) 2 A/S tubes
Main engines	Pielstick diesels; 1 large 5-bladed propeller; 1 900 bhp; electric motors
Speed, knots	15 surface; 20 submerged
Endurance	3 weeks
Complement	23

Albacore hull. Twin-decked. Diving depth 500 ft.

APPEARANCE.
Distinctive letters painted on the conning tower Sor, *Sjöormen:* Sbj, *Sjöbjörnen*; Shä, *Sjohästen:* Shu, *Sjöhunden*; Sle, *Sjölejoner.*

SJÖHUNDEN *1972, Royal Swedish Navy*

ICEBREAKERS

2 NEW CONSTRUCTION

ATLE **YMER**

Displacement, tons	8 000
Dimensions, feet	338 oa × 77 × 24·5
Main engines	5 Wärtsilä-Sulzer diesels; 4 Stromberg electric motors; 4 shafts (2 for'd, 2 aft); 20 000 hp = 17 knots

Under construction by the Wärtsilä concern in Finland. Due for completion in 1974 and 1975.

ALE

Displacement, tons	1 488
Dimensions, ft (*m*)	50·9 × 42·6 × 16·4 (*46* × *13* × *5*)
Main engines	Diesels; 4 750 hp = 14 knots

Completed in 1973.

NJORD

Displacement, tons	5 150 standard; 5 686 full load
Dimensions, feet	260·8 pp; 283·8 oa × 69·6 × 20·3
Main engines	Wärtsilä diesel-electric; 4 shafts, 2 forward, 2 aft; 12 000 hp = 18 knots

Built by Wärtsilä, Finland. Launched on 20 Oct 1968 and completed in Dec 1969 Near sister ship of *Tor*.

NJORD *1971, Royal Swedish Navy*

TOR

Displacement, tons	4 980 standard; 5 290 full load
Dimensions, feet	254·3 pp; 277·2 oa × 69·5 × 20·3
Main engines	Wärtsilä-Sulzer diesel-electric; 4 shafts; 2 forward; 2 aft; 12 000 hp = 18 knots

Launched from Wärtsilä's Crichton-Vulcan yard, Turku, on 25 May 1963. Towed to Sandvikens Skeppsdocka, Helsingfors, for completion. Delivered on 31 Jan 1964. Larger but generally similar to *Oden*, and a near-sister to *Tarmo* built for Finland.

TOR *1972, Royal Swedish Navy*

ODEN

Displacement, tons	4 950 standard; 5 220 full load
Dimensions, feet	255·9 pp; 273·5 oa × 63·7 × 22·7
Main engines	Diesel-electric; 4 shafts (2 for'd); 10 500 bhp = 16 knots
Oil fuel, tons	740
Complement	75

Similar to the Finnish *Voima* and 3 Soviet icebreakers. 4 screws, 2 forward, 2 aft. Built at Sandviken, Helsingfors. Launched on 16 Oct 1956. Completed in 1958.

ODEN *1972, Royal Swedish Navy*

THULE

Displacement, tons	2 200 standard; 2 280 full load
Dimensions, feet	187·0 wl; 204·2 oa × 52·8 × 19·4
Main engines	Diesel-electric; 3 shafts (1 for'd); 4 800 bhp = 14 knots
Complement	43

Launched at the Naval Dockyard, Karlskrona, in Oct 1951. Completed in 1953. A photograph appears in the 1969-70 and earlier editions. The icebreaker *Atle* was officially discarded in 1967.

YMER

Displacement, tons	4 330 standard; 4 645 full load
Dimensions, feet	240 wl; 258 oa × 63·1 × 22·3
Main engines	6 Atlas diesel-electric; 9 000 hp = 16 knots
Complement	44

Launched by Kockums MV A/B, Malmö in 1932. First large icebreaker with diesel-electric propulsion. Designed to carry a seaplane for ice spotting and survey.

YMER *1969, Royal Swedish Navy*

SUDAN

Establishment

The navy was established in 1962 to guard the Red Sea coast with a training staff from Yugoslavian Navy. This staff left in 1972.

Diplomatic Representation

Naval Military and Air Attaché in London:
Col. Hassan Yousif El-Hassan

Personnel

(a) 1974 600 officers and men
(b) Voluntary service

Mercantile Marine

Lloyd's Register of Shipping: 13 vessels of 38 278 tons gross

2 Ex-YUGOSLAV "PBR 500" CLASS (LARGE PATROL CRAFT)

FASHER PBR 1 **KHARTOUM** PBR 2

Displacement, tons	190 standard; 245 full load
Dimensions, feet	134·5 × 20·7 × 7·0
Guns	2—40 mm AA; 2—20 mm AA
Main engines	Diesel; 2 shafts; 3 300 bhp = 20 knots
Range, miles	1 500 at 12 knots

Built in 1953-55. Transferred from the Yugoslavian Navy during 1969.

4 Ex-YUGOSLAV PBR TYPE (LARGE PATROL CRAFT)

GIHAD PB 1 **HORRIYA** PB 2 **ISTIQLAL** PB 3 **SHAAB** PB 4

Displacement, tons	100
Dimensions, feet	115 × 16·5 × 5·2
Guns	1—40 mm AA; 1—20 mm AA; 2—7·6 mm MG
Main engines	Mercedes-Benz diesels; 2 shafts; 1 800 bhp = 20 knots
Range, miles	1 400 at 12 knots
Complement	20 officers and men

Built by Mosor Shipyard, Trogir, Yugoslavia, in 1961-62. Of steel construction. First craft acquired by the newly established Sudanese Navy.

HORRIYA *Sudanese Navy*

2 LANDING CRAFT

Two ex-Yugoslavian landing craft of the DTK 221 type were taken over during 1969.

FASHODA (ex-PN 17) (SUPPORT TANKER)

Displacement, tons	420 standard; 650 full load
Dimensions, feet	141·5 × 22·8 × 13·6
Main engines	300 bhp = 7 knots

Former Yugoslavian oiler rehabilitated and transferred to the Sudanese Navy in 1969.

TIENAGA (SURVEY SHIP)

A small vessel, converted into a hydrographic ship, acquired from Yugoslavia in 1969.

BARAKA (ex-PV 6) (WATER BOAT)

A small water carrier, transferred from Yugoslavia to the Sudanese Navy in 1969.

SWITZERLAND

The Swiss Army operates ten Coastal Patrol Craft on the frontier lakes. These were originally built in 1942 against possible German operations and have been modernised. Fitted with machine guns and radar.

SWISS PATROL CRAFT *1966, Swiss Army*

SYRIA

Personnel

(a) 1974: 2 200 officers and men
(b) 2½ years national service

Arab-Israeli War October 1973

Losses in the war with Israel were considerable. From the various reports available Syria appears to have lost both her original "Osas", three "Komars", one "T 43" and one "P 4". The replacement situation is uncertain but reports of "Osas" since the war suggest that this class is the first to receive attention.

Mercantile Marine

Lloyd's Register of Shipping: 8 vessels of 2 057 tons gross

3 Ex-USSR "OSA" CLASS (FAST ATTACK CRAFT—MISSILE)

Displacement, tons	165 standard; 200 full load
Dimensions, feet	128.7 × 25·1 × 5·9
Missile launchers	4, two pairs abreast, for SSN 2-A (Styx)
Guns	4—30 mm twins; 1 forward, 1 aft
Main engines	3 diesels; 13 000 bhp = 32 knots
Range, miles	800 at 25 knots
Complement	25

Original pair sunk in Oct 1973 war. Up to three replacements reported.

SYRIAN OSA CLASS *Dec. 1972*

3 Ex-USSR "KOMAR" CLASS (FAST ATTACK CRAFT—MISSILE)

Displacement, tons	70 standard; 80 full load
Dimensions, feet	83·7 × 19·8 × 5
Missile launchers	2 for SSN 2A (Styx)
Guns	2—25 mm AA
Main engines	4 diesels; 4 shafts; 4 800 bhp = 40 knots
Range, miles	400 at 30 knots

Transferred between 1963 and 1966. Three reported lost in Israeli war October 1973.

16 Ex-USSR "P 4 CLASS" (FAST ATTACK CRAFT—TORPEDO)

Displacement, tons	25 standard
Dimensions, feet	62·7 × 11·6 × 5·6
Tubes	2—18 in
Guns	2— MG (twin)
Main engines	2 diesels; 2 200 bhp 2 shafts = 50 knots

Five torpedo boats were transferred from the USSR at Latakia on 7 Feb 1957, and at least twelve subsequently. Only approximately ten of these can be considered operational. One reported lost in Israeli war October 1973.

3 Ex-FRENCH CH TYPE (LARGE PATROL CRAFT)

ABABEH IBN NEFEH **ABDULLAH IBN ARISSI** **TAREK IBN ZAYED**

Displacement, tons	107 standard; 131 full load
Dimensions, feet	116·5 pp; 121·8 oa × 17·5 × 6·5
Guns	1—3 in; 2—20 mm AA
A/S weapons	Depth charges
Main engines	MAN diesels; 2 shafts; 1 130 bhp = 16 knots
Oil fuel, tons	50
Range, miles	1 200 at 8 knots; 680 at 13 knots
Complement	28

All built in France and completed in 1940. Rebuilt in 1955-56 when the funnels were removed. These were transferred in 1962 to form the nucleus of the Syrian Navy. Two of these ships are probably non-operational.

1 Ex-USSR "T 43" CLASS (MINESWEEPER—OCEAN)

YARMOUK

Displacement, tons	500 standard; 610 full load
Dimensions, feet	191·5 × 28·1 × 6·9
Guns	4—37 mm AA; 4—25 mm AA
Main engines	2 diesel motors; 2 shafts 2 000 hp = 17 knots
Range, miles	1 600 at 10 knots
Complement	40

Reported in 1962 to have transferred from the Soviet Navy to the Syrian Navy. One of this class was sunk in the Israeli War October 1973.

TAIWAN (REPUBLIC OF CHINA)

Administration

Commander-in-Chief of the Navy:
Admiral Soong Chang-chih

Deputy Commander-in-Chief, Operations:
Vice Admiral Huang Hsi-lin

Deputy Commander-in-Chief, Administration:
Vice Admiral Lee Tun-chien

Commander, Fleet Command:
Vice Admiral Chen Ching-kun

Diplomatic Representation

Naval Attaché in Washington, D.C.:
Rear-Admiral Wang Hsi-ling

Personnel

38 000 officers and enlisted men in Navy plus
34 000 officers and enlisted men in Marine Corps.

Strength of the Fleet

2 Submarines	6 Torpedo Boats
19 Destroyers	1 Dock Landing Ship
8 Frigates	2 Amphibious Flagships
1 Frigate/Transport	21 Tank Landing Ships
3 Patrol Vessels	4 Medium Landing Ships
13 Coastal Minesweepers	22 Utility Landing Craft
9 Mine Boats & Launches	19 Auxiliary Ships
	5 Floating Dry Docks

Mercantile Marine

Lloyd's Register of Shipping:
399 vessels of 1 494 903 tons gross

SUBMARINES

2 Ex-US GUPPY II TYPE

Displacement, tons	1 870 standard; 2 420 submerged
Length, feet (*metres*)	307·5 (*93·6*) oa
Beam, feet (*metres*)	27·2 (*8·3*)
Draught, feet (*metres*)	18 (*5·5*)
Torpedo tubes	10—21 inch (*533 mm*); 6 fwd; 4 aft
Main engines	3 diesels (Fairbanks Morse); 4 800 bhp/ 2 electric motors (Elliott); 5 400 shp; 2 shafts
Speed, knots	18 surface; 15 submerged
Complement	81 (11 officers, 70 enlisted men)

Name	*No.*	*Launched*	*US Comm*	*Transferred*
HAI SHIH (ex-USS *Cutlass*, SS 478)	SS 91	5 Nov 1944	17 Mar 1945	12 Apr 1973
HAI PAO (ex-USS *Tusk*, SS 426)	SS 92	8 July 1945	11 Apr 1946	18 Oct 1973

Originally fleet-type submarines of the US Navy "Tench" class; extensively modernised under the GUPPY II programme. *Hai Shih* built by Portsmouth Navy Yard and *Hai Pao* by Federal SB & DD Co, Kearny, New Jersey. These submarines each have four 126-cell electric batteries; fitted with snorkel.
The *Cutlass* was the first US submarine to be transferred to an allied navy in the Western Pacific; provided primarily to improve anti-submarine training capabilities of the Republic of China Navy.

HAI SHIH — *1972, United States Navy*

HAI SHIH — *1973, US Navy*

DESTROYERS

4 Ex-US "GEARING" CLASS

Name	No.	Builder	Launched	US Comm	Transferred
DANG YANG (ex-USS *Lloyd Thomas*, DD 764)	DD 11	Bethlehem Steel (San Francisco)	5 Oct 1945	21 Mar 1947	12 Oct 1972
LIAO YANG (ex-USS *Hanson*, DD 832)	DD 12	Bath Iron Works Corp	11 Mar 1945	11 May 1945	18 Apr 1973
LAO YANG (ex-USS *Shelton*, DD 790)	DD 20	Todd Pacific Shipyards	8 Mar 1946	21 June 1946	18 Apr 1973
CHIEN YANG (ex-USS *James E. Kyes*, DD 787)	DD 12	Todd Pacific Shipyards	4 Aug 1945	8 Feb 1946	18 Apr 1973

Displacement, tons	2 425 standard; approx 3 500 full load
Length, feet (*metres*)	390·5 (*119·0*) oa
Beam, feet (*metres*)	40·9 (*12·4*)
Draught, feet (*metres*)	19 (*5·8*)
Guns	4—5 inch (*127 mm*) 38 cal DP (twin)
A/S weapons	1 ASROC 8-tube launcher except in *Dang Yang* which has trainable hedgehog (Mk 15); 6—12·75 inch (*324 mm*) torpedo tubes (Mk 32 triple)
Main engines	2 geared turbines (General Electric); 60 000 shp; 2 shafts
Boilers	4
Speed, knots	34
Complement	approx 275

Former US Navy destroyers of the "Gearing" class. The *Dang Yang* was modified to a special anti-submarine configuration and reclassified as a "hunter-killer" destroyer (DDK) in 1949; changed to "escort" destroyer (DDE) in 1950; changed again to "straight" DD upon modernisation in 1962. These ships have been extensively modernised under the Fleet Rehabilitation and Modernisation programme, all to FRAM I standard except *Dang Yang* which was FRAM II (no ASROC). All have helicopter platform and hangar.

Armament listed above was at time of transfer. The ex-*Shelton* has twin 5 inch gun mounts in "A" and "B" positions with A/S torpedo tubes alongside second funnel; other ships have the "A" and "Y" gun mounts with torpedo tubes in "B" position except *Dang Yang* has torpedo tubes between funnels.

The three FRAM I ships initially were scheduled for transfer to Spain; however; they were declined by Spain and allocated to Taiwan China.

ELECTRONICS. At the time of transfer the FRAM I ships had SPS-37 and SPS-10 search radar antennas on forward tripod mast except *James E. Kyes* which had SPS-40 and SPS-10 radars; *Lloyd Thomas* had SPS-6 and SPS-10 radars. Fitted with SQS-23 sonar except *Dang Yang* has SQS-29 series sonar.

DANG YANG (USS *Lloyd Thomas*) — *1970, United States Navy*

1 Ex-US "GEARING" CLASS RADAR PICKET

Name	No.	Builder	Launched	US Comm	Transferred
FU YANG (ex-USS *Ernest G. Small*, DD 838)	DD 7	Bath Iron Works Corp	14 June 1945	21 Aug 1945	19 Feb 1971

Displacement, tons	2 425 standard; approx 3 500 full load
Length, feet (*metres*)	390·5 (*119·0*) oa
Beam, feet (*metres*)	40·8 (*12·4*)
Draught, feet (*metres*)	19 (*5·8*)
Guns	6—5 inch (*127 mm*) 38 calibre DP (twin); several 40 mm (twin)
A/S weapons	6—12·75 inch (*324 mm*) torpedo tubes (Mk 32 triple); 2 fixed hedgehogs
Main engines	2 geared turbines; (General Electric); 60 000 shp; 2 shafts
Boilers	4 (Babcock & Wilcox)
Speed, knots	34
Complement	approx 275

Former US Navy radar picket destroyer of the "Gearing" class. Converted to a radar picket destroyer (DDR) during 1952 and subsequently modernised under the Fleet Rehabilitation and Modernisation (FRAM II) programme; redesignated as a "straight" destroyer (DD), but retained specialised electronic equipment. Not fitted with helicopter flight deck or hangar.

FU YANG (as USS *Ernest G. Small*) — *1970, United States Navy*

ELECTRONICS. At time of transfer the *Fu Yang* had SPS-37 and SPS-10 search radars on forward tripod mast, and large TACAN (tactical aircraft navigation) "beehive" antenna on second tripod mast. Fitted SQS-29 series hull-mounted sonar and SQA-10 variable depth sonar.

Destroyers—*continued*

6 Ex-US "ALLEN M. SUMNER" CLASS

Name	*No.*	*Builder*	*Launched*	*US Comm*	*Transferred*
HSIANG YANG (ex-USS *Brush*, DD 745)	DD 1	Bethlehem Steel (Staten Is)	28 Dec 1943	17 Apr 1944	Feb 1970
HENG YANG (ex-USS *Samuel N. Moore*, DD 747)	DD 2	Bethlehem Steel (Staten Is)	23 Feb 1944	24 June 1944	Feb 1970
HUA YANG (ex-USS *Bristol*, DD 857)	DD 3	Bethlehem Steel (San Pedro)	29 Oct 1944	17 Mar 1945	Feb 1970
YUEH YANG (ex-USS *Haynsworth*, DD 700)	DD 5	Federal SB & DD Co	15 Apr 1944	22 June 1944	May 1970
HUEI YANG (ex-USS *English*, DD 696)	DD 6	Federal SB & DD Co	27 Feb 1944	4 May 1944	Sep 1970
PO YANG (ex-USS *Maddox*, DD 731)	DD 10	Bath Iron Works Corp	19 Mar 1944	2 June 1944	July 1972

Displacement, tons: 2 200 standard; 3 320 full load
Length, feet (*metres*): 376·5 (*114·8*) oa
Beam, feet (*metres*): 40·9 (*12·4*)
Draught, feet (*metres*): 19 (*5·8*)
Guns: 6—5 inch (*127 mm*) 38 calibre DP (twin)
up to 6—3 inch (*76 mm*) 50 calibre AA (2 twin, 2 single) in most ships, some; including *Heng Yang* and *Yueh Yang*, have 8—40 mm (1 quad, 2 twin).
A/S weapons: 6—12·75 inch (*324 mm*) torpedo tubes (Mk 32 triple); 2 fixed hedgehogs; depth charges in some ships
Main engines: 2 geared turbines (General Electric or Westinghouse); 60 000 shp; 2 shafts
Boilers: 4 (Babcock & Wilcox)
Speed, knots: 34
Complement: approx 275

Former US Navy destroyers of the "Allen M. Sumner" class. These ships have not been modernised under the FRAM programmes, but retain their original configurations with removal of original torpedo tubes, and 40 mm and 20 mm AA guns, and installation of improved electronic equipment. Secondary gun battery now varies; during the 1950s most of these ships were rearmed with six 3 inch AA guns (two single alongside forward funnel and two twin amidships); number retained apparently varies from ship to ship, with some ships retaining original 40 mm guns. Tripod mast fitted.

ELECTRONICS. These ships have SPS-6 and SPS-10 search radars on their tripod mast.

PHOTOGRAPHS. The *Fu Yang* can be distinguished from the other six-gun destroyers operated by Taiwan China by the former ship's additional space between funnels and tripod mast forward of her second funnel. In the above photograph the *Yueh Yang*'s 40 mm guns, their separate gun directors in "tubs" aft of the second funnel, and depth charge rack are clearly evident.

YUEH YANG — *1973*

HSIANG YANG — *1971, United States Navy*

4 Ex-US "FLETCHER" CLASS

Name	*No.*	*Launched*	*US Comm*	*Transferred*
KWEI YANG (ex-USS *Twining*, DD 540)	DD 8	11 July 1943	1 Dec 1943	Aug 1971
CHING YANG (ex-USS *Mullany*, DD 528)	DD 9	12 Oct 1942	23 Apr 1943	Oct 1971
AN YANG (ex-USS *Kimberly*, DD 521)	DD 18	4 Feb 1943	22 May 1943	June 1967
KUEN YANG (ex-USS *Yarnall*, DD 541)	DD 19	25 July 1943	30 Dec 1943	June 1968

Displacement, tons: 2 100 standard; 3 050 full load
Length, feet (*metres*): 376·5 (*114·7*) oa
Beam, feet (*metres*): 35·9 (*11·9*)
Draught, feet (*metres*): 18 (*5·5*)
Guns: 5—5 inch (*127 mm*) 38 calibre DP (single) except 4 guns in *Ching Yang*
6—3 inch (*76 mm*) 50 calibre AA (twin) in *Kwei Yang* and *Ching Yang*; 6—40 mm AA (twin) in *An Yang* and *Kuen Yang*
A/S weapons: 2 fixed hedgehogs; depth charges
6—12·75 inch (*324 mm*) torpedo tubes (Mk 32 triple) in *Kwei Yang* and *Ching Yang*
Torpedo tubes: 5—21 inch (*533 mm*) quintuple in *Kuen Yang*
Main engines: 2 geared turbines (General Electric in *An Yang*, Allis Chalmers in *Kuen Yang*, Westinghouse in others); 60 000 shp; 2 shafts
Boilers: 4 (Babcock & Wilcox)
Speed, knots: 36
Complement: approx 250

Former US "Fletcher" class destroyers. Built by Bethlehem Steel .Co, San Francisco, except *An Yang* by Bethlehem at Staten Island, New York. *An Yang* retains original pole mast; others have tripod mast. Only *Kuen Yang* retains anti-ship torpedo tubes.

AN YANG — ***1971, courtesy Toshio Tamura***

Destroyers—*continued*

2 Ex-US "GLEAVES" CLASS

Name	No.	Launched	US Comm	Transferred
HSUEN YANG (ex-*Hatakze*, ex-USS *Macomb*, DMS 23, ex-DD 458)	DD 16	22 Sep 1941	26 Jan 1942	Aug 1970
NAN YANG (ex-USS *Plunkett*, DD 431)	DD 17	9 Mar 1940	16 July 1940	Feb 1959

Displacement, tons: 1 700 standard; 2 575 full load
Length, feet (*metres*): 341 (*104·0*) wl; 348·33 (*106·2*) oa
Beam, feet (*metres*): 36 (*11·0*)
Draught, feet (*metres*): 18 (*5·5*)
Guns: 4—5 inch (*127 mm*) 38 calibre DP (single) in *Nan Yang*; 3 guns in *Hsien Yang* (see Gunnery notes); several 40 mm AA; several 20 mm AA
A/S weapons: depth charges
Main engines: 2 geared turbines (Westinghouse in *Hsuen Yang*, General Electric in *Nan Yang*); 50 000 shp; 2 shafts
Boilers: 4 (Babcock & Wilcox)
Speed, knots: 34
Complement: 250

Former US destroyers of the "Gleaves" class. *Hsien Yang* built by Bath Iron Works Corp, and *Nan Yang* by Federal SB & DD Co.
The original *Hsien Yang* was the former USS *Rodman* (ex-DMS 21, ex-DD 456) transferred to Taiwan China in July 1955. After she ran aground and sustained severe damage two other ships of this class which had served with the Japanese Navy were transferred to Taiwan China for cannibalisation to repair the *Hsien Yang*. Subsequently, the ex-USS *Macomb* was judged in better condition than the damaged ship and was placed in service with the damaged ship's name and number.
Also acquired on 6 Aug 1970 for cannibalisation was the ex-Japanese *Asakaze*, ex-USS *Ellyson* (DMS 19, ex-DD 454). Both the ex-*Rodman* and ex-*Ellyson* were scrapped in Taiwan.
Reportedly, the *Nan Yang* was decommissioned in 1974 in preparation for scrapping.

HSUEN YANG (ex-Hatazke) — *1970, Toshio Tamura*

GUNNERY. As built *Nan Yang* mounted five 5 inch guns; reduced during World War II to four guns with removal of mount in "Q" position. The *Hsuen Yang* built with four guns but "Y" mount removed in 1944 when converted to high-speed minesweeper (DMS). In Japanese service the "Y" mount was again installed and the "B" 5 inch mounting was removed; 20 mm guns mounted in "B" position (see photograph).

2 Ex-US "BENSON" CLASS

Name	No.	Launched	US Comm	Transferred
HAN YANG (ex-USS *Hilary P. Jones*, DD 427)	DD 15	14 Dec 1939	7 Sep 1940	26 Feb 1954
LO YANG (ex-USS *Benson*, DD 421)	DD 14	15 Nov 1939	25 July 1940	26 Feb 1954

Displacement, tons: 1 620 standard; 2 575 full load
Length, feet (*metres*): 347·8 (*105·9*) oa
Beam, feet (*metres*): 36·1 (*10·9*)
Draught, feet (*metres*): 18·0 (*5·5*)
Guns: 4—5 inch (*127 mm*) 38 calibre DP (single); 4—40 mm AA (twin); several 20 mm AA
A/S weapons: depth charges
Main engines: 2 geared turbines (Bethlehem); 50 000 shp; 2 shafts
Boilers: 4 (Babcock & Wilcox in *Lo Yang*; Foster Wheeler in *Han Yang*)
Speed, knots: approx 34 (36·7 designed)
Complement: approx 230

Former US "Benson" class destroyers. *Lo Yang* built by Bethlehem Shipbuilding, Quincy, Massachusetts; *Han Yang* built by Charleston Navy Yard, South Carolina.

DISPOSALS
The destroyer **Tan Yan**, lately employed as a training ship, was scrapped in 1971. She is the former Japanese *Yukikaze* (see 1971-1972 and previous editions for descriptions).

HAN YANG — *Republic of China Navy*

FRIGATES

1 Ex-US "RUDDEROW" CLASS

Name	No.	Launched	US Comm	Transferred
TAI YUAN (ex-USS *Riley*, DE 579)	DE 27	29 Dec 1943	13 Mar 1944	10 July 1968

Displacement, tons: 1 450 standard; approx 2 000 full load
Length, feet (*metres*): 300 (*91·4*) wl; 306 (*93·3*) oa
Beam, feet (*metres*): 37 (*11·3*)
Draught, feet (*metres*): 14 (*4·3*)
Guns: 2—5 inch (*127 mm*) 38 calibre DP (single); 4—40 mm AA (twin); 4—20 mm AA (single)
A/S weapons: 6—12·75 inch (*324 mm*) torpedo tubes (Mk 32 triple); 1 hedgehog; depth charge
Main engines: Geared turbines (General Electric) with electric drive; 12 000 shp; 2 shafts
Boilers: 2 (Foster Wheeler)
Speed, knots: 24
Complement: approx 200

Former US Navy destroyer escort. Built by Bethlehem SB Co, Higham, Massachusetts. Refitted with tripod mast and platforms before bridge for 20 mm guns. (Hedgehog is on main deck, behind forward 5 inch mount). SPS-6 and SPS-10 search radars are installed.

TAI YUAN — *Iain G. B. Lovie*

Frigates—*continued*

DISPOSALS.
The frigate **Tai Kang** DE 21 (ex-USS *Wyffel*, DE 6) of the so-called "short-hull" type was scrapped in 1972 (see 1971-1972 and previous editions for description).

FU SHAN — *Courtesy "Ships of the World"*

1 Ex-US "BOSTWICK" CLASS

Name	No.	Launched	US Comm	Transferred
TAI HU (ex-USS *Bostwick*, DE 103)	DE 25	30 Aug 1943	1 Dec 1943	Nov 1948

Displacement, tons	1 240 standard; 1 900 full load
Length, feet (*metres*)	300 (*91·4*) wl; 306 (*93·3*) oa
Beam, feet (*metres*)	36·6 (*11·2*)
Draught, feet (*metres*)	14 (*4·3*)
Guns	2—5 inch (*127 mm*) 38 cal DP 8—40 mm AA (2 twin, 4 single) 4—20 mm AA (single)
A/S weapons	6—12·75 inch (*324 mm*) torpedo tubes (Mk 32 triple); 1 hedgehog depth charges
Main engines	Diesel-electric (4 General Motors diesels); 6 000 bhp; 2 shafts
Speed, knots	21
Complement	approx 200

Former US Navy destroyer escort; built by Dravo Corp, Wilmington, Delaware, but completed by Norfolk Navy Yard (Virginia).

GUNNERY. The original main battery of three 3 inch 50 cal guns have been replaced by two 5 inch guns in open mounts.

DISPOSALS
Tai Ho DE 23 (ex-USS *Thomas*, DE 102), **Tai Chong** DE 24 (ex-USS *Breeman*, DE 104), **Tai Chao** (ex-USS *Carter*, DE 112) decommissioned and scrapped 1972-1973.

TAI HO (5 inch guns, bridge refitted)—now stricken — *Toshio Tamura*

11 FRIGATES / 1 TRANSPORT } Ex-US APD TYPE

Name	No.	Launched	US Comm	Transferred
YU SHAN (ex-USS *Kinzer*, APD 91/DE 232)	PF 32	9 Dec 1943	1 Nov 1944	Apr 1965
HWA SHAN (ex-*Donald W. Wolf* APD 129/DE 713)	PF 33	22 July 1944	13 Apr 1945	May 1965
WEN SHAN (ex-*Gantner*, APD 42/DE 60)	PF 34	17 Apr 1943	23 July 1943	May 1966
FU SHAN (ex-*Truxtun*, APD 98/DE 282)	PF 35	9 Mar 1944	9 July 1954	Mar 1966
LU SHAN (ex-USS *Bull*, APD 78/DE 693)	PF 36	25 Mar 1943	12 Aug 1943	Aug 1966
SHOA SHAN (ex-*Kline*, APD 120/DE 687)	PF 37	27 June 1944	18 Oct 1944	Mar 1966
TAI SHAN (ex-*Register*, APD 92/DE 233)	PF 38	20 Jan 1944	11 Jan 1945	Oct 1966
HENG SHAN (*R. W. Herndon*, APD 121/DE 688)	PF 39	15 July 1944	3 Nov 1944	Oct 1966
KANG SHAN (*G. W. Ingram*, APD 43/DE 62)	PF 42	8 May 1943	11 Aug 1943	July 1967
CHUNG SHAN (ex-*Blessman*, APD 48/DE 69)	PF 43	19 June 1943	19 Sep 1943	July 1967
LUNG SHAN (ex-*Schmitt*, APD 76/DE 676)	PF 44	29 May 1943	24 July 1943	Feb 1969
TIEN SHAN (*Kleinsmith*, APD 132/DE 718)	APD 215	27 Jan 1945	12 June 1945	May 1960

Displacement, tons	1 400 standard; 2 130 full load
Length, feet (*metres*)	300 (*91·4*) wl; 306 (*93·3*) oa
Beam, feet (*metres*)	37 (*11·3*)
Draught, feet (*metres*)	12·6 (*3·2*)
Guns	2—5 inch (*127 mm*) 38 cal DP 6—40 mm AA (twin) 4—20 m AA (single) except *Hwa Shan* and possibly others have eight guns (twin mounts)
A/S weapons	6—12·75 inch (*324 mm*) torpedo tubes (Mk 32 triple) except *Heng Shan* and possibly others have two hedgehogs depth charges
Main engines	Geared turbines (General Electric) with electric drive; 12 000 shp; 2 shafts
Boilers	2 (Foster Wheeler)
Speed, knots	23·6
Complement	approx 200

LUNG SHAN — *1973*

Frigates—*continued*

Former US Navy high speed transports (APD) employed as frigates. All designated PF except *Tien Shan* which is designated APD.
All begun as destroyer escorts (DE), but converted during construction or after completion to high speed transports carrying 160 troops, commandos, or frogmen, PF 32 and 35 built by Charleston Navy Yard, South Carolina; PF 33, 36, and APD 215 by Defoe SB Co, Bay City, Michigan; PF 34, 42, and 43 by Bethlehem SB Co, Hingham, Massachusetts; PF 37, 39, and 44 by Bethlehem, Quincy, Mass.
The ex-USS *Walter B. Cobb* (APD 106/DE 596) transferred to Taiwan China in 1966 was lost at sea while under tow to Taiwan; replaced by ex-USS *Bull*.
Configurations differ: APD 37 class has high bridge; APD 87 class has low bridge. Radars and fire control equipment vary.
The *Heng Shan*, *Chung Shan*, and *Lung Shan* were reported to have been decommissioned in 1973.

GUNNERY. All ships are now believed to have been refitted with a second 5 inch gun aft. One twin 40 mm gun mount is forward of bridge and two twin mounts are amid ships. Note after 5 inch mount and depth charge racks in photo of *Lung Shan*. Davits amidships can hold four LCVP-type landing craft.

HWA SHAN — *1971, Iain G. B. Lovie*

PATROL VESSELS

3 Ex-US MSF TYPE

WU SHENG	(ex-USS *Redstart*, MSF 378)	PCE 66	18 Oct 1944
CHU YUNG	(ex-USS *Waxwing*, MSF 389)	PCE 67	10 Mar 1945
MO LING	(ex-USS *Steady*, MSF 118)	PCE 70	6 June 1942

Displacement, tons	890 standard; 1 250 full load
Dimensions, feet	215 wl; 221·1 oa × 32·1 × 10·8
Guns	2—3 inch (*76 mm*) 50 cal AA (single); 4—40 mm AA (twin); 4—20 mm AA (twin)
A/S weapons	1 hedgehog; 3—12·75 inch (*324 mm*) torpedo tubes (Mk 32 triple); depth charges
Main engines	Diesel-electric (General Motors diesels); 3 530 bhp; 2 shafts = 18 knots
Complement	approx 80

Former US Navy minesweepers of the "Auk" class; originally designated AM. *Wu Sheng* built by Savannah Machine & Foundry Co, Georgia, others by American SB Co, Cleveland, Ohio, respectivly; launch dates above. *Wu Sheng* transferred to Taiwan China in July 1965, *Chu Yung* in Nov 1965 and *Mo Ling* in Mar 1968.
Minesweeping equipment removed and second 3 inch gun fitted aft in Taiwan service. *Chein Men* PCE 45 (ex-USS *Toucan*, MSF 387) sunk by Communist Chinese warships south of Quemoy Island on 6 Aug 1965; *Mo Ling* reported still in service.

MO LING

Ex-US 185-ft PCE TYPE

All former US Navy 185-foot patrol escorts have been stricken. **Wei Yuan** PCE 68 (ex-*Yung Hsiang*, PF 42, ex-USS PCE 869) decommissioned in 1972 and subsequently scrapped. See 1973-1974 and previous editions for characteristics and earlier disposals.

ExUS 185 ft-AM TYPE

All former US Navy 185-foot minesweepers of the "Admirable" class have been stricken, including one ship reclassified as a minelayer and two reclassified as auxiliaries: **Yung Feng** MMC 150 (ex-USS *Prime*, AM 279), **Yang Ming** AGS 562 (ex-*Yung Ting*, MSF 45, ex-USS *Lucid*, AM 259), **Yung Hsiu** ADG 152 (ex-MSF 48, ex-USS *Pinnacle*, AM 274) all decommissioned in 1972 and reported subsequently stricken. See 1973-1974 and previous editions for characteristics.

Ex-US 173-ft PC/PGM TYPE

All former US Navy 173-foot submarine chasers and motor gunboats have been stricken. with two units now operated by the Customs Service (listed on later page). See 1971-1972 and previous editions for characteristics and ship lists.

Ex-US 110-ft SC TYPE

All former US Navy wood-hull, 110-foot submarine chasers have been stricken. See 1971-1972 and previous editions for characteristics and ship lists.

Several PATROL BOATS (PB)

Displacement, tons	approx 30 tons
Guns	1—40 mm

Small patrol boats designated PB. Constructed on Taiwan with the first of an estimated ten units completed about 1971.

PB 1

MINESWEEPERS

13 US MSC TYPE

YUNG PING	MSC 155 (ex-US MSC 140)
YUNG AN	MSC 156 (ex-US MSC 140)
YUNG NIEN	MSC 157 (ex-US MSC 277)
YUNG CHOU	MSC 158 (ex-US MSC 278)
YUNG HSIN	MSC 159 (ex-US MSC 302)
YUNG JU	MSC 160 (ex-US MSC 300)
YUNG LO	MSC 161 (ex-US MSC 306)
YUNG FU	MSC 162 (ex-*Diest*, ex-US MSC 77)
YUNG CHENG	MSC 165 (ex-*Maasieck*, ex-US *MSC* 78)
YUNG SHAN	MSC 164 (ex-*Lier*, ex-US MSC 63)
YUNG CHING	MSC 163 (ex-*Eekloo*, ex-US MSC 101)
YUNG LO	MSC 161 (ex-US MSC 306)
YUNG SUI	MSC 168 (ex-US *Diksmude*, ex-US MSC 65)

Displacement, tons	approx 380 full load
Dimensions, feet	144 oa × 28 × 8·5
Guns	2—20 mm AA (twin) in MSC 155-161
Main engines	Diesels (General Motors); 880 bhp; 2 shafts = 13·5 knots
Complement	40 to 50

Non-magnetic, wood-hulled minesweepers built in the United States specifically for transfer to allied navies. First seven units listed above transferred to Taiwan China upon completion: MSC 155 and 156 in June 1965, MSC 157 in Dec 1958, MSC 158 in July 1959, MSC 159 in Mar 1965. MSC 160 in Apr 1965, and MSC 161 in June 1966. The seven other units were transferred to Belgium upon completion in 1953-1955; retransferred to Taiwan China in Nov 1969. The *Yung Chi* MSC 166 (ex-*Charleroi*, ex-US AMS 152) reportedly has been cannibalised for spare parts.
All are of similar design; the ex-Belgium ships have a small boom aft on a pole mast. They carried a single 40 mm gun forward in Belgium service; current armament unknown. (Photograph shows ex-Belgium *Lier* under tow to Taiwan late in 1969; note gun removed; short pole mast aft).

YUNG LO *1966*

YUNG SHAN (under tow) *1969*

YUNG NIEN *1963, Official*

Minesweepers—*continued*

MSB 12 (ex-US MSB 4)

Former US Army minesweeping boat; assigned hull number MSB 4 in US Navy and transferred to Taiwan China in Dec 1961.

MSML 1	**MSML 5**	**MSML 7**	**MSML 11**
MSML 3	**MSML 6**	**MSML 8**	**MSML 12**

Fifty-foot minesweeping launches built in the United States and transferred to Taiwan China in Mar 1961.

TORPEDO BOATS

2 79-ft TYPE

FUH KWO PT 515 **TIAN KWO** PT 516

Displacement, tons	46 light; 53 full load
Dimensions, feet	79 oa × 23·25 × 5·5
Guns	1—40 mm AA; 2—·05 cal MG (single)
Torpedo launchers	2
Main engines	3 gasoline engines; 3 shafts = 39 knots max; 32 knots cruising
Complement	12

Built by Huckins Yacht Corp, Jacksonville, Florida. Transferred to Taiwan China on 1 Sep 1957.

2 71-ft TYPE

FAAN KONG PT 513 **SAO TANG** PT 514

Displacement, tons	39 light; 46 full load
Dimensions, feet	71 oa × 19 × 5
Guns	1—20 mm AA 4—·50 cal MG (twin)
Torpedo launchers	2 (?)
Main engines	3 gasoline engines; 3 shafts = 42 knots max; 32 knots cruising
Complement	12

Built by Annapolis Yacht Yard, Annapolis, Maryland. Transferred to Taiwan China on 19 Aug 1957 and 1 Nov 1957, respectively.

2 JAPANESE TYPE

FUH CHOW PT 511 **HSUEH CHIH** PT 512

Displacement, tons	33 light; 40 full load
Dimensions, feet	69 oa × 19·9
Guns	1—40 mm AA; 2—20 mm AA (twin)
Torpedo launchers	2—18 inch (457 *mm*)
Main engines	3 gasoline engines; 3 shafts = 40 knots max; 27 knots cruising
Complement	12

Built by Mitsubishi SB Co. Transferred to Taiwan China on 1 June 1957 and 6 Nov 1957, respectively. The 40 mm gun is not mounted in the adjacent photograph (can be fitted forward of bridge).

PT 511

Several small craft designated in the PT 600 series are used for frogmen operations.

DOCK LANDING SHIPS

1 Ex-US "ASHLAND" CLASS

TUNG HAI (ex-USS *White Marsh*, LSD 8) LSD 191

Displacement, tons	4 790 standard; 8 700 full load
Dimensions, feet	454 wl; 457·8 oa × 72 × 18
Guns	12—40 mm AA
Main engines	Skinner Unaflow; 7 400 ihp; 2 shafts = 15 knots
Boilers	2

Built by Moore Dry Dock Co, Launched on 19 July 1943. Designed to serve as parent ship for landing craft and coastal craft. Transferred from the US Navy to Taiwan on 17 Nov 1960.

TUNG HAI 1965

AMPHIBIOUS FLAGSHIPS

2 Ex-US LST TYPE

KAO HSIUNG (ex-*Chung Hai*, LST 219 ex-USS *Dukes County*, LST 735) AGC 2
(ex-*Chung Chih*, LST 226, ex-USS *Sagadahoc County*, LST 1091) AGC 1

Former US Navy tank landing ships employed as flagships for amphibious forces. The ex-USS *Dukes County* was transferred to Taiwan China in May 1957 for service as an LST; modified to flagship and redesignated AGC 1 in 1964 (renamed); a second LST is reported to have been subsequently modified for use as an amphibious command and support ship. See characteristics below.

KAO HSIUNG (ex-*Chung Hai*) as LST

TANK LANDING SHIPS

21 Ex-US LST TYPE

LST	Name	Transferred
201	**CHUNG HAI** (ex-USS LST 755)	Apr 1946
203	**CHUNG TING** (ex-USS LST 537)	Mar 1946
204	**CHUNG HSING** (ex-USS LST 557)	Mar 1946
205	**CHUNG CHIEN** (ex-USS LST 716)	June 1946
206	**CHUNG CHI** (ex-USS LST 1017)	Dec 1946
208	**CHUNG SHUN** (ex-USS LST 732)	Mar 1946
209	**CHUNG LIEN** (ex-USS LST 1050)	Jan 1947
210	**CHUNG YUNG** (ex-USS LST 574)	Mar 1959
216	**CHUNG KUANG** (ex-USS LST 503)	June 1960
217	**CHUNG SUO** (ex-USS *Bradley County*, LST 400)	Sep 1958
218	**CHUNG CHIH** (ex-USS *Berkley County*, LST 279)	June 1960
221	**CHUNG CHUAN** (ex-LST 1030)	Feb 1948
222	**CHUNG SHENG** (ex-LST 211, ex-USS LST 1033)	Dec 1947
223	**CHUNG FU** (ex-USS *Iron County*, LST 840)	July 1958
224	**CHUNG CHENG** (ex-USS *Lafayette County*, LST 859)	Aug 1958
225	**CHUNG CHIANG** (ex-USS *San Bernadino County*, LST 1110)	Aug 1958
227	**CHUNG MING** (ex-USS *Sweetwater County*, LST 1152)	Oct 1958
228	**CHUNG SHU** (ex-USS LST 520)	Sep 1958
229	**CHUNG WAN** (ex-USS LST 535)	Sep 1958
230	**CHUNG PANG** (ex-USS LST 578)	Sep 1958
231	**CHUNG YEH** (ex-USS *Sublette County*, LST 1144)	Sep 1961

Displacement, tons	1 653 standard; 4 080 full load
Dimensions, feet	316 wl; 328 oa × 50 × 14
Guns	varies; up to 10—40 mm AA (2 twin, 6 single) with some modernised ships rearmed with 2—3 inch AA (single) and 6—40 mm AA (twin) several 20 mm AA (twin or single)
Main engines	Diesel (General Motors); 1 700 bhp; 2 shafts = 11·6 knots
Complement	varies: 100 to 125 in most ships

Former US Navy tank landing ships constructed during World War II. Dates transferred to Taiwan China are listed above. These ships have been extensively modernised with several ships having been essentially rebuilt in Taiwan. Additional landing craft davits added to modernised ship.

LST 211 ex-USS LST 1033 changed to LST 222 on 13 Nov 1957. Other Taiwan pennant numbers in the LST series may have been assigned to more than one ship.

Several LSTs have been stricken: ex-USS LST 717 (no name assigned; acquired in 1946 and reported sunk in 1948); *Chung Cheng* LST 207 ex-USS LST 1075, *Chung Hsun* LST 208 ex-USS LST 993, *Chung Kung* LST 213 ex-USS LST 945, *Chung Yu* LST 215 ex-USS LST 330. One of these ships is believed to have been sunk by Communist Chinese torpedo boats off Quemoy Island on 25 Aug 1958.

MEDIUM LANDING SHIPS

4 Ex-US LSM TYPE

Name	No.	Transferred
MEI CHIN (ex-USS LSM 155)	LSM 341	May 1946
MEI SUNG (ex-USS LSM 431)	LSM 347	June 1946
MEI PING (ex-USS LSM 471)	LSM 353	Nov 1956
MEI LO (ex-USS LSM 362)	LSM 356	May 1962

Displacement, tons	1 095 full load
Dimensions, feet	196·5 wl; 203·5 oa × 34·5 × 7·3
Guns	2—40 mm AA (twin); 4 or 8—20 mm AA (4 single or 4 twin)
Main engines	Diesels; 2 800 bhp; 2 shafts = 12·5 knots
Complement	65 to 75

Former US Navy medium landing ships constructed during World War II. Originally numbered in the 200-series in Taiwan Chinese service, but changed in 300-series as above. Some numbers may have been assigned to more than one ship.

Several LSMs have been stricken: *Mei Peng* LSM 344 ex-USS LSM 344, *Mei Lo* LSM 242 ex-USS LSM 157 (destroyed by Communist Chinese artillery and beached on Quemoy Island on 8 Sep 1958), *Mei I* LSM 343 ex-USS LSM 285, *Mei Heng* LSM 245 ex-USS LSM 456, *Mei Hung* LSM 246 ex-USS LSM 442, *Mei Ho* LSM 248/ CMC 348 ex-USS LSM 13.

Mei Chien LSM 349 ex-USS LSM 76, *Mei Hwa* LSM 350 ex-USS LSM 256 (sunk 1969), *Mei Chen* LSM 351 ex-USS LSM 427, *Mei Kung* LSM 352 ex-USS LSM 478, *Mei Wen* LSM 354 ex-USS LSM 472, *Mei Ham* LSM 355 ex-LSM 474, *Mei Shen* LSM 249 ex-USS LSM 433 (sunk), *Me Hung* LSM 346 ex-USS LSM 442.

MEI KUNG (now stricken) *1962, Republic of China Navy*

UTILITY LANDING CRAFT

22 Ex-US LCU TYPE

Name	LCU	Name	LCU
HO CHUN (ex-LCU 892)	481	**HO CHUN** (ex-LCU 1225)	494
HO CH'UNG (ex-LCU 1213)	482	**HO YUNG** (ex-LCU 1271)	495
HO CHUNG (ex-LCU 849)	484	**HO CHIEN** (ex-LCU 1278)	496
HO CHANG (ex-LCU 512)	485	**HO CHI** (ex-LCU 1212)	501
HO CHENG (ex-LCU 1145)	486	**HO HOEI** (ex-LCU 1218)	502
HO SHAN (ex-LCU 1596)	488	**HO YAO** (ex-LCU 1244)	503
HO CHUAN (ex-LCU 489)	489	**HO DENG** (ex-LCU 1367)	504
HO SENG (ex-LCU 1598)	490	**HO FENG** (ex-LCU 1397)	505
HO MENG (ex-LCU 1599)	491	**HO CHAO** (es-LCU 1429)	506
HO MOU (ex-LCU 1600)	492	**HO TENG** (ex-LCU 1452)	507
HO SHOU (ex-LCU 1601)	493	**HO CHIE** (ex-LCU 700)	SB 1

21 Ex-US LCU TYPE

LCU 501 series:

Displacement, tons	158 light; 268 full load
Dimensions, feet	115·1 oa × 32 × 4·2
Guns	2—20 mm AA (single); some units also may have 2—·50 cal MG
Main engines	3 diesels; 675 bhp; 3 shafts = 10 knots
Complement	10 to 25 assigned

LCU 1466 series:

Displacment, tons	130 light; 280 full load
Dimensions, feet	115·1 oa × 34 × 4·1
Guns	3—20 mm AA (single); some units also have may 2—·50 cal MG
Main engines	3 diesels; 675 bhp; 3 shafts = 10 knots
Complement	15 to 25 assigned

The LCU 501 series formerly were built in the United States during World War II; initially designated LCT(6) series. LCU 1466 series built by Ishikowajima Heavy Industries Co, Tokyo, Japan, for transfer to Taiwan China; completed in 1955. All originally numbered in 200-series; subsequently changed to 400 and 500-series numbers.

LANDING SHIP INFANTRY AND SUPPORT SERIES

All former US Navy LSI(G), LSI(L), LSI(M), and LSS(L) ships transferred to Taiwan China have been stricken. See 1971-1972 and previous editions for ship lists and characteristics.

Utility Landing Craft—*continued*

HO MOU (LCU 492 ex-LCU 292) —see previous page

AUXILIARY SHIPS

1 REPAIR SHIP: Ex-US "LIBERTY" TYPE

PIEN TAI (ex-USS *Tutuila*, ARG 4)ARG 516

Displacement, tons	5 766 standard; 14 350 full load
Dimensions, feet	416 wl; 441·5 oa × 57 × 23
Guns	(current armament unknown)
Main engines	Triple expansion (General Machinery Corp); 2 500 ihp; 1 shaft = 12·5 knots
Boilers	2 (Babcock & Wilcox)

"Liberty" ship (EC2) built by Bethlehem Steel Co, Baltimore, Maryland; launched on 12 Sep 1943 and commissioned on 8 Apr 1944. Originally fitted to repair internal combustion engines, but capabilities subsequently expanded. Transferred from active US Fleet to Taiwan China on 21 Feb 1972.

PIEN TAI (as USS *Tutuila*) *United States Navy*

1 REPAIR SHIP: Ex-US C-3 TYPE

YU TAI (ex-USS *Cadmus*, AR 14) AR 521

Displacement, tons	7 826 standard; 14 490 full load
Dimensions, feet	456 wl; 492 oa × 70 × 27·5
Guns	1—5 inch (*127 mm*) 38 calibre DP
Main engines	Turbines (Westinghouse); 8 500 shp; 1 shaft = 16·5 knots
Boilers	2 (Foster Wheeler)

Former US Navy repair ship built by Tampa Shipbuilding Co, Tampa, Florida; launched on 5 Aug 1945; commissioned on 23 Apr 1946. Transferred to Taiwan China on 15 Jan 1973. A sister ship (ex-USS *Amphion*, AR 13) serves with the Iranian Navy.

1 TRANSPORT: Ex-US LST TYPE

YU TAI (ex-*Sung Shan*, ARL 236, ex-USS *Agenor*, ARL 3, ex-LST 490) AP 520

Displacement, tons	1 625 light; 4 100 full load
Dimensions, feet	316 wl; 328 oa × 50 × 11
Main engines	Diesels (General Motors); 1 800 bhp; 2 shafts = 11·6 knots
Troops	600

Begun for the US Navy as an LST but completed as a repair ship for landing craft (ARL); built by Kaiser Co, Vancouver, Washington; launched on 3 Apr 1943; commissioned on 20 Aug 1943. Transferred to France in 1951 for service in Indochina; subsequently returned to United States and retransferred to Taiwan China on 15 Sep 1957.
Employed as a repair ship (ARL 336, subsequently ARL 236) until converted in 1973-1974 to troop transport.

1 SURVEYING SHIP: Ex-US C1-M-AV1 TYPE

CHU HWA (ex-USNS *Sgt. George D. Keathley*, T-AGS 35, ex-T-APC 117) AGS 564

Displacement, tons	6 090 tons
Dimensions, feet	338·8 oa × 50·3 × 17·5
Guns	(current armament unknown)
Main engines	Diesel; 1 750 bhp; 1 shaft = 11·5 knots

Built in 1945 as merchant ship; subsequently acquired by US Army for use as transport, but assigned to Navy's Military Sea Transportation Service in 1950 and designated as coastal transport (T-APC 117). Refitted for oceanographic survey work in 1966-1967 and redesignated T-AGS 35. Transferred to Taiwan China on 29 Mar 1972.

Auxiliary Ships—*continued*

1 SURVEYING SHIP: Ex-US AUXILIARY TUG

CHIU LIEN (ex-USS *Geronimo*, ATA 207) AGS 563

LCU 1466 series:

Displacement, tons	835
Dimensions, feet	143 oa × 33·9 × 13·2
Guns	(current aramment unknown)
Main engines	Diesel (General Motors); 1 500 bhp; 1 shaft = 13 knots

Former US Navy auxiliary tug. Built by Gulfport Boiler & Welding Works, Port Arthur, Texas; launched 4 Jan 1945 and commissioned 1 Mar 1945. Transferred to Taiwan China in Feb 1969 and converted to surveying ship. Currently employed as maritime college training ship; Navy manned.

The surveying ship *Lien Chang* AGSC 466 ex-USS LSIL 1017 was stricken in 1972.

1 OILER: Ex-SOVIET MERCHANT TYPE

KUI CHI (ex-Soviet *Tuapse*) AOG 506 (ex-AOG 306)

Displacement, tons	18 100 full load
Dimensions, feet	489·75 oa × 62·8 × 25·4
Guns	AA weapons fitted
Main engines	Diesel; 5 520 bhp; 1 shaft = 14·5 knots
Cargo	11 000 tons fuel

Built by Burmeister & Wain, Copenhagen; completed in 1953 for Soviet merchant service. Seized by Taiwan China forces in Taiwan Straits in June 1954 and subsequently commissioned in naval service; commissioned 20 Oct 1955.

1 OILER: JAPANESE TYPE

WAN SHOU AOG 512

Displacement, tons	1 049 light; 4 150 full load
Dimensions, feet	283·8 oa × 54 × 18
Guns	2—40 mm AA (single); 2—20 mm AA
Main engines	Diesel; 2 100 bhp; 1 shaft = 13 knots
Complement	70
Cargo	73 600 gallons fuel; 62 000 gallons water

Built by Ujina Shipbuilding Co, Hiroshima, Japan for Taiwan China. Commissioned for naval service on 1 Nov 1969. Employed in resupply of offshore islands.

WAN SHOU *1969*

3 OILERS: Ex-US 310-ft AOG TYPE

CHANG PEI (ex-USS *Pecatonica* AOG 57)	AOG 307	17 Mar 1945
LUNG CHUAN (ex-HMNZS *Endeavour*, ex-USS *Namakagon*, AOG 53)	AOG 515	4 Nov 1944
HSIN LUNG (ex-USS *Elkhorn* AOG 7)	AOG 516	15 May 1943

Displacement, tons	1 850 light; 4 335 full load
Dimensions, feet	292 wl; 310·75 oa × 48·5 × 15·7
Guns	(current armament unknown)
Main engines	Diesels (General Motors); 3 300 bhp; 2 shafts = 14 knots

Former US gasoline tankers of the "Patapsco" class. Built by Cargill, Inc, Savage, Minnesota; launch dates above. The *Chang Pei* was transferred to Taiwan China on 24 Apr 1961. The ex-USS *Namakagon* was transferred to New Zealand on 5 Oct 1962 for use as an Antarctic resupply ship; strengthened for polar operations and renamed *Endeavour*; returned to the US Navy on 29 July 1971 and retransferred to Taiwan China the same date. The *Hsin Lung* was transferred to Taiwan China on 1 July 1972.
The smaller (220·5 ft) *Yu Chuan* AOG 303 ex-USS *Wantanga* AOG 22 stricken in 1959 after running aground; *Hsin Kao* AOG 502 (ex-AOG 302), ex-USS *Towalgia* AOG 42 stricken in 1973.

Auxiliary Ships—*continued*

2 OILERS: Ex-US YO TYPE

SZU MING (ex-USS YO 198) AOG 504 (ex-AOG 304)
TAI YUN (ex-USS YO 175) AOG 510

Displacement, tons	650 light; 1 595 full load
Dimensions, feet	174 oa × 32
Guns	*Szu Ming*: 1—40 mm AA; 5—20 mm AA (single)
Main engines	Diesel (Union); 560 bhp; 1 shaft = 10·5 knots
Complement	approx 65

Former US Navy self-propelled fuel oil barges. *Szu Ming* built by Manitowoc SB Co, Manitowoc, Wisconsin, in 1945; *Tai Yun* built by Albina Engine & Machinery Works, Portland, Oregon, in 1944. Transferred to Taiwan China in Dec 1949 and Mar 1968, respectively.

2 JAPANESE TYPE

Two small oilers of Japanese construction also are reported to be in service.

DISPOSALS

The *O Mei* AO 509 (ex-AO 309), formerly the USS *Maumee* AG 124 (ex-AO 2), was scrapped in 1967. The *Ho Lan* AO 305, formerly the Polish *Praca* was scrapped in 1964.

1 CARGO SHIP: Ex-US AKL TYPE

YUNG KANG (ex-USS *Mark*, AKL12 ex-AG 143, ex-US Army FS 214) AKL 514

Displacement, tons	approx 700
Dimensions, feet	176·5 oa × 32·8 × 10
Guns	(current armament unknown)
Main engines	Diesel; 1 000 bhp; 1 shaft = 10 knots

Built by Higgins in 1944 as a small cargo ship (freight amd supply) for the US Army. Transferred to US Navy on 30 Sep 1947; operated in Indochina area from 1963 until transferred to Taiwan China on 1 July 1971.

TUGS

TA TUNG (ex-USS *Chickasaw*, ATF 83) ATF 548 23 July 1942

Displacement, tons	1 235 standard; 1 675 full load
Dimensions, feet	195 wl; 205 oa × 38·5 × 15·5
Guns	1—3 inch (*76 mm*) 50 cal AA; several light AA
Main engines	Diesel-electric drive; 3 000 bhp; 1 shaft = 15 knots

Former US Navy "Apache" class fleet tug. Built by United Engineering Co, Alameda, California; launch date above. Transferred to Taiwan China in Jan 1966.

TA SUFH (ex-USS *Tonkawa*, ATA 176) ATR 547 1 Mar 1944
TA TENG (ex-USS *Cahokia*, ATA 186) ATA 549 18 Sep 1944

Displacement, tons	435 standard; 835 full load
Dimensions, feet	134·5 wl; 143 oa × 33·9 × 13
Guns	1—3 inch (*76 mm*) 50 cal AA; several light AA
Main engines	Diesel-electric (General Motors diesels); 1 500 bhp; 1 shaft = 13 knots

Former US Navy auxiliary ocean tugs. Built by Levingston SB Co, Orange, Texas; launch dates above. *Ta Sufh* transferred to Taiwan China in Apr 1966. *Ta Teng* assigned briefly to US Air Force in 1971; transferred to Taiwan China on 14 Apr 1972. A third tug of this type serves as a surveying ship.

TA WU (ex-US Army LT 1) ATA 542
TA MING (ex-US Army LT 220) ATA 543
TA YU (ex-US Army LT 310) ATA 545
TA CHING (ex-US Army LT 355) ATA

Former US Army harbour tugs; first three ships transferred in 1949 originally numbered in 300-series.

YTL 3 (ex-US Army ST 846)
YTL 8 (ex-US Army ST 2002)
YTL 9 (ex-US Army ST 2004)
YTL 10 (ex-US Army ST 2003)

Former US Army 76-foot harbour tugs.

Tugs—*continued*

YTL 11 (ex-USN YTL 454) **YTL 12** (ex-USN YTL 584) **YTL 13** (ex-USN YTL 585)

Former US Navy 66-foot harbour tugs.

MISCELLANEOUS

5 Ex-US FLOATING DRY DOCKS

HAY TAN (ex-USN AFDL 36) AFDL 1
KIM MEN (ex-USN AFDL 5) AFDL 2
HAN JIH (ex-USN AFDL 34) AFDL 3
FO WU 5 (ex-USN ARD 9) ARD 5
FO WU 6 (ex-USS *Windsor*, ARD 22) ARD 6

Former US Navy floating dry docks; see United States section for characteristics.

SERVICE CRAFT

Approximately 25 non-self-propelled service craft are in use; most are former US Navy service craft.

CUSTOMS SERVICE

Several small ships and small craft are in service with the Customs Service of Taiwan China, an agency of the Ministry of Finance. The larger ships include two former submarine chasers, listed below.

2 Ex-US PC TYPE

Name		RCN No.	Launched
TUNG KIANG	(ex-USS *Placerville*, PC 1087)	PC 119	21 Aug 1943
HSI KIANG	(ex-USS *Susanville*, PC 1149)	PC 120	11 Jan 1944

Displacement, tons	450 full load
Dimensions, feet	173·66 oa × 23 × 10·8
Guns	1—3 inch (*76 mm*)) 50 cal AA; several lighter guns
Main engines	Diesels (General Motors); 2 880 bhp; 2 shafts = 20 knots

Former US Navy steel-hulled submarine chasers. Launch dates above. Originally transferred to Taiwan China for naval use; subsequently allocated to the Customs Service. Armament believed to have been retained.

TANZANIA

Mercantile Marine

Lloyd's Register of Shipping: 11 vessels of 18 218 tons gross

FAST GUN BOATS

6 Ex-CHINESE "SHANGHAI" CLASS

Displacement, tons	100 full load
Dimensions, feet	120·0 × 18·0 × 6·0
Guns	4—37 mm (twin fore and aft)
Main engines	4 diesels; 4 800 bhp = 28 knots

Transferred by the Chinese People's Republic in 1970-71.
There are reported to be four small patrol boats, two of 50 tons and two of 27 tons. It was officially stated in 1967 that the four *Küstenwachboote* loaned to the Tanzania Government by the Federal Republic of Germany, KW 4, KW 5, KW 9 and KW 10, shipped from West Germany on 8 Dec 1963, and renamed *Rafiki*, *Papa*, *Uhura* and *Salama*, respectively, see full particulars in the 1966-67 edition, had been handed over to the Southern Engineering Company of Mombasa, Kenya.

THAILAND

Administration

Commander-in-Chief of the Navy:
Admiral Thavil Rayananon

Deputy Commander-in-Chief:
Admiral Kamol Sitakalin

Chief of the Naval Staff:
Vice-Admiral Jit Sangkhadul

Diplomatic Representation

Naval Attaché in London:
Captain Sam-Arng Kresupon

Naval Attaché in Washington:
Captain Kasem Rakcharcon

Strength of the Fleet

(No building programme known)

Type	*Active*
Frigates	7
Corvettes	14
Large Patrol Craft	14
Coastal Patrol Craft	16
Coastal Minelayers	6
MW Support Ship	1
MSB's	10
LST's	4
LSM's	3
LCG	1
LCI's	2
LCT's	6
LCM's	26
LCVP's	6
Survey Vessels	3
Support Tankers	2
Harbour Tankers	4
Water Boats	2
Tugs	4

Personnel

(a) 1974: *Navy,* 20 000 (2 000 officers and 18 000 ratings) including *Marine Corps:* 6 400 (400 officers and 6 000 men)
(b) 2 years National Service

Mercantile Marine

Lloyd's Register of Shipping:
78 vessels of 182 043 tons gross

Prefix to Ships' Names

HTMS.

Disposals

Frigates

1973 *Bangpakong, Maeklong*

Large Patrol Craft

1973 *SC 7*

Coastal Patrol Craft

1973 *CGC1* and *11, T 31, 33, 34* and *35*

FRIGATES

Name	*No.*	*Builders*	*Laid down*	*Launched*	*Completed*
MAKUT RAJAKUMARN	7	Yarrow & Co. Ltd. Scotstoun.	11 Jan 1970	18 Nov 1971	7 May 1973

Displacement, tons	1 780 standard; 1 900 full load
Length, feet (*metres*)	320·0 (*97·6*) oa
Beam, feet (*metres*)	36·0 (*11·0*)
Draught, feet (*metres*)	15·4 (*4·7*)
Missile launchers	1 quadruple "Seacat"
Guns, dual purpose	2—4·5 in Mk 8 (*114 mm*) (single)
Guns, AA	2—40 mm 60 cal Bofors (single)
A/S weapons	1 triple barrelled "Limbo" mortar; 1 DC rack; 2 depth charge throwers
Main engines	1 Rolls-Royce "Olympus" gas Turbine; 23 125 shp; 1 Crossley-Pielstick 12 PC2V diesel; 6 000 bhp
Speed, knots	26, 18 on diesel
Range, miles	5 000 at 18 knots (diesel) 1 200 at 26 knots
Complement	140 (16 officers, 124 ratings)

An order was placed with Yarrow & Co Ltd, Scotstoun, Glasgow on 21 Aug 1969 for a general purpose frigate. A long range vessel of a new design developed by Yarrow resulting in a comparative low cost ship with an armament/displacement ratio superior to that of any comparable warship. The ship is largely automated with a consequent saving in complement.

ELECTRONICS. HSA CIC system. Racal DF.

RADAR. LW 04 air surveillance amidships; M 20 series fire control system with co-mounted search and tracking radars in radome for guns; M 44 aft for seacat. NAVIGATION. Decca type 626. IFF—UK Mod Mk 10. Missile control—H. Signaal WM 22 and VM 44.

SONAR. UK Mod Type 170 and Plessey Type MS 27.

MAKUT RAJAKUMARN *1973, W Ralston Ltd.*

TAPI PF 107 **KHIRIRAT** PF 108

Displacement, tons	900 standard; 1 135 full load
Length, feet (*metres*)	275 (*83·8*) oa
Beam, feet (*metres*)	33 (*10·0*)
Draught, feet (*metres*)	10 (*3·0*)
Guns, surface	2—3 in (*76 mm*)
Guns, AA	2—40 mm
A/S weapons	Torpedoes, DCs, Hedgehogs
Main engines	FM Diesels; 6 000 bhp
Speed, knots	20

Of similar design to the Iranian ships of the "Bayandor" class. *Tapi* was ordered from the American Shipbuilding Co, Toledo, Ohio on June 27 1969 laid down 1 Apr 1970, launched 17 Oct 1970 and completed 1 Nov 1971. *Khirirat* was ordered from Norfolk SB & DD Co on 25 June 1971, laid down 18 Feb 1972 and completed in 1973.

MAKUT RAJAKUMARN *1973, Wright & Logan*

Frigates—*continued*

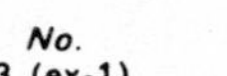

Name	*No.*	*Builders*	*Launched*	*Completed*
PIN KLAO (ex-USS *Hemminger DE* 746)	3 (ex-1)	Western Pipe & Steel Co	12 Sep 1943	30 May 1944

Displacement, tons	1 240 standard; 1 900 full load
Length, feet (*metres*)	306·0 (*93·3*) oa
Beam, feet (*metres*)	37·0 (*11·3*)
Draught, feet (*metres*)	14·1 (*4·3*)
Guns, dual purpose	3—3 in (*76 mm*) 50 cal
Guns, AA	6—40 mm
A/S weapons	8 DCT
Torpedo tubes	6 (2 triple) for A/S torpedoes
Main engines	GM diesels with electric drive; 2 shafts; 6 000 bhp
Speed, knots	20
Range, miles	11 500 at 11 knots
Oil fuel, tons	300
Complement	220

Ex-US "Cannon" class. Transferred from US Navy to Royal Thai Navy at New York Navy Shipyard in July 1959 under MDAP. The 3—21 in torpedo tubes were removed and the 4—20 mm AA guns were replaced by 4—40 mm AA. The six A/S torpedo tubes were fitted in 1966.

PIN KLAO *1966, Royal Thai Navy*

2 "PRASAE" CLASS

Name	*No.*	*Builders*	*Laid down*	*Launched*	*Completed*
PRASAE (ex-USS *Gallup, PF* 47)	2	Consolidated Steel Corpn, Los Angeles	18 Aug 1943	17 Sep 1943	29 Feb 1944
TAHCHIN (ex-USS *Glendale, PF* 36)	1	Consolidated Steel Corpn, Los Angeles	6 Apr 1943	28 May 1943	1 Oct 1943

Displacement, tons	1 430 standard; 2 100 full load
Length, feet (*metres*)	304·0 (*92·7*) oa
Beam, feet (*metres*)	37·5 (*11·4*)
Draught, feet (*metres*)	13·7 (*4·2*)
Guns, dual purpose	3—3 in (*76 mm*) 50 cal.
Guns, AA	2—40 mm; 9—20 mm
A/S weapons	8 DCT
Main engines	Triple expansion; 2 shafts; 5 500 ihp
Speed, knots	19
Boilers	2 small water tube 3-drum type
Oil fuel, tons	685
Range, miles	7 800 at 12 knots
Complement	180

Former US patrol frigates of the "Tacoma" class. Delivered to the Royal Thai Navy on 29 Oct 1951. They were of similar design to the British frigates of the "River" class. *Prasea* partially non-operational after collision in Jan 1972.

PRASAE *1971*

1 Ex-BRITISH "ALGERINE" CLASS

PHOSAMTON (ex-HMS *Minstrel*) MSF 1

Displacenemt, tons	1 040 standard; 1 335 full load
Length, feet (*metres*)	225·0 (*68·6*) oa
Beam, feet (*metres*)	35·5 (*10·8*)
Draught, feet (*metrer*)	10·5 (*3·2*)
Guns	1—4 in (*102 mm*) 6—20 mm
A/S weapons	4 DCT
Main engines	Triple expansion; 2 shafts; 2 000 ihp
Speed, knots	16
Boilers	2 three-drum type
Oil fuel, tons	270
Range, miles	5 000 at 10 knots
Complement	103

Former British "Algerine" class ocean minesweeper capable of fleet sweeping and escort duties. Built by Redfern Construction Co. Laid down in 1943, launched on 5 Oct 1944, completed in 1945. Transferred in Apr 1947. The 20 mm guns were increased from 3 to 6, and the DCTs from 2 to 4 in 1966. Marginally operational.

PHOSAMTON *1965 Royal Thai Navy*

CORVETTES

7 "TRAD" CLASS

CHANDHABURI 16 Dec 1936	No. 22	**PUKET** 28 Sep 1935	No. 12
CHUMPORN 18 Jan 1937	No. 31	**RAYONG** 11 Jan 1937	No. 23
PATTANI 16 Oct 1936	No. 13	**SURASDRA** 28 Nov 1936	No. 21
		TRAD 26 Oct 1935	No. 11

Displacement, tons	318 standard; 470 full load
Dimensions, feet	219 pp; 223 oa × 21 × 7
Guns	2—3 in AA; 1—40 mm AA; 2—20 mm AA; *Chumporn, Puket* and *Trad* 2—40 mm
Tubes	4—18 in (2 twin); *Chumporn, Puket* and *Trad* 2—18 in (twin)
Main engines	Parsons geared turbines; 2 shafts; 9 000 hp = 31 knots
Boilers	2 Yarrow
Oil fuel, tons	102
Range, miles	1 700 at 15 knots
Complement	70

Designed as torpedo boats, *Puket* and *Trad* were laid down on 8 Feb 1935 by Cantieri Riuniti dell'Adriatico, Monfalcone, for delivery by end of 1935. Launch dates above. Armament was supplied by Vickers-Armstrongs Ltd. First boat reached 32-34 knots on trials with 10 000 hp. All delivered by summer 1937. The 2 single 18 inch torpedo tubes and the 4—8 mm guns were removed.

TRAD

Corvettes—*cont.*

7 "LIULOM" CLASS (Ex US PC's)

LIULOM (ex-*PC* 1253) PC 7
LONGLOM (ex-*PC* 570) PC 8
PHALI (ex-*PC* 1185) PC 4
SARASIN (ex-*PC* 495) PC 1
SUKRIP (ex-*PC* 1218) PC 5
THAYANCHON (ex-*PC* 575) PC 2
TONGPLIU (ex-*PC* 616) PC 6

Displacement, tons	280 standard; 400 full load
Dimensions, feet	174 oa × 23·2 × 6
Guns	1—3 in AA; 1—40 mm AA; 5—20 mm AA
A/S weapons	2 ASW torpedo tubes (except *Sarasin*)
Main engines	Diesel; 2 shafts; 3 600 bhp = 19 knots
Oil fuel, tons	60
Range, miles	6 000 at 10 knots
Complement	62 to 71, *Sukeip* 69 (10 officers, 59 men)

Former US submarine chasers. Launched in 1941-43. Nos. PC 7, 8, 4, 1, 5, 2 and 6, respectively.

THAYANCHON — *1969, Royal Thai Navy*

LIGHT FORCES

3 "KLONGYAI" CLASS (LARGE PATROL CRAFT)

KANTANG No. 7 **KLONGYAI** No. 5 **SATTAHIP** No. 8

Displacement, tons	110 standard; 135 full load
Dimensions, feet	131·5 × 15·5 × 4
Guns	1—3 in 1—20 mm
Tubes	2—18 in
Main engines	Geared turbines = 2 shafts; 1 000 shp = 19 knots
Boilers	2 water-tube
Range, miles	480 at 15 knots
Oil fuel, tons	18
Complement	31

Sattahip was built by the Royal Thai Naval Dockyard, Bangkok, laid down on 21 Nov 1956, launched on 28 Oct 1957 and completed in 1958. The other two were built by Ishikawajima Co, Japan, both launched on 26 Mar 1937 and completed on 21 June 1937.

KANTANG — *1971*

3 THAI DESIGN (PATROL CRAFT—COASTAL)

T 91 **T 92** **T 93**

Displacement, tons	87·5 standard
Dimensions, feet	104·3 × 17·5 × 5·5
Guns	1—40 mm AA; 1—20 mm AA
Main engines	Diesels; 1 600 bhp = 25 knots
Complement	21

Built by the Royal Thai Naval Dockyard, Bangkok, Completed 1971.

T 91 — *1970, Royal Thai Navy*

Light Forces—*continued*

10 LARGE PATROL CRAFT

T 11 (ex-US *PGM* 71)
T 12 (ex-US *PGM* 79)
T 13 (ex-US *PGM* 107)
T 14 (ex-US *PGM* 116)
T 15 (ex-US *PGM* 117)
T 16 (ex-US *PGM* 115)
T 17 (ex-US *PGM 113*)
T 18 (ex-US *PGM 114*)
T 19 (ex-US *PGM* 123)
T 110 (ex-US *PGM* 124)

Displacement, tons	130 standard; 147 full load
Dimensions, feet	99·0 wl; 101·0 oa × 21·0 × 6·0
Guns	1—40 mm AA; 4—20 mm AA; 2—·50 cal
Main engines	Diesels; 2 shafts; 1 800 bhp = 18·5 knots
Range, miles	1 500 at 10 knots
Complement	30

T 11 was built by Peterson Builders Inc, launched on 5 May 1965 and transferred to the Royal Thai Navy on 1 Feb 1966. T 13 was transferred 28 Aug 1967, T 14, T 15 on 18 Aug 1969 and 2 Oct 1969, T 16, T 17 and T 19 on 12 Feb 1970, T 19 and T 110 on 25 Dec 1970.

T 12 — *1969, Royal Thai Navy*

7 COASTAL PATROL CRAFT

T 21 **T 22** **T 23** **T 24** **T 25** **T 26** **T 27**

Displacement, tons	20 standard, 22 full load
Dimensions, feet	50 × 13
Guns	2—0·50 cal (1 twin)
Main engines	Diesels; 2 shafts; 480 bhp = 25 knots
Complement	5

Swift class patrol craft transferred from USN; T22 in Oct 1968, T23-25 in Nov 1970.

2 COASTAL PATROL CRAFT

T 32 **T 36**

Displacement, tons	10·4 standard; 13·05 full load
Dimensions, feet	35 × 10
Guns	2—0·50 cal (1 twin); 2—0·30 cal
Main engines	Diesels; 2 shafts; 225 bhp = 14 knots
Complement	7

USN RPC type.

4 COASTAL PATROL CRAFT

CGC 3 (ex 13) **CGC 4** (ex 14) **CGC 5** (ex 15) **CGC 6** (ex 16)

Displacement, tons	95
Dimensions, feet	95 × 20·2 × 5
Guns	1—20 mm AA
A/S weapons	2 D.C. racks; 2 Mousetraps
Main engines	4 diesels; 2 shafts; 2 200 bhp = 21 knots
Range, miles	1 500 at 14 knots
Complement	15

US coastguard cutters transferred in 1954. Similar to those built for U.S.C.G. by US Coast Guard Yard, Curtis Bay, in 1953, Cost £475,000 each.

CGC 4 (as CGC 14) — *Royal Thai Navy*

1 Ex-US SC TYPE (LARGE PATROL CRAFT)

SC 8 (ex *SC*-32, ex-US *SC* 1633)

Displacement, tons	110 light; 125 full load
Dimensions, feet	111 × 17 × 6
Gun	1—40 mm; 3—20 mm
A/S weapons	Depth Charges, Mousetrap
Main engines	High-speed diesel = 18 knots
Range, miles	2 000 at 10 knots

Former US wooden submarine chaser. Built by South Coast Co, Newport Reach, California, in 1954-55. Non-operational.

MINE WARFARE FORCES

2 "BANGRACHAN" CLASS (COASTAL MINELAYERS)

BANGRACHAN MMC 1 **NHONG SARHAI** MMC 2

Displacement, tons	368 standard; 408 full load
Dimensions, feet	160·8 × 25·9 × 7·2
Guns	2—3 in AA; 2—20 mm AA
Mines	142 capacity
Main engines	Burmeister & Wain diesels; 2 shafts; 540 bhp = 12 knots
Oil fuel, tons	18
Range, miles	2 700 at 10 knots
Complement	55

Launched by Cantiere dell'Adriatico, Monfalcone in 1936, *Nhong Sarhai* on 22 July.

BANGRACHAN

4 COASTAL MINELAYERS

BANGKEO (ex-USS *MSC* 303) 6 **LADYA** (ex-USS *MSC* 297) 5
DONCHEDI (ex-USS *MSC* 313) 8 **TADINDENG** (ex-USS *MSC* 301) 7

Displacement, tons	330 standard; 362 full load
Dimensions, feet	145·3 oa × 27 × 8·5
Guns	2—20 mm AA
Main engines	4 GM diesels; 2 shafts; 1 000 bhp = 13 knots
Range, miles	2 500 at 10 knots
Complement	43 (7 officers, and 36 men)

Built by Peterson Builders Inc, Sturgeon Bay, Wisc, (*Ladya* and *Donchedi*), Tacoma Boat building Co Tacoma, Wash. (*Tadindeng*) and Dorchester Shipbuilding Corp, Camden (*Bangkeo*). *Ladya* was transferred on 14 Dec 1963, *Bangkeo* on 9 July 1965, *Tadindeng* on 26 Aug 1965, and *Donchedi* on 17 Sep 1965 (last three launched in 1964, 1 July, 11 Apr, 22 Dec). Of the ex-US *YMS* type, *Bangkeo* (ex-*YMS* 384), *Ladya* (ex-*YMS* 138) and *Tadindeng* (ex-*YMS* 21) were removed from the effective list in 1964 and 1965.

BANGKEO 1971

RANG KWIEN (ex-*Umihari Maru*) MCS 11 (MW SUPPORT SHIP)

Displacement, tons	586 standard
Dimensions, feet	162·3 × 31·2 × 13·0 max
Main engines	Triple expansion steam; Speed = 10 knots

Built in 1944 by Mitsubishi Co as a tug. Acquired by Royal Thai Navy on 6 Sep 1967.

RANG KWIEN *1969, Royal Thai Navy*

5 MSB

MSML 6-10

Thai built, 50 ft.

5 MSB

MSML 1-5

Thai built. 40 ft.

AMPHIBIOUS FORCES

4 Ex-US LST TYPE

ANGTHONG (ex-USS *LST* 294) LST 1
CHANG (ex-USS *Lincoln County LST* 898) LST 2
LANTA (ex-USS *Stone County LST* 1141) LST 4
PANGAN (ex-USS *Stark County LST* 1134) LST 3

Displacement, tons	1 625 standard; 4 080 full load
Dimensions, feet	316 wl; 328 oa × 50 × 14
Guns	6—40 mm; 4—20 mm
Main engines	GM diesels; 2 shafts; 1 700 bhp = 11knots
Range, miles	9 500 at 9 knots
Complement	80

Angthong is employed as training ship. *Chang*, transferred to Thailand in 1962, was built by Dravo Corp, laid down on 15 Oct 1944, launched on 25 Nov 1944 and completed on 29 Dec 1944. *Pangan* was transferred on 16 May 1966 and *Lanta* on 12 Mar 1970.

CHANG *1965, Royal Thai Navy*

3 Ex-US LSM TYPE

KRAM (ex-USS *LSM* 469) LSM 3 **KUT** (ex-USS *LSM* 338) LSM 1
PHAI (ex-USS *LSM* 333) LSM 2

Displacement, tons	743 standard; 1 095 full load
Dimensions, feet	196·5 wl; 203·5 oa × 34·5 × 8·3
Guns	2—40 mm AA
Main engines	Diesel direct drive; 2 shafts; 2 800 bhp = 12·5 knots
Range, miles	2 500 at 12 knots
Complement	55

Former United States landing ship of the LCM, later LSM (Medium Landing Ship), type. *Kram* was transferred to Thailand under MAP at Seattle, Wash, on 25 May 1962; she was built by Brown Shipbuilding Col, Houston, Tex, laid down on 27 Jan 1945, launched on 17 Feb 1945, and completed on 17 Mar 1945.

NAKA (ex-USS *LSSL* 102) LSSL 3 (LCG)

Displacement, tons	233 standard; 287 full load
Dimensions, feet	152 wl; 158 oa × 23 × 4·25
Guns	1—3 inch; 4—40 mm AA; 4—20 mm AA; 4—81 mm mortar
Main engines	Diesels; 2 shafts; 1 320 bhp = 15 knots
Range, miles	4 700 at 10 knots

Transferred in 1966. Acquired when Japan returned her to USA.

2 Ex-US LCI TYPE

PRAB (ex-*LCI M* 670) LCI 1 **SATAKUT** (ex-*LCI M* 739) LCI 2

Displacement, tons	230 standard; 387 full load
Dimensions, feet	157 × 23 × 6
Guns	2—20 mm AA
Main engines	Diesel; 2 shafts; 1 320 bhp = 14 knots
Complement	54

Former United States landing craft of the LCI (Infantry Landing Craft) type. Prab non-operational.

SATAKUT *Royal Thai Navy*

26 Ex-US LCM 6

14-16, 61-68, 71-78, 81-82, 85-87.

First 21 delivered 1969.

6 Ex-US LCVP

Amphibious Forces—*continued*

6 LCU Ex-US LCT (6) TYPE

ARDANG LCU 3 · **KOLUM** LCU 5 · **MATAPHON** LCU 1 · **PHETRA** LCU 4 · **RAWI** LCU 2 · **TALIBONG** LCU 6

Displacement, tons	134 standard; 279 full load
Dimensions, feet	112 × 32 × 4
Guns	2—20 mm AA
Main engines	Diesel; 3 shafts; 675 bhp = 10 knots
Complement	37

Former United States landing craft of the LCT (6) type. Employed as transport ferries.

SURVEY SHIP

CHANDHARA AGS 11

Displacement, tons	870 standard; 996 full load
Dimensions, feet	229·2 oa × 34·5 × 10
Gun	1—20 mm AA
Main engines	2 diesels; 2 shafts; 1 000 bhp = 13·25 knots
Range, miles	10 000 (cruising)
Complement	72

Built by C. Melchers & Co, Bremen, Germany. Laid down on 27 Sep 1960. Launched on 17 Dec 1960. Can also be used as training ship and yacht.

CHANDHARA *1962, Royal Thai Navy*

2 OCEANOGRAPHIC CRAFT

Of 90 tons, launched in 1955 with a crew of 8.

SUPPORT FORCES

CHULA AO 2 (SUPPORT TANKER)

Displacement, tons	2 395 standard
Dimensions, feet	328 × 43·2 × 25
Main engines	Steam turbines

This tanker and *Matra* (see below) were acquired for naval oiling and supply duties.

CHULA *1969, Royal Thai Navy*

MATRA AO 3 (SUPPORT TANKER)

Displacement, tons	4 744
Dimensions, feet	328 × 45·2 × 20
Main engines	Steam turbine

Employed as a freighting and fleet replenishment tanker and naval supply ship.

SAMED (HARBOUR TANKER)

Displacement, tons	360 standard; 485 full load
Dimensions, feet	120 × 20 × 10
Main engines	Diesel; 500 bhp = 9 knots

Built by Royal Thai Naval Dockyard, Bangkok. Launched on 8 July 1966. Commissioned on 15 Dec 1970.

Support Forces—*continued*

SAMUI (ex-USS YOG 60) YO 4 (HARBOUR TANKER)

Displacement, tons	422 standard
Dimensions, feet	174·5 × 32 × 15
Main engines	Diesel; 2 shafts; 600 bhp = 8 knots
Complement	29

Small tanker of the ex-YOG type. Employed as a fleet auxiliary attendant oiler.

PROET (HARBOUR TANKER)

Displacement, tons	360
Dimensions, feet	122·7 × 19·7 × 8·7
Main engines	Diesels; 500 bhp = 9 knots

Built by the Royal Thai Naval Dockyard, Bangkok. Commissioned on 16 Jan 1970.

PRONG YO 5 (HARBOUR TANKER)

Displacement, tons	150 standard
Dimensions, feet	95 × 18 × 7·5
Main engines	Diesel; 150 bhp = 10 knots
Complement	14

Launched in 1938. Employed as a small naval auxiliary servicing tanker.

SICHANG AKL 1 (TRANSPORT)

Displacement, tons	815 standard
Dimensions, feet	160 × 28 × 16
Main engines	Diesel; 2 shafts; 550 bhp = 16 knots
Complement	30

Built by Harima Co, Japan. *Sichang* was launched on 10 Nov 1937. Completed in Jan 1938.

KLED KEO AF 7 (TRANSPORT)

Displacement, tons	382 standard; 450 full load
Dimensions, feet	154·9 × 25·4 × 14
Guns	3—20 mm
Main engines	1 diesel; 600 hp = 12 knots
Complement	54

Operates with patrol boat squadron.

CHUANG YW 8 (WATER BOAT)

Displacement, tons	305 standard; 485 full load
Dimensions, feet	98 × 18 × 7·2
Main engines	GM diesel; 500 bhp = 11 knots
Complement	29

Built by the Royal Thai Naval Dockyard, Bangkok. Launched on 14 Jan 1965.

CHAN YW 6 (WATER BOAT)

Displacement, tons	355 standard
Dimensions, feet	139·5 × 24 × 10
Main engines	Diesel; Speed = 6 knots

Probably non-operational.

4 TUGS

SAMAE SAN (ex-*Empire Vincent*) YTM 1

Displacement, tons	503 full load
Dimensions, feet	105·0 × 26·5 × 13·0
Main engines	Triple expansion; 850 ihp = 10·5 knots
Complement	27

Built by Cochrane & Sons Ltd., Selby, Yorks, England.

KLUENG BADAN (ex-USN *YTL*) YTL 2 · **MARN VICHAI** (ex-USN *YTL*) YTL 3 · **RAD** (ex-USN *YTL*) YTL 1

Displacement, tons	63 standard (*Rad* 52 standard)
Dimensions, feet	64·7 × 16·5 × 6·0 (*Rad* 60·7 × 17·5 × 5·0)
Main engines	Diesels; speed = 8 knots (*Rad* 6 knots)

Rad transferred 1955 from US, the other pair bought from Canada 1953.

TRINIDAD AND TOBAGO

COAST GUARD

Administration

Commanding Officer, T. & T. Coast Guard: Captain D. F. A. Bloom MOM, GM

Personnel

(a) 1974: 200 (25 officers, 175 ratings)
(b) Voluntary

Mercantile Marine

Lloyd's Register of Shipping: 28 vessels of 15 659 tons gross

PATROL CRAFT

2 LATER VOSPER TYPE

BUCCO REEF CG 4 **CHAGUARAMUS** CG 3

Displacement, tons	100 standard; 125 full load
Dimensions, feet	95·0 wl; 103·0 × 19·8 × 5·8
Guns	1—20 mm Hispano Suiza
Main engines	2 Paxman Ventura diesels; 2 900 bhp = 24 knots
Oil fuel, tons	20
Range, miles	2 000 at 13 knots
Complement	19 (3 officers, 16 ratings)

Chaguaramus was laid down on 1 Feb 1971 and launched on 29 Mar 1971. Both commissioned at Portsmouth on 18 Mar 1972. Fitted with modern navigational equipment, air-conditioning and roll-damping.

CHAGUARAMUS *1972, Wright & Logan*

2 VOSPER TYPE

COURLAND BAY CG 2 **TRINITY** CG 1

Displacement, tons	96 standard; 123 full load
Dimensions, feet	95·0 wl; 102·6 oa × 19·7 × 5·5
Guns	1—40 mm Bofors
Main engines	2 Vee-form 12 cyl Paxman Ventura YJCM turbo-charged diesels; 2 910 bhp = 24·5 knots (max)
Oil fuel, tons	18
Range, miles	1 800 at 13·5 knots
Complement	17 (3 officers, 14 ratings)

Designed and built by Vosper Limited, Portsmouth. Of steel construction with aluminium alloy superstructure. Up-to-date radar and navigational equipment is fitted, and the boats are air-conditioned throughout except the engine room. Vosper roll-damping equipment is fitted for improved sea-keeping and greater efficiency and comfort of the crews. Laid down Oct 1963. *Trinity* was launched on 14 Apr 1964. Both were commissioned at Portsmouth on 20 Feb 1965. *Trinity* is named after Trinity Hills, so named by Columbus on making his landfall in 1498, and *Courland Bay* after a bay in Tobago where a settlement was founded by the Duke of Courland in the 17th century.

COURLAND BAY *1972, Trinidad & Tobago Coast Guard*

1 60 ft TYPE

SEA HAWK

Dimensions, feet	60 × 17·3 × 3·5
Guns	1 machine gun
Main engines	2 Rolls Royce diesels; 250 hp = 14·5 knots
Radius, miles	400
Complement	6 (1 officer, 5 men)

Built by J. Taylor (Shipbuilders) Ltd, Shoreham-by-Sea. Extensively refitted in 1969; but taken out of service in Dec 1971 and placed in reserve.

1 45ft TYPE

SEA SCOUT CG 5

Length, feet	45·0
Main engines	1 GM 671 diesel; speed - 12 knots

Built by J. Taylor (Shipbuilders) Ltd, Shoreham-oy-Sea. Refitted in 1970 with a single GM 671 diesel in place of the former two Perkins diesels.

SEA SCOUT *1972, Trinidad & Tobago Coast Guard*

4 INSHORE TYPE

CG 6 **CG 7** **CG 8** **CG 9**

Three Glastron glass fibre runabouts and one locally built (also of glass fibre), all capable of 27 knots, are used for inshore patrol work, mainly in the Gulf of Paria.

TONGA

On 10 Mar 1973 King Taufa 'ahau Tupou IV commissioned the first craft of Tonga's Maritime Force, a necessary service in a Kingdom of seven main groups of islands spread over 270 square miles.

NGAHAU KOULA P 101

Of 40 feet and armed with a machine gun. Manned by volunteers from the Royal Guard and Tongan Defence Force.

NGAHAU KOULA *1973 Statham*

TOGO

Togo, which proclaimed independence on 27 April 1960 and has a port at Lomé operates one 130 ft patrol vessel, three 100 ft patrol vessels, and one 95 ft river gunboat. Personnel is 250 officers and men.

TUNISIA

Administration

Chief of Naval Staff: Capitaine de Fregate Jedidi Bechir

Personnel

(a) 1974: 1 900 officers and men
(b) 1 year selective National Service

Mercantile Marine

Lloyds' Register of Shipping:
24 vessels of 28 408 tons gross

FRIGATE

1 Ex-US "EDSALL" CLASS

PRESIDENT BOURGUIBA (ex-USS *Thomas J. Gary* DER 326) E 7

Displacement, tons	1 590 standard; 1 850 full load
Dimensions, ft (*m*)	306 oa × 36·6 × 14 (*93·3 × 11·1 × 4·3*)
Guns	2—3 in (*76 mm*) 50 cal; 2—20 mm
Torpedo tubes	2 triple Mk 32
A/S weapon	1 Hedgehog
Main engines	4 diesels; 6 000 bhp; 2 shafts = 19 knots
Complement	169

Built by Consolidated Steel Corpn. Completed 27 Nov 1943. Converted to Radar Picket in 1958. Transferred 27 Oct 1973.

RADAR. SPS 28 and SPS 10.

CORVETTE

1 FRENCH A-69 TYPE AVISO

Displacement, tons	950 standard; 1 260 full load
Dimensions, feet	262·5 oa × 33·8 × 9·8
Guns	1—3·9 in AA (100 mm); 1—40 mm; 4—20 mm
A/S weapons	1 sextuple Mk 64 rocket launcher (375 mm) 4 fixed torpedo launchers for homing torpedoes
Main engines	2 SEMT Pielstick PC2V Diesels; 2 shafts; c-p propellers; 1 100 shp = 24 knots
Range, miles	4 500 at 15 knots
Complement	62

Ordered from France in 1972. (See Coastal minesweeper below).

COASTAL MINESWEEPER

HANNIBAL (ex-*Coquelicot* ex-USN MSC 84)

French minesweeper of the "Acacia" class loaned to Tunisia for one year in 1973 until completion of the A69 Type Aviso ordered from France is completed.

LIGHT FORCES

3 "P 48" CLASS

BIZERTE P 301 **HORRIA** (ex-*Liberté*) P 302 +1

Displacement, tons	250
Dimensions, feet	157·5 × 23·3 × 7
Guns	2—40 mm AA
Missiles	8 SS-12 M
Main engines	2 diesels; 4 800 bhp = 20 knots
Range, miles	2 000 at 16 knots

Built by Ch Franco-Belges (Villeneuve, la Garenne). *Bizerte* was launched on 20 Nov 1969 and completed 10 July 1970. *Horria* launched 12 Feb 1970 and completed Oct 1970. Third ship ordered from Soc. Francaise Constructions Navale for delivery in Nov 1974.

HORRIA 1972, Tunisian Navy

1 Ex "FOUGEUX" CLASS

SAKIET SIDI YOUSSEF (ex-*UW 12*) P 303

Displacement, tons	325 standard; 400 full load
Dimensions, feet	170 pp × 23 × 6·5
Guns	1—40 mm; 2—20 mm
A/S weapons	1 hedgehog; 2 DCT; 2 DC racks
Main engines	4 Pielstick-SEMT diesels; 2 340 bhp = 19 knots
Range, miles	2 000 at 15 knots
Complement	4 officers, 59 men

Patrol vessel of the "Fougueux" class. Built in France by Dubigeon, Nantes, under US off-shore order. Purchased by Federal Germany in 1957 and served as A/S trials vessel. Transferred to Tunisia in Dec 1969.

Light Forces—*continued*

SAKIET SIDI YOUSSEF *1971, Tunisian Navy*

4 COASTAL PATROL CRAFT

AL JALA P 203 **JOUMHOURIA** P 202
ISTIKLAL (ex-*VC* 11, *P* 761) P 201 **REMADA** P 204

Displacement, tons	75 standard; 82 full load
Dimensions, feet	104·5 × 15·5 × 5·5
Guns	2—20 mm AA
Main engines	2 Mercedes-Benz diesels; 2 shafts; 2 400 bhp = 29 knots
Range, miles	1 400 at 15 knots
Complement	17

Built by Ch Navals d'Esterel, 201-203 in 1961-63, 204 in 1967.

ISTIKLAL *1971, Tunisian Navy*

8 COASTAL PATROL CRAFT

V 101 **V 102** **V 103** **V 104** **V 105** **V 106** **V 107** **V 108**

Displacement, tons	38
Dimensions, feet	83 × 15·6 × 4·1
Guns	1—20 mm
Main engines	2 twim GM diesels; 2 400 hp = 23 knots
Range, miles	900 at 16 knots
Complement	11

V 101-106 built by Ch. Navals d'Esterel 1957-63. V 107 and V 108 were added to the flotilla in 1971.

V 104 *1970, Tunisian Navy*

TUG

2 COASTAL PATROL CRAFT

JAOUEL EL BAHR T 1
SABBACK EL BAHR T 2

25 metre patrol craft built by Ch. Navals d'Esterel.

RAS ADAR (ex-*Zeeland*, ex-*Pan American*, ex-*Ocean Pride*, ex-HMS *Oriana*, *BAT 1*)

Displacement, tons	540 standard
Dimensions, feet	144·4 × 33 × 13·5

Built by the Gulfport Boilerworks & Eng Co in 1942 and lend leased to the Royal Navy in that year as BAT 1 HMS *Oriana*, returned and sold in 1946 as *Ocean Pride*, then *Pan America* in 1947, then *Zeeland* in 1956.

TURKEY

Naval Command

Chief of the Navy:
Admiral Kemal Kayacan

Chief of Staff; Turkish Naval Forces:
Vice Admiral Hilmi Firat

Fleet Commander:
Vice-Admiral Bülent Ulusu

Diplomatic Representation

Defence Attaché in London:
Rear-Admiral Fuat Basol

Naval Attaché in Washington:
Captain Erhan Gürcan

Personnel

(a) 1974: 40 000 officers and ratings
(b) 20 months national service

Naval Bases

Headquarters: Ankara
Main Naval Base: Gölçük
Senior Flag Officers: Istanbul, Izmir
Other Flag Officers: Eregli, Bosphorus, Heybeli Ada (Training), Dardanelles, Iskenderun
Dockyards: Gölçük, Taskizak (Istanbul)

Strength of the Fleet

Type	*Active*	*Building*
Destroyers	14	—
Frigates	2	—
Corvettes	5	—
Submarines—Patrol	13	2
Fast Attack Craft—Missile	—	4
Fast Attack Craft—Torpedo	9	—
Large Patrol Craft	39	—
Coastal Patrol Craft	13	—
Minelayers—Large	3	—
Minelayers—Coastal	6	—
Minesweepers—Coastal	16	—
Minesweepers—Inshore	4	—
LST	1	—
LCT's	17	—
LCU's	16	—
LCM's	20	—
Support Tankers	8	—
Repair Ships	3	—
Transport	1	—
S/M Rescue Ships	2	—
BDV's	7	—
Gate Vessels	3	—
Tugs—Ocean	4	—
Tugs—Harbour	3	—
Floating Docks	7	—
Training Ship	1	—
Survey Vessels	6	—

Disposals

Destroyers

1973 *Gaziantep, Giresun*

Corvettes

1973 *Edremit, Eregli*

Submarines

(Most replaced by submarines of same name).

1973 *Birinci Inönü, Canakkale, Cerbe, Ikinci Inönü, Pirireis*

Fast Attack Craft

1973 *Dogan, Marti, AB 1-4, 6-7*

Naval Air Arm

3 AB-204B Helicopters
16 S2E ASW Aircraft

Mercantile Marine

Lloyd's Register of Shipping:
353 vessels of 756 807 tons gross

DESTROYERS

5 "TEPE" CLASS (Ex-US "GEARING" CLASS)

Name	*No.*	*Builders*	*Launched*	*Completed*
ADATEPE (ex-USS *Forest Royal*, DD 872)	D 353	Bethlehem (Staten Is.)	17 Jan 1946	28 June 1946
GAYRET (ex-USS *Eversole* DD 789)	D 352	Todd Pacific Shipyard	8 Jan 1946	10 July 1946
KOCATEPE (ex-USS *Harwood*, DD 861)	D 354	Bethlehem (San Pedro)	24 May 1945	28 Sep 1945
M. FEVZI ÇAKMAK (ex-USS *Charles H. Roan* DD 853)	D 351	Bethlehem Steel Co, Quincy	15 May 1945	12 Sep 1946
TINAZTEPE (ex-USS *Keppler*, DD 765)	D 355	Bethlehem (San Francisco)	24 June 1945	23 May 1947

Displacement, tons	2 425 standard; 3 500 full load
Length, feet (*metres*)	390·5 (*119·0*) oa
Beam, feet (*metres*)	40·9 (*12·5*)
Draught, feet (*metres*)	19·0 (*5·8*)
Guns	4—5 in (*127 mm*) 38 cal dual purpose (2 twin)
A/S weapons	Fram I; 1 Asroc 8-tube launcher; 2 triple torpedo tubes (Mk 32); Facilities for small helo Fram II; 1 Trainable Hedgehog; 2 Triple torpedo tubes (Mk 32); 2 Fixed Torpedo tubes (Mk 28). Facilities for small Helo
Main engines	2 geared turbines; 2 shafts; 60 000 shp
Boilers	4 Babcock & Wilcox
Speed	34 knots
Oil fuel, tons	650
Range, miles	4 800 at 15 knots, 2 400 at 25 knots
Complement	275 (15 officers, 260 ratings)

KOCATEPE (as Harwood) *Added 1972, USN*

GENERAL
Adatepe, Gayret and *Çakmak* FRAM I conversions and *Kocatepe Tinaztepe* FRAM II. They were transferred to Turkey on 27 Mar 1971 (*Adatepe*) 17 Dec 1971 (*Kocatepe*) 30 June 1972 (*Tinaztepe*) 11 July 1973 (*Gayret*) and 21 Sept 1973 (*Çakmak*), *Adatepe* and *Kocatepe* purchased 15 Feb 1973.

RADAR. Fram I: SPS 40 long range air search; SPS 10 surface search; gun fire control Mk 68 radar. Fram II; SPS 6 long range S band air surveillance; SPS 10 surface search; Mk 68 as above.

SONAR. Fram I SQS 23. Fram II SQS 29.

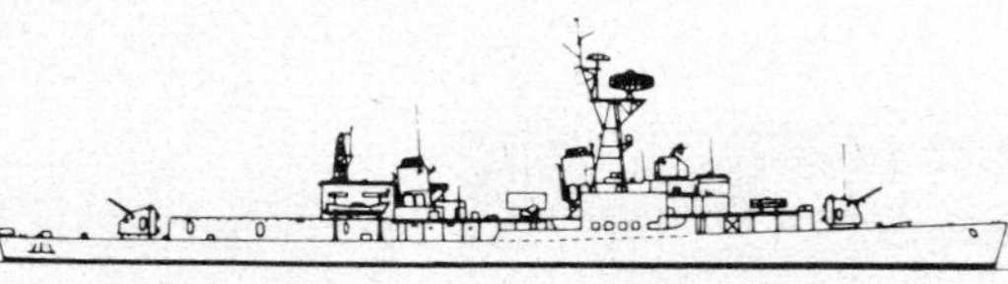
GEARING FRAM I

"ALLEN M. SUMNER" (FRAM II) CLASS

1 Ex-US "SMITH" CLASS

Name	*No.*	*Builders*	*Launched*	*Completed*
MUAVENET (ex-USS *Gwin*, ex- DM 33, ex DD 772)	D 357	Bethlehem, San Pedro	9 Apr 1944	30 Sep 1944

Displacement, tons	2 250 standard; 3 375 full load
Dimensions, ft (*m*)	376·5 × 41 × 19 (*114·8 × 12·5 × 5·8*)
Guns	6—5 in (*127 mm*) 38 cal (twins); 12—40 mm; 11—20 mm
Mines	80
Boilers	4 Babcock and Wilcox
Main engines	Geared turbines; 60 000 shp 2 shafts
Speed	34
Range, miles	4 600 at 15 knots
Complement	274

Modified "Allen M. Sumner" class converted for minelaying. After modernisation at Philadelphia she was transferred on 22 Oct 1971. R

RADAR. SPS 6 air search; Mk 68 radar director.

SONAR. SQS 29.

Destroyers—*continued*

ZAFER (ex-USS *Hugh, Purvis* ex-DD 709)

No.	Builders	Launched	Completed
D 356	Federal SB and DD Co	17 Dec 1944	1 Mar 1945

Displacement, tons	2 200 standard; 3 320 full load
Length, feet (*metres*)	376·5 (*114·8*)
Beam, feet (*metres*)	40·9 (*12·5*)
Draught, feet (*metres*)	19·0 (*5·8*)
Guns	6—5 in 38 cal (twins)
A/S weapons	2 Triple torpedo launchers Mk 32 2 Hedgehogs, 2 Mk 25 torpedo tubes
Machinery	2 geared turbines; 2 shafts; 60 000 shp
Boilers	4 Babcock & Wilcox
Speed	34 knots
Oil fuel, tons	650
Range, miles	4 600 at 15 knots
Complement	275 (15 officers, 260 ratings)

Allen M. Sumner Class FRAM II

GENERAL
Zafer is a standard FRAM II Sumner class purchased 15 Feb 1973.

RADAR. SPS 40 long range air search and SPS 10 surface search.

SONAR. SQS 29.

5 "I" CLASS
(Ex-US "FLETCHER" CLASS)

Name	No.	Builders	Launched	Completed
ICEL (ex-USS *Preston*, DD 795)	D 344	Bethlehem Company, San Pedro	12 Dec 1943	20 Mar 1944
ISKENDERUN (ex-USS *Boyd*, DD 544)	D 343	Bethlehem Company, San Pedro	29 Oct 1942	8 May 1943
ISTANBUL (ex-USS *Clarence K. Bronson* DD 668)	D 340	Federal SB & DD Co, Newark	18 Apr 1943	11 June 1943
IZMIR (ex-USS *Van Valkenburgh* DD 656)	D 341	Gulf Shipbuilding Corp	19 Dec 1943	2 Aug 1944
IZMIT (ex-USS *Cogswell*, DD 651)	D 392	Bath Iron Works Corpn	5 June 1943	17 Aug 1943

Displacement, tons	2 050 standard; 3 000 full load
Length, feet (*metres*)	376·5 (*114·8*) oa
Beam, feet (*metres*)	39·5 (*12·1*)
Draught, feet (*metres*)	18·0 (*5·5*)
Guns, surface	4—5 in (*127 mm*) 38 cal
Guns, AA	6—3 in (*76 mm*)
A/S weapons	2 Hedgehogs
Torpedo tubes	5—21 in (*533 mm*) quintupled
Main engines	GE geared turbines; 2 shafts; 60 000 shp
Speed, knots	34
Boilers	4 Babcock & Wilcox
Oil fuel, tons	650
Range, miles	5 000 at 15 knots
Complement	250

IZMIT — *1972, Turkish Navy*

TRANSFERS. Transferred as follows *Istanbul* 14 Jan 1967, *Izmir* 28 Feb 1967, *Iskenderun* and *Ismit* on 1 Oct 1969, and *Icel* on 15 Nov 1969.

RADAR. Search: SPS 6. Tactical: SPS 10. Fire Control: GFCS 68.

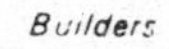

2 "G" CLASS
(Ex-US "GLEAVES" CLASS)

Name	No.	Builders	Laid down	Launched	Completed
GELIBOLU (ex-USS *Buchanan*, DD 484)	D 346	Federal SB & DD Co Port Newark	11 Feb 1941	22 Nov 1941	21 Mar 1942
GEMLIK (ex-USS *Lardner*, DD 487)	D 347	Federal SB & DD Co Port Newark	July 1941	20 Mar 1942	13 May 1942

Displacement, tons	1 810 standard; 2 580 full load
Length, feet (*mertes*)	341·0 (*103·9*)wl; 348·5 (*106·2*) oa
Beam, feet (*metres*)	36·0 (*11·0*)
Draught, feet (*metres*)	18·0 (*5·5*)
Guns, surface	*D346:* 3—5 in (*127 mm*) 38 cal; *D347:* 4—5 in (*127 mm*) 38 cal
Guns, AA	*D346:* 4—3 in (*76 mm*); *D347:* 4—40 mm
A/S weapons	2 Hedgehogs; homing torpedoes;
Torpedo tubes	5—21 in (*533 mm*)
Main engines	GE geared turbines; 2 shafts; 50 000 shp
Speed, knots	34
Boilers	4 Babcock & Wilcox
Range, miles	5 000 at 15 knots
Complement	250

GELIBOLU — *1970, Turkish Navy, Official*

GENERAL
Former US "Gleaves" class destroyers, acquired by Turkey early in 1949, *Gelibolu* was formally taken over on 29 Apr 1949, and *Gemlik* in 1950. Modernised in USA in 1957-58 and fitted with tripod instead of pole foremast and raised bridge.

GUNNERY. The 5 in gun in "X" position, 40 mm AA and 20 mm AA guns in *Gelibolu* and *Giresun* were replaced by four 3-in AA guns in two twin mountings.

RADAR. Search: SPS 6. Tactical: SPS 10. Fire Control: GFCS 68.

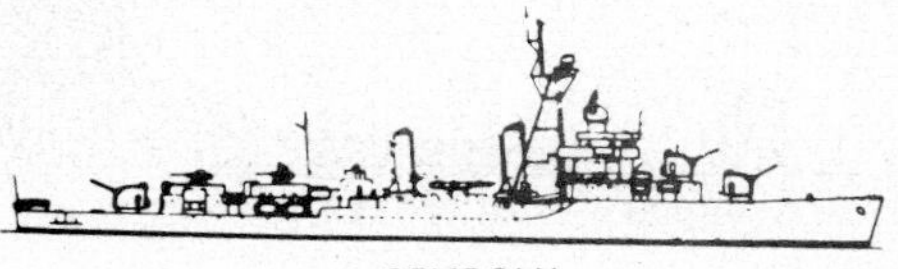
GELIBOLU

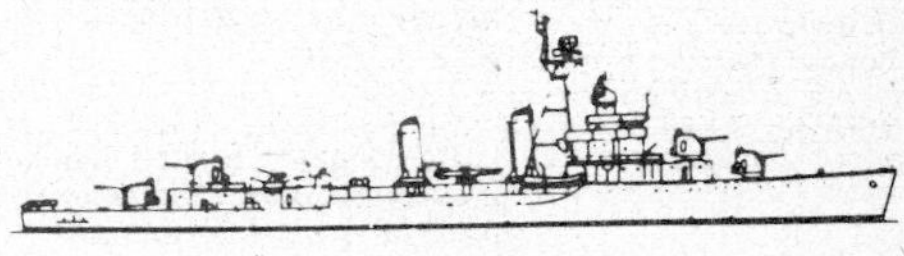
GEMLIK

FRIGATES

2 "BERK" CLASS

BERK D 358 **PEYK** D 359

Displacement, tons	1 450 standard; 1 950 full load
Length, feet (*metres*)	311·7 (*95·0*)
Beam, feet (*metres*)	38·7 (*11·8*)
Draught, feet (*metres*)	18·1 (*5·5*)
Guns	4—3 in (*76 mm*) 2 twin
Tubes	6—12·6 in (*320 mm*) 2 triple
Aircraft	1 helicopter
Main engines	4 Fiat diesels; 2 shafts; 24 000 bhp
Speed, knots	25

First major warships built in Turkey. The prototype, *Berk*, was laid down in the Gölcük naval yard on 9 Mar 1967, and *Peyk* on 18 Jan 1968. *Berk* was launched 25 June 1971 and completed 12 July 1972. *Peyk* was launched 7 June 1972 for completion in June 1974. Both are named after famous ships of the Ottoman Navy.

BERK *1972, Turkish Navy*

CORVETTES

3 "ÇESME" CLASS

CARDAK (ex-*Tourmaline*, 4 Oct 1942) A 596
ÇESME (ex-*Elfreda*, 25 Jan 1943) A 595
EDINICIK (ex-*Grecian*, 22 Sep 1943) A 597

Displacement, tons	1 010 standard; 1 250 full load
Length, feet (*metres*)	215·0 (*61·4*) wl; 221·0 (*67·4*) oa
Beam, feet (*metres*)	32·0 (*9·8*)
Draught, feet (*metres*)	10·8 (*3·3*)
Guns	1—3 in (*76 mm*); 6—40 mm
Main engines	Diesel electric; 2 shafts; 3 500 bhp
Speed, knots	18

CANDARLI *1972, Dr Giorgio Arra*

ÇESME *Class*

Former US fleet minesweepers of the "Auk" class. Transferred to Great Britain while under construction. Transferred to Turkey in Apr 1947. Built by Associated Shipbuilders, Cleveland (*Çesme* and *Edincik*); General Engineering & DD Co, Alameda, Gulf Shipbuilding Corporation, Houston (*Cardak*). Launch dates above. Named after Turkish ports. *Çesme* and *Cardak* are Head-quarters Ships. *Edincik* training ship, *Carsamba* and *Candarli* of the same class are Survey Ships.

2 "ALANYA" CLASS

Name	*No.*	*Builders*	*Launched*
ALANYA (ex-*Broome*)	A 589 (ex-M 501)	Evans Deakin, Brisbane	6 Oct 1941
AYVALIK (ex- *Antalya*, ex-*Geraldton*)	A 588 (ex-M 500)	Poole & Steele, Sydney	16 Aug 1941

Displacement, tons	790 standard; 1 025 full load
Length, feet (*metres*)	162·0 (*49·4*) pp; 186·0 (*56·7*) oa
Beam, feet (*metres*)	31·0 (*9·4*)
Draught, feet (*metres*)	8·5 (*2·6*)
Guns, surface	1—4 in (*102 mm*)
Guns, AA	1—40 mm; 4—20 mm
A/S weapons	2 DCT
Main engines	Triple expansion; 2 shafts; 1 800 ihp
Speed, knots	15
Boilers	2 water tube
Oil fuel, tons	170
Range, miles	4 500 at 10 knots
Complement	85

Both Australian built "Bathurst" class fleet minesweepers, 1940-42. Served in the Royal Navy. Acquired from Great Britain in Aug 1946. Named after Turkish ports. Both are now Logistic Support Ships.

AYVALIK *1968*

SUBMARINES

2 TYPE 209 (HOWALDTSWERKE)

Displacement, tons	990 surfaced; 1 290 dived
Length, feet (*metres*)	183·7 (*56·0*)
Beam, feet (*metres*)	20·3 (*6·2*)
Torpedo tubes	8—21 inch (with reloads)
Main machinery	Diesel electric. 4 MTU Siemens diesel-generators; 1 Siemens electric motor; 1 shaft
Speed, knots	10 surfaced; 22 dived
Range	50 days
Complement	31

Designed by Ingenieurkontor, Lübeck for construction by Howaldtswerke, Kiel and sale by Ferrostaal Essen all acting as a consortium.

TYPE 209 *1973 Howaldtswerke*

A single-hull design with two ballast tanks and forward and after trim tanks. Fitted with snort and remote machinery control. The single screw is slow revving. Very high capacity batteries with GRP lead-acid cells and battery cooling—by Wilh. Hagen and VARTA. Active and passive sonar, sonar detection equipment, sound ranging gear and underwater telephone. Fitted with two periscopes, radar and Omega receiver. Fore-planes retract. Building at Kiel. First boat laid down 2 Aug 1972.

Submarines—*continued*

2 Ex-US "GUPPY III" CLASS

Name	No.	Builder	Launched	Completed
CANAKKALE (ex-USS *Cobbler* SS 344)	S 341	Electric Boat Co.	1 Apr 1945	8 Aug 1945
IKINCI INONÜ (ex-USS *Corporal* SS 346)	S 333	Electric Boat Co.	10 June 1945	9 Nov 1945

Displacement, tons: 1 975 standard; 2 540 dived
Dimensions, ft (*m*): 326·5 × 27 × 17 (*99·4 × 8·2 × 5·2*)
Torpedo tubes: 10—21 inch (*533 mm*) 6 bow, 4 stern
Main machinery: 4 diesels; 6 400 shp; 2 electric motors 5 400 bhp; 2 shafts
Speed: 20 surfaced; 15 dived
Complement: 86

Transferred 21 Nov 1973.

CANAKKALE (as *Cobbler*) — *1970, A. & J. Pavia*

7 "GUPPY IIA" CLASS

Name	No.	Builders	Launched	Completed	Transferred
BIRINCI INÖNÜ (ex-USS *Threadfin*, SS 410)	346	Portsmouth Navy Yard	26 June 1944	30 Aug 1944	15 Aug 1973
BURAKREIS (ex-USS *Seafox*, SS 402)	335	Portsmouth Navy Yard	28 Mar 1944	13 June 1944	25 June 1971
CERBE (ex-USS *Trutta*, SS 421)	340	Portsmouth Navy Yard	22 May 1944	16 Nov 1944	24 Aug 1972
MURATREIS (ex-USS *Razorback*, SS 394)	336	Portsmouth Navy Yard	27 Jan 1944	3 Apr 1944	17 Dec 1971
ORUÇREIS (ex-USS *Pomfret*, SS 391)	337	Portsmouth Navy Yard	27 Oct 1943	19 Feb 1944	3 May 1972
PREVEZE (ex-USS *Entemedor*, SS 340)	345	Electric Boat Co.	17 Dec 1944	6 Apr 1945	24 Aug 1972
ULUÇALIREIS (ex-USS *Thornback*, SS 418)	338	Portsmouth Navy Yard	7 July 1944	13 Oct 1944	24 Aug 1972

1 "GUPPY IA" CLASS

Name	No.	Builders	Launched	Completed	Transferred
DUMLUPINAR (ex-USS *Caiman*, SS 323)	339	Electric Boat Co.	30 Mar 1944	17 July 1944	24 Aug 1972

Displacement, tons: 1 840 standard; 2 445 dived
Dimensions, ft (*m*): 306 × 27 × 17 (*93·2 × 8·2 × 5·2*)
Torpedo tubes: 10—21 in (*533 mm*) 6 bow, 4 stern; 24 torpedoes carried
Main machinery: 3 GM diesels; 4 800 hp; 2 electric motors; 5 400 hp
Speed, knots: 17 surfaced; 15 dived
Range, miles: 12 000 at 10 knots surfaced
Complement: 85

The fact that the same names are used for replacement submarines as for their predecessors can be confusing. eg "*Cerbe*" was used for both ex-USS *Hammerhead* and now for ex-USS *Trutta*.

ORUCREIS (as *Pomfret*) — *1972, Turkish Navy*

4 Ex-US MODIFIED FLEET TYPE (Ex-"BALAO" CLASS)

Name	No.	Builders	Launched	Completed	Transferred
GÜR (ex-USS *Chub*, SS 329)	334	Electric Boat Co.	7 May 1944	28 Apr 1945	23 May 1948
HIZIRREIS (ex-USS *Mero*, SS 378)	344	Manitowoc SB Co.	17 Jan 1945	17 Aug 1945	20 Apr 1960
SAKARYA (ex-USS *Boarfish*, SS 327)	332	Electric Boat Co.	18 June 1944	21 Oct 1944	23 May 1948
TURGUTREIS (ex-USS *Bergall*, SS 320)	342	Electric Boat Co.	16 Feb 1944	12 June 1944	17 Oct 1958

Displacement, tons: 1 526 standard; 1 829 surface; 2 424 dived
Dimensions, ft (*m*): 311·8 × 27·2 × 13·8 (*95 × 8·3 × 4·2*)
Torpedo tubes: 10—21 inch (*533 mm*); 6 bow, 4 stern; 24 torpedoes carried
Main machinery: 4 GM diesels; 6 400 shp; 2 electric motors; 5 400 shp
Speed, knots: 20 surfaced; 10 dived
Range, miles: 12 000 at 10 knots
Complement: 85

Streamlined boats of "Balao" class. Now becoming obsolescent. *Turgutreis* purchased 15 Aug 1973 probably for spare parts eventually.

GÜR — *1971, Turkish Navy*

LIGHT FORCES

4 FAST ATTACK CRAFT—MISSILE

These craft of 400 tons, one to be built in W. Germany and three in Turkey, have now been ordered.

2 Ex-US "ASHEVILLE" CLASS (LARGE PATROL CRAFT)

BORA (ex-USS *Surprise* PG97) P339
YILDIRIM (ex-USS *Defiance* PG 95) P 338

Displacement, tons: 225 standard; 245 full load
Dimensions, feet: 164·5 oa × 23·8 × *9·5*
Guns: 1—3 in 50 cal; 1—40 mm; 4—50 cal MG
Main engines: CODAG; 2 Cummins Diesels; 1 450 hp = 16 knots; 1 GE gas turbine; 13 300 shp = 40 knots
Complement: 25

These vessels belong to the largest Patrol Type built by the USN since World War II and the first of that Navy to have gas turbines. Built by Petersens, Wisconsin in 1969 for the USN and transferred to Turkey on 28th Feb 1973 and 11 June 1973 respectively.

YILDIRIM (as *Defiance*) — *1970, US Navy*

AMPHIBIOUS FORCES

1 Ex-US LST

ERTUGRUL (ex-USS *Windham County LST 1170*)

Displacement, tons: 2 590 light; 5 800 full load
Dimensions, feet: 384 oa × 55 × 17
Guns: 6—3 in 50 cal (twins)
Main engines: 4 GM diesels; 2 shafts (cp propellers); 6 000 bhp = 15 knots
Complement: 116
Troops: 395

Transferred by US June 1973. Built by Christy Corpn in 1954.

5 Ex-US LCT's

C 101 and 103-106

Displacement, tons: 500 light; 700 full load
Dimensions, feet: 180·9 × 27·7 × 5·4
Guns: 2—20 mm
Complement: 15

Built in USA in 1942. Transferred 25 Sept 1967.

12 TURKISH BUILT LCT's

C 107-118

Displacement, tons: 400 light; 600 full load
Dimensions, feet: 180·9 × 36·8 × 4·8
Guns: 2—20 mm
Speed, knots: 10·5
Complement: 15

Built in Turkey 1966-1973.

12 TURKISH-BUILT LCU's

C 205-216

Displacement, tons: 320 light; 405 full load
Dimensions, feet: 142 × 28 × 5·7
Guns: 2—20 mm
Main engines: GM diesels; 2 shafts; 600 bhp = 10 knots

Built in Turkey 1965-66.

4 Ex-US LCU 501 SERIES

C201-204

Displacement, tons: 160 light; 320 full load
Dimensions, feet: 119 oa × 32·7 × 5
Guns: 2—20 mm
Main engines: 3 diesels; 675 bhp = 10 knots
Complement: 13

Transferred from USA Oct-Dec 1966.

20 TURKISH-BUILT LCM8 TYPE

C 301-320

Displacement, tons: 58 light; 113 full load
Dimensions, feet: 72 × 20·5 × 4·8
Guns: 2—12·7 mm
Main engines: GM diesels; 2 shafts; 660 bhp = 9·5 knots
Complement: 9

Built in Turkey in 1965.

SURVEY SHIPS

ÇARSAMBA **CANDARLI**

Ex-US *"Auk"* Class minesweepers of 1 250 tons. For details see *"Çesme"* class under "Corvettes".

MESAHA 1 and 2

Of 45 tons with a complement of 8—built in 1966.

MESAHA 3 and 4

Of 60 tons with a complement of 10—built in 1943.

SERVICE FORCES

ULABAT **VAN** (SUPPORT TANKERS)

Displacement, tons: 1 200
Main engines: Designed for a speed of 14·5 knots

Two small tankers for the Turkish Navy built in the Gölcük Dockyard, Izmit, in 1968-70.

BINBASI SAADETTIN GÜRCAN A 573 (SUPPORT TANKER)

Displacement, tons: 1 505 tandard; 4 460 full load
Dimensions, feet: 299 × 39·4 × 18
Main engines: Diesels; 4 400 bhp

Built at Taskizak Naval Yard, Launched 1 July 1969.

ALBAY HAKKI BURAK A 572 (SUPPORT TANKER)

Displacement, tons: 3 800 full load
Dimensions, feet: 251·3 pp; 274·7 oa × 40·2 × 18
Main engines: 2 GM diesels; electric drive; 4,400 bhp = 16 knots
Complement: 88
Built in 1964.

ALBAY HAKKI BURAK *1972, Turkish Navy*

YUZBASI TOLUNAY A 571 (SUPPORT TANKER)

Displacement, tons: 2 500 standard; 3 500 full load
Dimensions, feet: 260 × 41 × 19·5
Main engines: Atlas Polar-diesels; 2 shafts; 1 920 bhp = 14 knots

Built at Taskizak by Haskoy Naval D.Y., Istanbul. Launched on 22 Aug 1950.

Service Forces—*continued*

YUZBASI TOLUNAY *1972, Turkish Navy*

AKAR (ex-*Istanbul*, ex-*Adour*) A 570 (SUPPORT TANKER)

Displacement, tons: 4 289 light; 13 200 full load
Dimensions, feet: 433 × 52·7 × 27
Main engines: Parsons geared turbines; 5 200 shp = 15 knots
Range, miles: 10 000 at 10 knots

AKAR *1970, Turkish Navy*

AKPINAR (ex-*Chiwaukum*) A 574 (SUPPORT TANKER)

Displacement, tons: 700 light; 2 700 full load
Measurement, feet: 1 453 deadweight
Dimensions, feet: 212·5 wl; 220·5 oa × 37 × 12·8
Main engines: Diesel; 800 bhp = 10 knots

Formerly the United States oiler *AOG 26*. Built by East Coast S.Y. Inc., Bayonne. Laid down on 2 Apr 1944. Launched on 5 May 1944. Completed on 22 July 1944. Transferred to Turkey in 1949.

GÖLÇUK (ex-A 573) Y 1207 (SUPPORT TANKER)

Displacement, tons: 1 255
Measurement, feet: 750 deadweight
Dimensions, feet: 185 × 31·1 × 10
Main engines: B. & W. diesel; 700 bhp = 12·5 knots

Built by Gölcük Dockyard, Ismit. Launched on 4 Nov 1953.

DONATAN (ex-USS *Anthedon, AS* 24) A 583 (REPAIR SHIP)

Displacement, tons: 8 100 standard
Dimensions, feet: 492 × 69·5 × 26·5
Main engines: Geared turbines; 1 shaft; 8 500 shp = 14·4 knots
Boilers: 2

Former US submarine tender of the "Aegir" class transferred to Turkey on 7 Feb 1969.

DONATAN *1972, Turkish Navy*

2 Ex-US REPAIR SHIPS

BASARAN (ex-*Patroclus, ARL* 19, ex-*LST* 955) A 582
ONARAN (ex-*Alecto, AGP* 14, ex-*LST* 558) A 581

Displacement, tons: 1 625 standard; 4 080 full load
Dimensions, feet: 316 wl; 328 oa × 50 × 14
Guns: 2—40 mm AA; 8—20 mm AA
Main engines: Diesel; 2 shafts; 1 700 bhp = 11 knots
Oil fuel (tons): 1 000
Range, miles: 9 000 at 9 knots
Complement: 80

Former US repair ship and MTB tender, respectively, of the LST type. *Basaran* was launched on 22 Oct 1944 by Bethlehem Hingham Shipyard, *Onaran* on 14 Apr 1944 by Missouri Valley Bridge & Iron Co. Acquired from the USA in 1952 and 1947, respectively.

ONARAN *1972, Turkish Navy*

Submarines—*continued*

2 Ex-US "GUPPY III" CLASS

Name	No.	Builder	Launched	Completed
CANAKKALE (ex-USS *Cobbler* SS 344)	S 341	Electric Boat Co.	1 Apr 1945	8 Aug 1945
IKINCI INONÜ (ex-USS *Corporal* SS 346)	S 333	Electric Boat Co.	10 June 1945	9 Nov 1945

Displacement, tons 1 975 standard; 2 540 dived
Dimensions, ft (*m*) 326·5 × 27 × 17 (*99·4* × *8·2* × *5·2*)
Torpedo tubes 10—21 inch (*533 mm*) 6 bow, 4 stern
Main machinery 4 diesels; 6 400 shp; 2 electric motors 5 400 bhp; 2 shafts
Speed 20 surfaced; 15 dived
Complement 86

Transferred 21 Nov 1973.

CANAKKALE (as *Cobbler*) 1970, A. & J. Pavia

7 "GUPPY IIA" CLASS

Name	No.	Builders	Launched	Completed	Transferred
BIRINCI INÖNÜ (ex-USS *Threadfin*, SS 410)	346	Portsmouth Navy Yard	26 June 1944	30 Aug 1944	15 Aug 1973
BURAKREIS (ex-USS *Seafox*, SS 402)	335	Portsmouth Navy Yard	28 Mar 1944	13 June 1944	25 June 1971
CERBE (ex-USS *Trutta*, SS 421)	340	Portsmouth Navy Yard	22 May 1944	16 Nov 1944	24 Aug 1972
MURATREIS (ex-USS *Razorback*, SS 394)	336	Portsmouth Navy Yard	27 Jan 1944	3 Apr 1944	17 Dec 1971
ORUÇREIS (ex-USS *Pomfret*, SS 391)	337	Portsmouth Navy Yard	27 Oct 1943	19 Feb 1944	3 May 1972
PREVEZE (ex-USS *Entemedor*, SS 340)	345	Electric Boat Co.	17 Dec 1944	6 Apr 1945	24 Aug 1972
ULUÇALIREIS (ex-USS *Thornback*, SS 418)	338	Portsmouth Navy Yard	7 July 1944	13 Oct 1944	24 Aug 1972

1 "GUPPY IA" CLASS

Name	No.	Builders	Launched	Completed	Transferred
DUMLUPINAR (ex-USS *Caiman*, SS 323)	339	Electric Boat Co.	30 Mar 1944	17 July 1944	24 Aug 1972

Displacement, tons 1 840 standard; 2 445 dived
Dimensions, ft (*m*) 306 × 27 × 17 (*93·2* × *8·2* × *5·2*)
Torpedo tubes 10—21 in (*533 mm*) 6 bow, 4 stern; 24 torpedoes carried
Main machinery 3 GM diesels; 4 800 hp; 2 electric motors; 5 400 hp
Speed, knots 17 surfaced; 15 dived
Range, miles 12 000 at 10 knots surfaced
Complement 85

The fact that the same names are used for replacement submarines as for their predecessors can be confusing. eg "*Cerbe*" was used for both ex-USS *Hammerhead* and now for ex-USS *Trutta*.

ORUCREIS (as *Pomfret*) 1972, Turkish Navy

4 Ex-US MODIFIED FLEET TYPE (Ex-"BALAO" CLASS)

Name	No.	Builders	Launched	Completed	Transferred
GÜR (ex-USS *Chub*, SS 329)	334	Electric Boat Co.	7 May 1944	28 Apr 1945	23 May 1948
HIZIRREIS (ex-USS *Mero*, SS 378)	344	Manitowoc SB Co.	17 Jan 1945	17 Aug 1945	20 Apr 1960
SAKARYA (ex-USS *Boarfish*, SS 327)	332	Electric Boat Co.	18 June 1944	21 Oct 1944	23 May 1948
TURGUTREIS (ex-USS *Bergall*, SS 320)	342	Electric Boat Co.	16 Feb 1944	12 June 1944	17 Oct 1958

Displacement, tons 1 526 standard; 1 829 surface; 2 424 dived
Dimensions, ft (*m*) 311·8 × 27·2 × 13·8 (*95* × *8·3* × *4·2*)
Torpedo tubes 10—21 inch (*533 mm*); 6 bow, 4 stern; 24 torpedoes carried
Main machinery 4 GM diesels; 6 400 shp; 2 electric motors; 5 400 shp
Speed, knots 20 surfaced; 10 dived
Range, miles 12 000 at 10 knots
Complement 85

Streamlined boats of "Balao" class. Now becoming obsolescent. *Turgutreis* purchased 15 Aug 1973 probably for spare parts eventually.

GÜR 1971, Turkish Navy

LIGHT FORCES

4 FAST ATTACK CRAFT—MISSILE

These craft of 400 tons, one to be built in W. Germany and three in Turkey, have now been ordered.

2 Ex-US "ASHEVILLE" CLASS (LARGE PATROL CRAFT)

BORA (ex-USS *Surprise* PG97) P339
YILDIRIM (ex-USS *Defiance* PG 95) P 338

Displacement, tons 225 standard; 245 full load
Dimensions, feet 164·5 oa × 23·8 × *9·5*
Guns 1—3 in 50 cal; 1—40 mm; 4—50 cal MG
Main engines CODAG; 2 Cummins Diesels; 1 450 hp = 16 knots; 1 GE gas turbine; 13 300 shp = 40 knots
Complement 25

These vessels belong to the largest Patrol Type built by the USN since World War II and the first of that Navy to have gas turbines. Built by Petersens, Wisconsin in 1969 for the USN and transferred to Turkey on 28th Feb 1973 and 11 June 1973 respectively.

YILDIRIM (as *Defiance*) 1970, US Navy

Light Forces—*continued*

6 "AKHISAR" CLASS (LARGE PATROL CRAFT)

AKHISAR (ex-*PC* 1641) P 114
DEMIRHISAR (ex-*PC* 1639) P 112
KOCHISAR (ex-*PC* 1643) P 116
SIVRIHISAR (ex-*PC* 1642) P 115
SULTANHISAR (ex-*PC* 1638) P 111
YARHISAR (ex-*PC* 1640) P 113

Displacement, tons	280 standard; 412 full load
Dimensions, feet	170 wl; 173·7 oa × 23 × 10·2
Guns	1—3 inch dp; 1—40 mm AA
A/S weapons	4 DCT
Main engines	2 FM Diesels; 2 shafts; 2 800 bhp = 19 knots
Range, miles	6 000 at 10 knots
Complement	65 (5 officers, and 60 men)

Similar to US 173 ft class submarine chasers. Built by Gunderson Bros. Engineering Co, Portland, Oregon, except *Kochisar* built in Gölcük Dockyard, Turkey. Transferred on 3 Dec 1964, 22 Apr 1965, 22 Apr 1965, 2 May 1964, 24 Sep 1964 and 22 Apr 1965 respectively.

YARHISAR *1972, Turkish Navy*

9 "KARTAL" CLASS (FAST ATTACK CRAFT—TORPEDO)

ALBATROS P 327 (ex-P 325)
ATMACA P 322 (ex-P 335)
DENIZKUSU P 321 (ex-P 336)
KARTAL P 324 (ex-P 333)
KASIRGA P 329 (ex-P 338)
MELTEM P 325 (ex-P 330)
PELIKAN P 326
SAHIN P 323 (ex-P 334)
SIMSEK P 328 (ex-P 332)

Displacement, tons	160 standard; 180 full load
Dimensions, feet	140·5 × 23·5 × 7·2
Guns	2—40 mm AA
Tubes	4—21 inch
Main engines	4 Maybach diesels; 4 shafts; 12 000 bhp = 42 knots

Of the German "Jaguar" type. Built by Lürssen, Vegesack, in 1966-67 (P 321, 322, 323, 324, 329, ex-P 336, 335, 334, 333, 338, respectively) others in 1968.

SIMSEK *1972, Turkish Navy*

10 LARGE PATROL CRAFT

AB 25 (P 1225)
AB 26 (P 1226)
AB 27 (P 1227)
AB 28 (P 1228)
AB 29 (P 1229)
AB 30 (P 1230)
AB 31 (P 1231)
AB 32 (P 1232)
AB 33 (P 1233)
AB 34 (P 1234)

Displacement, tons	170
Dimensions, feet	132 × 21 × 5·5
Guns	2—40 mm
Speed	22 knots

Built at Taskizak Naval Yard. First was launched on 9 Mar 1967. Six similar launches are operated by the Gendarmerie.

AB 28 *1970, Turkish Navy*

4 LARGE PATROL CRAFT

AB 21 (ex PGM-104)
AB 23 (ex PGM-106)
AB 22 (ex PGM-105)
AB 24 (ex PGM-106)

Displacement, tons	130 standard, 147 full load
Dimensions, feet	101 × 21 × 7
Guns	1—40 mm; 4—20 mm
Main engines	2 diesels; 2 shafts; 1 850 hp = 18·5 knots
Range, miles	1 500 at 10 knots
Complement	15

Patrol gunboat type supplied from the United States in 1967-68.

AB 23 *1970, Turkish Navy*

17 LARGE PATROL CRAFT

J 12-J 28

Displacement, tons	150
Dimensions, ft (*m*)	129·3 × 20·6 × 4·9 (*34·4 × 6·3 × 1·5*)
Guns	1—40 mm; 2—20 mm
Main engines	4 MB diesels; 2 shafts; 3 200 bhp = 22 knots

J 12-20 built in 1960-61 by Schweers, Bardenfleth. J 21 and 22 built at Gölcük Navy Yard. J 23 to 26 built at Taskizak in 1968 and J 27 and 28 at Taskizak in 1970.

J 21 *1972, Dr. Giorgio Arra*

4 COASTAL PATROL CRAFT

LS 9 P 1209
LS 11 P 1211
LS 10 P 1210
LS 12 P 1212

Displacement, tons	63 standard
Dimensions, feet	83·0 × 14·0 × 5·0
Gun	1—20 mm AA
A/S weapons	2 A/S Rocket launchers
Main engines	2 Cummins diesels; 1 100 bhp = 20 knots

Ex-US type, transferred on 25 June 1953.

9 COASTAL PATROL CRAFT

MTB 1 P 311
MTB 2 P 312
MTB 3 P 313
MTB 4 P 314
MTB 6 P 316
MTB 7 P 317
MTB 8 P 318
MTB 9 P 319
MTB 10 P 320

Displacement, tons	70 standard
Dimensions, feet	71·5 × 13·8 × 8·5
Main engines	Diesel; 2 000 bhp

All launched in 1942. General purpose craft. MTB 5 (315) was scrapped.

LS 9 *1972, Turkish Navy*

MINE WARFARE FORCES

1 LARGE MINELAYER

NUSRET N 110 (ex-N 108)

Displacement, tons	1 880 standard
Length feet (*metres*)	246 (*75·0*) pp; 252·7 (*77·0*) oa
Beam, feet (*metres*)	41 (*12·6*)
Draught, feet (*metres*)	11 (*3·4*)
Guns, dual purpose	4—3 in (*76 mm*), 2 twin mountings
Mines	400 capacity
Main engines	GM diesels; 4 800 hp; 2 shafts
Speed, knots	18
Complement	146

A new type of minelayer of special Scandinavian-NATO design. Built at Frederikshaven Dockyard, Denmark. Laid down in 1962, launched in 1964, and completed in 1965. Commissioned on 16 Sep 1964 at Copenhagen. Similar to Danish "Falster" class.

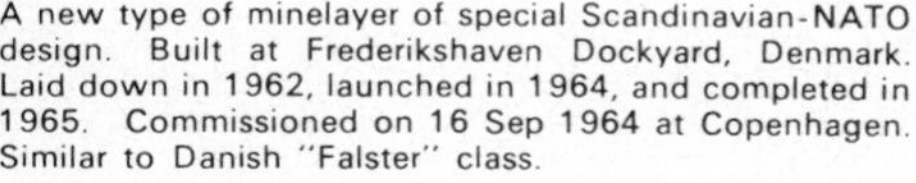

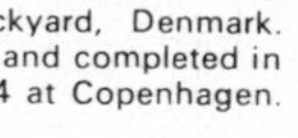

RADAR. Search: RAN 7S. Fire Control: X Band Navigation Radar.

NUSRET 1972, *Turkish Navy*

NUSRET

2 Ex-US LST TYPE (MINELAYERS)

SANCAKTAR (ex-German *Bochum*, ex-USS *Rice County*) A 580
BAYRAKTAR (ex-German *Bottrop*, ex-USS *Saline County*) A 579

Displacement, tons	1 653 standard; 4 080 full load
Dimensions, feet	328 oa × 50 × 14
Guns	6—40 mm (2 twin, 2 single)
Main engines	2 GM Diesels; 2 shafts; 1 700 bhp = 11 knots
Range, miles	15 000 at 9 knots
Complement	125

Formerly USN LST's, transferred to Germany in 1961 and thence to Turkey on 13 Dec 1972.

5 LSM TYPE (COASTAL MINELAYERS)

MARMARIS (ex-*LSM* 481) N 103
MERIÇ (ex-*LSM* 490) N 102
MERSIN (ex-*LSM* 492) N 104
MORDOGAN (ex-*LSM* 484) N 101
MÜREFTE (ex-*LSM* 493) N 105

Displacement, tons	743 standard; 1 100 full load
Dimensions, feet	196·5 wl; 203·2 oa × 34·5 × 8·5
Guns	2—40 mm AA; 2—20 mm AA
Main engines	Diesels; 2 shafts; 2 880 bhp = 12 knots
Oil fuel (tons)	60
Range, miles	2 500 at 12 knots
Complement	89

Ex-US Landing Ships Medium. All launched in 1945, converted into coastal minelayers by the US Navy in 1952 and taken over by the Turkish Navy (LSM 481, 484 and 490) and the Norwegian Navy (LSM 492 and 493) in Oct 1952 under MAP. LSM 492 (*Vale*) and LSM 493 (*Vidar*) were retransferred to the Turkish Navy on 1 Nov 1960 at Bergen, Norway.

MERSIN 1969

1 YMP TYPE (COASTAL MINELAYER)

MEHMETCIK (ex-USS *YMP* 3) N 115

Displacement, tons	540 full load
Dimensions, feet	130 × 35 × 6
Main engines	Diesels; 2 shafts; 600 bhp = 10 knots
Complement	22

Former US motor mine planter. Built by Higgins Inc, New Orleans. Completed in 1958. Steel hulled. Transferred under MAP in 1958. For harbour defence.

MEHMETCIK

12 MSC TYPE (MINESWEEPERS—COASTAL)

SAMSUN (ex-USS *MSC* 268) M 510
SAPANCA (ex-USS *MSC* 312) M 517
SARIYER (ex-USS *MSC* 315) M 518
SAROS (ex-USS *MSC* 305) M 515
SEDDULBAHIR (ex-*MSC* 272) M 513
SELÇUK (ex-*AMS* 124) M 508
SEYHAN (ex-*AMS* 142) M 509
SEYMEN (ex-*AMS* 131) M 507
SIGACIK (ex-USS *MSC* 311) M 516
SILIFKE (ex-USS *MSC* 304) M 514
SINOP (ex-USS *MSC* 270) M 511
SURMENE (ex-USS *MSC* 271) M 512

Displacement, tons	320 standard; 370 full load
Dimensions, feet	138·0 pp; 144·0 oa × 28·0 × 9·0
Guns	2—20 mm AA
Main engines	2 diesels; 2 shafts; 1 200 bhp = 14 knots
Oil fuel, tons	25
Range, miles	2 500 at 10 knots
Complement	38 (4 officers, 34 men)

Transferred on 30 Sep 1958, 26 July 1965, 8 Sep 1967, 8 Nov 1965, 9 July 1959, 24 Mar 1970, 24 Mar 1970, 19 Nov 1970, 29 May 1965, 25 Oct 1965, 30 Jan 1959, 27 Mar 1959, respectively. *Selçuk* (ex-AMS 124) and *Seyhan* (ex-AMS 142) were transferred from France (via USA) on 24 Mar 1970 and *Seyman* from Belgium (via USA) on 19 Nov 1970.

SAMSUN 1969

4 MCB TYPE (MINESWEEPERS—COASTAL)

TIREBOLU (ex-HMCS *Comax*) M 532
TEKIRDAG (ex-HMCS *Ungave*) M 533
TERME (ex-HMCS *Trinity*) M 531
TRABZON (ex-HMCS *Gaspe*) M 530

Displacement, tons	390 standard; 412 full load
Dimensions, feet	140·0 pp; 152·0 oa × 20·8 × 7·0
Gun	1—40 mm
Main engines	Diesels; 2 shafts; 2 400 bhp = 16 knots
Oil fuel, tons	52
Range, miles	4 500 at 11 knots
Complement	44

Ex-Canadian MCBs. Sailed from Sydney, Nova Scotia, to Turkey on 19 May 1958

TIREBOLU 1970, *Turkish Navy*

4 Ex-US MINESWEEPERS—INSHORE

FATSA (ex-*MSI* 17) M 502
FETHIYE (ex-*MSI* 16) M 501
FINIKE (ex-*MSI* 18) M 503
FOÇA (ex-*MSI* 15) M 500

Displacement, tons	180 standard; 235 full load
Dimensions, feet	111·9 × 23·5 × 7·9
Gun	1—50 cal
Main engines	4 diesels; 2 shafts; 960 bhp = 13 knots
Complement	30

Built in USA and transferred under MAP at Boston, Mass, Aug-Sep 1967. *Finike* was delivered by Peterson Builders Inc. on 8 Nov 1967.

FOCA 1970, *Turkish Navy*

AMPHIBIOUS FORCES

1 Ex-US LST

ERTUGRUL (ex-USS *Windham County LST 1170*)

Displacement, tons	2 590 light; 5 800 full load
Dimensions, feet	384 oa × 55 × 17
Guns	6—3 in 50 cal (twins)
Main engines	4 GM diesels; 2 shafts (cp propellers); 6 000 bhp = 15 knots
Complement	116
Troops	395

Transferred by US June 1973. Built by Christy Corpn in 1954.

5 Ex-US LCT's

C 101 and 103-106

Displacement, tons	500 light; 700 full load
Dimensions, feet	180·9 × 27·7 × 5·4
Guns	2—20 mm
Complement	15

Built in USA in 1942. Transferred 25 Sept 1967.

12 TURKISH BUILT LCT's

C 107-118

Displacement, tons	400 light; 600 full load
Dimensions, feet	180·9 × 36·8 × 4·8
Guns	2—20 mm
Speed, knots	10·5
Complement	15

Built in Turkey 1966-1973.

12 TURKISH-BUILT LCU's

C 205-216

Displacement, tons	320 light; 405 full load
Dimensions, feet	142 × 28 × 5·7
Guns	2—20 mm
Main engines	GM diesels; 2 shafts; 600 bhp = 10 knots

Built in Turkey 1965-66.

4 Ex-US LCU 501 SERIES

C201-204

Displacement, tons	160 light; 320 full load
Dimensions, feet	119 oa × 32·7 × 5
Guns	2—20 mm
Main engines	3 diesels; 675 bhp = 10 knots
Complement	13

Transferred from USA Oct-Dec 1966.

20 TURKISH-BUILT LCM8 TYPE

C 301-320

Displacement, tons	58 light; 113 full load
Dimensions, feet	72 × 20·5 × 4·8
Guns	2—12·7 mm
Main engines	GM diesels; 2 shafts; 660 bhp = 9·5 knots
Complement	9

Built in Turkey in 1965.

SURVEY SHIPS

ÇARSAMBA **CANDARLI**

Ex-US "*Auk*" Class minesweepers of 1 250 tons. For details see "*Çesme*" class under "Corvettes".

MESAHA 1 and 2

Of 45 tons with a complement of 8—built in 1966.

MESAHA 3 and 4

Of 60 tons with a complement of 10—built in 1943.

SERVICE FORCES

ULABAT **VAN** (SUPPORT TANKERS)

Displacement, tons	1 200
Main engines	Designed for a speed of 14·5 knots

Two small tankers for the Turkish Navy built in the Gölcük Dockyard, Izmit, in 1968-70.

BINBASI SAADETTIN GÜRCAN A 573 (SUPPORT TANKER)

Displacement, tons	1 505 tandard; 4 460 full load
Dimensions, feet	299 × 39·4 × 18
Main engines	Diesels; 4 400 bhp

Built at Taskizak Naval Yard, Launched 1 July 1969.

ALBAY HAKKI BURAK A 572 (SUPPORT TANKER)

Displacement, tons	3 800 full load
Dimensions, feet	251·3 pp; 274·7 oa × 40·2 × 18
Main engines	2 GM diesels; electric drive; 4,400 bhp = 16 knots
Complement	88

Built in 1964.

ALBAY HAKKI BURAK *1972, Turkish Navy*

YUZBASI TOLUNAY A 571 (SUPPORT TANKER)

Displacement, tons	2 500 standard; 3 500 full load
Dimensions, feet	260 × 41 × 19·5
Main engines	Atlas Polar-diesels; 2 shafts; 1 920 bhp = 14 knots

Built at Taskizak by Haskoy Naval D.Y., Istanbul. Launched on 22 Aug 1950.

Service Forces—*continued*

YUZBASI TOLUNAY *1972, Turkish Navy*

AKAR (ex-*Istanbul*, ex-*Adour*) A 570 (SUPPORT TANKER)

Displacement, tons	4 289 light; 13 200 full load
Dimensions, feet	433 × 52·7 × 27
Main engines	Parsons geared turbines; 5 200 shp = 15 knots
Range, miles	10 000 at 10 knots

AKAR *1970, Turkish Navy*

AKPINAR (ex-*Chiwaukum*) A 574 (SUPPORT TANKER)

Displacement, tons	700 light; 2 700 full load
Measurement, feet	1 453 deadweight
Dimensions, feet	212·5 wl; 220·5 oa × 37 × 12·8
Main engines	Diesel; 800 bhp = 10 knots

Formerly the United States oiler *AOG 26*. Built by East Coast S.Y. Inc., Bayonne. Laid down on 2 Apr 1944. Launched on 5 May 1944. Completed on 22 July 1944. Transferred to Turkey in 1949.

GÖLÇUK (ex-A 573) Y 1207 (SUPPORT TANKER)

Displacement, tons	1 255
Measurement, feet	750 deadweight
Dimensions, feet	185 × 31·1 × 10
Main engines	B. & W. diesel; 700 bhp = 12·5 knots

Built by Gölcük Dockyard, Ismit. Launched on 4 Nov 1953.

DONATAN (ex-USS *Anthedon, AS* 24) A 583 (REPAIR SHIP)

Displacement, tons	8 100 standard
Dimensions, feet	492 × 69·5 × 26·5
Main engines	Geared turbines; 1 shaft; 8 500 shp = 14·4 knots
Boilers	2

Former US submarine tender of the "Aegir" class transferred to Turkey on 7 Feb 1969.

DONATAN *1972, Turkish Navy*

2 Ex-US REPAIR SHIPS

BASARAN (ex-*Patroclus, ARL* 19, ex-*LST* 955) A 582
ONARAN (ex-*Alecto, AGP* 14, ex-*LST* 558) A 581

Displacement, tons	1 625 standard; 4 080 full load
Dimensions, feet	316 wl; 328 oa × 50 × 14
Guns	2—40 mm AA; 8—20 mm AA
Main engines	Diesel; 2 shafts; 1 700 bhp = 11 knots
Oil fuel (tons)	1 000
Range, miles	9 000 at 9 knots
Complement	80

Former US repair ship and MTB tender, respectively, of the LST type. *Basaran* was launched on 22 Oct 1944 by Bethlehem Hingham Shipyard, *Onaran* on 14 Apr 1944 by Missouri Valley Bridge & Iron Co. Acquired from the USA in 1952 and 1947, respectively.

ONARAN *1972, Turkish Navy*

Service Forces—*continued*

ÜLKÜ (ex-*Angeln*) A 586 (TRANSPORT)

Displacement, tons	3 088
Dimensions, feet	296·9 × 43·6 × 20·3
Main engines	Pielstick Diesel; 1 shaft; 3 000 bhp = 17 knots
Complement	57

Transferred by W. Germany. 22 March 1972.

KURTARAN (ex-*Bluebird*, ASR 19, ex-*Yurak*) A 584 (SUBMARINE RESCUE SHIP)

Displacement, tons	1 294 standard; 1 675 full load
Dimensions, feet	205·0 oa × 38·5 × 12·0
Guns	1—3 inch; 2—40 mm AA
Main engines	Diesel-electric; 3 000 bhp = 16 knots

Former salvage tug adapted as a submarine rescue vessel in 1947. Transferred from the US Navy on 15 Aug 1950.

KURTARAN 1971· A. & J. Pavia

AKIN (ex-*Greenlet ASR* 10) A 585 (SUBMARINE RESCUE SHIP)

Displacement, tons	1 770 standard; 2 321 full load
Dimensions, feet	251·3 × 42·2 × 14·7
Guns	1—40 mm; 2—20 mm (twin)
Main engines	Diesel-electric; 1 shaft; 3 000 bhp = 15 knots
Complement	85

Submarine rescue vessel, ex-USN "Chanticleer" class built by Moore SB & DD Co., Oakland in 1942. Transferred 12 June 1970 and purchased 15 Feb 1973.

ERKIN (ex-*Trabzon* ex-*Imperial*) A 591 (SUBMARINE SUPPORT)

Displacement, tons	10 900
Dimensions, feet	441 × 58·5 × 23
Guns	2—40 mm
Speed, knots	16
Complement	128

Built in 1938. Purchased in 1968 and placed on the Navy list in 1970.

AG 6 (ex-*Cerberus* A 895) P 306 (BOOM DEFENCE VESSEL)

Displacement, tons	780 standard; 902 full load
Dimensions, feet	165·0 × 33·0 × 10·0
Guns	1—3 in; 4—20 mm AA
Main engines	Diesel-electric; 1 shaft; 1 500 bhp = 12·8 knots

Netlayer built by Bethlehem Steel Co, Staten Island. Launched in May 1952 and completed on 10 Nov 1952. Transferred from USA to Netherlands in Dec 1952. Used first as a boom defence vessel and latterly as salvage and diving tender since 1961 but retained her netlaying capacity. Handed back to USN (formality) on 17 Sep 1970 but immediately turned over to the Turkish Navy.

AG 5 (*ex AN 104*) P 305 (BDV)

Displacement, tons	680 standard; 860 full load
Dimensions, feet	148·7 pp; 173·8 oa × 35·0 × 13·5
Guns	1—40 mm AA; 3—20 mm AA
Main engines	4 MAN diesels; 2 shafts; 1 450 bhp = 12 knots

Netlayer *AN 104* built in US off-shore programme by Kröger, Rendesburg for Turkey. Launched on 20 Oct 1960. Delivered on 35 Feb 1961.

AG 4 (ex-*Larch*, ex-*AN* 21) P 304 (BDV)

Displacement, tons	560 standard; 805 full load
Dimensions, feet	146·0 wl; 163·0 oa × 30·5 × 10·5
Guns	1—3 inch AA
Main engines	Diesel-electric; 800 bhp = 12 knots

Former US netlayer of the "Aloe" class. Built by American S.B. Co, Cleveland. Laid down in 1940. Launched on 2 July 1941. Completed in 1941. Acquired in 1947.

AG 4 1969

3 "BAR" CLASS (BDV's)

AG 1 (ex-*Barbarian*, 21 Oct 1937) P 301
AG 2 (ex-*Barbette*, 15 Dec 1937) P 302
AG 3 (ex-*Barfair*, 21 May 1938) P 303

Displacement, tons	750 standard; 1 000 full load
Dimensions, feet	150·0 pp; 173·8 oa × 32·2 × 9·5
Gun	1—3 inch AA
Main engines	Triple expansion; 850 ihp = 11·5 knots
Boilers	2 SE

Former British boom defence vessels. First two were built by Blyth S.B. Co. and the third by J. Lewis & Sons. Launch dates above.

KALDIRAY P 305 (BDV)

Measurement, tons	732 gross
Main engines	Steam reciprocating; 500 ihp = 10 knots
Complement	97

Built in 1938. Former French vessel. Purchased in 1964.

Y 1201 Y 1202 Y 1203 (GATE VESSELS)

Displacement, tons	360
Dimensions, feet	102·7 × 34 × 4·7

These gate vessels were built by US for transfer to Turkey under MAP.

TUGS

AKBAS Y 1118
KEPEZ Y 1119

Displacement, tons	971
Dimensions, feet	149 × 33·9 × 14
Speed, knots	12

GAZAL (ex USS *Sioux ATF* 75) A 587

Displacement, tons	1 235 standard; 1 675 full load
Dimensions, feet	205 oa × 38·5 × 16
Gun	1—3 inch
Main engines	Diesel electric; 3 000 bhp = 16 knots
Complement	85

ÖNCU **ÖNDER** Y 1124

Displacement, tons	500
Speed	12 knots

The US harbour tugs ex-YTL 155, 751 were transferred under MAP.

KUVVET Y 1122

Displacement, tons	390
Dimensions, feet	107 × 26·5 × 12

KUDRET Y 1229

Displacement, tons	128
Dimensions, feet	65 × 19·6 × 9

FLOATING DOCKS

Y 1081
16 000 tons lift.
Y 1082
12 000 tons lift.
Y 1084
4 500 tons lift.
Y 1087
3 500 tons lift.
Y 1086
3 000 tons lift.
Y 1083
2 500 tons lift.
Y 1085
400 tons lift.

TRAINING SHIP

SAVARONA

Displacement, tons	5 100
Length, feet (*metres*)	349·5 (*106·5*)wl; 408·5 (*124·5*)oa
Beam, feet (*metres*)	53 (*16·2*)
Draught, feet (*metres*)	20·5 (*6·2*)
Guns, surface	4—3 in (*76 mm*)
Guns, AA	2—40 mm; 2—20 mm
Main engines	6 geared turbines; 2 shafts; 10 750 shp
Speed, knots	18
Boilers	4 watertube; 400 psi
Oil fuel, tons	2 100
Range, miles	9 000 at 15 knots
Complement	132 + 81 midshipmen

Built by Blohm & Voss, Hamburg. Launched on 28 Feb 1931. Formerly probably the most sumptuously fitted yacht afloat. Equipment includes Sperry gyro-stabilisers. Converted into a training ship in 1952, the saloons and dining rooms being adapted as classrooms, workshops and libraries for midshipmen.

SAVARONA

UNITED KINGDOM

Admiralty Board

Secretary of State for Defence (Chairman):
The Right Honourable Mr. Roy Mason, MP
Minister of State: Ministry of Defence (Vice-Chairman) and Minister of State for Defence Procurement:
Mr William Rodgers, MP
Parliamentary Under-Secretary of State for Defence for the Royal Navy:
Mr Frank Judd, MP
Chief of the Naval Staff and First Sea Lord:
Admiral Sir Edward Ashmore, GCB, DSC
Chief of Naval Personnel and Second Sea Lord:
Admiral D. Williams
Controller of the Navy:
Admiral Sir Anthony Griffin, KCB
Chief of Fleet Support:
Vice-Admiral P. White, CBE
Vice-Chief of the Naval Staff:
Vice-Admiral J. D. Treacher
Chief Scientist (Royal Navy): Mr Basil Wilfred Lythall, CB, MA
Deputy Under Secretary of State (Navy): Mr Sydney Redman, CB
Second Permanent Under-Secretary for Administration: Mr J. M. Wilson, CBE
Second Permanent Uhder-Secterary for Equipment: Sir Martin Flett, KCB

Commanders-in-Chief

Commander in-Chief, Naval Home Command:
Admiral Sir Derek Empson, KCB
Commander-in-Chief, Fleet:
Admiral Sir Terence Lewin, KCB, MVO, DSC

Flag Officers

Flag Officer, 1st Flotilla:
Rear-Admiral H. C. Leach
Flag Officer, 2nd Flotilla:
Rear-Admiral R. P. Clayton
Flag Officer, Submarines:
Vice-Admiral I. G. Raikes, CBE, DSC
Flag Officer Naval Air Command:
Rear-Admiral P. M. Austin
Flag Officer Carriers and Amphibious Ships:
Rear-Admiral A. D. Cassidi
Flag Officer Scotland and Northern Ireland:
Rear-Admiral J. A. R. Troup, DSC and Bar
Flag Officer Medway:
Rear-Admiral S. F. Berthon
Flag Officer Plymouth:
Vice-Admiral A. M. Power, MBE
Flag Officer Sea Training:
Rear-Admiral J. W. F. Eberle
Flag Officer Malta:
Rear-Admiral D. A. Loram, MVO
Flag Officer Gibraltar:
Rear-Admiral R. S. Sandford
Flag Officer Spithead:
Rear-Admiral S. L. McArdle, MVO, GM

General Officers, Royal Marines

Commandant-General, Royal Marines:
General Sir Ian Gourlay, KCB, OBE, MC
Chief of Staff to Commandant-General, Royal Marines:
Major General P. J. Ovens, OBE, MC
Major General Training Group, Royal Marines:
Major-General Robert Loudon, CB, OBE
Major-General Commando Forces Royal Marines:
Major-General E. G. D. Pounds

Diplomatic Representation

British Naval Attaché in Washington:
Rear-Admiral L. R. Bell Davies

British Naval Attaché in Moscow:
Captain G. Hayne, RN

British Naval Attaché in Paris:
Captain L. A. Bird, RN

Personnel

(a) 1970: 89 000
1971: 87 000
1972: 83 000
1973: 84 000
1974: 81 000

(b) Voluntary Service

Mercantile Marine:

Lloyd's Register of Shipping: 3 628 vessels of 30 159 543 tons gross

Strength of the Fleet

Type	*Active*	*Building (Projected)*
Aircraft Carrier	1	—
Command Cruisers	1	(?2)
Helicopter Cruisers	2	—
Light Cruisers	9	—
Destroyers	—	6
Frigates	61	8
Sonar Trials Ship	1	—
SSBN's	4	—
Submarines—Fleet	7	4
Submarines—Patrol	22	—
Command Ships	2	—
Assault Ships (LSD)	2	—
LCT's	6	—
LCM's	16	—
LCVP's	26	—
LCPL's	2	—
Fast Attack Craft—Patrol	1	—
Large Patrol Craft	7	4
Fast Training Boats	3	—
MCM Support Ship	1	—
Minehunters	17	(?)
Minesweepers—Coastal	22	—
Minesweepers—Inshore	6	—
Maintenance Ships	3	—
Submarine Depot Ships	2	—
Surveys Ship	4	—
Coastal Survey Ships	4	—
Inshore Survey Craft	5	—
Ice Patrol Ship	1	—
Royal Yacht	1	—
Hovercraft	2	—
Diving Support Ship	1	—
Replenishment Tankers	9	—
Freighting Tankers	4	—
Bulk Tankers	2	—
Small Fleet Tankers	13	—
Helicopter Support Ship	1	—
Stores Support Ships	4	—
Fleet Replenishment Ships	4	2
Store Carriers	4	—
MSBV's	17	—
Trials Ships	3	1
TRV's	9	—
Cable Ships	2	—
Armament Carriers	6	—
Water Carriers	16	—
Ocean Tugs	14	—
Harbour Tugs	50	—
Water Tractors	36	—
Tenders	52	—
RNXS Craft	13	—
MFV's	61	—
DG Vessels	3	—
TCV's	7	—

Disposals

Carriers (of all kinds)

1972 *Centaur* and *Albion*

Destroyers

1970 *Aisne, Trafalgar, Camperdown*
1971 *Daring, Delight, Scorpion, Cambrian*
1972 *Crossbow, Defender, Saintes*

Frigates

1970 *Loch Killisport, Loch Fada, Ulysses, Zest, Murray*
1971 *Urania, Relentless, Pellew, Wakeful, Alert, Grafton*
1972 *Verulam, Venus*

Submarines

1970 *Talent, Thermopylae, Anchorite, Astute*
1971 *Ambush, Alaric, Trump, Taciturn*
1972 *Artemis, Acheron, Alderney*

NOTES. (a) These lists do not include a number of ships listed for disposal, destored and on the Reserve or Sales Lists eg *Eagle*. (b) There are also several ships used as accommodation ships or harbour Training ships which could be reactivated if required.

LIST OF PENNANT NUMBERS

Aircraft Carriers

R 09 Ark Royal

Commando Carriers

R 08 Bulwark
R 12 Hermes

Submarines

S 01 Porpoise
S 02 Rorqual
S 03 Narwhal
S 04 Grampus
S 05 Finwhale
S 06 Cachalot
S 07 Sealion
S 08 Walrus
S 09 Oberon
S 10 Odin
S 11 Orpheus
S 12 Olympus
S 13 Osiris
S 14 Onslaught
S 15 Otter
S 16 Oracle
S 17 Ocelot
S 18 Otus
S 19 Opossum
S 20 Opportune
S 21 Onyx
S 22 Resolution
S 23 Repulse
S 26 Renown
S 27 Revenge
S 46 Churchill
S 50 Courageous
S 63 Andrew
S 101 Dreadnought
S 102 Valiant
S 103 Warspite
S 104 Churchill
S 108 Sovereign
S 109 Superb
S 110 Sceptre
S 126 Swiftsure

Assault Ships

L 10 Fearless
L 11 Intrepid

Cruisers

C 20 Tiger
C 99 Blake

Light Cruisers and Destroyers

D 02 Devonshire
D 06 Hampshire
D 12 Kent
D 16 London
D 18 Antrim
D 19 Glamorgan
D 20 Fife
D 21 Norfolk
D 23 Bristol
D 35 Diamond
D 43 Matapan

Frigates

F 10 Aurora
F 12 Achilles
F 14 Leopard
F 15 Euryalus
F 16 Diomede
F 18 Galatea
F 27 Lynx
F 28 Cleopatra
F 32 Salisbury
F 34 Puma
F 36 Whitby
F 37 Jaguar
F 38 Arethusa
F 39 Naiad
F 40 Sirius
F 42 Phoebe
F 43 Torquay
F 45 Minerva
F 47 Danae
F 48 Dundas
F 52 Juno
F 53 Undaunted
F 54 Hardy
F 56 Argonaut
F 57 Andromeda
F 58 Hermione
F 59 Chichester
F 60 Jupiter
F 61 Llandaff
F 69 Bacchante
F 70 Apollo
F 71 Scylla
F 72 Ariadne
F 73 Eastbourne
F 75 Charybdis
F 76 Mermaid
F 77 Blackpool
F 80 Duncan
F 83 Ulster
F 84 Exmouth
F 85 Keppel
F 88 Malcolm
F 94 Pallister
F 97 Russell
F 99 Lincoln
F 101 Yarmouth
F 103 Lowestoft
F 104 Dido
F 106 Brighton
F 107 Rothesay
F 108 Londonderry
F 109 Leander
F 113 Falmouth
F 114 Ajax
F 115 Berwick
F 117 Ashanti
F 119 Eskimo
F 122 Gurkha
F 124 Zulu
F 125 Mohawk
F 126 Plymouth
F 127 Penelope
F 129 Rhyl
F 131 Nubian
F 133 Tartar
F 138 Rapid
F 169 Amazon
F 170 Antelope
F 171 Active
F 172 Ambuscade
F 173 Arrow
F 174 Alacrity
F 175 Ardent
F 176 Avenger
F 197 Grenville

Logistic Landing Ships

L 3004 Sir Bedivere
L 3005 Sir Galahad
L 3027 Sir Geraint
L 3029 Sir Lancelot
L 3036 Sir Percival
L 3505 Sir Tristram

Minelayers

N 13 Miner III
N 21 Abdiel

Helicopter Support Ship

K 08 Engadine

Support Ships & Auxiliaries

A 00 Britannia
A 70 Echo
A 71 Enterprise
A 72 Egeria
A 75 Tidespring
A 76 Tidepool
A 77 Pearleaf
A 78 Plumleaf
A 79 Bayleaf
A 80 Orangeleaf
A 81 Brambleleaf
A 84 Reliant
A 85 Faithful
A 86 Forceful
A 87 Favourite
A 88 Agile
A 89 Advice
A 90 Accord
A 91 Griper
A 92 Grinder
A 93 Dexterous
A 94 Director
A 95 Typhoon
A 96 Tidereach
A 97 Tideflow
A 98 Tidesurge
A 108 Triumph
A 111 Cyclone
A 122 Olwen
A 123 Olna
A 124 Olmeda
A 127 Torrent
A 128 Torrid
A 130 Gold Ranger
A 133 Hecla
A 134 Rame Head
A 135 Nordenfelt
A 137 Hecate
A 144 Hydra
A 160 Fort Dunvegan
A 163 Black Ranger
A 169 Brown Ranger
A 171 Endurance
A 176 Bullfinch
A 179 Whimbrel
A 185 Maidstone
A 186 Fort Rosalie
A 187 Forth
A 191 Berry Head
A 194 Tyne
A 200 Vidal
A 204 Robert Dundas
A 207 Wave Prince
A 218 Samsonia
A 222 Spapool
A 223 Nimble
A 224 Spabrook
A 230 Fort Langley
A 231 Reclaim
A 232 Kingarth
A 240 Bustler
A 241 Robert Middleton
A 257 Spaburn
A 259 St. Margarets
A 260 Spalake
A 261 Eddyfirth
A 262 Hartland Point
A 264 Reward
A 265 Wave Chief
A 268 Green Rover
A 269 Grey Rover
A 270 Blue Rover
A 280 Resurgent
A 281 Kinbrace
A 288 Sea Giant
A 289 Confiance
A 290 Confident
A 293 Careful
A 316 Fort Sandusky
A 329 Retainer
A 332 Caldy
A 333 Coll
A 334 Bern
A 336 Lundy
A 338 Skomer
A 339 Lyness
A 340 Graemsay
A 342 Foulness
A 344 Stromness
A 345 Tarbatness
A 346 Switha
A 377 Maxim
A 378 Kinterbury
A 387 Girdle Ness
A 390 Samson
A 404 Bacchus
A 406 Hebe
A 480 Resource
A 482 Kinloss
A 486 Regent
A 494 Salvalour
A 497 Salveda
A 499 Salvestor
A 500 Salvictor
A 503 Sea Salvor
A 505 Succour
A 506 Swin
A 507 Uplifter
A 508 Capable

Boom Defence Vessels

P 190 Laymoor
P 191 Layburn
P 192 Mandarin
P 193 Pintail
P 194 Garganey
P 195 Goldeneye
P 201 Barbain
P 202 Barfoot
P 232 Barmond
P 284 Moorsman
P 294 Barfoil

Light Forces

P 271 Scimitar
P 274 Cutlass
P 275 Sabre
P 276 Tenacity
P 1107 Beachampton
P 1155 Monkton
P 1189 Wasperton
P 1193 Wolverton
P 1196 Yarnton
P 3104 Dee (Beckford)
P 3113 Droxford

Coastal Minesweepers

M 1103 Kilmorey (Alfriston)
M 1109 Killiecrankie (Bickington)
M 1110 Bildeston
M 1113 Brereton
M 1114 Brinton
M 1115 Bronington
M 1124 St. David (Crichton)
M 1125 Cuxton
M 1126 Dalswinton
M 1130 Highburton
M 1133 Bossington
M 1136 Curzon (Fittleton)
M 1140 Gavinton
M 1141 Glasserton
M 1146 Venturer (Hodgeston)
M 1147 Hubberston
M 1150 Invermoriston
M 1151 Iveston
M 1153 Kedelston
M 1154 Kellington
M 1157 Kirkliston
M 1158 Laleston
M 1164 Maddiston
M 1165 Maxton
M 1166 Nurton
M 1167 Clyde (Repton)
M 1173 Mersey (Pollington)
M 1174 Puncheston
M 1175 Quainton
M 1180 Shavington
M 1181 Sheraton
M 1182 Shoulton
M 1187 Upton
M 1188 Walkerton
M 1192 Wilkieston
M 1194 Thames (Woolaston)
M 1195 Wotton
M 1198 Ashton
M 1199 Belton
M 1200 Soberton
M 1204 Montrose (Stubbington)
M 1205 Northumbria (Wiston)
M 1208 Lewiston
M 1209 Chawton
M 1216 Solent (Crofton)

Inshore Minesweepers

M 304 Waterwitch (Powderham 2720)
M 2002 Aveley
M 2010 Isis (Cradley)
M 2603 Arlingham (ex-TRV, ex-PAS)
M 2611 Bottisham R
M 2614 Bucklesham TRV
M 2616 Chelsham R
M 2621 Dittisham (ex-TRV)
M 2622 Downham TRV
M 2624 Elsenham TRV
M 2626 Everingham PAS
M 2628 Flintham (ex-TRV)
M 2630 Fritham TRV
M 2635 Haversham TRV
M 2636 Lasham TRV
M 2716 Pagham RNXS
M 2717 Fordham DGV
M 2726 Shipham RNXS
M 2733 Thakeham RNXS
M 2735 Tongham PAS
M 2737 Warmingham DGV
M 2780 Woodlark (Yaxham)
M 2781 Portisham RNXS
M 2783 Odiham RNXS
M 2784 Puttenham RNXS
M 2785 Birdham RNXS
M 2790 Thatcham DGV
M 2793 Thornham

DGV = *Degausing Vessels*
PAS = *Port Auxiliary Service*
RNXS = *Royal Naval Auxiliary Service*
TRV = *Torpedo Recovery Vessels*
R = Reserve (ex-RAF)

AIRCRAFT CARRIER

Name	Deck Letter	No.	Builders	Laid down	Launched	Completed
ARK ROYAL (ex-*Irresistable*)	R	R 09	Cammell Laird, Birkenhead	3 May 1943	3 May 1950	25 Feb 1955

ARK ROYAL 1972

Displacement, tons	43 060 standard; 50 786 full load
Length, feet (*metres*)	720·0 (*219·5*)pp; 845·0 (*257·6*)oa
Beam, feet (*metres*)	112·8 (*34·4*) hull
Draught, feet (*metres*)	36·0 (*11·0*)
Width, feet (*metres*)	166·0 (*50·6*)
Catapults	2 improved steam
Aircraft	30 fixed wing + 6 helicopters
Missile launchers	Fitted for four quadruple "Seacat" (not fitted)
Armour	4·5 in belt; 4 in flight deck; 2·5 in hangar deck; 1·5 in hangar side
Main engines	Parsons single reduction geared turbines; 4 shafts; 152 000 shp
Speed, knots	31·5
Boilers	8 Admiralty 3-drum type; pressure 400 psi (*28·1 kg/cm²*); superheat 600°F (316°C)
Oil fuel, tons	5 500 capacity
Complement	260 officers (as Flagship) 2 380 ratings (with Air Staff)

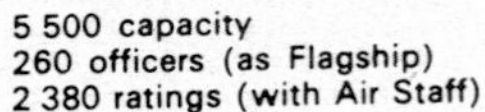
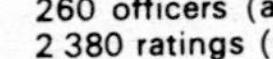

GENERAL
First British aircraft carrier with steam catapults. Had first side lift in a British aircraft carrier, situated amidships on the port side and serving the upper hangar but in 1959 this was removed, the deck park provided by the angled deck having obviated its necessity, leaving her with two centre lifts. In 1961, the deck landing projector sight, "Hilo" long range guidance system, and more powerful steam catapults were installed. Ship, originally cost £21 428 000. Due for disposal on completion of *Invincible*.

MODERNISATION. A three-years "special refit" and modernisation costing £32 500 000, from Mar 1967 to Feb 1970, enables her to operate both Phantom and Buccaneer Mk 2 aircraft. A fully angled deck 8·5 degrees off the centre line was fitted, involving two large extensions to the flight deck, and the size of the island was increased. A new waist catapult with an increased launching speed allows her to operate aircraft at almost "nil" wind conditions. A new direct acting gear was installed to enable bigger aircraft to be landed on at greater speeds.

CORVUS. Eight barrelled launcher fitted. Has multi-purpose use including launching of illuminants and "Chaff".

RADAR. Search: Type 965 (2 sets), Type 993. Aircraft Direction: Type 982 and Type 983 height finder. Miscellaneous: Carrier controlled Approach Radar.

DRAWING. Starboard elevation and plan. 1974 scale: 96 feet = 1 inch

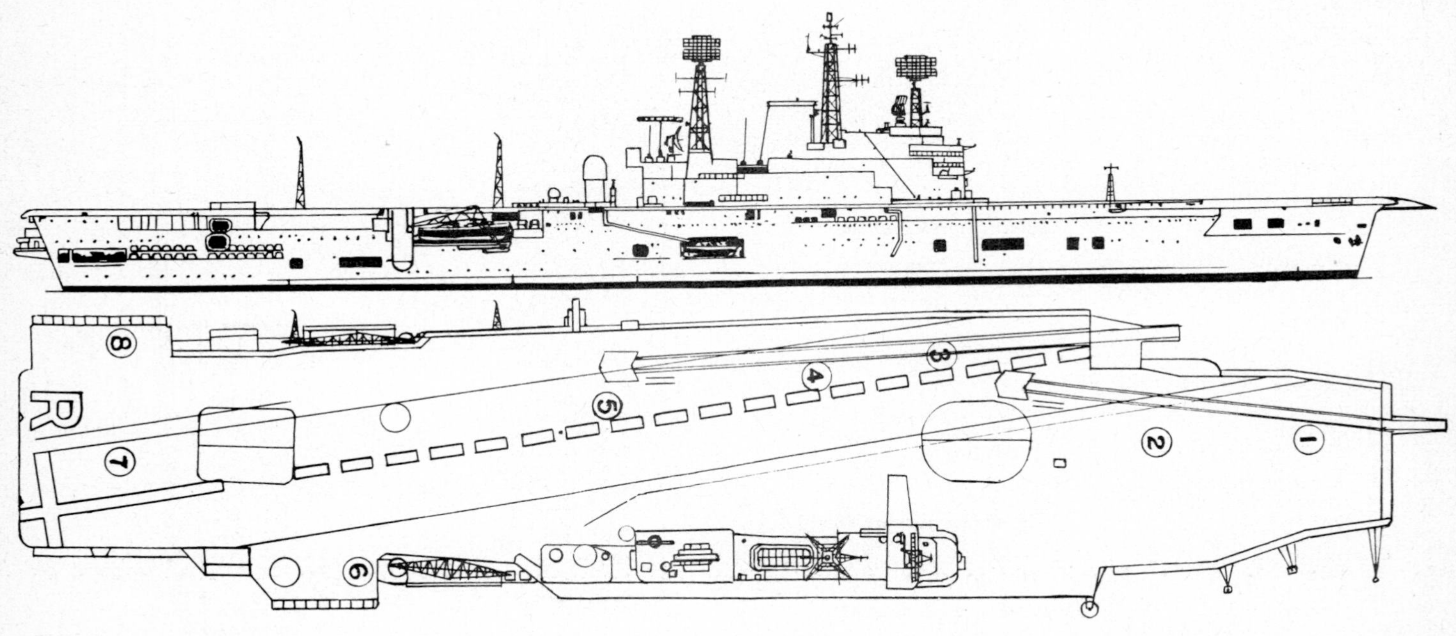

ARK ROYAL 1971

CRUISERS

NEW CONSTRUCTION

INVINCIBLE

Displacement, tons	19 000 to 20 000 estimated
Length, feet (*metres*)	650·0 (*198·1*) approx
Beam, feet (*metres*)	84·0 (*25·6*) approx
Flight Deck, ft (*m*)	100 (*30·5*)
Draught, feet (*metres*)	24·0 (*7·3*) approx
Aircraft	9 Sea King helicopters (could carry 6 Harriers)
Missile launchers	1 quadruple Exocet; 2 twin "Sea Dart"
Main engines	4 "Olympus" gas turbines; 112 000 shp; "Tyne" gas turbines
Speed, knots	30
Complement	1 200 (including aircrew)

First-of-class order from Vickers 17 April 1973, if follow-up orders are made, completion could be—first in 1978-79, second in 1980 and third in 1981-82. *Invincible* laid down at Barrow 20 July 1973.

She will be capable of providing a landing deck and hangar for helicopters, together with facilities for the command and control of naval and maritime air forces. The ship will be configured for a through deck, i.e. flight deck area, and approach will be unobstructed by superstructure, providing a limited run for V/STOL aircraft. With an angled deck she will virtually be a novel type of light fleet aircraft carrier. She will have two column masts and two funnels with an island bridge superstructure on the starboard side. Open forecastle head.

RADAR. As presently planned—Type 965 long range surveillance radar with double AKE-1 array; Type 992 Q general purpose radar; two Type 909 fire control and target radars for Sea Dart.

INVINCIBLE *1973, Vickers Ltd.*

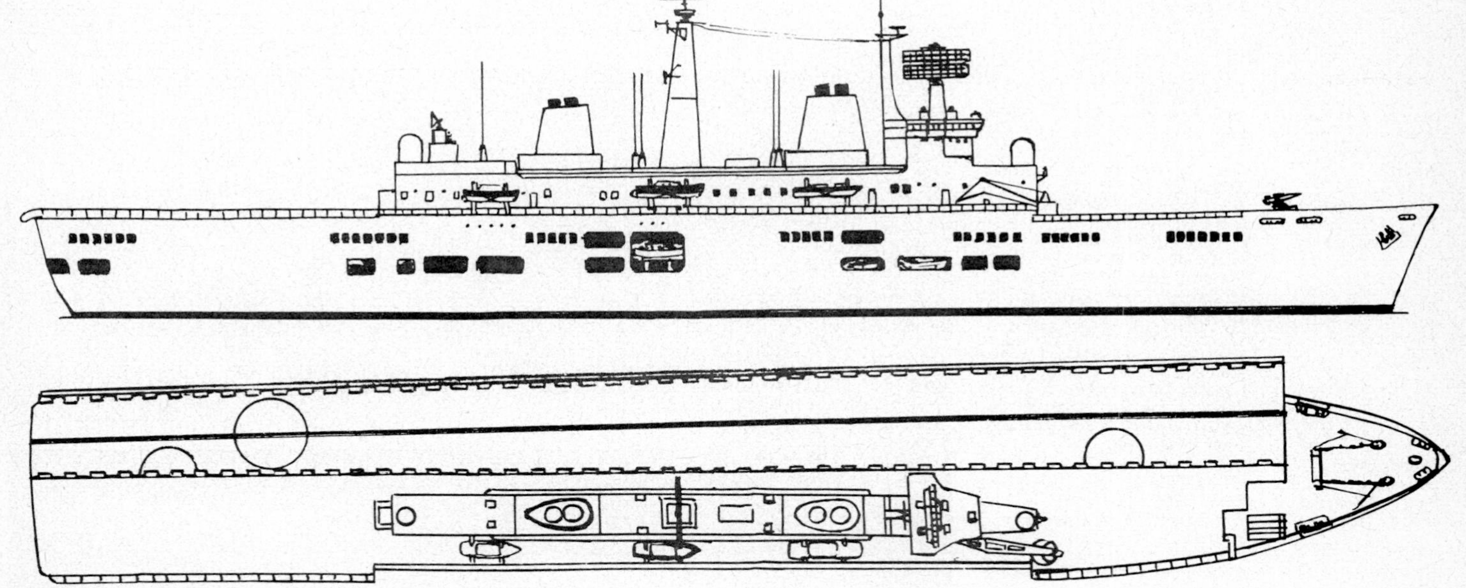

INVINCIBLE *1974*

Cruisers—*continued*

2 "TIGER" CLASS

Name	No.	Builders and Engineers	Laid down	Launched	Completed
BLAKE (ex-*Tiger*, ex-*Blake*)	C 99	Fairfield SB & Eng, Govan	17 Aug 42	20 Dec 45	8 Mar 61
TIGER (ex-*Bellerophon*)	C 20	John Brown, Clydebank	1 Oct 41	25 Oct 45	18 Mar 59

Displacement, tons	9 500 standard; 12 080 full load
Length, feet (*metres*)	538·0 (*164·0*) pp; 550·0 (*167·6*) wl; 566·5 (*172·8*) oa
Beam, feet (*metres*)	64·0 (*19·5*)
Draught, feet (*metres*)	23·0 (*7·0*)
Aircraft	4 Sea King helicopters
Missile launchers	2 quadruple "Seacat"
Guns	2—6 in (*152 mm*) 1 twin; 2—3 in (*76 mm*) (twin)
Armour	Belt 3·5 in—3·2 in (*89—83 mm*); deck 2 in (*51 mm*); turret 3 in—1 in (*76—25 mm*)
Main engines	4 Parsons geared turbines; 4 shafts; 80 000 shp
Boilers	4 Admiralty 3-drum type
Speed, knots	31·5 max
Range, miles	2 000 at 30 knots; 4 000 at 20 knots; 6 500 at 13 knots
Oil fuel, tons	1 850
Complement	85 officers, 800 ratings

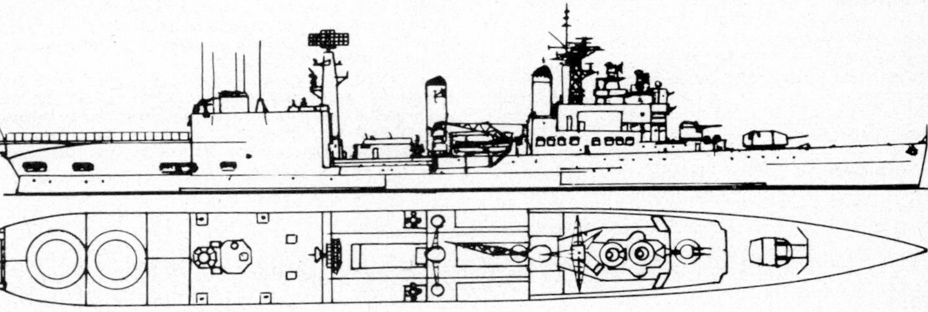

TIGER (Funnels higher than *Blake's*) 1974

Originally designed as orthodox cruisers. Work on the ships was stopped in July 1946, for eight years. The decision to complete them was announced on 15 Oct 1954. Delayed for resumption to a new design in 1955. *Tiger* cost £13 113 000 and *Blake* £14 940 000. Helicopter conversion cost £5 500 000 for *Blake* and the astonishing total of £13 250 000 for *Tiger*.

ELECTRICAL. 4 turbo-generators provide 4 000 kW ac, the first time this type of power used in British cruisers.

ENGINEERING. Main machinery is largely automatic and can be remotely controlled. Steam conditions 400 psi pressure and 640°F. Propellers 11 ft dia, 285 rpm.

CLASS. It was announced in Feb 1972 that the unconverted sister ship *Lion* had been approved for disposal by scrapping. *Hawke* of this class, laid down in HM Dockyard, Portsmouth in Aug 1944, was cancelled in 1946 as was *Bellerophon* (ex-*Tiger*) a cruiser of enlarged design ordered from Vickers-Armstrongs.

CONVERSION. *Blake* was converted to a command helicopter cruiser at HM Dockyard, Portsmouth from early 1965 until she recommissioned on 23 Apr 1969. *Tiger* was similarly converted during 1968 to 1972.

DRAWING. Starboard elevation and plan of *Tiger*. Redrawn in 1974.

GUNNERY. The 6 inch fully automatic guns of advanced design are equally effective in surface and anti-aircraft roles. Rate of fire is 20 rpm, more than twice that of any previous cruiser. The 3 inch guns are capable of 90 rpm.

RADAR. Search: Type 965 and Type 992. Height Finder: Type 277. Fire control: 4 MRS 3 fire control directors.

TIGER *1973, Wright and Logan*

LIGHT CRUISERS

1 TYPE 82

Name	No.	Builders	Laid down	Launched	Commissioned
BRISTOL	D 23	Swan Hunter & Tyne Shipbuilders Ltd	15 Nov 1967	30 June 1969	31 Mar 1973

Displacement, tons	5 650 standard (approx); 6 750 full load
Length, feet (*metres*)	490·0 (*149·4*) wl; 507·0 (*154·5*) oa
Beam, feet (*metres*)	55·0 (*16·8*)
Draught, feet (*metres*)	22·5 (*6·9*)
Aircraft	Landing platform for 1 "Wasp" helicopter
Missile launchers	1 twin "Seadart" GWS 30 launcher aft
A/S weapons	1 "Ikara" single launcher forward; 1 "Limbo" three-barrelled depth charge mortar (Mark 10) aft
Guns	1—4·5 in (*115 mm*) Mark 8 forward;
Main engines	COSAG arrangement (combined steam and gas turbines) 2 sets Standard Range geared steam turbines, 30 000 shp; 2 Bristol-Siddeley marine "Olympus" gas turbines, 44 600 shp; 2 shafts; Total 74 600 shp
Speed, knots	32
Boilers	2
Range, miles	Over 4 500 at 18 knots
Complement	433 (33 officers, 400 ratings)

GENERAL.
Three funnels, one amidships and two aft abreast the mainmast.
Designed around a new weapons system. Fully stabilised to present a steady weapon platform. The gas turbines provide emergency power and high speed boost. The machinery is remotely-controlled from a ship control centre. Automatic steering, obviating the need for a

BRISTOL *1973, Wright and Logan*

Light Cruisers—*continued*

quartermaster. Many labour-saving items of equipment fitted to make the most efficient and economical use of manpower resulting in a smaller ship's company for tonnage than any previous warship. Fitted with Action Data Automation Weapon System. Started trials 10 April 1972. Remainder of class cancelled owing to high cost.

COST. £22 500 000 (£27 000 000 overall). GEC-Marconi equipment for radar, weapons and communications cost over £3 000 000.

COMMUNICATIONS. By GEC-Marconi to include SCOT satellite system compatible with both SKYNET and the US Defence satellites.

MISSILES. The Seadart ship missile system, developed to meet the air threat of the 1970's and 1980's, also has a reasonable anti-ship capability.
Ikara is a long-range anti-submarine weapon system, developed in Australia.

RADAR. Type 965 long range search radar with AKE double aerial outfit and IFF; Type 992 General-purpose radar; Type 909 fire control and target radar for Sea Dart.

BRISTOL *1973, C. and S. Taxlor*

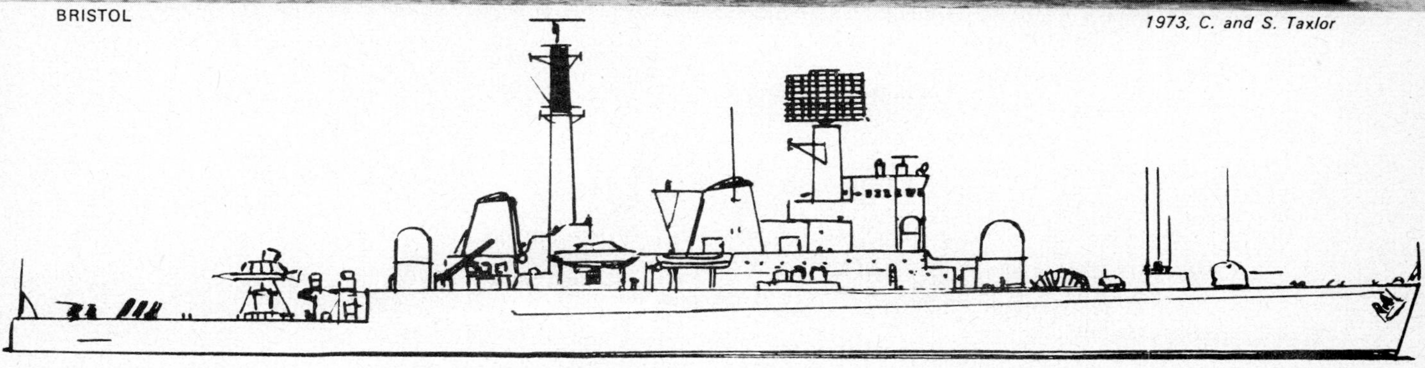
BRISTOL *1974*

8 "COUNTY" CLASS

Displacement, tons	5 440 standard; 6 200 full load
Length, feet (*metres*)	505·0 (*153·9*) wl; 520·5 (*158·7*) oa
Beam, feet (*metres*)	54·0 (*16·5*)
Draught, feet (*metres*)	20·0 (*6·1*) max
Aircraft	1 "Wessex" helicopter
Missile launchers	Exocet in four ships (see *Missile* note) 1 twin "Seaslug" aft; 2 quadruple "Seacat" either side abreast hangar.
Guns	4—4·5 in (*115 mm*), 2 twin turrets forward; 2—20 mm, single (2—4·5 only in ships with Exocet)
Boilers	2 Babcock & Wilcox
Main engines	Combined steam and gas turbines. 2 sets geared steam turbines, 30 000 shp; 4 gas turbines, 30 000 shp. 2 shafts; Total 60 000 shp; (see *Engineering* notes)
Speed, knots	32·5 max
Complement	471 (33 officers and 438 men)

Name	*No.*	*Builders*	*Laid down*	*Launched*	*Completed*
ANTRIM	D 18	Fairfield SB & Eng Co Ltd, Govan	20 Jan 66	19 Oct 67	**14 July 70**
DEVONSHIRE	D 02	Cammell Laird & Co Ltd, Birkenhead	9 Mar 59	10 June 60	**15 Nov 62**
FIFE	D 20	Fairfield SB & Eng Co Ltd, Govan	1 June 62	9 July 64	**21 June 66**
GLAMORGAN	D 19	Vickers-Armstrongs Ltd, Newcastle-on-Tyne	13 Sep 62	9 July 64	**11 Oct 66**
HAMPSHIRE	D 06	John Brown & Co (Clydebank) Ltd, Glasgow	26 Mar 59	16 Mar 61	**15 Mar 63**
KENT	D 12	Harland & Wolff Ltd, Belfast	1 Mar 60	27 Sep 61	**15 Aug 63**
LONDON	D 16	Swan, Hunter & Wigham Richardson, Wallsend	26 Feb 60	7 Dec 61	**4 Nov 63**
NORFOLK	D 21	Swan, Hunter & Wigham Richardson, Wallsend	15 Mar 66	16 Nov 67	**7 Mar 70**

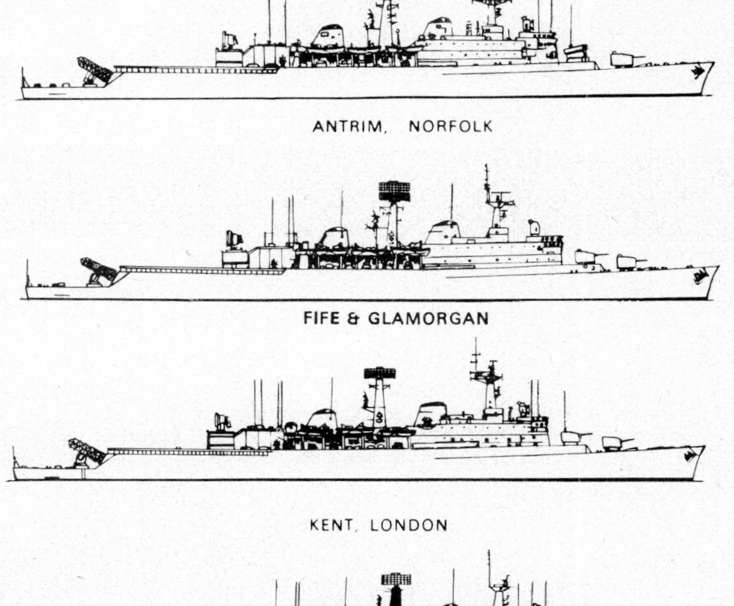
ANTRIM, NORFOLK

FIFE & GLAMORGAN

KENT, LONDON

DEVONSHIRE, HAMPSHIRE

GENERAL
Fife, Glamorgan, Antrim and *Norfolk*, have the more powerful "Seaslug" II systems. All fitted with stabilisers and are fully air-conditioned.

APPEARANCE. *Kent* and *London* have mainmast stepped further aft than remainder. The last four of the class have distinctive tubular foremast and twin radar "bedstead".

ELECTRICAL. Two 1 000 kW turbo-alternators and three gas turbines alternators total 3 750 kW, at 440 V.a.c.

ENGINEERING. These are the first ships of their size to have COSAG (combined steam and gas turbine machinery). Boilers work at a pressure of 700 psi and a temperature of 950 deg F. The steam and gas turbines are geared to the same shaft. Each shaft set consists of a high pressure and low pressure steam turbine of 15 000 shp combined output plus two G.6 gas turbines each of 7 500 shp. The gas turbines are able to develop their full power from cold within a few minutes, enabling ships lying in harbour without steam to get under way instantly in emergency.

GUNNERY. The 4—4·5 inch guns are radar controlled, fully automatic dual-purpose quick-firing. The 20 mm guns were added for picket duties in S.E. Asia, but have been retained for general close range duties.

MISSILES. Exocet being fitted in *Norfolk, Antrim, Fife* and *Glamorgan* in place of B turret. No reloads carried.

RADAR. Type 992 search radar; Height Finder Type 278; Type 901 fire control and Target radar aft for Seaslug; MRS 3 forward, port and starboard for gunnery fire control; GWS 22 (for Seacat) in *Kent, Norfolk, Antrim, Fife* and *Glamorgan*—remainder have optical sighting; Type 965 with double AKE-2 aerial outfit in *Norfolk, Glamorgan, Antrim* and *Fife* while the remainder have single AKE-1; IFF.

Light Cruisers—*continued*

NORFOLK with Exocet *1973, C. and S. Taylor*

ANTRIM before conversion *1973, Wright and Logan*

GLAMORGAN *1973, John Mortimer*

KENT *1973, Wright and Logan*

DESTROYERS

6 "TYPE" 42

Name	Builders	Ordered	Laid down	Launched	Completion
SHEFFIELD	Vickers Ltd Shipbuilding Group, Barrow	14 Nov 1968	15 Jan 1970	10 June 1971	1974
BIRMINGHAM	Cammell Laird & Co, Ltd, Birkenhead	21 May 1971	28 Mar 1972	30 July 1973	1976
COVENTRY	Cammell Laird & Co, Ltd, Birkenhead	21 May 1971	22 Mar 1972	—	—
CARDIFF	Vickers Ltd, Shipbuilding Group, Barrow	10 June 1971	3 Nov 1972	21 Feb 1974	—
NEWCASTLE	Swan Hunter & Tyne Shipbuilders, Ltd	11 Nov 1971	21 Feb 1973	—	—
GLASGOW	Swan Hunter & Tyne Shipbuilders, Ltd	11 Nov 1971	Feb 1974	—	—

NOTE. Work on prefabrication normally starts six months before lay down date.

Displacement, tons	3 500 approx full load
Length, feet (*metres*)	392·0 (*119·5*)wl; 410·0 (*125·0*) oa
Beam, feet (*metres*)	47·0 (*14·3*)
Draught, feet (*metres*)	22·0 (*6·7*)
Aircraft	1 twin engined "Lynx" anti-submarine helicopter
Missile launchers	1 twin "Sea Dart" medium range surface-to-air (surface-to-surface capability)
Guns	1—4·5 in automatic, Mark 8, 2—20 mm Oerlikon; 2 saluting
A/S weapons	Helicopter launched torpedoes
Main engines	COGOG arrangement of Rolls Royce Olympus gas turbines for full power; and 2 Rolls Royce Tyne gas turbines for cruising; reversible pitch propellers for manoeuvring; 2 shafts; 50 000 shp
Speed, knots	30 approx estimated max
Endurance	Over 4 000 miles at 18 knots
Complement	280 (20 officers and 260 ratings) (accommodation for 312)

GENERAL
The first "Type 42" all gas-turbine propelled destroyer with the Sea Dart guided missile as her main armament is scheduled for service in 1973. The helicopter will carry an air-to-surface weapon for use against lightly defended surface ship targets such as fast patrol boats. The gas turbine installation is a development of that in the frigate *Exmouth*. Advantages include ability to reach maximum speed with great rapidity, reduction in space and weight and 25 per cent reduction in technical manpower. To cost £17 000 000 per ship. All to be in service by end 1977.

ELECTRONICS. Twin Scot Skynet satellite communication aerials; ADAWS.

RADAR. Type 965 with AKE-2 and IFF; Type 992Q General-purpose radar; Type 1006 navigation radar; Two Type 909 Sea Dart fire control and target radars; ECM; D/F.

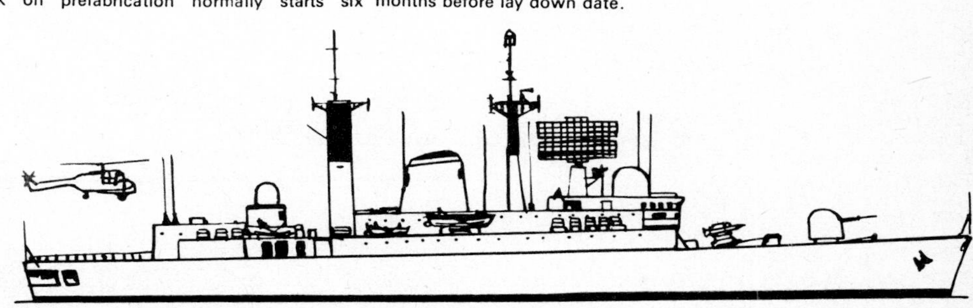

SHEFFIELD

SHEFFIELD (left) and CARDIFF fitting out at Vickers *1974, MOD (N)*

SHEFFIELD *1974, MOD (N)*

FRIGATES

1+7 "TYPE 21" AMAZON CLASS

Displacement, tons	2 500 full load
Length, feet (*metres*)	360·0 (*109·7*)wl; 384·0(*117·0*)oa
Beam, feet (*metres*)	41·8 (*12·7*)
Draught, feet (*metres*)	12·3 (*3·7*)
Aircraft	1 twin engined "Lynx" anti-submarine helicopter
Missile launchers	1 quadruple "Seacat" surface-to-air (later ships will have "Seawolf")
Guns	1—4·5 in Mark 8; 2—20 mm Oerlikon
A/S weapons	Helicopter launched torpedoes
Torpedo tubes	6 (2 triple)
Main engines	COGOG arrangement of 2 Rolls Royce "Olympus" gas turbines for speed; 2 Rolls Royce "Tyne" gas turbines for cruising; 2 shafts; 50 000 shp; controllable pitch propellers
Speed, knots	34
Range, miles	4 500 at 18 knots
Complement	170 (11 officers, and 159 ratings)

Name	*No.*	*Builders*	*Laid down*	*Launched*	*Completion*
AMAZON	F 169	Vosper Thornycroft, Woolston	6 Nov 1969	26 Apr 1971	July 1973
ANTELOPE	F 170	Vosper Thornycroft, Woolston	23 Mar 1971	16 Mar 1972	1974-5
ACTIVE	F 171	Vospre Thornycroft, Woolston	23 July 1971	23 Nov 1972	1974-5
AMBUSCADE	F 172	Yarrow & Co, Ltd, Glasgow	July 1971	18 Jan 1973	
ARROW	F 173	Yarrow & Co, Ltd, Glasgow	June 1972	5 Feb 1974	
ALACRITY	F 174	Yarrow & Co, Ltd, Glasgow	Feb 1973	Sep 1974	
ARDENT	F 175	Yarrow & Co, Ltd, Glasgow	Not yet laid down		
AVENGER	F 176	Yarrow & Co, Ltd, Glasgow			

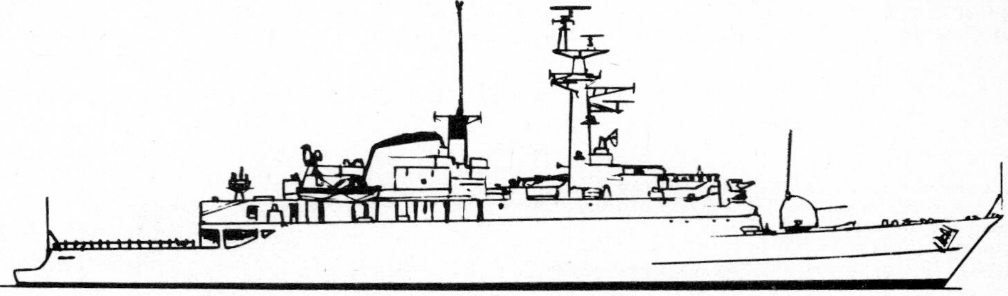

AMAZON

The Navy awarded Vosper Thornycroft, Portsmouth and Southampton, a contract on 27 Feb 1968 for the design of a patrol frigate to be prepared in full collaboration with Yarrow Ltd, Scotstoun. This is the first custom built gas turbine frigate (designed and constructed as such from the keel up, as opposed to conversion) and the first warship designed by commercial firms for many years. All eight should be completed by end 1977 but the completion of the last five building at Yarrows has been delayed by lack of technical information from beyond the shipyard.

RADAR. Type 992 Q general-purpose search radar; Type 978 navigation radar; GWS 24 fire control fore and aft for Seacat; Orion RTN-10X WSA-4 fire control system for guns; Cossor Type 1010 IFF interrogator; Plessey PTR 461 IFF transponder; CAAIS.

AMAZON *1973, Vosper Thornycroft Ltd.*

AMAZON *1973, John G. Callis*

"TYPE 22" PROJECTED

Displacement, tons	3 800
Length, feet (*metres*)	430 (*131·2*)
Aircraft	2 "Lynx" helicopters
Missile launchers	2 "Sea Wolf" surface-to-air system; 2 twin Exocet surface-to-surface launchers
Guns	2—40 mm
A/S weapons	2 Triple Torpedo tubes
Main engines	COGOG arrangement of 2 Rolls Royce "Olympus" gas turbines and 2 Rolls Royce "Tyne" gas turbines driving 2 shafts = Total 56 000 hp
Speed, knots	30

Designed as successors to the "Leander" class, the construction of which ceased with the completion of the scheduled programme of 26 ships. Order for first of class to be built by Yarrows was placed in Feb 1974.

Type 22 *1974*

Frigates—*continued*

16 "LEANDER" CLASS

10 "BROAD-BEAMED LEANDER" CLASS

Displacement, tons	2 450 standard; 2 860 full load (Leanders)
	2 500 standard; 2 962 full load (Broad-beamed)
Length, feet (*metres*)	360 (*109·7*) wl; 372 (*113·4*) oa
Beam, feet (*metres*)	41 (*12·5*) (Leanders)
	43 (*13·1*) (Broad-beamed)
Draught, feet (*metres*)	18 (*5·5*)
Aircraft	1 Wasp helicopter
Missiles	Exocet in some and Seacat (see *Notes*)
Guns (see *Notes*)	2—4·5 in (*115 mm*) (twin)
	2—40 mm (varies)
	2—20 mm (Seacat ships)
A/S weapons	Ikara in some (see *Notes*)
	1 "Limbo" 3 barrelled mortar
Main engines (see *Notes*)	2 double reduction geared turbines; 2 shafts; 30 000 shp
Boilers	2
Speed, knots	30
Oil fuel, tons	460
Complement	251 (Leanders)
	263 (Broad-beamed)

Name	No	Builders	Laid down	Launched	Completed
AJAX	F 114	Cammell Laird & Co Ltd, Birkenhead	12 Oct 59	16 Aug 62	10 Dec 63
DIDO	F 104	Yarrow & Co Ltd, Scotstoun, Glasgow	2 Dec 59	22 Dec 61	18 Sep 63
LEANDER	F 109	Harland & Wolff Ltd, Belfast	10 Apr 59	28 June 61	27 Mar 63
PENELOPE	F 127	Vickers Armstrongs Ltd, Tyne	14 Mar 61	17 Aug 62	31 Oct 63
AURORA	F 10	John Brown & Co (Clydebank) Ltd	1 June 61	28 Nov 62	9 Apr 64
EURYALUS	F 15	Scotts' Shipbuilding & Eng, Greenock	2 Nov 61	6 June 63	16 Sep 64
GALATEA	F 18	Swan, Hunter & Wigham Richardson, Tyne	29 Dec 61	23 May 63	25 Apr 64
ARETHUSA	F 38	J. Samuel White & Co Ltd, Cowes	7 Sep 62	5 Nov 63	24 Nov 65
NAIAD	F 39	Yarrow & Co Ltd, Scotstoun, Glasgow	30 Oct 62	4 Nov 63	15 Mar 65
CLEOPATRA	F 28	HM Dockyard, Devonport	19 June 63	25 Mar 64	4 Jan 66
SIRIUS	F 40	HM Dockyard, Portsmouth	9 Aug 63	22 Sep 64	15 June 66
MINERVA	F 45	Vickers-Armstrongs Ltd, Tyne	25 July 63	19 Dec 64	14 May 66
PHOEBE	F 42	Alex Stephen & Sons Ltd, Glasgow	3 June 63	8 July 64	15 Apr 66
DANAE	F 47	HM Dockyard, Devonport	16 Dec 64	31 Oct 65	7 Sep 67
JUNO	F 52	John I. Thornycroft Ltd, Woolston	16 July 64	24 Nov 65	18 July 67
ARGONAUT	F 56	Hawthorn Leslie, Ltd, Hebburn-on-Tyne	27 Nov 64	8 Feb 66	17 Aug 67

"BROAD BEAMED LEANDER" CLASS

Name	No	Builders	Laid down	Launched	Completed
ANDROMEDA	F 57	HM Dockyard, Portsmouth	25 May 66	24 May 67	2 Dec 68
JUPITER	F 60	Yarrow & Co Ltd, Scotstoun, Glasgow	3 Oct 66	4 Sep 67	9 Aug 69
HERMIONE	F 58	Alex Stephen & Sons Ltd, Glasgow	6 Dec 65	26 Apr 67	11 July 69
BACCHANTE	F 69	Vickers Ltd, High Walker, Newcastle	27 Oct 66	29 Feb 68	17 Oct 69
SCYLLA	F 71	HM Dockyard, Devonport	17 May 67	8 Aug 68	12 Feb 70
CHARYBDIS	F 75	Harland & Wolff Ltd, Belfast	27 Jan 67	28 Feb 68	2 June 69
ACHILLES	F 12	Yarrow & Co Ltd, Scotstoun	1 Dec 67	21 Nov 68	9 July 70
DIOMEDE	F 16	Yarrow & Co Ltd, Scotstoun	30 Jan 68	15 Apr 69	2 Apr 71
APOLLO	F 70	Yarrow & Co Ltd, Scotstoun	1 May 69	15 Oct 70	28 May 72
ARIADNE	F 72	Yarrow & Co Ltd, Scotstoun	1 Nov 69	10 Sep 71	10 Feb 73

GENERAL
This class, whose construction extended over ten years, was an improvement on the Type 12. As originally designed there were several significant improvements—a helicopter, VDS and long-range air warning radar being the most important. Recently a number of conversions have been put in hand (see *Notes* below).

ELECTRICAL. 440 volts, 60 cycle AC. 1 900 kw in earlier ships, 2 500 kw in later ones.

ENGINEERING. The first ten have Y-100 machinery, the remainder of the "Leanders" Y-136." Broad-beamed Leanders" have Y-160 machinery.

EXOCET. This is to be mounted forward in place of the 4·5 in turret in the following—*Cleopatra, Sirius, Minerva, Phoebe, Danae, Juno, Argonaut* and *Dido*.

GUNNERY. 4·5 in turret removed in Exocet and Ikara conversions and in *Penelope*. 40 mm are not fitted in unconverted ships mounting Seacat. Ikara conversions mount 2 twin 40 mm abaft the bridge. Two single 20 mm are mounted abaft the bridge in place of 40 mm in Seacat fitted ships.

IKARA. Already mounted in *Leander* in place of 4·5 in turret. To be fitted in *Ajax, Aurora, Euryalus, Galatea, Arethusa, Naiad* and in *Penelope* when Seawolf is removed.

RADAR. Search: Type 965 with single AKE aerial array, and Type 993 combined surface and air warning. Fire Control: X band. MRS.3/GWS-22 fire control directors. DF equipment. In Ikara conversions and *Penelope*. Type 965 aerial is removed to compensate for top-weight.

SEACAT. Single Seacat first fitted in *Naiad*, subsequently to replace 40 mm guns in all but Ikara conversions who have two Seacat mounts. *Penelope* currently has none.

SEAWOLF. An experimental outfit is mounted in *Penelope*, replacing the 4·5 in turret. She carries different radars and additional deckhouses, though no Seacat. Ikara will eventually replace Seawolf in this ship.

SONAR. VDS was originally fitted in all but *Diomede*. In some the VDS has been removed leaving the well—in others the well has been plated over to provide extra accommodation.

ACHILLES 1972

"Leander" class with 4·5 in guns and Seacat

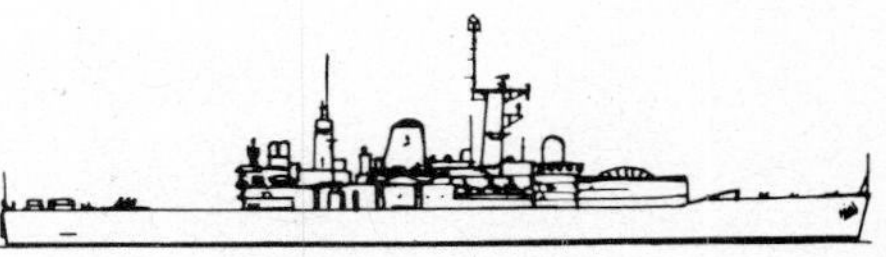
"Leander" class with Ikara

"Leander" class with Exocet

PENELOPE with Seawolf

Frigates—*continued*

APOLLO *1972, C. and S. Taylor*

LEANDER with Ikara *1973, Wright and Logan*

ARGONAUT *1973, C. and S. Taylor*

Frigates—*continued*

PENELOPE with Seawolf — *1973, Wright and Logan*

9 "ROTHESAY" CLASS

MODIFIED TYPE 12

Displacement, tons	2 380 standard; 2 800 full load
Length, feet (*metres*)	360·0 (*109·7*)wl; 370·0 (*112·8*)oa
Beam, feet (*metres*)	41·0 (*12·5*)
Draught, feet (*metres*)	17·3 (*5·3*) max (props)
Aircraft	1 "Wasp" helicopter
Missile launchers	1 quadruple for "Seacat"
Guns	2—4·5 in (*115 mm*) dp (1 twin) 2—20 mm AA single
A/S weapons	1 Limbo 3-barrelled DC mortar
Main engines	2 double reduction geared turbines; 2 shafts; 30 000 shp
Speed, knots	30
Boilers	2 Babcock & Wilcox
Oil fuel, tons	400
Complement	235 (15 officers and 220 ratings)

Name	No.	Builders	Laid down	Launched	Completed
BERWICK	F 115	Harland & Wolff Ltd, Belfast	16 June 1958	15 Dec 1959	1 June 1961
BRIGHTON	F 106	Yarrow & Co Ltd, Scotstoun	23 July 1957	30 Oct 1959	28 Sep 1961
FALMOUTH	F 113	Swan Hunter, Wigham Richardson	23 Nov 1957	15 Dec 1959	25 July 1961
LONDONDERRY	F 108	J. Samuel White & Co Ltd, Cowes	15 Nov 1956	20 May 1958	22 July 1960
LOWESTOFT	F 103	Alex Stephen & Sons Ltd, Govan	9 June 1958	23 June 1960	18 Oct 1961
PLYMOUTH	F 126	HM Dockyard, Devonport	1 July 1958	20 July 1959	11 May 1961
RHYL	F 129	HM Dockyard, Portsmouth	29 Jan 1958	23 Apr 1959	31 Oct 1960
ROTHESAY	F 107	Yarrow & Co Ltd, Scotstoun	6 Nov 1956	9 Dec 1957	23 Apr 1960
YARMOUTH	F 101	John Brown & Co Ltd, Clydebank	29 Nov 1957	23 Mar 1959	26 Mar 1960

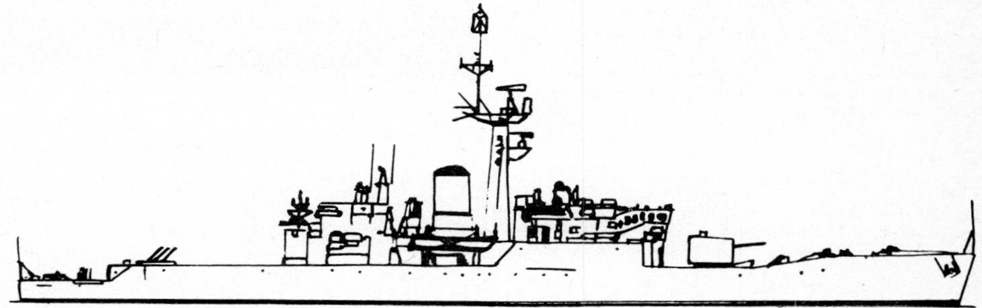
ROTHESAY *Class*

Provided under the 1954-55 programme. Originally basically similar to the "Whitby" class but with modifications in layout as a result of experience gained.

ELECTRICAL. Two turbo generators and two diesel generators in all ships. Total 1 140 kW. Alternating current, 440 volts, three phase, 60 cycles per second.

ENGINEERING. Two Admiralty Standard Range turbines each rated at 15 000 shp. Propeller revolutions 220 rpm. Steam conditions 550 psi (*38·7 kg/cm²*) pressure and 850° F (450°C) temperature at boilers.

MODERNISATION. The "Rothesay" class was reconstructed and modernised from 1966-72 during which time they were equipped to operate a Wessex Wasp helicopter armed with homing torpedoes. A flight deck and hangar were built on aft, necessitating the removal of one of her anti-submarine mortars. A "Seacat" replaced the 40 mm gun.

RADAR. Search: Some ships are fitted with Type 993 and others with Type 293. Fire Control: MRS.3. fire control: Type 978 air warning radar; optical Seacat director; DF.

LONDONDERRY — *1973, Wright and Logan*

FALMOUTH — *1973, John G. Callis*

Frigates—*continued*

4 "WHITBY" CLASS TYPE 12

Name	No.	Builders	Laid down	Launched	Completed
BLACKPOOL	F 77	Harland & Wolff Ltd Belfast	20 Dec 1954	14 Feb 1957	13 Aug 1958
EASTBOURNE	F 73	Vickers-Armstrongs Ltd Tyne	13 Jan 1954	29 Dec 1955	9 Jan 1958
TORQUAY	F 43	Harland & Wolff Ltd, Belfast	11 Mar 1953	1 July 1954	10 May 1956
WHITBY	F 36	Cammell Laird & Co Ltd, Birkenhead	30 Sep 1952	2 July 1954	19 July 1956

Displacement, tons	2 150 standard; 2 560 full load
Length, feet (*metres*)	360·0 (*109·7*)wl; 369·8 (*112·7*)oa
Beam, feet (*metres*)	41·0 (*12·5*)
Draught, feet (*metres*)	17 (*5·2*)
Guns, dual purpose	2—4·5 in (*115 mm*) 1 twin 1—40 mm Bofors (1 twin) (not in *Torquay*)
A/S weapons	2 Limbo 3-barrelled DC mortars (1 only in *Torquay*)
Boilers	2 Babcock & Wilcox Pressure 550 psi (*38·7 kg/cm²*) Temperature 850°F (454°C)
Main engines	2 sets d.r. geared turbines; 2 shafts; 30 430 shp
Speed, knots	31
Oil fuel (tons)	370
Complement	225 (12 officers and 213 ratings)

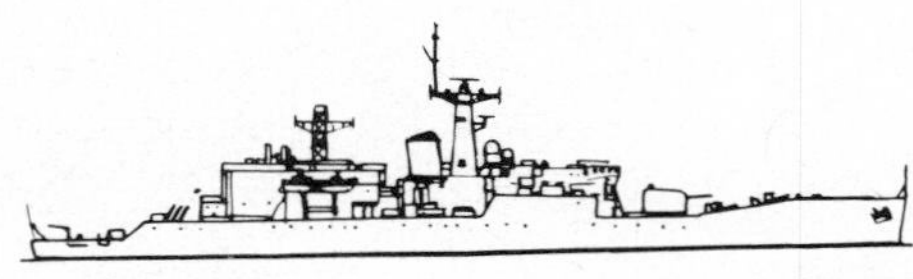
WHITBY 1974

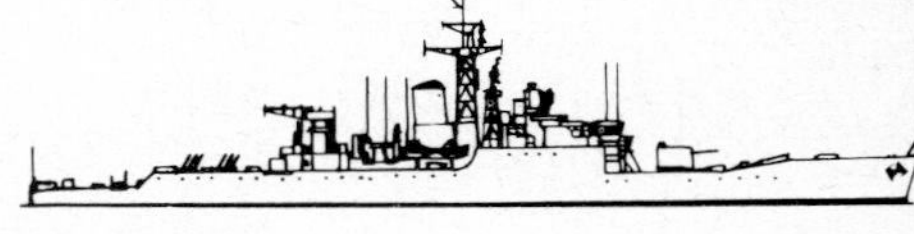
TORQUAY 1974

Ordered in 1951. Good sea-keeping qualities enable them to maintain their high speed in rough seas. Their twin-rudders improve manoeuvrability. They are all welded and were specially designed with the lightest possible structure.

CLASS. *Whitby* remains operational. *Torquay* used as Navigation/Direction trainingand trials ship at Portsmouth, having a large deck-house aft and carrying the first CAAIS (Computer Assisted Action Information System) to go to sea. *Eastbourne*, stripped of her gun and A/S armament, is based at Rosyth for engine-room trainees from HMS *Caledonia*. *Blackpool*, after service with RNZN until April 1971, is in reserve without her 4·5 in turret pending a decision on her disposal. *Tenby* and *Scarborough* sold to Pakistan in 1974.

ELECTRICAL. System is alternating current, 440 volts; three phase, 60 cycles per second. Two turbo alternators and two diesel alternators. Total 1 140 kilowatts.

ENGINEERING. Propelling machinery includes geared turbines of Y 100 design and high power. Double reduction gearing allows low propeller revolutions of 220 rpm at high power and the propeller efficiency is correspondingly high. This, with improvements in hull design, enables these frigates to achieve over 30 knots on only 75 per cent of the power required by older destroyers of comparable displacement.

RADAR. Search: Type 293 and Type 277 for surface search. Fire Control: Mk 6M DCT with Type 275.

WHITBY 1971, *John Mortimer*

EASTBOURNE after removal of armament 1973, *C. and S. Taylor*

TORQUAY 1972, *MOD (N)*

Frigates—*continued*

7 "BLACKWOOD" CLASS TYPE 14

Displacement, tons	1 180 standard; 1 456 full load
Length, feet (*metres*)	300 (*91·4*) wl; 310 (*94·5*) oa
Beam, feet (*metres*)	33·0 (*10·1*)
Draught, feet (*metres*)	15·5 (*4·7*)
Guns, AA	2—40 mm Bofors
A/S weapons	2 "Limbo" 3-barrelled DC mortars
Boilers	2 Babcock & Wilcox Pressure 550 psi (*38·7 kg/cm²*) Temperature 850°F (454°C)
Main engines	1 set geared turbines; 1 shaft; 15 000 shp
Speed, knots	27·8
Range, miles	4 000 at 12 knots
Oil fuel, tons	275
Complement	140 (8 officers, and 132 ratings)

Of comparatively simple construction. Built in prefabricated sections. In 1958-59 their hulls were strengthened to withstand severe and prolonged sea and weather conditions on fishery protection in Icelandic waters.

RADAR. Equipped with Type 978 search radar.

TORPEDOES. 4—21 inch tubes (2 twin) mounted in *Exmouth*, and *Malcolm* were removed.

ENGINEERING. All engined by their builders, except *Russell*, by Wallsend Slipway & Eng Co Ltd, Four-bladed, 12 ft diameter propeller, 220 rpm.

"Blackwood" Class 1974

THREE ACTIVE SHIPS

Name	*No.*	*Builders*	*Laid down*	*Launched*	*Completed*
DUNDAS	F 48	J. Samuel White & Co. Ltd.	17 Oct 1952	25 Sep 1953	16 Mar 1956
HARDY	F 54	Yarrow & Co. Ltd.	4 Feb 1953	25 Nov 1953	15 Dec 1955
RUSSELL	F 97	Swan Hunter & Wigham Richardson	11 Nov 1953	10 Dec 1954	7 Feb 1957
TWO HARBOUR TRAINING SHIPS					
BLACKWOOD	F 78	John I. Thornycroft & Co. Ltd.	14 Sep 1953	4 Oct 1955	22 Aug 1957
DUNCAN	F 80	John I. Thorncroft & Co. Ltd.	17 Dec 1953	30 May 1957	21 Oct 1958
TWO RESERVE SHIPS					
KEPPEL	F 85	Yarrow & Co. Ltd.	27 Mar 1953	31 Aug 1954	6 July 1956
PALLISER	F 94	Alex Stephen & Sons Ltd.	15 Mar 1955	10 May 1956	13 Dec 1957

DUNDAS 1973, *Wright and Logan*

1 TYPE 14 CONVERSION

Name	*No.*	*Builder*	*Laid down*	*Launched*	*Completed*
EXMOUTH	F 84	J. Samuel White & Co. Ltd.	24 Mar 1954	16 Nov 1955	20 Dec 1957

Details of displacement, dimensions and armament as for "Blackwood" Class Type 14 above.

Main engines	1 Olympus Gas Turbine; 22 500 hp 2 Proteus Gas Turbines; 6 500 hp 1 shaft; controllable pitch propeller
Speed, knots	28

GENERAL
The conversion of *Exmouth* to gas-turbine propulsion was completed in Chatham Dockyard on 20 July 1968. She was the first all gas-turbine major warship in the Royal Navy.

ENGINEERING. She can be propelled on only one system at a time, either the Olympus or the pair of Proteus engines.

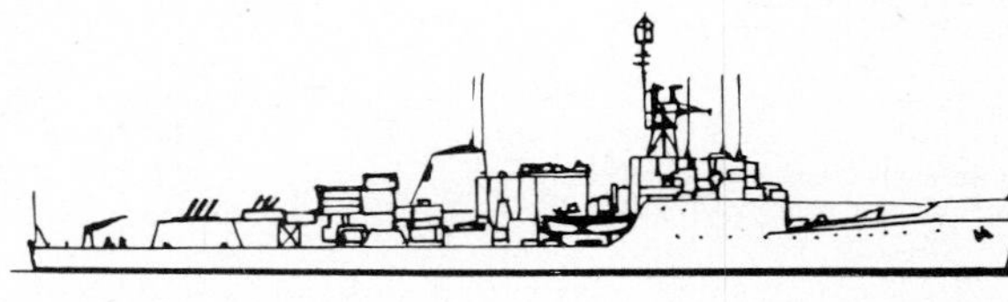

EXMOUTH 1974

EXMOUTH 1973, *C. and S. Taylor*

Frigates—*continued*

7 "TRIBAL" CLASS. TYPE 81

Name	No	Builders	Laid down	Launched	Completed
ASHANTI	F 117	Yarrow & Co Ltd, Scotstoun	15 Jan 1958	9 Mar 1959	23 Nov 1961
ESKIMO	F 119	J. Samuel White & Co Ltd, Cowes	22 Oct 1958	20 Mar 1960	21 Feb 1963
GURKHA	F 122	J. I. Thornycroft & Co Ltd, Woolston	3 Nov 1958	11 July 1960	13 Feb 1963
MOHAWK	F 125	Vickers-Armstrongs Ltd, Barrow	23 Dec 1960	5 Apr 1962	29 Nov 1963
NUBIAN	F 131	HM Dockyard, Portsmouth	7 Sep 1959	6 Sep 1960	9 Oct 1962
TARTAR	F 133	HM Dockyard, Devonport	22 Oct 1959	19 Sep 1960	26 Feb 1962
ZULU	F 124	Alex Stephen & Sons Ltd, Govan	13 Dec 1960	3 July 1962	17 Apr 1964

Displacement, tons	2 300 standard; 2 700 full load
Length, feet (*metres*)	350·0 (*106·7*)wl; 360·0 (*109·7*)oa
Beam, feet (*metres*)	42·3 (*12·9*)
Draught, feet (*metres*)	17·5 (*5·3*) max (props)
Aircraft	1 "Wasp" helicopter
Missile launchers	2 quadruple Seacats in all but *Eskimo* and *Tartar*
Guns	2—4·5 in dp (singles) 2—40 mm in non-Seacat ships 2—20 mm in others
A/S weapons	1 "Limbo" 3-barrelled DC mortar
Main engines	Combined steam and gas turbine; Metrovick steam turbine; 12 500 shp. Metrovick gas turbine; 7 500 shp; 1 shaft; 20 000 shp
Speed, knots	28
Boilers	1 Babcock & Wilcox (plus 1 auxiliary boiler)
Oil fuel, tons	400
Complement	253 (13 officers and 240 ratings)

Ashanti, Eskimo and *Gurkha* were ordered under the 1955-56 estimates, *Nubian* and *Tartar* 1956-57, and *Mohawk* and *Zulu* 1957-58 designed as self-contained units for service in such areas as the Persian Gulf. *Ashanti* cost £5 220 000.

GURKHA — *1973, C. and S. Taylor*

CONSTRUCTION. All-welded prefabrication. Denny Brown stabilisers fitted to reduce rolling in heavy seas. Enclosed bridge and twin rudders.

ELECTRICAL. Generator capacity of 1 500 kW.

ENGINEERING. The gas turbine is used to boost the steam turbines for sustained bursts of high speed and also enables the ship lying in harbour without steam up to get under way instantly in emergency. The machinery is remotely controlled. The main boiler works at a pressure of 550 psi and a temperature of 850 deg F. Five-bladed propeller, 11·75 ft diameter, 280 rpm. The forward funnel serves the boiler, the after one the gas turbine.

MOHAWK — *1972, John G. Callis*

GUNNERY. Optical Seacat directors in *Gurkha, Mohawk, Nubian* and *Zulu*.

RADAR. Search: Type 965 with single AKEI with IFF. Air and surface warning; Type 293. Fire Control; MRS 3.

SONAR. *Ashanti* and *Gurkha* were fitted with variable depth sonar equipment in the counter well in 1970, see photographs.

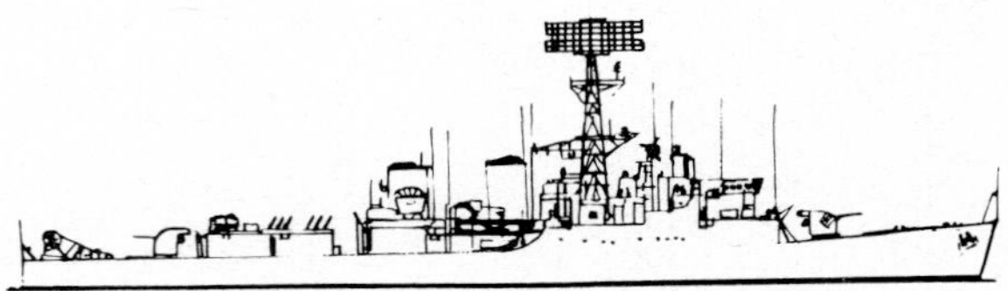
"TRIBAL" Class — *1974*

NUBIAN — *1973, C. and S. Taylor*

Frigates—*continued*

3 "LEOPARD" CLASS TYPE 41

Name	No	Builders	Laid down	Launched	Completed
JAGUAR	F 37	Wm Denny & Bros Ltd, Dumbarton	2 Nov 1953	30 July 1957	12 Dec 1959
LEOPARD	F 14	H.M. Dockyard, Portsmouth	25 Mar 1953	23 May 1955	30 Sep 1958
LYNX	F 27	John Brown & Co Ltd, Clydebank	13 Aug 1953	12 Jan 1955	14 Mar 1957

Displacement, tons	2 300 standard; 2 520 full load
Length, feet (*metres*)	320 (*97·5*) pp; 330 (*100·6*) wl; 339·8 (*103·6*) oa
Beam, feet (*metres*)	40 (*12·2*)
Draught, feet (*metres*)	16 (*4·9*)
Guns, dual purpose	4—4·5 in (*115 mm*), 2 twin turrets
Guns, AA	1—40 mm
A/S weapons	1 Squid 3-barrelled DC mortar
Main engines	8 ASR 1 diesels in three engine rooms; 14 400 bhp; 2 shafts; 4 engines geared to each shaft
Speed, knots	24
Range, miles	2 300 at full power; 7 500 at 16 knots
Oil fuel (tons)	220
Complement	235 (15 officers, 220 ratings)

Designed primarily for anti-aircraft protection. All welded. *Jaguar* and *Lynx* were ordered on 28 June 1951.– Fitted with stabilisers.

ENGINEERING. The propelling machinery comprises Admiralty Standard Range 1 diesels coupled to the propeller shafting through hydraulic gear boxes. These diesels are of light weight, about 17 lb/shp. *Jaguar* is the only ship of this class to be fitted with controllable pitch propellers, 12 ft diameter 200 rpm. The fuel tanks have a compensating system, so that sea water replaces oil fuel as it is used.

RADAR. Search: Type 965 with single AKE 1 aerial and IFF and Type 993. Fire Control: Mk 6M X-bandfire control director unit with Type 275. Type 975 nav radar. ECM and DF.

RECONSTRUCTION. *Lynx* was extensively refitted in 1963 with new mainmast. *Leopard* was similarly refitted in Oct 1964-Feb 1966, followed by *Jaguar*.

TRANSFER. Another ship of this class, *Panther*, was transferred to India while building and renamed *Brahmaputra*.

LEOPARD *1973, Wright and Logan*

JAGUAR *1973, Wright and Logan*

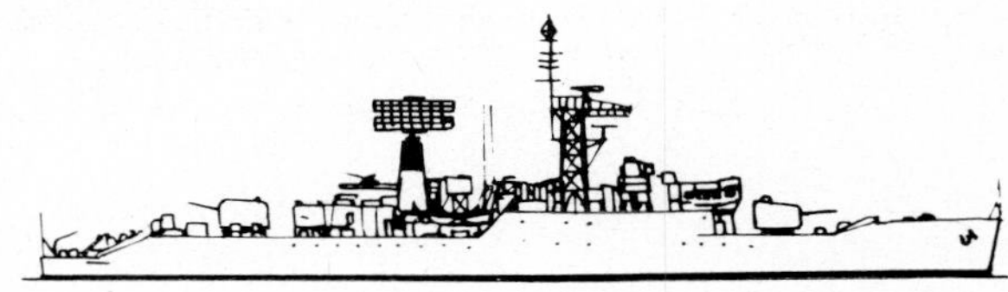

"LEOPARD" Class *1974*

LYNX

Frigates—*continued*

4 "SALISBURY" CLASS TYPE 61

Name	No.	Builders	Laid down	Launched	Completed
CHICHESTER	F 59	Fairfield SB & Eng Co Ltd, Govan	25 Jan 1953	21 Apr 1955	16 May 1958
LINCOLN	F 99	Fairfield SB & Eng Co Ltd, Govan	20 May 1955	6 Apr 1959	7 July 1960
LLANDAFF	F 61	Hawthorn Leslie Ltd, Hebburn-on-Tyne	27 Aug 1953	30 Nov 1955	11 Apr 1958
SALISBURY	F 32	HM Dockyard, Devonport	23 Jan 1952	25 June 1953	27 Feb 1957

Displacement, tons	2 170 standard; 2 408 full load
Length, feet (*metres*)	320·0 (*97·5*) pp; 330·0 (*100·6*) oa 339·8 (*103·6*) oa
Beam, feet (*metres*)	40·0 (*12·2*)
Draught, feet (*metres*)	15·5 (*4·7*) max (props)
Missile launchers	1 quadruple "Seacat" in *Lincoln* and *Salisbury* which also have 2 sextuple 3 in rocket launchers
Guns	2—4·5 in (*115 mm*) 4—40 mm (*Chichester*); 2 mm (*Llandaff*); 2—20 mm (all but *Llandaff*)
A/S weapons	1 Squid triple-barrelled DC mortar
Main engines	8 ASR 1 diesels in three engine rooms; 2 shafts; 14 400 bhp
Speed, knots	24
Range, miles	2 300 at full power; 7 500 at 16 knots
Oil fuel, tons	230
Complement	237 (14 officers and 223 ratings)

Designed primarily for the direction of carrier-borne and shore-based aircraft. Ordered on 28 June 1951 except *Salisbury*, the prototype ship. Construction was all welded and largely prefabricated. The construction of the three other ships *Exeter, Gloucester* and *Coventry* cancelled in the 1957 defence economies. Fitted with stabilisers (except *Lincoln*). Original lattice masts replaced by tower masts during 1960's.

ENGINEERING. Powered by Admiralty Standard Range 1 heavy oil engines coupled to the propeller shafts through hydraulic couplings and oil operated reverse and reduction gear boxes. *Llandaff* is the only Type 61 frigate to have a 500 kW gas-turbine alternator and three diesel generators *Lincoln* is fitted with controllable pitch propellers, rotating at 200 rpm, which are 12 feet in diameter, manufactured by Stone Marine & Engineering Co Ltd. The fuel tanks have a compensating system whereby sea water replaces oil fuel as it is consumed.

HONG KONG GUARDSHIP. In 1973 *Chichester* was re-equipped for service as permanent HK Guardship. This involved removal of Type 965, the top weight saved being used to mount extra 40 mm guns.

RADAR. Type 965 long-range surveillance with double AKE 2 with IFF (except in *Chichester*); Type 993 combined air and surface warning; Type 277 Q height finder; Type 982 high definition target indicator; Mk 6M fire control director with Type 275; GWS-22 radar director aft for Seacat (*Salisbury* and *Lincoln* only); Type 975 nav radar.

LINCOLN — *1974, Wright and Logan*

CHICHESTER as Hong Kong guardship — *1973*

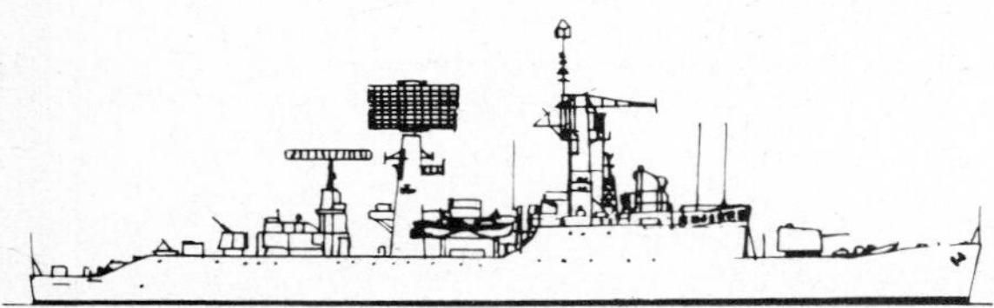

"SALISBURY" Class except *Chichester* — *1974*

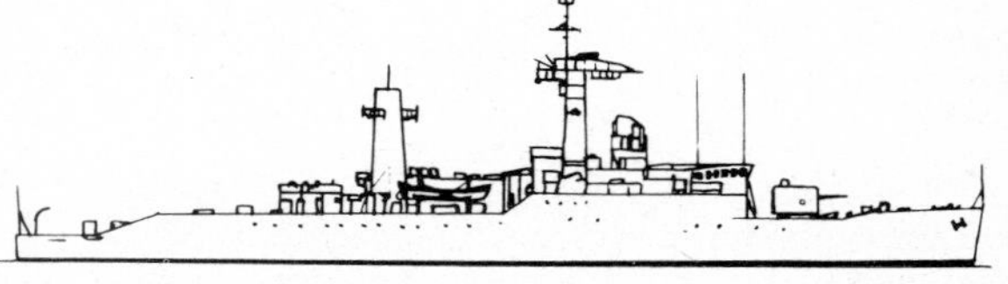

CHICHESTER — *1974*

LLANDAFF — *1973, C. and S. Taylor*

Frigates—*continued*

2 "TYPE 15"

Name	No.	Builders	Laid down	Launched	Completed
GRENVILLE	F 197	Swan, Hunter & Wigham Richardson, Ltd	1 Nov 41	12 Oct 42	27 May 43
UNDAUNTED	F 53	Cammell Laird & Co Ltd, Birkenhead	8 Sep 42	19 July 43	3 Mar 44

Displacement, tons	2 240 standard; 2 880 full load
Length, feet (*metres*)	339·5 (*103·5*) pp; 350·0 (*106·7*) wl; 362·8 (*110·6*) oa
Beam, feet (*metres*)	35·7 (*10·9*)
Draught, feet (*metres*)	17·0 (*5·2*)
Guns	2—40 mm (1 twin)
A/S weapons	2 Limbo 3-barrelled DC mortars (*Undaunted*)
Main engines	Parsons geared turbines; 2 shafts; 40 000 shp
Speed, knots	32
Boilers	2 Admiralty 3 drum; Pressure 300 psi (*21·1 kg/cm²*) Superheat 640°F (*338°C*)
Range, miles	1 300 at full power; 2 800 to 3 000 at 20 knots
Oil fuel, tons	570 to 600
Complement	195 (15 officers and 180 men)

RADAR. Search: Type 993 and Type 277 height finder (*Grenville* 978 on mainmast) ECM. DF. Nav radar 975.

These are the sole survivors of the wartime "R", "T", "U", "V", "W" and "Z" classes of destroyers, launched in 1942-43. Of the 48 ships of these classes 33 were converted into Type 15 frigates and 7 ("T" Class") into Type 16 (limited conversion) frigates. A number have been transferred to other navies and now only *Undaunted* with the 2nd Frigate Squadron and *Grenville* refitting for service as the Navigation School tender remain on the active list. *Ulster* is employed as an accommodation ship at Portsmouth and *Rapid* is on the scrap list.

UNDAUNTED *1973, Wright and Logan*

1 YARROW TYPE

Name	No.	Builders	Launched	Completed
MERMAID	F 76	Yarrow Shipbuilders & Co Ltd	29 Dec 1966	May 1973 (see *Notes*)

Displacement, tons	2 300 standard; 2 520 full load
Dimensions	320 pp; 330 wl; 339·3 oa × 40 × 12
Guns	2—4 inch (twin). 4—40 mm
A/S weapons	1 Squid
Main engines	8 Diesels; 2 shafts; 2cp. propellers
Oil fuel, tons	230
Range, miles	4 800 at 15 knots

Similar in hull and machinery to "Leopard" and "Salisbury" classes. Originally built for Ghana as a display ship for Nkrumah at a cost of £5 m. but put up for sale after his departure. She was launched without ceremony on 29 Dec 1966 and completed in 1968. She was transferred to Portsmouth dockyard in April 1972 being acquired by the Royal Navy. Refit started October 1972 at Chatham. Commissioned in Royal Navy 16 May 1973.

MERMAID *1973, MOD (N)*

SONAR TRIALS SHIP

Name	No.	Builders	Laid down	Launched	Completed	Converted
MATAPAN	D 43	John Brown, Clydebank	11 Mar 1944	30 Apr 1945	5 Sep 1947	1971-1972

Displacement, tons	3 835 full load
Length, feet (*metres*)	388 (*118·3*) oa
Beam, feet (*metres*)	40·5 (*12·3*)
Draught, feet (*metres*)	27 (*8·2*)
Boilers	2 Admiralty 3-drum; 400 psi (*28·1 kg/cm²*); (650°F (*343°C*)
Main engines	Parsons geared turbines; 50 000 shp; 2 shafts
Speed, knots	31
Range, miles	1 300 at full power; 3 000 at 20 knots; 4 400 at 12 knots
Oil fuel, tons	680

A former standard "Battle Class" destroyer which went into reserve almost immediately after being completed. Attached to the Admiralty Underwater Weapons Establishment at Portland after conversion.

CONVERSION. Taken in hand at HM Dockyard, Portsmouth in Jan 1971 for conversion into a Sonar Trials Ship. The rebuilding involved a new clipper bow, different bridge, remodelled superstructure, extension of the forecastle deck aft all the way to the counter, thus converting her into a flushdecker, adding a second funnel, and a helicopter landing deck. Commissioned 2 Feb 1973 after a £2½m conversion.

MATAPAN *1973, C. and S. Taylor*

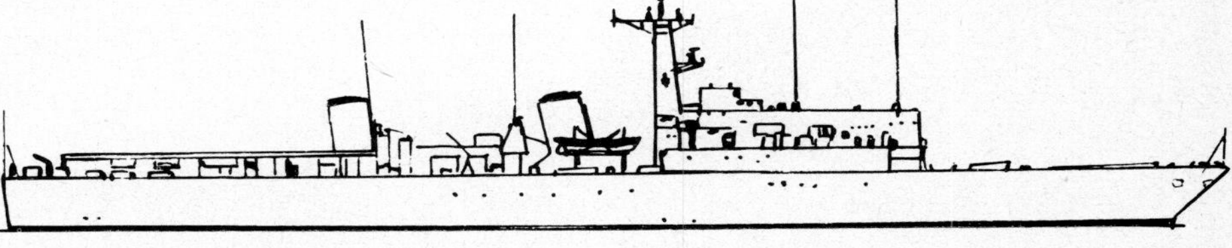

MATAPAN *1974*

SUBMARINES

Nuclear Powered Ballistic Missile Submarines (SSBN)

4 "RESOLUTION" CLASS

Name	*No.*	*Builders*	*Laid down*	*Launched*	*Completion*
RENOWN	S 26	Cammell Laird & Co Ltd, Birkenhead	25 June 1964	25 Feb 1967	15 Nov 1968
REPULSE	S 23	Vickers-Armstrongs Ltd, Barrow-in-Furness	12 Mar 1965	4 Nov 1967	28 Sept 1968
RESOLUTION	S 22	Vickers-Armstrongs Ltd, Barrow-in-Furness	26 Feb 1964	15 Sep 1966	2 Oct 1967
REVENGE	S 27	Cammell Laird & Co Ltd, Birkenhead	19 May 1965	15 Mar 1968	4 Dec 1969

Displacement, tons	7 500 surface; 8 400 submerged
Length, feet (*metres*)	360 (*109·7*) pp; 425 (*129·5*) oa
Beam, feet (*metres*)	33 (*10·1*)
Draught, feet (*metres*)	30 (*9·1*)
Missiles, surface	16 tubes amidships for "Polaris" A—3's IRBM's, range 2 500 nautical miles
Torpedo tubes	6—21 in (*533 mm*) forward
Nuclear reactors	1 pressurised water cooled
Main engines	Geared steam turbines; 1 shaft
Speed, knots	20 on surface; 25 submerged
Complement	141 (13 officers, 128 ratings); 2 crews (see *Personnel*)

In Feb 1963 it was officially stated that it was intended to order four or five 7 000 ton nuclear powered submarines, each to carry 16 "Polaris" missiles, and it was planned that the first would be on patrol in 1968. Their hulls and machinery would be of British design. As well as building two submarines Vickers-Armstrongs would give lead yard service to the builder of the other two. Four "Polaris" submarines were in fact ordered in May 1963. The plan to build a fifth Polaris submarine was cancelled on 15 Feb 1965. Britain's first SSBN *Resolution*, put to sea on 22 June 1967 and completed 6 weeks trial in the Firth of Clyde and Atlantic on 17 Aug 1967.

SONAR AND RADAR. Fitted with a large sonar array mounted in the chin position and an X band short range surveillance radar.

PERSONNEL. Each submarine, which has accommodation for 19 officers and 135 ratings is manned on a two-crew basis, in order to get maximum operational time at sea.

COST. £40 240 000, *Resolution*; £39 950 000, *Renown*; £37 500 000, *Repulse*; £38 600 000, *Revenge*; completed ships excluding missiles.

RESOLUTION *1967*

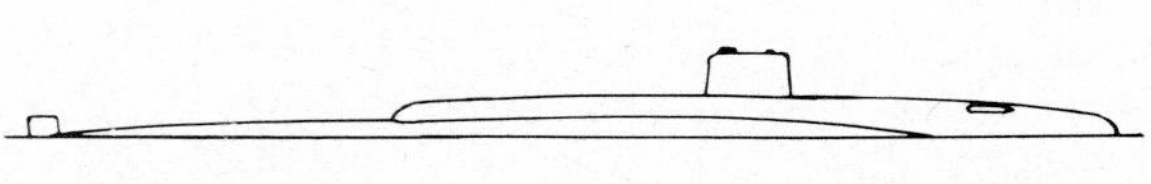

"RESOLUTION" Class *1974*

REVENGE *1971*

REPULSE ***1971***

Submarines—*continued*

Fleet Submarines

2 "VALIANT" CLASS (A)
3 "CHURCHILL" CLASS (B)
5 "SWIFTSURE" CLASS (C)

	Name	No.	Builder	Ordered	Laid down	Launched	Completed (Commissioned)
(A)	**VALIANT**	S 102	Vickers Ltd Shipbuilding Group, Barrow	31 Aug 1960	22 Jan 1962	3 Dec 1963	18 July 1966
	WARSPITE	S 103	Vickers Ltd Shipbuilding Group, Barrow	12 Dec 1962	10 Dec 1963	25 Sep 1965	18 Apr 1967
(B)	**CHURCHILL**	S 46	Vickers Ltd Shipbuilding Group, Barrow	21 Oct 1965	30 June 1967	20 Dec 1968	15 July 1970
	CONQUEROR	S 105	Cammell Laird & Co Ltd, Birkenhead	9 Aug 1966	5 Dec 1967	28 Aug 1969	9 Nov 1971
	COURAGEOUS	S 50	Vickers Ltd Shipbuilding Group, Barrow	1 Mar 1967	15 May 1968	7 Mar 1970	16 Oct 1971
(C)	**SWIFTSURE**	S 126	Vickers Ltd Shipbuilding Group, Barrow	3 Nov 1967	6 June 1969	7 Sep 1971	17 Apr 1973
	SOVEREIGN	S 108	Vickers Ltd Shipbuilding Group, Barrow	16 May 1969	18 Sep 1970	17 Feb 1973	—
	SUPERB	S 109	Vickers Ltd Shipbuilding Group, Barrow	20 May 1970	1 Jan 1971	—	—
	SCEPTRE	S 110	Vickers Ltd Shipbuilding Group, Barrow	1 Sep 1971	16 Mar 1973	—	—
	—	S 111	Vickers Ltd Shipbuilding Group, Barrow	17 Feb 1973	—	—	—

Displacement, tons	3 500 standard; 4 500 submerged
Length, feet (*metres*)	285 (*86·9*); *Swiftsure* 272·0 (*82·9*)
Beam, feet (*metres*)	33·2 (*10·1*)
Draught, feet (*metres*)	27 (*8·2*)
Torpedo tubes	6—21 in (*533 mm*) homing; *Swiftsure* 5—21 in
Nuclear reactors	1 pressurised water-cooled
Main engines	EE Geared steam turbines; 1 shaft
Speed, knots	30 approx
Complement	103 (13 officers, 90 men) 97 (12 and 85) in *Swiftsure* class

CHURCHILL, CONQUEROR, VALIANT, WARSPITE

It was announced on 31 Aug 1960 that the contract for a second nuclear powered submarine (*Valiant*) had been awarded to Vickers-Armstrong (Shipbuilders) Ltd, the principal sub-contractors being Vickers-Armstrong (Engineers) Ltd, for the machinery and its installation, and Rolls Royce and Associates for the nuclear steam raising plant. The class, of which she is the first, is broadly of the same design as that of *Dreadnought*, but slightly larger. She was originally scheduled to be completed in Sep 1965, but work was held up by the "Polaris" programme. All the above boats will be in service by end-1977 on present plans.

SONAR AND RADAR. Fitted with a large sonar array mounted in the "chin" position around the bow. Also fitted with X band short range surveillance radar.

ENDURANCE. On 25 Apr 1967 *Valiant* completed the 12 000-mile homeward voyage from Singapore, the record submerged passage by a British submarine, after 28 days non-stop.

ENGINEERING. *Valiant's* reactor core was made in Great Britain, with machinery of British design and manufacture similar to the shore prototype installed in the Admiralty Reactor Test Establishment at Dounreay. The main steam turbines and condensers were designed and manufactured by the English Electric Company, Rugby, and the electrical propulsion machinery and control gear by Laurence, Scott & Electromotors Ltd.

CONQUEROR

VALIANT *1974, Wright and Logan*

Submarines—*continued*

1 "DREADNOUGHT" CLASS (FLEET SUBMARINE)

Name	*No.*	*Builders*	*Engineers*	*Laid down*	*Launched*	*Commissioned*
DREADNOUGHT	S 101	Vickers-Armstrongs, Barrow	Rolls-Royce and Westinghouse	12 June 1959	21 Oct 1960	17 Apr 1963

Displacement, tons	3 000 standard; 3 500 surface; 4 000 submerged
Length, feet (*metres*)	265·8 (*81·0*)
Beam, feet (*metres*)	32·2 (*9·8*)
Draught, feet (*metres*)	26 (*7·9*)
Torpedo tubes	6—21 in (*533 mm*) bow, all internal
Nuclear reactor	1 S5W pressurised water-cooled
Main engines	Geared steam turbines; 1 shaft
Speed, knots	30 approx
Complement	88 (11 officers, 77 men)

As originally planned *Dreadnought* was to have been fitted with a British designed and built nuclear reactor, but in 1958 an agreement was concluded with the United States Government for the purchase of a complete set of propulsion machinery of the type fitted in USS *Skipjack*. This agreement enabled the submarine to be launched far earlier. The supply of this machinery was made under a contract between the Westinghouse Electric Corporation and Rolls-Royce. The latter were also supplied with design and manufacturing details of the reactor and with safety information and set up a factory in this country to manufacture similar cores. *Dreadnought* has a hull of British design both as regards structural strength and hydrodynamic features, although the latter are based on the pioneering work of the US Navy in *Skipjack* and *Albacore*. From about amidships aft, the hull lines closely resemble *Skipjack* to accommodate the propulsion machinery. The forward end is wholly British in concept. In the Control Room and Attack Centre the instruments are fitted into consoles.

The improved water distilling plant for the first time provides unlimited fresh water for shower baths and for washing machines in the fully equipped laundry.

She is fitted with an inertial navigation system and with means of measuring her depth below ice and was the first British submarine to surface at the North Pole in 1970.

SONAR AND RADAR. Fitted with a large sonar array mounted in the "chin" position around the bow. Also fitted with X band short range surveillance radar.

DREADNOUGHT *1971, C. and S. Taylor*

Patrol Submarines

1 "A" CLASS

Name	*No*	*Builders*	*Laid down*	*Launched*	*Completed*
ANDREW	S 63	Vickers-Armstrongs Ltd. Barrow	13 Aug 1945	6 Apr 1946	16 Mar 1948

Displacement, tons	1 120 standard; 1 385 surface; 1 620 submerged
Dimensions, feet	283 × 22·2 × 17·1
Torpedo tubes	6—21 in (*533 mm*) internal, 4 bow 2 stern; 16 torpedoes carried
Main machinery	2 8-cyl diesels; 4 300 bhp 2 electric motors, 1 250 hp
Speed, knots	19 on surface, 8 submerged
Complement	60 to 68 (5 officers, 63 men)

Only survivor of a class of fifteen. These submarines were originally designed for service in the Pacific. Construction was entirely welded. Streamlined fin fitted in late 1950's.

SLAM. *Aeneas* of this class was hired by Vickers in July 1972 for most successful trials of SLAM anti-helicopter weapon.

SONAR AND RADAR. Fitted with sonar array on Fore casing. Fitted with X Band surveillance radar.

ANDREW with gun in Far East *1968, MOD (N)*

Submarines—*continued*

Patrol Submarines

13 "OBERON" CLASS
8 "PORPOISE" CLASS

Displacement, tons	1 610 standard; 2 030 surface; 2 410 submerged
Length, feet (*metres*)	241 (*73·5*) pp; 295·2 (*90·0*) oa
Beam, feet (*metres*)	26·5 (*8·1*)
Draught, feet (*metres*)	18 (*5·5*)
Torpedo tubes	8—21 in (*533 mm*) 6 bow 2 stern; 30 torpedoes carried
Main machinery	2 ASR 1, 16 VMS diesels; 3 680 bhp; 2 electric motors; 6 000 shp; 2 shafts;
Speed, knots	12 surface, 17 submerged
Complement	68 (6 officers, 62 men) 71 (6 officers, 65 men) in "Porpoise" class

"OBERON" CLASS

Name	*No.*	*Builders*	*Laid down*	*Launched*	*Completed*
OBERON	S 09	H.M. Dockyard, Chatham	28 Nov 1957	18 July 1959	24 Feb 1961
OCELOT	S 17	H.M. Dockyard, Chatham	17 Nov 1960	5 May 1962	31 Jan 1964
ODIN	S 10	Cammell Laird & Co Ltd, Birkenhead	27 Apr 1959	4 Nov 1960	3 May 1962
OLYMPUS	S 12	Vickers-Armstrongs Ltd, Barrow	4 Mar 1960	14 June 1961	7 July 1962
ONSLAUGHT	S 14	H.M. Dockyard, Chatham	8 Apr 1959	24 Sep 1960	14 Aug 1962
ONYX	S 21	Cammell Laird & Co Ltd, Birkenhead	16 Nov 1964	18 Aug 1966	20 Nov 1967
OPOSSUM	S 19	Cammell Laird & Co Ltd, Birkenhead	21 Dec 1961	23 May 1963	5 June 1964
OPPORTUNE	S 20	Scotts' S.B. & Eng Co Ltd, Greenock	26 Oct 1962	14 Feb 1964	29 Dec 1964
ORACLE	S 16	Cammell Laird & Co Ltd, Birkenhead	26 Apr 1960	26 Sep 1961	14 Feb 1963
ORPHEUS	S 11	Vickers-Armstrongs Ltd, Barrow	16 Apr 1959	17 Nov 1959	25 Nov 1960
OSIRIS	S 13	Vickers-Armstrongs Ltd, Barrow	26 Jan 1962	29 Nov 1962	11 Jan 1964
OTTER	S 15	Scotts' S.B. & Eng Co Ltd, Greenock	14 Jan 1960	15 May 1961	20 Aug 1962
OTUS	S 18	Scotts' S.B. & Eng Co Ltd, Greenock	31 May 1961	17 Oct 1962	5 Oct 1963

"PORPOISE" CLASS

Name	*No*	*Builders*	*Laid down*	*Launched*	*Completed*
CACHALOT	S 06	Scotts S.B. & Eng Co Ltd, Greenock	1 Aug 1955	11 Dec 1957	1 Sep 1959
FINWHALE	S 05	Cammell Laird & Co Ltd, Birkenhead	18 Sep 1956	21 July 1959	19 Aug 1960
GRAMPUS	S 04	Cammell Laird & Co Ltd, Birkenhead	16 Apr 1955	30 May 1957	19 Dec 1958
NARWHAL	S 03	Vickers-Armstrongs Ltd, Barrow	15 Mar 1956	25 Oct 1957	4 May 1959
PORPOISE	S 01	Vickers-Armstrongs Ltd, Barrow	15 June 1954	25 Apr 1956	17 Apr 1958
RORQUAL	S 02	Vickers-Armstrongs Ltd, Barrow	15 Jan 1955	5 Dec 1956	24 Oct 1958
SEALION	S 07	Cammell Laird & Co Ltd, Birkenhead	5 June 1958	31 Dec 1959	25 July 1961
WALRUS	S 08	Scotts' S.B. & Eng Co Ltd, Greenock	12 Feb 1958	22 Sep 1959	10 Feb 1961

CONSTRUCTION. For the first time in British submarines plastic was used in the superstructure construction of the Oberon class. Before and abaft the bridge the superstructure is mainly of glass fibre laminate in most units of this class. The superstructure of *Orpheus* is of light alloy aluminium.

RCN. The submarine of the Oberon class laid down on 27 Sep 1962 at HM Dockyard, Chatham, as *Onyx* for the Royal Navy was launched on 29 Feb 1964 as *Ojibwa* for the Royal Canadian Navy. She was replaced by another "Oberon" class submarine named *Onyx* for the Royal Navy built by Cammell Laird, Birkenhead.

SONAR AND RADAR. Fitted with sonar with bow dome; and X Band surveillance radar.

GUNNERY. "O" class submarines serving in the Far East carried an Oerlikon gun during Indonesian Confrontation.

MODIFICATION. *Oberon* has been modified with deeper casing to house equipment for the initial training of personnel for nuclear powered submarines. Others of of this class are currently undergoing modification.

ONSLAUGHT — *1973, Wright and Logan*

GRAMPUS — *1973, Wright and Logan*

OBERON — *1973*

WALRUS — *1973, John G. Callis*

AMPHIBIOUS WARFARE SHIPS

Name	*Dock Letter*	*No.*	*Builders*	*Laid down*	*Launched*	*Completed*
HERMES (ex-*Elephant*)	H	R 12	Vickers-Armstrongs, Barrow-in-Furness	21 June 1944	16 Feb 1953	18 Nov 1959

Displacement, tons	23 900 standard; 28 700 full load
Length, feet (*metres*)	650·0 (*198·1*) pp; 744·3 (*226·9*) oa
Beam, feet (*metres*)	90·0 (*27·4*) hull
Draught, feet (*metres*)	29·0 (*8·8*)
Width, feet (*metres*)	160·0 (*48·8*) overall
Aircraft	20 Wessex Sea King, and Sioux helicopters
Armour	Reinforced flight deck
Missiles	2 quadruple Seacat launchers either side abaft the after lift
Boilers	4 Admiralty 3-drum type
Main engines	Parsons geared turbines; 2 shafts; 76 000 shp
Speed, knots	28
Oil fuel, tons	3 880 furnace; 320 diesel;
Complement	980 plus Commando of 750. In emergency a second commando can be embarked

HERMES *1973, C. and S. Taylor*

Originally name ship of a class including *Albion*, *Bulwark* and *Centaur*, but design was modified to a more advanced type, incorporating new equipment and improved arrangements, including five post-war developments—angled deck, steam catapult, landing sight, 3-D radar, and deck edge-lift. Air-conditioned. Embarked air squadrons and joined the Fleet summer 1960. Long refit 1964 to 1966, costing £10 000 000.

CONVERSION. *Hermes* was taken in hand for conversion to a Commando Carrier on 1 Mar 1971, commissioning for this role on 17 Aug 1973. Fixed wing facilities such as catapults and arrester gear were removed. The whole performance cost over £25 million. Although she retains a STOL/VTOL capability:

FLIGHT DECK. Angled 6·5 deg off centre line of ship, the biggest angle that could be contrived in an aircraft carrier of the size. Strengthened to take Harrier aircraft.

RADAR. Type 984; Type 992Q; GWS-22 for Seacat; Tacan beacon.

HERMES *1973, Wright and Logan*

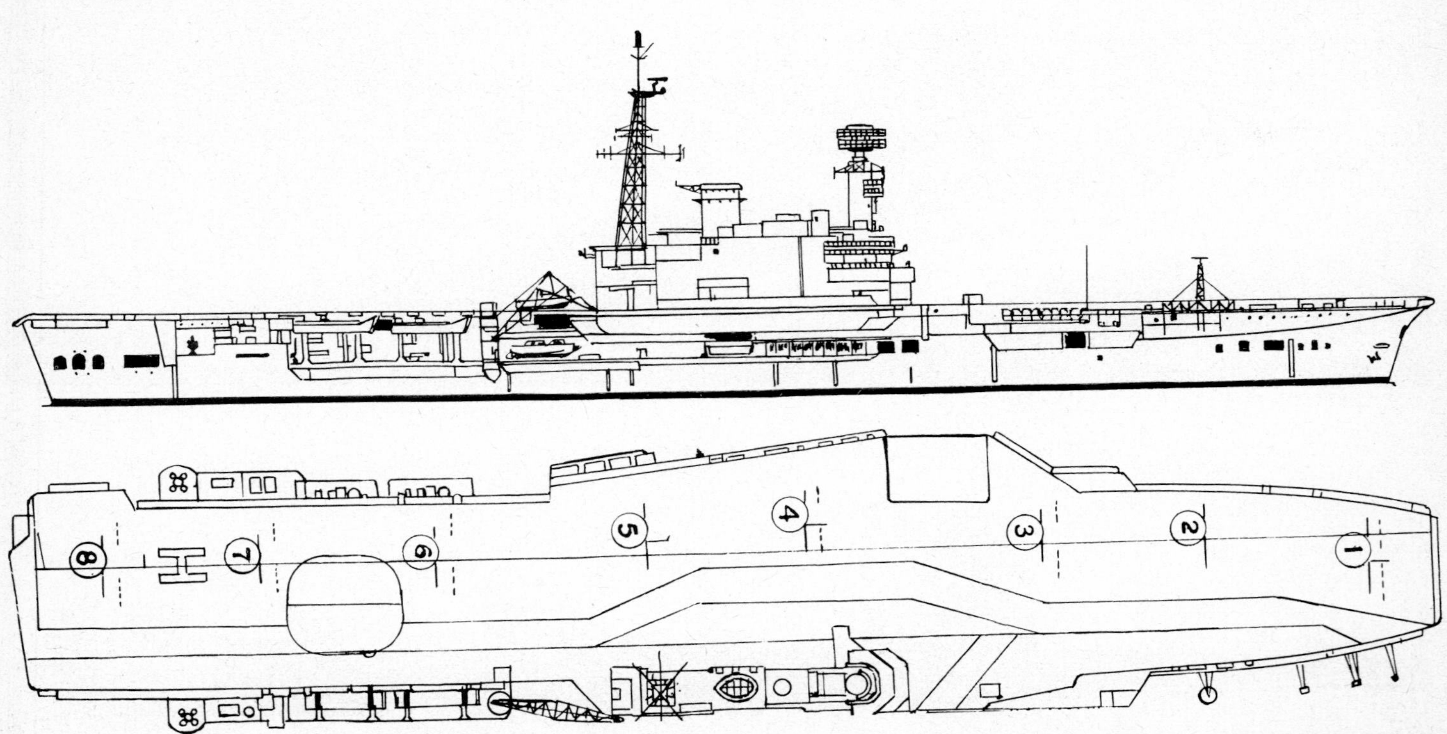

HERMES *1974*

Amphibious Warfare Ships—*continued*

Name	*Deck Letter*	*No.*	*Builders*	*Laid down*	*Launched*	*Completed*	*Converted*
BULWARK	B	R 08	Harland & Wolff Ltd, Belfast	10 May 1945	22 June 1948	4 Nov 1954	1959-60

Displacement, tons 23 300 standard; 27 705 full load
Length, feet (*metres*) 650 (*198·1*) pp; 737·8 (*224·9*) oa
Beam, feet (*metres*) 90 (*27·4*) hull
Draught, feet (*metres*) 28 (*8·5*)
Width, feet (*metres*) 123·5 (*37·7*) overall
Aircraft 20 Wessex and Sioux helicopters
Landing craft 4 LCVP
Guns 8—40 mm (twins) Bofors Mk V
Boilers 4 Admiralty 3 drum
Main engines Parsons geared turbines 76 000 shp; 2 shafts
Speed, knots 28
Oil fuel, tons 3 880 furnace; 320 diesel
Complement 980 plus 750 Royal Marine Commando and troops

GENERAL

Former fixed-wing aircraft carrier. Converted into commando ship in Portsmouth Dockyard, Jan 1959 to Jan 1960. A full strength commando is available, which the ship can quickly transport and land with equipment. Their helicopters can disembark the commando's vehicles. The ship has sufficient stores and fuel to support the commandos in operations ashore.

ENGINEERING. The three-bladed propellers in *Bulwark* were replaced by four-bladed propellers. Propeller diameter 15·5 feet. At 28 knots the propellers work at 230 rpm.

CONVERSION. Basically *Bulwark* was not changed during her initial conversion, although the fixed wing capability, arrester wires and catapults were removed. Alterations and modifications were made to render the ship suitable as an all-helicopter troop carrier with 16 Westland Whirlwind aircraft, replaced at a later date by the Wessex, and four landing craft (vehicle or personnel).

RADAR. Search: Type 293; Aircraft Direction: Type 982, Type 983.

BULWARK 1973, C. and S. Taylor

BULWARK 1972, MOD (N)

BULWARK with Harriers on deck 1973, C. and S. Taylor

DRAWING. Starboard elevation and plan of *Albion*. Drawn in 1972. Scale: 87 feet = 1 inch

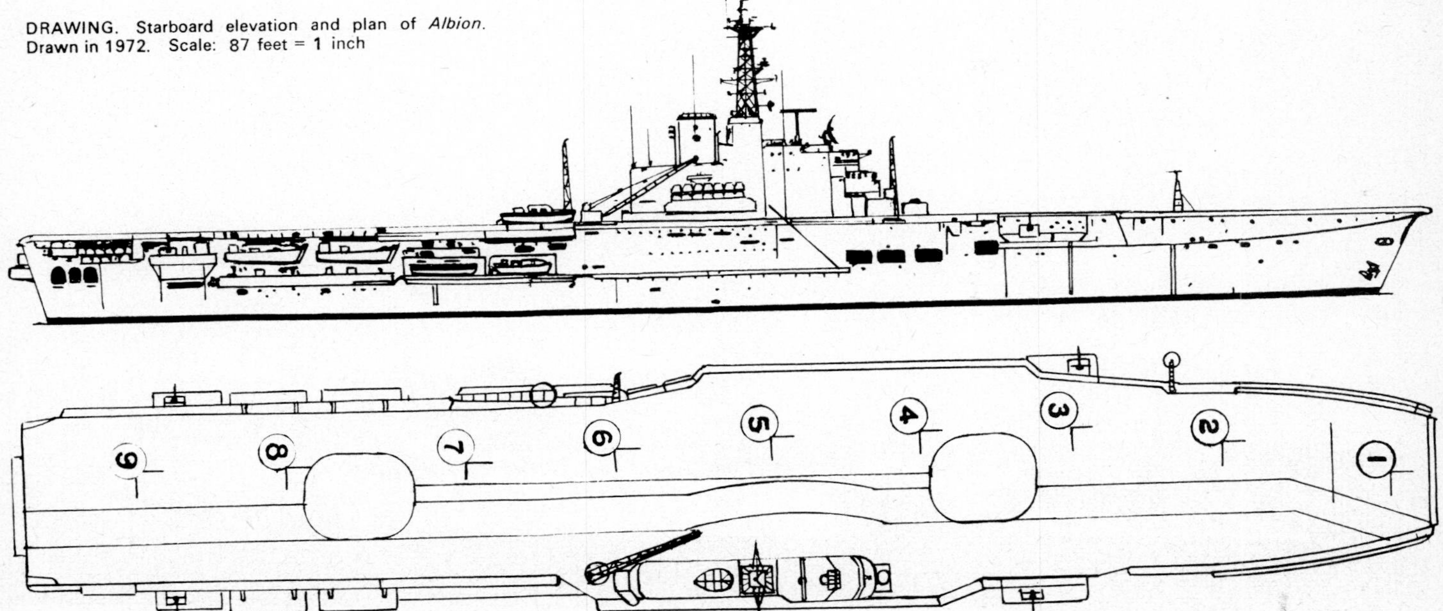

Amphibious Warfare Ships—*continued*

2 ASSAULT SHIPS (LPD)

Name	*No*	*Builders*	*Ordered*	*Laid down*	*Launched*	*Completed*
FEARLESS	L 10 (ex-L 3004)	Harland & Wolff Ltd, Belfast	1 Dec 1961	25 July 1962	19 Dec 1963	25 Nov 1965
INTREPID	L 11 (ex-L 3005)	John Brown & Co. (Clydebank) Ltd	1 May 1962	19 Dec 1962	25 June 1964	11 Mar 1967

Displacement, tons	11 060 standard; 12 120 full load 16 950 ballasted
Length, feet (*metres*)	500 (*152·4*) wl; 520 (*158·5*) oa
Beam, feet (*metres*)	80 (*24·4*)
Draught, feet (*metres*)	20·5 (*6·2*)
Draught, ballasted	32 (*9·8*) aft, 23 (*7·0*) fwd; 27·5 (*8·4*) mean
Landing craft	4 LCM(9) in dock; 4 LCVP at davits
Vehicles	*Specimen load:* 15 tanks, 7 three-ton and 20 quarter-ton trucks (20 three tonners on flight deck)
Aircraft	Flight deck facilities for 5 Wessex helicopters
Missiles, AA	4 "Seacat" systems
Guns, AA	2—40 mm Bofors
Boilers	2 Babcock & Wilcox
Main engines	2 EE turbines 22 000 shp; 2 shafts
Speed, knots	21
Range, miles	5 000 at 20 knots
Complement	580 (see Troops note)

These assault ships, with commando carriers, replace the former ships of the Amphibious Warfare Squadron. They carry landing craft which are floated through the open stern by flooding compartments of the ship and lowering her in the water; are able to deploy tanks, vehicles and men; have seakeeping qualities much superior to those of tank landing ships, and greater speed and range. Capable of operating independently. Another valuable feature is a helicopter platform which is also the deckhead of the dock from which the landing craft are floated out. Officially estimated building cost: *Fearless* £11 250 000; *Intrepid* £10 300 000.

ELECTRICAL. Power at 440V 60 c/s 3-phase a.c. is supplied by four 1 000 kW AE1 turbo-alternators.

ENGINEERING. The two funnels are staggered across the beam of the ship, indicating that the engines and boilers are arranged *en echelon*, two machinery spaces having one turbine and one boiler installed in each space. The turbines were manufactured by the English Electric Co Rugby, the gearing by David Brown & Co, Huddersfield. Boilers work at a pressure of 550 lbs per sq in and a temperature of 850 deg F. Two 5-bladed propellers, 12·5 feet diameter, 200 rpm in *Fearless*.

OPERATIONAL. Each ship is fitted out as a Naval Assault Group/Brigade Headquarters with an assault Operations Room from which naval and military personnel, can mount and control the progress of an assault operation.

RADAR. Fitted with type 993 air and surface warning radar.

SATELLITE SYSTEM. The Royal Navy fitted its first operational satellite communications system in *Intrepid* in 1969, the contract having been awarded to Plessey Radar —now removed.

TRAINING. *Intrepid* used for the sea training of officers from the Britannia Royal Naval College, Dartmouth. When *Intrepid* is refitting *Fearless* will take over. Both retain full amphibious capabilities.

TROOPS. Each ship can carry 380 to 400 troops at ship's company standards, and an overload of 700 marines and military personnel can be accommodated for short periods.

FEARLESS 1972

INTREPID 1973, C. and S. Taylor

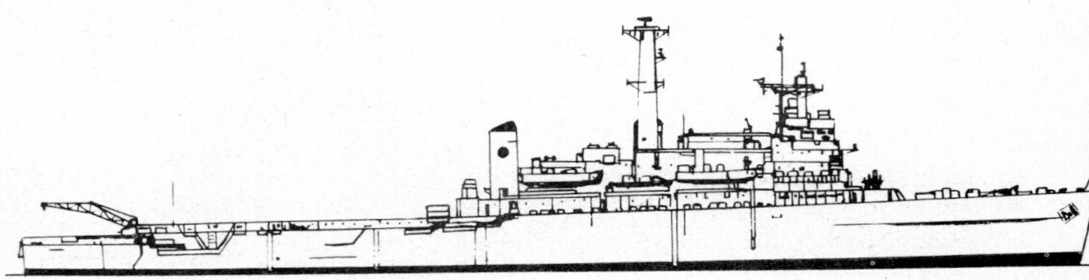

FEARLESS, INTREPID 1974

INTREPID flooded down 1973, C. and S. Taylor

Amphibious Warfare Ships—*continued*

6 LOGISTIC LANDING SHIPS

(RFA MANNED)

Name	No.	Builder	Laid down	Launched	Completed
SIR LANCELOT	L 3029	Fairfield	Mar 1962	June 1963	Jan 1964
SIR GALAHAD	L 3005	Alex Stephen	Feb 1965	19 Apr 1966	17 Dec 1966
SIR GERAINT	L 3027	Alex Stephen	June 1965	26 Jan 1967	12 July 1967
SIR BEDIVERE	L 3004	Hawthorn Leslie	Oct 1965	20 July 1966	18 May 1967
SIR PERCIVAL	L 3036	Hawthorn Leslie	Apr 1966	4 Oct 1967	23 Mar 1968
SIR TRISTRAM	L 3505	Hawthorn Leslie	Feb 1966	12 Dec 1966	14 Sep 1967

Displacement, tons	3 270 light; 5 674 full load (3 370 and 5 550 in *Sir Lancelot*)
Dimensions, feet	366·3 pp; 412·1 oa × 59·8 × 13·0
Aircraft	Can carry 20 Wessex helicopters
Guns	Fitted for 2—40 mm—not normally carried
Main engines	2 Mirrlees Diesels; 9 400 bhp; 2 shafts; (2 Denny/Sulzer diesels; 9 520 bhp in *Sir Lancelot*)
Speed, knots	17
Oil fuel, tons	815
Range, miles	8 000 at 15 knots
Complement	68 (18 officers, 50 ratings)
Military lift	340

SIR LANCELOT — *1973, John G. Callis*

GENERAL
Sir Lancelot was the prototype of this class which was originally built for the Army but transferred to RFA in Jan and Mar 1970. Fitted for bow and stern loading with drive-through facilities and deck-to-deck ramps. Facilities provided for on-board maintenance of vehicles and for laying out pontoon equipment.

AIRCRAFT. Helicopters can be operated from the well-deck and the after platform by day or night in the later ships. In *Sir Lancelot* well-deck operations are limited to fair weather-day conditions. If required to carry helicopters 11 can be stowed on the Tank Deck and 9 on the Vehicle Deck.

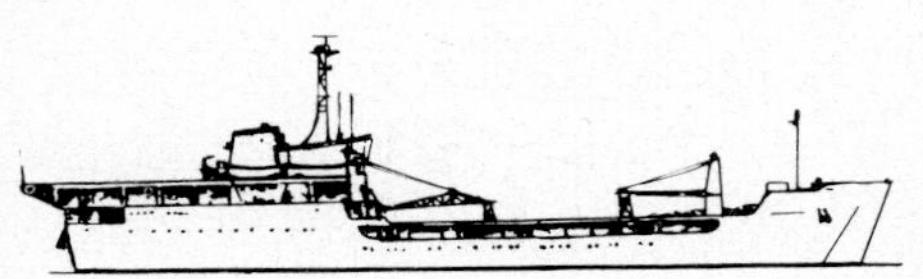

LSL — *1973*

SIR TRISTRAM — *1973, John G. Callis*

14 LCM (9) TYPE

LCM (9) 700	**LCM (9) 703**	**LCM (9) 706**	**LCM (9) 710**
LCM (9) 701	**LCM (9) 704**	**LCM (9) 707**	**LCM (9) 711**
LCM (9) 702	**LCM (9) 705**	**LCM (9) 708**	**LCM (9) 3507**
		LCM (9) 709	**LCM (9) 3508**

Displacement, tons	75 light; 176 loaded
Dimensions, feet	77 pp; 85 oa × 21·5 × 5·5
Capacity	2 battle tanks or 100 tons of vehicles
Main engines	2 Paxman 6 cyl. YHXAM diesels; 2 shafts; 624 bhp = 10 knots. Screws enclosed in Kort nozzles to improve manoeuvrability.

LCM (9) 3507 and LCM (9) 3508 were the first operational minor landing craft to be built since the Second World War. Ramped in the traditional manner forward, a completely enclosed radar-fitted wheelhouse is positioned aft. Upon completion they carried out familiarisation trials to perfect the new techniques required in launching and recovering LCMs from the flooded sterns of the parent assault ships. Four each of the 700 Series allocated to assault ships.

L 705 (F2) — *1972, A. & J. Pavia*

2 LCM (7) 7,000 SERIES (and NSB)

Displacement, tons	28 light; 63 loaded
Dimensions, feet	60·2 × 16 × 3·7
Main Engines	290 bhp = 9·8 knots

Nos. 7037, 7100. Three are employed as naval servicing boats and store carriers: 7037 (NSB 351), 7100 (NSB 359), 7104 (NSB 358). Some of the LCM (7) type were re-engined with Gray Marine diesels. 7087 and 7104 were removed from the list in 1968 and 7016 in 1969.

26 LCVP 100 SERIES

Displacement, tons	8·5 light; 13·5 full load; LCVP (ex-LCA (2)s 11·5 light 16 full load
Dimensions, feet	41·5 LCVP (2)s; 43 × 10 × 2·5
Main engines	130 bhp = 8 knots; LCVP (2)s: 2 Foden diesels, 200 bhp 10 knots

There are 12 LCVP (1)s Nos between Nos 102 and 136 and 14 LCVP (2)s, Nos 137 to 150. There were also a number of variations and prototypes of about the same length (43 feet).
Raiding Landing Craft, including LCR 5507 and 5508, and Navigational Landing Craft, including LCN 604 (ex-LCR 5505). LCA (1) 1275, 1330 1481, 1485, 1644 1678, 1705, 1712. 1733, 1745, 1779, and 1787 were for disposal in 1961, eleven more in 1963, and 1272, 1543, 1639, 1972 and 1891 in 1964, 1485 and 1700 in 1968. LCVP (2)s carried by *Intrepid* and *Fearless* can carry 35 troops or 2 Land Rovers. Crew 4. LCA (2)s were redesignated LCVPs (Landing Craft Vehicle and Personnel) in 1966.

2 LCP (L) 3 500 SERIES

Displacement, tons	6·5 light; 10 loaded
Dimensions, feet	37 × 11 × 3·2
Main engines	225 bhp = 12 knots

There are two LCP (L) 3s Nos 501 and 503. Aurora gas turbines were installed in LCP (L) 3 No. 502.

NOTE. Five LCT (8)'s operated by the Royal Corps of Transport are listed under auxiliaries.

1 "LST" (3) CLASS

EMPIRE GULL (ex-*Trouncer*) L 2523

Measurements, tons	4 257·9 gross
Dimensions, feet	347 × 54·1 × 12
Main engines	2 Triple Expansion; 2 shafts; 5 500 shp
Boilers	2 Water Tube
Oil fuel	950 tons
Complement	63 officers and men
Troop accommodation	8 officers, 72 ORs

Launched 9 July 1945. In commission until Oct 1974 at least.

MINE WARFARE FORCES

ABDIEL N 21

Displacement, tons	1 375 standard; 1 500 full load
Dimensions, feet	244·5 pp; 265 oa × 38·5 × 10
Mines	44 carried
Main engines	2 Paxman Ventura 16 cyl pressure charged diesels; 1 250 rpm; 2 690 bhp = 16 knots
Complement	77

Exercise minelayer ordered in June 1965 from John I. Thornycroft & Co Ltd, Woolston, Southampton. Laid down on 23 May 1966. Launched on 27 Jan 1967. Completed on 17 Oct 1967. Main machinery manufactured by Davey Paxman, Colchester. Main gearing supplied by Messrs Wisemans. Her function is to support mine counter-measure forces, maintain these forces when they are operating away from their shore bases, and lay exercise mines. Cost £1 500 000.

ABDIEL *1967, MOD (N)*

NEW GRP MCM VESSELS

A new class of MCM Vessels is still in the design stage—a contract is being negotiated with Vosper-Thornycroft. The cost of these ships is likely to be in the region of £4-5 million.

Artists Impression of new MCMV *1973, MOD (N)*

WILTON M 1116

Displacement, tons	450 standard
Dimensions, feet	153·0 oa × 28·8 × 8·5
Main engines	2 English Electric Deltic 18 diesels; 2 shafts; 3 000 bhp = 16 knots estimated max
Guns	1—40 mm Mark VII
Cost	£2 000 000
Complement	37 (5 officers and 32 ratings)

The world's first GRP warship. Contract signed on 11 Feb 1970. Laid down 16 Nov 1970. Launched on 18 Jan 1972 and commissioned 14 July 1973. Prototype built of glass reinforced plastic to the existing minehunter design by Vosper Thornycroft at Woolston. Similar to the "Ton" class and fitted with reconditioned machinery and equipment from the scrapped *Derriton*.

WILTON *1973, MOD (N)*

Mine Warfare Forces —*continued*

38 "TON" CLASS

16 MINEHUNTERS

BILDESTON	M 1110	**HUBBERSTON**	M 1147
BOSSINGTON	M 1133	**IVESTON**	M 1151
BRERETON	M 1113	**KEDLESTON**	M 1153
BRINTON	M 1114	**KELLINGTON**	M 1154
BRONINGTON	M 1115	**KIRKLISTON**	M 1157
GAVINTON	M 1140	**MAXTON**	M 1165
GLASSERTON	M 1141	**SHERATON**	M 1181
HIGHBURTON	M 1130	**SHOULTON**	M 1182

11 MINESWEEPERS—COASTAL

ASHTON	M 1198	**NURTON**	M 1166
CHAWTON	M 1209	**SHAVINGTON**	M 1180
CUXTON	M 1125	**SOBERTON**	M 1200
LALESTON	M 1158	**UPTON**	M 1187
LEWISTON	M 1208	**WALKERTON**	M 1188
		WOTTON	M 1195

11 MINESWEEPERS—COASTAL (RNR)

CLYDE (ex-*Repton*)	M 1167	**NORTHUMBRIA** (ex-*Wiston*)	M 1204
CURZON (ex-*Fittleton*)	M 1136	**ST DAVID** (ex-*Crichton*)	M 1124
KILLIECRANKIE (ex-*Bickington*)	M 1109	**SOLENT** (ex-*Crofton*)	M 1216
KILMOREY (ex-*Alfriston*)	M 1103	**THAMES** (ex-*Woolaston*)	M 1194
MERSEY (ex-*Pollington*)	M 1173	**VENTURER** (ex-*Hodgeston*)	M 1146
MONTROSE (ex-*Stubbington*)	M 1204		

Displacement, tons	360 standard; 425 full load
Dimensions, feet	140·0 pp; 153·0 oa × 28·8 × 8·2
Guns	Vary in different ships, some sweepers having no 40 mm, some 1—40 mm whilst hunters have 1 or 2—40 mm; 2—20 mm
Main engines	2 diesels; 2 shafts; 2 500 bhp (JVSS 12 Mirrlees), 3 000 bhp (18A-7A Deltic) = 15 knots; see *Engineering*
Oil fuel, tons	45
Range, miles	2 300 at 13 knots
Complement	29 (38 in minehunters, 5 officers and 33 ratings)

The survivors of a class of 118 built between 1953 and 1960, largely as a result of lessons from the Korean War. John I. Thornycroft & Co Ltd, Southampton were the lead yard for these ships which have double mahogany hull and incorporate a considerable amount of non-magnetic material. Fitted with Vospers stabilisers. The majority has now been fitted with nylon in place of copper sheathing.
APPEARANCE. Enclosed bridges in *Ashton, Bossington, Bronington, Chawton, Clyde, Gavinton, Hubberston, Kedleston, Maxton, Mersey, Montrose, Northumbria, Nurton, Sheraton, Shoulton, Soberton, Walkerton.*

CONVERSIONS. *Beachampton, Monkton, Wasperton, Wolverton,* and *Yarnton* were converted into coastal patrol vessels late in 1971, (see Light Forces). *Laleston* was converted into diving trials ship in 1966-67.

ENGINEERING. Earlier vessels had Mirrlees diesels, but later units had Napier Deltic lightweight diesels. *Highburton,* the first with Deltic diesels, was accepted on 21 Apr 1955. All minehunters have Deltics and active rudders. Generators for electrical power are in a separate engine room. Three-bladed propellers, 6 ft diameter, 400 rpm. *Shoulton,* refitted 1965-67, has pump-jet propulsion.

MINEHUNTERS. *Shoulton* was the first fitted with British Type 193 mine-hunting equipment, *Glasserton* is fitted with derricks for Osbourne sweep.

ROYAL NAVAL RESERVE. Eleven units were renamed and attached to Royal Naval Reserve Division Headquarters as follows (Division under *Name*):—

Thames	*Curzon*	*Solent*	*Venturer*	*St. David*	*Mersey*
London	Sussex	Solent	Severn	S. Wales	Mersey
Kilmorey	*Clyde*	*Montrose*	*Killiecrankie*	*Northumbria*	
Ulster	Clyde	Tay	Forth	Tyne	

TRANSFERS. Argentine (6 in 1968), Australia (6 in 1962), Ghana (1 in 1964), India (4 in 1956), Ireland (3 in 1971), Malaysia (7 in 1960-68), South Africa (10 in 1958-59).

BOSSINGTON *1973, C. and S. Taylor*

LEWISTON, MINESWEEPER *1973, Wright and Logan*

MONTROSE RNR MINESWEEPER *1973, Wright and Logan*

4 "HAM" CLASS (MINESWEEPERS—INSHORE)

ARLINGHAM	M 2603
DITTISHAM	M 2621
FLINTHAM	M 2628
THORNHAM (ABERDEEN)	M 2793

Displacement, tons	120 standard; 159 full load
Dimensions, feet	2601 Series; 100 pp; 106·5 oa × 21·2 × 5·5 2793 100 p ; 107·5 oa × 22 × 5·8
Gun	1—20 mm Oerlikon AA forward
Main engines	2 Paxman diesels; 1 100 bhp = 14 knots
Oil fuel (tons)	15
Complement	15 (2 officers, 13 ratings)

The first inshore minesweeper, *Inglesham,* was launched by J Samuel White & Co Ltd, Cowes, on 23 Apr 1952. The 2601 series were of composite construction. In all 95 of this class were built.

TRANSFERS. Australia (3 in 1966-68), France (15 in 1954-55) Ghana (2 in 1959), India (2 in 1955), Libya (2 in 1963), Malaysia (4 in 1958-59), South Yemen (3 in 1967). Ships subsequently returned are not listed.

DITTISHAM *1973, John G. Callis*

2 "LEY" CLASS. M 2001 SERIES

AVELEY M 2002 **ISIS** (ex-*Cradley*) M 2010

Displacement, tons	123 standard; 164 full load
Dimensions, feet	100 pp; 107 oa × 21·8 × 5·5
Guns	1—40 mm AA or 1—20 mm AA forward
Main engines	2 Paxman diesels; 700 bhp = 13 knots
Complement	15 (2 officers, 13 ratings)

The "Ley" class differed from the "Ham" class. They were of composite (non-magnetic metal and wooden) construction, instead of all wooden construction. Their superstructure and other features also differed. They had no winch or sweeping gear, as they were minehunters, not sweepers. *Aveley* is attached to Plymouth. *Cradley* was allocated to London Division R.N.R. in 1953 and renamed *Isis*.

MAINTENANCE SHIPS

Name	No.	Builders	Laid down	Launched	Completed
TRIUMPH	A 108 (ex-*R* 16)	R & W Hawthorn Leslie, Hebburn	27 Jan 1943	2 Oct 1944	9 Apr 1946

Displacement, tons	13 500 standard; 17 500 full load
Length, feet (*metres*)	630·0 (*192·0*) pp; 650·0 (*198·1*) wl; 699·0 (*213·1*) oa
Beam, feet (*metres*)	80·0 (*24·4*)
Draught, feet (*metres*)	23·5 (*7·2*)
Width, feet (*metres*)	112·5 (*34·3*) overall
Aircraft	3 helicopters in flight deck hangar
Guns	4—40 mm AA; 3 saluting
Main engines	Parsons geared turbines; 2 shafts; 40 000 shp
Speed, knots	24·25
Boilers	4 Admiralty 3-drum type; Pressure 400 psi (*28·1 kg/cm²*); Temperature 700°F (*371°C*)
Range, miles	10 000 at 14 knots; 5 500 at full speed
Oil fuel, tons	3 000
Complement	500 (27 officers, 473 men) plus 285 (15 officers, 270 men) of maintenance staff

Originally an aircraft carrier of the "Colossus" class. Converted for present role at a cost of £10·2 mill. at Portsmouth between 1958 and 1965. Now in reserve at Chatham.

TRIUMPH 1974, *Wright and Logan*

2 "HEAD" CLASS

Name	No.	Builders	Laid down	Launched	Completed
BERRY HEAD	A 191	North Vancouver Ship Repairs	15 June 1944	21 Oct 1944	30 May 1945
RAME HEAD	A 134	Burrard DD Co, Vancouver	12 July 1944	22 Nov 1944	18 Aug 1945

Displacement, tons	9 000 standard; 11 270 full load
Length, feet (*metres*)	416·0 (*126·8*) pp; 441·5 (*134·6*) oa
Beam, feet (*metres*)	57·5 (*17·5*)
Draught, feet (*metres*)	22·5 (*6·9*)
Guns, AA	11—40 mm
Boilers	2 Foster Wheeler
Main engines	Triple expansion; 2 500 ihp
Speed, knots	10 approx
Oil fuel, tons	1 600 capacity
Complement	425

Escort Maintenance Ships. In reserve in 1972. *Berry Head* was refitted in 1968-69 to relieve HMS *Triumph* in the Far East, but returned in 1970 and is now in reserve at Chatham. *Rame Head* accommodation ship at Londonderry.

SUBMARINE DEPOT SHIPS

Name	No.	Builders	Laid down	Launched	Completed	Reconstructed
FORTH	A 187	John Brown, Clydebank	30 June 1937	11 Aug 1938	14 May 1939	1962-1966
MAIDSTONE	A 185	John Brown, Clydebank	17 Aug 1936	21 Oct 1937	5 May 1938	1958-1962

Displacement, tons	10 000 standard; 13 000 full load
Length, feet (*metres*)	497·0 (*151·5*) pp; 531·0 (*161·8*) oa
Beam, feet (*metres*)	73·0 (*22·3*)
Draught, feet (*metres*)	21·2 (*6·5*)
Guns, AA	5—40 mm Bofors (see *Gunnery*)
Boilers	4 Admiralty 3-drum type
Main engines	Geared turbines (Brown Curtis in *Forth*: Parsons in *Maidstone*) 2 shafts; 7 000 shp
Speed, knots	16
Oil fuel, tons	2 300
Complement	695 (45 officers and 650 men) Accommodation for 1 159 (119 officers and 1 040 men) normal; over 1 500 max

Equipment includes foundry, coppersmith's, plumbers', carpenters'; heavy and light machine, electrical and torpedo repair shops and plant for charging submarine batteries. Designed for maintaining nine operational submarines, and supplying over 140 torpedoes and a similar number of mines. Repair facilities on board for all material in attached submarines, and extensive diving and salvage equipment. There are steam laundry, hospital, chapel, two canteens, bakery, barber shops, operating theatre and dental surgery.

In Oct 1969, *Maidstone* was restored and recommissioned as an accommodation ship for 2 000 troops and sent to Belfast.

As the Fleet Maintenance Base, Devonport and parent ship of the 2nd Submarine Squadron *Forth* became part of HMS *Defiance*.

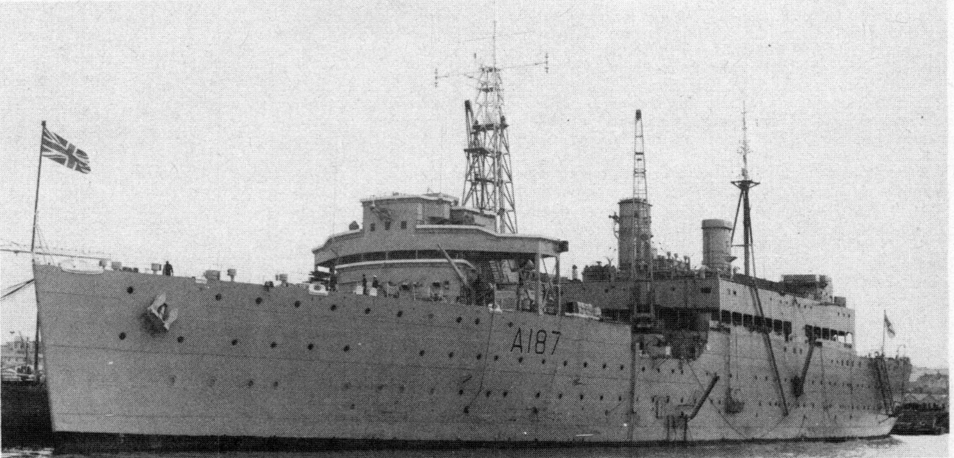

FORTH 1973, *John G. Callis*

RECONSTRUCTION. *Maidstone* was extensively reconstructed in HM Dockyard, Portsmouth in 1958-62 as support ship for nuclear powered submarines with a lattice foremast and additional superstructure amidships. The conversion and modernisation included refitting as parent ship for the nuclear-powered submarine *Dreadnought*. *Forth* was similarly modernised and converted into a support ship for nuclear powered submarines in HM Dockyard Chatham, in 1962-63.

ROYAL YACHT

BRITANNIA A 00

Displacement, tons	3 990 light; 4 961 full load
Measurement, tons	5 769 gross
Dimensions, feet	360·0 pp; 380·0 wl; 412·2 oa × 55·0 × 17·0 max
Main engines	Single reduction geared turbines; 2 shafts; 12 000 shp = 21 knots continuous cruising; 22·75 knots max (trials)
Boilers	2
Radius, miles	2 100 at 20 knots; 2 400 at 18 knots; 3 000 miles at 15 knots
Oil fuel, tons	330 (490 with auxiliary fuel tanks)
Complement	270

Designed as a medium sized naval hospital ship for use by Her Majesty The Queen in peacetime as the Royal Yacht. Built by John Brown & Co Ltd, Clydebank. Completed on 14 Jan 1954. Construction conformed to mercantile practice. Fitted with Denny-Brown single fin stabilisers to reduce roll in bad weather from 20 deg to 6 deg. Cost £2 098 000. To pass under the bridges of the St. Lawrence Seaway when she visited Canada, the top 20 feet of her mainmast and the radio aerial on her foremast were hinged in Nov 1958 so that they could be lowered as required. Total cost of refits to date to £12 million.

BRITANNIA 1973, *Wright and Logan*

SURVEY SHIPS

3 "HECLA" CLASS

Name	No	Builders	Laid down	Launched	Completed
HECATE	A 137	Yarrow & Co Ltd, Scotstoun	26 Oct 1964	31 Mar 1965	20 Dec 1965
HECLA	A 133	Yarrow & Co and Blythswood	6 May 1964	21 Dec 1964	9 Sep 1965
HYDRA	A 144	Yarrow & Co and Blythswood	14 May 1964	14 July 1965	5 May 1966

Displacement, tons 1 915 light; 2 733 full load
Measurement, tons 2 898 gross
Length, feet (*metres*) 235 (*71·6*) pp; 260 1 (*79·3*) oa
Beam, feet (*metres*) 49·1 (*15·0*)
Draught, feet (*metres*) 15·6 (*4·7*)
Aircraft 1 Wasp helicopter
Main engines Diesel-electric drive; 1 shaft. 3 Paxman "Ventura" 12-cyl Vee turbocharged diesels; 3,840 bhp. 1 electric motor, 2 000 shp
Speed, knots 14·35 on trials
Range, miles 20 000 at 9 knots
Oil fuel, tons 450
Complement 118 (14 officers, 104 ratings)
Accommodation 123 (19 officers, 104 ratings)

The first to be designed with a combined oceanographical and hydrographical role. Of merchant ship design and similar in many respects to the Royal Research ship *Discovery*, they have range and endurance to fit them for their specialised work. The hull is strengthened for navigation in ice, and a propeller built into a transverse tunnel in the bow for good manoeuvrability. The fore end of the superstructure incorporates a Landrover garage and the after end a helicopter hanger with adjacent flight deck. Equipped with chartroom, drawing office and photographic studio; two laboratories, dry and wet; electrical engineering and shipwright workshops, and large storerooms. Capable of operating independently of shore support for long periods. Air-conditioned throughout.

HECATE, HECLA, HYDRA (Survey)

1 IMPROVED "HECLA" CLASS

HERALD

Displacement, tons 2 000 standard
Measurement, tons 2 900 gross
Aircraft 1 Wasp helicopter
Main engines Diesel-electric drive; 1 shaft
Speed, knots 14 approx
Range, miles 20 000 at 9 knots
Complement 118

A later version of the "Hecla" class design. Ordered under the 1972-73 Supply (Ministry of Defence) Estimates. Being built by Robb Caledon, Leith, with main machinery manufactured by GEC/AEI Projects Ltd. Fitted with Hydroplot Satellite navigation system.

Launched by Mrs Mary Hall, wife of the Hydrographer on 4 Oct 1973.

HYDRA AND HECLA *1971, MOD (N)*

COASTAL SURVEY SHIPS

4 "FAWN" CLASS

BEAGLE A 319 **BULLDOG** A 317 **FAWN** A 325 **FOX** A 320

Displacement, tons 800 approx standard (official figure); 1 088 full load
Dimensions, feet 189 oa × 37·5 × 12
Main engines 4 Lister Blackstone ERS8M, 8 cyl. 4 str. diesels, coupled to 2 shafts, 2 000 bhp = 15 knots max designed, controllable pitch propellers
Range, miles 4 000 at 12 knots cruising
Complement 38 (4 officers, 34 ratings)

Designed for duty overseas, working in pairs. *Fawn* and *Fox* replaced the coastal minesweeper conversions. The first ship of the class launched was *Bulldog* on 12 July 1967 at Brooke Marine Ltd, Lowestoft, followed by *Beagle* on 7 Sep 1967, *Fox* on 6 Nov 1967 and *Fawn* on 29 Feb 1968. *Bulldog* was commissioned on 21 Mar 1968 and the others by the end of 1968. Built to commercial standards. Fitted with passive tank stabilizer to reduce rolling, most modern echo sounders, precision ranging radar, Decca "Hifix" system, automatic steering. Air-conditioned throughout. Carry 28·5 ft survey motor launch in davits.

BEAGLE *1974, Wright and Logan*

BULLDOG *1974, Wright and Logan*

INSHORE SURVEY CRAFT

3 "E" CLASS

ECHO A 70 **EGERIA** A 72 **ENTERPRISE** A 71

Displacement, tons 120 standard; 160 full load
Dimensions, feet 100·0 pp; 106·8 oa × 22·0 × 6·8 max
Main engines 2 Paxman diesels; 2 shafts; controllable pitch propellers; 700 bhp = 14 knots max; 12 knots normal
Oil fuel, tons 15 capacity
Endurance, miles 1 600 at 10 knots
Complement 18 (2 officers, 16 ratings); accommodation for 22 (4 officers, 18 ratings)

Echo, the first Inshore Survey Craft, was built by J. Samuel White & Co Ltd, Cowes, launched on 1 May 1957, and commissioned on 12 Sep 1958. *Egeria* was built by Wm Weatherhead & Sons Ltd, Cockenzie, and *Enterprise* by M. W. Blackmore & Sons Ltd, Bideford. Equipped with two echo sounding machines, sonar, radar, wire sweep gear and echo sounding launch.

ENTERPRISE *1970*

2 "HAM" CLASS

MODIFIED INSHORE MINESWEEPERS

WATERWITCH (ex-*Powderham*) M 272 **WOODLARK** ex-*Yaxham*) M 2780

Displacement, tons 120 standard; 160 full load
Dimensions, feet 107·5 oa × 22 × 5·5
Main engines Diesels; 2 shafts; 1 100 bhp = 14 knots
Endurance, miles 1 500 at 12 knots
Complement 18 (2 officers, 16 ratings)

Former inshore minesweepers of the "Ham" class converted to replace the old survey motor launches *Meda* and *Medusa* for operation in inshore waters at home. *Waterwitch*, ex-M 2720, was seconded to Port Auxiliary Service in 1968.

LIGHT FORCES

4 NEW CONSTRUCTION (LARGE PATROL CRAFT)

CYGNET P 261
KINGFISHER P 260
PETREL P 262
SANDPIPER P 236

Length, feet	120
Main engines	Ruston diesels

Built by Dunston (Thorne) at Hessle. Of similar type to "Seal" class RAF rescue launches with improved sea-keeping qualities and fitted with stabilisers. To be used initially for Fishery Protection duties.

1 VOSPER THORNYCROFT (FAST ATTACK CRAFT—PATROL)

TENACITY P 276

Displacement, tons	165 standard; 220 full load
Dimensions, feet	130·0 wl; 142·0 deck, 144·5 oa × 26·6 × 7·8
Guns	2 MGs
Main engines	3 Rolls Royce Proteus gas turbines; 3 shafts; 12 750 bhp = 40 knots max 2 Paxman Ventura 6 cyl diesels on wing shafts for cruising = 16 knots
Range, miles	2 500 at 15 knots
Complement	32 (4 officers, 28 ratings)

Built as a private venture by Vosper Thornycroft Limited. Launched on 18 Feb 1969 at Camber Shipyard, Portsmouth. Steel hull and aluminium alloy superstructure. Purchased by the Ministry of Defence (Navy) on 25 Jan 1972 for approximately £750 000 "as lying" and refitted with minor alterations and additions to meet naval requirements. To be used for exercises and fishery protection. Decca nav, radar. Commissioned 17 Feb 1973.

TENACITY *1973, John G. Callis*

3 FAST TRAINING BOATS

CUTLASS P 274 **SABRE** P 275 **SCIMITAR** P 271

Displacement, tons	102 full load
Dimensions, feet	90·0 wl; 100·0 oa × 26·6 × 6·4
Main engines	2 Rolls Royce Proteus gas turbines = 40 knots (2 Foden diesels for cruising in CODAG arrangement)
Range, miles	425 at 35 knots; 1 500 at 11·5 knots
Complement	12 (2 officers, 10 ratings)

Hull of glued laminated wood construction. Design developed from that of "Brave" class fast patrol boats. Complete July—December 1970. All built by Vosper Thornycroft Group, Porchester Shipyard. Design permits fitting of third gas-turbines and a gun armament if required.

SCIMITAR *1972, C. and S. Taylor*

5 MODIFIED "TON" CLASS

(FORMER COASTAL MINESWEEPERS)

BEACHAMPTON P 1007 (ex-M 1107)
MONKTON P 1055 (ex-M 1155)
WASPERTON P 1089 (ex-M 1189)
WOLVERTON P 1093 (ex-M 1193)
YARNTON P 1096 (ex-M 1196)

Displacement, tons	360 standard; 425 full load
Dimensions, feet	140·0 pp; 153·0 oa × 28·8 × 8·2
Guns	2—40 mm Bofors AA, single, 1 forward, 1 aft
Main engines	2 diesels; 2 shafts; 3 000 bhp = 15 knots max
Oil fuel, tons	45 bunkerage
Range, miles	2 300 at 13 knots
Complement	30 (5 officers and 25 ratings, but varies)

Former coastal minesweepers of the "Ton" class, refitted as gunboats at the end of 1971, re-designated as coastal patrol vessels. Form 6th Patrol Squadron Hong Kong.

WOLVERTON *1972, Michael D. J. Lennon*

2 "FORD" CLASS (SDB's)

DEE (ex-*Beckford*) P 3104 (Mersey RNR) **DROXFORD** P 3113 (Clyde RNR)

Displacement, tons	120 standard; 142 full load
Dimensions, feet	110·0 wl; 117·2 oa × 20·0 × 7·0 props
Guns	1—40 mm Bofors AA
A/S weapons	DC rails; large and small DC
Main engines	Davey Paxman diesels. Foden engine on centre shaft. 1 100 bhp = 18 knots max; 15 knots sea
Oil fuel, tons	23
Complement	19

Built in 1953-57. Last survivors of a class of 20.

DROXFORD *1972, Wright & Logan*

ICE PATROL SHIP

ENDURANCE (ex-*Anita Dan*) A 171

Displacement, tons	*circa* 3 600 (official)
Measurement, tons	2 641 gross
Length, feet (*metres*)	300 (*91·44*) oa; 305 (*92·96*) including helicopter deck extension
Beam, feet (*metres*)	46 (*14·02*)
Draught, feet (*metres*)	16·5 (*5·03*); 18 (*5·5*) max
Aircraft	2 Whirlwind Mk IX helicopters
Guns	2—20 mm
Main engines	B & W 550 VTBF diesels; 3 220 ihp; 1 shaft
Speed knots	14·5
Range, miles	12 000 at 14·5 knots
Complement	119 (13 officers, 106 men, including a small Royal Marine detachment) plus 12 spare berths for scientists

ENDURANCE *1972 MoD (UK)*

Designed and built by Krögerwerft, Rendsburg completing in 1956. Purchased from J. Lauritzen Lines, Copenhagen (announced on 20 Feb 1967). Strengthened for operation in ice. Converted by Harland & Wolff, Belfast, into an ice patrol ship for southern waters to replace *Protector*, undertaking hydrographic and oceanographic surveys and acting as support ship and guard vessel.

An unusual feature for one of HM ships is her hull painted a vivid red for easy identification in the ice. Another feature is that the ship can be controlled from the crow's nest.

HOVERCRAFT

1 "WINCHESTER" (SRN6) TYPE

Displacement, tons	10 normal gross weight
Dimensions, feet	48·4 × 23·0 × 15·0 oa (height) × 4·0 (skirt)
Main engines	1 Rolls Royce Gnome gas turbine; 900 shp = 50 knots
Range	200 miles

Modified with radar and military communications equipment for its primary role of a fast amphibious communication craft to support Royal Marine units.

1 "WELLINGTON" (BHN7) TYPE

Displacement, tons	50 max weight; 33 light
Dimensions, feet	78·33 × 45·5 × 34·0 oa (height) × 5·5 (skirt)
Main engines	1 Rolls Royce Proteus gas turbine; 4 250 shp = 60 knots
Complement	14 plus trials crew

First "hover warship" costing about £700 000, delivered to the inter-Service Hovercraft Trials Unit at the Royal Naval Air Station, Lee-on-Solent, in Apr 1970. She could be used as a missile armed fast patrol craft or amphibious assault craft. Winter trials in Swedish waters in Feb 1972. Records established: longest open sea voyage, furthest north, and sustained speeds of over 55 knots in the Baltic.

SRN6 *1971*

DIVING SHIP

RECLAIM ((ex-*Salverdant*) A 231

Displacement, tons	1 200 standard; 1 800 full load
Dimensions, feet	200 pp; 217·8 oa × 38 × 15·5
Main engines	Triple expansion; 2 shafts; 1 500 ihp = 12 knots
Oil fuel, tons	310
Range, miles	3 000
Complement	100

Built by Wm. Simons & Co Ltd, Renfrew. Engined by Aitchison Blair Ltd. Laid down on 9 Apr 1946. Launched on 12 Mar 1948. Completed on Oct 1948. Construction based on the design of a "King Salvor" class naval ocean salvage vessel. First deep diving and submarine rescue vessel built as such for the Royal Navy. Fitted with sonar, radar, echo-sounding apparatus for detection of sunken wrecks, and equipped for submarine rescue work.

RECLAIM *1972*

ROYAL FLEET AUXILIARY SERVICE
FLEET REPLENISHMENT TANKERS

3 "OL" CLASS

OLMEDA (ex-*Oleander*) A 124
OLNA A 123
OLWEN (ex-*Olynthus*) A 122

Displacement, tons	10 890 light; 33 240 full load
Measurement, tons	22 350 deadweight; 18 600 gross
Dimensions, feet	611·1 pp; 648·0 oa × 84·0 × 34·0
Aircraft	2 Wessex helicopters (can carry 3)
Main engines	Pametrada double reduction geared turbines; 26 500 shp = 19 knots (21·2 on trials)
Boilers	2 Babcock & Wilcox, 750 lbs sq in, 950 deg F
Complement	87 (25 officers and 62 ratings)

Largest and fastest ships when they joined the Royal Fleet Auxiliary Service. *Olmeda* was launched on 19 Nov 1964 and completed on 18 Oct 1965 by Swan Hunter, Wallsend, with machinery by Wallsend Slipway & Eng Co Ltd, while *Olna* and *Olwen* were launched on 28 July 1965 and 10 July 1964 and completed on 1 Apr 1966 and 21 June 1965, respectively, by Hawthorn Leslie, Hebburn, engined by Hawthorn Leslie (Engineers) Ltd.

Designed for support of the Fleet, with handling gear for transferring fuels and stores by jackstay and derricks whilst steaming at speed A helicopter landing platform and hangar enable ships to collect stores by air. Specially strengthened for operations in ice. Accommodation of a high standard, fully air-conditioned. *Olna* has a transverse bow thrust unit for improved manoeuvrability in confined waters and a new design of replenishment at sea systems.

OLMEDA *1973, Wright and Logan*

OLWEN *1974, Wright and Logan*

2 LATER "TIDE" CLASS

TIDESPRING A 75
TIDEPOOL A 76

Displacement, tons	8 531 light; 25 931 full load
Measurement, tons	17 400 deadweight; 14 130 gross
Dimensions, feet	550·0 pp; 583·0 oa × 71·0 × 32·0
Main engines	Double reduction geared turbines; 15 000 shp = 17 knots
Boilers	2 Babcock & Wilcox
Complement	110 (30 officers and 80 ratings

Built by Hawthorn Leslie, Hebburn with machinery by Hawthorn Leslie (Engineers) Ltd. Highly specialised ships for fuelling (13 000 tons cargo fuel) and storing naval vessels at sea and capable of high performance under rigorous service conditions. Their all-round capability is enhanced by a helicopter platform and hangar. *Tidespring* was laid down on 24 July 1961, launched on 3 May 1962, and accepted on 18 Jan 1963. *Tidepool* was laid down on 4 Dec 1961 launched on 11 Dec 1962 and accepted on 28 June 1963.

TIDEPOOL *1971*

3 "TIDE" CLASS

TIDEFLOW (ex-*Tiderace*) A 97
TIDESURGE (ex-*Tiderange*) A 98
TIDEREACH A 96

Displacement, tons	9 040 light; 25 940 full load
Measurement, tons	16 900 deadweight; 13 700 gross
Dimensions, feet	550 pp; 583 oa × 71 × 32 max
Main engines	Double reduction geared turbines; 15 000 shp = 17 knots

Tidereach, launched by Swan Hunter & Wigham Richardson Ltd, Wallsend-on-Tyne, on 2 June 1954, and completed on 30 Aug 1955, was the first of the new Fleet Replenishment Tankers. The main machinery was manufactured by the Wallsend Slipway Co. Designed for the support of the Fleet and replenishment under way. *Tiderange* (renamed *Tidesurge* in 1958) was launched at I. L. Thompson & Sons Ltd, Sunderland, on 30 Aug 1954, the main machinery being manufactured by North Eastern Marine Engineering Co Ltd, Wallsend. A fourth ship, *Tide Austral*, built for Australia, was renamed *Supply* on 7 Sep 1962.

TIDEFLOW *1973, John Mortimer*

FREIGHTING TANKERS

Name	No.	Builders	Launched
WAVE CHIEF (ex-*Empire Edgehill*)	A 265	Harland & Wolff, Ltd Govan, Glasgow	4 Apr 1946

Displacement, tons	4 750 light; 8 200 standard; 16 650 full load
Measurement, tons	11 900 deadweight; 8 447 gross
Dimensions, feet	465·3 pp; 492·5 oa × 64·5 × 28·5
Main engines	Double reduction geared turbines; 6 800 shp = 14·5 knots
Boilers	Three-drum type
Complement	60

WAVE CHIEF *1973, Wright and Logan*

CHERRYLEAF (ex-*Overseas Adventurer*) A 82

Measurement, tons	18 560 deadweight; 12 402 gross; 7 338 net
Dimensions, feet	544 × 72·7 × 30·6
Machinery	6 cyl Doxford diesel; 6 800 bhp = 13 knots

Built by Sir James Laing & Sons Ltd in 1953. Transferred to RFA in March 1973.

CHERRYLEAF *1973, John G. Callis*

CHERRYLEAF *1973, MOD (N)*

PLUMLEAF A 78

Displacement, tons	24 920 full load
Measurement, tons	18 562 deadweight; 12 692 gross
Dimensions, feet	534 pp; 560 oa × 72 × 30
Main engines	N.E. Doxford 6-cyl diesels; 9 350 bhp = 15·5 knots

Built by Blyth DD & Eng Co Ltd. Launched 29 Mar 1960. Completed July 1960. Astern and abeam fuelling.

PLUMLEAF *1972, Wright & Logan*

Freighting Tankers—*continued*

ORANGELEAF (ex-M.V. *Southern Satellite*) A 80

Measurement, tons	17 475 deadweight; 12 481 gross; 6 949 net
Dimensions, feet	525 pp; 556·5 oa × 71·7 × 30·5 mean
Main engines	Doxford 6-cyl. diesel; 6 800 bhp = 15 knots
Oil fuel (tons)	1 610

Built by Furness Shipbuilding Co Ltd, Haverton Hill on Tees. Launched on 8 Feb 1955. Completed June 1955. From South Georgia Co Ltd, 25 May 1959. Astern and abeam fuelling.

ORANGELEAF *1969, MOD (N)*

PEARLEAF A 77

Displacement, tons	24 900 full load
Measurement, tons	18 045 deadweight; 12 139 gross; 7 216 net
Dimensions, feet	535 pp; 568 oa × 71·7 × 30
Main engines	Rowan Doxford 6-cyl. diesels; 8 800 bhp = 15·8 knots

Built by Scotstoun Yard of Blythswood Shipbuilding Co Ltd, for Jacobs and Partners Ltd, London. Launched on 15 Oct 1959 and completed in Jan 1960. Chartered by the Royal Navy on completion. Can carry three different grades of cargo. Astern and abeam fuelling.

PEARLEAF *1970, MOD (N)*

MOBILE BULK TANKERS

DERWENTDALE (ex-M.V. *Halcyon Breeze*)

Displacement, tons	88 555 full load
Measurement, tons	28 288 net; 42 343 gross; 72 550 deadweight
Dimensions, feet	761·0 pp; 799·0 oa × 117·8 × 42·3
Main engines	B. & W. 9 cyl diesels; 1 shaft; 20 700 bhp = 15·5 knots
Complement	56

Commercial oil tanker built by Hitachi, Japan. Launched on 8 Jan 1964. Taken over by Great Britain in 1967. Chartered for Royal Fleet Auxiliary Service from the Court Line but is returning to her owners in 1974.

DERWENTDALE *1972*

DEWDALE (ex-M.V. *Edenfield*)

Measurement, tons	21 542 net; 35 805 gross; 63 588 deadweight
Dimensions, feet	747·0 pp; 774·5 oa × 107·8 × 41·5
Main engines	B. & W. 9 cyl diesels; 1 shaft; 17 000 bhp = 15 knots
Complement	51

In July 1967 the Ministry of Defence chartered three large tankers for service East of Suez. After limited modifications the ships operated in the Indian Ocean area. But *Ennerdale* sank on 1 June 1970 after striking a submerged hazard in the Indian Ocean. *Dewdale* is the largest RFA tanker at present in service.

DEWDALE *1969, Wright & Logan*

SMALL FLEET TANKERS

5 "ROVER" CLASS

GREEN ROVER A 268 **GREY ROVER** A 269 **BLUE ROVER** A 270

GOLD ROVER A 271 **BLACK ROVER** A 273

Displacement, tons	11 522 full load
Measurement, tons	3 185 net; 7 060 deadweight; 7 510 gross
Dimensions, feet	461·0 × 63·0 × 24·0
Main engines	2 Ruston & Hornsby 16 cyl. uni-directional diesels; 1 shaft; controllable pitch propeller; 16 000 bhp = 19 knots (Pielstick diesels in new construction).
Complement	47 (16 officers and 31 men)

Small fleet tankers designed to replenish HM ships at sea with fuel, fresh water, limited dry cargo and refrigerated stores under all conditions while underway. *Blue Rover* is classified as "Fleet Replenishment Tanker". A helicopter landing platform is provided, served by a stores lift, to enable stores to be transferred at sea by helicopter. Built at Swan Hunter, Hebburn-on-Tyne, *Green Rover* was launched on 19 Dec 1968, *Grey Rover* on 17 Apr 1969, *Blue Rover* on 11 Nov 1969 and *Gold Rover* on 7 Mar 1973. The cost of *Black Rover* was £7 mill. an increase of £4 mill. on the price of the original ships.

GREY ROVER *May, 1970, Wright & Logan*

1 "RANGER" CLASS (ATTENDANT TANKER)

BROWN RANGER (12 Dec 1940) A 169

Displacement, tons	6 630 full load
Measurement, tons	3 435 to 3 781 deadweight
Dimensions, feet	349·5 pp; 365·8 oa × 47·0 × 20·0
Main engines	Burmeister & Wain diesels; 2 750 bhp = 12 knots

Built by Harland & Wolff Ltd, Govan, Glasgow. Launch date above. The funnel is on the port side.

1 "EDDY" CLASS (WHITE OIL TANKER)

EDDYFIRTH A 261

Displacement, tons	1 960 light; 4 160 full load
Measurement, tons	2 300 gross; 2 200 deadweight
Dimensions, feet	270 pp; 286 oa × 44 × 17·2
Main engines	1 set triple expansion; 1 shaft; 1 750 ihp = 12 knots
Boilers	2 oil burning cylindrical

Built bu Lobnitz & Co Ltd, Renfrew. Completed on 10 Feb 1954. Cargo capacity: 1 650 tons oil.

EDDYFIRTH *1973, C. and S. Taylor*

FLEET REPLENISHMENT SHIPS

2 NEW CONSTRUCTION

Dimensions, feet	603 × 79 × 25
Aircraft	1 Wessex helicopter
Main engines	Diesel; single screw

Ordered from Scott-Lithgow in Nov 1971. To be fitted with a helicopter flight-deck and hangar, thus allowing not only for vertical replenishment but also a fuelling point for Force A/S helicopters.

New Construction Fleet Replenishment Ship *1972, MOD (N) Drawing*

REGENT A 486 **RESOURCE** A 480

Displacement, tons	19 000 full load
Measurements, tons	18 029 gross
Dimensions, feet	600·0 pp; 640·0 oa × 77·2 × 26·1
Aircraft	1 Wessex helicopter
Guns	Fitted for 2—40 mm Bofors (single) which are not normally carried
Main engines	AEI steam turbines; 20 000 shp = 20 knots
Complement	119 R.F.A. officers and ratings; 52 Naval Dept industrial and non-industrial civil servants; 11 Royal Navy (1 officer and 10 ratings) for helicopter flying and maintenance

Ordered on 24 Jan 1963. Built by Scott's Shipbuilding & Engineering Co, Greenock, and Harland & Wolff, Belfast. They have lifts for armaments and stores, and helicopter platforms for transferring loads at sea. Designed from the outset as Fleet Replenishment Ships (previous ships had been converted merchant vessels). Air-conditioned. *Resource* was launched at Greenock on 11 Feb 1966, *Regent* at Belfast on 9 Mar 1966. Official title is Ammunition, Food, Explosives, Stores Ship (AFES).

RESOURCE *1973, John Mortimer*

RESURGENT (ex-*Changchow*) A 280 **RETAINER** (ex-*Chungking*) A 329

Displacement, tons	14 000 (approx)
Measurement, tons	*Resurgent* 9 511 gross; *Retainer* 9 301 gross
Dimensions, feet	451 pp; 477·2 oa × 62 × 29 max
Main engines	Doxford diesel; 1 shaft; 6 500 bhp = 15 knots
Oil fuel (tons)	925
Complement	107

Built by Scotts' Shipbuilding and Engineering Co Ltd, Greenock, and completed in 1951 and 1950, respectively. *Retainer* was purchased in 1952 and converted into a naval storeship during autumn 1954-April 1955 by Palmers Hebburn Co Ltd, where further conversion was carried out Mar-Aug 1957 to extend her facilities as a stores ship, including the fitting out of holds to carry naval stores, the installation of lifts for stores, the provision of extra cargo handling gear and new bridge wings. *Resurgent* was taken over on completion for employment as a fleet replenishment ship.

RESURGENT *1973, MOD (N)*

HELICOPTER SUPPORT SHIP

ENGADINE K 08

Displacement, tons	8 000 to 9 000 full load
Measurement, tons	6 384 gross; 2 848 net
Dimensions, feet	424·0 oa × 58·4 × 22·1
Aircraft	4 Wessex and 2 Wasp or 2 Sea King helicopters
Main engines	1 Sulzer two stroke, 5 cyl turbo charged 5RD68 diesel; 5 500 bhp = 16 knots
Complement	RFA: 63 (15 officers, 48 men); RN: 14 (2 officers, 12 ratings) Accommodation for a further RN 113 (29 officers and 84 ratings)

Projected under the 1964-65 Navy Estimates. Built by Henry Robb Ltd, Leith. Ordered on 18 Aug 1964. Laid down on 9 Aug 1965. Officially named on 15 Sep 1966. Accepted into service on 15 Dec 1967. Largest ship then built by the company. Intended for the training of helicopter crews in deep water operations. Fitted with Denny Brown stabilisers to provide greater ship control during helicopter operations, the only RFA vessel so equipped.

ENGADINE *1972, Wright & Logan*

ENGADINE *1969*

STORES SUPPORT SHIP

LYNESS A 339 **STROMNESS** A 344 **TARBATNESS** A 345

Displacement, tons	16 500 laden
Measurements, tons	12 359 gross; 4 744 net; 7 782 deadweight
Dimensions, feet	490 pp; 524 oa × 72 × 25·5
Aircraft	Facilities for helicopters
Main engines	Wallsend-Sulzer 8-cyl RD.76 diesel; 11 520 bhp = 17 knots
Complement	105

Designed and built by Swan Hunter & Wigham Richardson Ltd, Wallsend-on-Tyne. Lifts and mobile appliances provided for handling stores internally, and a new replenishment at sea system and a helicopter landing platform for transferring loads at sea. A novel feature of the ships is the use of close circuit television to monitor the movement of stores. All air-conditioned. *Lyness* was completed on 22 Dec 1966, *Stromness* on 21 Mar 1967, and *Tarbatness* Sept 1967. *Lyness* is an Air-Stores Support Ship.

LYNESS *1972*

AIR STORES SUPPORT SHIPS

(See Lyness above)

RELIANT (ex-*Somersby*) A 84

Displacement, tons	4 447 light as built; 13 737 full load
Measurement, tons	9 290 deadweight (summer), 8 460 gross
Dimensions, feet	440 pp; 468·8 oa × 61·5 × 26·2
Main engines	Doxford 6 cyl, diesel; 8 250 bhp = 18 knots
Complement	102

Built by Sir James Laing & Sons Ltd, Sunderland. Engined by Hawthorne Leslie. Completed in 1954. Converted for her new role at North Shields. Sailed from Chatham on 4 Nov 1958 for the Far East as the Royal Navy's first air/victualling stores issuing ship capable of replenishing aircraft carriers at sea. Has an endurance of 50 days steaming at 16 knots, and carries 40 000 different patterns of aircraft spares and general naval stores. As refitted she has a helicopter pad aft for stores transfer. In reserve at Rosyth since 1972.

Air Stores Support Ships—*continued*

RELIANT *1969, MOD (N)*

STORE CARRIERS

2 "BACCHUS" CLASS

BACCHUS A 404 **HEBE** A 406

Displacement, tons	2 740 light; 7 958 full load
Measurement, tons	4 823 gross; 2 441 net; 5 218 deadweight
Dimensions, feet	350 pp; 379 oa × 55 × 22 max
Main engines	Swan Hunter Sulzer diesel; 1 shaft; 5 500 bhp 15 knots
Oil fuel, tons	720
Complement	57

Built by Henry Robb Ltd. Leith, for the British India Steam Navigation Co. Taken over by the Royal Navy on completion on long term "bare-boat" charter. *Bacchus* was completed in Sep 1962, *Hebe* in May 1962. Crew accommodation and engines aft as in tankers. In 1973 both purchased by P and O SN Co, remaining on charter to MOD (N).

HEBE *1973, C. and S. Taylor*

Storecarriers—*continued*

ROBERT MIDDLETON A 241

Displacement, tons	900 light; 1 900 full load
Measurement, tons	1 000 deadweight; 1 125 gross
Dimensions, feet	210 pp; 222·5 oa × 36 × 13·5 mean
Main engines	Atlas Polar Diesel; 1 shaft; 960 bhp = 10·5 knots
Oil fuel, tons	60
Complement	17

Coastal store carrier. Built by Grangemouth Dockyard Co Ltd. Machinery by British Auxiliaries Ltd, Govan. Launched on 29 June 1938.

ROBERT MIDDLETON *1969, Godfrey H. Walker*

ROYAL MARITIME AUXILIARY SERVICE AND PORT AUXILIARY SERVICE

NOTE. To avoid over complication the ships and vessels of the Royal Naval Auxiliary Service and some of the Royal Corps of Transport are included here.

MOORING SALVAGE AND BOOM VESSELS

2 "WILD DUCK" CLASS

2 "IMPROVED WILD DUCK" CLASS

2 "LATER WILD DUCK" CLASS

RMAS	PAS
GARGANEY P 194	**GOLDENEYE** P 195
MANDARIN P 192	**PINTAIL** P 193
GOOSANDER	
POCHARD	

Displacement, tons	950
Measurement, tons	283 deadweight
Dimensions, feet	190 including horns (*Garganey* and *Goldeneye*). 182 including horns (*Mandarin* and *Pintail*)
Main engines	1 Davey Paxman 16 cyl diesel; 1 shaft; controllable pitch propeller; 550 bhp = 10 knots
Range, miles	3 000 at 10 knots
Complement	24 (6 officers, 6 petty officers, 12 ratings)

Mandarin was the first of a new class of marine service vessels. Launched on 17 Sep 1963 and handed over on 5 Mar 1964. *Pintail* was launched on 3 Dec 1963. Both built by Cammell Laird & Co Ltd, Birkenhead. Previously their three tasks were separately undertaken by specialist vessels. Capable of laying out and servicing the heaviest moorings used by the Fleet and also maintaining booms for harbour defence. Heavy lifting equipment enables a wide range of salvage operations to be performed, especially in harbour clearance work. The special heavy winches have an ability for tidal lifts over the apron of 200 tons. *Garganey* and *Goldeneye* were built in 1965-67 by Brooke Marine Ltd, Lowestoft. *Goosander* and *Pochard* of the later "Wild Duck" class were built by Robb Caledon Ltd and launched 12 Apr 1973 and 21 June 1973 respectively. Completion early 1974.

GOLDENEYE *1972, Wright and Logan*

BARFOOT P 202 **BARMOND** P 232

Displacement, tons	750 standard; 1 000 full load
Dimensions, feet	150 pp; 173·8 oa; 182 over horns × 23·2 × 11·5
Main engines	Triple expansion; 850 ihp = 11 knots (Sea speed 9 knots)
Boilers	2 single ended (200 lbs per sq in)
Fuel, tons	214 coal (*Barfoam* and *Barmond* converted to oil in 1966)
Radius, miles	3 000
Complement	32

Launched by Blyth DD & SB Co on 8 Jan 1940, John Lewis & Sons Ltd, Aberdeen on 25 Sep 1942, Philip & Son Ltd, Dartmouth on 18 July 1942, and Wm Simons & Co Ltd, Renfrew on 24 Dec 1942, respectively.
Bow lift of 27 to 70 tons. *Barfoot* and *Barmond* are civilian manned.

BARFOOT

TRANSFERS. *Barbrake* and *Barcross* were transferred to South Africa, *Barbarian*, *Barbette* (first of this name in the class, launched on 15 Dec 1937) and *Barfair* to Turkey, *Baron* to Ceylon in 1958 (purchased by the Colombo Port Commission).

LAYBURN P 191 RMAS **LAYMOOR** P 190 RN

Displacement, tons	800 standard; 1 050 full load
Dimensions, feet	160 pp; 192·7 oa × 34·5 × 11·5 feet
Main engines	Triple expansion; 1 shaft; 1 300 ihp = 10 knots
Boilers	2 Foster Wheeler "D" type; 200 psi
Complement	2 officers; 29 to 34 ratings

Both built by Wm. Simons & Co Ltd (Simons-Lobnitz Ltd). *Layburn*, which cost £565 000 was completed on 7 June 1960. *Laymoor* was accepted on 9 Dec 1959. Designed for naval or civilian manning. Lifting capacity is greater than that of predecessors; improvement in accommodation enables them to be operated in any climate.

LAYBURN *1973, John G. Callis*

Mooring, Salvage and Boom Vessels—*continued*

7 "KIN" CLASS RMAS

DISPENSER	(22 Apr 43)	**KINLOSS** A 482	(14 Apr 45) PAS
KINBRACE A 281	(17 Jan 45) PAS	**UPLIFTER** A 507	(29 Nov 43)
KINGARTH A 232	(22 May 44)		

Displacement, tons: 950 standard; 1 050 full load
Measurement, tons: 775 gross; 262 deadweight
Dimensions, feet: 150·0 pp; 179·2 oa × 35·2 × 9·5 mean; 12·0 max
Main engines: *Kinbrace, Kingarth, Kinloss, Uplifter:* 1 British Polar Atlas M44M diesel; 630 bhp = 9 knots; Others: Triple expansion; 1 shaft; 600 ihp = 9 knots
Boilers: 1 return tube cylindrical (30 ton) in others
Complement: 34

Originally classified as Coastal Salvage Vessels, but re-rated Mooring, Salvage and Boom Vessels in 1971. Launch dates above. Equipped with horns and heavy rollers. Can lift 200 tons deadweight over the bow. *Kinbrace, Kingarth, Kinloss* were built by A. Hall, Aberdeen, *Uplifter* by Smith's Dock Co Ltd. *Dispenser* was on charter to Liverpool & Glasgow Salvage Association, but returned in 1971. *Kinbrace, Kingarth* and *Uplifter* were refitted with diesel engines in 1966-67, and *Kinloss* in 1963-64.

KINLOSS *1972, Wright and Logan*

OILERS

6 "OILPRESS" CLASS

OILBIRD	Y 25	**OILMAN**	Y 26	**OILSTONE**	Y 22
OILFIELD	Y 24	**OILPRESS**	Y 21	**OILWELL**	Y 23

Displacement, tons: 280 standard; 530 full load
Dimensions, feet: 130·0 wl; 139·5 oa × 30·0 × 8·3
Main engines: 1 Lister Blackstone ES6 diesel; 1 shaft; 405 shp at 900 rpm
Complement: 11 (4 officers and 7 ratings)

Coastal tankers. Ordered on 10 May 1967 from Appledore Shipbuilders Ltd. Three are diesel oil carriers and three FFO carriers.

OILWELL *1972, Wright and Logan*

TRIALS SHIPS

1 NEW CONSTRUCTION

Ordered from Scott-Lithgow November 1971. To be launched Oct 1974. Similar to *Whitehead* below. Prime duty sonar propagation trials.

WHITEHEAD ETV 01

Displacement, tons: 3 040 full load
Dimensions, feet: 291·0 wl; 319·0 oa × 48·0 × 17·0
Main engines: 2 Paxman 12 YLCM diesels; 1 shaft; 3 400 bhp = 15·5 knots
Range, miles: 4 000 at 12 knots
Complement: 10 officers, 32 ratings, 15 trials and scientific staff

Designed to provide mobile preparation, firing and control facilities for weapons and research vehicles. Built by Scotts, Shipbuilding Co Ltd, Greenock. Launched on 5 May 1970. Named after Robert Whitehead, the torpedo development pioneer and engineer. Fitted with equipment for tracking weapons and targets and for analysing the results of trials.

WHITEHEAD *1972*

CRYSTAL RDV 01 Dockyard control

Displacement, tons: 3 040 deep
Dimensions, feet: 410·0 wl; 413·5 × 56·0 × 5·5
Complement: 60, including scientists

Unpowered floating platform for Sonar Research and Development. Built at H.M. Dockyard, Devonport. Ordered in Dec 1969. Begun in Mar 1970 for completion in Sep 1971. A harbour-based laboratory without propulsion machinery or steering which provides the Admiralty Underwater Weapons Establishment at Portland with a stable platform on which to carry out acoustic tests and other research projects.

Trials Ships—*continued*

CRYSTAL *1972*

ICEWHALE PAS

Displacement, tons: 289 standard; 350 full load
Dimensions, feet: 120 × 24 × 9
Main engines: Speed = 9 knots
Complement: 12 (Master, Mate and 10 ratings)
Range, miles: 4 000 at 12 knots
Complement: 10 officers, 32 ratings, 15 trials and scientific staff

Experimental Trials Vessel for the Underwater Weapons Establishment, Portland.

ICEWHALE *1968, John G. Callis*

3 "MINER" CLASS

MINER III (RMAS) **BRITANNIC** (PAS) **STEADY** (PAS)

Displacement, tons: 300 standard; (355 full load)
Dimensions, feet: 110·2 × 26·5 × 8·0
Main engines: Ruston & Hornsby diesels; 2 shafts; 360 bhp = 10 knots

All built by Philip & Son Ltd, Dartmouth, and engined by Ruston & Hornsby Ltd, Lincoln. *Miner V* was converted into a cable lighter and renamed *Britannic* in 1960 with PAS as store carrier. *Miner VII* was adapted as a stabilisation trials ship at Portsmouth and renamed *Steady* in 1960 with PAS. *Miner III* is now RMAS diving tender at Pembroke Dock.

TORPEDO RECOVERY VESSELS

TORRENT A 127 **TORRID** A 128

Measurement, tons: 550 gross
Dimensions, feet: 151·0 × 31·5 × 11
Main engines: Paxman diesels; 700 bhp = 12 knots
Complement: 19

Torrent was completed on 10 Sept 1971 and *Torrid* in Jan 1972 by Swan Hunter (Tyne). These ships have a stern well for torpedo recovery—can carry 22 torpedoes in hold and 10 on deck.

TORRENT *1972*

THOMAS GRANT PAS

Displacement, tons: 209 light; 461 full load
Measurement, tons: 252 deadweight; 218 gross
Dimensions, feet: 113·5 × 25·5 × 8·8
Main engines: 2 diesels; Speed = 9 knots

Built as a local store carrier by Charles Hill & Sons Ltd, Bristol. Launched on 11 May 1953 and completed in July 1953. Converted into a torpedo recovery vessel in 1968.

THOMAS GRANT *Added 1969*

6 "HAM" CLASS PAS

BUCKLESHAM, DOWNHAM, EVERINGHAM, FRITHAM, HAVERSHAM LASHAM

Details similar to other "Ham" class in mine warfare section but converted for TRV in 1964 onwards. Now fitted with stern well.

CABLE SHIPS

RMAS

BULLFINCH (19 Aug 1940) A 176 **ST. MARGARETS** (13 Oct 1943) A 259

Displacement, tons	1 300 light; 2 500 full load
Measurement, tons	1 524 gross; 1 200 deadweight
Dimensions, feet	228·8 pp; 252 oa × 36·5 × 16·3 mean
Main engines	Triple expansion; 2 shafts; 1 250 ihp = 12 knots

Both built by Swan, Hunter & Wigham Richardson Ltd. Launch dates above. Provision was made for mounting one 4 inch gun and four 20 mm AA guns but no armament is fitted.

BULLFINCH *1970*

LANDING CRAFT

5 LCT (8) TYPE (RCT)

AACHEN L 4062
ABBEVILLE L 4041
AGHEILA L 4002
ANDALNES L 4097
AUDEMER L 4061

Displacement, tons	657 light; 895 to 1 017 loaded
Dimensions, feet	225 pp; 231·2 oa × 39 × 3·2 forward; 5 aft Beaching draughts
Main engines	4 Paxman engines; 1 840 bhp 12·6 knots (9 knots cruising)
Complement	33 to 37

All transferred to the Army's Royal Corps of Transport from the Royal Navy.

APPEARANCE. *Aachen* has twin funnels. *Audemer* has an enlarged bridge.

AACHEN *1973, Wright and Logan*

ANDALNES *1969 Skyfotos*

ARMAMENT CARRIERS

KINTERBURY A 378 **THROSK**

Displacement, tons	1 490 standard; 1 770 full load
Measurement, tons	600 deadweight
Dimensions, feet	185 pp; 199·8 × 34·3 × 13
Main engines	Triple expansion; 1 shaft; 900 ihp = 11 knots
Coal, tons	154

Launched on 14 Nov 1942 and in 1943 and completed on 4 Mar 1943 and 22 Dec 1943, respectively. Both built by Philip & Son Ltd. Rated as naval armament carriers Converted in 1959 with hold stowage and a derrick for handling guided missiles for attending and servicing the guided weapons trials ship *Girdle Ness*.

KINTERBURY *1972, Wright & Logan*

BOWSTRING **CATAPULT** **FLINTLOCK**

Of various displacements and data.

MAXIM A 377

Displacement, tons	604 to 663
Measurement, tons	340 deadweight
Dimensions, feet	144·5 × 25 × 8
Main engines	Reciprocating; 500 ihp = 9 knots
Complement	13

Built by Lobnitz & Co Ltd, Renfrew.

WATER CARRIERS

6 "WATER" CLASS

WATERFALL Y 17
WATERSHED Y 18
WATERSIDE Y 20
WATERSPOUT Y 19
WATERCOURSE
WATERFOWL

Measurement, tons	285 gross
Dimensions, feet	123 pp; 131·5 oa × 24·8 × 8
Main engines	Diesels; 1 shaft; 1 100 bhp = 11 knots

Built by Drypool Engineering & Drydock Co, Hull. Launched on 30 Mar 1966, 3 Aug 1966, 20 June 1967 and 29 Dec 1966, respectively and last pair in 1973.

WATERFALL *1972, Wright & Logan*

4 "SPA" CLASS

SPALAKE (10 Aug 1946) A 260
SPAPOOL (28 Feb 1946) A 222
SPABROOK (24 Aug 1944) A 224
SPABURN (5 Jan 1946) A 257

Displacement, tons	1 219 full load
Measurement, tons	630 deadweight; 672 to 719 gross
Dimensions, feet	160 pp; 172 oa × 30 × 12
Main engines	Triple expansion; 675 ihp = 9 knots
Coal, tons	90

Spalake and *Spapool* were built by Charles Hill & Sons Ltd, Bristol and *Spabrook* and *Spaburn* by Philip & Son Ltd, Dartmouth. *Spapool* in Mombasa.

SPAPOOL *1967, MOD (N)*

6 "FRESH" CLASS

FRESHBURN
FRESHLAKE
FRESHMERE
FRESHPOND
FRESHPOOL
FRESHSPRING

Displacement, tons	594
Dimensions, feet	126·2 × 25·5 × 10·8 max
Main engines	Triple expansion; 450 ihp = 9 knots

Freshspring was converted from coal to oil fuel, in 1961. *Freshpool* is in reserve.

FRESHPOOL *1966, courtesy Dr. Giorgio Arra*

TUGS

3 OCEAN TUGS RMAS

ROBUST PAS **ROLLICKER** **ROYSTERER**

Displacement, tons	1 630 full load
Dimensions, feet	162·0 pp; 179·7 oa × 38·5 × 18·0
Main engines	2 Mirrlees KMR 6 diesels (by Lister Blackstone Mirrlees Marine Ltd); 2 shafts; 4 500 bhp at 525 rpm = 15 knots
Range, miles	13 000 at 12 knots
Complement	31 (10 officers and 21 ratings) (and able to carry salvage party of 10 RN officers and ratings)

These are the biggest and most powerful ocean tugs ever built for the Royal Navy. Bollard pull—50 tons. Built by Charles D. Holmes at Beverley Shipyard, Hull. Designed principally for salvage and long range towage but can be used for general harbour duties, which *Robust* now undertakes. Cost well over £2 million apiece. Completion dates *Roysterer* 26 Apr 1972, *Rollicker* Feb 1973, *Robust* Oct 1973.

ROYSTERER *1973, Wright and Logan*

TYPHOON A 95

Displacement, tons	800 standard; 1 380 full load
Dimensions, feet	181·0 pp; 200·0 oa × 40·0 × 13·0
Main engines	2 turbocharged vee type 12-cyl diesels; 1 shaft; 2 750 bhp = over 16 knots

Built by Henry Robb & Co Ltd, Leith. Launched on 14 Oct 1958. Completed in 1960. Diesels manufactured by Vickers-Armstrongs Ltd, Barrow-in-Furness. The machinery arrangement of two diesels geared to a single shaft was an innovation for naval ocean tugs. Controllable pitch propeller, 150 rpm. Fitted for fire fighting, salvage and ocean rescue, with a heavy mainmast and derrick attached. Bollard pull 32 tons.

TYPHOON *1973, Wright and Logan*

5 "CONFIANCE" CLASS RMAS

ACCORD (17 Sept 1957) A 90
ADVICE (16 Oct 1958) A 89
AGILE (2 July 1958) A 88
CONFIANCE (15 Nov 1955) A 289
CONFIDENT (17 Jan 1956) A 290

Displacement, tons	760 full load
Dimensions, feet	140·0 pp; 154·8 oa × 35·0 × 11·0
Main engines	4 Paxman HAXM diesels; 2 shafts; 1 800 bhp = 13 knots
Complement	29 plus 13 salvage party

Confiance and *Confident* were built by A. & J. Inglis Ltd, Glasgow. Launch dates above. *Confiance* was completed on 27 Mar 1956. Fitted with 2·50 m diam Stone Kamewa controllable pitch propellers. *Accord, Advice* and *Agile*, formerly rated as dockyard tugs' were officially added to the "Confiance "class in 1971 as part of the Royal Maritime Auxiliary Service ocean towing force. Fitted for 1—40 mm AA.

AGILE *1974, Wright and Logan*

3 "SAMSON" CLASS PAS

SAMSON (14 May 1953) A 390
SEA GIANT (2 June 1954) A 288
SUPERMAN (23 Nov 1953)

Displacement, tons	1 200 full load
Measurement, tons	850 gross
Dimensions, feet	165 pp; 180 oa × 37 × 14
Main engines	Triple expansion; 2 shafts; 3 000 ihp = 15 knots

All built and engined by Alexander Hall & Co Ltd, Aberdeen. Launch dates above.

SEA GIANT *1972, John G. Callis*

2 "BUSTLER" CLASS

CYCLONE (ex-*Growler*, 10 Sep 1942) A 111 **REWARD** (13 Oct 1944) A 264

Displacement, tons	1 118 light; 1 630 full load
Dimensions, feet	190·0 pp; 205·0 oa × 40·2 × 16·8
Main engines	2 Atlas Polar 8-cyl diesels; 1 shaft; 4 000 bhp = 16 knots
Oil fuel, tons	405
Range, miles	17 000
Complement	42

All built by Henry Robb Ltd, Leith.

CYCLONE *1974, Wright and Logan*

6 FLEET SERVICING TUGS PAS

EMPIRE ACE **EMPIRE DEMON** **EMPIRE FRED**
EMPIRE ROSA

All slightly different.

17 HARBOUR TUGS PAS

DIVER	**EMINENT**	**HANDMAID**	**SECURITY**
DRIVER	**FIDGET**	**IMPETUS**	**TAMPEON**
	FOREMOST	**INTEGRITY**	**TRUNNION**
	FREEDOM	**PROMPT**	**VAGRANT**
	FRISKY	**RESOLVE**	**WEASEL**

A miscellany of steam and diesel tugs.

7 "DIRECTOR" CLASS PAS

DEXTROUS A93
DIRECTOR A94
FAITHFUL A85
FORCEFUL A86
FAVOURITE A87
GRIPER A91
GRINDER A92

Displacement, tons	710 full load
Dimensions, feet	157·2 oa × 30 (60 over paddle boxes) × 10
Main engines	Paxman diesels and BTH motors; diesel electric; 2 shafts; 2 paddle wheels; 2 000 bhp = 13 knots
Complement	21

Modern paddlers.

FORCEFUL *1973, Wright and Logan*

Tugs—*continued*

20 "DOG" CLASS PAS

AIREDALE **ALSATIAN** **BASSET** **BEAGLE** **BOXER** **CAIRN** **COLLIE** **CORGI** **DALMATIAN** **DEERHOUND** **ELKHOUND** **HUSKY** **LABRADOR** **MASTIFF** **POINTER** **SALUKI** **SEALYHAM** **SETTER** **SHEEPDOG** **SPANIEL**

Harbour berthing tugs.

BOXER 1972, *Wright and Logan*

8 "GIRL" CLASS

AGATHA **AGNES** **ALICE** **AUDREY** **BARBARA** **BETTY** **BRENDA** **BRIDGET**

The first of a new class of harbour berthing tugs, later to be known for some reason, as "Water tractors".

10 "IMPROVED GIRL" CLASS

CELIA **CHARLOTTE** **CHRISTINE** **CLARE** **DAISY** **DAPHNE** **DORIS** **DOROTHY** **EDITH** **FELICITY**

18 "SUPER GIRL" CLASS

FIONA **GEORGINA** **GWENDOLINE** **HELEN** **IRENE** **ISABEL** **JOAN** **JOYCE** **KATHLEEN** **KITTY** **LESLEY** **LILIAN** **LILAH** **MAY** **MARY** **MYRTLE** **NANCY** **NORAH**

GEORGINA 1973, *Wright and Logan*

FLEET TENDERS

7 "INSECT" CLASS

BEE **CICALA** **COCKCHAFER** **CRICKET** **GNAT** **LADYBIRD** **SCARAB** (RMAS)

Displacement, tons	450 full load
Dimensions, feet	111·8 oa × 28 × 11
Main engines	Lister-Blackstone Diesels; 1 shaft; 660 bhp = 10·5 knots
Complement	10

All built by C. D. Holmes Ltd, Beverley, Yorks in 1970-71, first three as stores carriers, two as armament carriers and *Scarab*, as mooring vessel.

CICALA 1971, *Wright and Logan*

12 "ABERDOVEY" CLASS

ABERDOVEY **ABINGER** **ALNESS** **ALNMOUTH** **APPLEBY** **ASHCOTT** **BEAULIEU** **BEDDGELERT** **BEMBRIDGE** **BIBURY** **BLAKENEY** **BRODICK**

Displacement, tons	117·5 full load
Dimensions, feet	79·8 oa × 18 × 5·5
Main engines	1 Lister-Blackstone Diesel; 1 shaft; 225 bhp = 10·5 knots
Complement	6

'A" names built by Isaac Pimblott & Sons, Northwich. "B" names by J. S. Doig, Grimsby 1963-71. Sixty fleet tenders are planned to replace the ageing MFV's. Multi-purpose for stores (25 tons), passengers (200 standing) plus a couple of torpedos

APPLEBY 1973, *Wright and Logan*

30 CARTMEL CLASS

CARTMEL **CAWSAND** **CLOVELLY** **CRICCIETH** **CRICKLADE** **CROMARTY** **DATCHET** **DENMEAD** **DORNOCH** **DUNSTER** **ELKSTONE** **ELSING** **EPWORTH** **ETTRICK** **FELSTEDC** (RMAS) **FINTRY** **FOTHERBY** **FROXFIELD** **FULBECK** **GLENCOVE** **GRASMERE** **HAMBLEDON** **HARLECH** **HEADCORN** **HEVER** **HOLMWOOD** **HORNING** **LAMLASH** **LECHLADE** **LLANDOVERY**

Displacement, tons	143 full load
Dimensions, feet	80 oa × 21 × 6·5
Main engines	1 Lister-Blackstone diesel; 1 shaft; 320 bhp = 10·5 knots
Complement	6

All fleet tenders as *"Aberdovey"* class except *Datchet*, diving tender with Gray diesels, 2 shafts, 450 bhp = 12 knots and *Felsted* with RMAS. Builders — first 4 "C"s and *Glencove* by Pimblott; *Cricklade, Denmead* and *Fulbeck* by C. D. Holmes, Beverley; *Cromarty, Dornoch, Fintry* and *Grasmere* by J. Lewis, Aberdeen; four "E"s by J. Cook Wivenhoe; *Datchet* by Vospers; remainder by R. Dunston, Thorne.

5 "LOYAL" CLASS

LOYAL FACTOR A 382
LOYAL GOVERNOR A510
LOYAL MODERATOR
LOYAL CHANCELLOR
LOYAL PROCTOR

Details as for "Cartmel "class. All employed by RNXS.

8 "HAM" CLASS

BIRDHAM **ODIHAM** **PAGHAM** **PORTISHAM** **PUTTENHAM** **SHIPHAM** **THAKEHAM** **TONGAM**

RNXS manned. Details in Minewarfare Section.

61 MFV TYPES

MFV 2, 7, 15, 63, 93, 96, 119, 139, 140, 175, 205, 256, 278, 289,
Length: 61·5 feet
MFV 642, 658, 686, 715, 740, 767, 775, 816, 911,
Length: 45 feet
MFV 1021, 1033, 1037, 1048, 1051, 1062, 1077, 1151, 1190, 1255
Length: 75 feet
MV 1527 Length: 90 feet

TANK CLEANING VESSELS

7 "ISLES" CLASS PAS

BERN	(2 May 1942)	**LUNDY** A 366	(29 Aug 1942)
CALDY A 332	(31 Aug 1943)	**SWITHA** A 346	(3 Apr 1942)
COLL A 333	(7 Apr 1942)	**SKOMER** A 332	(17 June 1943)
GRAEMSAY A 340	(3 Aug 1942)		

Dimensions, feet	150 pp; 164 oa × 27·5 × 14
Main engines	Triple expansion; 1 shaft; 850 ihp = 12 knots
Boilers	1 cylindrical
Coal, tons	183

Built by Ardrossan Dockyard (2) *Cook, Welton* and Gemmell (2), John Lewis and Sons (2) A. & J. Inglis Ltd (1). Launch dates above. Former minesweeping trawlers converted to tank cleaning vessels. Classed as port auxiliary service craft and have "A" pennant numbers.

DEGAUSSING VESSELS

Fordham, Thatcham, Warmingham of the "Ham' 'Class. See Mine Warfare Section for details.

NUCLEAR DECONTAMINATION VESSEL

MAC 1012 **MAC 1013**

1012 launched at Chatham early in 1971. 1013 built at Devonport 1973. Length 180 feet, beam 30 feet. To be used in connection with the disposal of radio active waste from the Chatham nuclear powered submarine refitting complex.

UNITED STATES OF AMERICA

Compiled and Edited by Norman Polmar

ADMINISTRATION

Secretary of the Navy:
J. William Middendorf, II

PRINCIPAL FLAG OFFICERS

Chairman, Joint Chiefs of Staff:
Admiral Thomas H. Moorer, USN

Chief of Naval Operations:
Admiral James Holloway, III, USN

Vice Chief of Naval Operations:
Admiral Worth H. Bagley, USN

Deputy Chief of Naval Operations (Manpower and Naval Reserve):
Vice Admiral David H. Bagley, USN

Deputy Chief of Naval Operations (Submarine Warfare):
Vice Admiral Eugene P. Wilkinson, USN

Deputy Chief of Naval Operations (Surface Warfare):
Vice Admiral Frank H. Price, Jnr, USN

Deputy Chief of Naval Opreations (Air Warfare):
Vice Admiral William D. Houser, USN

Deputy Chief of Naval Operations (Logistics):
Vice Admiral Walter D. Gaddis, USN

Deputy Chief of Naval Operations (Plans and Policy):
Vice Admiral George C. Talley, Jnr, USN

* **Commander-in-Chief Atlantic and Commander-in-Chief Atlantic Fleet:*
Admiral Ralph W. Cousins, USN

**Commander-in-Chief Pacific:*
Admiral Noel A. M. Gayler, USN

Commander-in-Chief Pacific Fleet:
Admiral Maurice F. Weisner, USN

Commander Third Fleet (Eastern Pacific):
Vice Admiral William T. Rapp, USN

Commander Second Fleet (Atlantic):
Vice Admiral John G. Finneran, USN

Commander Sixth Fleet (Mediterranean):
Vice Admiral Daniel J. Murphy, USN

Commander Seventh Fleet (Western Pacific):
Vice Admiral George P. Steele, II, USN

Commander Military Sealift Command:
Rear Admiral John D. Chase, USN

Chief of Naval Education and Training:
Vice Admiral Malcolm W. Cagle, USN

Chief of Naval Reserve:
Vice Admiral Pierre N. Charbonnet, Jnr, USN

Oceanographer of the Navy:
Rear Admiral Joseph E. Snyder, Jnr, USN

MARINE CORPS

Commandant of the Marine Corps:
General Robert E. Cushman, Jnr, USMC

Assistant Commandant of the Marine Corps:
General Earl E. Anderson, USMC

Chief of Staff:
Lieutenant General Foster C. Lahue, USMC

MATERIÉL

Chief of Naval Material:
Admiral Isaac C. Kidd, Jnr, USN

Commander Naval Air Systems Command:
Vice Admiral Kent L. Lee, USN

Commander Naval Electronic Systems Command:
Rear Admiral R. J. Schneider (ED), USN

Commander Naval Facilities Engineering Command:
Rear Admiral Albert R. Marschall, (CEC), USN

Commander Naval Ordnance Systems Command:
Rear Admiral Roger E. Spreen, USN

Commander Naval Ship Systems Command:
Rear Admiral Robert C. Gooding, (ED), USN

Commander Naval Supply Systems Command:
Rear Admiral Wallace R. Dowd, Jnr (SC), USN

NOTES: *Unified Command with the Commander-in-Chief directing all US Army, Navy, and Air Force activities in the area. Only naval officers serving as Unified Commanders-in-Chief are listed. **In addition to Unified Commander, also Supreme Allied Commander Atlantic (NATO position). In July 1974 the Naval Ordnance Systems Command and Naval Ship Systems Command were merged into the new Naval Sea Systems Command.

DIPLOMATIC

Defense Attaché and Naval Attaché in London:
Rear Admiral James C. Longino, USN

Defense Attaché and Naval Attaché in Moscow:
Rear Admiral James Mayo, USN

Naval Attaché and Naval Attaché for Air in Paris:
Captain George La Rocque, USN

STRENGTH OF THE FLEET

The following table provides a tabulation of the ship strength of the United States Navy and an index to the ship listings within the United States section of this edition. Ship arrangement is based on function and employment; the official arrangement of ship types is contained in the "List of classifications of naval ships and service craft" which appears on a later page in this section. Numbers of ships listed in the table are estimated as of 1 July 1974 based on official and unofficial sources.

	Category-Type	*Active* a	*Building* b	*Reserve*
STRATEGIC MISSILE SUBMARINES				
SSBN	Ballistic Missile Submarines	41	1	—
SUBMARINES				
SSN	Attack Submarines (nuclear)	59	27	1
SSN	Research Submarines (nuclear)	2	—	—
SS	Attack Submarines (diesel post-war)	10	—	—
SS	Attack Submarines (diesel war-built)	2	—	—
SSG	Guided Missile Submarines (diesel)	—	—	1
LPSS	Transport Submarines	1	—	1
AGSS	Research Submarines	2	—	1
AIRCRAFT CARRIERS				
CVAN	Attack Carriers (nuclear)	1	3	—
CVA	Attack Carriers	13	—	1
CVS	Anti-Submarine Carriers	—	—	4
CVT	Training Carriers	1	—	—
SURFACE COMBATANTS				
	Sea Control Ships	1	—	—
CG	Missile Cruisers	3	—	—
CGN	Missile Cruisers (nuclear)	1	—	—
CLG	Light Missile Cruisers	2	—	3
DLGN	Missile Frigates (nuclear)	3	4	—
DLG	Missile Frigates	28	—	—
DDG	Missile Destroyers	29	—	—
DD	Destroyers (all-gun)	70	23	34
OCEAN ESCORTS				
PF	Patrol Frigates	—	1	—
DEG	Missile Escort Ships	6	—	—
DE-AGDE	Escort Ships (all-gun)	60	1	—
DER	Escort Ships (war-built)	—	—	15
FIRE SUPPORT SHIPS				
BB	Battleships	—	—	4
CA	Heavy Cruisers	1	—	4
COMMAND AND COMMUNICATION SHIPS				
AGF	Miscellaneous Flagships	1	—	—
CC	National Command Ships	—	—	2
AGMR	Communication Relay Ships	—	—	2
AMPHIBIOUS WAFARE SHIPS				
LCC	Amphibious Command Ships	2	—	4
LHA	Amphibious Assault Ships	—	5	—
LPH	Amphibious Assault Ships	6	—	—
LKA	Amphibious Cargo Ships	6	—	5
LPA	Amphibious Transports	2	—	7
LPR	Amphibious Transports (small)	—	—	10
LPD	Amphibious Transport Docks	14	—	—
LSD	Dock Landing Ships	13	—	11
LST	Tank Landing Ships	20	—	24
PATROL SHIPS AND CRAFT				
PHM	Patrol Hydrofoil Missile Ships	—	2	—
PGH	Patrol Gunboats (hydrofoil)	1	—	—
PCH	Patrol Craft (hydrofoil)	1	—	—
PG	Patrol Gunboats/Missile Boats	14	—	—
PTF	Fast Patrol Craft	17	—	—
MINE WARFARE SHIPS				
MSO	Ocean Minesweepers	25	—	19
MSC	Coastal Minesweepers	9	—	2
UNDERWAY REPLENISHMENT SHIPS		54	1	13
FLEET SUPPORT SHIPS		82	3	28
SEALIFT SHIPS		38	6	16
EXPERIMENTAL, RESEARCH AND SURVEYING SHIPS		42	—	5

NOTES: (a) Includes ships undergoing overhaul and refuelling in the case of nuclear-powered ships; also includes 37 destroyers and 31 minesweepers (MSO-MSC) assigned to the Naval Reserve Force. (b) Generally includes ships authorised through Fiscal Year 1974 new construction programme although construction may not have begun.

Mercantile Marine

US Maritime Administration: 569 vessels of 9 127 000 tons gross (13 155 000 tons deadweight) active as of 1 Mar 1974. Approx 400 additional vessels inactive, many of which are scheduled to be scrapped.

Lloyd's Register of Shipping: 4063 vessels of 14912432 tons gross.

Fiscal Year 1975 New Construction Programme

2 Nuclear-Powered FBM Submarines (Trident)
3 Nuclear-Powered Attack Submarines (SSN 688 class)
1 Sea Control Ship (SCS)
1 Nuclear-Powered Missile Frigate (DLGN 38 class)
7 Destroyers (DD 963 class)
7 Patrol Frigates (PF)
4 Guided Missile Patrol Hydrofoils (PHM 1 class)
1 Destroyer Tender (AD)
1 Oiler (AO)
1 Fleet Tug (ATF)

Fiscal Year 1975 Conversion Programme

3 Nuclear-Powered FBM Submarines (SSBN) to Poseidon
1 Submarine Tender (AS) to Poseidon support capability

Fiscal Year 1974 New Construction Programme

1 Nuclear-Powered FBM Submarine (Trident)
5 Nuclear-Powered Attack Submarines (SSN 688 class)
1 Nuclear-Powered Aircraft Carrier (CVAN 68 Class)
7 Destroyers (DD 963 Class)

Fiscal Year 1974 Conversion Programme

5 Nuclear-Powered FBM Submarines (SSBN) to Poseidon
1 Nuclear-Powered GM Frigate (DLGN) to improve AAW capability
2 Guided Missile Frigates (DLG) to improve AAW capability

Fiscal Year 1973 New Construction Programme

6 Nuclear-Powered Attack Submarines (SSN 688 class)
7 Destroyers (DD 963 class)
1 Patrol Frigate (PF)
2 Guided Missile Patrol Hydrofoils (PHM)
1 Destroyer Tender (AD 37 class)
1 Submarine Tender (AS 36 class)
2 Salvage and Rescue Tugs (ATS 1 class)

Fiscal Year 1973 Conversion Programme

2 Guided Missile Frigates (DLG) to improve AAW capability
6 Nuclear-Powered FBM Submarines (SSBN) to Poseidon
1 Submarine Tender (AS) to Poseidon support capability

Fiscal Year 1972 New Construction Programme

5 Nuclear-Powered Attack Submarines (SSN 688 class)
1 Nuclear-Powered Guided Missile Frigate (DLGN 38 class)
7 Destroyers (DD 963 class)
1 Replenishment Oiler (AOR 1 class)
1 Submarine Tender (AS 36 class)
1 Salvage and Rescue Tug (ATS 1 class)

Fiscal Year 1972 Conversion Programme

2 Guided Missile Frigates (DLG) to improve AAW capability
6 Nuclear-Powered Fleet Ballistic Missile Submarines (SSBN) to Poseidon

Fiscal Year 1971 New Construction Programme

1 Nuclear-Powered Guided Missile Frigate (DLGN)
4 Nuclear-Powered Attack Submarines (SSN)
6 Destroyers (DD)
2 Amphibious Assault Ships (LHA)
2 Oceanographic Research Ships (AGOR)

Fiscal Year 1971 Conversion Programme

6 Nuclear-Powered Fleet Ballistic Missile Submarines (SSBN) to Poseidon
4 Guided Missile Frigates (DLG) to improve AAW capability
The original FY 1971 programme has been modified as reflected above.

Fiscal Year 1970 New Construction Programme

1 Nuclear-Powered Attack Carrier (CVAN)
1 Nuclear-Powered Guided Missile Frigate (DLGN)
3 Destroyers (DD)
3 Nuclear-Powered Attack Submarines (SSN)
2 Amphibious Assault Ships (LHA)

Fiscal Year 1970 Conversion Programme

4 Nuclear-Powered Fleet Ballistic Missile Submarines (SSBN) to Poseidon
1 Guided Missile Frigate (DLG) to improve AAW capability
5 Ocean Minesweepers (MSO)
The original FY 1970 programme has been modified to reflect the above data.

SPECIAL NOTES

United States Navy Ships that are in active commission are indicated by an asterisk next to the particular ship's name. It should be noted that this marking for active ships applies ONLY to the United States Navy section of *Jane's Fighting Ships*.

The introductory passages in the United States section of this edition are based primarily on official United States Government statements and congressional hearings on the Fiscal Year 1975 Defence Budget. Any interpretation of these statements and hearings is solely the responsibility of the Compiler and Editor of the United States section, Mr. Norman Polmar.

Personnel

	30 June 1973 (Actual)	30 June 1974 (Planned)	30 June 1975 (Planned)
Navy			
Officers	67 600	67 600	66 150
Enlisted men and women	490 009	479 240	469 980
Marine Corps			
Officers	19 282	18 880	18 670
Enlisted men and women	176 816	177 135	177 725

Naval Aviation

US Naval Aviation currently consists of approx 6 600 aircraft flown by the Navy and Marine Corps. The principal naval aviation organisations are 14 carrier air wings, 24 maritime reconnaissance/patrol squadrons, and three Marine Aircraft Wings. In addition, the Naval Reserve and Marine Corps Reserve operate 7 fighter squadrons, 11 attack squadrons, and 12 patrol squadrons, plus various helicopter and transport units.

Fighters: approx 965 flown by 28 Navy carrier-based squadrons (F-14, F-8, F-4) and 12 Marine fighter squadrons (F-4). F-14 Tomcat procurement planned for 12 Navy squadrons and 4 Marine squadrons; F-8 Crusaders will be phased out with deactivation of carriers *Oriskany* (CVA 34) and *Hancock* (CVA 19). Seven reserve fighter squadrons fly F-4 and F-8 aircraft.
Attack Aircraft: approx 1 540 flown by 42 Navy carrier-based squadrons (A-7, A-6, A-4) and 13 Marine attack squadrons (AV-8A, A-6, A-4). Eleven reserve attack squadrons fly primarily A-4 aircraft.
(In addition to fighter and attack aircraft, carrier air wings have various combinations of E-1B Tracer or E-2A/2C Hawkeye early warning aircraft, EA-6 Prowler or EKA-3B Skywarrior electronic warfare aircraft, RA-5C Vigilante or RF-8G Crusader reconnaissance aircraft, KA-6 Intruder tanker aircraft, S-2 Tracker or S-3 Vigilante anti-submarine aircraft, SH-3 Sea King anti-submarine helicopters, and utility aircraft and helicopters; Marine aircraft wings also have EA-6 electronic warfare, RF-4 reconnaissance, KC-130 cargo-tanker, spotting, and utility aircraft, in addition to several squadrons of helicopters).
Patrol Aircraft: approx 450 P-3 Orion aircraft flown by 24 active Navy patrol squadrons plus special mission squadrons and detachments flying EP-3, RP-3, and WP-3 Orion variants for reconnaissance, weather reporting, and research. Reserve Patrol squadrons fly P-3 Orions and P-2 Neptunes.
Training Aircraft: approx 1 430 assigned to 27 Navy training squadrons (which train Marine and Coast Guard fliers in addition to Navy personnel).
Helicopters: approx 1 310 of all types used by Navy and Marine Corps.
Cargo, Transport, and Utility Aircraft: approx 760 of all types used by Navy and Marine Corps.

MAJOR SHIPYARDS

Naval Shipyards

Boston Naval Shipyard, Boston, Massachusetts; closed in 1973-1974
Charleston Naval Shipyard, Charleston, South Carolina
Hunters Point Naval Shipyard, San Francisco, California (formerly a division of the San Francisco Bay Naval Shipyard and before that the San Francisco Naval Shipyard)
Long Beach Naval Shipyard, Long Beach, California
Mare Island Naval Shipyard, Vallejo, California (formerly a division of the San Francisco Bay Naval Shipyard); closed in 1973-1974
Norfolk Naval Shipyard, Portsmouth, Virginia
Pearl Harbour Shipyard, Pearl Harbour, Hawaii
Philadelphia Naval Shipyard, Philadelphia, Pennsylvania
Portsmouth Naval Shipyard, Portsmouth, New Hampshire (located in Kittery, Maine)
Puget Sound Naval Shipyard, Bremerton, Washington

(Note: None of the above shipyards now is engaged in new construction, but are used for the overhaul and conversion of warships and auxiliaries.)

Commercial Shipyards

Avondale Shipyards, Inc, New Orleans, Louisiana
Bath Iron Works Corp, Bath, Maine
Bethlehem Steel Corp, Sparrows Point, Maryland
General Dynamics Corp, Electric Boat Division, Groton, Connecticut (formerly Electric Boat Company)
General Dynamics Corp, Quincy Shipbuilding Division, Quincy, Massachusetts (formerly Bethlehem Steel Corp Yard)
Ingalls Shipbuilding Corp (Litton Industries), East Bank Yard, Pascagoula, Mississippi
Ingalls Shipbuilding Corp (Litton Industries), West Bank Yard, Pascagoula, Mississippi
Lockheed Shipbuilding & Construction Co, Seattle, Washington
National Steel & Shipbuilding Co, San Diego, California
Newport News Shipbuilding & Dry Dock Co, Newport News, Virginia
Todd Shipyards Corp, San Pedro, California
Todd Shipyards Corp, Seattle, Washington

(Note: All of the above yards are engaged in naval and commercial shipbuilding, overhaul, and modernisation except for the General Dynamics/Electric Boat yard which is engaged only in submarine work.)

CLASSIFICATION OF NAVAL SHIPS AND SERVICE CRAFT

The following is the official US Navy list of classifications of naval ships and service craft as promulgated by the Secretary of the Navy.
In actual usage, symbols preceded by the letter "E" indicate that the ship or craft is a prototype in an experimental or developmental status; the prefix "T" indicates that the ship is assigned to the Navy's Military Sealift Command and is civilian manned; and the prefix "F" indicates a ship being constructed by the United States for a foreign government

COMBATANT SHIPS

(1) Warships

Aircraft Carriers:	
Aircraft Carrier	CV
Attack Aircraft Carrier	CVA
Attack Aircraft Carrier (nuclear propulsion)	CVAN
Aircraft Carrier (nuclear propulsion)	CVN
ASW Aircraft Carrier	CVS
Surface Combatants:	
Battleship	BB
Heavy Cruiser	CA
Guided Missile Cruiser	CG
Guided Missile Cruiser (nuclear propulsion)	CGN
Light Cruiser	CL
Guided Missile Light Cruiser	CLG
Destroyer	DD
Guided Missile Destroyer	DDG
Radar Picket Destroyer	DDR
AEGIS Missile Destroyer	DG
Frigate	DL
Guided Missile Frigate	DLG
Guided Missile Frigate (nuclear propulsion)	DLGN
Surface Effect Destroyer	DS
Patrol Frigate	PF
Ocean Escorts:	
Escort Ship	DE
Guided Missile Escort Ship	DEG
Radar Picket Escort Ship	DER
Command Ship	CC
Submarines:	
Submarine	SS
Submarine (nuclear propulsion)	SSN
Guided Missile Submarine	SSG
Fleet Ballistic Missile Submarine (nuclear propulsion)	SSBN
Patrol Ships:	
Patrol Escort	PCE
Patrol Rescue Escort	PCER
Patrol Gunboat	PG
Guided Missile Patrol Hydrofoil	PHM

(2) Amphibious Warfare Ships

Amphibious Command Ship	LCC
Inshore Fire Support Ship	LFR
Amphibious Fire Support Ship	LFS
Amphibious Assault Ship (general purpose)	LHA
Amphibious Cargo Ship	LKA
Amphibious Transport	LPA
Amphibious Transport Dock	LPD
Amphibious Assault Ship	LPH
Amphibious Transport (small)	LPR
Amphibious Transport Submarine	LPSS
Dock Landing Ship	LSD
Tank Landing Ship	LST

(3) Mine Warfare Ships

Mine Countermeasures Ship	MCS
Minesweeper, Coastal (non-magnetic)	MSC
Minesweeper, Fleet (steel hulled)	MSF
Minesweeper, Ocean (non-magnetic)	MSO

COMBATANT CRAFT

(1) Patrol Craft

Patrol Craft (hydrofoil)	PCH
Patrol Gunboat (hydrofoil)	PGH
Fast Patrol Craft	PTF

(2) Landing Craft

Landing Craft, Assault	LCA
Landing Craft, Mechanised	LCM
Landing Craft, Personnel, Large	LCPL
Landing Craft, Personnel, Ramped	LCPR
Landing Craft, Utility	LCU
Landing Craft, Vehicle, Personnel	LCVP
Amphibious Warping Tug	LWT

(3) Mine Countermeasures Craft

Minesweeping Boat	MSB
Minesweeper, Drone	MSD
Minesweeper, Inshore	MSI
Minesweeping Launch	MSL
Minesweeper, River	MSM
Minesweeper, Patrol	MSR
Minesweeper, Special (Device)	MSS

(4) Riverine Warfare Craft

Assault Support Patrol Boat	ASPB
Armoured Troop Carrier	ATC
Command and Control Boat	CCB
Monitor	MON
River Patrol Boat	PBR
Patrol Craft, Inshore	PCF
Quiet Fast Boat	QFB
Riverine Utility Craft	RUC
Strike Assault Boat	STAB

(5) SEAL Support Craft

Landing Craft Swimmer Reconnaissance	LCSR
Light SEAL Support Craft	LSSC
Medium SEAL Support Craft	MSSC
Swimmer Delivery Vehicle	SDV

(6) Mobile Inshore Underseas Warfare (MIUW) Craft

MIUW Attack Craft	MAC

AUXILIARY SHIPS

Destroyer Tender	AD
Degaussing Ship	ADG
Ammunition Ship	AE
Store Ship	AF
Combat Store Ship	AFS
Miscellaneous	AG
Escort Research Ship	AGDE
Hydrofoil Research Ship	AGEH
Environmental Research Ship	AGER
Miscellaneous Command Ship	AGF
Missile Range Instrumentation Ship	AGM
Major Communications Relay Ship	AGMR
Oceanographic Research Ship	AGOR
Patrol Craft Tender	AGP
Radar Picket Ship	AGR
Surveying Ship	AGS
Auxiliary Submarine	AGSS
Technical Research Ship	AGTR
Hospital Ship	AH
Cargo Ship	AK
Cargo Ship Dock	AKD
Light Cargo Ship	AKL
Vehicle Cargo Ship	AKR
Stores Issue Ship	AKS
Cargo Ship and Aircraft Ferry	AKV
Net Laying Ship	ANL
Oiler	AO
Fast Combat Support Ship	AOE
Gasoline Tanker	AOG
Replenishment Oiler	AOR
Transport	AP
Self-propelled Barracks Ship	APB
Repair Ship	AR
Battle Damage Repair Ship	ARB
Cable Repairing Ship	ARC
Internal Combustion Engine Repair Ship	ARG
Landing Craft Repair Ship	ARL
Salvage Ship	ARS
Salvage Lifting Ship	ARSD
Salvage Craft Tender	ARST
Aircraft Repair Ship (Aircraft)	ARVA
Aircraft Repair Ship (Engine)	ARVE
Aircraft Repair Ship (Helicopter)	ARVH
Submarine Tender	AS
Submarine Rescue Ship	ASR
Auxiliary Ocean Tug	ATA
Fleet Ocean Tug	ATF
Salvage and Rescue Ship	ATS
Auxiliary Training Submarine	ATSS
Seaplane Tender	AV
Guided Missile Ship	AVM
Aviation Supply Ship	AVS
Auxiliary Aircraft Transport	AVT
Distilling Ship	AW
Training Aircraft Carrier	CVT
Fast Deployment Logistic Ship	FDL

SERVICE CRAFT*

Large Auxiliary Floating Dry Dock	AFDB
Small Auxiliary Floating Dry Dock	AFDL
Medium Auxiliary Floating Dry Dock	AFDM
Auxiliary Deep Submergence Support Vehicle	AGDS
Barracks Craft (non-self propelled)	APL
Auxiliary Repair Dry Dock	ARD
Medium Auxiliary Repair Dry Dock	ARDM
Deep Submergence Rescue Vehicle	DSRV
Deep Submergence Vehicle	DSV
Unclassified Miscellaneous	IX
Unclassified Miscellaneous Submarine	IXSS
Submersible Research Vehicle (nuclear propulsion)	NR
Target and Training Submarine (self-propelled)	SST
Submersible Craft (self-propelled)	X
Miscellaneous Auxiliary (self-propelled)	YAG
Open Lighter	YC
Car Float	YCF
Aircraft Transportation Lighter	YCV
Floating Crane	YD
Diving Tender	YDT
Covered Lighter (self-propelled)	YF
Ferryboat or Launch (self-propelled)	YFB
Yard Floating Dry Dock	YFD
Covered Lighter	YFN
Large Covered Lighter	YFNB
Dry Dock Companion Craft	YFND
Lighter (special purpose)	YFNX
Floating Power Barge	YFP
Refrigerated Covered Lighter (self-propelled)	YFR
Refrigerated Covered Lighter	YFRN
Covered Lighter (Range Tender) (self-propelled)	YFRT
Harbour Utility Craft (self-propelled)	YFU
Garbage Lighter (self-propelled)	YG
Garbage Lighter (non-self-propelled)	YGN
Salvage Lift Craft, Heavy	YHLC
Salvage Lift Craft, Light (self-propelled)	YLLC
Dredge (self-propelled)	YM
Salvage Lift Craft, Medium	YMLC
Gate Craft	YNG
Fuel Oil Barge (self-propelled)	YO
Gasoline Barge (self-propelled)	YOG
Gasoline Barge	YOGN
Fuel Oil Barge	YON
Oil Storage Barge	YOS
Patrol Craft (self-propelled)	YP
Floating Pile Driver	YPD
Floating Workshop	YR
Repair and Berthing Barge	YRB
Repair, Berthing and Messing Barge	YRBM
Floating Dry Dock Workshop (Hull)	YRDH
Floating Dry Dock Workshop (Machine)	YRDM
Radiological Repair Barge	YRR
Salvage Craft Tender	YRST
Seaplane Wrecking Derrick (self-propelled)	YSD
Sludge Removal Barge	YSR
Large Harbour Tug (self-propelled)	YTB
Small Harbour Tug (self-propelled)	YTL
Medium Harbour Tug (self-propelled)	YTM
Water Barge (self-propelled)	YW
Water Distilling Barge	YWDN
Water Barge	YWN

*Self-propelled barges are indicated in parenthesis. The final letter "N" generally indicates non-self-propelled.

CLASSIFICATION OF MARITIME COMMISSION SHIP DESIGNS

Ships constructed under the jurisdiction of the US Maritime Commission by private shipyards are assigned Maritime Commission design classifications. These classifications consist of three groups of letters and numbers.

First group letter(s) indicate type of ship and number indicates size class. The letters of Maritime Commission ship classifications now on the US Navy List are:

Cargo	C
Emergency Cargo (Liberty)	EC
Passenger	P
Refrigerator	R
Special Purpose	S
Tanker	T
Victory Cargo	VC

Second group letter(s) indicate type of propulsion and number "2" indicates twin shaft ship and "4" quadruple shaft ship.

Motor (diesel)	M
Motor (diesel) Electric	ME
Steam (reciprocating or turbine)	S
Steam (turbine) Electric	SE

Third group of letters and numbers indicates the design of a particular type of ship, beginning with A1.

FLEET BALLISTIC MISSILES

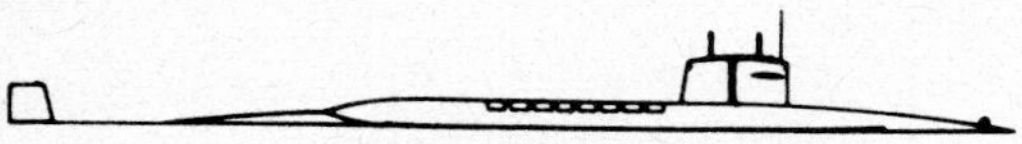

LAFAYETTE (SSBN 616)

GEORGE WASHINGTON (SSBN 598)

SUBMARINES

STURGEON (SSN 637)

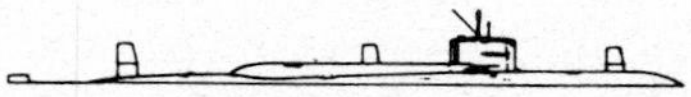

TULLIBEE (SSN 597)

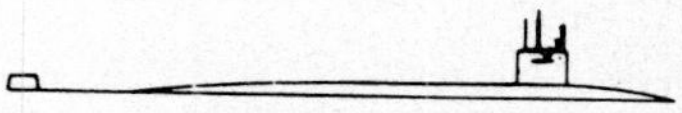

PERMIT (SSN 594)

HALIBUT (SSN 587)

TRITON (SSN 586)

SKIPJACK (SSN 585)

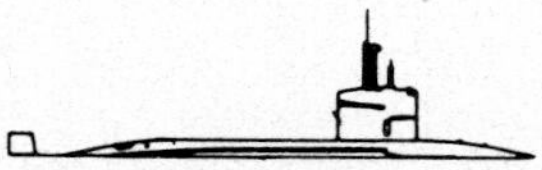

BARBEL (SS 580)

SWORDFISH (SSN 579)

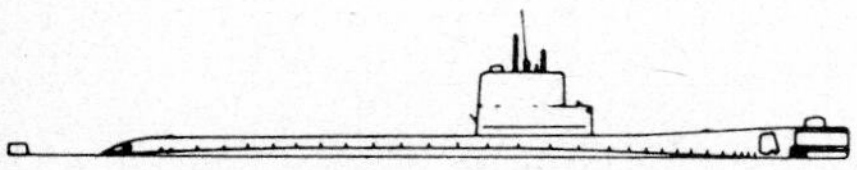

SEAWOLF (SSN 575)

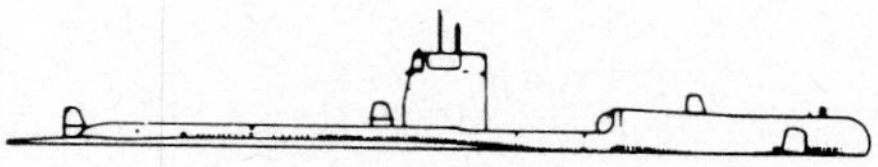

GRAYBACK (LPSS 574)

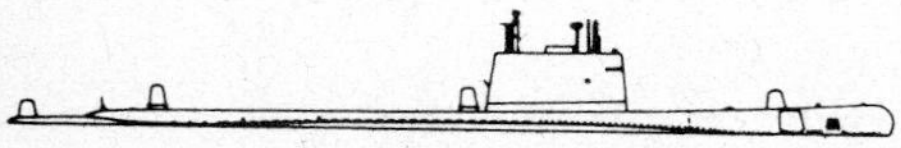

SAILFISH (SS 572)

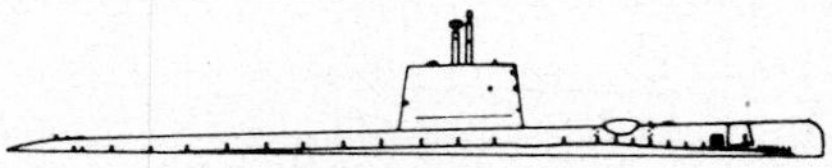

NAUTILUS (SSN 571)

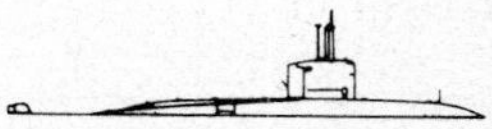

ALBACORE (AGSS 569)

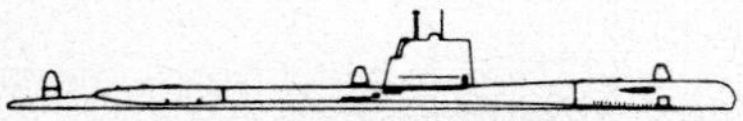

WAHOO (SS 565) Tang Class

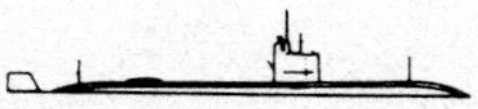

DOLPHIN (AGSS 555)

Guppy III Type

AIRCRAFT CARRIERS

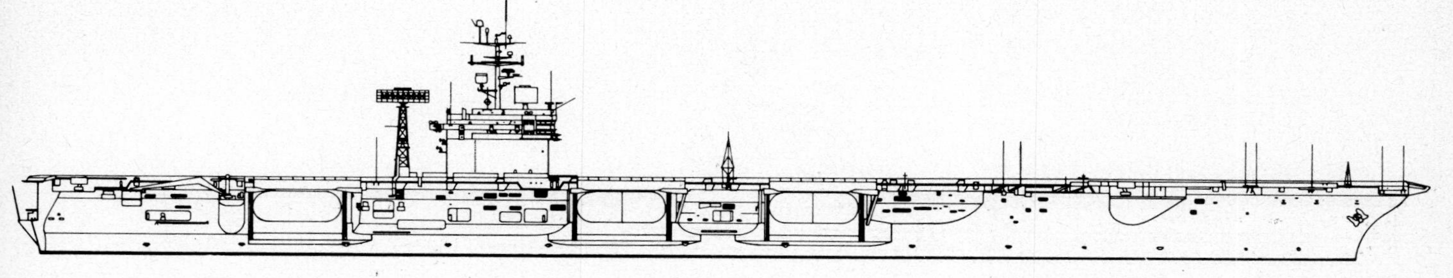

NIMITIZ (CVAN 68)

Scale: 1 inch = 150 feet (1 : 1 800)

Drawings by A. D. Baker

Aircraft Carriers *—continued*

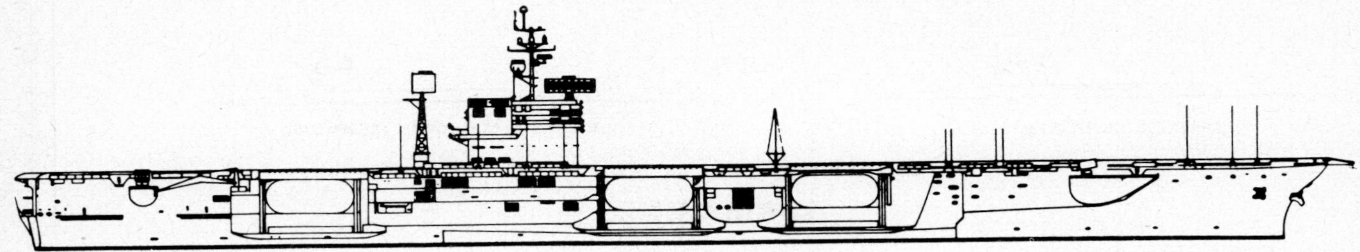

JOHN F. KENNEDY (CVA 67)

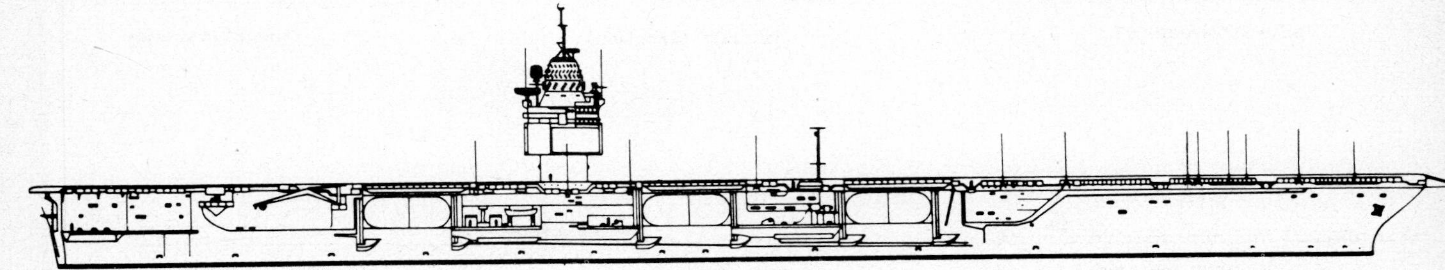

ENTERPRISE (CVAN 65)

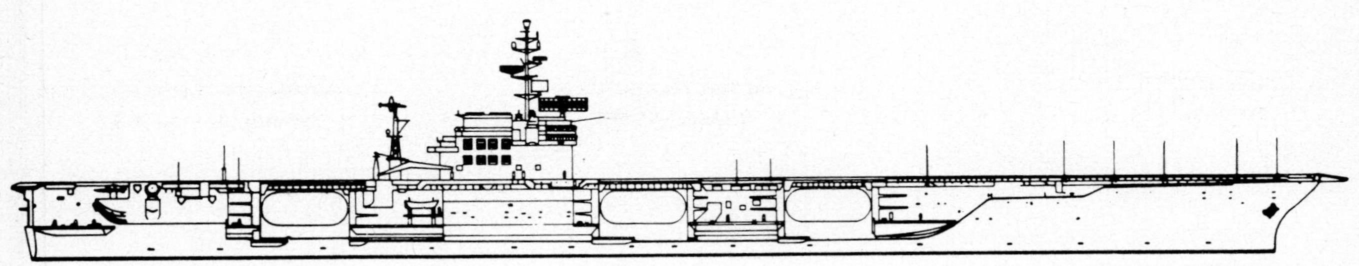

KITTY HAWK (CVA 63)

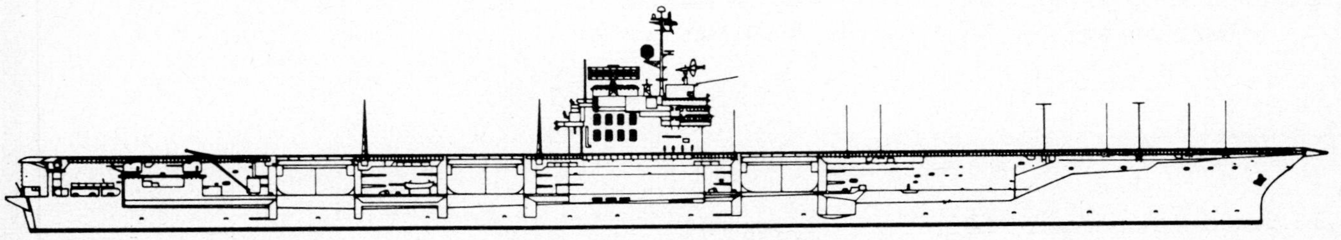

SARATOGA (CVA 60) Forrestal Class

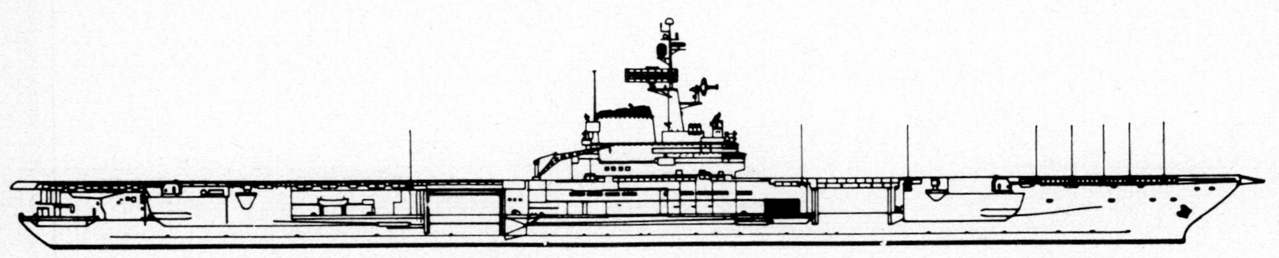

CORAL SEA (CVA 43) Midway Class (ROOSEVELT similar)

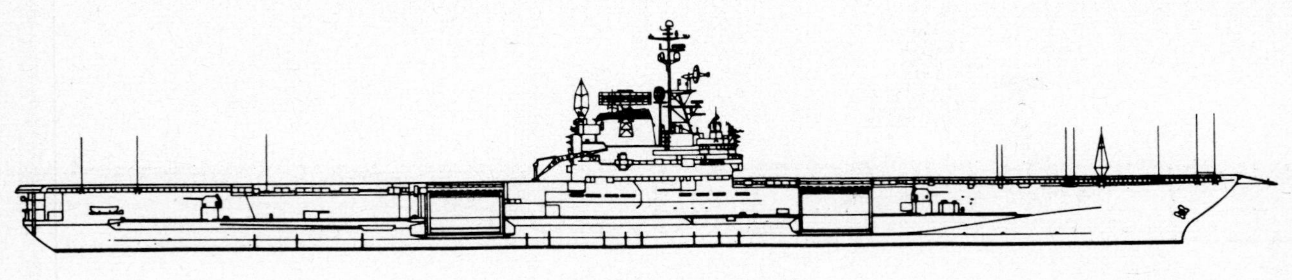

MIDWAY (CVA 41)

Scale: 1 inch = 150 feet (1 : 1 800)

Aircraft Carriers—*continued*

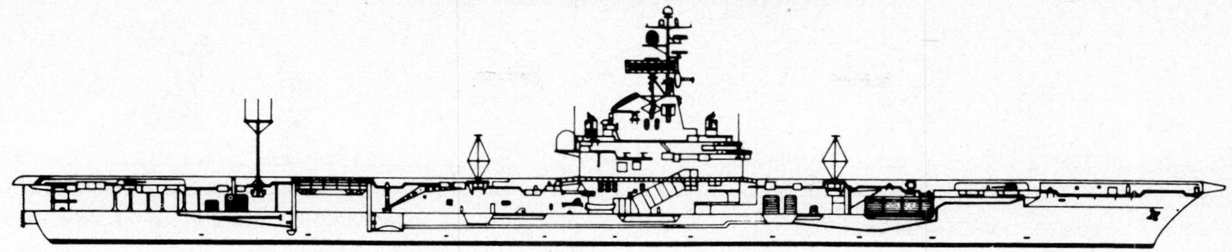

HANCOCK (CVA 19)

GUIDED MISSILE CRUISERS

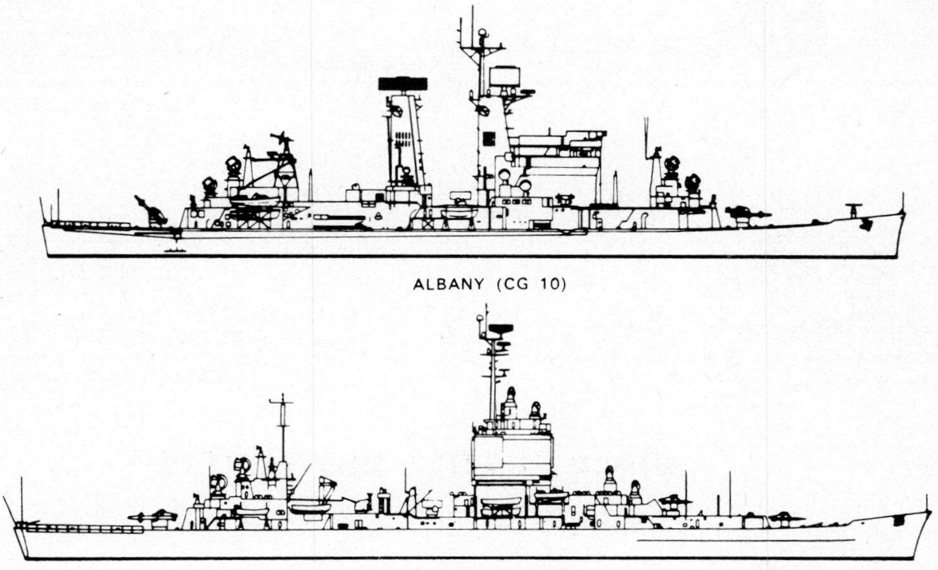

ALBANY (CG 10)

LONG BEACH (CGN 9)

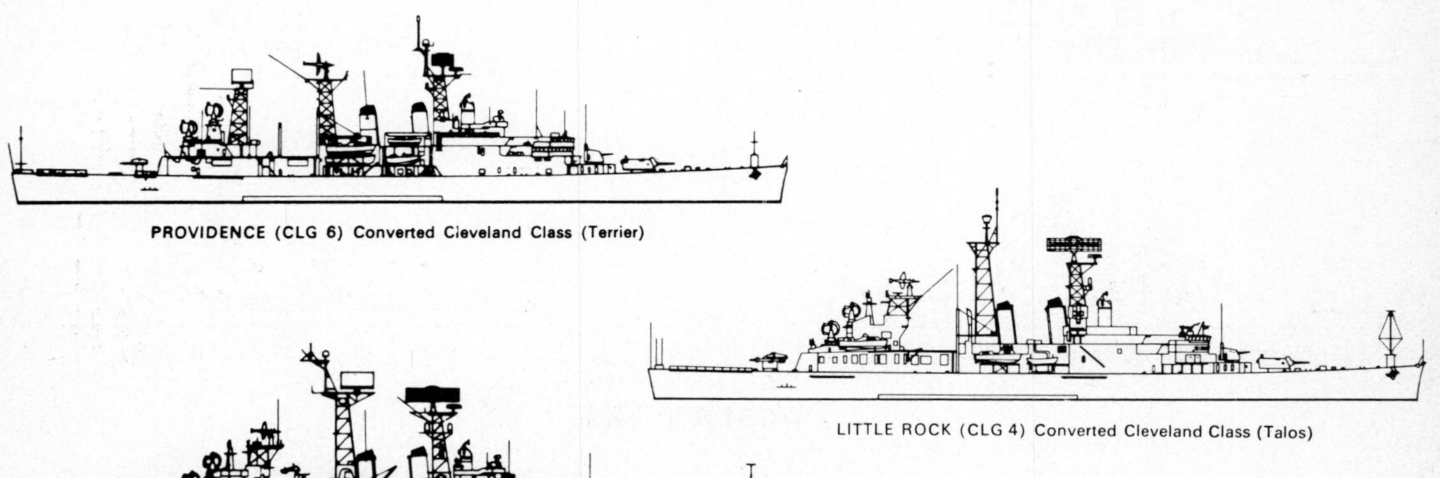

PROVIDENCE (CLG 6) Converted Cleveland Class (Terrier)

LITTLE ROCK (CLG 4) Converted Cleveland Class (Talos)

GALVESTON (CLG 3) Converted Cleveland Class (Talos)

GUIDED MISSILE FRIGATES

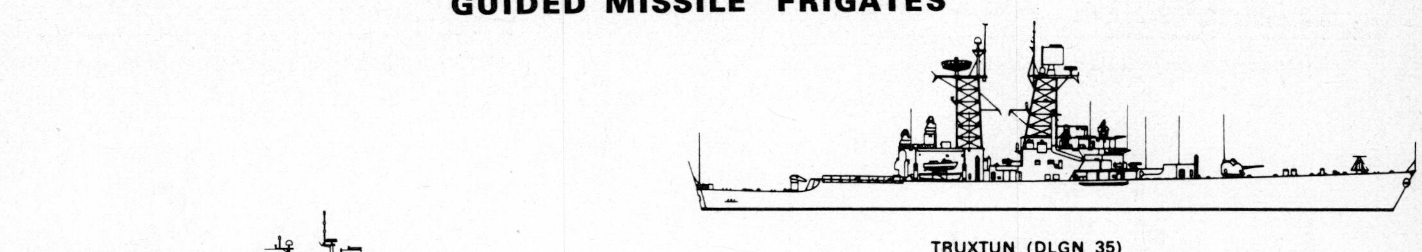

TRUXTUN (DLGN 35)

CALIFORNIA (DLGN 36)

Scale: 1 inch = 150 feet (1 : 1 800)

Guided Missile Frigates—*continued*

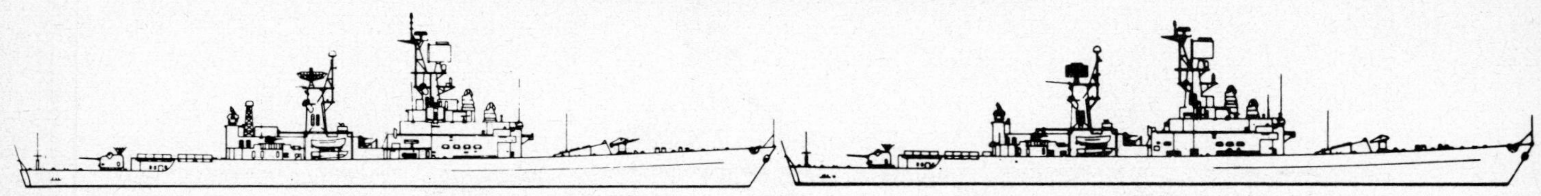

FOX (DLG 33) Belknap Class

WAINWRIGHT (DLG 28) Belknap Class

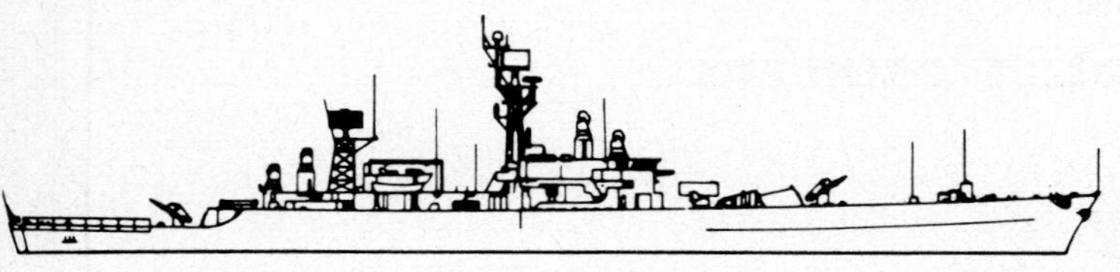

BAINBRIDGE (DLGN 25)

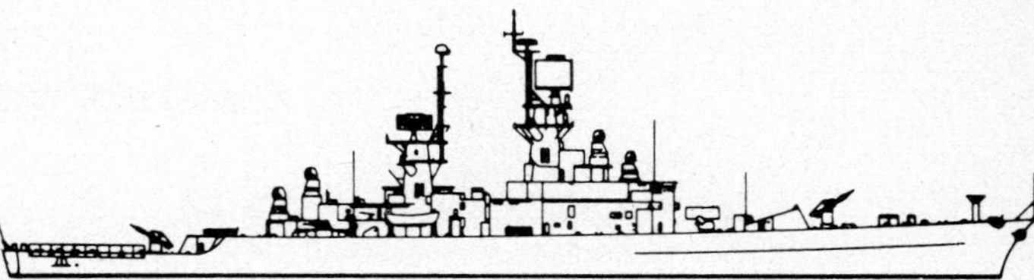

LEAHY (DLG 16)

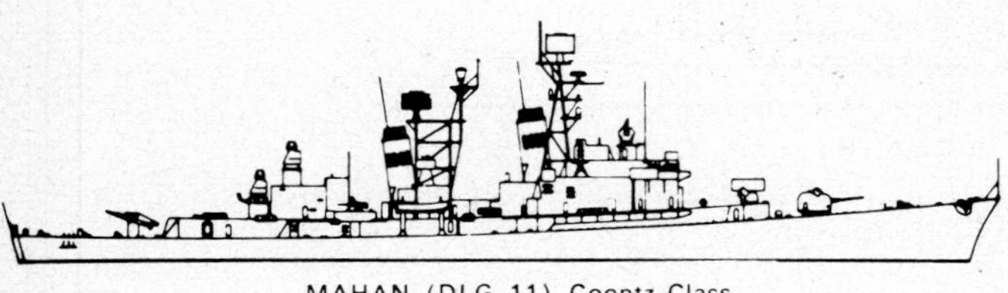

MAHAN (DLG 11) Coontz Class

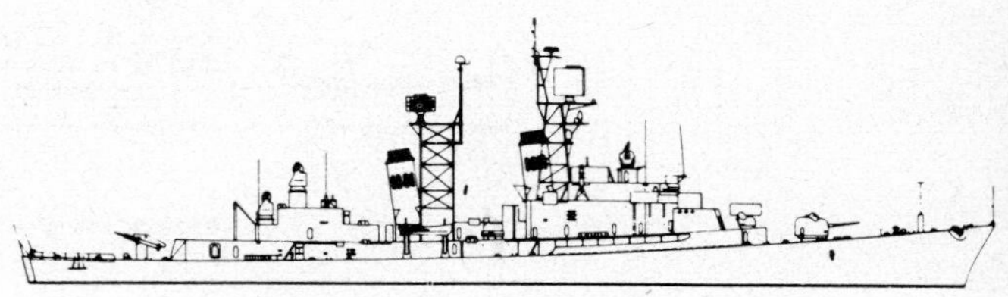

FARRAGUT (DLG 6) Coontz Class

GUIDED MISSILE DESTROYERS

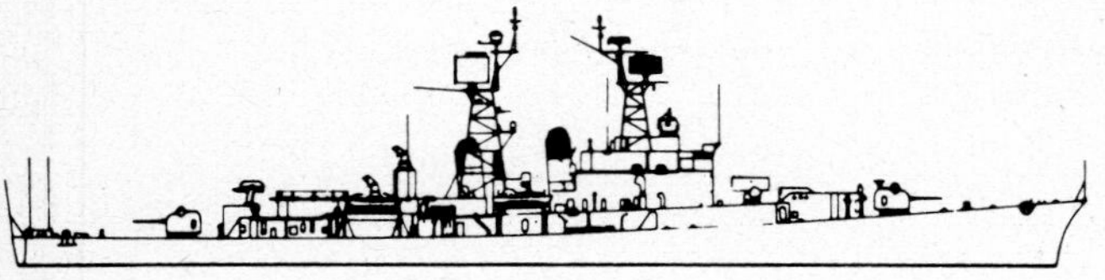

MITSCHER (DDG 35)

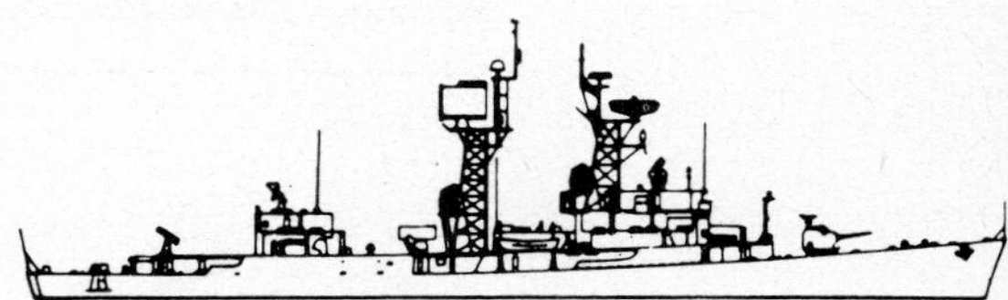

SOMERS (DDG 34) Converted Forrest Sherman Class

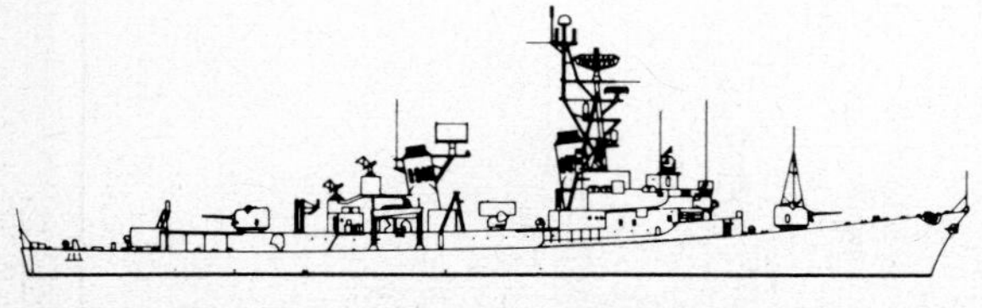

WADDELL (DDG 24) Charles F. Adams Class

BARNEY (DDG 6) Charles F. Adams Class

DESTROYERS

MANLEY (DD 940) Forrest Sherman Class

JONAS INGRAM (DD 938) Forrest Sherman Class (ASW)

BARRY (DD 933) Forrest Sherman Class (ASW)

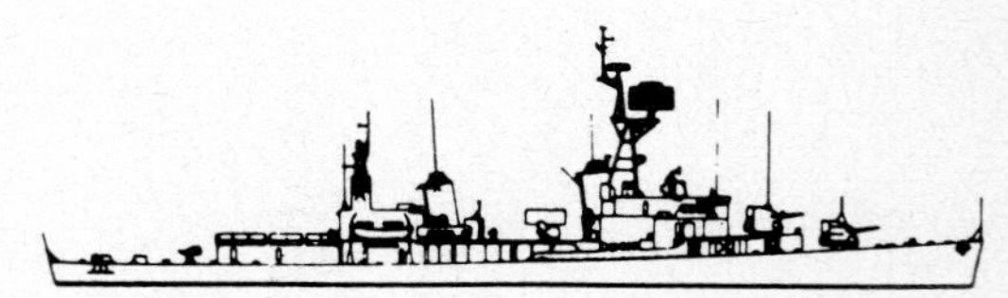

Gearing Class FRAM I (all guns forward)

Scale: 1 inch = 150 feet (1 : 1 800)

Destroyers—*continued*

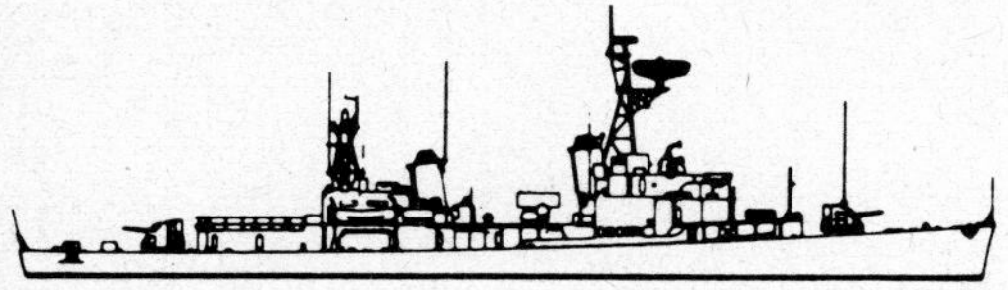
Gearing Class FRAM I (guns forward and aft)

ROBERT A. OWENS (DD 827) Carpenter Class FRAM I

Allen M. Sumner Class FRAM II

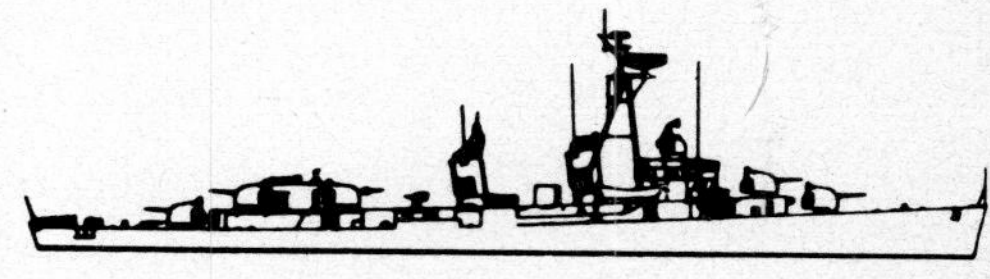
Fletcher Class (5 guns)

Fletcher Class (4 guns)

ESCORT SHIPS

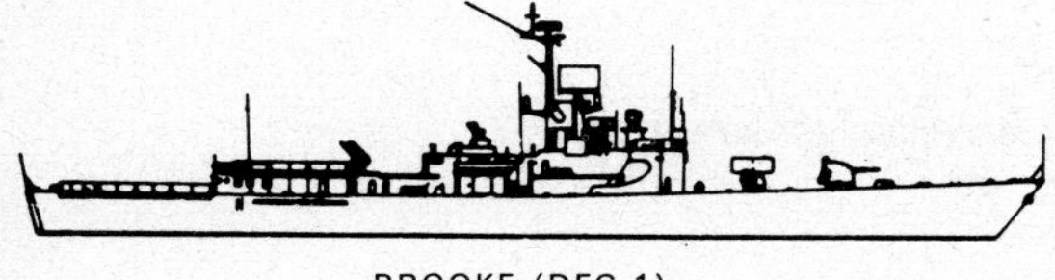
BROOKE (DEG 1)

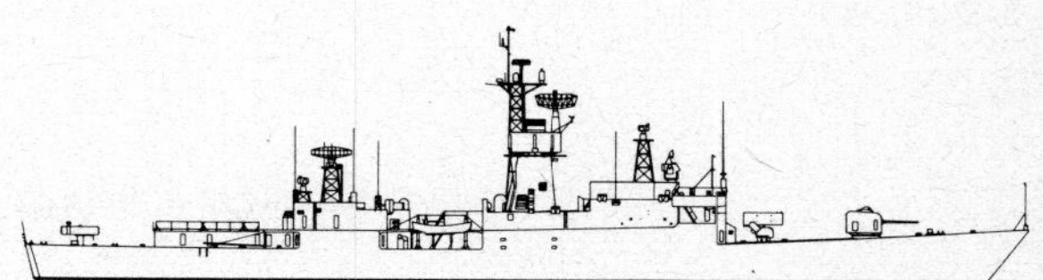
DOWNES (DE 1070) NATO Sea Sparrow

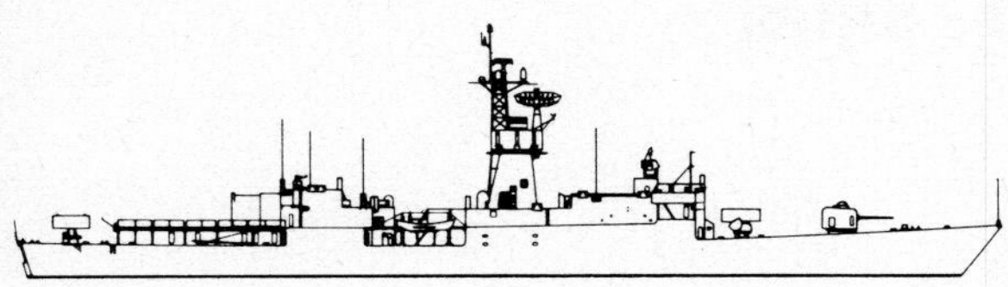
Knox Class (improved)

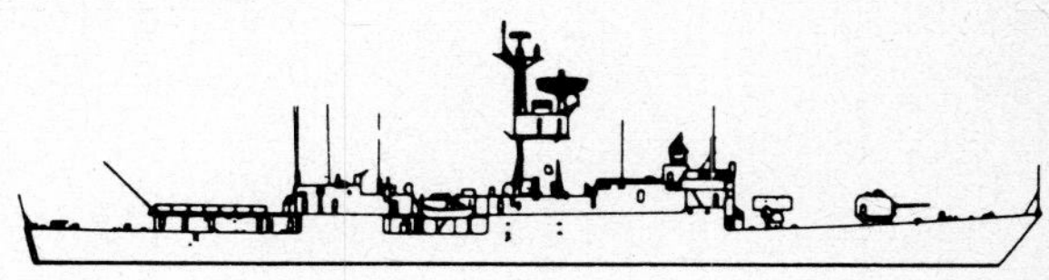
Knox Class

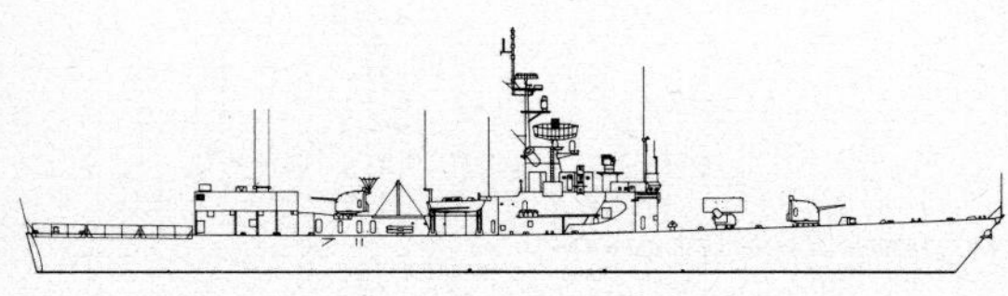
Garcia Class (LAMPS Modification)

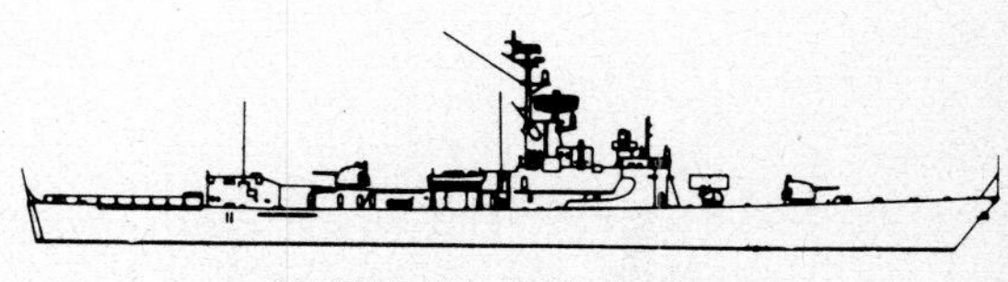
SAMPLE (DE 1048) Garcia Class

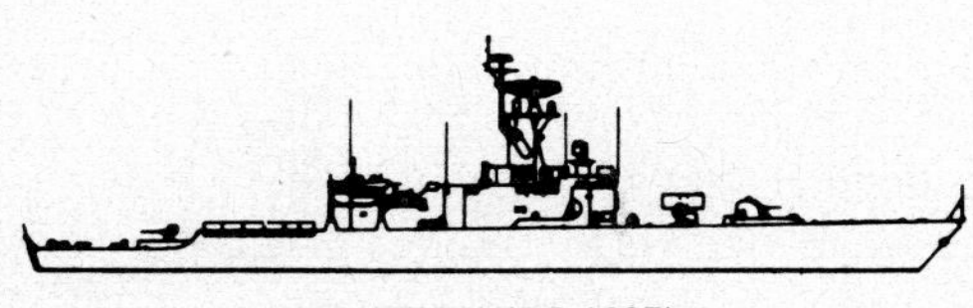
BRONSTEIN (DE 1037)

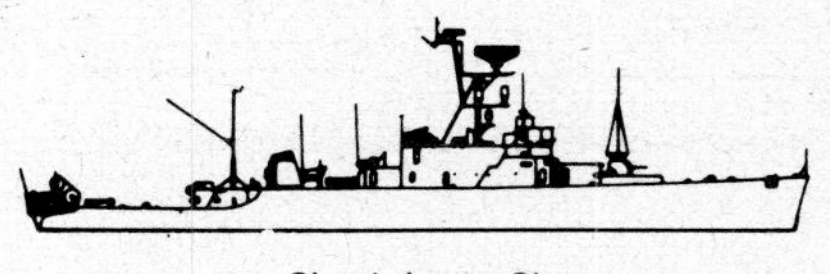
Claud Jones Class

CALCATERRA (DER 390)
Edsall Class Radar Pickets

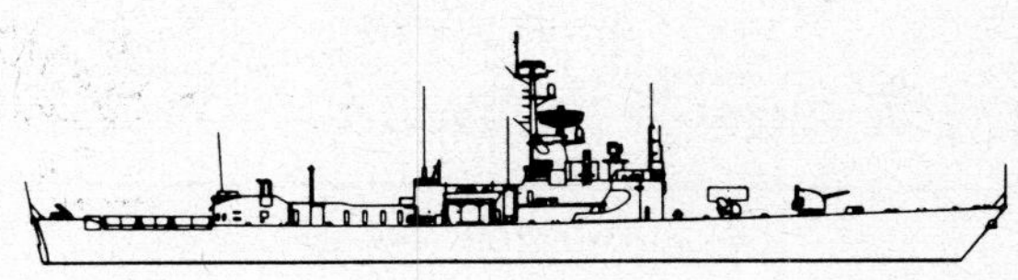
GLOVER (AGDE 1)

Scale: 1 inch = 150 feet (1 : 1 800)

FIRE SUPPORT SHIPS/CRUISERS

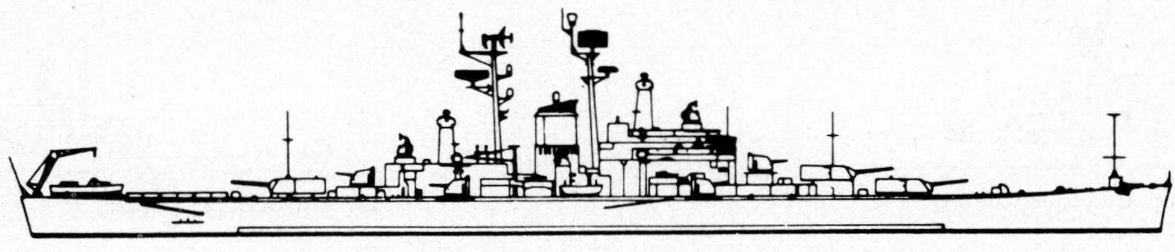

NEWPORT NEWS (CA 148) Des Moines Class

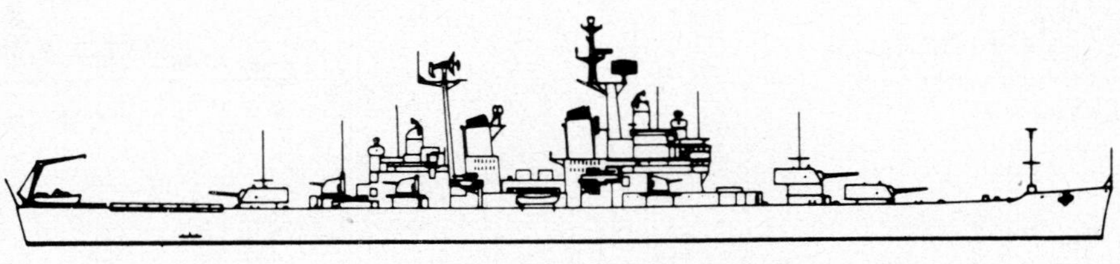

ST. PAUL (CA 73) Baltimore Class

COMMAND SHIPS

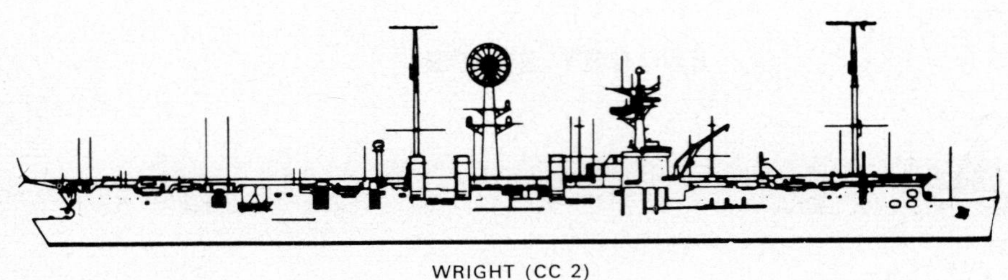

WRIGHT (CC 2)

AMPHIBIOUS WARFARE SHIPS

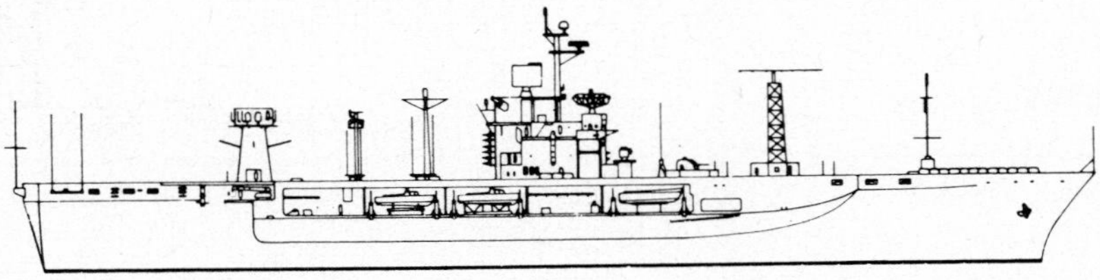

BLUE RIDGE (LCC 19)

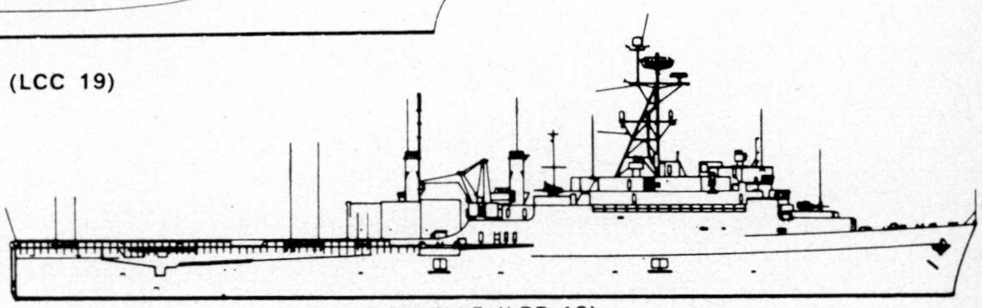

NASHVILLE (LPD 13)

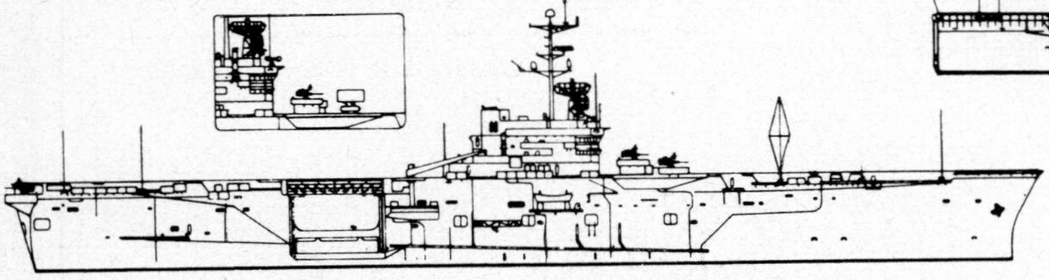

TRIPOLI (LPH 10) Iwo Jima Class (BPDMS inset)

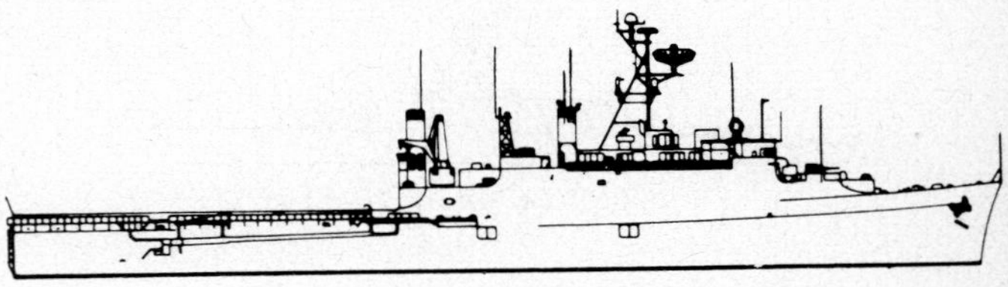

RALEIGH (LPD 1)

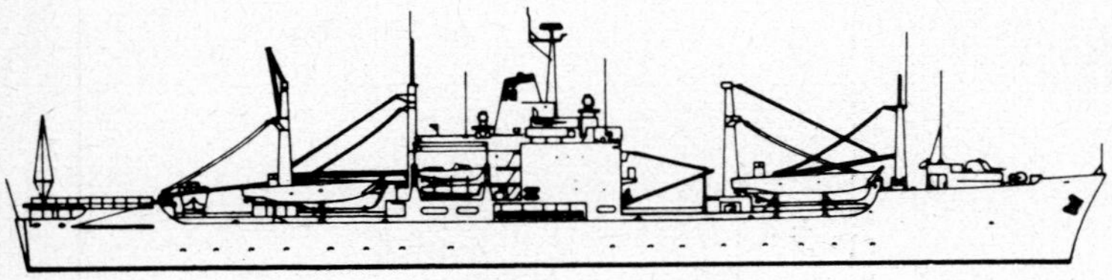

CHARLESTON (LKA 113)

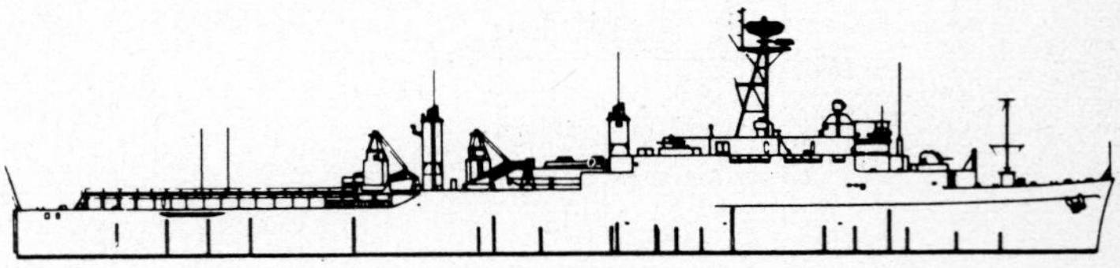

ANCHORAGE (LSD 36)

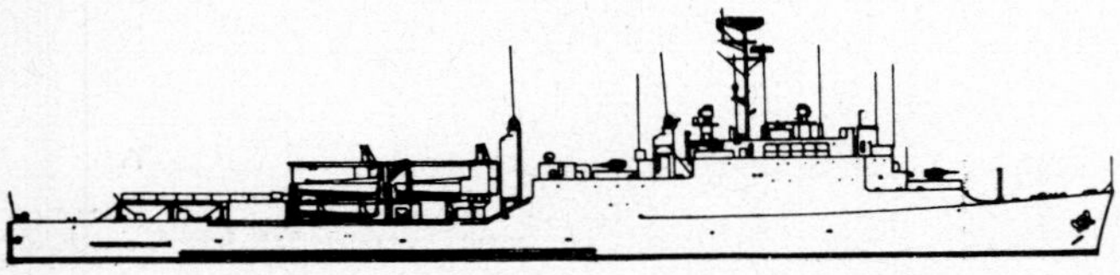

HERMITAGE (LSD 34) Thomaston Class

Scale: 1 inch = 150 feet (1 : 1 800)

Amphibious Warfare Ships—*continued*

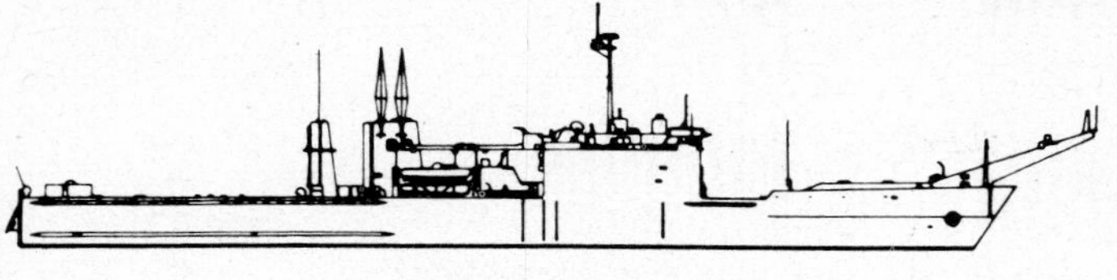

NEWPORT (LST 1179)

Suffolk County Class (LST 1171)

AUXILIARY SHIPS

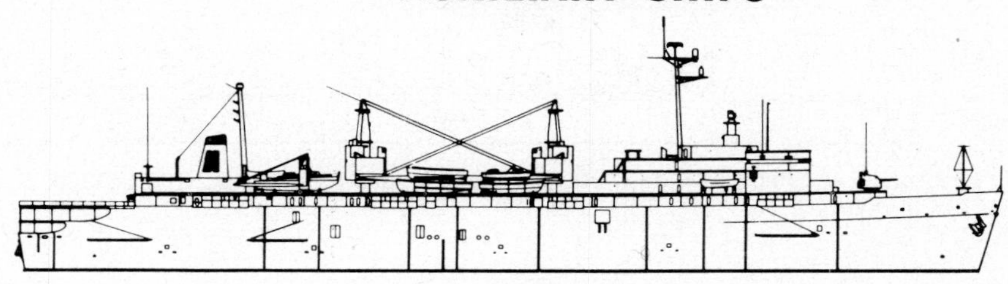

SAMUEL GOMPERS Class (AD 37)

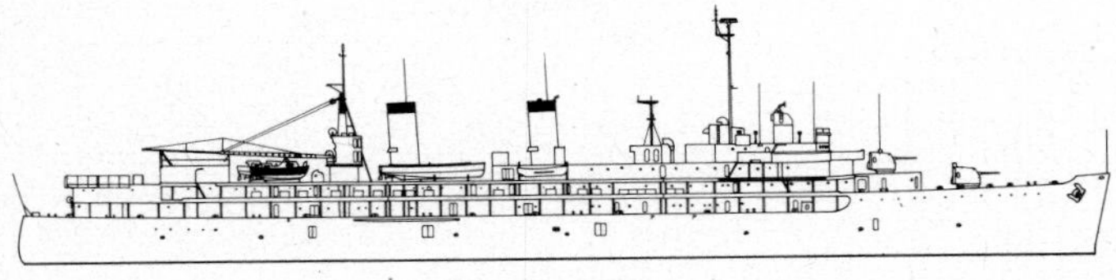

YOSEMITE (AD 19)

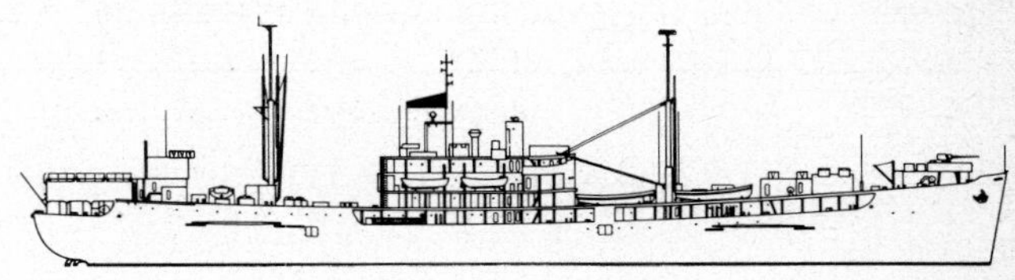

SHENANDOAH (AD 26)

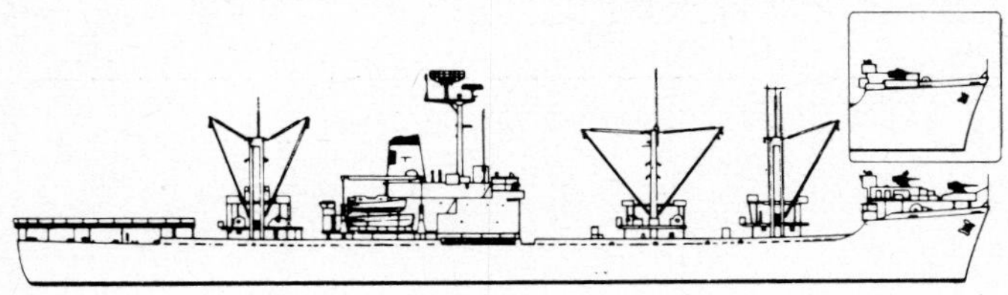

MAUNA KEA (AE 22) Suribachi Class
(inset shows gun variation)

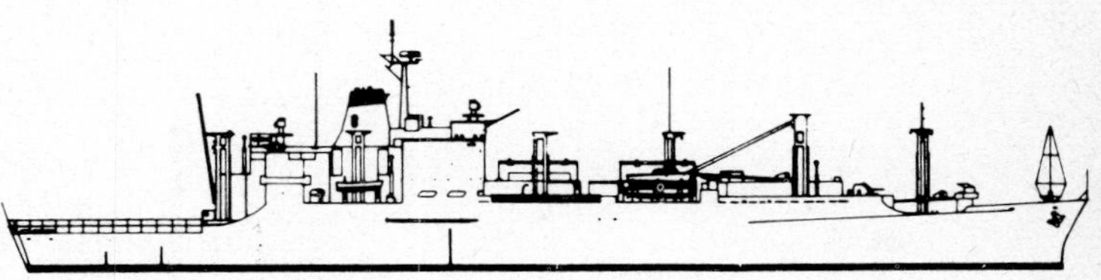

SANTA BARBARA (AE 28) Kilauea Class

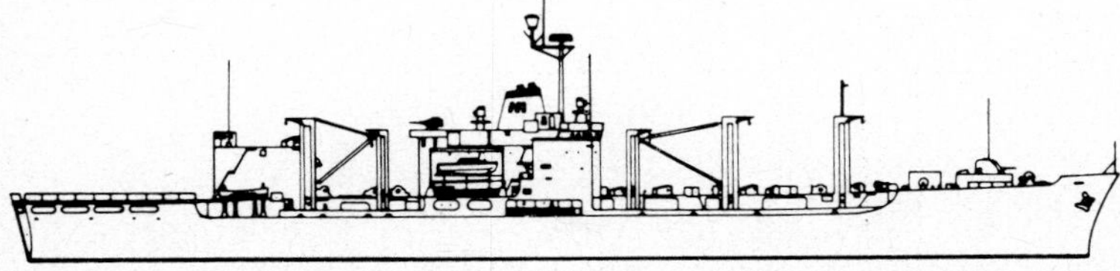

SAN JOSE (AFS 7) Mars Class

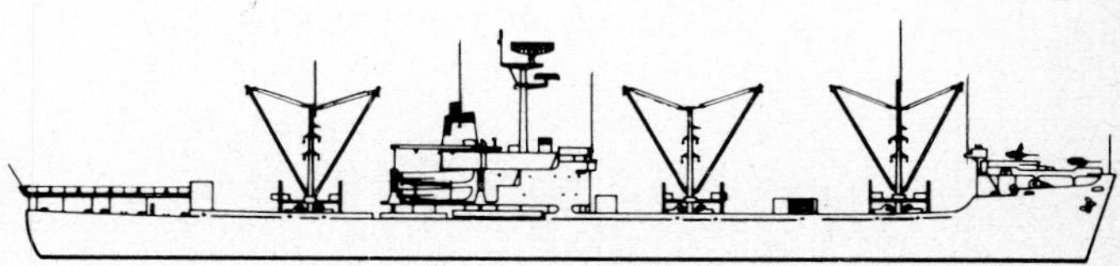

RIGEL (AF 58) R3-S-4A Type

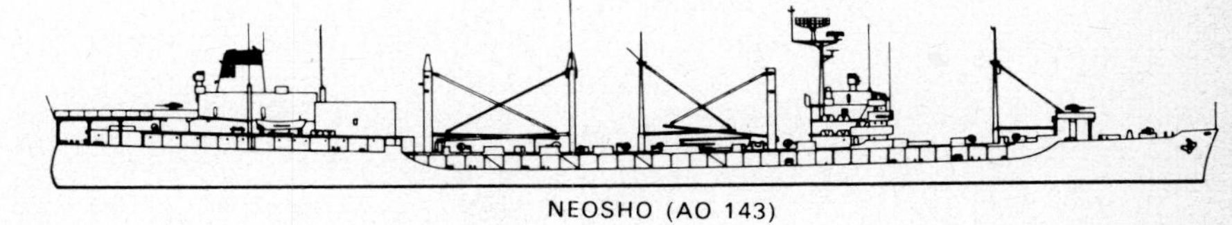

NEOSHO (AO 143)

MISPILLION (AO 105) Jumboised T3-S2-A3

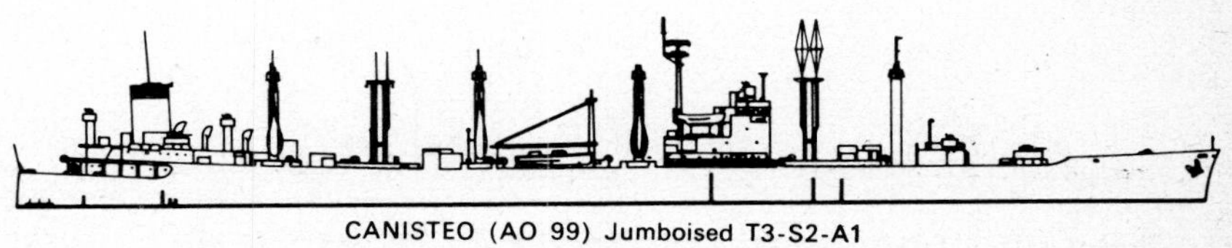

CANISTEO (AO 99) Jumboised T3-S2-A1

Scale: 1 inch = 150 feet (1 : 1 800)

Auxiliary Ships—*continued*

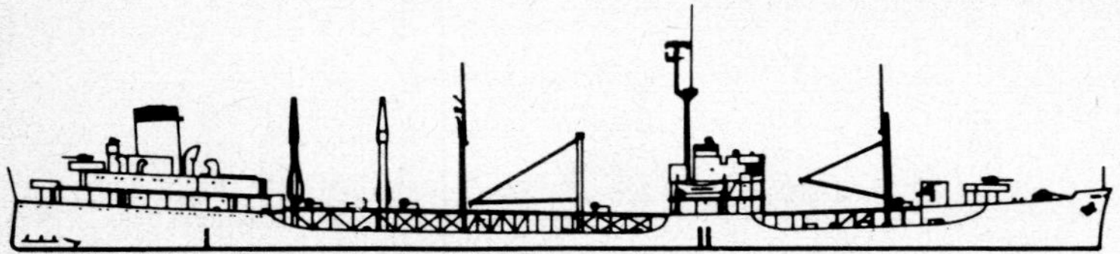

GUADALUPE (AO 32) T3-S2-A1 Type

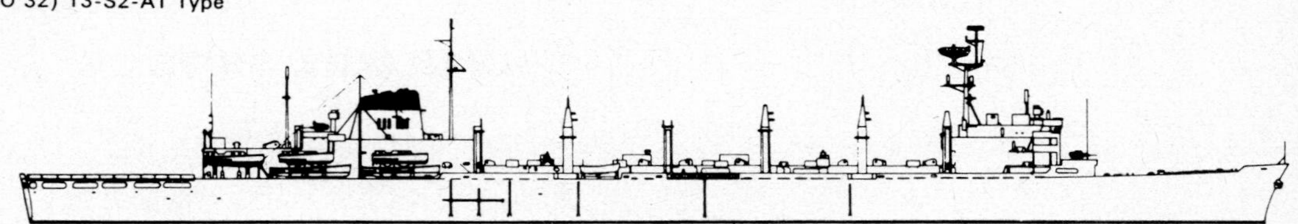

CAMDEN (AOE 2) Sacramento Class

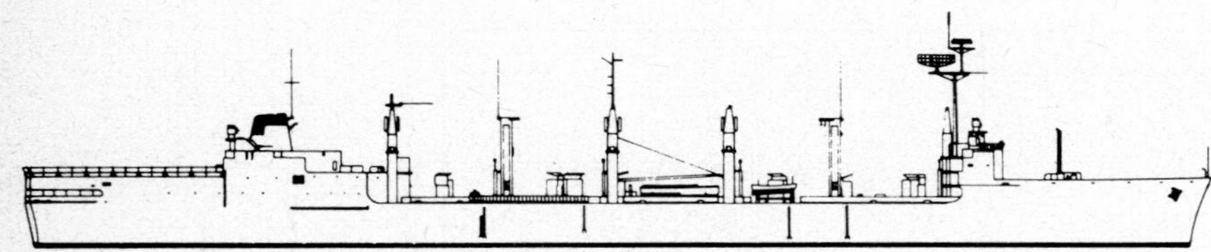

WABASH (AOR 5) Wichita Class

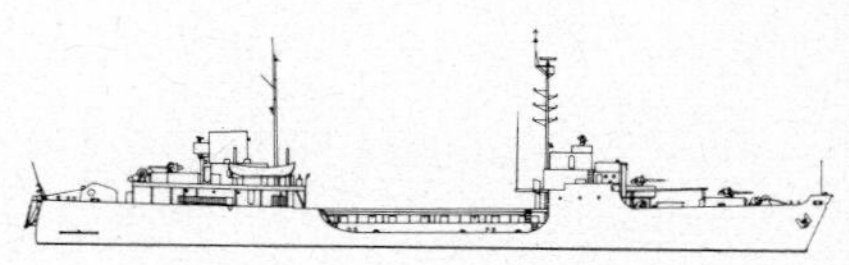

Patapsco Class

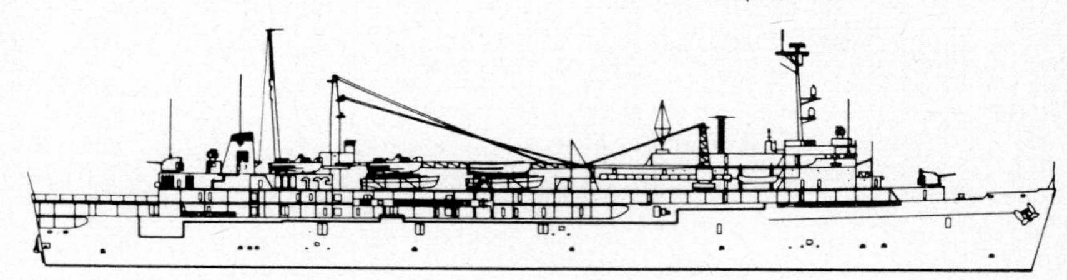

L. Y. SPEAR (AS 36)

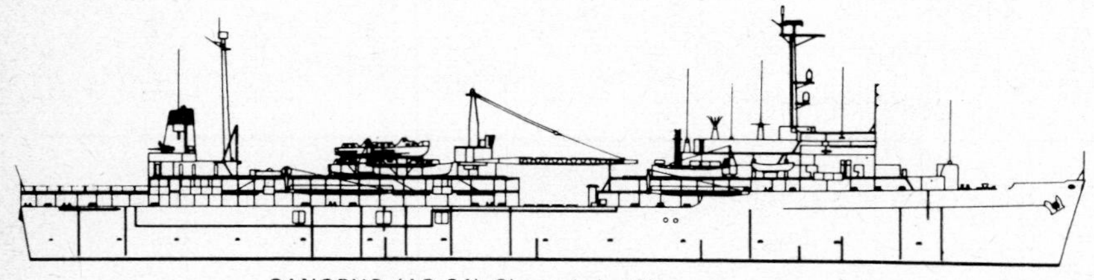

CANOPUS (AS 34) Simon Lake Class

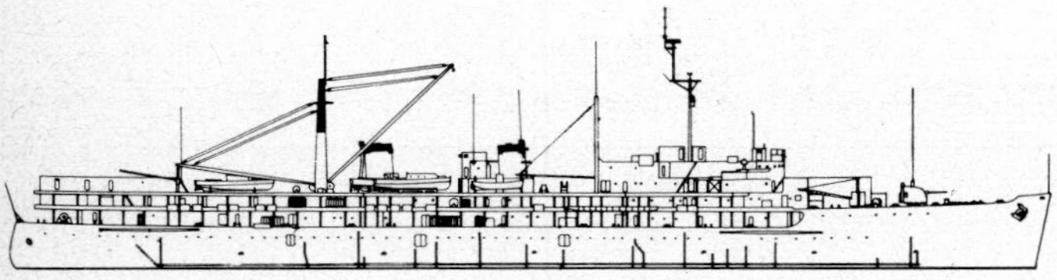

HOWARD W. GILMORE (AS 16)

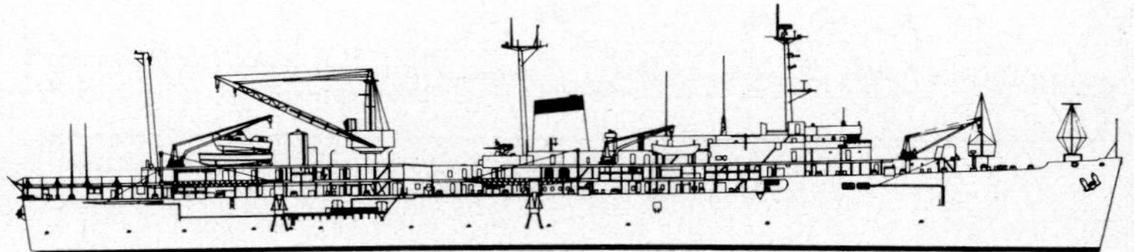

HUNLEY (AS 31)

EDENTON (ATS 1)

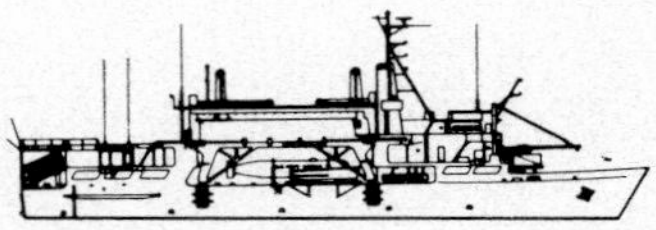

PIGEON (ASR 21)

Scale: 1 inch = 150 feet (1 : 1 800)

PATROL SHIPS AND CRAFT

ANTELOPE (PG 86) Asheville Class

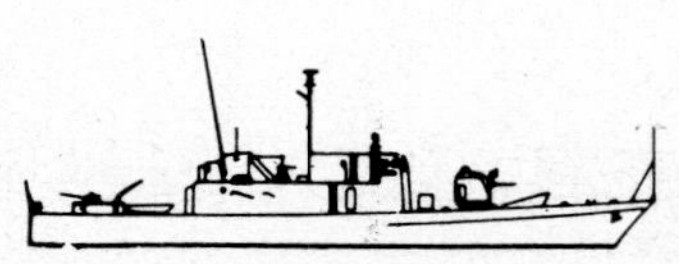

BEACON (PG 99) Asheville Class

MINE WARFARE SHIPS

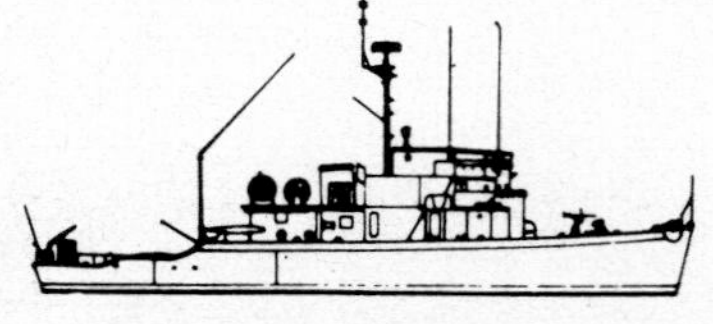

PIVOT (MSO 463) Agile Class

BLUEBIRD (MSC 121) Bluebird Class

Scale: 1 inch = 100 feet (1 : 1 200)

UNITED STATES SHIP HULL NUMBERS

(Type designations in order of arrangement within this volume; ships in numerical sequence)

Strategic Missile Submarines

SSBN—Fleet Ballistic Missile Submarines

"Geo. Washington" Class
598 George Washington
599 Patrick Henry
600 Theodore Roosevelt
601 Robert E. Lee
602 Abraham Lincoln

"Ethan Allen" Class
608 Ethan Allen
609 Sam Houston
610 Thomas A. Edison
611 John Marshall

"Lafayette" Class
616 Lafayette
617 Alexander Hamilton

"Ethan Allen" Class (Cont'd)
618 Thomas Jefferson

"Lafayette" Class (Cont'd)
619 Andrew Jackson
620 John Adams
622 James Monroe
623 Nathan Hale
624 Woodrow Wilson
624 Henry Clay
626 Daniel Webster
627 James Madison
628 Tecumseh
629 Daniel Boone
630 John C. Calhoun
631 Ulysses S. Grant
632 Von Steuben
633 Casimir Pulaski
634 Stonewall Jackson
635 Sam Rayburn
636 Nathanael Greene
640 Benjamin Franklin
641 Simon Bolivier
642 Kamehameha
643 George Bancroft
644 Lewis and Clark
645 James K. Polk
654 George C. Marshall
655 Henry L. Stimson
656 George Washington Carver
657 Francis Scott Key
658 Mariano G. Vallejo
659 Will Rogers

Submarines

SS SSN—Attack Submarines
AGSS—Auxiliary Submarines
LPSS—Amphibious Transport Submarines
SSG—Guided Missile Submarines

"Sealion" Type
315 Sealion LPSS

GUPPY III Type
343 Clamagore
416 Tiru

"Tigrone" Type
419 Tigrone AGSS

"Dolphin" Type
555 Dolphin AGSS

"Tang" Class
563 Tang

565 Wahoo
566 Trout
567 Gudgeon

"Albacore" Type
569 Albacore AGSS

"Nautilus" Type (SSN)
571 Nautilus

"Sailfish" Class
572 Sailfish
573 Salmon

"Grayback" Type
574 Grayback LPSS

"Seawolf" Type (SSN)
575 Seawolf

"Darter" Type
576 Darter

"Grayback" Type
577 Growler SSG

"Skate" Class (SSN)
578 Skate
579 Swordfish

"Barbel" Class
580 Barbel
581 Blueback
582 Bonefish

"Skate" Class (SSN) (Cont'd)
583 Sargo
584 Seadragon

"Skipjack" Class (SSN)
585 Skipjack

"Triton" Type (SSN)
586 Triton

"Halibut" Type (SSN)
587 Halibut

"Skipjack" Class (SSN) (Cont'd)
588 Scamp
590 Sculpin
591 Shark
592 Snook

"Permit" Class (SSN)
594 Permit
595 Plunger
596 Barb

"Tullibee" Type (SSN)
597 Tullibee

"Permit" Class (SSN) (Cont'd)
603 Pollack
604 Haddo
605 Jack
606 Tinosa
607 Dace
612 Guardfish
613 Flasher
614 Greenling
615 Gato
621 Haddock

"Sturgeon" Class (SSN)
637 Sturgeon
638 Whale
639 Tautog
646 Grayling
647 Pogy
648 Aspro
649 Sunfish
650 Pargo
651 Queenfish
652 Puffer
653 Ray
660 Sand Lance
661 Lapon
662 Gurnard
663 Hammerhead
664 Sea Devil
665 Guitarro
666 Hawkbill
667 Bergall
668 Spadefish
669 Seahorse
670 Finback

"Narwhal" Type (SSN)
671 Narwhal
672 Pintado
673 Flying Fish
674 Trepang
675 Bluefish
676 Billfish

"Sturgeon" Class (SSN) (Cont'd)
667 Drum
678 Archerfish
679 Silversides
680 William H. Bates
681 Batfish
682 Tunny
683 Parche
684 Cavalla

"Lipscomb" Type (SSN)
685 Glenard P. Lipscomb

"Sturgeon" Class (SSN) (Cont'd)
686 L. Mendel Rivers
687 Richard B. Russell

"Los Angeles" Class (SSN)
688 Los Angeles
689 Baton Rouge
690 Philadelphia
691 Memphis
692 Omaha
693 Cincinnati
694 Groton
695 Birmingham
696 New York City
697 Indianapolis
698 Bremerton
699 Jacksonville

Aircraft Carriers

CV CVA CVAN CVN— Attack Aircraft Carriers
CVS—ASW—Aircraft Carriers
CVT—Training Aircraft Carriers

"Hancock" Class
11 Intrepid CVS

Modernised "Essex" Class
12 Hornet CVS

"Hancock" class (Cont'd)

16 Lexington CVT
19 Hancock

Modernised "Essex" Class (Cont'd)
20 Bennington CVS

"Hancock" Class (Cont'd)
31 Bon Homme Richard
34 Oriskany
38 Shangri-La CVS

"Midway" Class
40 Mississippi
41 Midway
42 Franklin D. Roosevelt
43 Coral Sea

"Forrestal" Class
59 Forrestal
60 Saratoga
61 Ranger
62 Independance

"Kitty Hawk" Class
63 Kitty Hawk
64 Constellation

"Enterprise" Type (CVAN)
65 Enterprise

"Kitty Hawk" Class (Cont'd)
66 America
67 John F. Kennedy

"Nimitz" Class (CVAN)
68 Nimitz
69 Dwight D. Eisenhower
70 Carl Vinson

Surface Combatants

Sea Control Ships

9 Guam LPH

CG CGN—Guided Missile Cruisers

"Long Beach" Type (CGN)
9 Long Beach

"Albany" Class
10 Albany
11 Chicago
12 Columbus

CLG—Guided Missile Light Cruisers

Converted "Cleveland" Class
3 Galveston
4 Little Rock
5 Oklahoma City
6 Province
7 Springfield
8 Topeka

DLG DLGN—Guided Missile Frigates

"Coontz" Class
6 Farragut
7 Luce
8 MacDonough
9 Coontz
10 King
11 Mahan
12 Dahlgren
13 William V. Pratt
14 Dewey
15 Preble

"Leahy" Class
16 Leahy
17 Harry E. Yarnell
18 Worden
19 Dale
20 Richmond K. Turner
21 Gridley
22 England
23 Halsey
24 Reeves

"Bainbridge" Type (DLGN)
25 Bainbridge

"Belknap" Class
26 Bellknap
27 Josephus Daniels
28 Wainwright
29 Jouett
30 Horne
31 Sterett
32 William H. Standley
33 Fox
34 Biddle

"Truxtun" Type (DLGN)
35 Truxtun

"California" Class (DLGN)
36 California
37 South Carolina

"Virginia" Class (DLGN)
38 Virginia
39 Texas

DDG—Guided Missile Destroyers

"Chas F. Adams" Class
2 Charles F. Adams
3 John King
4 Lawrence
5 Claude V. Ricketts
6 Barney
7 Henry B. Wilson
8 Lynde McCormick
9 Towers
10 Sampson
11 Sellers
12 Robinson
13 Hoel
14 Buchanan
15 Berkeley
16 Joseph Strauss
17 Conyngham
18 Semmes
19 Tattnall
20 Goldsborough
21 Cochrane
22 Benjamin Stoddert
23 Richard E. Byrd
24 Waddell

Converted "Sherman" Class
31 Decatur
32 John Paul Jones
33 Parsons
34 Somers

Converted "Mitscher" Class
35 Mitscher
36 John S. McCain

DD—Destroyers

"Fletcher" Class
448 La Vallettee
499 Renshaw
502 Sigsbee
507 Conway
513 Terry
519 Daly
531 Hazelwood
537 Sullivans
562 Robinson
563 Ross
564 Rowe
566 Stoddard
568 Wren
575 McKee
589 Izard
596 Shields
629 Abbott
630 Braine
643 Sigourney

Later "Fletcher" Class
649 Albert W. Grant
650 Caperton
651 Cogswell
652 Ingersoll
653 Knapp
654 Bearss
659 Dashiell
661 Kidd
665 Bryant
666 Balck
669 Cotton
671 Gatling
672 Healy
674 Hunt
679 McNair
680 Melvin
682 Porterfield
683 Stockholm
684 Wedderburn
685 Picking
688 Remey
691 Mertz

"Allen M. Sumner" Class
698 Ault
702 Hank
707 Soley
708 Harlan R. Dickson

"Gearing" Class
714 William R. Rush
715 William M. Wood
716 Wiltsie
717 Theo E. Chandler
718 Hammer
719 Epperson

"Allen M. Sumner" Class (Cont'd)
723 Walke
724 Laffey
728 Mansfield
729 Lyman K. Swenson
730 Collett
732 Hyman

"Gearing" Class (Cont'd)
743 Southerland

"Allen M. Sumner" Class (Cont'd)
744 Blue
755 John A. Bole
756 Beatty
759 Lofberg
760 John W. Thomason
762 Henley

"Gearing" Class (Cont'd)
763 William C. Lawe

"Allen M. Sumner" Class (Cont'd)
775 Willard Keith
775 James C. Owens

"Gearing" Class (Cont'd)
782 Rowan
783 Gurke
784 McKean
785 Henderson
786 Richard B. Anderson
788 Hollister

Later "Fletcher" Class (Cont'd)
793 Cassin Young

"Gearing" Class (Cont'd)
805 Chevalier
806 Highbee
817 Corry
818 New
819 Holder
820 Rich
821 Johnson
822 Robert H. McCard
824 Basilone

"Carpenter" Type
825 Carpenter

"Gearing" Class (Cont'd)
826 Agerholm

"Carpenter" Type (Cont'd)
827 Robert A. Owens

"Gearing" Class (Cont'd)
829 Myles C. Fox
835 Charles P. Cecil
836 George K. Mackenzie
837 Sarsfield
839 Power
840 Glennon
842 Fiske
844 Perry
845 Bausell
846 Ozbourn
847 Robert L. Wilson
849 Richard E. Kraus
850 Joseph P. Kennedy Jr.
852 Leonard F. Mason

Gearing Class (Cont'd)
858 Fred T. Berry
862 Vogelgesang
863 Steinaker
864 Harold J. Ellison
865 Charles R. Ware
866 Cone
867 Stribling
868 Brownson
871 Damato
873 Hawkins
876 Rogers
877 Perkins
878 Vesole
880 Dyess
881 Bordelon
883 Newman K. Perry
885 John F. Craig
886 Orleck
888 Stickell
890 Meredith

"Forrest Sherman" Class
931 Forrest Sherman
933 Barry
937 George F. Davis
938 Jonas Ingram
940 Manley
941 Dupont
942 Bigelow
943 Blandy
944 Mullinnix
945 Hull
946 Edson
948 Morton
950 Richard S. Edwards
951 Turner Joy

"Spruance" Class
963 Spruance
964 Paul F. Foster
965 Kinkaid
966 Hewitt
967 Elliot
968 Arthur W. Radford
969 Peterson
970 Caron

DEG—Guided Missile Escort Ships

"Brooke" Class
1 Brooke
2 Ramsey
3 Schofield
4 Talbot
5 Richard L. Page
6 Julius A. Furer

AGDE—Escort Research Ship

1 Glover

DE—Escort Ships/DER—Radar Picket Escort Ships

"Edsall" Class
244 Otterstetter/DER
318 Kirkpatrick/DER
342 Falgout/DER
332 Price DER
336 Roy O. Hale/DER
382 Ramsden/DER
383 Mills/DER
384 Rhodes/DER
386 Savage/DER
387 Vance/DER
389 Durant/DER
390 Calcaterra/DER
391 Chambers/DER
400 Hissem/DER

"John C. Butler" Class
539 Wagner/DER
540 Vandivier/DER

"Claud Jones" Class
1033 Claud Jones
1036 McMorris

"Bronstein" Class
1037 Bronstein
1038 McCloy

"Garcia" Class
1040 Garcia
1041 Bradley
1043 Edward McDonnell
1044 Brumby
1045 Davidson
1047 Voge
1048 Sample
1049 Koelsch
1050 Albert David
1051 O'Callahan

"Knox" Class
1052 Knox
1053 Roark
1054 Gray
1055 Hepburn
1056 Connole
1057 Rathburne
1058 Mayerkord
1059 W. S. Sims
1060 Lang
1061 Patterson
1062 Whipple
1063 Reasoner
1064 Lockwood
1065 Stein
1066 Marvin Shields
1067 Francis Hammond
1068 Vreeland
1069 Bagley
1070 Downes
1071 Badger
1072 Blakely
1073 Robert E. Peary
1074 Harold E. Holt
1075 Trippe
1076 Fanning
1077 Ouellet
1078 Joseph Hewes
1079 Bowen
1080 Paul
1081 Aylwin
1082 Elmer Montgomery
1083 Cook
1084 McCandless
1085 Donald B. Beary
1086 Brewton
1087 Kirk
1088 Barbey
1089 Jesse L. Brown
1090 Ainsworth
1091 Miller
1092 Thomas C. Hart
1093 Capodanno
1094 Pharris
1095 Truitt
1096 Valdez
1097 Moinester

Fire Support Ships

BB—Battleships

"Iowa" Class
61 Iowa
62 New Jersey
63 Missouri
64 Wisconsin

CA—Heavy Cruisers

"Baltimore" Class
70 Canberra
73 St. Paul

"Salem" Class
134 Des Moines

"Baltimore" Class (Cont'd)
135 Los Angeles

"Salem" Class (Cont'd)
139 Salem
148 Newport News

Command and Communication Ships

AGF—Miscellaneous Flagships

3 La Salle

CC—Command Ships

1 Northampton
2 Wright

AGMR—Major Communication Relay Ships

1 Annapolis
2 Arlington

Amphibious Warships

LCC—Amphibious Command Ships (ex-AGC)

"Mount McKinley" Class
7 Mount McKinley
12 Estes
16 Pocono
17 Taconic

"Blue Ridge" Class
19 Blue Ridge
20 Mount Whitney

LHA—Amphibious Assault Ships

1 Tarawa
2 Saipan
3 Da Nang
4 Belleau Wood
5 Nassau

LPH—Amphibious Assault Ships

"Iwo Jima" Class
2 Iwo Jima
3 Okinawa
7 Guadalcanal
9 Guam
11 New Orleans
12 Inchon

LKA—Amphibious Cargo Ships

"Andromeda" Class
54 Algol
57 Capricornus
61 Muliphen
88 Uvalde
93 Yancey
94 Winston
97 Merrick

"Rankin" Class
103 Rankin
104 Seminole
105 Skagit
106 Union
107 Vermilion
108 Washburn

"Tulare" Type
112 Tulare

"Charleston" Class
113 Charleston
114 Durham
115 Mobile
116 St. Louis
117 El Paso

LPA—Amphibious Transports

"Haskell" Class
194 Sandoval
199 Maggoffin
208 Talladega
213 Mountrail
215 Navarro
222 Pickaway
237 Bexar

"Paul Revere" Class
248 Paul Revere
249 Francis Marion

LPR—Amphibious Transports (Small)

55 Laning
86 Hollis
90 Kirwin
100 Ringness
119 Beverley W. Reid
123 Diachenko
124 Horace A. Bass
127 Begor
132 Balduck
135 Weiss

LPD—Amphibious Transport Docks

"Raleigh" Class
1 Raleigh
2 Vancouver

"Austin" Class
4 Austin
5 Ogden
6 Duluth
7 Cleveland
8 Dubuque
9 Denver
10 Juneau
11 Coronado
12 Shreveport
13 Nashville
14 Trenton
15 Ponce

LSD—Dock Landing Ships

"Casa Grande" Class
13 Casa Grande
14 Rushmore
15 Shadwell
16 Cabildo
17 Catamount
18 Colonial
19 Comstock
20 Donner
22 Fort Marion
26 Tortuga
27 Whetstone

"Thomaston" Class
28 Thomaston
29 Plymouth Rock
30 Fort Snelling
31 Point Defiance
32 Speigel Grove
33 Alamo
34 Hermitage
35 Monticello

"Anchorage" Class
36 Anchorage
37 Portland
38 Pensacola
39 Mt. Vernon
40 Fort Fisher

LST—Tank Landing Ships

1—510 series
344 Blanco County

511-1152 series
525 Caroline County
533 Cheboygan County
583 Churchill County
722 Dodge County
758 Duval County
762 Floyd County
819 Hampshire County
854 Kemper County
901 Litchfield County
980 Meeker County
983 Middlesex County
1082 Pitkin County
1084 Polk County
1096 St. Clair County
1123 Sedgwick County
1148 Sumner County
1150 Sutter County

"Terrebonne Parish" Class
1157 Terrell County
1161 Vernon County
1166 Washtenaw County
1167 Westchester County
1169 Whitfield County

"Suffolk County" Class
1173 Suffolk County
1174 Grant County
1177 Lorain County
1178 Wood County

"Newport" Class
1179 Newport
1180 Manitowac
1181 Sumter
1182 Fresno
1183 Peroria
1184 Frederick
1185 Schenectady
1186 Cayuga
1187 Tuscaloosa
1188 Saginaw
1189 San Bernadino
1190 Boulder
1191 Racine
1192 Spartanburg County
1193 Fairfax County
1194 Lamour County
1195 Barbour County
1196 Harlan County
1197 Barnstaple County
1198 Bristol County

PHM—Hydrofoil Missile Boats

1 Pegasus
2 Hercules

PGH—Hydrofoil Gunboats

1 Flagstaff

PCH—Hydrofoil Patrol Craft

1 High Point

PG—Patrol Gunboats

84 Asheville
85 Gallup
86 Antelope
86 Ready
88 Crockett
89 Marathon
90 Canon
92 Tacoma
93 Welch
94 Chehalis
98 Grand Rapids
99 Beacon
100 Douglas
101 Green Bay

ADVANCED SHIPBOARD SYSTEMS

ASROC (Anti-Submarine Rocket)
Anti-submarine missile launched from surface ships with homing torpedo or nuclear depth charge as warhead. Launcher is Mk 10 or Mk 26 combination ASROC/surface-to-air missile launcher or Mk 16 eight-cell "pepper box". Installed in US Navy cruisers (CG, CGN), frigates (DLG, DLGN), destroyers (DD,DDG), and escort ships (DE, DEG); Japanese, Italian, West German, and Canadian destroyer-type ships.
Weight of missile approximately 1 000 lbs; length 15 ft; diameter 1 ft; span of fins 2·5 ft; payload: Mk 44 or Mk 46 acoustic-homing torpedo or nuclear depth charge; range one to six miles.
Prime Contractors: Honeywell. Designation: RUR-5. Status: Operational.

AEGIS (formerly Advanced Surface Missile System)
Advanced surface-to-air missile system intended for use in planned DGX ships tentatively scheduled for construction during the 1980s. To have a capability against high-performance aircraft and air-launched, anti-ship missiles. Launcher is Mk 26 with combined surface-to-air and ASW missile capability. Aegis will have an electronic scanning radar with fixed antennae, and will be capable of controlling friendly aircraft as well as detection. Additional components will include the UYK-7 computer (a component of the Naval Tactical Data System) and SPY-1 radar "illuminators" for missile guidance. Prime contractor: RCA. Status: Development (radars only; initially to use Standard missile). Being evaluated in *Norton Sound* (AVM 1).

BPDMS (Basic Point Defence Missile System)
Close-in air defence system employing the Sparrow AIM-7E or 7F series missile designated Sea Sparrow} and a modified ASROC-type "pepper box" launcher. Installed in aircraft carriers, ocean escorts, and amphibious ships. Status: Operational.

CAPTOR (Encapsulated Torpedo). Mk 46 torpedo inserted in mine casing. Prime contractor: Goodyear. Status: Operational.

CHAPARRAL Close-in Weapon System for defence against anti-ship missile and aircraft firing the Sidewinder AIM-9C missile. Adapted from Army MIM-72 Chaparral system.

CIWS (Close-in Weapon System) "Family" of advanced gun and missile systems to provide close-in or "point" defence for ships against anti-ship missiles and aircraft. Specific weapons being developed or evaluated under this programme include the Chaparral, Hybrid launcher, Pintle, Vulcan Air Defence, and Vulcan/Phalanx described on this page as well as the OTO Melara 35 mm twin gun mount.

HYBRID Close-in Weapon System consisting of a launcher capable of firing different missiles against anti-ship missiles and aircraft, providing the opportunity of engaging a target at different ranges and aspects. Missiles being considered for the launcher include various Sidewinder and Sparrow modes, the Redeye (FIM-43) missile, and Hornet (AGM-64) missile.
Status: Development.

LAMPS (Light Airborne Multi-Purpose System)
Ship-launched helicopter intended for anti-submarine and missile-defence missions, with secondary roles of search-and-rescue and utility (e.g., parts and personnel transfer) For use aboard destroyer-type ships with hangars and certain amphibious warfare ships. Sensors include dipping sonar, magnetic airborne detection (MAD), and sonobuoys with digital relays to permit control and attack direction by launching ship. Radar provided to extend detection range vis-a-vis hostile surface missile ships. Weapons: 2 Mk 46 ASW torpedoes. Crew: pilot and 2 operators.
Status: Approximately 100 Kaman Seasprite helicopters being modified to SH-2D configuration as interim LAMPS. Initially being deployed on frigates and escort ships.

NTDS (Naval Tactical Data System)
Combination of digital computers, displays, and transmission links to increase an individual ship commander's capability to assess tactical data and take action by integrating input from various sensors (e.g., radars) and providing display of tactical situation and the defence or offence options available. Data can be transmitted among NTDS-equipped ships. An automatic mode initiates action to respond to greatest threats in a tactical situation. Also can be linked to Airborne Tactical Data System (ATDS) in E-2 Hawkeye aircraft.
Fitted in all US Navy aircraft carriers, missile-armed cruisers and frigates, new amphibious command ships, and two escort ships (*Voge* and *Koelsch*).
Status: Operational

NATO Sea Sparrow Follow-on to BPDMS with a Target Acquisition System (TAS), powered director, smaller launcher, and control console combined with the Sea Sparrow missile.
Status: Under development; also a NATO co-operative programme with Belgium, Denmark, Italy, Netherlands and Norway. Being evaluated in *Downes* (DE 1070).

PINTLE Rapid-fire, close-in gun system similar to Vulcan/Phalanx weapon but firing 20 mm ammunition from a three-barrel, light-weight "Gatling" gun.
Status: Development.

SINS (Ships' Inertial Navigation System) Navigation system providing exact navigation information without active input from terrestrial sources. Prime components are gyroscopes and accelerometers that relate movement of the ship in all directions, ship speed through water and over ocean floor, and true north to give a continuous report of the ship's position.
Status: Operational

SUBROC (Submarine Rocket)
Anti-submarine missile launched from submarines with nuclear warhead. Launched from 21-inch torpedo tube. Carried in US Navy submarines of "Permit" and later classes with amidships torpedo tubes, BQQ-2 or BQQ-5 sonar and Mk 113 torpedo fire control systems. The missile is fired from the submerged submarine, rises up through the surface, travels through air towards the hostile submarine, and then re-enters the water to detonate.
Weight of missile approximately 4 000 lbs, length 21 ft; diameter 1·75 ft (maximum); estimated range 25 to 30 miles.
Prime contractor: Goodyear. Designation: UUM-44A. Status: Operational.

TASS (Towed Array Surveillance System) Ship-towed sonar array.

VULCAN/PHALANX
Rapid-fire, close-in gun system being developed to provide "last-ditch" defence against anti-ship missiles. Fires 20 mm ammunition from six-barrel "gatling" gun with "dynamic gun aiming" with fire control radar tracking projectiles and target(s). Initially planned for "Spruance" class destroyers, sea control ships (SCS), and patrol frigates (PF); tentative programme calls for approx 360 units in 220 ships. Prime contractor: General Dynamics Corp, Pamona Division. Status: Development.

TORPEDOES

Designation	*Launch Platforms*	*Weight (pounds)*	*Length (feet)*	*Diameter (inches)*	*Propulsion*	*Guidance*	*Notes*
Mk 37 Mod 2	Submarines	1 690	13·5	19	Electric	Wire	Anti-submarine
Mk 37 Mod 3	Submarines	1 400	11·3	19	Electric	Active-passive acoustic homing	Anti-submarine
Mk 44 Mod 1	Surface ships (Mk 32 tubes and ASROC); aircraft	433	8·5	12·75	Electric	Active acoustic homing	Anti-submarine
Mk 45 Mod 1 & Mod 2 (ASTOR)	Submarines	2 400	19·9	19	Electric	Wire	Anti-submarine; nuclear warhead; 10+ mile range
Mk 46 Mod 0	Surface ships (Mk 32 tubes and ASROC); aircraft	580	8·4	12·75	Solid-propellant	Active-passive acoustic homing	Anti-submarine; successor to Mk 44
Mk 46 Mod 1	Surface ships (Mk 32 tubes and ASROC); aircraft	512	8·4	12·75	Liquid mono-propellant	Active-passive acoustic homing	Anti-submarine; successor to Mk 44
Mk 48 Mod 0	Submarines	Approx 3 600	19	21	Liquid mono-propellant	Wire/terminal acoustic homing	Anti-submarine; development only; some will convert to Mod 2; approx 25 mile range; Westinghouse
Mk 48 Mod 1	Submarines	approx 3 600	19	21	Liquid mono-propellant	Wire/terminal acoustic homing	Anti-submarine and anti-shipping; larger warhead than Mod 0; in production by Gould Inc (formerly Clevite)
Mk 48 Mod 2	Submarines	approx 3 600	19	21	Liquid mono-propellant	Wire/terminal acoustic homing	Anti-submarine and anti-shipping; version of Mod 0; Westinghouse; effort terminated in favour of Mod 1

STRATEGIC MISSILE SUBMARINES

The US Navy's contribution to the nation's strategic striking forces consist of 41 nuclear-propelled submarines (SSBN) armed with Polaris and Poseidon ballistic missiles. In addition, construction has been authorized for the first of the Trident ballistic missile submarines and design efforts have been initiated with the goal of developing a smaller, lower-cost submarine that could be armed with the Trident missile. This concept is now known as the "Narwhal" programme because of use of the S5G reactor plant developed in conjunction with the attack submarine *Narwhal* (SSN 671).

The nation's strategic offensive forces now are composed of 1,054 land-based ICBMs, almost 500 B-52 and FB-111 bombers, and the 41 Polaris and Poseidon submarines. By the late 1970s this force will be reduced slightly as 54 of the older ICBMs probably will be phased out as well as some of the manned bombers; however, the number of warheads or "re-entry vehicles" will increase as the remaining ICBMs and submarine-launched missiles are fitted with Multiple Independently Targeted Re-entry Vehicles (MIRV). Of an estimated 8 000 strategic offensive warheads planned for the US arsenal in the late 1970's the 31 Poseidon-armed submarines will carry 4 960 warheads and the ten remaining Polaris submarines will carry 160 warheads. (Although each Polaris A-3 missile has three RVs, they are "shot-gunned" at a single target and cannot be directed to separated targets as are MIRV warheads.)

The number of RVs is only one measure of strategic offensive forces, the others including the number of launch vehicles (the bombers and missiles) and megatonnage. At this time the United States apparently has superiority over the USSR in quantity and quality of RVs; however, the USSR has a greater number of launch vehicles and can deliver about four times the megatonnage. Further MIRVs are being developed in the USSR. The Soviet Navy's contribution to that nation's strategic offensive forces includes a larger number of nuclear-propelled missile submarines with more missiles at sea than the US Navy's Polaris-Poseidon force.

TRIDENT PROGRAMME. The Trident submarine missile programme, originally proposed by the STRAT-X study and known as the Underwater Long-range Missile System (ULMS), was conceived in the late 1960s. The programme was to have a long-range strategic missile (approximately 6 000 miles) launched from an advanced-technology submarine.

In February 1972, the Secretary of Defense announced that the programme would be accelerated because "the at sea portion of our sea-based strategic forces has the best long term prospect for high pre-launch survivability." Subsequently, the Trident programme was accelerated and, employing Poseidon missile technology, the effort was divided into a Phase I and II with the former resulting in a missile range of only some 3 000 to 4 000 miles which could be carried in the existing Poseidon submarines. The Phase II missile, with a planned range of 6 000 miles, could still be developed but would only be compatible with the Trident missile submarines. This approach will result in an improved submarine missile being available in the late 1970s, but at the same time dictates a very conservative design approach to the new Trident submarine.

The first Trident SSBN is scheduled to be completed late in 1978 when the Trident I missile becomes operational. A total of ten Trident SSBNs now are planned, all to be initially armed with the Trident I missile which will have either MIRV or Maneuvering Re-entry Vehicle (MaRV) warheads. In addition, the backfitting of Trident I missiles into ten Poseidon submarines is scheduled to begin in 1979.

NARWHAL PROGRAMME. The Fiscal Year 1975 budget requested funds to initiate design of a smaller and less costly SSBN than the Trident design (described below). Poseidon submarines could be rearmed with the Trident I missile to place that weapon at sea at a comparatively low cost, but the design and age of these submarines will make them comparatively vulnerable to advanced detection systems in the 1980s and 1990s. Consequently, additional SSBNs beyond the ten planned Trident submarines would have to be constructed to maintain a significant force of strategic missiles at sea as the older Polaris-Poseidon submarines are phased out. The characteristics of the new SSBN have not been determined, but the submarine would probably be only slightly larger than the "Lafayette" class ballistic missile submarines and would have a *Narwhal*-type nuclear reactor plant. According to official statements, the "Narwhal" SSBN would have about 16 missile tubes compared to the 24-tube Trident SSBN design.

STRATEGIC CRUISE MISSILE. The US Navy is studying the feasibility of a strategic cruise missile, a submarine-launched weapon with ram-jet propulsion that could deliver nuclear warheads on urban targets.

According to a 1972 statement by the Director Defense Research & Engineering: "Informal Navy studies with respect to the development or sea-based strategic cruise missiles have led us to the conclusion that such a missile could effectively diversify our strategic forces. Development of a strategic cruise missile system is within the state of the art and is technically feasible without major new developments".

At this time there are no proposals for construction of strategic cruise missile submarines; rather, if such a weapon is developed the Navy's older Polaris missile submarines would be refitted to launch the new missile or possibly some attack submarines would be adopted to that role.

The strategic cruise missile would have a low-level, terrain following flight path over land, much like that of a manned bomber in contrast to the ballistic trajectory of a Polaris/Poseidon missile.

NOMENCLATURE. FBM submarines are named for "famous Americans", including South American and Hawaiian leaders as well as Europeans who aided the United States war for independence. The lead ship of the class is named after the French aristocrat who served with George Washington in the American Revolution.

FLEET BALLISTIC MISSILE SUBMARINES (SSBN): TRIDENT PROGRAMME

No.	*Programme*	*Commission*
SSBN 726	Fiscal Year 1974 programme	1979
SSBN 727	Proposed FY 1975 programme	
SSBN 728	Proposed FY 1975 programme	
SSBN 729	Planned FY 1976 programme	
SSBN 730	Planned FY 1976 programme	
SSBN 731	Planned FY 1977 programme	
SSBN 732	Planned FY 1977 programme	
SSBN 733	Planned FY 1978 programme	
SSBN 734	Planned FY 1978 programme	
SSBN 735	Planned FY 1979 programme	

Displacement, tons	approx 8 000 to 12 000 surface; approx 15 000 submerged
Length, feet	approx 550 oa
Missiles	24 tubes for Trident I submarine-launched ballistic missile
Main engines	geared turbines; 1 shaft
Reactors	1 pressurised-water cooled S6G (General Electric)
Complement	approx 150

The first of ten planned Trident fleet ballistic missile submarines was authorised in the Fiscal Year 1974 new construction programme. The remaining Trident SSBNs are planned for construction at the rate of two per year (instead of three per year as originally planned but opposed by many members of Congress). The lead submarine probably will be built by General Dynamics/Electric Boat, with completion scheduled for late 1978 (almost 12 years after the last Polaris submarine was completed). The above characteristics are unofficial estimates based on the statements of Navy officials before Congressional committees.

The principal characteristics of the Trident concept as proposed were: (1) long-range missile (circa 6 000 miles) to permit targeting the Soviet Union while the submarine cruises in remote areas, making effective ASW virtually impossible for the foreseeable future, (2) extremely quiet submarines, (3) a high at-sea to in-port ratio, (4) high systems reliability, (5) dedicated systems design to provide the most effective submarine, and (6) underwater launch capability. Modular construction techniques could greatly facilitate maintenance, overhaul, and subsequent modernisation.

DESIGN. The size of the Trident submarine is dictated primarily by the larger size missile required for 6 000-mile range and the larger reactor plant to drive the ship. The submarine will have 24 tubes in a vertical position penetrating the main submarine pressure hull. Early studies had indicated several advantages would accrue from advanced design concepts, such as housing the missiles in a horizontal position external to the main pressure hull. However, a conservative submarine design was adopted.

DESIGNATION. Initially the hull number SSBN 711 was planned for the first Trident submarine. However, on 21 Feb 1974 the designation SSBN 1 was assigned, confusing the Navy's submarine designation system which goes back to the USS *Holland* (SS 1), commissioned in 1900. Subsequently, the designation was again changed on 10 Apr 1974, with the "block" SSBN 726-735 being reserved for the Trident programme.

FISCAL. Construction of the lead Trident SSBN was funded at $781 000 000 in the Fiscal Year 1974 budget; SSBN 727 and SSBN 728 were to be funded at $604 000 000 per submarine ($281 000 000 in long-lead component funding in FY 1974 and $927 000 000 requested in FY 1975). An addition $25 000 000 was requested in the "Supplemental" FY 1974 budget to "protect the option" for the SSBN 727 and SSBN 728. These requests do not include funding for submarine component development and missile development.

MISSILES. The Trident submarines initially will be armed with the Trident I missile, scheduled to become operational late in 1978. This missile is expected to have a range of 3 000 to 4 000 nautical miles, a range already exceeded by the SS-N-8 missile in the Soviet "Delta" class submarines. However, the US missile will have a MIRV warhead while at this writing no statements by US officials have indicated that the SS-N-8 has a multiple warhead (the SS-N-6 missile associate with the "Yankee' class submarine has been tested with a MRV warhead).

The Trident missile is expected to carry more than the 10 to 14 re-entry vehicles that the Poseidon can lift. In addition, the Mk 500 MaRV (Maneuvering Re-entry Vehicle) is under development for the purpose of demonstrating its compatability with the Trident I missile. This re-entry vehicle is intended to evade ABM interceptor missiles and is not terminally guided to increase its accuracy. The Mk 500 MaRV is expected to be less accurate than previous submarine launched-ballistic missile warheads, according to official statements.

THOMAS A. EDISON (SSBN 610), in rear, passing FRANCIS SCOTT KEY (SSBN 654) in Panama Canal *1973, United States Navy*

Strategic Missile Submarines—*Continued*

31 FLEET BALLISTIC MISSILE SUBMARINES (FBM): "LAFAYETTE" CLASS

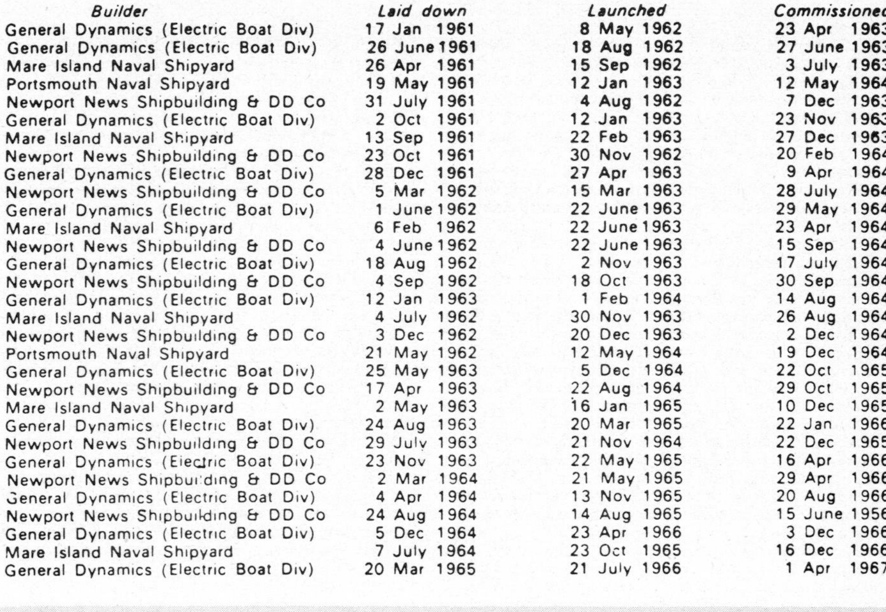

Name	*No.*	*Builder*	*Laid down*	*Launched*	*Commissioned*
***LAFAYETTE**	SSBN 616	General Dynamics (Electric Boat Div)	17 Jan 1961	8 May 1962	23 Apr 1963
***ALEXANDER HAMILTON**	SSBN 617	General Dynamics (Electric Boat Div)	26 June 1961	18 Aug 1962	27 June 1963
***ANDREW JACKSON**	SSBN 619	Mare Island Naval Shipyard	26 Apr 1961	15 Sep 1962	3 July 1963
***JOHN ADAMS**	SSBN 620	Portsmouth Naval Shipyard	19 May 1961	12 Jan 1963	12 May 1964
***JAMES MONROE**	SSBN 622	Newport News Shipbuilding & DD Co	31 July 1961	4 Aug 1962	7 Dec 1963
***NATHAN HALE**	SSBN 623	General Dynamics (Electric Boat Div)	2 Oct 1961	12 Jan 1963	23 Nov 1963
***WOODROW WILSON**	SSBN 624	Mare Island Naval Shipyard	13 Sep 1961	22 Feb 1963	27 Dec 1963
***HENRY CLAY**	SSBN 625	Newport News Shipbuilding & DD Co	23 Oct 1961	30 Nov 1962	20 Feb 1964
***DANIEL WEBSTER**	SSBN 626	General Dynamics (Electric Boat Div)	28 Dec 1961	27 Apr 1963	9 Apr 1964
***JAMES MADISON**	SSBN 627	Newport News Shipbuilding & DD Co	5 Mar 1962	15 Mar 1963	28 July 1964
***TECUMSEH**	SSBN 628	General Dynamics (Electric Boat Div)	1 June 1962	22 June 1963	29 May 1964
***DANIEL BOONE**	SSBN 629	Mare Island Naval Shipyard	6 Feb 1962	22 June 1963	23 Apr 1964
***JOHN C. CALHOUN**	SSBN 630	Newport News Shipbuilding & DD Co	4 June 1962	22 June 1963	15 Sep 1964
***ULYSSES S. GRANT**	SSBN 631	General Dynamics (Electric Boat Div)	18 Aug 1962	2 Nov 1963	17 July 1964
***VON STEUBEN**	SSBN 632	Newport News Shipbuilding & DD Co	4 Sep 1962	18 Oct 1963	30 Sep 1964
***CASIMIR PULASKI**	SSBN 633	General Dynamics (Electric Boat Div)	12 Jan 1963	1 Feb 1964	14 Aug 1964
***STONEWALL JACKSON**	SSBN 634	Mare Island Naval Shipyard	4 July 1962	30 Nov 1963	26 Aug 1964
***SAM RAYBURN**	SSBN 635	Newport News Shipbuilding & DD Co	3 Dec 1962	20 Dec 1963	2 Dec 1964
***NATHANAEL GREENE**	SSBN 636	Portsmouth Naval Shipyard	21 May 1962	12 May 1964	19 Dec 1964
***BENJAMIN FRANKLIN**	SSBN 640	General Dynamics (Electric Boat Div)	25 May 1963	5 Dec 1964	22 Oct 1965
***SIMON BOLIVAR**	SSBN 641	Newport News Shipbuilding & DD Co	17 Apr 1963	22 Aug 1964	29 Oct 1965
***KAMEHAMEHA**	SSBN 642	Mare Island Naval Shipyard	2 May 1963	16 Jan 1965	10 Dec 1965
***GEORGE BANCROFT**	SSBN 643	General Dynamics (Electric Boat Div)	24 Aug 1963	20 Mar 1965	22 Jan 1966
***LEWIS AND CLARK**	SSBN 644	Newport News Shipbuilding & DD Co	29 July 1963	21 Nov 1964	22 Dec 1965
***JAMES K. POLK**	SSBN 645	General Dynamics (Electric Boat Div)	23 Nov 1963	22 May 1965	16 Apr 1966
***GEORGE C. MARSHALL**	SSBN 654	Newport News Shipbuilding & DD Co	2 Mar 1964	21 May 1965	29 Apr 1966
***HENRY L. STIMSON**	SSBN 655	General Dynamics (Electric Boat Div)	4 Apr 1964	13 Nov 1965	20 Aug 1966
***GEORGE WASHINGTON CARVER**	SSBN 656	Newport News Shipbuilding & DD Co	24 Aug 1964	14 Aug 1965	15 June 1956
***FRANCIS SCOTT KEY**	SSBN 657	General Dynamics (Electric Boat Div)	5 Dec 1964	23 Apr 1966	3 Dec 1966
***MARIANO G. VALLEJO**	SSBN 658	Mare Island Naval Shipyard	7 July 1964	23 Oct 1965	16 Dec 1966
***WILL ROGERS**	SSBN 659	General Dynamics (Electric Boat Div)	20 Mar 1965	21 July 1966	1 Apr 1967

Displacement, tons	6 650 light surface; 7 320 standard surface; 8 250 submerged
Length, feet (*metres*)	425 (*129·5*) oa
Beam, feet (*metres*)	33 (*10·1*)
Draft, feet (*metres*)	31·5 (*9·6*)
Missile launchers	16 tubes for Polaris A-3 or Poseidon C-3 (see *Missile* notes)
Torpedo tubes	4—21 inch (*533 mm*) forward
Main engines	2 geared turbines 15 000 shp; 1 shaft
Nuclear reactor	1 pressurised-water cooled S5W (Westinghouse)
Speed, knots	20 surface; approx 30 submerged
Complement	147 (14 officers, 133 enlisted men)

These Fleet Ballistic Missile (FBM) submarines are the largest undersea craft ever built in the West. The first four submarines (SSBN 616-620) of this class were authorised in the Fiscal Year 1961 shipbuilding programme with five additional submarines (SSBN 622-626) authorised in a supplemental FY 1961 programme; SSBN 627-636 (ten) in FY 1962, SSBN 640-645 (six) in FY 1963, and SSBN 654-659 (six) in FY 1964. Cost for the earlier ships of this class was approximately $109 500 000 per submarine.

CLASSIFICATION. The *Benjamin Franklin* and later submarines officially are considered a separate class; however, differences are minimal (eg, quieter machinery) and all 31 submarines generally are considered as a single class.

DESIGN. The *Daniel Webster* has diving planes mounted on bow in lieu of sail-mounted planes, the only "16-tube" FBM submarine of any navy with this configuration. (See photograph this page).

ENGINEERING. The *Benjamin Franklin* and subsequent submarines of this class have been fitted with quieter machinery. All SSBNs have diesel-electric stand-by machinery, snorkels, and "outboard" auxiliary propeller for emergency use.
The nuclear cores inserted in refuelling these submarines during the late 1960s and early 1970s cost approximately $3 500 000 and provide energy for approximately 400 000 miles.

MISSILES. The first eight ships of this class were fitted with the Polaris A-2 missile (1 725 statute mile range) and the 23 later ships with the Polaris A-3 missile (2 880 statute mile range).
The SSBN 620 and SSBN 622-625 (5 ships) were rearmed with the Polaris A-3 missile during overhaul-refuellings from 1968 to 1970. Subsequently, all converted to carry the Poseidon C-3 missile.
The *James Madison* was the first submarine to undergo conversion to carry the Poseidon missile. She began conversion in February 1969 and was completed in June 1970. (See conversion table on following page.)
Poseidon conversion, overhaul, and reactor refuelling are conducted simultaneously. In addition to changes in missile tubes to accommodate larger Poseidon, the conversion provides replacement of Mk 84 fire control system with Mk 88 system. The Poseidon conversion programme is scheduled to complete in April 1977.
Some of the options for the Trident missile programme include the rearming submarines of this class with an advanced missile, providing a longer range capability than available with the Poseidon missile.

DANIEL WEBSTER (SSBN 626) *United States Navy*

DANIEL BOONE (SSBN 629) *United States Navy*

Strategic Missile Submarines—*Continued*

JAMES MONROE (SSBN 662) *1972, United States Navy*

DANIEL BOONE (SSBN 629) *1970, United States Navy*

"LAFAYETTE" CLASS—*continued*

NAVIGATION. FBM submarines are equipped with an elaborate Ship's Inertial Navigation System (SINS), a system of gyroscopes and accelerometers which relates movement of the ship in all directions, true speed through the water and over the ocean floor, and true north to give a continuous report of the submarine's position. The system includes the capability of both optical and electronic checks. Navigation data produced by SINS can be provided to each missile's guidance package until the instant the missile is fired.
The polaris-armed submarines each have two Mk 2 Mod 3 SINS inertial navigation systems; as converted all Poseidon submarines have three Mk 2 Mod 4 SINS; all fitted with navigational satellite receivers.

OPERATIONAL. The *Andrew Jackson* launched the first Polaris A-3 missile from a submarine on 26 Oct 1963. The *Daniel Webster* was the first submarine to deploy with the A-3 missile, beginning her first patrol on 28 Sep 1964. The *Daniel Boone* was the first Polaris submarine to deploy to the Pacific, beginning her first patrol with the A-3 missile on 25 Dec 1964. The *James Madison* launched the first Poseidon C-3 missile from a submarine on 3 Aug 1970; the submarine began the first Poseidon deployment on 31 Mar 1971.

PERSONNEL. Each FBM submarine is assigned two alternating crews designated "Blue" and "Gold" Each crew mans the submarine during a 60-day patrol and partially assists during the intermediate 28-day refit alongside a Polaris tender. The "off-duty" crew is undergoing training or is on leave. All FBM submarines are fully air conditioned and the newer ships have elaborate crew study and recreation facilities.

POSEIDON CONVERSION SCHEDULE

No.	*Programme*	*Conversion*	*Start*	*Complete*
SSBN 616	FY 1973	General Dynamics Corp (Electric Boat)	Oct 1972	July 1974
SSBN 617	FY 1973	Newport News SB & DD Co.	Jan 1973	Sep 1974
SSBN 619	FY 1973	General Dynamics Corp (Electric Boat)	Mar 1973	Dec 1974
SSBN 620	FY 1974			
SSBN 622	FY 1975			
SSBN 623	FY 1973	Puget Sound Naval Shipyard	June 1973	Nov 1974
SSBN 624	FY 1974	Newport News SB & DD Co.	Oct 1973	Mar 1975
SSBN 625	FY 1975			
SSBN 626	FY 1975			
SSBN 627	FY 1968	General Dynamics Corp (Electric Boat)	Feb 1969	June 1970
SSBN 628	FY 1970	Newport News SB & DD Co	Nov 1969	Feb 1971
SSBN 629	FY 1968	Newport News SB & DD Co	May 1969	Aug 1970
SSBN 630	FY 1969	Mare Island Naval Shipyard	Aug 1969	Feb 1971
SSBN 631	FY 1970	Puget Sound Naval Shipyard	Oct 1969	Dec 1970
SSBN 632	FY 1969	General Dynamics Corp (Electric Boat)	July 1969	Nov 1970
SSBN 633	FY 1970	General Dynamics Corp (Electric Boat)	Jan 1970	Apr 1971
SSBN 634	FY 1971	General Dynamics (Electric Boat)	July 1970	Oct 1971
SSBN 635	FY 1970	Portsmouth Naval Shipyard	Jan 1970	Sep 1971
SSBN 636	FY 1971	Newport News SB & DD Co	July 1970	Sep 1971
SSBN 640	FY 1971	General Dynamics Corp (Electric Boat)	Feb 1971	May 1972
SSBN 641	FY 1971	Newport News SB & DD Co	Feb 1971	May 1972
SSBN 642	FY 1972	General Dynamics Corp (Electric Boat)	July 1971	Oct 1972
SSBN 643	FY 1971	Portsmouth Naval Shipyard	Apr 1971	Aug 1972
SSBN 644	FY 1971	Puget Sound Naval Shipyard	Apr 1971	July 1972
SSBN 645	FY 1972	Newport News SB & DD Co	July 1971	Nov 1972
SSBN 654	FY 1972	Puget Sound Naval Shipyard	Sep 1971	Feb 1973
SSBN 655	FY 1972	Newport News SB & DD Co	Nov 1971	Mar 1973
SSBN 656	FY 1972	General Dynamics Corp (Electric Boat)	Nov 1971	Apr 1973
SSBN 657	FY 1972	Puget Sound Naval Shipyard	Feb 1972	Apr 1973
SSBN 658	FY 1973	Newport News SB & DD Co	Aug 1972	Dec 1973
SSBN 659	FY 1973	Portsmouth Naval Shipyard	Oct 1972	Feb 1974

PHOTOGRAPHS. Fleet ballistic missile submarines converted to Poseidon are virtually indistinguishable from pre-conversion appearance. FBM submarines rarely operate on the surface and photographs are difficult to obtain. Note that the *John C. Calhoun*, shown below entering Holy Loch, Scotland, has her sail number painted out.

JOHN C CALHOUN (SSBM 630) *1970, United States Navy, PH1 T. Milton Putray*

Strategic Missile Submarines —*continued*

5 FLEET BALLISTIC MISSILE SUBMARINES (SSBN): "ETHAN ALLEN" CLASS

Name	*No.*	*Builder*	*Laid down*	*Launched*	*Commissioned*
***ETHAN ALLEN**	SSBN **608**	General Dynamics (Electric Boat Div, Groton)	14 Sep 1959	22 Nov 1960	**8 Aug 1961**
***SAM HOUSTON**	SSBN **609**	Newport News Shipbuilding & DD Co	28 Dec 1959	2 Feb 1961	**6 Mar 1962**
***THOMAS A. EDISON**	SSBN **610**	General Dynamics (Electric Boat Div, Groton)	15 Mar 1960	15 June 1961	**10 Mar 1962**
***JOHN MARSHALL**	SSBN 611	Newport News Shipbuilding & DD Co	4 Apr 1960	15 July 1961	**21 May 1962**
***THOMAS JEFFERSON**	SSBN 618	Newport News Shipbuilding & DD Co	3 Feb 1961	24 Feb 1962	**4 Jan 1963**

Displacement, tons	6 900 standard surface; 7 900 submerged
Length, feet (*metres*)	410·5 (*125·1*) oa
Beam, feet (*metres*)	33 (*10·1*)
Draft, feet (*metres*)	30 (*9·4*)
Missile launchers	16 tubes for Polaris A-3
Torpedo tubes	4—21 inch (*533 mm*) forward
Main engines	2 geared turbines (General Electric); 15 000 shp; 1 shaft
Nuclear reactor	1 pressurised-water cooled S5W (Westinghouse)
Speed, knots	20 surface; approx 30 submerged
Complement	139 (12 officers, 127 enlisted men)

JOHN MARSHALL (SSBN 611) *1967, United States Navy*

These submarines were designed specifically for the FBM role and are larger and better arranged than the earlier "George Washington" class submarines. The first four ships of this class were authorised in the Fiscal Year 1959 programme; the *Thomas Jefferson* (which is out of numerical sequence) was in the FY 1961 programme. These submarines and the previous "George Washington" class will not be converted to carry the Poseidon missile because of material limitations and the age they would be after conversion. Also the "George Washington" class submarines are depth limited compared to the later FBM classes which, according to official statements, are based on the "Permit" SSN design.

DESIGN. These submarines and the subsequent "Lafayette" class are deep-diving submarines with a depth capability similar to the "Permit" class attack submarines; pressure hulls of HY-80 steel.

MISSILES. These ships were initially armed with the Polaris A-2 missile (1 725 statute mile range). The *Ethan Allan* launched the first A-2 missile fired from a submarine on 23 Oct 1961. She was the first submarine to deploy with the A-2 missile, beginning her first patrol on 26 June 1962. The *Ethan Allan* fired a Polaris A-2 missile in the Christmas Island Pacific Test Area on 6 May 1962 in what was the first complete US test of a ballistic missile including detonation of the nuclear warhead. All five of these ships have been modified to fire the A-3 missile (2,880 statute mile range). They will not be fitted with the advanced Poseidon missile. Originally fitted with Mk 80 fire control system and compressed air missile ejectors; provided with Mk 84 fire control systems and gas-steam missile ejectors with A-3 missile.

NAVIGATION. Fitted with two Mk 2 Mod 3 Ship's Inertial Navigation Systems (SINS) and navigational satellite receiver.

PERSONNEL. Alternating "Blue" and "Gold" crews are assigned to these submarines as in "Lafayette" class submarines.

PHOTOGRAPHS. Note sail number is painted out in view of *Ethan Allen* underway off Rota, Spain.

ETHAN ALLEN (SSBN 608) *1971, United States Navy, PH3 P. J. Roberts*

ETHAN ALLEN (SSBN 608) *1971, United States Navy*

Strategic Missile Submarines—*Continued*

5 FLEET BALLISTIC MISSILE SUBMARINES (SSBN): "GEORGE WASHINGTON" CLASS

Name	*No.*	*Builder*	*Laid down*	*Launched*	*Commissioned*
***GEORGE WASHINGTON**	SSBN 598	General Dynamics (Electric Boat Div, Groton)	1 Nov 1957	9 June 1959	30 Dec 1959
***PATRICK HENRY**	SSBN 599	General Dynamics (Electric Boat Div, Groton)	27 May 1958	22 Sep 1959	9 Apr 1960
***THEODORE ROOSEVELT**	SSBN 600	Mare Island Naval Shipyard	20 May 1958	3 Oct 1959	13 Feb 1961
***ROBERT E. LEE**	SSBN 601	Newport News Shipbuilding & DD Co	25 Aug 1958	18 Dec 1959	16 Sep 1960
***ABRAHAM LINCOLN**	SSBN 602	Portsmouth Naval Shipyard	1 Nov 1958	14 May 1960	11 Mar 1961

Displacement, tons	5 900 standard surface; 6 700 submerged
Length, feet (*metres*)	381·7 (*115·8*) oa
Beam, feet (*metres*)	33 (*10·1*)
Draft, feet (*metres*)	29 (*8·8*)
Missile launchers	16 tubes for Polaris A-3
Torpedo tubes	6—21 inch (*533 mm*) forward
Main engines	2 geared turbines (General Electric); 15 000 shp; 1 shaft
Nuclear reactor	1 pressurised-water cooled S5W (Westinghouse)
Speed, knots	20 surface; approx 30 submerged
Complement	140 (13 officers, 127 enlisted men)

The *George Washington* was the West's first ship to be armed with ballistic missiles. A supplement to the Fiscal Year 1958 new construction programme signed on 11 Feb 1958 provided for the construction of the first three Fleet Ballistic Missile (FBM) submarines. The Navy had already ordered the just-begun attack submarine *Scorpion* (SSN 589) to be completed as a missile submarine on 31 Dec 1957; the hull was redesignated SSBN 598 and completed as the *George Washington*. The *Patrick Henry* similarly was re-ordered on the last day of 1957, her materials having originally been intended for the not-yet-started SSN 590. These submarines and three sister ships (two authorised in FY 1959) were built to a modified "Skipjack" class design with almost 130 feet being added to the original design to accommodate two rows of eight missile tubes, fire control and navigation equipment, and auxiliary machinery.

ENGINEERING. The *George Washington* was the first FBM submarine to be overhauled and "refuelled". During her 4½ years of operation on her initial reactor core she carried out 15 submerged missile patrols and steamed more than 100 000 miles.

MISSILES. These ships were initially armed with the Polaris A-1 missile (1 380 statute mile range). The *George Washington* successfully fired two Polaris A-1 missiles while submerged off Cape Canaveral (Kennedy) on 20 July 1960 in the first underwater launching of a ballistic missile from a US submarine. She departed on her initial patrol on 15 Nov 1960 and remained submerged for 66 days, 10 hours. All five submarines of this class have been refitted to fire the improved Polaris A-3 missile (2 880 statute mile range). Missile refit and first reactor refuelling were accomplished simultaneously during overhaul: *George Washington* from 20 June 1964 to 2 Feb 1966, *Patrick Henry* from 4 Jan 1965 to 21 July 1966, *Theodore Roosevelt* from 28 July 1965 to 14 Jan 1967, *Robert E. Lee* from 23 Feb 1965 to 2 July 1966, and *Abraham Lincoln* from 25 Oct 1965 to 3 June 1967; four at Electric Boat yard in Groton, Connecticut, and *Robert E. Lee* at Mare Island Naval Shipyard (California).

These submarines all have Mk 84 fire control systems and gas-steam missile ejectors (originally fitted with Mk 80 fire control systems and compressed air missile ejectors, changed during A-3 missile refit).

These submarines will not be modified to carry and launch the advanced Poseidon ballistic missile.

GEORGE WASHINGTON (SSBN 598) *United States Navy*

ABRAHAM LINCOLN (SSBN 602) *United States Navy*

NAVIGATION. Fitted with three Mk 2 Mod 4 Ship's Inertial Navigation Systems (SINS) and navigational satellite receiver.

PERSONNEL. Alternating "Blue" and "Gold" crews are assigned to these submarines as in "Lafayette" class submarines.

PHOTOGRAPHS. Note that "hump" of hull extension for housing missile tubes is more pronounced in these submarines than later classes. Note the bitts and capstans visible in view of *Abraham Lincoln* while mooring; as in SSNs, most hull projects are removable or retractable to provide a "clean" hull and reduce noise as submarine passes through water.

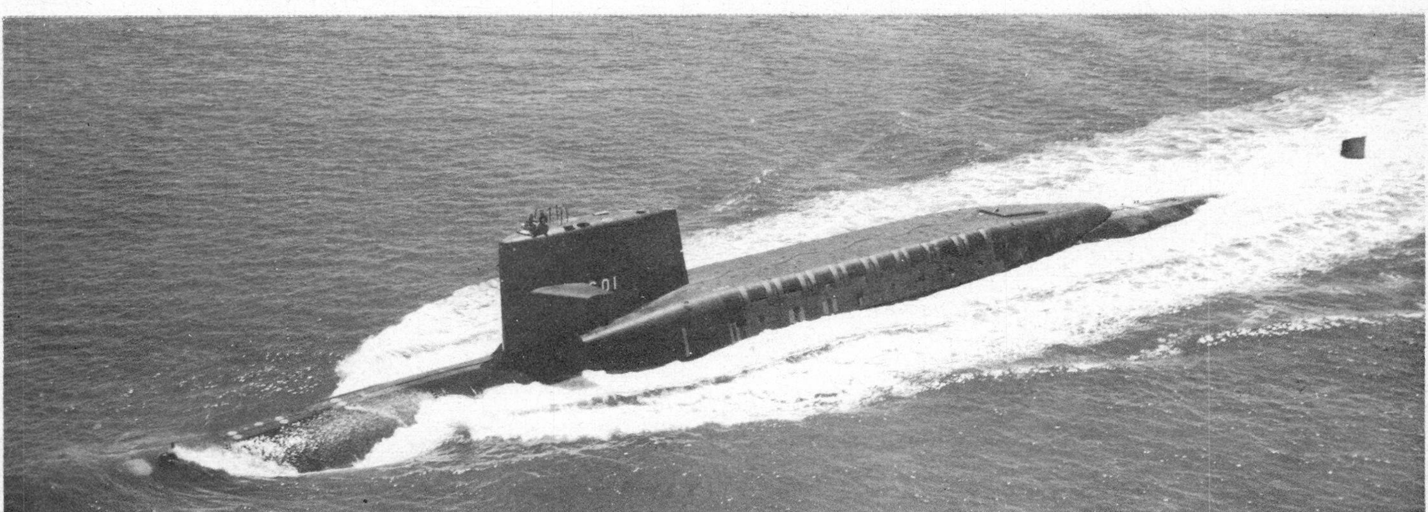

ROBERT E. LEE (SSBN 601) ***1966, United States Navy***

SUBMARINES

The US Navy's submarine forces consist of two principal categories: fleet ballistic missile submarines (SSBN), listed in the previous section, and attack submarines (SS and SSN).

The current US attack submarine force goal is 90 nuclear-propelled submarines. This number will not be attained until at least the early 1980s when the Navy will have 26 "Los Angeles" class (including three proposed in the Fiscal Year 1975 programme), 53 other first-line SSNs ("Skipjack" class and later), and eight older SSNs suitable only for training and research. By that time the Soviet Navy, assuming continuation of the current construction rate of about five per year, could have over 130 nuclear attack submarines (SSN/SSGN) in service. Obviously the age of some of the Soviet craft also would make them of limited combat value by that time.

Additional nuclear attack submarines will be built by the United States at the rate of five every two years to provide replacements for older SSNs being retired. The size of the "Los Angeles" programme, the limited number of submarine construction yards available (probably only two after 1974), and the planned Trident SSBN effort will preclude a major increase in attack submarine construction.

Current SSN construction is limited to the "Los Angeles" class, a large submarine intended in part to counter the high-speed submarines of the Soviet Navy. US nuclear submarines classes have grownsteadily in size since the reactor plant; accordingly, submarine performance has "Skipjack" class of 1959 while retaining the same S5W deteriorated. In contrast, Soviet attack submarine speeds appear to have steadily increased. Unofficial sources indicate that the lack of US progress in submarine reactor development required modification of a surface ship nuclear reactor plant for use in the "Los Angeles" class which, in turn, necessitated a larger submarine.

Similarly, proposals for follow-on attack submarines (see below) probably will require still larger hulls to accommodate sensors and weapons for new missions, as well as larger reactor plants if high submerged speeds are sought.

MISSIONS. Nuclear-powered attacks submarines are primarily considered anti-submarine platforms because of their ability to operate covertly, especially in waters which are otherwise under the control of enemy surface and air forces where other US anti-submarine forces could not operate.

The US Navy is investigating the use of SSNs in other roles, including the open-ocean escorting of high-value surface ships such as aircraft carriers. Also, the increasing capabilities and oceanic operations of Soviet surface forces have caused renewed US Navy interest in the employment of the submarines in the antiship role, armed with torpedoes and anti-ship missiles.

ANTI-SHIP MISSILES. An encapsulated version of the Harpoon anti-ship missile is being developed for launching from submarines. The Harpoon, also capable of surface ship and aircraft launch, is a 15-foot weapon carrying a conventional high-explosive warhead. In the encapsulated version, the Harpoon is launched from a torpedo tube and travels to the surface where the protective capsule is discarded, the missile's fins extend, and the rocket engine ignites. The Harpoon has a range of about 60 nautical miles. Production will begin in 1975 with later submarines of the "Los Angeles" class to be armed with the weapon. Consideration is being given to retrofitting the missile in submarines of the "Permit" and "Sturgeon" classes as well as the early units of the "Los Angeles" class. The limited number of torpedo tubes in these submarines will restrict arming flexibility.

ADVANCED SUBMARINES. Two advanced submarine concepts are under consideration for follow-on construction to the "Los Angeles" class:

A built-for-the-purpose cruise missile submarine with improved weapons, having anti-submarine and anti-ship capabilities, possibly carrying nuclear as well as conventional tactical cruise missiles. Provision of advanced tactical missiles could result in an attack submarime even larger than the "Los Angeles".

A smaller and less costly nuclear attack submarine than the "Los Angeles" class. Details of this concept have not been explained, but probably would require a reduction in some combat capabilities (eg, a less sophisticated sonar system than the larger and expensive albeit highly capable BQQ-5).

In addition, apparently some consideration is being given to construction of advanced-technology, diesel-electric combat submarines. Although restricted in high-speed underwater endurance, such craft would be useful in certain anti-submarine scenarios and other roles. Beyond combat operations, non-nuclear submarines would be useful in the training role and for transfer to foreign allied navies that are primarily dependent upon Germany, Britain, and France for submarines of post-war construction.

CONVENTIONAL SUBMARINES. The US Navy now operates only 12 diesel-electric attack submarines, ten of post-World War II construction and two older GUPPY conversions. The latter are expected to be transferred to Turkey in mid-1975. In addition, one diesel transport submarine and two diesel research submarines are in service, with the former scheduled for layup in the near future. A few specialized submarines remain in the reserve or "mothball" fleet: the nuclear underwater giant *Triton* (SSN 586), the guided missile submarine *Growler* (SSG 577), the research submarine *Albacore* (AGSS 569), and the transport submarine *Sealion* (LPSS 315).

NOMENCLATURE. US submarines generally have been named for fish and other marine life except that fleet ballistic missile submarines have been named for famous Americans. The tradition of naming "fleet" and "attack" submarines for fish was broken in 1971 when three submarines of the "Sturgeon" class and the one-of-a-kind SSN 685 were named for deceased members of the Congress. Previously US destroyer-type ships have honoured members of the Congress.

Later in 1971 the SSN 688, lead ship for a new class of attack submarines, was named *Los Angeles*, introducing "city" names to US submarines. This was the third name source applied to US submarines within a year, indicating the considerable confusion in ship nomenclature within the Navy.

(Of late, several types of auxiliary ships also have been named for cities, a name source traditionally applied to cruisers in the US Navy)

23 + 3 NUCLEAR-POWERED ATTACK SUBMARINES (SSN): "LOS ANGELES" CLASS

Displacement, tons	6 900 submerged
Length, feet	360 oa
Beam, feet	33
Draft, feet	32 max
Torpedo tubes	4—21 inch (*533 mm*) amidships
A/S weapons	SUBROC and Mk 48 A/S torpedoes
Main engines	2 geared turbines; 1 shaft
Nuclear reactor	1 pressurised-water cooled
Speed, knots	30+ submerged
Complement	102

Name	*No.*	*Builder*	*Laid down*	*Launched*	*Commission*
LOS ANGELES	SSN 688	Newport News SB & DD Co	8 Jan 1972	6 Apr 1974	Feb 1975
BATON ROUGE	SSN 689	Newport News SB & DD Co	18 Nov 1972	1975	late 1975
PHILADELPHIA	SSN 690	General Dynamics (Electric Boat)	12 Aug 1972	Sep 1974	mid 1975
MEMPHIS	SSN 691	Newport News SB & DD Co	23 June 1973	1975	1976
OMAHA	SSN 692	General Dynamics (Electric Boat)	27 Jan 1973	1975	late 1975
CINCINNATI	SSN 693	Newport News SB & DD Co	6 Apr 1974	1976	1976
GROTON	SSN 694	General Dynamics (Electric Boat)	3 Aug 1973	Dec 1974	1976
BIRMINGHAM	SSN 695	Newport News SB & DD Co	1975	1975	1976
NEW YORK CITY	SSN 696	General Dynamics (Electric Boat)	15 Dec 1973	1975	1976
INDIANAPOLIS	SSN 697	General Dynamics (Electric Boat)	Sep 1974	1975	1976
BREMERTON	SSN 698	General Dynamics (Electric Boat)	Dec 1974	1976	1977
JACKSONVILLE	SSN 699	General Dynamcis (Electric Boat)	1975	1976	1977
Six submarines	**SSN 700-705**	General Dynamics (Electric Boat)			
Five submarines	**SSN 706-710**	Fiscal Year 1974 programme			1977-1979
Three submarines	**SSN 711-713**	Proposed FY 1975 programme			

These are "high-speed" attack submarines intended to counter the new Soviet classes of submarines that went to sea during the late 1960s and early 1970s.

The SSN 688-690 (3 ships) were authorised in the Fiscal Year 1970 new construction programme, SSN 691-694 (4 ships) in FY 1971, SSN 695-699 (5 ships) in FY 1972, SSN 700-705 (6 ships) in FY 1973, SSN 706-711 (5 ships) in FY 1974, and SSN 711-713 (3 ships) requested in FY 1975 programme. Additional submarines are planned at the rate of five units every two years.

Detailed design of the SSN 688 class as well as construction of the lead submarine was contracted to the Newport News Shipbuilding & Dry Dock Company, Newport News, Virginia; the follow-on ships were awarded to Newport News and to the General Dynamics Electric Boat Division yard at Groton, Connecticut.

These ships are considerably behind schedule, in part because of delays in the delivery of contractor-furnished equipment and a slower-than-planned build up of the work force at Newport News.

DESIGN. These submarines will be considerably larger than the previous "Sturgeon" class. All construction features, including sail size, hull shape, propulsion plant design, machinery mounting technique, auxiliary machinery, etc. will be designed to provide the maximum degree of quietness possible. Their sound level will be similar to the "Sturgeon" class when both submarines are travelling at comparable speeds.

ELECTRONICS. Electronic equipment planned for these submarines includes BQQ-5 (formerly BQS-13DNA) long-range detection sonar, BQS-15 close contact avoidance sonar, and BPS-15 surface search radar. A towed sonar array will be fitted.

UYK-7 computer will be installed to assist command and control functions.

ENGINEERING. Unofficial sources indicate that a modified surface ship nuclear reactor plant may be used in this class. The "smallest" surface ship reactor now available for submarine use is the D2G type used in the frigates *Bainbridge* and *Truxtun*: these reactors each produce approximately 30 000 shp. Reactor core life between "refuelings" has been estimated as high as ten years

FISCAL. The costs of these submarines have increased in every fiscal year programme; the estimated cost of the lead ship *Los Angeles* is $232 000 000; for the other FY 1970 submarines $153 700 000, for FY 1971 submarines $162 300 000, for FY 1972 submarines $177 600 000, for FY 1973 submarines $178 200 000, for FY 1974 submarines $183 400 000, and for FY 1975 submarines $193 600 000. These estimates are based on data available prior to completion of any of the submarines; subsequent units probably will cost in excess of $200 000 000 each.

1 NUCLEAR POWERED ATTACK SUBMARINE (SSN): QUIET DESIGN

Displacement, tons	over 5 000 submerged
Length, feet	over 300 oa
Torpedo tubes	4—21 inch (*533 mm*) amidships
A/S weapons	SUBROC and A/S torpedoes
Main engines	Turbine-electric drive (General Electric); 1 shaft
Nuclear reactor	1 pressurised-water cooled S5WA (Westinghouse)
Speed, knots	approx 25 submerged
Complement	over 100

Name	*No.*	*Builder*	*Laid down*	*Launch*	*Commission*
GLENARD P. LIPSCOMB	(SSN 685)	*General Dynamics,*	5 June 1971	4 Aug 1973	Aug 1974

The Turbine-Electric Drive Submarine (TEDS) is being built to test "a combination of advanced silencing techniques" involving "a new kind of propulsion system, and new and quieter machinery of various kinds", according to the Department of Defense. The noise level produced by an operating submarine is an important factor in its ability to remain undetected by an opponent's passive listening devices and its own ability to detect the opponent. The TEDS project will permit an at-sea evaluation of improvements in ASW effectiveness due to noise reduction. The SSN 685 will be slightly larger than "Sturgeon" class submarines and somewhat slower.

No class of turbine-electric nuclear submarines is planned at this time. Rather, quieting features developed in the SSN 685 which do not detract from speed probably will be incorporated in the SSN 688 design and subsequent SSN classes. (The TEDS design is several years ahead of the SSN 688 design)

Authorised in the Fiscal Year 1968 new construction programme; estimated construction cost will be between $150 000 000 and $200 000 000.

Design of an advanced submarine specifically intended for quiet operation began with Navy studies which commenced in October 1964. Approval to construct the submarine was revoked on at least one occasion by the Department of Defense in an effort to combine several desired characteristics in a single submarine design. However, high speed and silent operation apparently are not compatible with available technolgy.

Final Department of Defense approval for construction of the turbine-electric drive submarine was announced on 25 Oct 1968. A contract was awarded to GD/EB for construction of the SSN 685 on 16 Dec 1968.

GLENARD P. LIPSCOMB *1973,*

Submarines—*continued*

1 NUCLEAR POWERED SUBMARINE — QUIET DESIGN

ENGINEERING. Turbine-electric drive eliminates the noisy reduction gears of standard steam turbine power plants, the major source of noise in a nuclear-powered submarine. The turbine-electric power plant is larger and heavier than comparable steam turbine submarine machinery.

The *Tullibee* (SSN 597) was an earlier effort at noise reduction through a turbine-electric nuclear plant.

1 NUCLEAR POWERED ATTACK SUBMARINE (SSN): "NARWHAL" TYPE

Displacement, tons	4 450 standard; 5 350 submerged
Length, feet (*metres*)	314 (*95·7*) oa
Beam, feet (*metres*)	38 (*11·5*)
Draft, feet (*metres*)	26 (*7·9*)
Torpedo tubes	4—21 inch (*533 mm*) amidships
A/S weapons	SUBROC and A/S torpedoes
Main engines	2 steam turbines; approx 17 000 shp; 1 shaft
Nuclear reactor	1 pressurised water-cooled S5G (General Electric)
Speed, knots	approx 20 surface; approx 30 submerged
Complement	107 (12 officers, 95 enlisted men)

Name	*No*	*Builder*	*Laid down*	*Launched*	*Commissioned*
•NARWHAL	SSN 671	General Dynamics (Electric Boat)	17 Jan 1966	9 Sep 1967	12 July 1969

The *Narwhal* is a large attack submarine with an improved propulsion system. Authorised in the Fiscal Year 1964 new construction programme.

DESIGN. The *Narwhal* is similar to the "Sturgeon" class submarines in design.

ELECTRONICS. Fitted with BQQ-2 sonar system. See "Sturgeon" and "Permit" classes for general notes.

ENGINEERING. The *Narwhal* is fitted with the prototype sea-going S5G natural circulation reactor plant. According to Admiral H. G. Rickover the natural circulation reactor "offers promise of increased reactor plant reliability, simplicity, and noise reduction due to the elimination of the need for large reactor coolant pumps and associated electrical and control equipment by taking maximum advantage of natural convection to circulate the reactor coolant".
Natural circulation eliminates the requirement for primary coolant pumps, the second noisiest component of a pressurised-water propulsion system after the steam turbines.
The Atomic Energy Commission's Knolls Atomic Power Laboratory was given prime responsibility for development of the power plant. Construction of a land-based prototype plant began in May 1961 at the National Reactor Testing Station in Idaho. The reactor achieved initial criticality on 12 Sep 1965.

NARWHAL (SSN 671) *1969, General Dynamics, Electric Boat Division*

NARWHAL (SSN 671) ***1969, General Dynamics, Electric Boat Division***

POGY (SSN 647) *1973, United States Navy*

Submarines—*continued*

37 NUCLEAR-POWERED ATTACK SUBMARINES (SSN): "STURGEON" CLASS

Displacement, tons	3 860 standard; 4 630 submerged
Length, feet (*metres*)	292·2 (*89·0*) oa
Beam, feet (*metres*)	31·7 (*9·5*)
Draft, feet (*metres*)	26 (*7·9*)
Torpedo tubes	4—21 inch (*533 mm*) amidships
A/S weapons	SUBROC and A/S torpedoes
Main engines	2 steam turbines; approx 15 000 shp; 1 shaft
Nuclear reactor	1 pressurised-water cooled S5W (Westinghouse)
Speed, knots	approx 20 surface; approx 30 submerged
Complement	107 (12 officers, 95 enlisted men)

Name	*No.*	*Builder*	*Laid down*	*Launched*	*Commissioned*
*STURGEON	SSN 637	General Dynamics (Electric Boat)	10 Aug 1963	26 Feb 1966	3 Mar 1967
*WHALE	SSN 638	General Dynamics (Quincy)	27 May 1964	14 Oct 1966	12 Oct 1968
*TAUTOG	SSN 639	Ingalls Shipbuilding Corp	27 Jan 1964	15 Apr 1967	17 Aug 1968
*GRAYLING	SSN 646	Portsmouth Naval Shipyard	12 May 1964	22 June 1967	11 Oct 1969
*POGY	SSN 647	Ingalls Shipbuilding Corp	4 May 1964	3 June 1967	15 May 1971
*ASPRO	SSN 648	Ingalls Shipbuilding Corp	23 Nov 1964	29 Nov 1967	20 Feb 1969
*SUNFISH	SSN 649	General Dynamics (Quincy)	15 Jan 1965	14 Oct 1966	15 Mar 1969
*PARGO	SSN 650	General Dynamics (Electric Boat)	3 June 1964	17 Sep 1966	5 Dec 1967
*QUEENFISH	SSN 651	Newport News SB & DD Co	11 May 1965	25 Feb 1966	6 Dec 1966
*PUFFER	SSN 652	Ingalls Shipbuilding Corp	8 Feb 1965	30 Mar 1968	9 Aug 1969
*RAY	SSN 653	Newport News SB & DD Co	1 Apr 1965	21 June 1966	12 Apr 1967
*SAND LANCE	SSN 660	Portsmouth Naval Shipyard	15 Jan 1965	11 Nov 1969	25 Sep 1971
*LAPON	SSN 661	Newport News SB & DD Co	26 July 1965	16 Dec 1966	14 Dec 1967
*GURNARD	SSN 662	San Francisco NSY (Mare Island)	22 Dec 1964	20 May 1967	6 Dec 1968
*HAMMERHEAD	SSN 663	Newport News SB & DD Co	29 Nov 1965	14 Apr 1967	28 June 1968
*SEA DEVIL	SSN 664	Newport News SB & DD Co	12 Apr 1966	5 Oct 1967	30 Jan 1969
*GUITARRO	SSN 665	San Francisco NSY (Mare Island)	9 Dec 1965	27 July 1968	9 Sep 1972
*HAWKBILL	SSN 666	San Francisco NSY (Mare Island)	12 Sep 1966	12 Apr 1969	4 Feb 1971
*BERGALL	SSN 667	General Dynamics (Electric Boat)	16 Apr 1966	17 Feb 1968	13 June 1969
*SPADEFISH	SSN 668	Newport News SB & DD Co	21 Dec 1966	15 May 1968	31 July 1969
*SEAHORSE	SSN 669	General Dynamics (Electric Boat)	13 Aug 1966	15 June 1968	19 Sep 1969
*FINBACK	SSN 670	Newport News SB & DD Co	26 June 1967	7 Dec 1968	4 Feb 1970
*PINTADO	SSN 672	San Francisco NSY (Mare Island)	27 Oct 1967	16 Aug 1969	29 Apr 1971
*FLYING FISH	SSN 673	General Dynamics (Electric Boat)	30 June 1967	17 May 1969	29 Apr 1970
*TREPANG	SSN 674	General Dynamics (Electric Boat)	28 Oct 1967	27 Sep 1969	14 Aug 1970
*BLUEFISH	SSN 675	General Dynamics (Electric Boat)	13 Mar 1968	10 Jan 1970	8 Jan 1971
*BILLFISH	SSN 676	General Dynamics (Electric Boat)	20 Sep 1968	1 May 1970	11 Sep 1971
*DRUM	SSN 677	San Francisco NSY (Mare Island)	20 Aug 1968	23 May 1970	15 Apr 1972
*ARCHERFISH	SSN 678	General Dynamics (Electric Boat)	19 June 1969	16 Jan 1971	17 Dec 1971
*SILVERSIDES	SSN 679	General Dynamics (Electric Boat)	13 Oct 1969	4 June 1971	5 May 1972
*WILLIAM H. BATES	SSN 680	Ingalls Shipbuilding (Litton)	4 Aug 1969	11 Dec 1971	12 Apr 1973
*BATFISH	SSN 681	General Dynamics(Electric Boat)	9 Feb 1970	9 Oct 1971	1 Sep 1972
*TUNNY	SSN 682	Ingalls Shipbuilding (Litton)	22 May 1970	10 June 1972	26 Jan 1974
PARCHE	SSN 683	Ingalls Shipbuilding (Litton)	10 Dec 1970	13 Jan 1973	mid-1974
*CAVALLA	SSN 684	General Dynamics (Electric Boat)	4 June 1970	19 Feb 1972	9 Feb 1973
L. MENDEL RIVERS	SSN 686	Newport News SB & DD Co	26 June 1971	2 June 1973	late 1974
RICHARD B. RUSSELL	SSN 687	Newport News SB & DD Co	19 Oct 1971	12 Jan 1974	early 1975

The 37 "Sturgeon" class attack submarines comprise the largest US Navy group of nuclear powered-ships built to the same design (followed by the 31 "Lafayette" class ballistic missile submarines; the Soviet Navy has built 33 submarines of the same design in the "Delta" class).
These submarines are intended to seek out and destroy enemy submarines. They are similar in design to the previous "Permit" (ex-"Thresher") class but are slightly larger. SSN 637-639 (3 ships) were authorised in the Fiscal Year 1962 new construction programme. SSN 646-653 (8 ships) in FY 1963, SSN 660-664 (5 ships) in FY 1964, SSN 665-670 (6 ships) in FY 1965, SSN 672-677 (6 ships) in FY 1966, SSN 678-682 (5 ships) in FY 1967, SSN 683-684 (2 ships) in FY 1968, and SSN 686 and SSN 687 in FY 1969.
Some of these ships are requiring *seven* years for construction (keel laying to completion).

CONSTRUCTION. The *Pogy* was begun by the New York Shipbuilding Corp (Camden, New Jersey), but was towed to Ingalls Shipbuilding Corp for completion; contract with the New York Shipbuilding Corp was terminated on 5 June 1967; contract for completion awarded to Ingalls Shipbuilding Corp on 7 Dec 1967.
The *Guitarro* sank in 35 feet of water on 15 May 1969 while being fitted out at the San Francisco Bay Naval Shipyard. According to a congressional report, the sinking, caused by shipyard workers, was "wholly avoidable". Subsequently raised; damage estimated at $25 000 000 to repair damage due to interior flooding. Completion delayed more than two years.

DESIGN. These submarines are slightly larger than the previous "Permit" (ex-"Thresher") class and can be identified by their taller sail structure and the lower position of their diving planes on the sail (to improve control at periscope depth). Sail height is 20 feet, 6 inches above deck. Sail-mounted diving planes rotate to vertical for breaking through ice when surfacing in arctic regions.
These ships incorporate modifications of the submarine safety (SUBSAFE) programme established after the loss of the *Thresher*. These submarines probably are slightly slower than the previous "Permit" and "Skipjack" classes because of their increased size with the same propulsion system as in the earlier classes.

ELECTRONICS. These submarines are fitted with the advanced BQQ-2 sonar system. Principal components of the BQQ-2 include the BQS-6 active sonar, with transducers mounted in a 15-foot diameter sonar sphere, and BQR-7 passive sonar, with hydrophones in a conformal array on sides of forward hull. The active sonar sphere is fitted in the optimum bow position, requiring placement of torpedo tubes amidships. These submarines also have BQS-8 and BQS-13 active passive sonars; transducers for the former are in two small domes aft of sail structure. BQS-8 sonar is intended primarily for under-ice-navigation. Sonar suits of *Guitarro* and *Cavalla* are of improved designs. BPS-14 surface search radar fitted. These submarines have the Mk 113 torpedo fire control director.

MISSILES. Compatability tests were conducted during 1972-1973 with several submarines of this class and the encapsulated Harpoon anti-ship missile.

NOMENCLATURE. *William H. Bates* ex-*Redfish*, renamed 25 June 1971 to honour deceased member of Congress.

OPERATIONAL. The *Whale*, *Pargo*, and older nuclear submarine *Sargo* conducted exercises in the Arctic ice pack during March-April 1969. The *Whale* surfaced at the geographic North Pole on April 6, the 60th anniversary of Rear Admiral Robert E. Peary reaching the North Pole. This was believed the first instance of single-screw US nuclear submarines surfacing in the Arctic ice.
The *Hammerhead* and the older nuclear submarine *Skate* conducted exercises in the Arctic during November-December 1970, with the *Hammerhead* surfacing at the North Pole on 20 Nov 1970.
The *Trepang* operated in the Arctic with the *Skate* during the spring of 1971.

SUBMERSIBLES. The *Hawkbill* has been modified to carry and support the Navy's Deep Submergence Rescue Vehicles (DSRV). The *Hawkbill* can transport a 50-foot DSRV "piggyback" on her after deck and while submerged can launch and recover the DSRV. The DSRV also can "land" on the submarine's forward hatch as well as the after hatch to transfer personnel. See section on Deep Submergence Vehicles for additional DSRV details. The research submarine *Halibut* (SSN 587) also is fitted to carry the DSRV. The modifications do not affect the *Hawkbill's* combat capabilities.

BATFISH (SSN 681) — *1972, General Dynamics, Electric Boat Division*

ARCHERFISH (SSN 678) — *1971, General Dynamics, Electric Boat Division*

PHOTOGRAPHS. These submarines have streamlined hulls with few deck projections to interrupt their clean lines; the two small domes on the main deck aft of the sail structure are BQS-8 sonar transducers and the darker "windows" on the sail structure (forward of diving planes) are BQS-8 hydrophones. Capstans and cleats are retractable.
The *Hawkbill* is shown carrying the submersible DSRV-1 The markings on the submarines' sail and around her forward hatch are luminescent to assist underwater "mating" operations.
A photograph of the *Whale* surfaced through ice at the North Pole, with her diving planes rotated to the vertical position, appears in the 1971-1972 and 1972-1973 editions.

Submarines—*continued*

HAWKBILL (SSN 666) with DSRV-1 *1971, United States Navy*

13 NUCLEAR-POWERED ATTACK SUBMARINES (SSN): "PERMIT" CLASS

Name	No	Builder	Laid down	Launched	Commissioned
***PERMIT**	SSN 594	Mare Island Naval Shipyard	16 July 1959	1 July 1961	29 May 1962
***PLUNGER**	SSN 595	Mare Island Naval Shipyard	2 Mar 1960	9 Dec 1961	21 Nov 1962
***BARB**	SSN 596	Ingalls Shipbuilding Corp	9 Nov 1959	12 Feb 1962	24 Aug 1963
***POLLACK**	SSN 603	New York Shipbuilding Corp	14 Mar 1960	17 Mar 1962	26 May 1964
***HADDO**	SSN 604	New York Shipbuilding Corp	9 Sep 1960	18 Aug 1962	16 Dec 1964
***JACK**	SSN 605	Portsmouth Naval Shipyard	16 Sep 1960	24 Apr 1963	31 Mar 1967
***TINOSA**	SSN 606	Portsmouth Naval Shipyard	24 Nov 1959	9 Dec 1961	17 Oct 1964
***DACE**	SSN 607	Ingalls Shipbuilding Corp	6 June 1960	18 Aug 1962	4 Apr 1964
***GUARDFISH**	SSN 612	New York Shipbuilding Corp	28 Feb 1961	15 May 1965	20 Dec 1966
***FLASHER**	SSN 613	General Dynamics (Electric Boat)	14 Apr 1961	22 June 1963	22 July 1966
***GREENLING**	SSN 614	General Dynamics (Electric Boat)	15 Aug 1961	4 Apr 1964	3 Nov 1967
***GATO**	SSN 615	Ingalls Shipbuilding Corp	15 Dec 1961	14 May 1964	25 Jan 1968
***HADDOCK**	SSN 621	Ingalls Shipbuilding Corp	24 Apr 1961	21 May 1966	22 Dec 1967

Displacement, tons	3 750 standard, *Flasher, Greenling*, and *Gato* 3 800 tons; 4 300 submerged except *Jack* 4 500, submerged, *Flasher, Greenling*, and *Gato* 4 600 submerged
Length, feet (*metres*)	278·5 (*84·9*) oa except *Jack* 295·7 (*89·5*), *Flasher, Greenling* and *Gato* 292·2 (*89·1*)
Beam, feet (*metres*)	31·7 (*9·6*)
Draft, feet (*metres*)	25·2 (*7·6*)
Torpedo tubes	4—21 inch (*533 mm*) amidships
A/S weapons	SUBROC and A/S torpedoes
Main engines	2 steam turbines, approx 15 000 shp; 1 shaft
Nuclear reactor	1 pressurised-water cooled S5W (Westinghouse)
Speed, knots	approx 20 surface; approx 30 submerged
Complement	107 (12 officers, 95 enlisted men)

These submarines were the first of a series of advanced attack submarines intended to seek out and destroy enemy submarines. They have a greater depth capability than previous nuclear-powered submarines and are the first to combine the SUBROC anti-submarine missile capability with the advanced BQQ-2 sonar system. The lead ship of the class, the ill-fated *Thresher* (SSN 593), was authorised in the Fiscal Year 1957 new construction programme, the SSN 594-596 (3 ships) in FY 1958, SSN 603-607 (5 ships) in FY 1959, SSN 612-615 (4 ships) in FY 1960, and SSN 621 in FY 1961.

The *Thresher* (SSN 593) was lost off the coast of New England on 10 Apr 1963 while on post-overhaul trials. She went down with 129 men on board (108 crewmen plus four naval officers and 17 civilians on board for trials).

Later submarines of this class were delayed because of the Submarine Safety (SUBSAFE) program modifications, increased quality control of submarine construction, and specific problems at shipyards.

CLASS. These submarines were originally listed as belonging to the "Thresher" class; now referred to as the "Permit" class after loss of the *Thresher* in 1963.

CONSTRUCTION. *Greenling* and *Gato* were launched by the Electric Boat Division of the General Dynamics Corp (Groton, Connecticut); towed to Quincy Division (Massachusetts) for lengthening and completion.

DESIGN. The *Plunger, Barb, Pollack*, and *Dace* were ordered as guided missile submarines (SSGN) and were to each carry four Regulus II missiles. They were re-ordered as "Thresher" class attack submarines after the Regulus II programme was cancelled on 18 Dec 1958 (retaining numerical sequence in the submarine series). The *Jack* was built to a modified design to test a different power plant (see *Engineering* notes).

The *Flasher, Gato*, and *Greenling* were modified during construction; fitted with SUBSAFE features, heavier machinery, and larger sail structures.

These submarines have a modified "tear-drop" hull design. Their bows are devoted to sonar and their four torpedo tubes are amidships, angled out, two to port and two to starboard.

The sail structure height of these submarines is 13 feet, 9 inches to 15 feet above the deck, with later submarines of this class having a sail height of 20 feet.

ELECTRONICS. These submarines are fitted with the advanced BQQ-2 sonar system (first installed in the *Tullibee*, SSN 597). Principal components of the BQQ-2 include the BQS 6 active sonar, with transducers mounted in a 15-foot diameter sonar sphere, and BQR-7 passive sonar, with hydrophones in a conformal array along sides of forward hull. The active sonar sphere is fitted in the optimum bow position, requiring placement of torpedo tubes amidships. The advanced BQS-13DNA active/passive sonar will be fitted in these submarines.

These submarines have the Mk 113 torpedo fire control director.

ENGINEERING. The *Jack* is fitted with two propellers on essentially one shaft (actually a single shaft within a sleeve-like shaft) and a counter-rotating turbine without a reduction gear. Both innovations are designed to reduce operating noises. To accommodate the larger turbine the engine spaces were lengthened ten feet and the shaft structure was lengthened seven feet to mount the two propellers. The propellers are of different size and are smaller than in the other submarines of this class.

PLUNGER (SSN 595) *United States Navy*

BARB (SSN 596) *1973, United States Navy*

Also eliminated in *Jack* was a clutch and secondary-propulsion electric motor.

The *Jack's* propulsion arrangement provides a ten per cent increase in power efficiency, but no increase in speed.

NOMENCLATURE. **Names changed during construction: *Plunger* ex-*Pollack*: *Barb* ex-*Pollack*: ex-*Plunger*: *Pollack* ex-*Barb*.**

Submarines—*continued*

1 NUCLEAR-POWERED ATTACK SUBMARINE (SSN): "TULLIBEE" TYPE

Displacement, tons	2 317 standard; 2 640 submerged
Length, feet (*metres*)	273 (*83·2*) oa
Beam, feet (*metres*)	23·3 (*7·1*)
Draft, feet (*metres*)	21 (*6·4*)
Torpedo tubes	4—21 inch (*533 mm*) amidships
A/S weapons	A/S torpedoes
Main engines	Turbo-electric drive with steam turbine (Westinghouse) 2 500 shp; 1 shaft
Nuclear reactor	1 pressurised water cooled S2C (Combustion Engineering)
Speed, knots	approx 15 surface; 15+ submerged)
Complement	56 (6 officers, 50 enlisted men)

Name	*No*	*Builder*	*Laid down*	*Launched*	*Commissioned*
•TULLIBEE	SSN 597	General Dynamics (Electric Boat)	26 May 1958	27 Apr 1960	9 Nov 1960

The *Tullibee* was designed specifically for anti-submarine operations and was the first US submarine with the optimum bow position devoted entirely to sonar. No additional submarines of this type were constructed because of the success of the larger, more-versatile "Permit" class. The *Tullibee* was authorised in the Fiscal Year 1958 new construction programme. She is no longer considered a "first line" submarine.

DESIGN. The *Tullibee* has a modified, elongated "tear-drop" hull design. Originally she was planned as a 1 000-ton craft, but reactor requirements and other considerations increased her size during design and construction.
The *Tullibee* has four amidships torpedo tubes angled out from the centreline, two to port and two to starboard. However, she is not fitted to fire the SUBROC anti-submarine missile. She cannot match the "Thresher" and later SSN classes in underwater speed or manoeuvrability.

ELECTRONICS. The *Tullibee* was the first submarine fitted with the advanced BQQ-2 sonar system (see "Permit" class listing for details). The fin-like sonar domes are PUFFs for BQG-4 passive fire control sonar; in the earlier photograph only two PUFF domes are installed (not to be confused with fin-like rudder); later photograph shows three PUFF domes with second dome (aft of sail structure) painted light color.

PUFF is an acronym for Passive Underwater Fire-control Feasibility system. Fitted with Mk 112-1 torpedo fire control system.

TULLIBEE (SSN 597) *1960, United States Navy*

ENGINEERING. The *Tullibee* has a small nuclear power plant designed and developed by the Combustion Engineering Company.
The *Tullibee* propulsion system features turbo-electric drive rather than conventional steam turbines with reduction gears in an effort to reduce operating noises.

NAVIGATION. The *Tullibee* is fitted with Ships Inertial Navigation System (SINS).

5 NUCLEAR-POWERED ATTACK SUBMARINES (SSN): "SKIPJACK" CLASS

Displacement, tons	3 075 standard; 3 500 submerged
Length, feet (*metres*)	251·7 (*76·7*) oa
Beam, feet (*metres*)	31·5 (*9·6*)
Draft, feet (*metres*)	28 (*8·5*)
Torpedo tubes	6—21 inch (*533 mm*) forward
A/S weapons	A/S torpedoes
Main engines	2 steam turbines (Westinghouse in *Skipjack*; General Electric in others); approx 15 000 shp; 1 shaft
Nuclear reactor	1 pressurised-water cooled S5W (Westinghouse)
Speed, knots	approx 20 surface; 30+ submerged
Complement	93 (8 officers, 85 enlisted men)

Name	*No*	*Builder*	*Laid down*	*Launched*	*Commissioned*
•SKIPJACK	SSN 585	General Dynamics (Electric Boat)	29 May 1956	26 May 1958	15 Apr 1959
•SCAMP	SSN 588	Mare Island Naval Shipyard	23 Jan 1959	8 Oct 1960	5 June 1961
•SCULPIN	SSN 590	Ingalls Shipbuilding Corp	3 Feb 1958	31 Mar 1960	1 June 1961
•SHARK	SSN 591	Newport News SB & DD Co	24 Feb 1958	16 Mar 1960	9 Feb 1961
•SNOOK	SSN 592	Ingalls Shipbuilding Corp	7 Apr 1958	31 Oct 1960	24 Oct 1961

The "Skipjack" class combines the high-speed endurance of nuclear propulsion with the high-speed "tear-drop" hull design tested in the conventionally powered submarine *Albacore* (AGSS 569). (See *Design* and *Engineering* notes). The *Skipjack* was authorised in the Fiscal Year 1956 new construction programme; the five other submarines of this class were authorised in FY 1957. Although they are now nearing their first decade of service, these submarines are still considered suitable for "first line" service. Officially described as fastest US nuclear submarines in service.
Each cost approximately $40 000 000.
The *Scorpion* (SSN 589) of this class was lost some 400 miles southwest of the Azores while en route from the Mediterranean to Norfolk, Virginia, in May 1968. She went down with 99 men on board.

CONSTRUCTION. The *Scorpion's* keel was laid down twice: the original keel laid down on 1 Nov 1957 was renumbered SSBN 598 and became the Polaris submarine *George Washington*; the second SSN 589 keel became the *Scorpion*. The *Scamp's* keel laying was delayed when material for her was diverted to the SSBN 599. This class introduced the Newport News Shipbuilding and Dry Dock Company and the Ingalls Shipbuilding Corporation to nuclear submarine construction. Newport News had not previously built any submarine since before World War I; Ingalls previously had built only one submarine, the *Blueback* (SS 581), launched in 1959.

SNOOK (SSN 592) *1964, United States Navy*

DESIGN. The *Skipjack* was the first US nuclear submarine built to the "tear-drop" or modified spindle hull design for improved underwater performance. These submarines have a single propeller shaft (vice two in earlier nuclear submarines) and their diving planes are mounted on sail structures to improve underwater manoeuvrability. No after torpedo tubes are fitted because of their tapering sterns.

Submarines—*continued*

1 NUCLEAR-POWERED RESEARCH SUBMARINE (SSN): "HALIBUT" TYPE

Name	No.	Builder	Laid down	Launched	Commissioned
*HALIBUT	SSN 587 (ex-SSGN 587)	Mare Island Naval Shipyard, Vallejo, Calif	11 Apr 1957	9 Jan 1959	4 Jan 1960

Displacement, tons	3 850 standard; 5 000 submerged
Length, feet (*metres*)	350 (*106·6*) oa
Beam, feet (*metres*)	29·5 (*8·9*)
Draft, feet (*metres*)	21·5 (*6·5*)
Torpedo tubes	6—21 inch (*533 mm*) 4 fwd; 2 aft
Main engines	2 steam turbines (Westinghouse), approx 6 000 shp; 2 shafts
Nuclear reactor	1 pressurised-water cooled S3W (Westinghouse)
Speed, knots	15·5 surface; 15+ submerged
Complement	97 (9 officers, 88 enlisted men)

The *Halibut* is believed to have been the first submarine designed and constructed specifically to fire guided missiles. The Soviet "Juliett" class guided missile submarines with diesel-electric propulsion were constructed after the *Halibut*.

She was originally intended to have diesel-electric propulsion but on 27 Feb 1956 the Navy announced she would have nuclear propulsion. She was the US Navy's only nuclear powered *guided* missile submarine (SSGN) to be completed. Authorised in the Fiscal Year 1956 new construction programme and built for an estimated cost of $45 000 000.

The *Halibut* was reclassifed as an attack submarine on 25 July 1965 after the Navy discarded the Regulus submarine-launched missile force. Her missile equipment was removed; she is no longer considered a "first line" submarine and is employed in experimental work. The submarine's large missile compartment makes her an excellent ship for underwater projects.

The Navy has stated that the *Halibut* and earlier *Seawolf* have been designated as "mother" submarines for the deep submergence research programmes. Reportedly the *Halibut* has been fitted with a ducted bow thruster to permit precise control and manoeuvering.

She can carry the 50-foot Deep Submergence Rescue Vehicle (DSRV) and other submersibles on her after deck; the submersibles can "take off" from and land" on" the *Halibut* while the larger craft is submerged.

DESIGN. The *Halibut* was built with a large missile hangar faired into her bow. Her hull was intended primarily to provide a stable surface launching platform rather than for speed or manoeuvrability.

ENGINEERING. Fitted with same reactor propulsion plant as *Skate* and *Sargo*. Submerged speed of *Halibut* is less than "Skate" class because of larger hull volume and shape.

HALIBUT (SSN 587) — *1970, United States Navy*

MISSILES. The *Halibut* was designed to carry two Regulus II surface-to-surface missiles. The Regulus II was a transonic missile which could carry a nuclear warhead and had a range of 1 000 miles. The Regulus II was cancelled before becoming operational and the *Halibut* operated from 1960 to 1964 carrying five Regulus I missiles, subsonic cruise missiles which could deliver a nuclear warhead on targets 500 miles from the launching ship or submarine.

During this period the US Navy operated a maximum of five Regulus "guided" (cruise) missile submarines, the *Halibut*, the post-war constructed *Grayback* (SSG 574 now LPSS 574) and *Growler* (SSG 577), and the World War II-built *Tunny* (SSG 282 subsequently LPSS 282) and *Barbero* (SSG 317). The *Grayback* and *Growler* each could carry four Regulus I missiles and the older submarines each carried two missiles.

As SSGN carried a complement of 11 officers and 108 enlisted men.

NAVIGATION. The *Halibut* is fitted with Ship's Inertial Navigation System (SINS).

PHOTOGRAPHS. Both views of the *Halibut* presented here show the submarine carrying a submersible simulator on deck. Note forward "bulge" of missile hangar door.

1 NUCLEAR-POWERED ATTACK SUBMARINE (SSN): "TRITON" TYPE

Name	No.	Builder	Laid down	Launched	Commissioned
TRITON	SSN 586 (ex-SSRN 586)	General Dynamics Corp (Electric Boat), Groton, Conn	29 May 1956	19 Aug 1958	10 Nov 1959

Displacement, tons	5 940 standard; 7 780 submerged
Length, feet (*metres*)	447·5 (*136·3*) oa
Beam, feet (*metres*)	37 (*11·3*)
Draft, feet (*metres*)	24 (*7·3*)
Torpedo tubes	6—21 inch (*533 mm*) 4 fwd; 2 aft
Main engines	2 steam turbines (General Electric); approx 34 000 shp; 2 shafts
Nuclear reactors	2 pressurised-water cooled S4G (General Electric)
Speed, knots	27 surface; 20+ submerged
Complement as SSRN	172 (16 officers, 156 men enlisted

The *Triton* was designed and constructed to serve as a radar picket submarine to operate in conjunction with surface carrier task forces. She is the longest submarine ever constructed and is exceeded in displacement only by the later Polaris missile submarines. Authorised in the Fiscal Year 1956 new construction programme and built for an estimated cost of $109 000 000.

The *Triton* circumnavigated the globe in 1960, remaining submerged except when her sail structure broke the surface to enable an ill sailor to be taken off near the Falkland Islands. The 41 500-mile cruise took 83 days and was made at an average speed of 18 knots.

The underwater giant was reclassified as an attack submarine (SSN) on 1 Mar 1961 as the Navy dropped the radar picket submarine programme. She is no longer considered a "first line" submarine and was decommissioned on 3 May 1969 to become the first US nuclear submarine to be relegated to the "mothball fleet".

There had been proposals to operate the *Triton* as an underwater national command post afloat, but no funds were provided.

DESIGN. The *Triton* was designed to operate as a surface radar picket, submerging when in danger of enemy attack. She was fitted with an elaborate combat information centre and large radar antenna which retracted into the sail structure.

ENGINEERING. The *Triton* is the only US submarine with two nuclear reactors. The Atomic Energy Commission's Knolls Atomic Power Laboratory was given prime responsibility for development of the power plant. After 2½ years of operation, during which she steamed more than 110 000 miles, the *Triton* was overhauled and refuelled from July 1962 to March 1964.

TRITON (SSN 586) — *United States Navy*

Submarines—*continued*

4 NUCLEAR-POWERED ATTACK SUBMARINES (SSN): "SKATE" CLASS

Displacement, tons	2 570 standard; 2 861 submerged
Length, feet (*metres*)	267·7 (*81·5*) oa
Beam, feet (*metres*)	25 (*7·6*)
Draft, feet (*metres*)	21 (*6·4*)
Torpedo tubes	8—21 inch (*533 mm*) 6 forward; 2 aft (short)
Main engines	2 steam turbines (Westinghouse) approx 6 600 shp 2 shafts
Nuclear reactor	1 pressurised-water cooled S3W (Westinghouse) in *Skate* and *Sargo*. 1 pressurised-water cooled S4W (Westinghouse) in *Swordfish* and *Seadragon*
Speed, knots	15·5 surface; 20+ submerged
Complement	95 (8 officers, 87 enlisted men)

Name	*No.*	*Builder*	*Laid down*	*Launched*	*Commissioned*
***SKATE**	SSN 578	General Dynamics (Electric Boat)	21 July 1955	16 May 1957	23 Dec 1957
***SWORDFISH**	SSN 579	Portsmouth Naval Shipyard	25 Jan 1956	27 Aug 1957	15 Sep 1958
***SARGO**	SSN 583	Mare Island Naval Shipyard	21 Feb 1956	10 Oct 1957	1 Oct 1958
***SEADRAGON**	SSN 584	Portsmouth Naval Shipyard	20 June 1956	16 Aug 1958	5 Dec 1959

The "Skate" class submarines were the first production model nuclear-powered submarines. They are similar in design to the *Nautilus*, but smaller. The *Skate* and *Swordfish* were authorised in the Fiscal Year 1955 new construction programme, and the *Sargo* and *Seadragon* in FY 1956.

The *Skate* was the first submarine to make a completely submerged transatlantic crossing, in 1958 she established a (then) record of 31 days submerged with a sealed atmosphere; on 11 Aug 1958 she passed under the North Pole during a polar cruise, and on 17 Mar 1959 she became the first submarine to surface at the North Pole. The *Sargo* undertook a polar cruise during January-February 1960 and surfaced at the North Pole on 9 Feb 1960. The *Seadragon* transited from the Atlantic to the Pacific via the Northwest Passage (Lancaster Sound, Barrow and McClure Straits) in August 1960. The *Skate*, operating from New London, Connecticut, and the *Seadragon*, based at Pearl Harbour, rendezvoused under the North Pole on 2 Aug 1962 and then conducted anti-submarine exercises under the polar ice pack and surfaced together at the North Pole.

The *Skate* also operated in the Arctic Ocean during April-May 1969, conducting exercises under the Arctic ice pack with the later nuclear-powered attack submarines *Pargo* and *Whale*; and again during the spring of 1971 with the nuclear attack submarine *Trepang*.

SEADRAGON (SSN 584) *1965, United States Navy*

DESIGN. The "Skate" design is similar to the *Nautilus-Seawolf* design with GUPPY hull, bow diving planes, and twin propellers.

ENGINEERING. The reactors for this class were developed by the Atomic Energy Commission's Bettis Atomic Power Laboratory, the new propulsion system was similar to that of the *Nautilus* but considerably simplified with improved operation and maintenance. The propulsion plant developed under this programme had two arrangements, the S3W configuration in the *Skate*, *Sargo* and *Halibut* and the S4W configuration in the *Swordfish* and *Seadragon*. Both arrangements have proven satisfactory. The *Skate* began her first overhaul and refuelling in January 1961 after steaming 120 862 miles on her initial reactor core during three years of operation. The *Swordfish* began her first overhaul and refuelling in early 1962 after more than three years of operation in which time she steamed 112 000 miles.

SWORDFISH (SSN 579) *1970, United States Navy, PH1 John D. Osborne*

SKATE (SSN 578)—See following page *United States Navy*

Submarines—*continued*

1 NUCLEAR-POWERED RESEARCH SUBMARINE (SSN): "SEAWOLF" TYPE

Name	*No*	*Builder*	*Laid down*	*Launched*	*Commissioned*
*SEAWOLF	SSN 575	General Dynamics (Electric Boat), Groton, Connecticut	15 Sep 1953	21 July 1955	30 Mar 1957

Displacement, tons	3 720 standard; 4 280 submerged
Length, feet (*metres*)	337·5 (*102·9*) oa
Beam, feet (*metres*)	27·7 (*8·4*)
Draft, feet (*metres*)	22 (*6·7*)
Torpedo tubes	6—21 in (*533 mm*) forward
Main engines	2 steam turbines (General Electric), approx 15 000 shp; 2 shafts
Nuclear reactor	1 pressurised-water cooled S2Wa (Westinghouse)
Speed, knots	19 surface; 20+ submerged
Complement	105 (10 officers, 95 enlisted men)

The *Seawolf* was the world's second nuclear-propelled vehicle she was constructed almost simultaneously with the *Nautilus* to test a competitive reactor design. Funds for the *Seawolf* were authorised in the Fiscal Year 1952 new construction programme.

The *Seawolf* established a submerged endurance record in 1958 when she remained submerged for 60 consecutive days, travelling a distance of 13 761 miles with a completely sealed atmosphere. She is no longer considered a "first line" submarine and has been engaged primarily in research work since 1969.

ENGINEERING. Initial work in the development of naval nuclear propulsion plants investigated a number of concepts, two of which were of sufficient interest to warrant full development: the pressurised water and liquid metal (sodium). The *Nautilus* was provided with a pressurised-water reactor plant and the *Seawolf* was fitted initially with a liquid-metal reactor.

Originally known as the Submarine Intermediate Reactor (SIR), the liquid metal-plant was developed by the Atomic Energy Commission's Knolls Atomic Power Laboratory.

The SIR Mark II/S2G reactor in the *Seawolf* achieved initial criticality on 25 June 1956. Steam leaks developed during the dockside testing. The plant was shut down and it was determined that the leaks were caused by sodium-potassium alloy which had entered the superheater steam piping. After repairs and testing the *Seawolf* began sea trials on 21 Jan 1957. The trials were run at reduced power and after two years of operation the *Seawolf* entered the Electric Boat yard for removal of her sodium-cooled plant and installation of a pressurised-water plant similar to that installed in the *Nautilus* (designated S2Wa). When the original *Seawolf* plant was shut down in December 1958 the submarine had steamed a total of 71 611 miles. She was recommissioned on 30 Sep 1960. The pressurised-water reactor was refuelled for the first between May 1965 and August 1967, having propelled the *Seawolf* for more than 161 000 miles on its initial fuel core.

SEAWOLF (SSN 575) — *1967, United States Navy*

1 NUCLEAR POWERED ATTACK SUBMARINE (SSN): "NAUTILUS" TYPE

Name	*No.*	*Builder*	*Laid down*	*Launched*	*Commissioned*
*NAUTILUS	SSN 571	General Dynamics (Electric Boat) Groton, Connecticut	14 June 1952	21 Jan 1954	30 Sep 1954

Displacement, tons	3 530 standard; 4 040 submerged
Length, feet (*metres*)	323·7 (*98·6*) oa
Beam, feet (*metres*)	27·6 (*8·4*)
Draft, feet (*metres*)	22 (*6·7*)
Torpedo tubes	6—21 inch (*533 mm*) forward
Main engines	2 steam turbines (Westinghouse), approx 15 000 shp; 2 shafts
Nuclear reactor	1 pressurised-water cooled S2W (Westinghouse)
Speed, knots	18 surface; 20+ submerged
Complement	105 (10 officers, 95 enlisted men)

The *Nautilus* was the world's first nuclear-propelled vehicle. She predated the first Soviet nuclear-powered submarine by an estimated five years.

The Chief of Naval Operations initially established a requirement for a nuclear-propelled submarine in August 1949 and specified a "ready-for-sea" date of January 1955. The funds for construction of the *Nautilus* were authorised in the Fiscal Year 1952 budget. The *Nautilus* put to sea for the first time on 17 Jan 1955 and signalled the historic message: "Underway on nuclear power".

On her shakedown cruise in May 1955 the *Nautilus* steamed submerged from London, Connecticut, to San Juan, Puerto Rico, travelling more than 1 300 miles in 84 hours at an average speed of almost 16 knots; she later steamed submerged from Key West, Florida, to New London, a distance of 1 397 miles, at an average speed of more than 20 knots.

During 1958 the *Nautilus* undertook extensive operations under the Arctic ice pack and in August she made history's first polar transit from the Pacific to the Atlantic, steaming from Pearl Harbour to Portland, England. She passed under the geographic North Pole on 3 Aug 1958.

The *Nautilus* is no longer considered a "first line" submarine and can be expected to be decommissioned in the near future.

DESIGN. The *Nautilus* and *Seawolf* have GUPPY-type hull configurations. The *Seawolf* has a stepped sail and a slight rise at the bow.

ENGINEERING. In January 1948 the Department of Defense requested the Atomic Energy Commission to undertake the design, development, and construction of a nuclear reactor for submarine propulsion. Initial research and conceptual design of the Submarine Thermal Reactor (STR) was undertaken by the Argonne National Laboratory. Subsequently the Atomic Energy Commission's Bettis Atomic Power Laboratory, operated by the Westinghouse Electric Corporation, undertook development of the first nuclear propulsion plant.

The *Nautilus* STR Mark II nuclear plant (redesignated S2W) was first operated on 20 Dec 1954 and first developed full power on 3 Jan 1955.

After more than two years of operation, during which she steamed 62 562 miles, the *Nautilus* began an overhaul which included refuelling in April 1957. She was again refuelled in 1959 after steaming 91 324 miles on her second fuel core, and again in 1964 after steaming approximately 150 000 miles on her third fuel core. (The prototype Mark I/S1W plant was refuelled in 1955, 1958, 1960, and 1967; it remains in operation as an experimental and training facility)

PHOTOGRAPH. Two light areas on deck are emergency, tethered marker buoys (fitted to all US submarines) for localisation of sunken submarine and to winch down McCann submarine rescue chamber.

NAUTILUS (SSN 571) — ***United States Navy***

Submarines—*continued*

3 ATTACK SUBMARINES (SS): "BARBEL" CLASS

Displacement, tons	2 145 surface; 2 895 submerged
Length, feet (*metres*)	219·5 (*66·8*) oa
Beam, feet (*metres*)	29 (*8·8*)
Draft, feet (*metres*)	28 (*8·5*)
Torpedo tubes	6—21 in (*533 mm*) forward
Main engines	3 diesels 4 800 bhp (Fairbanks Morse); 2 electric motors (General Electric) 3 150 shp; 1 shaft
Speed, knots	15 on surface; 25 submerged
Complement	79 (10 officers, 69 men)

Name	*No.*	*Builder*	*Laid down*	*Launched*	*Commissioned*
*BARBEL	SS 580	Portsmouth Naval Shipyard	18 May 1956	19 July 1958	17 Jan 1959
*BLUEBACK	SS 581	Ingalls Shipbuilding Corporation	15 Apr 1957	16 May 1959	15 Oct 1959
*BONEFISH	SS 582	New York Shipbuilding Corp	3 June 1957	22 Nov 1958	9 July 1959

These submarines were the last non-nuclear combatant submarines built by the US Navy. All three were authorised in the Fiscal Year 1956 new construction programme.

CONSTRUCTION. The *Blueback* was the first submarine built by the Ingalls Shipbuilding Corp at Pascagoula, Mississippi, and the *Bonefish* was the first constructed at the New York Shipbuilding Corp yard in Camden, New Jersey. None of the three shipyards that built this class is now employed in submarine construction.

DESIGN. These submarines have the "tear drop" or modified spindle hull design which was tested in the experimental submarine *Albacore*. As built their diving planes were bow-mounted; subsequently relocated to the sail structure.
These submarines introduced a new concept in centralised arrangement of controls in an "attack centre" to increase efficiency; the concept has been adapted for all later US combat submarines.

PHOTOGRAPHS. Note forward position of diving planes on sail structure, bow configuration for maximum underwater performance, and clear decks that are void of projections.

BLUEBACK (SS 581) *1967, United States Navy*

BONEFISH (SS 582) *1969, United States Navy*

1 ATTACK SUBMARINE (SS): "DARTER" TYPE

Displacement, tons	1 720 surface; 2 388 submerged
Length, feet (*metres*)	268·6 (*81·9*) oa
Beam, feet (*metres*)	27·2 (*8·3*)
Draft, feet (*metres*)	19 (*5·8*)
Torpedo tubes	8—21 in (*533 mm*) 6 fwd; 2 aft
Main engines	3 diesels (Fairbanks Morse); 4 500 bhp electric motors (Elliott); 2 shafts
Speed, knots	19·5 surface; 14 submerged
Complement	83 (8 officers, 75 men)

Name	*No.*	*Builder*	*Laid down*	*Launched*	*Commissioned*
*DARTER	SS 576	General Dynamics Corp (Electric Boat)	10 Nov 1954	28 May 1956	20 Oct 1956

Designed for high submerged speed with quiet machinery. Planned sister submarines *Growler* and *Grayback* were completed to missile-launching configuration.

Basic design of the *Darter* is similar to the "Tang" class described on a later page.

Authorised in Fiscal Year 1954 shipbuilding programme. No additional submarines of this type were built because of shift to high-speed hull design and nuclear propulsion.

DARTER (SS 576) *United States Navy*

Submarines—*continued*

2 ATTACK SUBMARINES (SS): "SAILFISH" CLASS

Name	No.	Builder	Laid down	Launched	Commissioned
*SAILFISH	SS 572 (ex-SSR 572)	Portsmouth Naval Shipyard	8 Dec 1953	7 Sep 1955	14 Apr 1956
*SALMON	SS 573 (ex-AGSS 573, ex-SSR 573)	Portsmouth Naval Shipyard	10 Mar 1954	25 Feb 1956	25 Aug 1956

Displacement, tons	2 625 surface; 3 168 submerged
Length, feet (*metres*)	350·4 (*106·8*) oa
Beam, feet (*metres*)	28·4 (*8·8*)
Draft, feet (*metres*)	18 (*5·5*) max
Torpedo tubes	6—21 inch (*533 mm*) forward
Main engines	4 diesels (Fairbanks Morse); 6 000 bhp/2 electric motors (Elliott); 8 200 shp; 2 shafts
Speed, knots	19·5 on surface; 14 submerged
Complement	95 (12 officers, 83 enlisted men)

Largest non-nuclear submarines built by the US Navy since the *Narwhal* (SS 167) and *Nautilus* (SS 168) completed in 1956. The *Sailfish* and *Salmon* were built as radar picket submarines (SSR) with air search radar antennas on deck and elaborate air control centres. Authorised in Fiscal Year 1952 programme. Both submarines underwent FRAM II modernisation.
These are believed to be the largest non-nuclear submarines in service with any navy.

CLASSIFICATION. Reclassified from radar picket submarines (SSR) to SS on 1 Mar 1961; *Salmon* reclassified AGSS on 29 June 1968 to serve at test and evaluation submarine for Navy's Deep Submergence Rescue Vehicle (DSRV). However, the DSRV programme was delayed and the *Salmon* reverted to the SS designation on 30 June 1969.

All ten of the World War II-built submarines that had been converted to radar picket configurations have been stricken except for the *Tigrone* (AGSS 419), which survives as a research submarine (described on a later page in this section).

Radar picket submarines were to operate ahead of carrier task forces to provide early warning of air attack; upon coming under attack themselves they would submerge for safety. The Soviet Navy operates several modified "W" class submarines in the radar picket role.

ELECTRONICS. Fitted with BQG-4 passive fire control sonar (note three fin-like PUFF sonar domes). The fourth "fin" at stern is the upper rudder. See "Tong" class listing for details.

PHOTOGRAPHS. Note size of PUFF fins in comparison to men in photograph of the *Salmon*.

SAILFISH (SS 572) *1966, United States Navy*

SALMON (SS 573) *United States Navy*

1 GUIDED MISSILE SUBMARINE (SSG): "GROWLER" TYPE

Name	No.	Builder	Laid down	Launched	Commissioned
GROWLER	SSG 577	Portsmouth Naval Shipyard	15 Feb 1955	5 Apr 1959	30 Apr 1958

Displacement, tons	2 540 standard; 3 515 submerged
Length, feet (*metres*)	317·6 (*96·8*) oa
Beam, feet(*metres*)	27·2 (*8·2*)
Draft, feet (*metres*)	19 (*5·8*)"
Torpedo tubes	6—21 inch (*533 mm*) 4 fwd; 2 aft
Main engines	3 diesels (Fairbanks Morse); 4 600 bhp/2 electric motors (Elliott); 5 600 shp; 2 shafts
Speed, knots	20 surface; 17 submerged
Complement	84 officers and enlisted men

The *Growler* was authorised in the Fiscal Year 1955 new construction programme; completed as a guided missile submarine to fire the Regulus surface-to-surface cruise missile (see *Halibut*, SSN 587, for *Missile* notes).
When the Regulus submarine missile programme ended in 1964 the *Growler* and her near-sister submarine *Grayback* were withdrawn from service; the *Grayback* subsequently converted to an amphibious transport submarine (LPSS). The *Growler* was scheduled to undergo a similar conversion when the *Grayback* was completed, but the second conversion was deferred late in 1968 because of rising ship conversion costs.
The *Growler* is in reserve as an SSG.

DESIGN. The *Grayback* and *Growler* initially were designed as attack submarines similar to the *Darter*. Upon redesign as missile submarines they were cut in half on the building ways and were lengthened approximately 50 feet, two cylindrical hangars, each 11 feet high and 70 feet long, were superimposed on their bows, a missile launcher was installed between the hangars and sail structure, and elaborate navigation and fire control systems were fitted. The height of the sail structure on the *Growler* is approximately 30 feet above the deck; the *Grayback's* lower sail structure was increased during LPSS conversion.

GRAYBACK (left), GROWLER (right) *1964, United States Navy*

Submarines—*continued*

1 AMPHIBIOUS TRANSPORT SUBMARINE (LPSS): "GRAYBACK" TYPE

Name	*No.*	*Builder*	*Laid down*	*Launched*	*Commissioned*	*LPSS Comm.*
***GRAYBACK**	LPSS 574 (ex-SSG 574)	Mare Island Naval Shipyard	1 July 1954	2 July 1957	7 Mar 1958	9 May 1969

Displacement, tons	2 670 standard; 3 650 submerged
Length, feet (*metres*)	334 (*101·8*) oa
Beam, feet (*metres*)	30 (*9·0*)
Draft, feet (*metres*)	19 (*5·8*)
Torpedo tubes	8—21 inch (*533 mm*) 6 fwd; 2 aft
Main engines	3 diesels (Fairbanks Morse); 4 500 bhp/2 electric motors (Elliott); 5 600 shp; 2 shafts
Speed, knots	20 surface; 17 submerged
Complement	87 (9 officers, 78 enlisted men)
Troops	67 (7 officers, 60 enlisted men)

The *Grayback* has been fully converted to a transport submarine and is officially classified as an amphibious warfare ship. She was originally intended to be an attack submarine, being authorised in the Fiscal Year 1953 new construction programme, but redesigned in 1956 to provide a Regulus missile launching capability; completed as SSG 574 in 1958, similar in design to the *Growler* (SSG 577). See *Growler* listing for basic design notes. The *Grayback* probably will be decommissioned in mid-1975.

CONVERSION. The *Grayback* began conversion to a transport submarine at the San Francisco Bay Naval Shipyard (Mare Island) in November 1967. The conversion was originally estimated at $15 200 000 but was actually about $30 000 000. She was reclassified from SSG to LPSS on 30 Aug 1968 (never officially designated APSS).
During conversion the *Grayback* was fitted to berth and mess 67 troops and carry their equipment including landing craft or swimmer delivery vehicles (SDV). Her torpedo tubes and hence attack capability are retained. As completed (SSG) the *Grayback* had an overall length of 322 ft 4 in; lengthened 12 ft during LPSS conversion. Conversion was authorised in Fiscal Year 1965 programme and completed in June 1969; delayed because of higher priorities being allocated to other submarine projects.

ELECTRONICS. Fitted with BQG-4 passive fire control sonar (note three fin-like PUFF sonar domes). See "Tang" class listing for details.

PHOTOGRAPHS. Bow and stern views of the *Grayback* appear in the 1972-1973 edition.

GRAYBACK (LPSS 574) — *1969, United States Navy*

4 ATTACK SUBMARINES (SS): "TANG" CLASS

Displacement, tons	2 100 surface; 2 700 submerged
Length, feet (*metres*)	287 (*87·4*) oa
Beam, feet (*metres*)	27·3 (*8·3*)
Draft, feet (*metres*)	19 (*6·2*)
Torpedo tubes	8—21 in (*533 mm*) 6 fwd, 2 aft
Main engines	3 diesels (Fairbanks-Morse); 4 500 bhp/2 electric motors; 5 600 shp; 2 shafts
Speed, knots	16 surface; 16 submerged
Complement	83 (8 officers, 75 men)

Name	*No.*	*Builder*	*Laid down*	*Launched*	*Commissioned*
***TANG**	SS 563	Portsmouth Naval Shipyard	18 Apr 1949	19 June 1951	25 Oct 1951
***WAHOO**	SS 565	Portsmouth Naval Shipyard	24 Oct 1949	16 Oct 1951	30 May 1952
***TROUT**	SS 566	Electric Boat Co, Groton	1 Dec 1949	21 Aug 1951	27 June 1952
***GUDGEON**	SS 567	Portsmouth Naval Shipyard	20 May 1950	11 June 1952	21 Nov 1952

Six submarines of this class were constructed, incorporating improvements based on German World War II submarine developments. The *Tang* was authorised in the Fiscal Year 1947 new construction programme, *Wahoo* and *Trout* in FY 1948, and *Gudgeon* in FY 1949. The *Gudgeon* was the first US submarine to circumnavigate the world during Sep 1957-Feb 1958.
All remaining submarines of this class are active.

ELECTRONICS. BQG-4 fire control sonar fitted in some of these submarines; the small, fin-like structures are antenna domes for the sonar (referred to as PUFFS—an acronym for Passive Underwater Fire Control Feasibility System).

ENGINEERING. *Tang, Trout* and *Wahoo* were originally powered by a compact, radial type engine produced after five years of development work, comprising a 16-cylinder 2-cycle plant, mounted vertically with four rows of cylinders radially arranged. These new engines were half the weight and two-thirds the size of the engines previously available for submarines. They proved to be unsatisfactory and were replaced by machinery similar to that in *Gudgeon* which has Fairbanks-Morse high speed lightweight engines mounted horizontally. The electric motors are Elliott in *Tang*, General Electric in *Wahoo* and *Trout*, Westinghouse in *Gudgeon*.
Snorkel fitted as in all later US nuclear and conventionally propelled submarines.

RECONSTRUCTION. All six submarines of this class were built with an overall length of 269 ft 2 in. The units had their original diesel engines replaced during the late 1950's were cut in half and a 9 ft section inserted amidships. All six submarines were modernised during the 1960's with the installation of improved electronics equipment and other features; additional sections were added to give an overall length of 287 ft.

DISPOSALS AND TRANSFERS
Trigger (SS 564) transferred to Italy on 10 July 1973; **Harder** (SS 568) transferred to Italy on 15 Mar 1974 (corrections to previous editions).

GUDGEON (SS 567) — *1970, United States Navy*

WAHOO (SS 565) — *1968, United States Navy*

Submarines—*continued*

1 RESEARCH SUBMARINE (AGSS): "DOLPHIN" TYPE

Name	*No.*	*Builder*	*Laid down*	*Launched*	*Commissioned*
***DOLPHIN**	AGSS 555	Portsmouth Naval Shipyard	9 Nov 1962	8 June 1968	17 Aug 1968

Displacement, tons	800 standard; 930 full load
Length, feet	152
Beam, feet	19·3
Diameter, feet	18 (maximum)
Torpedo tubes	Removed
Main engines	Diesel/electric (2 Detroit 12V71 diesels), 1 500 hp; 1 shaft
Speed, knots	12+ submerged
Complement	23 (3 officers, 20 enlisted men) plus 4 to 7 scientists

DOLPHIN (AGSS 555) *United States Navy*

The *Dolphin* is an auxiliary submarine specifically designed for deep-diving operations. Authorised in Fiscal Year 1961 new construction programme, but delayed because of changes in mission and equipment coupled with higher priorities being given to other submarine projects The *Dolphin* is fitted for deep-ocean sonar and oceanographic research. She is highly automated and has three computer-operated systems, a safety system, hovering system, and one that is classified. The digital-computer submarine safety system monitors equipment and provides data on closed-circuit television screens; malfunctions in equipment or trends towards potentially dangerous situations set off an alarm and if they are not corrected within the prescribed time the system, unless overridden by an operator, automatically brings the submarine to the surface. There are several research stations for scientists in the *Dolphin* and she is fitted to take water samples down to her operating (test) depth. The single, experimental torpedo tube was removed in 1970. Underwater endurance is limited (endurance and habitability were considered of secondary importance in design). On 24 Nov 1968 the *Dolphin* "descended to a depth greater than that recorded by any other operational submarine" according to official statements.

CLASSIFICATION. The *Dolphin's* number was taken from a block (551-562) authorised but cancelled late in World War II with no construction being assigned. (Submarines built in Norway and Denmark were assigned the hull numbers SS 553 and SS 554, respectively, for financial accounting purposes; hull numbers SS 551 and SS 552 in this series were assigned to the late hunter-killer submarines *Bass*, ex-SSK 2 and *Bonita* ex-SSK 3 respectively).

DESIGN. The *Dolphin* has a constant diameter cylindrical pressure hull approximately 15 feet in outer diameter closed at both ends with hemispherical heads. Pressure hull fabricated of HY-80 steel with aluminium and fibreglass used in secondary structures to reduce weight, a critical factor in retaining buoyancy at deep depths. No conventional diving planes are mounted; improved rudder design and other features provide manoeuvring control and hovering capability. Access is through a single hatch in the pressure hull (opening into sail structure).

ENGINEERING. Fitted with 330 cell silver zinc battery. Submerged endurance is approximately 24 hours with an at-sea endurance of 14 days.

STATUS. Completed in early 1969, approximately five years behind official schedule at time of keel laying. The *Dolphin* is in commission and has a commanding officer.

PHOTOGRAPHS. Note the *Dolphin's* rounded, constant-diameter hull configuration in the above photograph; note her small deck area, narrow sail structure raised periscope. A photograph of the *Dolphin* being launched, showing her stern configuration, appeared in the 1970-1971 edition and a photograph of the *Dolphin* design model appeared in the 1969-1970 edition.

DOLPHIN (AGSS 555) *United States Navy*

1 RESEARCH SUBMARINE (AGSS): "ALBACORE" TYPE

Name	*No.*	*Builder*	*Laid down*	*Launched*	*Commissioned*
ALBACORE	AGSS 569	Portsmouth Naval Shipyard	15 Mar 1952	1 Aug 1953	5 Dec 1953

Displacement, tons	1 500 surface; 1 850 submerged
Length, feet (*metres*)	210·5 (*63·6*) oa
Beam, feet (*metres*)	27·5 (*8·4*)
Draft, feet (*metres*)	18·5 (*5·6*)
Torpedo tubes	None
Main engines	2 diesels, radial pancake type (General Motors) electric motor (Westinghouse) 15 000 shp; 1 shaft
Speed, knots	25 on surface; 33 submerged
Complement	52 (5 officers, 47 men)

High speed experimental submarine. Conventionally powered submarine of radical design with new hull form which makes her faster and more manoeuverable than any other conventional submarine. Officially described as a hydrodynamic test vehicle. Streamlined, whale shaped without the naval flat-topped deck. Conning tower resembles a fish's dorsal fin.

The *Albacore* was decommissioned and placed in reserve on 1 Sep 1972.

EXPERIMENTAL. The *Albacore* has been extensively modified to test advanced submarine design and engineering concepts.
Phase I modifications were made from July 1954 to February 1955 to eliminate the many "bugs" inherent with completely new construction and equipment.
Phase II modifications from Dec 1955 to Mar 1956 during which conventional propeller-rudder-stern diving plane arrangement was modified; the new design provided for the propeller to be installed *aft* of the control surfaces. (At this time a small auxiliary rudder on the sail was removed)
A concave bow sonar dome was fitted for tests in 1960.
Phase III modifications from Nov 1960 to Aug 1961 during which an entirely new stern was installed featuring the stern planes in an "X" configuration, a system of ten hydraulic operated dive brakes around the hull amidships, a dorsal rudder, and a new bow sonar dome. Phase IV modifications from Dec 1962 to Mar 1965 during which a silver-zinc battery was installed and counter-rotating stern propellers rotating around the same axis were fitted.
The *Albacore* conducted trials with towed sonar arrays from May to July 1966.
All modifications were made at the Portsmouth Naval Shipyard.

PHOTOGRAPH. Note stern rudder configuration; rounded hull without superstructure deck common to previous and contemporary submarines. Round electronic "ball" antenna on sail structure. Deck cleats and other equipment are recessed into hull.

Submarines—*continued*

ALBACORE (AGSS 569) *United States Navy*

2 ATTACK SUBMARINES (SS): GUPPY III TYPE

Displacement, tons	1 975 standard; 2 450 submerged
Length, feet (*metres*)	326·5 (*99·4*) oa
Beam, feet (*metres*)	27 (*8·2*)
Draft, feet (*metres*)	17 (*5·2*)
Torpedo tubes	10—21 inch (*533 mm*) 6 fwd, 4 aft
Main engines	*Clamagore* 4 diesels; (General Motors); 6 400 bhp; *Tiru* 3 diesels (Fairbanks Morse); 4 800 bhp/2 electric motors (General Electric); 5 400 shp; 2 shafts
Speed, knots	approx 20 surface; 15 submerged
Complement	approx 85

Name	*No.*	*Builder*	*Laid down*	*Launched*	*Commissioned*
***CLAMAGORE**	SS 343	Electric Boat Co (Groton, Conn)	16 Mar 1944	25 Feb 1945	28 June 1945
***TIRU**	SS 416	Mare Island Navy Yard	17 Apr 1944	16 Sep 1947	1 Sep 1948

Nine submarines of the "Balao" and "Tench" classes were modernised under the GUPPY III programme in 1960-1962. Fifteen additional planned GUPPY III conversions were dropped in favour of new construction nuclear-propelled submarines.
The *Clamagore* and *Tiru* are the last of 52 submarines of World War II construction modernised under the GUPPY programme (an acronym for Greater Underwater Propulsion Project); both are expected to be transferred to Turkey during 1975.

CONVERSION. The GUPPY III concept evolved after World War II as a method to improve the underwater performance of existing US submarines. The concept was based on the German Type XXI submarines which were massed produced in 1944-1945. The Type XXI characteristics included a streamlined hull and superstructure, snorkel, and increased battery power. The US Navy's GUPPY conversions had similar features, with resulting increases in underwater speed and endurance.

ELECTRONICS. Both submarines are fitted with the BQR-2 sonar and BQG-4 fire control sonar.

ENGINEERING. Fitted with two increased capacity, 126-cell electric batteries; also snorkel to permit operation of diesel engines to charge batteries and for propulsion while at periscope depth.

PHOTOGRAPHS. Small, fin-like structures on these submarines are antenna domes for the BQG-4 fire control sonar (referred to as PUFFs—an acronym for Passive Underwater Fire control Feasibility System, an anti-submarine targeting system). GUPPY conversions have rounded bows as opposed to "ship" bows in streamlined fleet-type submarines.

CLAMAGORE (SS 343) and CORPORAL (SS 346) *United States Navy*

TIRU (SS 416) *1969, United States Navy*

DISPOSALS AND TRANSFERS

Volador (SS 490), **Pickerel** (SS 524) transferred to Italy on 18 Aug 1972; **Trumpetfish** (SS 425) transferred to Brazil on 15 Oct 1973; **Remora** (SS 487) transferred to Greece on 29 Oct 1973; **Cobbler** (SS 344), **Corporal** (SS 346) transferred to Turkey on 21 Nov 1973; **Greenfish** (SS 351) transferred to Brazil on 30 Nov 1973.

Submarines—*continued*

1 RESEARCH SUBMARINE (AGSS): "TIGRONE" TYPE

Displacement, tons	1 840 standard; 2 400 submerged
Length, feet (*metres*)	312 (*95·1*) oa
Beam, feet (*metres*)	27·2 (*8·3*)
Draft, feet (*metres*)	16·5 (*5·0*)
Torpedo tubes	10—21 inch (*533 mm*) 6 fwd, 4 aft
Main engines	4 diesels (Fairbanks Morse); 5 400 bhp/4 electric motors (General Electric); 2 shafts
Speed, knots	approx 20 surface; 10 submerged
Complement	approx 85

Name	*No.*	*Builder*	*Laid down*	*Launched*	*Commissioned*
***TIGRONE**	AGSS 419	Portsmouth Navy Yard	8 May 1944	20 July 1944	25 Oct 1944

Originally a "Tench" class fleet submarine refitted as a radar picket submarine in 1947-1948, being provided with elaborate air search radars and an air control centre. Reverted to fleet submarine status in 1959 with the end of the submarine radar picket programme. Subsequently fitted with large bow sonar installation and used for research and experimental work.

Disposal of the *Tigrone* has been periodically delayed; she probably will be the last submarine of World War II construction in active US service.

CLASSIFICATION. *Tigrone* changed from SS to radar picket submarine (SSR) on 31 Mar 1948; reverted to SS designation on 15 Aug 1959; changed to auxiliary submarine (AGSS) on 1 Dec 1963.

ENGINEERING. Fitted with snorkel installation.

PHOTOGRAPHS. Note large bow sonar structure housing surface ship sonar installed for acoustic research. Two "ball" electronic antennas are fitted atop the sonar structure; similar antennas are found on the bows of later US nuclear-propelled submarines and on some Soviet undersea craft.

TIGRONE (AGSS 419) — *1968, United States Navy*

1 AMPHIBIOUS TRANSPORT SUBMARINE (LPSS): "SEALION" TYPE

Displacement, tons	2 145 surface; 2 500 submerged
Length, feet (*metres*)	311·5 (*95·0*)
Beam, feet (*metres*)	27 (*8·2*)
Draft, feet (*metres*)	17 (*5·2*)
Torpedo tubes	Removed
Guns	Removed
Main engines	2 diesels (General Motors), 2 305 bhp/4 electric motors (General Electric); 2 shafts
Speed, knots	13 surface; 10 submerged
Complement	74 (6 officers, 68 men)
Troops	160

Name	*No.*	*Builder*	*Laid down*	*Launched*	*Commissioned*
SEALION	LPSS 315	Electric Boat Company, Groton	25 Feb 1943	31 Oct 1943	8 Mar 1944

Originally a "Balao" class submarine converted to underwater transport for carrying Marines, commandos or frogmen in covert operations where surface ships would be too vulnerable. The *Sealion* was to have been replaced by conversion of the *Growler* (SSG 577) to a transport submarine; however, conversion of *Growler* was cancelled.

The *Sealion* was decommissioned and placed in reserve in Feb 1970.

The *Sealion* is the last submarine of World War II construction remaining on the Naval Register.

CLASSIFICATION. *Sealion* changed from SS to transport submarine (SSP) in March 1948; changed to auxiliary transport submarine (ASSP) in January 1950; changed to APSS in October 1956; changed again to amphibious transport submarine (LPSS) on 1 Jan 1969.

CONVERSION. The *Sealion* was converted to a transport submarine at the San Francisco Naval Shipyard in 1948. All torpedo tubes and half of her diesel propulsion plant were removed to provide berthing for 160 troops; stowage provided for rubber rafts and other equipment in enlarged superstructure deck aft of conning tower.

ENGINEERING. Fitted with snorkel installation.

GUNNERY. The two 40 mm single guns shown on conning tower steps were removed prior to the *Sealion* being decommissioned.

SEALION (LPSS 315) — *1965, United States Navy*

STATUS. In 1960 the *Sealion* was assigned to operational reserve training duties; recommissioned late in 1961 with increase of US conventional warfare capabilities.

See 1971-1972 edition for disposals of earlier transport submarines.

GUPPY SUBMARINES

Except for the two GUPPY III submarines listed on the previous page, all other U.S. submarines modernised under the GUPPY programmes have been stricken or transferred (with two submarines lost operationally, the *Cochino* (SS 345) of the GUPPY II type off Norway in 1949, and the *Stickleback* (SS 415) of the GUPPY IIA type off Hawaii in 1958).

A total of 52 submarines of World War II construction were modernised to GUPPY configurations between 1946 and 1962. See 1973-1974 and previous editions for characteristics.

GUPPY III TYPE

Volador (SS 490), **Pickerel** (SS 524) transferred to Italy on 18 Aug 1972; **Trumpetfish** (SS 425) stricken on 15 Oct 1973; **Remora** (SS 487) transferred to Greece on 29 Oct 1973; **Cobbler** (SS 344), **Corporal** (SS 346) stricken on 21 Nov 1973; **Greenfish** (SS 351) stricken on 19 Dec 1973; **Clamagore** (SS 343), **Tiru** (SS 416) stricken in June 1974.

GUPPY II TYPE

DISPOSALS AND TRANSFERS

Pomodon (SS 486) stricken on 1 Aug 1970, **Diodon** (SS 349) stricken on 15 Jan 1971; **Halfbeak** (SS 352) stricken on 1 July 1971; **Catfish** (SS 339) transferred to Argentina on 1 July 1971; **Cubera** (SS 347) transferred to Venezuela on 5 Jan 1972; **Grampus** (SS 523) to Brazil 13 May 1972; **Sirago** (SS 485) stricken on 1 June 1972; **Odax** (SS 484) transferred to Brazil on 8 July 1972, **Dogfish** (SS 350) to Brazil on 28 July 1972; **Sea Leopard** (SS 483) transferred to Brazil on 27 Mar 1973; **Cutlass** (SS 478) transferred to Taiwan China on 12 Apr 1973; **Grenadier** (SS 525) transferred to Venezuela on 15 May 1973; **Amberjack** (SS 522) transferred to Brazil on 17 Oct 1973; **Tusk** (SS 426) transferred to Taiwan China on 18 Oct 1973.

GUPPY IIA TYPE

DISPOSALS AND TRANSFERS

Razorback (SS 394) transferred to Turkey on 30 Nov 1970, **Sea Fox** (SS 402) transferred to Turkey on 15 Dec 1970, **Ronquil** (SS 396) transferred to Spain on 1 July 1971, **Pomfret** (SS 391) and **Thornback** (SS 418) transferred to Turkey on 1 July 1971; **Hardhead** (SS 365) transferred to Greece on 26 July 1972; **Entemedor** (SS 340) and **Trutta** (SS 421) to Turkey on 31 July 1972; **Threadfin** (SS 410) to Turkey on 18 Aug 1972; **Picuda** (SS 382) and **Bang** (SS 385) transferred to Spain on 1 Oct 1972, **Quillback** (SS 424) stricken on 23 Mar 1973; **Menhaden** (SS 377) stricken on 15 Aug 1973; **Tirante** (SS 420) stricken on 1 Oct 1973; **Jallao** (SS 368) stricken on 26 June 1974.

GUPPY IA TYPE

DISPOSALS AND TRANSFERS

Sea Robin (SS 407) stricken on 1 Oct 1970; **Chivo** (SS 341) transferred to Argentina on 1 July 1971; **Chopper** (IXSS 342/AGSS 342/SS 342) stricken on 1 Oct 1971; **Caiman** (SS 323) transferred to Turkey on 30 June 1972; **Blackfin** (SS 322) stricken on 15 Sep 1972; **Becuna** (SS 319/AGSS 319), **Blenny** (SS 324/AGSS 324), **Atule** (SS 403/AGSS 403), **Sea Poacher** (SS 406/AGSS 406), **Tench** (SS 417/AGSS 417) stricken on 15 Aug 1973.

TRAINING SUBMARINES (SST)

All specifically designated target and training submarines have been stricken. See 1973-1974 and previous editions for characteristics.

The former "hunter-killer" type submarine **Barracuda** (SS-T3/SST 3/SSK 1) stricken on 1 Oct 1973.

The built-for-the-purpose training submarines **Mackerel** (SST 1/AGSS 570) and **Marlin** (SST 2) stricken on 31 Jan 1973.

AIRCRAFT CARRIERS

The US Navy operated 14 aircraft carriers into 1974. The completion of the nuclear-propelled *Nimitz* (CVAN 68) late in 1974 was to permit a temporary return to a 15-carrier force level.
At 14 ships the US Navy's total carrier force is at the lowest level since the Korean War (1950-1953). Although the number of *attack* aircraft carriers had declined to 14 ships in 1959-1960, during the past two decades as many as nine anti-submarine aircraft carriers (CVS) were also in service for a total carrier force of over 20 ships. The specialised anti-submarine carriers have been discarded and all attack carriers (CVA/CVAN) will be provided with anti-submarine helicopters and fixed-wing aircraft, and the related command centres to permit the ships to function as multi-mission "aircraft carriers" (CV/CVN).
In addition to the *Nimitz*, two other nuclear-propelled aircraft carriers are under construction. With the nuclear-propelled *Enterprise* (CVAN 65) and eight ships of the conventional "Forrestal" classes, the Navy will have 12 "modern" carriers in service in the early 1980s. By that time the five surviving attack carriers of World War II-era construction, two "Hancock" class and three "Midway" class ships, will have been discarded (although one possibly would be retained as a training ship). It was planned to decommission the two smaller ships, the *Hancock* (CVA 19) and *Oriskany*, (CVA 34) in 1974-1975, reducing the carrier force level to 13 ships. However, the difficulties encountered in home porting a US carrier in Greece and the recent need to deploy a carrier periodically in the Indian Ocean has led to retention of these two older carriers.
Currently the Navy has six carriers in the Atlantic and eight in the Pacific, with two of these ships normally forward deployed in the Mediterranean and three in the western Pacific-Indian Ocean areas. All carriers are based in US ports and forward deploy for about six months at a time, except for the carrier *Midway* (CVA 41) which was homeported in Japan during 1973.

ADVANCED AIRCRAFT CARRIERS. The first carriers of the "Forrestal" design will reach their 30th year of service in the mid-1980s and a replacement programme is being planned. This follows-on carrier has been designated CVX until specific characteristics are determined. The first CVX is believed scheduled for the Fiscal Year 1978 new construction programme.
According to official statements, CVX conceptual studies and preliminary design work are underway, oriented toward ship dimensions, propulsion system, and other features that would be compatible with a design-to-cost goal of about $550 000 000 (in Fiscal Year 1973 dollars). This compares to a cost of about twice that for the last "Nimitz" class carrier.
Unofficial estimates provide for a CVX of about 50 000 to 60 000 tons full load, capable of embarking an air wing of perhaps 70 aircraft (compared to about 100 for a 90 000 ton "Nimitz" class ship). Key factors in the final determination of the CVX characteristics could be the capabilities of future V/STOL high-performance aircraft and the question of nuclear propulsion. The value of nuclear propulsion has been amply demonstrated in over a decade of operations by the carrier *Enterprise*. However, an aircraft carrier, perhaps more than any other warship, is tied to attendant escorts and to underway replenishment forces (for aircraft fuels and munitions); thus in many situations the nuclear carrier's high sustained speeds cannot be fully exploited.
The four nuclear carriers available in the 1980s will provide four quick reaction-nuclear task groups, two in each ocean area. In view of increasing ship costs, the reluctance of the navy to request and of the Congress to provide large amounts of "front end" money to finance nuclear surface ships (with resulting lower operational costs), and the probable need for replacement carriers during the remainder of the 20th Century, the CVX could evolve as a non-nuclear ship.

SEA CONTROL SHIPS. The Navy's plans to construct eight so-called Sea Control Ships (SCS) are described in the subsequent listing of Surface Combatants in this edition of *Jane's Fighting Ships*. This categorisation follows the US Navy's consideration of the ship. With respect to actual capabilities the sea control ship concept does "fit" between aircraft carriers and the various missile-armed cruisers, frigates, and destroyers described under Surface Combatants.
The sea control ship will operate less-capable aircraft than the aircraft carriers listed herein, will be a slower ship, and have minimal shipboard weapons and sensors. Thus, the sea control ship is perhaps comparable with the escort or "jeep" aircraft carrier of World War II with respect to both characteristics and role.

TRAINING CARRIER. The "Hancock" class carrier *Lexington* (CVT 16) operates as a training carrier and is based at Pensacola, Florida. The ship has no aircraft maintenance or arming capabilities, and hence cannot be considered as a combat ship. In an emergency situation aircraft could be embarked to conduct anti-submarine or amphibious assault operations on a very restricted basis. The designation CVT officially is classified as an auxiliary ship.

AIR WINGS. Each large attack carrier normally operates an air wing of 85 to 95 aircraft; two fighter squadrons with 24 F-4 Phantoms or F-14 Tomcats as they become available, two or three light attack squadrons with 24 or 36 A-7 Corsairs, one medium attack squadron with 9 or 12 A-6 Intruders, and smaller squadrons or detachments with three or four RA-5C Vigilantes for reconnaissance, four EA-6B Prowlers for electronic warfare, four E-2L Hawkeyes for early warning, and four KA-6 Intruders for in-flight refueling.
In the CV/CVN configuration the carrier trade off A-7 Corsiars and possibly RA-5C Vigilantes for a ten-plane squadron of S-2 Tracker or S-3 Viking anti-submarine aircraft, and eight SH-3 Sea King helicopters. The "Nimitz" class ships will accommodate all of the above simultaneously.
The "Hancock" class ships operate F-8 Crusader fighters, A-7 Corsair attack planes, RF-8G Crusader photo-reconnaissance airvraft, EKA-SB Skywarriors in the electronic warfare-tanker role, and E-1B Tracers for airborne early warning.
Attack carriers generally have a C-1 Trader carrier on-board delivery (COD) cargo aircraft and UH-2 utility helicopters assigned.

3 NUCLEAR-POWERED ATTACK AIRCRAFT CARRIERS (CVAN/CVN): "NIMITZ" CLASS

Displacement, tons	91 400 full load
Length, feet (*metres*)	1 040 (*317·0*) wl; 1 092 (*332·0*) oa
Beam, feet (*metres*)	134 (*40·8*)
Draft, feet (*metres*)	37 (*11·3*)
Flight deck width, feet (*metres*)	252 (*76·8*)
Catapults	4 steam
Aircraft	approx 100
Missiles	3 Basic Point Defence Missile System (BPDMS) launchers with Sea Sparrow missiles
Main engines	Geared steam turbines; 260 000 shp; 4 shafts
Nuclear reactors	2 pressurised-water cooled
Speed, knots	30+
Complement	3 300 plus approx 2 800 assigned to air wing for a total of 6 100 per ship

Name	*No.*	*Builders*	*Laid down*	*Launch*	*Commission*
NIMITZ	CVAN 68	Newport News	22 June 1968	13 May 1972	late 1974
DWIGHT D. EISENHOWER	CVAN 69	Newport News	14 Aug 1970	Oct 1974	early 1976
CARL VINSON	CVN 70	Newport News	Nov 1975	Mar 1979	1981

NIMITZ (CVAN 68) at launching — *1972, United States Navy, PH1 T. Hilton Putnam*

The lead ship for this class and the world's second nuclear-powered aircraft carrier was ordered 9½ years after the first such ship, the USS *Enterprise*. The *Nimitz* was authorised in the Fiscal Year 1967 new construction programme; the *Dwight D. Eisenhower* in the FY 1970 programme, and the *Carl Vinson* in the FY 1973-1974 programmes. All three ships are being constructed by the Newport News Shipbuilding & Dry Dock Co (Virginia), the only US shipyard now capable of constructing large, nuclear-propelled warships.
The completion of the first two ships is being delayed approximately one year because of delays in the delivery and testing of nuclear plant components. The *Eisenhower* is contracted for delivery to the Navy 21 months after the *Nimitz*. The delays in these ships could further increase their costs. (See *Fiscal* notes).

DESIGNATION. The third ship of this class is designated an "aircraft carrier" (CV) because she will carry fighter, attack, and anti-submarine aircraft; the other ships will be modified to CV status after completion.

ELECTRONICS. These ships will have the Naval Tactical Data System (NTDS) and the following radars: SPS-10 surface search, SPS-43A two-dimensional air search, and SPS-48 three-dimensional air search, and SPN-42, SPN-43, and SPN-44 navigation equipment. These ships will not have sonar.

ENGINEERING. These carriers will each have only two nuclear reactors compared to the eight reactors required for the carrier *Enterprise*. The nuclear cores for the reactors in these ships are expected to provide sufficient energy for the ships to each steam for at least 13 years, an estimated 800 000 to 1 million miles between "refuelling". The two cores in one of these carriers will have the energy equivalent to 462 000 000 gallons (US) or 1 620 000 long tons of fuel oil.

FISCAL. The latest reported ship costs for the "Nimitz" class programme are $594 000 000 for the *Nimitz*, $679 000 000 for the *Eishenhower*, and $956 000 000 for the *Vinson*. In addition, each ship will have "outfitting and post-delivery" costs (amounting to an estimated $16 000 000 for the *Vinson*). The *Vinson* was funded with $299 000 000 in the FY 1973 budget and $657 000 000 in the FY 1974 budget.

NOMENCLATURE. The *Nimitz* honours Fleet Admiral Chester W. Nimitz who was Commander-in-Chief Pacific Fleet and Commander-in-Chief Pacific Ocean Areas during World War II, and Chief of Naval Operations from December 1945 to December 1947.
The *Dwight D. Eisenhower* is believed the first major US surface warship to be named for an Army officer; General of the Army Eisenhower commanded Allied Forces in Western Europe in 1944-45, subsequently was first Supreme Allied Commander in NATO, and President of the United States from January 1953 to January 1961. The CVAN 69 was named *Eisenhower* on 21 Feb 1970; renamed *Dwight D. Eisenhower* on 25 May 1970, but Secretary of Defense Laird dedicated the ship as the "USS *Eisenhower*" at the keel laying on 15 Aug 1970.

Aircraft Carriers—*continued*

"NIMITZ" CLASS—*continued*

The *Carl Vinson* is believed the first US naval ship to be named for a living person since the American Revolution when a small naval craft was named *Franklin* for American patriot Benjamin Franklin. Carl Vinson was a member of the House of Representatives from Georgia from 1914 to 1965; he served as Chairman of the House Naval Affairs Committee and later the House Armed Services Committee.

PHOTOGRAPHS. The *Nimitz* is shown on the previous page at "launching" (flooding of building dock).
The photograph at right shows the *John F. Kennedy* (CVA 67) at anchor in a Mediterranean port. The SPS-48 radar antenna on the separate after mast appears to dominate the ship's island structure in this photograph.
The *Forrestal* photograph below shows 55 aircraft or just over half of the ship's air wing "spotted" on the flight deck. Note the several hundred sailors spelling out the word "people" on the forward portion of the flight deck.
The four earlier "Forrestal" carriers can be distinguished from the later ships by the farther forward position of the island structure in the earlier ships.

JOHN F. KENNEDY (CVA 67) (see following page) *1973, Giorgio Arra*

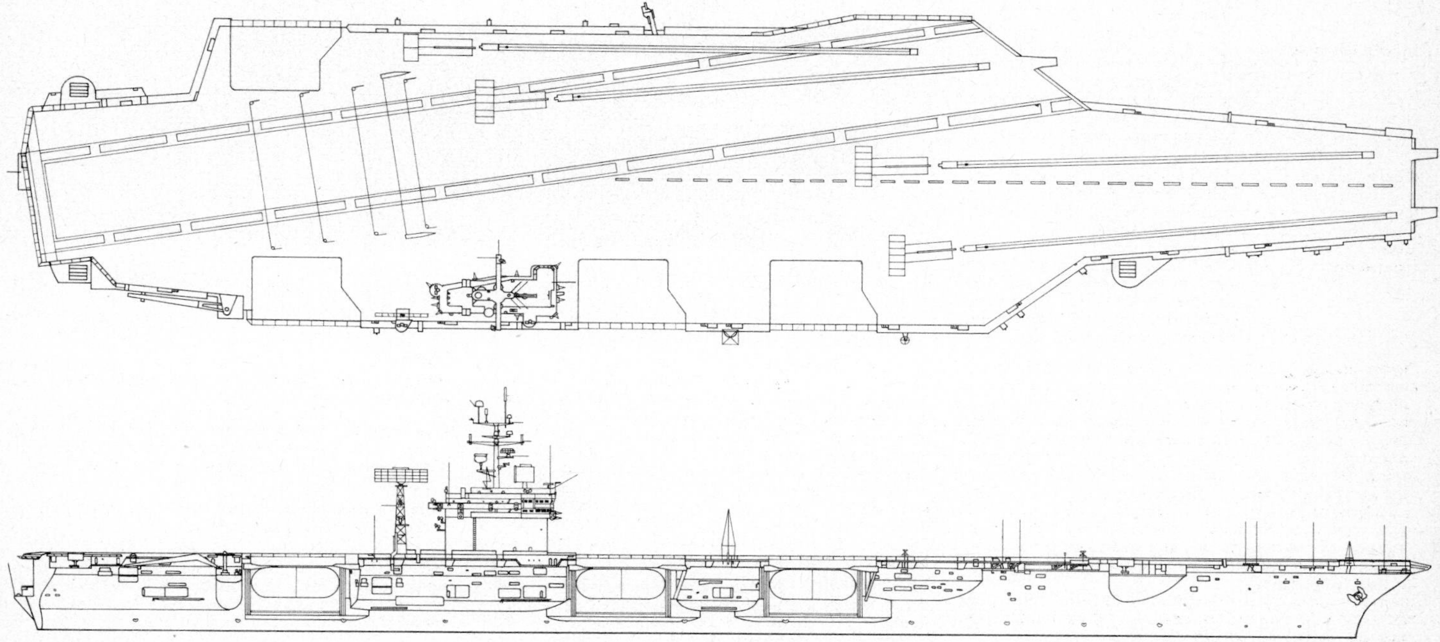

NIMITZ (CVAN 68) *Drawing by A. D. Baker*

FORRESTAL (CVA 59) *United States Navy, PH1 D. Withrow*

Aircraft Carriers—*Continued*

4 ATTACK AIRCRAFT CARRIERS (CVA/CV): "KITTY HAWK" CLASS

Name	*No.*	*Builder*	*Laid down*	*Launched*	*Commissioned*
***KITTY HAWK**	CV 63	New York Shipbuilding Corp, Camden, NJ	27 Dec 1956	21 May 1960	29 Apr 1961
***CONSTELLATION**	CVA 64	New York Naval Shipyard	14 Sep 1957	8 Oct 1960	27 Oct 1961
***AMERICA**	CVA 66	Newport News Shipbuilding & Dry Dock Co	9 Jan 1961	1 Feb 1964	23 Jan 1965
***JOHN F. KENNEDY**	CVA 67	Newport News Shipbuilding & Dry Dock Co	22 Oct 1964	27 May 1967	7 Sep 1968

Displacement, tons	
Kitty Hawk	60 100 standard; 80 800 full load
Constellation	60 100 standard; 80 800 full load
America	60 300 standard; 80 800 full load
John F. Kennedy	61 000 standard; 87 000 full load
Length, feet (*metres*)	990 (*301·8*) wl
Kitty Hawk	1 062·5 (*323·9*) oa
Constellation	1 072·5 (*326·9*) oa
America J.F.K.	1047·5 (*319·3*) oa
Beam, feet (*metres*)	
Kitty Hawk, Constellation	129·5 (*38·5*)
America, J.F.K.	130 (*39·6*)
Draft, feet (*metres*)	35·9 (*10·9*)
Flight deck width, feet, (*metres*)	
J.F.K.	252 (*76·9*) maximum
Others	249 (*76·0*) maximum
Catapults	4 steam
Aircraft	approx 85 in *Kitty Hawk* and *Constellation*; approx 95 in *America* and *John F. Kennedy*
Missile launchers	2 twin Terrier surface-to-air launchers (Mk 10) in *Kitty Hawk, Constellation, America*; 3 Basic Point Defence Missile System (BPDMS) launchers with Sea Sparrow missiles in *John F. Kennedy*
Main engines	4 geared turbines (Westinghouse) 280 000 shp; 4 shafts
Boilers	8—1 200 psi (*83·4 kg/cm²*) (Foster Wheeler)
Speed	35 knots
Complement	2 795 (150 officers, approx 2 645 enlisted men) plus approx 2 150 assigned to attack air wing for a total of 4 950 officers and enlisted men per ship

JOHN F. KENNEDY (CVA 67) *1973, United States Navy*

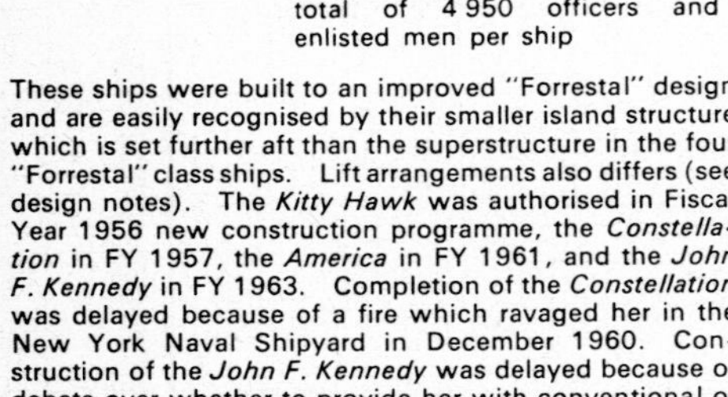

These ships were built to an improved "Forrestal" design and are easily recognised by their smaller island structure which is set further aft than the superstructure in the four "Forrestal" class ships. Lift arrangements also differs (see design notes). The *Kitty Hawk* was authorised in Fiscal Year 1956 new construction programme, the *Constellation* in FY 1957, the *America* in FY 1961, and the *John F. Kennedy* in FY 1963. Completion of the *Constellation* was delayed because of a fire which ravaged her in the New York Naval Shipyard in December 1960. Construction of the *John F. Kennedy* was delayed because of debate over whether to provide her with conventional or nuclear propulsion.
Construction costs were $265 200 000 for *Kitty Hawk*, $264 500 000 for *Constellation*, $248 800 000 for *America*, and $277 000 000 for *John F. Kennedy*.

CLASSIFICATION. Officially known as the "Kitty Hawk" class; generally referred to as improved "Forrestals". The *John F. Kennedy* Is officially a separate one-ship class.

These ships are being modified to operate as multi-purpose aircraft carriers, embarking anti-submarine aircraft as well as fighter/attack aircraft. *Kitty Hawk* redesignated CV 63 vice CVA 63 on 29 Apr 1973. The three other ships were to be modified for CV operations during 1974-1975.

DESIGN. These ships are officially considered to be of a different design than the "Forrestal" class. The island structure is smaller and set farther aft in the newer ships with two deck-edge lifts forward of the superstructure, a third lift aft of the structure, and the port-side left on the after quarter (compared with two lifts aft of the island and the port-side lift at the forward end of the angled deck in the earlier ships). This lift arrangement considerably improves flight deck operations. All four of these ships also have a small radar mast aft of the island structure. The *John F. Kennedy* and *America* have stem anchors because of their bow sonar domes.

ELECTRONICS. All four ships of this class have highly sophisticated electronic equipment including the Naval Tactical Data System (NTDS). The *America* and *John F. Kennedy* have bow-mounted SQS-23 sonar, the first US attack carriers with anti-submarine sonar (several ASW carriers have been fitted with sonar during modernisations).

All four ships have SPS-43 search radar antenna on island structure; three ships also have a three-dimensional SPS-52 search radar antenna on island and an SPS-30 search radar antenna on second mast while the *John F. Kennedy* has SPS-48 antenna on second mast; being fitted with SPS-58 radar to detect low-flying aircraft and missiles. All ships have TACAN navigation pods or "bee-hives".

MISSILES. The three Terrier-armed ships have an Mk10 Mod 3 launcher on the starboard quarter and a Mod 4 launcher on the post quarter.

The *America* has updated Terrier launchers and guidance system that can accommodate Standard missiles; the *Constellation* and *Kitty Hawk* retain older Terrier HT systems.

Three Sea Sparrow BPDMS launchers were fitted in the *John F. Kennedy* early in 1969.

NOMENCLATURE. US aircraft carriers are generally named after battles and historic ships. However, the *Kitty Hawk* better honours the site where the Wright brothers made their historic flights than the converted aircraft ferry of that name which served in World War II. The *Constellation* remembers a frigate built in 1797 and a later ship still afloat at Baltimore, Maryland, although no longer in Navy commission. The name "America" was previously carried by a 74-gun ship of the line launched in 1782, and presented to France, by the racing schooner which gave her name to the America's Cup, and by the German liner *Amerika* which was taken over by the US Navy in World War I, renamed, and used as a troop transport. The *John F. Kennedy* remembers the martyred president who was assassinated in 1963. The destroyer *Joseph P. Kennedy Jr.* (DD 850) honours his older brother who

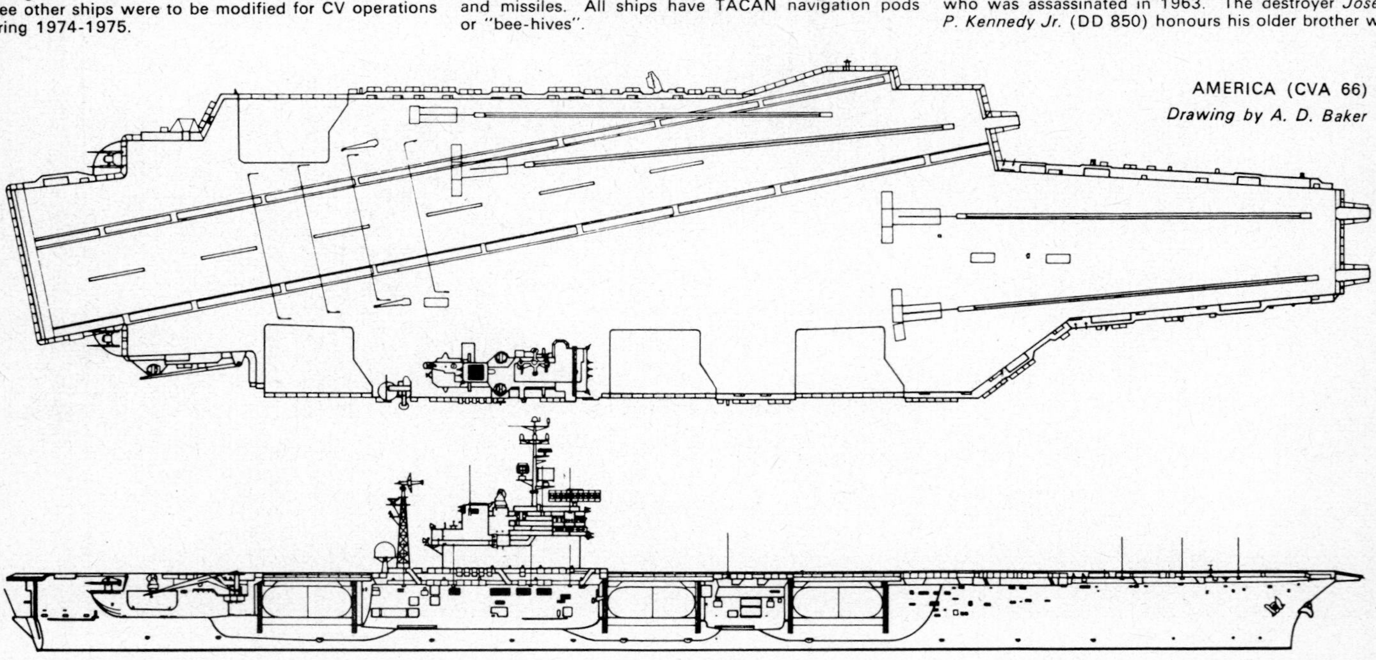

AMERICA (CVA 66)
Drawing by A. D. Baker

Aircraft Carriers—*continued*

"KITTY HAWK" CLASS—*continued*

was killed in a bomber explosion over England in World War II.

PHOTOGRAPHS. Note the angled funnel and Sea Sparrow BPDMS launchers of the *John F. Kennedy.* These ships can be distinguished from the earlier "Forrestal" class carriers by the position of the island structure and the small radar mast aft of the island.

JOHN F. KENNEDY (CVA 67) — *1973, United States Navy, PH1 D. D. Deverman*

AMERICA (CVA 66) — *1972, United States Navy, PH3 G. R. Stromquist*

CONSTELLATION (CVA 64) — *1971· United States Navy, PH1 V. P. Koon*

Aircraft Carriers—*continued*

1 NUCLEAR-POWERED ATTACK AIRCRAFT CARRIER (CVAN): "ENTERPRISE" TYPE

Name	*No.*	*Builder*	*Laid down*	*Launched*	*Commissioned*
***ENTERPRISE**	CVAN 65	Newport News Shipbuilding & Dry Dock Co	4 Feb 1958	24 Sep 1960	25 Nov 1961

Displacement, tons	75 700 standard; 89 600 full load
Length, feet (*metres*)	1 040 (*317·0*) wl; 1 123 (*341·3*) oa
Beam, feet (*metres*)	133 (*40·5*)
Draft, feet (*metres*)	35·8 (*10·8*)
Flight deck width, feet (*metres*)	257 (*78·3*) maximum
Catapults	4 Steam
Aircraft	approx 95
Missile launchers	2 Basic Point Defence Missile System (BPDMS) launchers with Sea Sparrow missiles (see *Armament* notes)
Main engines	4 geared steam turbines (Westinghouse); approx 280 000 shp; 4 shafts
Nuclear reactors	8 pressurised-water cooled A2W (Westinghouse)
Speed, knots	35
Complement	3 100 (162 officers, approx 2 940 enlisted men) plus 2 400 assigned to attack air wing for a total of 5 500

ENTERPRISE (CVAN 65) — *1969, United States Navy*

The *Enterprise* was the largest warship ever built at the time of her construction and will be rivalled in size only by the nuclear-powered "Nimitz" class ships. The *Enterprise* was authorised in the Fiscal Year 1958 new construction programme. She was launched only 19 months after her keel was laid down.

The *Enterprise* was flagship of Task Force One during Operation Sea Orbit when the carrier, the nuclear-powered cruiser *Long Beach* (CGN 9), and the nuclear-powered frigate *Bainbridge* (DLGN 25) circumnavigated the world, in 1964, cruising more than 30 000 miles in 64 days (underway 57 days) without refuelling.

The cost of the *Enterprise* was $451 300 000.

The Fiscal Year 1960 budget provided $35 000 000 to prepare plans and place orders for components of a second nuclear-powered carrier, but the project was deferred.

ARMAMENT. The *Enterprise* — "the world's largest warship"—was completed without any armament in an effort to hold down construction costs. Space for Terrier missile system was provided. Short-range Sea Sparrow BPDMS subsequently was installed in late 1967.

DESIGN. Built to a modified "Forrestal" Class design The most distinctive feature is the island structure. Nuclear propulsion eliminated requirement for smoke stack and boiler air intakes, reducing size of superstructure, and reducing vulnerability to battle damage, radioactivity and biological agents. Rectangular fixed-array radar antennas ("billboards") are mounted on sides of island; electronic countermeasures (ECM) antennas ring cone-shaped upper levels of island structure. Fixed antennas have increased range and performance (see listing for cruiser *Long Beach*). The *Enterprise* has four deck-edge lifts, two forward of island and one aft on starboard side and one aft on port side (as in "Kitty Hawk" class).

CLASSIFICATION. The *Enterprise* will refit as a multi-purpose carrier in 1975-1976; will change from CVAN 65 to CVN 65.

ELECTRONICS. Fitted with the Naval Tactical Data System (NTDS). In addition to SPS-32 and SPS-33 "billboard" radar systems, the *Enterprise* has SPS-10 and SPS-12 search radars and various navigation radar antennas atop her island structure; SPS-58 radar fitted to detect low-flying aircraft and missiles. TACAN navigation pod caps mast.

ENGINEERING. The *Enterprise* is the world's second nuclear-powered warship (the cruiser *Long Beach* was completed a few months earlier). Design of the first nuclear powered aircraft carrier began in 1950 and work continued until 1953 when the programme was deferred pending further work on the submarine reactor programme. The large ship reactor project was reinstated in 1954 on the basis of technological advancements made in the previous 14 months. The Atomic Energy Commission's Bettis Atomic Power Laboratory was given prime responsibility for developing the nuclear power plant.

The first of the eight reactors installed in the *Enterprise* achieved initial criticality on 2 Dec 1960, shortly after the carrier was launched. After three years of operation during which she steamed more than 207 000 miles, the *Enterprise* was overhauled and refuelled from November 1964 to July 1965. Her second set of cores provided

ENTERPRISE (CVAN 65)
Drawing by A. D. Baker

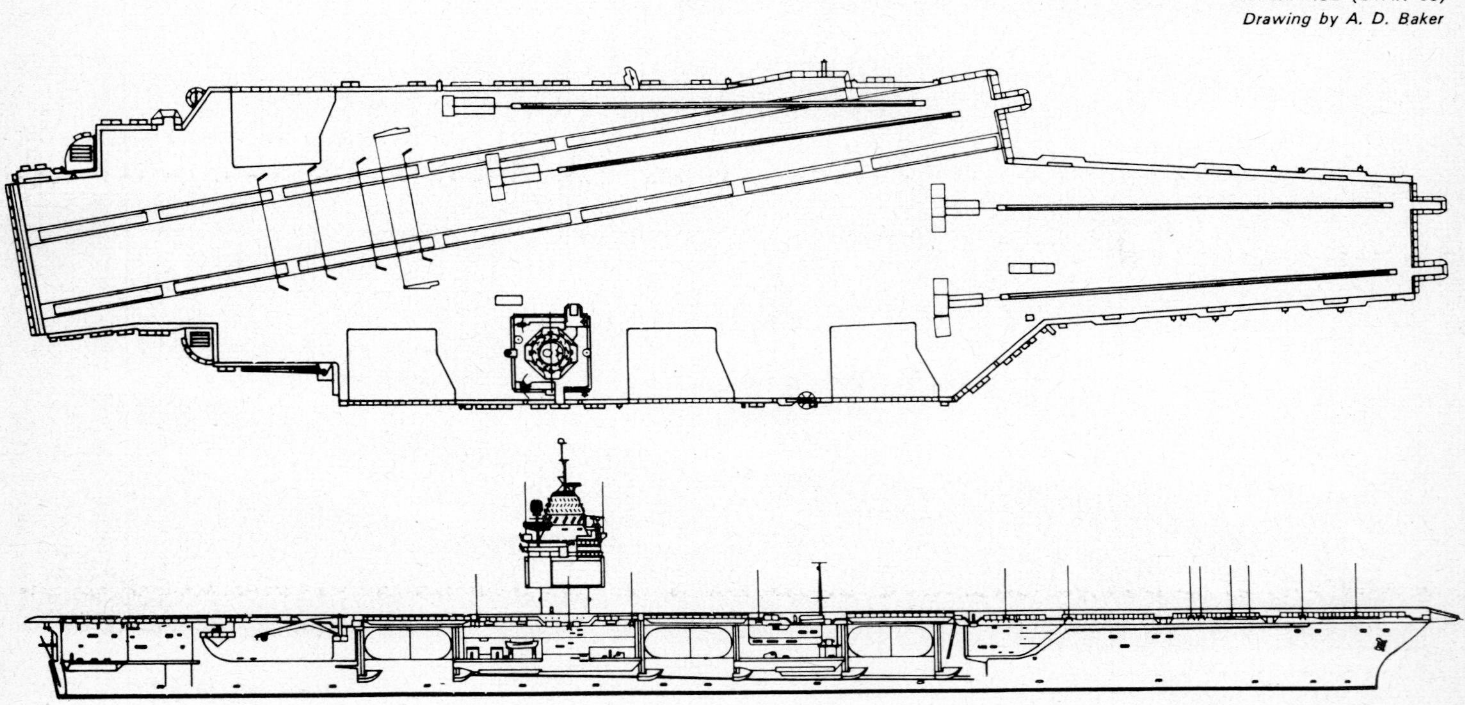

Aircraft Carriers—*continued*

ENTERPRISE (CVAN 65) ***1969, United States Navy***

"ENTERPRISE" TYPE—*continued*

about 300 000 miles steaming. The eight cores initially installed in the *Enterprise* cost $64 000 000; the second set cost about $20 000 000.

The *Enterprise* underwent an extensive overhaul from October 1969 to January 1971, which included installation of a new set of uranium cores in the ship's eight nuclear reactors. The overhaul and refuelling took place at the Newport News shipyard. Estimated cost of the overhaul was approximately $30 000 000, with $13 000 000 being for non-nuclear repairs and alterations, and $17 000 000 being associated with installation of the new nuclear cores (the latter amount being in addition to the $80 000 000 cost of the eight cores). This third set of cores is expected to fuel the ship for 10 to 13 years, according to Vice Adm H. G. Rickover.

In addition to virtually unlimited high-speed endurance nuclear propulsion for aircraft carriers provides additional space for aviation fuels and ordnance, elimination of stack gases and smoke which have corrosive effects on electronic antennas and aircraft, virtually unlimited electrical power, and the ability to quickly change speed without affecting the number of personnel on watch in the engineering spaces.

There are two reactors for each of the ship's four shafts. The eight reactors feed 32 heat exchangers. The *Enterprise* developed more horsepower during her propulsion trials than any other ship in history (officially "in excess of 200 000 shaft horsepower"; subsequently Navy officials stated that she can generate 280 000 hp).

NOMENCLATURE. Eight US Navy ships have carried the name *Enterprise*. The first was a British supply sloop captured in 1775 and armed for use on Lake Champlain.

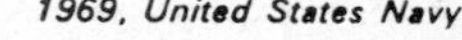

ENTERPRISE (CVAN 65) *1968, United States Navy*

The seventh *Enterprise* (CV 6) was the most famous US carrier of World War II. She earned 20 battle stars. That "Big E" was sold in 1958 and scrapped.

PHOTOGRAPHS. In the above photograph note the Sea Sparrow missile launcher at near full elevation on a sponson on the ship's port quarter. In the bottom photograph on this page an A-6 Intruder with wings folded is on the ship's forward starboard deck-edge elevator.

ENTERPRISE (CVAN 65) ***1968, United States Navy***

Aircraft Carriers—*continued*

4 ATTACK AIRCRAFT CARRIERS (CVA/CV): "FORRESTAL" CLASS

Name	*No.*	*Builder*	*Laid down*	*Launched*	*Commissioned*
***FORRESTAL**	CVA 59	Newport News SB & DD Co	14 July 1952	11 Dec 1954	1 Oct 1955
***SARATOGA**	CV 60	New York Naval Shipyard	16 Dec 1952	8 Oct 1955	14 Apr 1956
***RANGER**	CVA 61	Newport News SB & DD Co	2 Aug 1954	29 Sep 1956	10 Aug 1957
***INDEPENDENCE**	CV 62	New York Naval Shipyard	1 July 1955	6 June 1958	10 Jan 1959

Displacement, tons	
Forrestal	59 650 standard; 78 000 full load
Others	60 000 standard; 78 000 full load
Length, feet (*metres*)	990 (*301·8*) wl
Forrestal, Saratoga	
Ranger	1 039 (*316·7*) oa
Independence	1 046·5 (*319·0*) oa
Beam, feet (*metres*)	129·5 (*38·5*)
Draft, feet (*metres*)	37 (*11·3*)
Flight deck width, feet (*metres*)	
Ranger	260 (*79·2*) maximum
Others	252 (*76·8*) maximum
Catapults	4 Steam
Aircraft	approx 85
Guns	4—5 inch (*127 mm*) 54 cal DP single in *Ranger*
Missile launchers	2 Basic Point Defence Missile System (BPDMS) launchers with Sea Sparrow missiles in all except *Ranger*
Main engines	4 geared turbines (Westinghouse) 4 shafts 260 000 shp in *Forrestal* 280 000 shp in others
Boilers	8—615 psi (*42·7 kg/cm²*) in *Forrestal* 1 200 psi (*83·4 kg/cm²*) in others (all Babcock & Wilcox)
Speed, knots	
Forrestal	33
Others	35
Complement	2 790 (145 officers, approx 2 645 enlisted men) plus approx 2 150 assigned to attack air wing for a total of 4 940+ per ship

The *Forrestal* was the world's first aircraft carrier designed and built after World War II. The *Forrestal* design drew heavily from the aircraft carrier *United States* (CVA 58) which was cancelled immediately after being laid down in April 1949. The *Forrestal* was authorised in the Fiscal Year 1952 new construction programme; the *Saratoga* followed in the FY 1953 programme, the *Ranger*. in the FY 1954 programme, and the *Independence* in the FY 1955 programme.

Construction costs were $188 900 000 for *Forrestal*, $213 900 000 for *Saratoga*, $173 300 000 for *Ranger*, and $225 300 000 for *Independence*.

CLASSIFICATION. The *Forrestal* and *Saratoga* were initially classified as Large Aircraft Carriers CVB 59 and 60, respectively; reclassified as Attack Aircraft Carriers (CVA) in October 1952 to reflect their purpose rather than size. The ill-fated *United States* was a "heavy" carrier (CVA).

The ships are being modified to operate as multi-purpose aircraft carriers, embarking anti-submarine aircraft as well as fighter/attack aircraft. *Saratoga* redesignated CV 60 vice CVA 60 on 30 June 1972; *Independence* to CV 62 on 28 Feb 1973; *Forrestal* and *Ranger* will be reclassified CV in 1975-1976.

DESIGN. The "Forrestal" Class ships were the first aircraft carriers designed and built specifically to operate jet-propelled aircraft. The *Forrestal* was redesigned early in construction to incorporate British-developed angled flight deck and steam catapults. These were the first US aircraft carriers built with an enclosed bow area to improve seaworthiness. Four large deck-edge lifts are fitted, one forward of island structure to starboard, two aft of island structure to starboard and one at forward edge of angled flight deck to port. Other features include armoured flight deck and advanced underwater protection and internal compartmentation to reduce effects of conventional and nuclear attack. Mast configurations differ; the *Forrestal* originally had two masts, one of which was removed in 1967.

ELECTRONICS. The primary radars installed in these ships are SPS-43, SPS-30, and SPS-10 search radars, and SPN-10 navigation radar. Small TACAN navigation pods top the masts of these ships.

SPS-58 radar being installed to detect low-flying aircraft and missiles.

Naval Tactical Data System (NTDS) is installed in all four ships.

ENGINEERING. The *Saratoga* and later ships have an improved steam plant; increased machinery weight of the improved plant is more than compensated by increased performance and decreased fuel consumption.

GUNNERY. All four ships initially mounted 8—5 inch guns in single mounts, two mounts on each quarter. The forward sponsons carrying the guns interfered with ship operations in rough weather, tending to slow the ships down. The forward sponsons and guns were subsequently removed (except in *Ranger*), reducing armament to four guns per ship.

The after guns have been removed with installation of BPDMS launchers (see below).

MISSILES. The four after 5 inch guns were removed from the *Forrestal* late in 1967 and a single BPDMS launcher for Sea Sparrow missiles was installed forward on the starboard side. An additional launcher was provided aft on the port side in 1972. Two BPDMS launchers fitted in *Independence* in 1973 and two launchers in *Saratoga* in 1974. *Ranger* will receive similar armament.

NOMENCLATURE. The *Forrestal* honours James V. Forrestal, Secretary of the Navy from 1944 until he was appointed the first US Secretary of Defense in 1947, a post he held until shortly before his death in 1949. The *Saratoga* commemorates the battle at Saratoga, New York, in the American Revolution and five earlier US warships including a carrier of World War II fame (CV 3). The first USS *Ranger* was a sloop built in 1777 and a later ship of that name was the first US built-for-the-purpose carriers (CV 4). The first USS *Independence* was a sloop built in 1775 and a later ship of that name was a light carrier (CVL 22) that saw extensive combat in World War II.

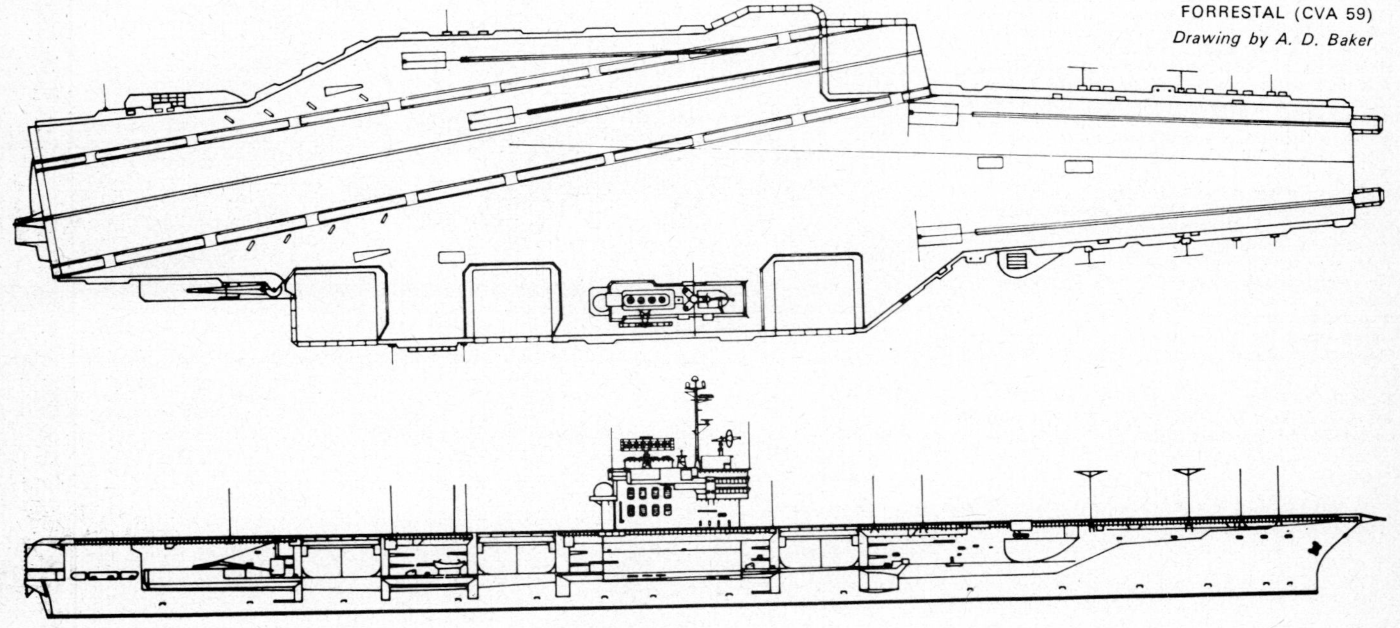

FORRESTAL (CVA 59)
Drawing by A. D. Baker

SARATOGA (CV 60) *1970, United States Navy, PH1 R. D. Williams*

Aircraft Carriers—*continued*

RANGER (CVA 61) *1968, United States Navy*

FORRESTAL (CVA 59) *United States Navy*

FORRESTAL (CVA 59) *1971, United States Navy*

INDEPENDENCE (CV 62) *1970, United States Navy*

Aircraft Carriers—*continued*

3 ATTACK AIRCRAFT CARRIERS (CVA): "MIDWAY" CLASS

Name	No	Builder	Laid down	Launched	Commissioned
•MIDWAY	CVA 41	Newport News SB & DD Co	27 Oct 1943	20 Mar 1945	10 Sep 1945
•FRANKLIN D. ROOSEVELT	CVA 42	New York Navy Yard	1 Dec 1943	29 Apr 1945	3 Nov 1945
•CORAL SEA	CVA 43	Newport News SB & DD Co	10 July 1944	2 Apr 1946	1 Oct 1947

Displacement, tons	
Midway	51 000 standard
F. D. Roosevelt	51 000 standard
Coral Sea	52 500 standard
	all approx 64 000 full load
Length, feet (*metres*)	900 (*274·3*) wl; 979 (*298·4*) oa
Beam, feet (*metres*)	121 (*36·9*)
Draft, feet (*metres*)	35·3 (*10·8*)
Flight deck width, feet (*metres*)	238 (*72·5*) maximum
Catapults	2 steam except 3 in *Coral Sea*
Aircraft	approx 75
Guns	4—5 inch (*127 mm*) 54 cal DP in *F. D. Roosevelt*; three guns in *Midway* and *Coral Sea* (see *Gunnery* notes)
Main engines	4 geared turbines (Westinghouse in *Midway* and *Coral Sea*; General Electric in *F. D. Roosevelt*); 212 000 shp; 4 shafts
Boilers	12—615 psi (*41·7 kg/cm²*) (Babcock & Wilcox)
Speed, knots	33
Complement	2 615 (140 officers, approx 2 475 enlisted men) except *Coral Sea* 2 710 (165 officers, approx 2 545 enlisted men) plus approx 1 800 assigned to attack air wing for a total of 4 400 to 4 500 per ship

These carriers were the largest US warships constructed during World War II. Completed too late for service in that conflict, they were the backbone of US naval strength for the first decade of the Cold War. Beginning in 1949 they were modified to store, assemble, and load nuclear weapons, making them the world's first warships with a nuclear strike capability. (P2V-3C Neptunes and AJ-1 Savages were the first delivery aircraft.) All three ships operated in the Atlantic and Mediterranean during the Korean War, but subsequently they have operated in the Pacific. The entire class has been in active service (except for overhaul and modernisation) since the ships were completed almost 30 years ago.

The *Midway* was homeported in Japan in 1973, the first US aircraft carrier to be based overseas. Plans to homeport another carrier in Greece have been delayed.

Construction cost of *Midway* was $85 600 000, *F. D. Roosevelt* $85 700 000, and *Coral Sea* $87 600 000.

MIDWAY (CVA 41) — *1971, United States Navy*

CORAL SEA (CVA 43) — *1970, United States Navy, PH2 George W. Estaver*

CLASSIFICATION. These ships were initially classified as Large Aircraft Carriers CVB 41-43, respectively, reclassified as Attack Aircraft Carriers (CVA) in October 1952.

DESIGN. These ships were built to the same design with a standard displacement of 45 000 tons, full load displacement of 60 100 tons, and an overall length of 968 feet. They have been extensively modified since completion (see notes below). These ships were the first US aircraft carriers with an armoured flight deck and the first US warships with a designed width too large to enable them to pass through the Panama Canal.

The unnamed CVB 44, 56 and 57 of this class were cancelled prior to the start of construction.

ELECTRONICS. Naval Tactical Data System (NTDS) in *Midway* and *Coral Sea*.

The principal radars installed on these ships are SPS-10, SPS-30, SPS-43, SPN-6, and SPN-10. *Midway* fitted with SPS-58 radar to detect low-flying aircraft and missiles. Note that *Coral Sea* retains large TACAN (Tactical Air Navigation) "bee hive" antenna atop mast compared to smaller antenna pods on *Midway* and *Franklin D. Roosevelt*.

GUNNERY. As built these ships mounted 18—5 inch guns (14 in *Coral Sea*), 84—40 mm guns, and 28—20 mm guns. Armament reduced periodically with 3 inch guns replacing lighter weapons. Minimal 5 inch armament remains. The 5 inch guns are 54 calibre Mk 39, essentially modified 5 inch/38 calibre with a longer barrel for greater range; not to be confused with rapid-fire 5 inch 54s of newer US warships.

MODERNISATION. All three "Midway" Class carriers have been extensively modernised. Their most extensive conversion "package" gave them angled flight decks, steam catapults, enclosed "hurricane" bows, new electronics, and new lift arrangement (*Franklin D. Roosevelt* from 1953 to 1956, *Midway* from 1954 to 1957, and *Coral Sea* from 1956 to 1960; all at Puget Sound Naval Shipyard). Lift arrangement was changed in *Franklin D. Roosevelt* and *Midway* to one centreline lift forward, one deck-edge list aft of island on starboard side, and one deck-edge lift at forward end of angled deck on port side. The *Coral Sea* has an improved arrangement with one lift forward and one aft of island on starboard side and third lift outboard on port side aft. The *Midway* began another extensive modernisation at the San Francisco Bay Naval Shipyard in February 1966; she was recommissioned on 31 Jan 1970 and went to sea in March 1970. Her modernisation included provisions for handling newer aircraft, new catapults, new lifts (arranged as in *Coral Sea*), and new electronics. A similar modernisation planned for the *Franklin D. Roosevelt*, to have begun in Fiscal Year 1970, has been cancelled because the *Midway* modernisation is taking longer and costing more than originally estimated (24 months and $88 000 000 was planned; actual work required approximately 52 months and $202 300 000). The *Franklin D. Roosevelt* completed an austere overhaul in June 1969 which enables her to operate the new A-6 Intruder and A-7 Corsair II attack aircraft; cost of overhaul was $46 000 000.

The *Midway* is now the most capable of the three ships (for example, her lifts can handle aircraft weights to 100 000 pounds compared to 74 000 pounds for the *Coral Sea* and *Franklin D. Roosevelt*).

Aircraft Carriers—*continued*

FRANKLIN D. ROOSEVELT (CVA 42) *1972, Giorgio Arra*

MIDWAY (CVA 41) *1970, United States Navy*

CORAL SEA (CVA 43) *1971, United States Navy*

FRANKLIN D. ROOSEVELT (CVA 42)
Drawing by A. D. Baker

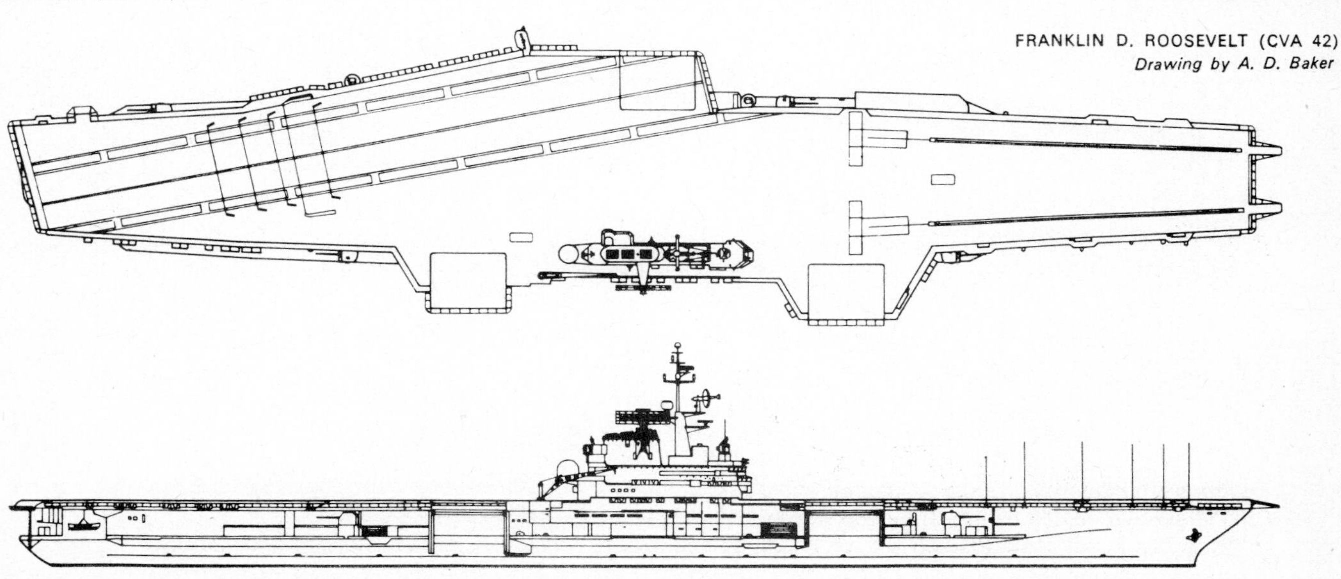

Aircraft Carriers—*Continued*

3 ATTACK AIRCRAFT CARRIERS (CVA) / 2 ASW AIRCRAFT CARRIERS (CVS) / 1 TRAINING CARRIER (CVT) — "HANCOCK" CLASS

Name	No.	Builder	Laid down	Launched	Commissioned
INTREPID	CVS 11	Newport News Shipbuilding & Dry Dock Co	1 Dec 1941	26 Apr 1943	16 Aug 1943
***LEXINGTON**	CVT 16	Bethlehem Steel Co, Quincy, Mass	15 July 1941	26 Sep 1942	17 Feb 1943
***HANCOCK**	CVA 19	Bethlehem Steel Co, Quincy, Mass	26 Jan 1943	24 Jan 1944	15 Apr 1944
BON HOMME RICHARD	CVA 31	New York Navy Yard	1 Feb 1943	29 Apr 1944	26 Nov 1944
***ORISKANY**	CVA 34	New York Navy Yard	1 May 1944	13 Oct 1945	25 Sep 1950
SHANGRI-LA	CVS 38	Norfolk Navy Yard	15 Jan 1943	24 Feb 1944	15 Sep 1944

Displacement, tons	approx 32 800 standard, except *Oriskany* 33 250
CVA type	approx 44 700 full load
Others	approx 42 000 full load except *Lexington* 39 000
Length, feet (*metres*)	894·5 (*272·6*) oa except *Oriskany* 890 (*271·3*); 820 (*249·9*) wl
Beam, feet (*metres*)	103 (*30·8*) except *Oriskany* 106·5 (*32·5*)
Draft, feet (*metres*)	31 (*9·4*)
Flight deck width feet (*metres*)	192 (*58·5*) maximum except *Oriskany* 195 (*59·5*)
Catapults	2 steam
Aircraft	70 to 80 for CVA type; approx 45 for CVS type; none assigned to *Lexington*
Guns	4—5 inch (*127 mm*) 38 cal dual-purpose (single); removed from *Lexington*
Main engines	4 geared turbines (Westinghouse) 150 000 shp; 4 shafts
Boilers	8 (Babcock & Wilcox)
Speed, knots	30+
Complement	
CVA type	2 130 (130 officers, approx 2 000 enlisted men) plus approx 1 500 assigned to attack air wing for a total of 3 630 per ship
CVS type	1 615 (115 officers, approx 1 500 enlisted men) plus approx 800 assigned to ASW air group for a total of 2 400 per ship
Lexington	1 440 (75 officers, 1 365 enlisted men); no air unit assigned

ORISKANY (CVA 34) — *1970, United States Navy*

These ships originally were "Essex" class aircraft carriers; extensively modernised during 1950s, being provided with enclosed, hurricane-bow, angled flight deck, improved elevators, increased aviation fuel storage, and steam catapults (last feature permits operation of more-advanced aircraft that can be flown from modernised "Essex" class). Construction of *Oriskany* suspended after World War II and she was completed in 1950 to a modified "Essex" design. See "Essex" class listing for additional notes.

Bon Homme Richard decommissioned on 2 July 1971, *Shangri-La* on 30 July 1971, and *Intrepid* on 30 March 1974. The *Intrepid* was the last "dedicated" anti-submarine carrier in service. All three ships are in reserve. Decommissioning of the *Hancock* and *Oriskany* have been delayed to provide a 14 or 15 carrier-force level through at least 1976.

CLASSIFICATION. All "Essex" class ships originally were designated as Aircraft Carriers (CV); reclassified as Attack Aircraft Carriers (CVA) in Oct 1952. *Intrepid* reclassified as ASW Support Aircraft Carrier (CVS) on 31 Mar 1962, *Lexington* on 1 Oct 1962, *Shangri-La* on 30 June 1969. The *Lexington* became the Navy's training aircraft carrier in the Gulf of Mexico on 29 Dec 1962 (correction from previous edition); reclassified CVT on 1 Jan 1969.

ELECTRONICS. The *Oriskany* and the frigates *King* (DLG 10) and *Mahan* (DLG 11) conducted the initial sea trials of the Naval Tactical Data System (NTDS) in 1961-1962.

The principal radars in these ships are SPS-43, SPS-30, and SPS-10 search radars, and SPN-10 navigation radar, except *Lexington* has SPS-43 SPS-12, SPS-10, and SPN-10 (the SPS-8 formerly mounted has been removed). TACAN aircraft navigation pods stop their masts.

MODERNISATION. These ships have been modernised under several programmes to increase their ability to operate more-advanced aircraft. The *Oriskany* was completed with some post-war ("jet age") features incorporated. The most prominent difference from their original configuration is angled flight deck and removal of twin 5-inch gun mounts from flight deck forward and aft of island structure. Three elevators fitted: "Pointed" centreline lift forward between catapults, deckedge lift on portside at leading edge of angled deck, and deckedge lift on starboard side aft of island structure. Minimal gun battery retained (see description of original armament under "Essex" class listings). Remaining guns removed from *Lexington* in 1969.

OPERATIONAL. The *Shangri-La* while designated as an anti-submarine carrier operated as a "limited attack carrier" off Vietnam during 1969-1970, carrying an air wing of A-4 Skyhawk and A-1 Skyraider attack planes, with the latter being phased out of the Navy during that period, and later F-8 Crusader fighters.

As of early 1973 the *Lexington* had recorded 329 000 arrested aircraft landings during her operational career (1934-1947, 1955-present).

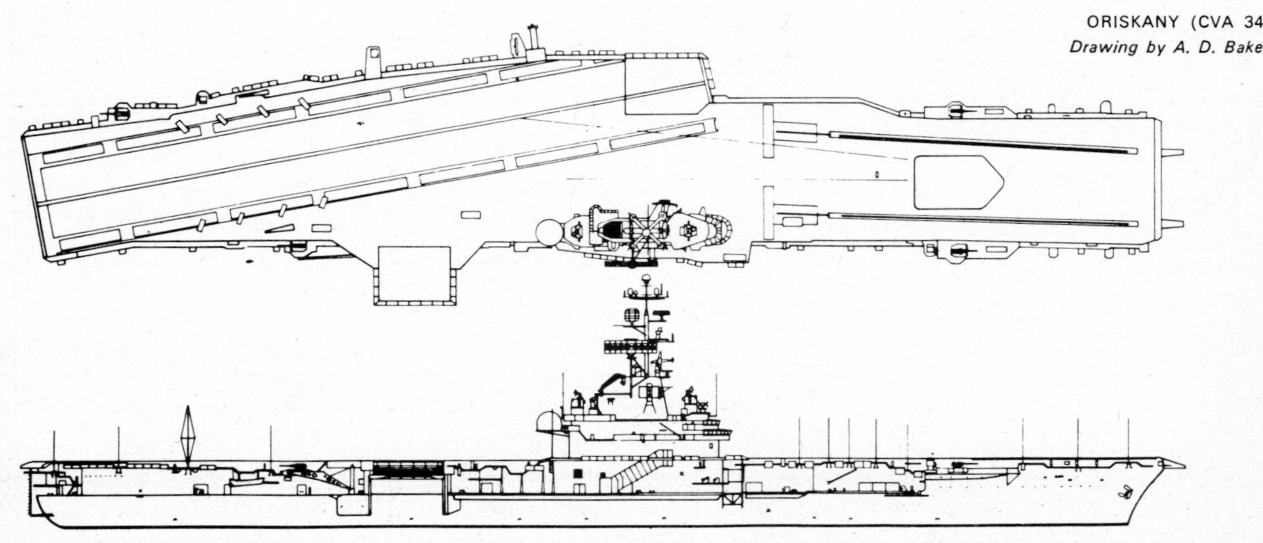

ORISKANY (CVA 34)
Drawing by A. D. Baker

Aircraft Carriers—*Continued*

"HANCOCK" CLASS—*continued*

NOMENCLATURE. All 24 "Essex" class carriers are named for early American ships or battles except for *Shangri-La*, which is named for the imaginary locale in James Hilton's novel which President Roosevelt told the press was the base for the Doolittle-Halsey raid against Japan in 1942. Several ships renamed during construction to carry on names of carriers lost in battle. The *Hancock* and *Ticonderoga* exchanged names during construction.

DISPOSALS
Nine "straight-deck" carriers of this class have been stricken: **Franklin** (AVT 8, ex-CVS 13) stricken on 1 Oct 1964; **Bunker Hill** (AVT 8, ex-CVS 17) stricken on 1 Nov 1966, but retained as moored electronic test ship at San Diego, California, until Nov 1972; **Tarawa** (AVT 12, ex-CVS 40) stricken on 1 June 1967; **Leyte** (AVT 10, ex-CVS 32) stricken on 1 June 1969; **Philippine Sea** (AVT 11, ex-CVS 47), **Lake Champlain** (CVS 39), and **Boxer** (LPH 4, ex-CVS 21) stricken on 1 Dec 1969; **Princeton** (LPH 5, es-CVS 37) stricken on 30 Jan 1970; **Valley Forge** (LPH 8, ex-CVS 45) stricken on 15 Jan 1970.
Of the "Essex" class ships modernised to an angled-deck configuration: **Wasp** (CVS 18) stricken on 1 July 1972;
Of the "Essex" class ships modernised to an angled-deck configuration: **Wasp** (CVS 18) stricken on 1 July 1972; **Kearsarge** (CVS 33), **Antietam** (CVS 36) stricken on 1 May 1973; **Essex** (CVS 9), **Yorktown** (CVS 10), **Randolph** (CVS 15) stricken on 1 June 1973; **Ticonderoga** (CVS 14) stricken on 16 Nov 1973.

ORISKANY (CVA 34) — *1970, United States Navy*

HANCOCK (CVA 19) — *1971, United States Navy, PH2 M. E. Mowbray*

LEXINGTON (CVT 16) — *1972, United States Navy PH2 Gabriel Benzur*

Aircraft Carriers—*Continued*

2 ASW AIRCRAFT CARRIERS (CVS): MODERNISED "ESSEX" CLASS

Name	*No.*	*Builder*	*Laid down*	*Launched*	*Commissioned*
HORNET	CVS 12	Newport News Shipbuilding & Dry Dock Co	3 Aug 1942	29 Aug 1943	29 Nov 1943
BENNINGTON	CVS 20	New York Navy Yard	15 Dec 1942	26 Feb 1944	6 Aug 1944

Displacement, tons	approx 33 000 standard; approx 40 060 full load
Length, feet (*metres*)	820 (*249·9*) wl; 8900 (*271·3*) oa
Beam, feet (*metres*)	102 (*31*); 93 (*28·4*)
Draft, feet (*metres*)	31· (*9·4*)
Flight deck width feet (*metres*)	196 (*59·7*) maximum
Catapults	2 hydraulic
Aircraft	approx 45 (including 16 to 18 helicopters)
Guns	4—5 inch (*127 mm*) 38 cal dual-purpose (single)
Main engines	4 geared turbines (Westinghouse); 150 000 shp; 4 shafts
Boilers	8—600 psi (*41·7 kg/cm²*) (Babcock & Wilcox)
Speed, knots	30+
Complement	1 615 (115 officers, approx 1 500 enlisted men) plus approx 800 assigned to ASW air group for a total of 2 400 per ship.

The two above ships and the previously listed "Hancock" class are the survivors of the 24 "Essex" class fleet carriers built during the World War II (with one ship, *Oriskany*, not completed until 1950). Both of the above ships were extensively modernised during the 1950s; however, they lack the steam catapults and other features of the "Hancock" class.

The late *Antietam* of this class was the world's first aircraft carrier to be fitted with an angled flight deck to increase efficiency and safety of high-performance aircraft operations aboard carriers.
The *Bennington* was decommissioned on 15 Jan 1970 and the *Hornet* on 26 June 1970; both ships are in reserve.

CLASSIFICATION. These ships originally were designated as Aircraft Carriers (CV); reclassified as Attack Carriers(CVA) in Oct 1952. Subsequently they became ASW Support Aircraft Carriers (CVS): *Hornet* on 27 June 1958, and *Bennington* on 30 June 1959.

DESIGN. All 24 "Essex" class ships were built to the same basic design except for the delayed *Oriskany*. Standard displacement as built was 27 100 tons, full load displacement was 36 380 tons, and overall length 888 or 972 feet. Two additional ships of this class were cancelled while under construction, the *Reprisal* (CV 35) and *Iwo Jima* (CV 46), and six others were cancelled prior to keel laying, the unnamed CV 50-55. See 1971-1972 and previous editions for notes on armament as originally completed and ship nomenclature.

ELECTRONICS. The primary radars in these ships are SPS-43, SPS-30, and SPS-10 search radars, and SPN-10 navigation radars; TACAN aircraft navigation pods top masts. Both ships have SQS-23 bow-mounted sonar.

MODERNISATION. These ships have been modernised under several programmes to increase their ability to operate advanced aircraft and to improve sea keeping. Also modernised to improve anti-submarine capabilities under the Fleet Rehabilitation and Modernisation (FRAM II) programme.

PHOTOGRAPHS. The *Bennington* is shown during an underway replenishment, fueling from an oiler which also is fueling a destroyer. Note *Bennington's* starboard deck-edge elevator is hinged upwards during replenishment. Both carriers have S-2 Tracker and E-1 Tracer aircraft, and SH-3 Sea King helicopters on their decks.

LIGHT AIRCRAFT CARRIERS (CVL)

All light aircraft carriers have been stricken from the Navy List, transferred or reclassified.
See 1973-1974 and previous editions for disposals of the nine ship "Independence" class light aircraft carriers (CVL 22-30).
The larger, built-for-the-purpose light carriers of the "Saipan" class have been converted to other roles: *Saipan* (AVT 6, ex-CVL 48) converted to major communications relay ship (AGMR 2) and *Wright* (AVT 7, ex-CVL 49) converted to command ship (CC 2).

BENNINGTON (CVS 20) — *1968, United States Navy*

HORNET (CVS 12) — *1968, United States Navy*

SURFACE COMBATANTS

The US Navy categorisation Surface Combatants includes battleships, cruisers, frigates, and destroyers. The various types of escort ships (DE/DEG/DER) generally addressed within the context of destroyer-type ships officially are categorised as Ocean Escorts and follow the listings for Surface Combatants. The escort ships have speeds below the 30-knot-plus speeds of surface combatants and thus cannot operate with the Navy's aircraft carriers. *Jane's Fighting Ships* lists the US Navy's remaining battleships and non-missile cruisers (CA) as Fire Support Ships because of their limited capabilities for anti-air, anti-submarine, and surface warfare in the context of modern naval operations.

As of mid-1974 the US Navy's active ships in the Surface Combatant category consisted of six guided missile cruisers (CG/CGN/CLG), 31 missile frigates (DLG/DLGN), 29 missile destroyers (DDG), and about 30 all-gun destroyers (DD). In addition, 37 destroyers are operational with the Naval Reserve Force with composite active duty-reserve crews.

During the 1970s deliveries will be made of five additional nuclear-propelled missile frigates (DLGN 37-41) and 30 large, all-gun destroyers of the "Spruance" class (DD 963-992). Both of these ships types have been criticised for their limited capabilities and high costs. The later nuclear frigates, displacing over 10 000 tons full load and costing almost $275 000 per ship, have become too costly to procure in large numbers. Although nuclear propulsion provides a most-valuable high sustained speed capability, the US ships are clearly inferior in several respects to their conventionally propelled Soviet contemporaries. The eight nuclear "escorts" ship built and now under construction (CGN/DLGN) would provide two nuclear escorts for each of the Navy's four nuclear aircraft carriers, with the DLGN 41 proposed in the Fiscal Year 1975 programme providing a "spare." By employing attack submarines in the carrier escort role as well as conventional escorts in some situations, the construction of additional DLGNs could be deferred until smaller nuclear power plants are developed which would permit "destroyer size" nuclear escorts, or an advanced surface combatant design could be developed. The latter possibly would incorporate increased aviation capabilities, both manned and remote piloted vehicles (RPVs), as well as advanced missile systems suitable for use against aircraft and surface targets, with conventional or tactical nuclear warheads.

The 30 "Spruance" class destroyers being completed during the later 1970s also are characterised by large size (7 800 tons) and high cost (approximately $100 000 000 per ship) and limited combat capabilities. Although the ships have advanced anti-submarine sensors and weapons, their lack of effective anti-air and anti-ship weapons will limit their effectiveness in many combat situations. Indeed, the "patrol frigates" (PF) now planned—described with Ocean Escorts in this edition—probably will have greater anti-air and anti-ship capabilities in a ship of less than half the displacement and a speed only two or three knots less than the "Spruance" class.

Because of the reduction in surface combatant ships during the past few years, the US Navy will increasingly use ocean escorts (DE/DEG) and later the patrol frigates (PF) in roles previously assigned to larger ships; similarly, the patrol missile boats (PHM) may be employed for some coastal operations in lieu of destroyer-type ships. "On the horizon" is the promise of the air capable or "sea control ship" concept described below. However, the currently planned sea control ship (SCS) is an austere design, cost-limited to operate in a low-threat"" combat environment. The increasing capabilities and open-ocean operations of the Soviet Navy have made the potential value of such a ship questionable in view of the limited numbers of surface combat ships that will be available to the US Navy in the 1980s and beyond.

DGX PROGRAMME. A new class of area defence "destroyer", now known as the DGX design, has been proposed as a replacement for the older DLG/DDG-type ships as they reach retirement age beginning in the early 1980s. The DGX would have the new AEGIS fleet air defence system, which has a high-power, long-range phased array radar, and a single launcher for an improved Standard surface-to-air missile.

The Navy estimates that design efforts could be sufficiently advanced to request funding for the first DGX in the Fiscal Year 1977 new construction programme with a total of 16 ships tentatively planned. Preliminary design goals provide for a GXD of about 6 000 tons at an average cost per follow-on ship (after certain research, development, and start-up costs) of $125 000 000 per ship (in Fiscal Year 1973 dollars). That size and cost constraint probably would preclude the use of nuclear propulsion in this ship.

DSX PROGRAMME. Research and development also is underway on a high-speed, "surface effect" destroyer concept, now known as the DSX design. The surface effect ship is a variation of the air cushion vehicle with rigid sidewalls to permit deep-water operation. Because current DSX efforts are directed toward a warship of 2 000 tons, additional discussion, characteristics, and an artists' impression are provided under the listing for Ocean Escorts in this edition.

SEA CONTROL SHIPS: PROPOSED

	Commission
one SCS proposed FY 1975 programme	1978
three SCS planned FY 1976 programme	1979
two SCS planned FY 1977 programme	1980
two SCS planned FY 1978 programme	1981

Displacement, tons	14 300 full load
Length, feet	approx 650 oa
Beam, feet	80
Draft, feet	22
Aircraft	3 AV-8 Harrier V/STOL strike aircraft (or successor); 14 SH-3 Sea King helicopters (or successor); 2 LAMPS helicopters (see *Aircraft* notes)
Guns	2—20 mm Vulcan/Phalanx rapid-fire CIWS
Main engines	2 gas turbines (General Electric); 40 000 shp; 1 shaft
Speed, knots	approx 26
Complement	700 (including air wing; accommodations for 750 planned)

MODEL OF SEA CONTROL SHIP (SCS) *United States Navy*

The Navy has proposed the sea control ship to operate V/STOL fixed-wing aircraft and helicopters in defence of underway replenishment groups, amphibious task forces, and merchant convoys. Because of the limited capabilities of the ships and their embarked aircraft they could operate only in areas of limited enemy threat. The sea control ship will have minimum sensors and weapons, relying instead upon embarked aircraft and the capabilities of escorting warships. In addition to operating and maintaining its embarked aircraft, the sea control ship would provide maintenance to helicopters on destroyers and escort ships.

The National Steel and Shipbuilding Co of San Diego, California, has been awarded a contract for detailed design of the ship; it is anticipated that the sea control ships will be built by National Steel and at least one other shipyard.

The first sea control ship was proposed by the Navy in the Fiscal Year 1974 new construction programme; however, only funds for continuation of studies and design efforts were provided by the Congress. Subsequently, the lead ship was again requested in the FY 1975 programme, with seven additional ships planned for the FY 1976-1978 programmes.

AIRCRAFT. Aircraft capacity is based on one radar warning and up to two anti-submarine helicopters being airborne at all times and at least one V/STOL aircraft and another A/S helicopter on deck ready for immediate launch.

The sea control ship also would provide maintenance facilities for the LAMPS (Light Airborne Multi-Purpose System) helicopters embarked in accompanying destroyer-type ships. Probably two LAMPS helicopters would be carried in the sea control ship as replacements and for temporary operation from ships that have a helicopter deck but no support facilities.

DESIGN. Preliminary designs provide for a ship resembling World War II-era escort carriers or the "Iwo Jima" class amphibious assault ships with a clear flight deck and "island" structure to starboard. Two aircraft elevators are planned, but no catapult or arresting wires.

Flight deck dimensions will be approximately 575 × 105 feet.

DESIGNATION. As originally conceived this ship was known as an "air capable ship" and given the tentative designation DH indicating it would be a "destroyer type" warship with helicopter capability. However, on 8 May 1971 Admiral Zumwalt, the Chief of Naval Operations, said that the ship would be designated as the "sea control ship" in an apparent move to arouse interest and support for the programme. The initials SCS are being used in official documentation. Reportedly, the designation CH is being considered for the ship.

ELECTRONICS. The sea control ship will have austere electronics equipment with helicopters serving in the Airborne Early Warning (AEW) role to provide long-range detection and warning of hostile ships and aircraft.

The SPS-52 and SPS 55-radar antennas are reportedly planned for the ship.

GUNNERY. Official models and drawings indicate that the sea control ship will be armed with two 20 mm Vulcan/Phalanx rapid-fire Close-In Weapon Systems (CIWS) to provide defence against enemy anti-ship missiles that penetrate "area defence" systems of accompanying warships or aircraft.

FISCAL. The lead sea control ship is estimated to cost $172 000 000 with a follow-on ship cost goal of $117 000 000 each.

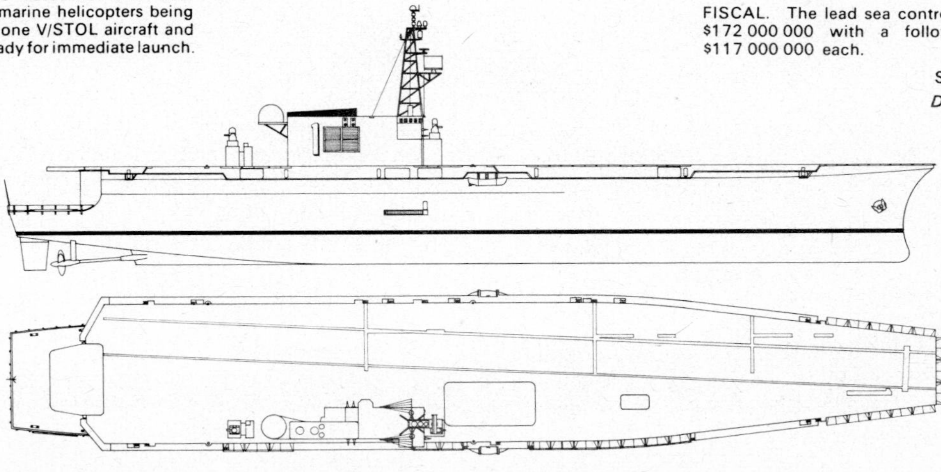

SEA CONTROL SHIP
Drawing by A. D. Baker

1 INTERIM SEA CONTROL SHIP: "IWO JIMA" CLASS

Name	*No.*	*Builder*	*Laid down*	*Launched*	*Commissioned*
***GUAM**	LPH 9	Philadelphia Naval Shipyard	15 Nov 1962	22 Aug 1964	16 Jan 1965

Displacement, tons: 18 300 full load
Length, feet (*metres*): 592 (*180·0*) oa
Beam, feet (*metres*): 84 (*25·6*)
Draft, feet (*metres*): 26 (*7·9*)
Flight deck width, feet (*metres*): 105 (*31·9*) maximum
Aircraft: AV-8A Harrier V/STOL strike aircraft; SH-2F Sea Sprite A/S helicopters; SH-3H Sea King A/S helicopters
Missile launchers: 2 Basic Point Defence Missile System (BPDMS) launchers with Sea Sparrow missile
Guns: 4—3 inch (*76 mm*) 50 calibre AA (twin)
Main engines: 1 geared turbine; 23 000 shp; 1 shaft
Boilers: 2 (Babcock & Wilcox)
Speed, knots: 20 (sustained)
Complement: 621 (52 officers, 569 enlisted men)

The amphibious assault ship *Guam* (LPH 9) is being employed as an interim sea control ship to develop operational concepts and tactics for the planned new construction ships described above.

The *Guam* was modified from Oct 1971 to Jan 1972, receiving improved aircraft maintenance capabilities, new deck markings, modified deck lighting and aircraft control/direction facilities, and being provided with an anti-submarine sensor analysis centre.

The ship began operations as an interim sea control ship early in 1972. She now operates various combinations of SH-2F Seasprite and SH-3H Sea King helicopters from Helicopter A/S Squadron 15 (HS-15) and AV-8A Harrier V/STOL aircraft from Marine Attack Squadron 513 (VMA-513). See "Iwo Jima" class listing under Amphibious Warfare Ships for additional notes.

ELECTRONICS. The *Guam* has SPS-10 and SPS-40 search radar antennas, SPN-10 navigation radar, and Carrier-Control Approach (CCA) radar; small TACAN (Tactical Air Navigation) pod atop mast.

MISSILES. During 1974 two BPDMS multiple launchers installed for Sea Sparrow missiles; two 3 inch twin gun mounts removed.

PHOTOGRAPHS. The photograph below shows the *Guam* with an AV-8A Harrier about to touch down on her flight deck while two other Harriers are parked forward.

GUAM (LPH 9) — *1972, United States Navy PH2 John E. Koppari*

ALBANY (CG 10) (see following page) — *1972, Giorgio Arra*

CHICAGO (CG 11) (see following page) — *1968, United States Navy*

Surface Combatants—*continued*

3 GUIDED MISSILE CRUISERS (CG): "ALBANY" CLASS

Name	*No*	*Builder*	*Laid down*	*Launched*	*Commissioned*	*CG Comm.*
• **ALBANY**	CG 10 (ex-CA 123)	Bethlehem Steel Co (Quincy)	6 Mar 1944	30 June 1945	15 June 1946	3 Nov 1962
• **CHICAGO**	CG 11 (ex-CA 136)	Philadelphia Navy Yard	28 July 1943	20 Aug 1944	1 Jan 1945	2 May 1964
• **COLUMBUS**	CG 12 (ex-CA 74)	Bethlehem Steel Co (Quincy)	28 June 1943	30 Nov 1944	8 June 1945	1 Dec 1962

Displacement, tons	13 700 standard; 17 500 full load
Length, feet (*metres*)	664 (*202.4*) wl; 673 (*205.3*) oa
Beam, feet (*metres*)	70 (*21.6*)
Draft, feet (*metres*)	27 (*8.2*)
Missile launchers	2 twin Talos surface-to-air launchers; 2 twin Tartar surface-to-air launchers
Missile launchers	2 twin Talos surface-to-air launchers 2 twin Tartar surface-to-air launchers
Guns	2—5 in (*127 mm*) 38 calibre dual-purpose (see *Gunnery* notes)
A/S weapons	1 ASROC 8-tube launcher 2 triple torpedo tubes (Mk 32)
Helicopter	utility helicopter carried
Main engines	4 geared turbines (General Electric); 120 000 shp; 4 shafts
Boilers	4 (Babcock & Wilcox)
Speed, knots	33
Complement	1 000 (60 officers, approx 940 enlisted men)

These ships were fully converted from heavy cruisers, the *Albany* having been a unit of the "Oregon City" class and the *Chicago* and *Columbus* of the "Baltimore" class. Although the two heavy cruiser classes differ in appearance (see Fire Support Ships), they have the same hull dimensions and machinery. These three missile ships now form a new, homogeneous class.
The cruiser *Fall River* (CA 131) was originally scheduled for missile conversion, but was replaced by the *Columbus*. **Proposals to convert two additional heavy cruisers (CA 124 and CA 130) to missile ships (CG 13 and CG 14) were dropped, primarily because of high conversion costs and improved capabilities of newer missile-armed frigates.**

The *Columbus* was to decommission in late 1974.

CONVERSION. During conversion to missile configuration these ships were stripped down to their main hulls with all cruiser armament and superstructure being removed. New superstructures make extensive use of aluminium to reduce weight and improve stability. Former masts and stacks were replaced by "macks" which support electronic antennas and have machinery exhausts vented from sides near top. The *Albany* was converted at the Boston Naval Shipyard between January 1959 and November 1962; the *Columbus* at Puget Sound Naval Shipyard from June 1959 to March 1963; and *Chicago* at San Francisco Naval Shipyard from July 1959 to September 1964.
Helicopter landing area on fantail, but no hangar or support facilities.

ELECTRONICS. These ships are fitted with SQS-23 sonar which is linked to the ASROC fire control system. The Naval Tactical Data System (NTDS) is fitted in the *Albany* and *Chicago*.
The radar arrangements differ slightly: the *Albany* has SPS-48 three-dimensional and SPS-10 search radars on her forward "mack", an SPS-43 radar on her second "mack", and an SPS-30 on the after platform (no SPS-30 atop bridge structure); the *Chicago* has SPS-30 forward and aft, SPS-52 and SPS-10 on her forward "mack", and an SPS-43 on her after "mack"; the *Columbus* has SPS-30 forward and aft, and an SPS-10 search radar on her forward "mack", and an SPS-43 on her after "mack"

GUNNERY. No guns were fitted when these ships were converted to missile cruisers. Two single, *open-mount* 5 inch guns were fitted subsequently to provide minimal defence against low-flying, subsonic aircraft or torpedo boat attacks.
Two Mk 56 directors installed for gun control.

MISSILES. One twin Talos launcher is forward and one aft; a twin Tartar launcher is on each side of the main bridge structure. During conversion space was allocated amidships for installation of eight Polaris missile tubes, but the plan to install ballistic missiles in cruisers was cancelled in mid-1959. Reportedly, 92 Talos and 80 Tartar missiles are carried.

MODERNISATION. The *Albany* underwent an extensive anti-air warfare modernisation at the Boston Naval Shipyard; "conversion" began in February 1967 and was completed in August 1969. She was formally recommissioned on 9 Nov 1968. The *Chicago* and *Columbus* will not have AAW modernisations.
The *Albany's* AAW conversion included installation of NTDS, a digital Talos fire-control system which provides faster and more-reliable operation, and improved SPS-48 and SPS-30 air search radars (the *Albany* also has an SPS-43 long-range and SPS-10 short-range search radars, and SPG-51C fire-control radar).

PHOTOGRAPHS. On the previous page note the differing radar antennae and antenna arrangement on the forward "mack" of the *Albany* and *Chicago*.

ALBANY (CG 10) — *1970, Anthony & Joseph Pavia*

COLOMBUS (CG 12) — *1972, Giorgio Arra*

COLUMBUS (CG 12) — *1972, Giorgio Arra*

Surface Combatants—*continued*

1 NUCLEAR-POWERED GUIDED MISSILE CRUISER (CGN): "LONG BEACH" TYPE

Name	*No.*	*Builder*	*Laid down*	*Launched*	*Commissioned*
•LONG BEACH	CGN 9 (ex-CGN 160, CLGN 160)	Bethlehem Steel Co, (Quincy, Massachusetts)	2 Dec 1957	14 July 1959	**9 Sep 1961**

Displacement, tons	14 200 standard; 17 350 full load
Length, feet (*metres*)	721·2 (*220*) oa
Beam, feet (*metres*)	73·2 (*22·3*)
Draft, feet (*metres*)	29 (*8·8*)
Missile launchers	1 twin Talos surface-to-air launcher (Mk 12 Mod 0) 2 twin Terrier surface-to-air launchers (Mk 10 Mod 1 and 2)
Guns	2—5 inch (*127 mm*) 38 calibre dual-purpose (see *Gunnery* notes)
A/S weapons	1 ASROC 8-tube launcher 2 triple torpedo tubes (Mk 32)
Helicopter	utility helicopter carried
Main engines	2 geared turbines (General Electric); approx 80 000 shp; 2 shafts
Reactors	2 pressurised-water cooled C1W (Westinghouse)
Speed, knots	approx 35
Complement	1 000 (60 officers, approx 950 enlisted men)

The *Long Beach* was the first ship to be designed and constructed from the keel up as a cruiser for the United States since the end of World War II. She is the world's first nuclear-powered surface warship and the first warship to have a guided missile main battery. She was authorised in the Fiscal Year 1957 new construction programme. Estimated construction cost was $332 850 000. Construction was delayed because of shipyard strike.
No additional cruisers were constructed by the US Navy because of the capabilities of new guided-missile frigates (DLG and DLGN), which are approaching the size of World War II-era light cruisers.

CLASSIFICATION. The *Long Beach* was ordered as a Guided Missile Light Cruiser (CLGN 160) on 15 Oct 1956; reclassified as a Guided Missile Cruiser (CGN 160) early in 1957 and renumbered (CGN 9) on 1 July 1957.

DESIGN. The *Long Beach* was initially planned as a large destroyer or "frigate" of about 7 800 tons (standard displacement) to test the feasibility of a nuclear powered surface warship. Early in 1956 the decision was made to capitalise on the capabilities of nuclear propulsion and her displacement was increased to 11 000 tons and a second Terrier missile launcher was added to the design. A Talos missile launcher was also added to the design which, with other features, increased displacement to 14 000 tons by the time the contract was signed for her construction on 15 October 1956.

ELECTRONICS. The *Long Beach* has fixed-array ("billboard") radar which provides increased range over rotating antennas. Horizontal antennas on bridge superstructure are for SPS-32 bearing and range radar; vertical antennas are for SPS-33 target tracking radar. The SPS-33 uses an "S" band frequency and the SPS-32 is VHF; both frequency scan in elevation. Developed and produced by Hughes Aircraft, they are believed the first operational fixed-array radar systems in the Western world. Also installed in the nuclear-powered aircraft carrier *Enterprise* (CVAN 65).
SPS-12 and SPS-10 search radars are mounted on the forward mast.
The SPS-32/33 "Scanfar" radars and the associated computers were modified in 1970 to improve performance. She is equipped with Naval Tactical Data System (NTDS) and SQS-23 sonar.

LONG BEACH (CGN 9) — *1968, United States Navy*

ENGINEERING. The reactors are similar to those of the nuclear-powered aircraft carrier *Enterprise* (CVAN 65). The *Long Beach* first got underway on nuclear power on 5 July 1961. After four years of operation and having steamed more than 167 000 miles she underwent her first overhaul and refuelling at the Newport News Shipbuilding and Dry Dock Company from August 1965 to February 1966.

GUNNERY. Completed with an all-missile armament. Two single 5 inch mounts were fitted during 1962-1963 yard period to provide defence against low-flying subsonic aircraft and torpedo boats.

MISSILES. Initial plans provided for installation of the Regulus II surface-to-surface missile, a transonic missile which carried a nuclear warhead and had a 1 000-mile range. Upon cancellation of the Regulus II programme, provision was made for providing eight Polaris missile tubes, but they were never installed. Plans to provide Polaris were dropped early in 1961 in an effort to reduce construction costs.
Reportedly, the *Long Beach* carries 40 Talos and 240 Terrier missiles.

NOMENCLATURE. Cruisers are named for American cities. Since 1971 the Navy also has named attack submarines for cities, beginning with the SSN 688 (*Los Angeles*).

OPERATIONAL. Talos missiles fired from the *Long Beach* have downed Communist aircraft in what are believed to have been the first surface-to-air "kills" in combat with ship-launched missiles.
While operating in the Tonkin Gulf, the ship's Talos missiles shot down one supersonic MiG fighter on May 23, 1968, and a second MiG in June 1968; both aircraft were over North Vietnam at the time of their destruction.

LONG BEACH (CGN 9) — *1968, United States Navy*

Surface Combatants—*continued*

5 GUIDED MISSILE LIGHT CRUISERS (CLG): CONVERTED "CLEVELAND" CLASS

Name	*No.*	*Builder*	*Laid down*	*Launched*	*Commissioned*	*CLG Comm.*
GALVESTON	CLG 3 (ex-CL 93)	Cramp Shipbuilding (Philadelphia)	20 Feb 1944	22 Apr 1945	(see notes)	28 May 1958
***LITTLE ROCK**	CLG 4 (ex-CL 92)	Cramp Shipbuilding (Philadelphia)	6 Mar 1943	27 Aug 1944	17 June 1945	3 June 1960
***OKLAHOMA CITY**	CLG 5 (ex-CL 91)	Cramp Shipbuilding (Philadelphia)	8 Mar 1942	20 Feb 1944	22 Dec 1944	7 Sep 1960
PROVIDENCE	CLG 6 (ex-CL 82)	Bethlehem Steel Co. (Quincy)	27 July 1943	28 Dec 1944	15 May 1945	17 Sep 1959
SPRINGFIELD	CLG 7 (ex-CL 66)	Bethlehem Steel Co. (Quincy)	13 Feb 1943	9 Mar 1944	9 Sep 1944	2 July 1960

Displacement, tons: 10 670 standard; 14 600 full load
Length, feet (*metres*): 600 (*182·9*) wl; 610 (*185·9*) oa
Beam, feet (*metres*): 66·3 (*20·2*)
Draft, feet (*metres*): 25 (*7·6*)
Missile launchers:
CLG 3, 4, 5: 1 twin Talos surface-to-air launcher (Mk 7 Mod 0)
CLG 6, 7: 1 twin Terrier surface-to-air launcher (Mk 9 Mod 1)
Guns CLG 4-7: 3—6 inch (*152 mm*) 47 cal; 2—5 inch (*127 mm*) 38 cal dual-purpose
CLG 3: 6—6 inch (*152 mm*) 47 cal; 6—5 inch (*27 mm*) 38 cal dual-purpose
Helicopters: utility helicopter carried
Main engines: 4 geared turbines (General Electric); 100 000 shp; 4 shafts
Boilers: 4 (Babcock & Wilcox)
Speed: 31·6 knots
Complement CLG 4-7: 1 680 officers and enlisted men (including fleet staff)
CLG 3: 1 200 officers and enlisted men

PROVIDENCE (CLG 6) *United States Navy*

Originally a series of six ships converted from light cruisers of the "Cleveland" class; three ships converted to Terrier missile configuration aft and three ships to Talos missile, with two ships of each missile type configured to serve as fleet flagships.
The surviving ships are the *Little Rock* and *Oklahoma* armed with Talos and fitted as fleet flagships; the *Providence* and *Springfield* armed with Terrier and fitted as fleet flagships; and the *Galveston* armed with Terrier. The *Galveston* was decommissioned on 25 May 1970; *Providence* decommissioned on 31 Aug 1973; and *Springfield* decommissioned in June 1974. All in reserve and can be expected to strike in the near future.
The *Little Rock* serves in the Mediterranean as flagship of the US Sixth Fleet and the *Oklahoma City* in the Western Pacific as flagship of the US Seventh Fleet.

CLASSIFICATION. All US Navy guided missile cruisers are numbered in a single series (CAG 1-2, CLG 3-8, CGN 9).

CONSTRUCTION. The construction of the *Galveston* was suspended on 24 June 1946 when nearly complete; placed in reserve until 1956 when taken in hand for conversion to a missile ship. She got underway for the first time on 30 June 1958.

CONVERSION. All six of these ships had their two after 6 inch gun turrets replaced by a twin surface-to-air missile launcher, superstructure enlarged to support missile fire control equipment, lattice masts fitted to carry antennas, 5 inch battery reduced from original 12 guns), and all 40 mm and 20 mm light anti-aircraft guns removed. The four ships fitted as fleet flagships additionally had their No. 2 turret of 6 inch guns removed and their forward superstructure enlarged to provide command and communications spaces for the flag staff.

The *Galveston* began conversion at the Philadelphia Naval Shipyard in August 1956 and was completed in September 1958; the *Little Rock* began conversion at the New York Shipbuilding Corp (Camden, New Jersey) in January 1957 and was completed in June 1960; the *Oklahoma City* began conversion at the Bethlehem Steel shipyard in San Francisco in May 1957 and was completed in September 1960; the *Providence* began conversion at the Boston Naval Shipyard in June 1957 and was completed in September 1959; the *Springfield* began conversion at the Bethlehem Steel shipyard in Quincy, Massachusetts, in August 1957, but was moved to the Boston Naval Shipyard in March 1960 for completion in July 1960.
There is a helicopter landing area on the fantail, but only limited support facilities are provided; no hangar.

ELECTRONICS. The Terrier-armed ships have SPS-43 and SPS-10 radars on their forward mast, an SPS-30 radar on the second mast, and an SPS-52 or SPS-39 three-dimensional radar on the third mast; the Talos-armed ships have SPS-43 and SPS-10 radars on their forward mast, an SPS-52 or SPS-39 three dimensional radar on their after mast, and an SPS-30 on the after platform.
The *Little Rock* has had her SPS-39 three-dimensional search radar removed.
These ships have no ASW sonar.

GUNNERY. As converted to missile-gun cruisers these ships each retained one Mk 37 and one Mk 39 gunfire control directors forward; some directors have been removed.

MISSILES. Reportedly, the two cruisers armed with Terrier each carry 120 missiles and the three ships armed with Talos each carry 46 missiles.

DISPOSALS
Topeka (CLG 8, ex-CL 67) stricken on 1 Dec 1973.

SPRINGFIELD (CLG 7) *1973, United States Navy, PH2 H. E. Deffenbaugh*

Surface Combatants—*continued*

3+1 NUCLEAR-POWERED GUIDED MISSILE FRIGATES (DLGN): "VIRGINIA" CLASS

Name	*No.*	*Builder*	*Laid down*	*Launch*	*Commission*
VIRGINIA	DLGN 38	Newport News Shipbuilding & Dry Dock Co.	19 Aug 1972	July 1974	late 1975
TEXAS	DLGN 39	Newport News Shipbuilding & Dry Dock Co.	18 Aug 1973	mid 1975	1976
	DLGN 40	Newport News Shipbuilding & Dry Dock Co.	July 1974	late 1975	1977
	DLGN 41	Proposed FY 1975 programme.			

Displacement, tons	approx 10 000 full load
Length, feet (*metres*)	585 (*177·3*) oa
Beam, feet (*metres*)	61 (*18·5*)
Draft, feet (*metres*)	29·5 (*9·0*)
Helicopters	2 (see *Helicopter* notes)
Missile launchers	2 combination twin Tartar-D/ASROC launchers firing Standard MR surface-to-air missile (Mk 26)
Guns	2—5 inch (*127 mm*) 54 calibre dual-purpose (Mk 45) (single)
A/S weapons	ASROC (*see above*) 2 triple torpedo tubes (Mk 32)
Main engines	2 geared turbines; 2 shafts
Reactors	2 pressurised-water cooled D2G (General Electric)
Speed, knots	30+
Complement	442 (27 officers, 415 enlisted men)

The DLGN 38 was authorised in the Fiscal Year 1970 new construction programme, DLGN 39 in FY 1971 programme, and DLGN 40 in FY 1972 programme. Subsequently, the Department of Defense did not request additional nuclear-propelled frigates because of their high cost; however, the Congress added funds for advanced procurement of DLGN 41 and DLGN 42 components in the FY 1974 budget. Accordingly, the DLGN 41 was proposed in the FY 1975 construction programme and the decision was made to "protect the option" of the DLGN 42 in the FY 1976 programme.

According to Admiral H. G. Rickover, the long-range Navy plan in effect until April 1971 was to construct a total of 28 nuclear escort ships (CGN/DLGN) with the construction of one additional DLGN per year for the next two decades. This ambitious plan has been terminated and the construction of these ships is uncertain beyond the DLGN 41.

Construction of the first three ships has been delayed about seven months each because of a shortage of skilled labour in the shipyard. The Newport News yard is the only one in the United States now engaged in the construction of nuclear surface ships.

DESIGN. The principal differences between the DLGN 38 class and the "California" class will be the improved anti-air warfare capability, electronic warfare equipment, anti-submarine fire control system, and the combat information centre (CIC) facilities. The deletion of the ASROC "pepper-box" launcher permitted the later ships to be ten feet shorter.

ELECTRONICS. These ships will have bow-mounted SQS-53A sonar (improved SQS-26 series); also to have Naval Tactical Data System (NTDS), SPS-48A three-dimensional radar, SPS-40B and SPS-55 radar antennas.

FISCAL. Estimated cost is $222 000 000 for the DLGN 38 and $113 800 000 for DLGN 39, although shipyard delays and inflation probably will drive their costs higher. The Secretary of Defense has estimated that the cost of the DLGN 41 would be "at least" $268 000 000 and that of the DLGN 42 $278 000 000.

According to the Secretary of Defense: "Clearly, we will not be able to afford many (more) surface combatant ships at these prices".

See 1973-1974 and previous editions for funding details.

GUNNERY. These ships will have Mk 86 gunfire control directors.

HELICOPTERS. A hangar for helicopters is installed beneath the fantail flight-deck with a telescoping hatch cover and an electro-mechanical elevator provided to transport helicopters between the main deck and hangar. These are the first US post-World War II destroyer/cruiser ships with a hull hangar.

MISSILES. The initial design for this class provided for a single surface-to-air missile launcher; revised in 1969 to provide two Mk 26 launchers that will fire the Standard-Medium Range (MR) surface-to-air missile and the ASROC anti-submarine missile. "Mixed" Standard/ASROC magazines are planned for each launcher. The digital Mk 116 ASW fire control system will simplify weapon system interfaces compared to previous US missile-armed warships. Mk 74 missile control directors.

DRAWING. Chaff-rocket (CHAFROC) launchers are shown forward of bridge and aft of boat davits with triple anti-submarine torpedo tubes also aft of boat davits; "California" design on the following page has the torpedo tubes built into superstructure. Note enclosed radar towers, similar to "California" class.

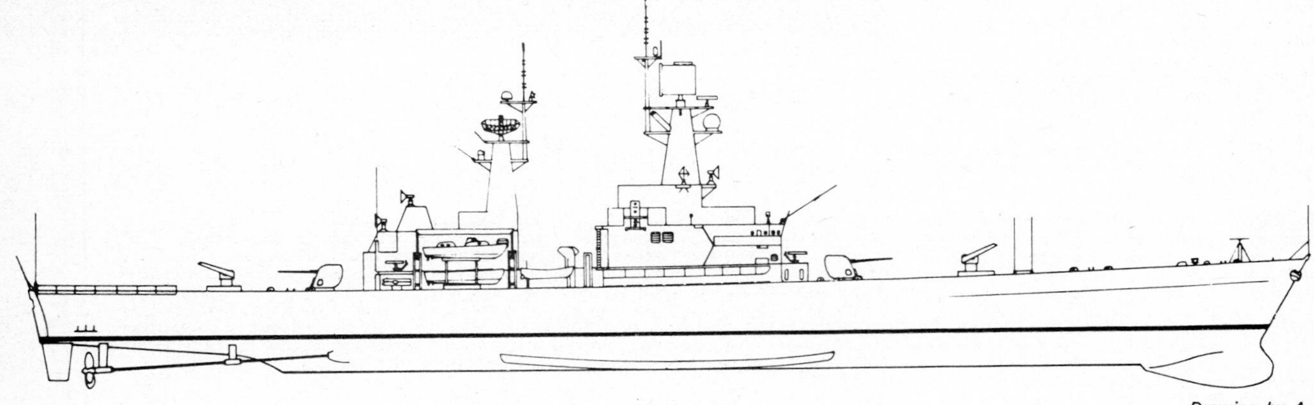

Drawing by A. D. Baker

LITTLE ROCK (CLG 4)—see previous page

United States Navy

Surface Combatants—*continued*

2 NUCLEAR-POWERED GUIDED MISSILE FRIGATES (DLGN): "CALIFORNIA" CLASS

Name	*No.*	*Builder*	*Laid down*	*Launch*	*Commissioned*
*CALIFORNIA	DLGN 36	Newport News Shipbuilding & Dry Dock Co	23 Jan 1970	22 Sep 1971	16 Feb 1974
SOUTH CAROLINA	DLGN 37	Newport News Shipbuilding & Dry Dock Co	1 Dec 1970	1 July 1972	Sep 1974

Displacement tons	10 150 full load
Length, feet (*metres*)	596 (*181·7*) oa
Beam, feet (*metres*)	61 (*18·6*)
Draft, feet (*metres*)	31·5 (*9·6*)
Missile launchers	2 single Tartar-D surface-to-air launchers firing Standard MR (Mk 13 Mod 3)
Guns	2—5 inch (*127 mm*) 54 calibre dual-purpose (Mk 45) (single)
A/S weapons	4 torpedo tubes (Mk 32) 1 ASROC 8-tube launcher
Main engines	2 geared turbines; 2 shafts
Reactors	2 pressurised-water cooled D2G (General Electric)
Speed, knots	30+
Complement	540 (28 officers, 512 enlisted men)

These are large, multi-purpose warships intended primarily to operate with fast carrier forces. Their high-speed and endurance capabilities also make them suitable for independent operations.

The *California* was authorised in the Fiscal Year 1967 new construction programme and the *South Carolina* in the FY 1968 programme. The construction of a third ship of this class (DLGN 38) also was authorised in FY 1968, but the rising costs of these ships and development of the DXGN/DLGN 38 design caused the third ship to be deferred.

The contract for both ships was awarded on 13 June 1968. The frigate *California* together with the three previously built nuclear escort ships (*Long Beach, Bainbridge, Truxtun*) will provide one all-nuclear carrier task group consisting of one attack aircraft carrier and four escorts.

DESIGN. These ships have tall, enclosed towers supporting radar antennae in contrast to the open lattice masts of the previous nuclear frigates *Truxtun* and *Bainbridge*.

ELECTRONICS Fitted with bow-mounted SQS-26CX sonar and the Naval Tactical Data System (NTDS). These ships have SPS-48 three-dimensional, SPS-10 and SPS-40 search radar antennas.

ENGINEERING. Estimated nuclear core life for these ships provide 700 000 miles "range"; estimated cost is $11 500 000 for the two initial nuclear cores.

CALIFORNIA (DLGN 36) — *1973, Newport News SB & DD Co.*

CALIFORNIA (DLGN 36) — *1973, Newport News SB & DD Co.*

CALIFORNIA (DLGN 36) launching — *1971, Newport News*

FISCAL. Estimated cost is $200 000 000 for *California* and $180 000 000 for *South Carolina*. See 1971-1972 edition for funding history.

GUNNERY. These ships are the heaviest gunned missile frigates yet built. Fitted with Mk 86 gunfire control system.

MISSILES. Reportedly, these ships carry some 80 surface-to-air missiles divided equally between a magazine beneath each launcher. The launchers will fire the Standard-MR missile. Fitted with Mk 74 missile control directors.

NOMENCLATURE. Destroyer-type ships in the US Navy have traditionally been named for officers and enlisted personnel of the Navy and Marine Corps, Secretaries of the Navy, members of Congress who have influenced naval affairs, and inventors. The frigates generally honour admirals and commodores of the Navy; however, in January 1970 it was announced that henceforth frigates would be named for states of the Union with the first frigate so named honouring California, home state of the incumbant president. The DLGN 37 honours the home state of the late L. Mendel Rivers, chairman of the House of Representatives Committee on Armed Services from 1965 until his death in 1971. The "Sturgeon" class submarine SSN 686 was renamed while under construction to honour the late representative.

PHOTOGRAPHS. The "California" class can be distinguished from the subsequent "Virginia" class frigates by the ASROC launcher and "reload house" forward of the bridge and the after 5 inch gun being one level above the main deck in the earlier ships. Note the tower-like mast structures in both US classes; similar to the Soviet missile cruiser designs.

Surface Combatants—*continued*

1 NUCLEAR-POWERED GUIDED MISSILE FRIGATE (DLGN): "TRUXTUN" TYPE

Name	*No.*	*Builder*	*Laid down*	*Launched*	*Commissioned*
***TRUXTUN**	DLGN 35	New York Shipbuilding Corp (Camden)	17 June 1963	19 Dec 1964	27 May 1967

Displacement, tons	8 200 standard; 9 200 full load
Length, feet (*metres*)	64 (*117·9*) oa
Beam, feet (*metres*)	58 (*17·7*)
Draft, feet (*metres*)	31 (*9·4*)
Missile launchers	1 twin Terrier/ASROC launcher (Mk 10 Mod 7)
Guns	1—5 inch (*127 mm*) 54 calibre dual purpose 2—3 inch (*76 mm*) 50 calibre anti-aircraft (single)
A/S weapons	ASROC (see above) 4 fixed torpedo tubes (Mk 32) facilities for helicopter
Main engines	2 geared turbines; approx 60 000 shp; 2 shafts
Reactors	2 pressurised water-cooled D2G (General Electric)
Speed, knots	30+
Complement	approx 500 (35 officers, 456 enlisted men)

The *Truxtun* was the US Navy's fourth nuclear powered surface warship. The Navy has requested seven oil-burning frigates in the Fiscal Year 1962 shipbuilding programme, the Congress authorised seven ships; but stipulated that one ship must be nuclear powered. Although the *Truxtun* design is adapted from the "Belknap" class design, the nuclear ship's gun-missile launcher arrangement is reversed from the non-nuclear ships. Construction cost was $138 667 000.

ELECTRONICS. The *Truxtun* has bow-mounted SQS-26 sonar and the Naval Tactical Data System (NTDS). Fitted with SPS-48 three-dimensional and SPS-10 search radars on forward mast and an SPS-40 search radar and TACAN (Tactical Aircraft Navigation) "pod" on after mast.

ENGINEERING. Power plant is identical to that of the frigate *Bainbridge*.

MISSILES. The twin missile launcher aft can fire both Terrier anti-aircraft missiles and ASROC anti-submarine rockets.

TRUXTUN (DLGN 35) *1970, United States Navy*

NOMENCLATURE. The *Truxtun* is the fifth ship to be named for Commodore Thomas Truxton (sic) who commanded the frigate *Constellation* (38 guns) in her successful encounter with the French frigate *L'Insurgente* (44) in 1799.

TORPEDOES. Fixed Mk 32 tubes are below 3-inch gun "tubs", built into superstructure. The two Mk 25 torpedo tubes built into her stern are not used.

PHOTOGRAPHS. The *Truxtun* can be readily identified by her squared lattice radar masts, empty "B" gun position and lack of funnel. Two chaff rocket (CHAFROC) launchers subsequently have been fitted in the "B" position.

TRUXTUN (DLGN 35) *1970, United States Navy, PH1 E. L. Goligoski*

CALIFORNIA (DLGN 36)—see previous page *1973, Newport News SB & DD Co.*

Surface Combatants—*continued*

1 NUCLEAR-POWERED GUIDED MISSILE FRIGATE (DLGN): "BAINBRIDGE" TYPE

Name	*No.*	*Builder*	*Laid down*	*Launched*	*Commissioned*
*BAINBRIDGE	DLGN 25	Bethlehem Steel Co (Quincy)	15 May 1959	15 Apr 1961	6 Oct 1962

Displacement, tons	7 600 standard; 8 580 full load
Length, feet (*metres*)	550 (*167·6*)wl; 565 (*172·5*) oa
Beam, feet (*metres*)	57·9 (*17·6*)
Draft, feet (*metres*)	29 (*7·9*)
Missile launchers	2 twin Terrier surface-to-air launchers
Guns	4—3 inch (*76 mm*) 50 calibre anti-aircraft (twin)
A/S weapons	1 ASROC 8-tube launcher; 2 triple torpedo tubes (Mk 32)
Main engines	2 geared turbines; approx 60 000 shp; 2 shafts
Reactors	2 pressurised-water cooled D2G (General Electric)
Speed, knots	30+
Complement	approx 450 (26 officers, approx 425 enlisted men)

The *Bainbridge* was the US Navy's third nuclear-powered surface warship and the world's first "destroyer type" ship to have nuclear propulsion. She is larger than the light anti-aircraft cruisers the United States built during World war II. Authorised in Fiscal Year 1956 shipbuilding programme. Construction cost was $163 610 000.

DESIGN. The *Bainbridge* is similar in basic arrangement to the "Leahy" class frigates. However, the nuclear ship has two heavy lattice radar masts in place of the "mack" structures of the conventional ships.

ELECTRONICS. Fitted with SQS-23 bow-mounted sonar.
The *Bainbridge* has SPS-52 three-dimensional search radar and SPS-10 search radar on her forward mast, and an SPS-37 search radar antenna on her after mast.

ENGINEERING. Development of a nuclear power plant suitable for use in a large "destroyer type" warship began in 1957. The Atomic Energy Commission's Knolls Atomic Power Laboratory undertook development of the destroyer power plant (designated D1G/D2G).

MISSILES. The *Bainbridge* has a Terrier Mk 10 Mod 5 launcher forward and a Mk 10 Mod 6 launcher aft. Reportedly, the ship carries 80 missiles divided between the forward and aft Terrier magazines.

MODERNISATION. The *Bainbridge* began an Anti-Air Warfare (AAW) modernisation at the Puget Sound Naval Shipyard in June 1974; completion scheduled for early 1976. The ship will be fitted with the Naval Tactical Data System (NTDS) and improved guidance capability for Terrier and Standard missiles. Estimated cost of modernisation $103 000 000.

BAINBRIDGE (DLGN 25) — *1971, United States Navy*

DALE (DLG 19)—"Leahy" class — *1972, United States Navy*

WILLIAM H. STANDLEY (DLG 32)—"Belknap" class — *1972, Giorgio Arra*

Surface Combatants—*continued*

9 GUIDED MISSILE FRIGATES (DLG): "BELKNAP" CLASS

Displacement, tons	6 570 standard; 7 930 full load
Length, feet (*metres*)	547 (*166·7*) oa
Beam, feet (*metres*)	54·8 (*16·7*)
Draft, feet (*metres*)	28·8 (*8·7*)
Missile launchers	1 twin Terrier/ASROC launcher (Mk 10 Mod 7)
Guns	1—5 inch (*127 mm*) 54 cal dual-purpose 2—3 inch (*76 mm*) 50 cal anti-aircraft (single)
A/S weapons	ASROC (see above) 2 triple torpedo tubes (Mk 32) 1 SH-2D LAMPS helicopter
Main engines	**2 geared turbines (General Electric in DLG 26-28, 32, 34; De Laval in DLG 29-31, 33); 85 000 shp; 2 shafts**
Boilers	**4 (Babcock & Wilcox in DLG 26-28, 32, 34; Combustion Engineering in DLG 29-31, 33)**
Speed, knots	**34**
Complement	**418 (31 officers, 387 enlisted men) including squadron staff**

Name	*No*		*Builder*	*Laid down*	*Launched*	*Commissioned*
***BELKNAP**	DLG	26	Bath Iron Works Corp	5 Feb 1962	20 July 1963	7 Nov 1964
***JOSEPHUS DANIELS**	DLG	27	Bath Iron Works Corp	23 Apr 1962	2 Dec 1963	8 May 1965
***WAINWRIGHT**	DLG	28	Bath Iron Works Corp	2 July 1962	25 Apr 1964	8 Jan 1966
***JOUETT**	DLG	29	Puget Sound Naval Yard	25 Sep 1962	30 June 1964	3 Dec 1966
***HORNE**	DLG	30	San Francisco Naval Yard	12 Dec 1962	30 Oct 1964	15 Apr 1967
***STERETT**	DLG	31	Puget Sound Naval Yard	25 Sep 1962	30 June 1964	8 Apr 1967
***WILLIAM H. STANDLEY**	DLG	32	Bath Iron Works Corp	29 July 1963	19 Dec 1964	9 July 1966
***FOX**	DLG	33	Todd Shipyard Corp	15 Jan 1963	21 Nov 1964	8 May 1966
***BIDDLE**	DLG	34	Bath Iron Works Corp	9 Dec 1963	2 July 1965	21 Jan 1967

These ships are considered excellent anti-submarine and anti-air warfare ships, intended to screen fast carrier task forces. The DLG 26-28 were authorised in the Fiscal Year 1961 new construction programme; the DLG 29-34 in FY 1962 programme.

DESIGN. These ships are distinctive by having their single missile launcher forward and 5 inch gun mount aft. This arrangement allowed missile stowage in the larger bow section and provided space aft of the superstructure for a helicopter hangar and platform. **The reverse gun-missile arrangement, preferred by some commanding officers, is found in the *Truxtun*. The "Belknap" class ships have their masts and stacks combined into "mack" structures.**

ELECTRONICS. SQS-26 bow-mounted sonar installed. These ships have the Naval Tactical Data System (NTDS). Fitted with SPS-48 three-dimensional and SPS-10 search radars on their forward "mack" and an SPS-37 (first three ships) or SPS-40 search radar and small TACAN (Tactical Aircraft Navigation) pod on their after "mack"

GUNNERY. The 5 inch guns were installed previously on forward sponsons of the "Forrestal" class carriers. They are rapid fire-Mk 42 single 5 inch guns and the single 3 inch guns are Mk 34.

HELICOPTERS. These ships are the only conventionally powered US frigates with a full helicopter support capability. All being fitted with the Light Airborne Multi-Purpose System, now the SH-2D helicopter. The *Belknap* embarked the first operational SH-2D/LAMPS in December 1971.

MISSILES. The *Truxtun* and "Belknap" class ships have a twin Terrier/ASROC Mk 10 missile launcher. A "triple-ring" rotating magazine stocks both Terrier anti-aircraft missiles and ASROC anti-submarine rockets, feeding either weapon to the launcher's two firing arms. The rate of fire and reliability of the launcher provide a potent AAW/ASW capability to these ships.

TORPEDOES. As built, these ships each had two 21 inch tubes for anti-submarine torpedoes installed in the structure immediately forward of the 5 inch mount, one tube angled out to port and one to starboard; subsequently removed.

STERETT (DLG 31) — *1972, United States Navy, PHAN Delvin D. Bren*

JOSEPHUS DANIELS (DLG 27) — *1972, Giorgio Arra*

JOSEPHUS DANIELS (DLG 27) — *1973, Giorgio Arra*

Surface Combatants—*continued*

9 GUIDED MISSILE FRIGATES (DLG:) "LEAHY" CLASS

Displacement, tons	5 670 standard; 7 800 full load
Length, feet (*metres*)	533 (*162·5*) oa
Beam, feet (*metres*)	54·9 (*16·6*)
Draft, feet (*metres*)	24·5 (*7·4*)
Missile launchers	2 twin Terrier surface-to-air launchers (Mk 10 Mod 5)
Guns	4—3 inch (*76 mm*) 50 cal anti-aircraft (twin)
A/S weapons	1 ASROC 8-tube launcher 2 triple torpedo tubes (Mk 32)
Main engines	2 geared turbines (see *Engineering* notes); 85 000 shp; 2 shafts
Boilers	4 (Babcock & Wilcox in DLG 16-18; Foster Wheeler in DLG 19-24)
Speed, knots	34
Complement	396 (31 officers, 365 enlisted men) including squadron staff

These ships are "double-end" missile frigates especially designed to screen fast carrier task forces. They are limited in only having 3 inch guns in comparision wth 5 inch guns on other DLG classes. The DLG 16-18 authorised in the Fiscal Year 1958 new construction programme; DLG 19-24 in the FY 1959 programme.

DESIGN. These ships are distinctive in having twin missile launchers forward and aft with ASROC "pepper box" launcher between the forward missile launcher and bridge on main deck level. Masts and stacks are combined into "macks".
There is a helicopter landing area aft but only limited support facilities are provided; no hangar.

ELECTRONICS. These ships were fitted with the Naval Tactical Data System (NTDS) during AAW modernisation. SQS-23 bow mounted sonar installed. These ships have SPS-10 and SPS-48 search radars on forward mast (the latter replacing SPS-39 or SPS-52 in some ships) and an SPS-37 search radar on their after mast.
Halsey, *Worden*, *Richmond K. Turner*, and *Reeves* completed with only two Mk 76 missile directors; two additional directors were installed during AAW modernisation.

ENGINEERING. General Electric turbines in DLG 16-18; De Laval turbines in DLG 19-22; and Allis-Chalmers turbines in DLG 23 and DLG 24.

MISSILES. Reportedly, each ship carries 80 missiles divided between the two Terrier magazines.

MODERNISATION. These ships were modernised between 1967 and 1972 to improve their Anti-Air Warfare (AAW) capabilities. Superstructure enlarged to provide space for additional electronic equipment, including NTDS; improved TACAN fitted and improved guidance system for Terrier/Standard missiles installed, and larger ship's service turbo generators provided.
All ships modernised at Bath Iron Works except *Leahy* at Philadelphia Naval Shipyard.

Cost of *Leahy* modernisation was $36 100 000.

NOMENCLATURE. The *England* is the second US warship to honour a sailor killed at Pearl Harbour on 7 Dec 1941; the first *England* (DE 635) sank six Japanese submarines in just 12 days during May of 1944.

PHOTOGRAPHS. These ships can be distinguished from other non-nuclear frigates by having twin surface-to-air missile launchers forward and aft, and from all other frigates by the absence of distinctive 5 inch gun mounts.

Name	*No*	*Builder*	*Laid down*	*Launched*	*Commissioned*
*LEAHY	DLG 16	Bath Iron Works Corp	3 Dec 1959	1 July 1961	4 Aug 1962
*HARRY E YARNELL	DLG 17	Bath Iron Works Corp	31 May 1960	9 Dec 1961	2 Feb 1963
*WORDEN	DLG 18	Bath Iron Works Corp	19 Sep 1960	2 June 1962	3 Aug 1963
*DALE	DLG 19	New York SB Corp	6 Sep 1960	28 July 1962	23 Nov 1963
*RICHMOND K TURNER	DLG 20	New York SB Corp	9 Jan 1961	6 Apr 1963	13 June 1964
*GRIDLEY	DLG 21	Puget Sound B & D Co	15 July 1960	31 July 1961	25 May 1963
*ENGLAND	DLG 22	Todd Shipyards Corp	4 Oct 1960	6 Mar 1962	7 Dec 1963
*HALSEY	DLG 23	San Francisco Naval Yard	26 Aug 1960	15 Jan 1962	20 July 1963
*REEVES	DLG 24	Fuget Sound Naval Yard	1 July 1960	12 May 1962	16 May 1964

HARRY E. YARNELL (DLG 17) *1972, Giorgio Arra*

GRIDLEY (DLG 21) *1970, United States Navy*

HARRY E. YARNELL (DLG 17) *1972, Giorgio Arra*

Surface Combatants—*continued*

10 GUIDED MISSILE FRIGATES (DLG): "COONTZ" CLASS

Displacement, tons	4 700 standard; 5 800 full load
Length, feet (*metres*)	512·5 (*156·2*) oa
Beam, feet (*metres*)	52·5 (*15·9*)
Draft, feet (*metres*)	25 (*7·6*)
Missile launchers	1 twin Terrier surface-to-air launcher (Mk 10 Mod 0)
Guns	1—5 inch (*127 mm*) 54 cal dual purpose
A/S weapons	1 ASROC 8-tube launcher 2 triple torpedo tubes (Mk 32)
Main engines	2 geared turbines; 85 000 shp; 2 shafts
Boilers	4 (Foster Wheeler in DLG 6-8; Babcock & Wilcox in DLG 9-15)
Speed, knots	34
Complement	377 (21 officers, 356 enlisted men)
Flag Staff	19 (7 officers, 12 enlisted men)

Name	*No.*	*Builder*	*Laid down*	*Launched*	*Commissioned*
*FARRAGUT	DLG 6	Bethlehem Co. Quincy	3 June 1957	18 July 1958	10 Dec 1960
*LUCE	DLG 7	Bethlehem Co. Quincy	1 Oct 1957	11 Dec 1958	20 May 1961
*MACDONOUGH	DLG 8	Bethlehem Co. Quincy	15 Apr 1958	9 July 1959	4 Nov 1961
*COONTZ	DLG 9	Puget Sound Naval Yard	1 Mar 1957	6 Dec 1958	15 July 1960
*KING	DLG 10	Puget Sound Naval Yard	1 Mar 1957	6 Dec 1958	17 Nov 1960
*MAHAN	DLG 11	San Francisco Naval Yard	31 July 1957	7 Oct 1959	25 Aug 1960
*DAHLGREN	DLG 12	Philadelphia Naval Yard	1 Mar 1958	16 Mar 1960	8 Apr 1961
*WILLIAM V PRATT	DLG 13	Philadelphia Naval Yard	1 Mar 1958	16 Mar 1960	4 Nov 1961
*DEWEY	DLG 14	Bath Iron Works, Maine	10 Aug 1957	30 Nov 1958	7 Dec 1959
*PREBLE	DLG 15	Bath Iron Works, Maine	16 Dec 1957	23 May 1959	9 May 1960

These ships are "single-end" missile frigates intended to screen fast carrier task forces. Their design is based on the "Mitscher" class (DL/DDG). The DLG 6-11 were authorised in the Fiscal Year 1956 shipbuilding programme; the DLG 12-15 in FY 1957 programme. Average cost per ship was $52 000 000.

CLASSIFICATION. The *Farragut*, *Luce* and *McDonough* initially were classified as DL 6-8, respectively; changed to DLG on 14 Nov 1956. These ships are known officially as the "Coontz" class as that ship was the first to be ordered as a DLG (DLG 9-11 ordered on 18 Nov 1955; DLG 6-8 ordered on 27 Jan 1956).

DESIGN. These ships are the only US guided missile "frigates" with separate masts and funnels. They have aluminium superstructures to reduce weight and improve stability. Early designs for this class had a second 5 inch gun mount in the "B" position; design revised when ASROC "pepper box" launcher was developed. Helicopter landing area on stern, but no hangar and limited support capability.

ELECTRONICS. The *King* and *Mahan* along with the aircraft carrier *Oriskany* (CVA 34) were the first ships fitted with the Naval Tactical Data System (NTDS), conducting operational evaluation of the equipment in 1961-1962.
As completed these ships had an SPS-10 and three-dimensional SPS-39 search radars on their forward mast, and an SPS-37 search radar and TACAN (Tactical Aircraft Navigation) "bee hive" antenna on second mast. Prior to AAW modernisation some ships had the SPS-39 replaced with the SPS-52 radar. During modernisation SPS-48 three-dimensional search radar fitted on the forward mast, an improved TACAN "pod" is fitted on the second mast, and NTDS installed. These ships have SQS-23 sonar.

The *Coontz* was fitted with the SSM-5 Test Evaluation and Monitoring System (TEAMS) in 1968 for operational evaluation of the electronic check-out system, subsequently removed. See *Knox* (DE 1052) for details.

ENGINEERING. De Laval turbines in DLG 6-8 and DLG 15; Allis-Chalmers turbines in DLG 9-14.

GUNNERY. These ships have Mk 42 single 5 inch guns. As built these ships also had two 3 inch 50 cal AA twin mounts amidships; removed during modernisation.
The *King* was used as a test ship for the 20 mm Vulcan/Phalanx Close-In Weapon System (CIWS) during 1973-1974.

MISSILES. The first five ships of this class were built with Terrier BW-1 beam-riding missile systems; five later ships built with Terrier BT-3 homing missile systems. See *Modernisation* notes for conversion of earlier ships to improved missile capability. Reportedly, each ship carries 40 missiles.

MODERNISATION. These ships were modernised between 1968 and 1975 to improve their Anti-Air Warfare (AAW) capabilities. Superstructure enlarged to provide space for additional electronic equipment, including NTDS (previously fitted in *King* and *Mahan*); improved TACAN installed, first five ships given improved guidance system for Terrier/Standard missiles (Mk 76 fire control system), and larger ship's service turbo generators fitted. The *Farragut* also had improved ASROC reload capability provided (with additional structure forward of bridge) and second mast increased in height.
All ships modernised at Philadelphia Naval Shipyard, except *Mahan* at Bath Iron Works, Bath, Maine, and *King* at Boland Machine & Manufacturing Co, New Orleans, Louisiana.
Cost of modernisation was $39 000 000 per ship in FY 1970 conversion programme.

NOMENCLATURE. The DLG 7 was to have been named *Dewey*, named *Luce* in 1957.

PHOTOGRAPHS. Note the separate mast and funnel structures compared to later US guided missile frigates. Subsequent DLG/DLGN designs have bow-mounted sonar and stem anchors.

PRATT (DLG 13) *1972, Giorgio Arra*

FARRAGUT (DLG 6) *1970, United States Navy, PHC F. W. Gotavco*

LUCE (DLG 7) *1971, United States Navy, D. V. Angelucci*

FRIGATES (DL)

The surviving all-gun frigates (DL) have been stricken. Of the "Mitscher" class, **Willis A. Lee** (DL 4) stricken on 15 May 1972; **Wilkinson** (DL 5) stricken on 1 May 1974. Two other ships of this class converted to guided missile destroyers (DDG). See 1973-1974 and previous editions for characteristics.
The one-of-a kind **Norfolk** (DL 1) stricken on 1 Nov 1973. See 1973-1974 and previous editions for characteristics.

Surface Combatants—*continued*

4 GUIDED MISSILE DESTROYERS (DDG): CONVERTED "FORREST SHERMAN" CLASS

Name	*No.*	*Builder*	*Laid down*	*Launched*	*DD Comm.*	*DDG Comm*
*DECATUR	DDG 31 (ex-DD 936)	Bethlehem Steel Co (Quincy)	13 Sep 1954	15 Dec 1955	7 Dec 1956	29 Apr 1967
*JOHN PAUL JONES	DDG 32 (ex-DD 932)	Bath Iron Works	18 Jan 1954	7 May 1955	5 Apr 1956	23 Sep 1967
*PARSONS	DDG 33 (ex-DD 949)	Ingalls Shipbuilding Corp	17 June 1957	19 Aug 1958	29 Oct 1959	3 Nov 1967
*SOMERS	DDG 34 (ex-DD 947)	Bath Iron Works	4 Mar 1957	30 May 1958	3 Apr 1959	10 Feb 1968

Displacement, tons	4 150 full load
Length, feet (*metres*)	
DDG 31-32	418·4 (*127·5*) oa
DDG 33-34	418 (*127·4*) oa
Beam, feet (*metres*)	
DDG 31-32	45·2 (*13·8*)
DDG 33-34	45 (*13·7*)
Draft, feet (*metres*)	20 (*6·1*)
Missile launchers	1 single Tartar surface-to-air launcher (Mk 13 Mod 1)
Guns	1—5 inch (*127 mm*) 54 calibre dual-purpose
A/S weapons	1 ASROC 8-tube launcher 2 triple torpedo tubes (Mk 32)
Main engines	2 geared turbines (Westinghouse in *John Paul Jones*; General Electric in others); 70 000 shp; 2 shafts
Boilers	4 (Foster Wheeler in *Decatur* and *Parsons*; Babcock & Wilcox in *John Paul Jones* and *Somers*)
Speed	33 knots
Complement	335 (22 officers, 313 enlisted men)

These four ships are former "Forrest Sherman" class destroyers that have been converted to a guided missile and improved ASW configuration. Plans for additional DDG conversions of this class were dropped (the *Turner Joy*, DD 951, was to have been the fifth missile ship of this type). The *Decatur* was reclassified as DDG 31 on 15 Sep 1966; the *John Paul Jones*, *Somers*, and *Parsons* became DDG on 15 Mar 1967. See "Forrest Sherman" class for additional notes.

CONVERSION. The *Decatur* began conversion to a DDG at the Boston Naval Shipyard on 15 June 1965, the *John Paul Jones* at the Philadelphia Naval Shipyard on 2 Dec 1965, the *Parsons* at the Long Beach (California) Naval Shipyard on 30 June 1965, and the *Somers* at the San Francisco Bay Naval Shipyard on 30 Mar 1966.
During conversion all existing armament was removed except the forward 5 inch gun; two triple ASW torpedo tubes were installed forward of the bridge; two heavy lattice masts fitted; ASROC launcher mounted aft of second stack; single Tartar Mk 13 launcher installed aft (on 01 level; system weighs approximately 135 000 pounds).
Original DDG conversion plans provided for Drone Anti-Submarine Helicopter (DASH) facilities; however, ASROC was substituted in all four ships as DASH lost favour in the Navy.

ELECTRONICS. SQS-23 sonar installed. SPS-10 and SPS-37 search radars on forward mast except *Somers* has SPS-40 in lieu of SPS-37; all have SPS-48 three-dimensional search radar on after mast.

GUNNERY. The original Mk 42 forward gun mount has been replaced by a modified Mk 42 mount with the local anti-aircraft control deleted (starboard "bubble" or "frog-eye" on mount removed; port dome is for local anti-surface control).

These are the only US destroyers with one 5 inch gun.

MISSILES. Reportedly Tartar magazine capacity is 40 missiles.

NOMENCLATURE. The *John Paul Jones* honours the Scottish-born father of the American Navy who later served as a rear-admiral in the Russian Navy (1788).

DECATUR (DDG 31) *1972, United States Navy, PH3 D. L. Pierce*

PARSONS (DDG 33) *1968, United States Navy*

PARSONS (DDG 33) *1972, United States Navy*

Surface Combatants—*continued*

23 GUIDED MISSILE DESTROYERS (DDG): "CHARLES F. ADAMS" CLASS

Displacement, tons	3 370 standard; 4 500 full load
Length, feet (*metres*)	437 (*132·8*) oa
Beam, feet (*metres*)	47 (*14·3*)
Draft, feet (*metres*)	20 (*6·1*)
Missile launchers	
DDG 2-14	1 twin Tartar surface-to-air launcher (Mk 11 Mod 0)
DDG 15-24	1 single Tartar surface-to-air launcher (Mk 13 Mod 0)
DDG 4 and 13	1 multiple launcher for Chaparral (see *Missile* notes)
Guns	2—5 inch (*127 mm*) 54 calibre DP (single)
A/S weapons	1 ASROC 8-tube launcher 2 triple torpedo tubes (Mk 32)
Main engines	2 geared steam turbines (General Electric in DDG 2, 3, 7, 8, 10-13, 15-22; Westinghouse in DDG 4-6, 9, 14, 23, 24,); 70 000 shp; 2 shafts
Boilers	4 (Babcock & Wilcox in DDG2, 3, 7, 8, 10-13, 20-22; Foster Wheeler in DDG 4-6, 9, 14; Combustion Engineering in DDG 15-19)
Speed, knots	35
Complement	354 (24 officers, 330 enlisted men).

Name	*No.*	*Builder*	*Laid down*	*Launched*	*Commissioned*
*CHARLES F. ADAMS	DDG 2	Bath Iron Works	16 June 1958	8 Sep 1959	10 Sep 1960
*JOHN KING	DDG 3	Bath Iron Works	25 Aug 1958	30 Jan 1960	4 Feb 1961
*LAWRENCE	DDG 4	New York Shipbuilding Corp	27 Oct 1958	27 Feb 1960	6 Jan 1962
*CLAUDE V. RICKETTS	DDG 5	New York Shipbuilding Corp	18 May 1959	4 June 1960	6 Jan 1962
*BARNEY	DDG 6	New York Shipbuilding Corp	18 May 1959	10 Dec 1960	11 Aug 1962
*HENRY B. WILSON	DDG 7	Defoe Shipbuilding Co	28 Feb 1958	23 Apr 1959	17 Dec 1960
*LYNDE McCORMICK	DDG 8	Defoe Shipbuilding Co	4 Apr 1958	9 Sep 1960	3 June 1961
*TOWERS	DDG 9	Todd Shipyards Inc, Seattle	1 Apr 1958	23 Apr 1959	6 June 1961
*SAMPSON	DDG 10	Bath Iron Works	2 Mar 1959	9 Sep 1960	24 June 1961
*SELLERS	DDG 11	Bath Iron Works	3 Aug 1959	9 Sep 1960	28 Oct 1961
*ROBISON	DDG 12	Defoe Shipbuilding Co	23 Apr 1959	27 Apr 1960	9 Dec 1961
*HOEL	DDG 13	Defoe Shipbuilding Co	1 June 1960	4 Aug 1960	16 June 1962
*BUCHANAN	DDG 14	Todd Shipyards Inc, Seattle	23 Apr 1959	11 May 1960	7 Feb 1962
*BERKELEY	DDG 15	New York Shipbuilding Corp	1 June 1960	29 July 1961	15 Dec 1962
*JOSEPH STRAUSS	DDG 16	New York Shipbuilding Corp	27 Dec 1960	9 Dec 1961	20 Apr 1963
*CONYNGHAM	DDG 17	New York Shipbuilding Corp	1 May 1961	19 May 1962	13 July 1963
*SEMMES	DDG 18	Avondale Marine Ways Inc	18 Aug 1960	20 May 1961	10 Dec 1962
*TATTNALL	DDG 19	Avondale Marine Ways Inc	14 Nov 1960	26 Aug 1961	13 Apr 1963
*GOLDSBOROUGH	DDG 20	Puget Sound B & DD Co	3 Jan 1961	15 Dec 1961	9 Nov 1963
*COCHRANE	DDG 21	Puget Sound B & DD Co	31 July 1961	18 July 1962	21 Mar 1964
*BENJAMIN STODDERT	DDG 22	Puget Sound B & DD Co	11 June 1962	8 Jan 1963	12 Sep 1964
*RICHARD E. BYRD	DDG 23	Todd Shipyards Inc, Seattle	12 Apr 1961	6 Feb 1962	7 Mar 1964
*WADDELL	DDG 24	Todd Shipyards Inc, Seattle	6 Feb 1962	26 Feb 1963	28 Aug 1964

These destroyers are considered excellent multi-purpose ships. The DDG 2-9 were authorised in the Fiscal Year 1957 new construction programme, DDG 10-14 in FY 1958, DDG 15-19 in FY 1959, DDG 20-22 in FY 1960, DDG 23 and DDG 24 in FY 1961. Three additional ships of this design have been built in US shipyards for Australia (DDG 25-27) and three for West Germany (DDG 28-30).

CLASSIFICATION. **The first eight ships were initially assigned hull numbers in the standard DD series (DDG 952-959); renumbered while under construction. The DDG 1 was the *Gyatt* (ex-DD 712), which operated as a missile destroyer from 1956 to 1962; armed with a twin Terrier launcher.**

DESIGN. **These ships were built to an improved "Forrest Sherman" class design with aluminium superstructures and a high level of habitability including air conditioning in all living spaces. They do not have the second radar trellis mast nor secondary gun battery of the earlier class. DDG 20-24 have stem anchors because of sonar arrangements.**

Several ships have been modified with an extension of the bridge structure on the starboard side on the 02 level, providing additional space for storage.

BARNEY (DDG 6) *1971, United States Navy*

ELECTRONICS. DDG 20-24 have bow-mounted SQS-23 sonar; earlier ships have SQS-23 sonar with hull domes.
DDG 2-14 have SPS-37 and SPS-10 search radars on tripod mast; DDG 15-24 have SPS-40 and SPS-10. All ships apparently being fitted with antenna associated with SPS-52 radar, but the ships retain SPS-39 system (three-dimensional search antenna on second stack); these ships were completed with SPS-39 radar antenna aft.
Mk-74 guided missile fire control system is provided. The *Towers* is the first US Navy ship to be fitted with the Ship Anti-Missile Integrated Defence (SAMID) to counter the Soviet cruise missile threat (Styx, etc); this system integrates existing electronic equipment and weapons to reduce reaction time when under attack. Also fitted with chaff rockets (CHAFFROC).

GUNNERY. **These ships have rapid-fire Mk 42 guns. The *Charles F. Adams* has modified mounts with local anti-aircraft controls deleted (starboard "bubble" or "frog-eye" on mounts removed; port dome is for local anti-surface control).**

CONYNGHAM (DDG 17) ***1971, US Navy, PH1 Robert L. Varney***

RICHARD E. BYRD (DDG 23) ***1970, Anthony & Joseph Pavia***

Surface Combatants—*continued*

"C.F. ADAMS" CLASS *continued*

MISSILES. The DDG 2-14 have a twin Mk 11 Tartar missile launcher while the DDG 15-24 have a single Mk 13 Tartar launcher. The Mk 11 launcher installation weighs 165 240 pounds while the Mk 13 weighs only 132 561 pounds. Reportedly, their magazine capacities are 42 and 40 missiles, respectively, and ships equipped with either launcher can load, direct, and fire about six missiles per minute. (The twin Mk 11 launcher is installed in the cruisers CG 10-12; the "Mitscher" and "Forrest Sherman" DDG conversions have a similar Mk 13 launcher which weighs approximately 135 000 pounds.)

***Lawrence* and *Hoel* fitted in 1972-1973 with multiple launcher for Chaparral (MIM-72A) and other point-defence missiles in addition to their Tartar launcher.**

NOMENCLATURE. The DDG 5 was originally named *Biddle*; renamed *Claude V. Ricketts* on 28 July 1964 to honour the late Vice Chief of Naval Operations who had supported multi-national NATO manning of ballistic missile surface ships. (The name *Biddle* subsequently was assigned to the DLG 34.) The DDG 23 honours the famed polar explorer and naval aviator.

PHOTOGRAPHS. Note difference in radars on tripod mast and missile launchers on DDG 2-14 and DDG 15-24 series of this class. The *Buchanan*, below, has only one missile on her twin Tartar launcher.

SELLERS (DDG 11) *1972, Giorgio Arra*

RICHARD E. BYRD (DDG 23) *1973, Giorgio Arra*

BUCHANAN (DDG 14) *United States Navy*

RICHARD S. EDWARDS (DD 950)—see subsequent page ("Forrest Sherman" class) *United States Navy*

Surface Combatants—*continued*

23 + 7 DESTROYERS (DD): "SPRUANCE" CLASS

Name	*No.*	*Start Erection*	*Launch*	*Commission*
SPRUANCE	DD 963	17 Nov 1972	10 Nov 1973	Oct 1974
PAUL F. FOSTER	DD 964	6 Feb 1973	23 Feb 1974	Apr 1975
KINCAID	DD 965	19 Apr 1973	20 Apr 1974	June 1975
HEWITT	DD 966	23 July 1973	July 1974	July 1975
ELLIOTT	DD 967	15 Oct 1973	Sep 1974	Oct 1975
ARTHUR W. RADFORD	DD 968	14 Jan 1974	Dec 1974	1976
PETERSON	**DD 969**	1 Apr 1974	1975	1976
	DD 970	July 1974	1975	1976
	DD 971	Aug 1974	1975	1976
	DD 972	Nov 1974	1975	1976
	DD 973	Jan 1975	1975	9176
5 ships	**DD 974-978**	1975	1976	1977
7 ships	**DD 979-985**			1978
7 ships	**DD 986-992**	Proposed FY 1975 programme		

Displacement, tons	7 800 full load
Length, feet (*metres*)	529 (*161·2*) wl; 563·3 (*171·1*) oa
Beam, feet (*metres*)	55 (*17·6*)
Draft, feet (*metres*)	29 (*8·8*)
Guns	2—5 inch (*127 mm*) 54 calibre DP (Mk 45) (single)
Missile launchers	1 NATO Sea Sparrow multiple launcher
A/S weapons	1 SH-2 or SH-3 LAMPS helicopter 1 ASROC 8-tube launcher 2 triple torpedo tubes (Mk 32)
Main engines	4 gas turbines (General Electric); 80 000 shp; 2 shafts
Speed, knots	30+
Complement	approx 250 (18 officers, 232 enlisted men)

SPRUANCE (DD 963) *1973, Litton Industries*

These ships were intended as replacements for the large number of World War II-built destroyers that have undergone extensive modernisation (FRAM) to enable them to serve into the 1970s. According to official statements: "The primary mission of these ships is anti-submarine warfare including operations as an integral part of attack carrier task forces. They also have the capability for shore bombardment and for surface warfare, and will have short range missiles for defense against airborne threats, including enemy missiles. Their effectiveness against submarines is expected to be far greater, particularly at high speeds, than that of current Navy ships due to ship silencing techniques and improved sea-keeping capabilities."

The Fiscal Year 1969 new construction programme proposed by the Department of Defense requested funding for the first five ships of this class; however; funds were denied by the Congress because of the design status. In the FY 1970 programme the Congress approved funds for five ships, but increasing costs forced the Department of Defense to construct only three ships under the FY 1970 programme (DD 963-965); six ships were authorised in the FY 1971 programme (DD 966-971); seven ships (DD 972-978) in the FY 1972 programme; and seven ships (DD 979-985) in the FY 1974 programme. The final seven ships were requested in the FY 1975 budget.

These ships have been the subject of severe criticism because of their large size and limited anti-air/anti-ship capabilities. They are believed to be the largest surface warships of contemporary design except for aircraft carriers which do not have a major surface-to-air missile system.

The Iranian Navy has ordered two additional ships of the "Spruance" class, which would be completed in the late 1970s. The Iranian ships reportedly will be armed with launchers for Standard surface-to-air and surface-to-surface missiles.

CONSTRUCTION. All ships of this class are being constructed by the Litton Ship Systems Division of Litton Industries in Pascagoula, Mississippi. The "production facility" is a new shipyard which launched its first ship (a commercial freighter) in 1971. Advanced production techniques including modular assembly of large ship components is featured. A contract for the development and production of the entire DD 963 class was awarded to Litton on 23 June 1970; that award also provided go-ahead for the first three ships.

CLASSIFICATION. During the early proposal stage these ships were designated as the DX project, the letter "X" signifying that the characteristics were not fully defined.

DESIGN. Extensive use of the modular concept is used to facilitate initial construction and bloc modernisation of the ships.

The ships will be highly automated, resulting in about 20 per cent reduction in personnel over a similar ship with conventional systems.

ELECTRONICS. These ships will have SQS-26 sonar and will be the first US warships with a completely digital command and control system, which will reduce complexity and speed up production. (Most existing systems have a mixture of digital and analog components.)

To be fitted with SPS-40A and SPS-55 radars, SQS-26CX sonar, and Mk 116 underwater fire control system. Advanced electronic countermeasure (ECM) equipment. Provision in stern for eventual installation of SQS-35 Independent Variable Depth Sonar (IVDS).

Fire control system for guns is Mk 86.

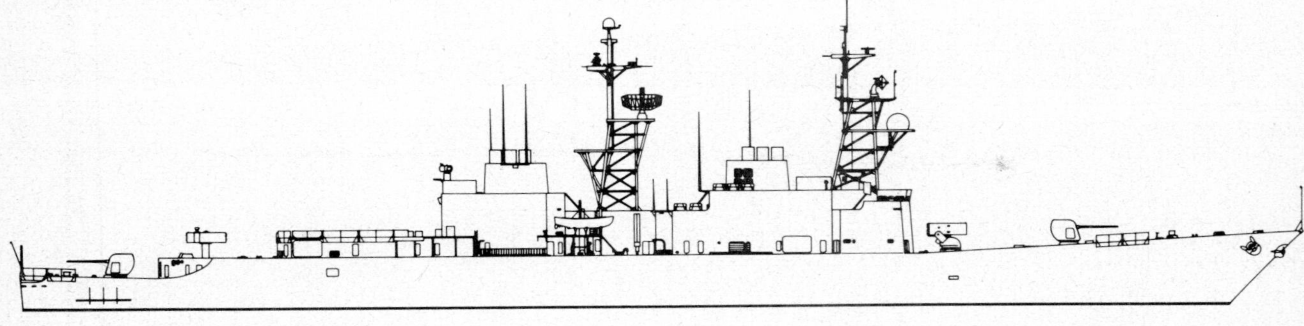

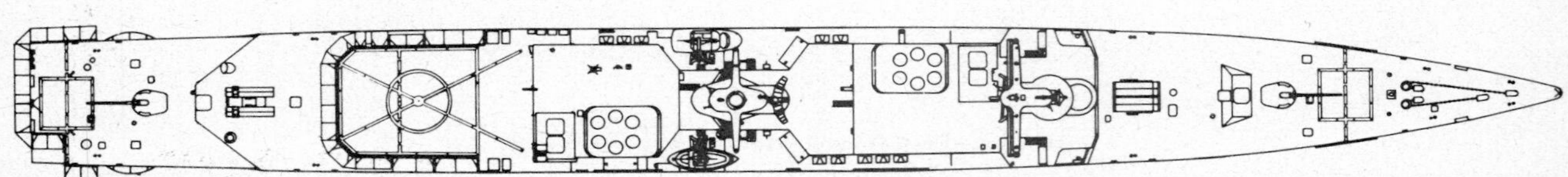

SPRUANCE (DD 963)

Surface Combatants—*continued*

"SPRUANCE" CLASS —*continued*

ENGINEERING. These ships will be the first large US warships to employ gas turbine propulsion. Each ship will have four General Electric LM2500 marine gas turbine engines, a shaft-power version of the TF39 turbofan aircraft engine. The LM2500 is rated at approximately 20 000 horsepower. The gas turbine was selected because of comparatively low operating costs, smaller space requirements, rapid replacement capability, and cold-start capability (the engines can go from "cold iron" to full power in 12 minutes).
These ships will have controllable-pitch propellers because gas turbine engines cannot use a reversible shaft; to be fitted with advanced self-noise reduction features.
During normal operations these ships will "steam" on two engines, going to three and then four engines for higher speeds. Range is estimated at 6 000 miles at 20 knots.

As designed these ships have provision in stern for installation of SQS-35 Independent Variable Depth Sonar (IVDS); however, success of bow-mounted SQS-53 sonar has alleviated need for the second sonar system.

FISCAL. The proposed FY 1973 defence budget requested $612 000 000 for the DD 979-985 (seven ships). Only $247 000 000 was approved in FY 1973 for long-lead time components. The FY 1974 budget provided $590 900 000 to complete funding of the ships.
The average cost per ship of this class is officially estimated at $85 000 000, but more likely will be in excess of $100 000 000 per ship. See 1971-1972 edition for additional fiscal data.

GUNNERY. These ships have the 5 inch 54 calibre, light-weight Mk 45 gun which has a limited rate-of-fire (approx 20 rounds-per-minute) but reduced manning requirements. An improved 5 inch 54 calibre Mk 65 gun is being considered for use in later ships of the class. Also, an 8 inch light-weight gun intended primarily for shore bombardment may be developed for installation in a few of these ships.
The 20 mm Vulcan/Phalanx rapid-fire Close-In Weapon System (CIWS) probably will be installed in these ships as a terminal defence against cruise missile attack.

HELICOPTERS. Full helicopter facilities are provided to accommodate the Light Airborne Multi-Purpose System (LAMPS), now the SH-2D helicopter. However, the ship can handle the larger SH-3 Sea King series.

NOMENCLATURE. The *Spruance* is named for Admiral Raymond A. Spruance, who had tactical command of the US carriers in the Battle of Midway (June 1942) and of the US fleet in the Battle of the Marianas (June 1944), two of the major engagements of the Pacific War. He also was considered one of the leading intellectuals of the US Navy.

PHOTOGRAPHS. The accompanying Litton artist's concept shows a 20 mm CIWS installed on the starboard side of the bridge structure; another is indicated on top of the helicopter hangar. An earlier artist's concept appears in the 1973-1974 and previous edition. The stern configuration of later ships differ.

SPRUANCE (DD 963) *Litton artist's concept*

SPRUANCE (DD 963) at launching *1973, Litton Industries*

SPRUANCE (DD 963) *1973, Litton Industries*

Surface Combatants—*continued*

14 DESTROYERS (DD) "FORREST SHERMAN" CLASS

Displacement, tons	approx 2 800 standard approx 4 050 standard
Length, feet (*metres*)	
DD 931-944	418·4 (*127·5*) oa
except DD 933	425
DD 945-951	418 (*127·4*) oa
Beam, feet (*metres*)	
DD 931-944	45·2 (*13·8*)
DD 945-951	45 (*13·7*)
Draft, feet (*metres*)	20 (*6·1*)
Guns A/S Mod	2—5 in (127 *mm*) 54 calibre dual-purpose (single)
Others	3—5 in (*127 mm*) 54 calibre dual-purpose (single) 2—3 in (*76 mm*) 50 calibre anti-aircraft (twin) in DD 931, 944, 945, 946
A/S weapons	
A/S Mod	1 ASROC 8-tube launcher 2 triple torpedo tubes (Mk 32)
Others	2 hedgehogs; depth charges retained in a few ships 2 triple torpedo tubes (Mk 32)
Main engines	2 geared turbines (Westinghouse in DD 931 and 933; General Electric in others); 70 000 shp; 2 shafts
Boilers	4 (Babcock & Wilcox in DD 931 and 933, 940-942, 945, 946, 950, 951; Foster Wheeler in others)
Speed	33 knots
Complement	292 (17 officers, 275 enlisted men) in unmodified ships; 304 in A/S Mod ships (17 officers, 287 enlisted men)

Name	*No*	*Builder*	*Laid down*	*Launched*	*Commissioned*
***FORREST SHERMAN**	DD 931	Bath Iron Works	27 Oct 1953	5 Feb 1955	9 Nov 1955
***BIGELOW**	DD 942	Bath Iron Works	6 July 1955	2 Feb 1957	8 Nov 1957
***MULLINNIX**	DD 944	Bethlehem Steel Co (Quincy)	5 Apr 1956	18 Mar 1957	7 Mar 1958
***HULL**	DD 945	Bath Iron Works	12 Sep 1956	10 Aug 1957	3 July 1958
***EDSON**	DD 946	Bath Iron Works	3 Dec 1956	1 Jan 1958	7 Nov 1958
***TURNER JOY**	DD 951	Puget Sound Bridge & DD	30 Sep 1957	5 May 1958	3 Aug 1959
		ANTI-SUBMARINE MODIFIED			
***BARRY**	DD 933	Bath Iron Works	15 Mar 1954	1 Oct 1955	31 Aug 1956
***DAVIS**	DD 937	Bethlehem Steel Co (Quincy)	1 Feb 1955	28 Mar 1956	28 Feb 1957
***JONAS INGRAM**	DD 938	Bethlehem Steel Co (Quincy)	15 June 1955	8 July 1956	19 July 1957
***MANLEY**	DD 940	Bath Iron Works	10 Feb 1955	12 Apr 1956	1 Feb 1957
***DU PONT**	DD 941	Bath Iron Works	11 May 1955	8 Sep 1956	1 July 1957
***BLANDY**	DD 943	Bethlehem Steel Co (Quincy)	29 Dec 1955	19 Dec 1956	26 Nov 1957
***MORTON**	DD 948	Ingalls Shipbuilding Corp	4 Mar 1957	23 May 1958	26 May 1959
***RICHARD S. EDWARDS**	DD 950	Puget Sound Bridge & DD	20 Dec 1956	24 Sep 1957	5 Feb 1959

These ships were the first US destroyers of post-World War II design and construction. Four have been converted to a guided missile configuration and are listed separately. They were authorised in the Fiscal Year 1952-1956 new construction programmes. These ships each cost approximately $26 000 000.
All of these ships are active.

ARMAMENT. As built all 18 ships of this class had three single 5 inch guns, two twin 3 inch mounts, four fixed 21 inch ASW torpedo tubes (amidships); two ASW hedgehogs (forward of bridge), and depth charge racks.

DESIGN. The entire superstructures of these ships are of aluminium to obtain maximum stability with minimum displacement. All living spaces are air conditioned. The *Decatur* and later ships have higher bows; the *Hull* and later ships have slightly different bow designs. The *Barry* had her sonar dome moved forward in 1959 and a stem anchor fitted.

ELECTRONICS. SQS-23 sonar installed with the *Barry* being the first US warship fitted with bow mounted sonar. Variable depth sonar installed on stern of A/S modified ships.
All of these ships have an SPS-10 search radar antenna and most also have SPS-40 (DD 933, 937, 940, 942, and 946 have SPS-37, and DD 944 retains older SPS-12). Several of the unmodified ships have elaborate electronic warfare electronic pods on the after mast (see photograph of *Hull*). (Correction to previous edition).

BARRY (DD 933) *1972, United States Navy*

GUNNERY. With original armament of one 5 inch mount forward and two 5 inch mounts aft, these were the first US warships with more firepower aft than forward. Note that *Barry* and later ships have their Mk 68 gunfire control director forward and Mk 56 director aft; positions reversed in earlier ships.

MODERNISATION. Eight ships of this class were extensively modified in 1967-1971 to improve their anti-submarine capabilities: *Barry, Davis, Du Pont* at the Boston Naval Shipyard; *Jonas Ingram, Manley, Blandy* at the Philadelphia Naval Shipyard; and *Morton, Richard S. Edwards* at the Long Beach (California) Naval Shipyard. During modernisation the anti-submarine torpedo tubes installed forward of bridge (on 01 level), deckhouse aft of second funnel extended to full width of ship, ASROC launcher installed in place of after gun mounts on 01 level, and variable depth sonar fitted at stern. Six ships of this class were not provided improved A/S capabilities because of increased costs.

During 1974 the *Hull* was experimentally fitted with an 8 inch gun forward to determine feasibility of installing a Major Calibre Light Weight Gun (MCLWG) in destroyer-type ship for shore bombardment.

PHOTOGRAPHS. Compare electronic pods on after masts of *Manley* and *Hull*. The latter ship is one of the Pacific Fleet "Sherman" class destroyers that retained hedgehogs forward of bridge and depth charge racks on stern late into their careers; she also has twin 3 inch gun mount between after funnel and after 5 inch gun battery.

MANLEY (DD 940) *1973, Giorgio Arra*

HULL (DD 945) *1971, United States Navy, PH1 B. L. Kuykendall*

Surface Combatants—*continued*

54 DESTROYERS (DD): MODERNISED "GEARING" CLASS (FRAM I)

Displacement, tons	2 425 standard; 3 480 to 3 520 full load
Length, feet (*metres*)	390·5 (*119·0*) oa
Beam, feet (*metres*)	40·9 (*12·4*)
Draft, feet (*metres*)	19 (*5·8*)
Guns	4—5 inch (*127 mm*) 38 calibre DP (twin)
A/S weapons	1 ASROC 8-tube launcher 2 triple torpedo tubes (Mk 32) facilities for small helicopter
Main engines	2 geared turbines (General Electric or Westinghouse); 60 000 shp 2 shafts
Boilers	4 (Babcock & Wilcox or combination Babcock & Wilcox and Foster-Wheeler)
Speed, knots	34
Complement	274 (14 officers, 260 enlisted men) 305 in Naval Reserve training ships (12 officers, 176 enlisted active duty; 5 officers, 112 enlisted reserve)

Name	*No.*	*Builder*	*Launched*	*Commissioned*
*WILLIAM R. RUSH (NRF)	DD 714	Federal SB & DD Co	8 July 1945	21 Sep 1945
*WILLIAM M. WOOD	DD 715	Federal SB & DD Co	29 July 1945	24 Nov 1945
*WILTSIE	DD 716	Federal SB & DD Co	31 Aug 1945	12 Jan 1946
*THEODORE E. CHANDLER (NRF)	DD 717	Federal SB & DD Co	20 Oct 1945	22 Mar 1946
*HAMNER (NRF)	DD 718	Federal SB & DD Co	24 Nov 1945	11 July 1946
*EPPERSON (NRF)	DD 719	Federal SB & DD Co	22 Dec 1945	19 Mar 1949
*SOUTHERLAND (NRF)	DD 743	Bath Iron Works Corp	5 Oct 1944	22 Dec 1944
*WILLIAM C. LAWE (NRF)	DD 763	Bethlehem (San Francisco)	21 May 1945	18 Dec 1946
*ROWAN	DD 782	Todd Pacific Shipyards	29 Dec 1944	31 Mar 1945
*GURKE	DD 783	Todd Pacific Shipyards	15 Feb 1945	12 May 1945
*McKEAN (NRF)	DD 784	Todd Pacific Shipyards	31 Mar 1945	9 June 1945
*HENDERSON (NRF)	DD 785	Todd Pacific Shipyards	28 May 1945	4 Aug 1945
*RICHARD B. ANDERSON	DD 786	Todd Pacific Shipyards	7 July 1945	26 Oct 1945
*HOLLISTER (NRF)	DD 788	Todd Pacific Shipyards	9 Oct 1945	26 Mar 1946
*HIGBEE (NRF)	DD 806	Bath Iron Works Corp	12 Nov 1944	27 Jan 1945
*CORRY (NRF)	DD 817	Consolidated Steel Corp	28 July 1945	26 Feb 1946
*NEW	DD 818	Consolidated Steel Corp	18 Aug 1945	5 Apr 1946
*HOLDER (NRF)	DD 819	Consolidated Steel Corp	25 Aug 1945	18 May 1946
*RICH (NRF)	DD 820	Consolidated Steel Corp	5 Oct 1945	4 July 1946
*JOHNSTON (NRF)	DD 821	Consolidated Steel Corp	19 Oct 1945	10 Oct 1945
*ROBERT H. McCARD (NRF)	DD 822	Consolidated Steel Corp	9 Nov 1945	26 Oct 1946
*BASILONE	DD 824	Consolidated Steel Corp	21 Dec 1945	26 July 1949
*AGERHOLM	DD 826	Bath Iron Works Corp	30 Mar 1946	20 June 1946
*MYLES C. FOX (NRF)	DD 829	Bath Iron Works Corp	13 Jan 1945	20 Mar 1945
*CHARLES P. CECIL (NRF)	DD 835	Bath Iron Works Corp	22 Apr 1945	29 June 1945
*GEORGE K. MacKENZIE	DD 836	Bath Iron Works Corp	13 May 1945	13 July 1945
*SARSFIELD	DD 837	Bath Iron Works Corp	27 May 1945	31 July 1945
*POWER (NRF)	DD 839	Bath Iron Works Corp	30 June 1945	13 Sep 1945
*GLENNON	DD 840	Bath Iron Works Corp	14 July 1945	4 Oct 1945
*FISKE (NRF)	DD 842	Bath Iron Works Corp	8 Sep 1945	28 Nov 1945
*BAUSELL	DD 845	Bath Iron Works Corp	19 Nov 1945	7 Feb 1947
*OZBOURN (NRF)	DD 846	Bath Iron Works Corp	22 Dec 1945	5 Mar 1946
*ROBERT L. WILSON (NRF)	DD 847	Bath Iron Works Corp	5 Jan 1946	28 Mar 1946
*RICHARD E. KRAUS (ex-AG 151)	DD 849	Bath Iron Works Corp	2 Mar 1946	23 May 1946
*LEONARD F. MASON	DD 852	Bethlehem (Quincy)	4 Jan 1946	28 June 1946
*VOGELGESANG (NRF)	DD 862	Bethlehem (Staten Island)	15 Jan 1945	28 Apr 1945
*STEINAKER (NRF)	DD 863	Bethlehem (Staten Island)	13 Feb 1945	26 May 1945
*HAROLD J. ELLISON (NRF)	DD 864	Bethlehem (Staten Island)	14 Mar 1945	23 June 1945
CHARLES R. WARE (NRF)	DD 865	Bethlehem (Staten Island)	12 Apr 1945	21 July 1945
*CONE (NRF)	DD 866	Bethlehem (Staten Island)	10 May 1945	18 Aug 1945
*STRIBLING	DD 867	Bethlehem (Staten Island)	8 June 1945	29 Sep 1945
*BROWNSON	DD 868	Bethlehem (Staten Island)	15 Mar 1945	17 Nov 1945
*DAMATO (NRF)	DD 871	Bethlehem (Staten Island)	21 Nov 1945	27 Apr 1946
*HAWKINS	DD 873	Consolidated Steel Corp	7 Oct 1944	10 Feb 1945
*ROGERS (NRF)	DD 876	Consolidated Steel Corp	20 Nov 1944	26 Mar 1945
*VESOLE	DD 878	Consolidated Steel Corp	29 Dec 1944	23 Apr 1945
*DYESS (NRF)	DD 880	Consolidated Steel Corp	26 Jan 1945	21 May 1945
*BORDELON	DD 881	Consolidated Steel Corp	3 Mar 1945	5 June 1945
*NEWMAN K. PERRY (NRF)	DD 883	Consolidated Steel Corp	17 Mar 1945	26 July 1945
*JOHN R. CRAIG (NRF)	DD 885	Consolidated Steel Corp	14 Apr 1945	20 Aug 1945
*ORLECK (NRF)	DD 886	Consolidated Steel Corp	12 May 1945	15 Sep 1945
*MEREDITH (NRF)	DD 890	Consolidated Steel Corp	28 June 1945	31 Dec 1945

These ships are enlarged versions of the "Allen M. Sumner" class with an additional 14-foot section amidships for additional fuel tanks. All of the above listed ships have been extensively modernised under the FRAM I programme (see *Modernisation* notes). The *Richard E. Kraus* (ex-AG 151) and *Sarsfield* are used for experimental work (EDD). (The former ship was designated AG 151 from 24 Aug 1949 to 11 Dec 1953). The "Gearing" class initially covered hull numbers DD 710-721, 742, 743, 763-769, 782-791, 805-926. Forty-nine of these ships were cancelled in 1945 (DD 768, 769, 809-816, 854-856, and 891-926); four ships were never completed and were scrapped in the 1950s: *Castle* (DD 720), *Woodrow R. Thompson* (DD 721), *Lansdale* (DD 766), and *Seymour D. Owens* (DD 767).

After World War II several "Gearing" class destroyers were completed to specialised anti-submarine configurations (DDK "hunter-killer"); other ships were converted to escort (DDE) and radar picket (DDR) configurations. Subsequently all surviving ships modernised under FRAM I and FRAM II programmes.

All surviving ships of this class are active. Thirty-four ships are assigned to Naval Reserve training and are manned by composite active duty-reserve crews. These ships are noted as NRF (Naval Reserve Force).

ARMAMENT-DESIGN. As built these ships had a pole mast and carried an armament of six 5 inch guns (twin mounts), 12 40 mm AA guns (2 quad, 2 twin), 11 20 mm AA guns (single), and 10 21 inch torpedo tubes (quin). After World War II the after bank of tubes was replaced by an additional quad 40 mm mount. All 40 mm and 20 mm guns were replaced subsequently by six 3 inch guns (2 twin, 2 single) and a tripod mast was installed to support heavier radar antennas. The 3 inch guns and remaining torpedo tubes were removed during FRAM conversion.

ELECTRONICS. These ships have SPS-10 and SPS-40 or SPS-37 search radars on their forward tripod mast; advanced electronic warfare equipment fitted to most ships with an enlarged electronic "stack" atop the helicopter hangar-ASROC magazine structure. Fitted with SQS-23 sonar. *Brownson* fitted with SQQ-23 (modified SQS-23) for evaluation.

ENGINEERING. Range is 5 800 miles at 15 knots.

HELICOPTERS. These ships no longer operate drone helicopters, but rely on ASROC and tube-launched torpedoes for anti-submarine weapons. They had been fitted to operate the Drone Anti-Submarine Helicopter (DASH) during FRAM modernisation.

MODERNISATION. All of these ships have undergone extensive modernisation under the Fleet Rehabilitation and Modernisation (FRAM I) programme. They were stripped of all armament except two 5 inch mounts, new anti-submarine weapons were installed including facilities for operating ASW helicopters, new electronic equipment was installed, machinery was overhauled, living and working spaces were rehabilitated. For budgeting reasons FRAM I work was officially considered a "conversion". The *Perry* was the first ship to undergo FRAM I conversion, the work being accomplished at the Boston Naval Shipyard from May 1959 to April 1960, her FRAM I cost an estimated $7 700 000.

There are two basic FRAM I configurations: the DD 786, 790, 826, 841, 844, 845, 847, and 890 (eight ships)6 have twin 5 inch mounts in "A" and "B" positions and Mk 32 torpedo launchers abaft second funnel; others have twin 5 inch mounts in "A" and "Y" positions and Mk 32 launchers on 01 level in "B" position.

The *Herbert J. Thomas* was additionally modified for protection against biological, chemical, and atomic attack; the ship is fully "sealed" with enclosed lookout and control positions, special air conditioning provisions, *et cetera*. (Modified at Mare Island Naval Shipyard from July 1963 to July 1964.)

POWER (DD 839) — *1973, Giorgio Arra*

SARSFIELD (DD 837) — *1973, Giorgio Arra*

Surface Combatants—*continued*

"GEARING" CLASS FRAM I—*continued*

DISPOSALS AND TRANSFERS (since 1 Jan 1970) **Fechteler** (DD 870) stricken on 11 Sep 1970; **Samuel B. Roberts** (DD 823) stricken on 2 Nov 1970; **Forrest Royal** (DD 872) transferred to Turkey on 27 Mar 1971; **Stickell** (DD 888) transferred to Greece on 1 July 1972; **Eugene A. Greene** (DD 711), **Furse** (DD 882) transferred to Spain on 31 Aug 1972; **Warrington** (DD 843) stricken on 1 Oct 1972; **Shelton** (DD 790) transferred to Spain on 15 Mar 1973; **James E. Kyes** (DD 787), **Hanson** (DD 832) to Spain on 31 Mar 1973; **Gearing** (DD 710), **Dennis J. Buckley** (DD 808), **Perry** (DD 844), **Joseph P. Kennedy Jr.** (DD 850), **Floyd B. Parks** (DD 884) stricken on 2 July 1973; **Rupertus** (DD 851) transferred to Greece on 10 July 1973; **Eversole** (DD 789) transferred to Turkey on 11 July 1973; **Charles H. Roan** (DD 853) to Turkey on 21 Sep 1973; **Noa** (DD 841), **Leary** (DD 879), **O'Hare** (DD 889) transferred to Spain on 31 Oct 1973; **Henry W. Tucker** (DD 875), **Brinkley Bass** (DD 887) transferred to Brazil on 3 Dec 1973; **Arnold J. Isbell** (DD 869) transferred to Greece on 3 Dec 1973. **Herbert J. Thomas** (DD 833) stricken on 1st Apr 1974.

"GEARING" CLASS FRAM II

The 16 "Gearing" class destroyers modernised under the FRAM II programme have been stricken or transferred to foreign navies. See 1973-1974 and previous editions for characteristics and photographs.

Ex-ESCORT TYPE

Fred T. Berry (DD 858) stricken on 15 Sep 1970; **Harwood** (DD 861) transferred to Turkey on 17 Dec 1971; **Keppler** (DD 765) transferred to Turkey on 30 June 1972; **Lloyd Thomas** (DD 764) transferred to Taiwan China on 30 Oct 1972; **McCaffery** (DD 860) stricken on 30 Sep 1973; **Norris** (DD 859) stricken on 1 Feb 1974.

Ex-RADAR PICKET TYPE

Turner (DD 834) stricken on 26 Sep 1969; **Frank Knox** (DD 742) transferred to Greece on 23 Jan 1971; **Ernest G. Small** (DD 838) transferred to Taiwan China on 19 Feb 1971; **Chevalier** (DD 805) transferred to South Korea on 5 July 1972; **Everett F. Larson** (DD 830) to South Korea on 30 Oct 1972; **Perkins** (DD 877) transferred to Argentina on 15 Jan 1973; **Duncan** (DD 874) stricken on 1 Sep 1973; **Benner** (DD 807), **Kenneth D. Bailey** (DD 713), **Goodrich** (DD 831) stricken on 1 Feb 1974.

HAROLD J. ELLISON (DD 864) passing Belgian container ship DART EUROPE *1972, US Navy*

WILLIAM R. RUSH (DD 714) *1970, United States Navy*

WILLIAM M. WOOD (DD 715) *1971, Anthony & Joseph Pavia*

CORRY (DD 817) *1972, United States Navy, PH1 James G. Seagle*

Surface Combatants—*continued*

2 DESTROYERS (DD): "CARPENTER" TYPE (FRAM I)

Name	No.	Builder	Launched	Commissioned
*CARPENTER	DD 825	Consolidated Steel Corp	30 Dec 1945	15 Dec 1946
*ROBERT A. OWENS	DD 827	Bath Iron Works Corp	15 July 1946	5 Nov 1949

Displacement, tons: 2 425 standard; 3 410 full load
Length, feet (*metres*): 390·5 (*119·0*) oa
Beam, feet (*metres*): 40·9 (*12·4*)
Draft, feet (*metres*): 19 (*5·8*)
Guns: 2—5 inch (*127 mm*) 38 calibre DP (twin)
A/S weapons: 1 ASROC 8-tube launcher; 2 triple torpedo tubes (Mk 32); facilities for small helicopter
Main engines: 2 geared turbines (Westinghouse in *Carpenter*, General Electric in *Robert A. Owens*); 60 000 shp; 2 shafts
Boilers: 4 (Babcock & Wilcox)
Speed, knots: 34
Complement: 305 (12 officers, 176 enlisted active duty; 5 officers, 112 enlisted reserve)

These ships were laid down as units of the "Gearing" class. Their construction was suspended after World War II until 1947 when they were towed to the Newport News Shipbuilding and Drydock Co for completion as "hunter-killer" destroyers (DDK). As specialised ASW ships they mounted 3 inch (76 mm) guns in place of 5 inch mounts and were armed with improved ahead-firing anti-submarine weapons (hedgehogs and Weapon Able/Alfa); special sonar equipment installed. The DDK and DDE classifications were merged in 1950 with both of these ships being designated DDE on 4 March 1950. Upon being modernised to the FRAM I configuration they were reclassified DD on 30 June 1962.

Both of these ships are assigned to Naval Reserve training; they are manned by composite active duty reserve crews.

ELECTRONICS. These ships have SPS-10 and SPS-40 search radars on their forward tripod mast and electronic warfare "pods" on a smaller tripod mast forward of their second funnel.

PHOTOGRAPHS The *Carpenter* and *Robert A. Owens* are distinguished as the only surviving war-built US destroyers with one twin 5 inch gun mount.

ROBERT A. OWENS (DD 827) — *1969, A. & J. Pavia*

1 DESTROYER (DD): MODERNISED "ALLEN M. SUMNER" CLASS (FRAM II)

Name	No.	Builder	Launched	Commissioned
*LAFFEY	DD 724	Bath Iron Works Corp	21 Nov 1943	8 Feb 1944
LYMAN K. SWENSON	DD 729	Bath Iron Works Corp	12 Feb 1944	2 May 1944
JOHN A. BOLE	DD 755	Bethlehem (Staten Island)	1 Nov 1944	3 Mar 1945
LOFBERG	DD 759	Bethlehem (San Francisco)	12 Aug 1944	26 Apr 1945
JOHN W. THOMASON	DD 760	Bethlehem (San Francisco)	30 Sep 1944	11 Oct 1945

Displacement, tons: 2 200 standard; 3 320 full load
Length, feet (*metres*): 376·5 (*114·8*) oa
Beam, feet (*metres*): 40·9 (*12·4*)
Draft, feet (*metres*): 19 (*5·8*)
Guns: 6—5 inch (*127 mm*) 38 calibre DP (twin)
A/S Weapons: 2 triple torpedo tubes (Mk 32); 2 ahead-firing hedgehogs; facilities for small helicopter
Main engines: 2 geared turbines; 60 000 shp; 2 shafts
Boilers: 4
Speed, knots: 34
Complement: *Laffey* 283 (12 officers, 176 enlisted active duty; 5 officers, 94 enlisted reserve)

The *Laffey* is the only survivor of 70 ships completed 1943-1945 58 as destroyers (DD) and 12 as destroyer minelayers (DM). Of the former, 33 ships were modernized under the FRAM II programme of the late 1950s (see *Modernization* notes).
Frank E. Evans (DD 754) was cut in half by the Australian carrier *Melbourne* on 2 June 1969; bow sank with loss of 74 crewmen. Officially stricken from the Naval Register on 1 July 1969 (with stern section sunk as a target on 10 Oct 1969).
The *Laffey*, employed as a Naval Reserve training ship based at Alexandria, Virginia, a suburb of Washington, DC. The ship is manned by a composite active duty-reserve crew.

ELECTRONICS. These ships have SQS-29 series hull-mounted sonar (SQS-29 to -31 designation, depending upon frequency); variable depth sonar in most ships; fitted with SPS-40 or SPS-37 and small SPS-10 search radars on tripod mast.

MODERNISATION. All of these ships have been modernised under the fleet Rehabilitation and Modernisation (FRAM II) programme. New ASW torpedo tubes were installed as were facilities for operating drone ASW helicopters and variable depth sonar (VDS). Machinery was overhauled, new electronic equipment was installed, and living and working spaces were rehabilitated.

PHOTOGRAPHS. The *Lyman K. Swenson* has an SPS-37 search radar antenna and no variable depth sonar; the *Lofberg*, on the following page, has an SPS-40 radar antenna and a VDS installation on the fantail. Note amount of space between funnels compared to the larger "Gearing" class ships on the previous page.

LYMAN K. SWENSON (DD 729) — *1970, United States Navy, PHC T. J. Taylor*

DISPOSALS AND TRANSFERS
Zellars (DD 777) transferred to Iran on 19 Mar 1971; **Ingraham** (DD 694) to Greece on 16 July 1971; **Stormes** (DD 780) to Iran on 16 Feb 1972; **O'Brien** (DD 725) stricken on 18 Feb 1972; **Borie** (DD 704) transferred to Argentina on 1 July 1972; **Hugh Purvis** (DD 709) transferred to Turkey on 1 July 1972; **Moale** (DD 693) stricken on 2 July 1973; **Buck** (DD 761), **James C. Owens** (DD 776) transferred to Brazil on 15 July 1973; **Ault** (DD 698) stricken on 16 July 1973; **Putnam** (DD 757) stricken on 6 Aug 1973; **Allen M. Sumner** (DD 692) stricken on 15 Aug 1973; **Taussig** (DD 746) stricken on 1 Sep 1973; **Massey** (DD 778) stricken on 17 Sep 1973; **Lowry** (DD 770) stricken on 29 Oct 1973; **Waldron** (DD 699) transferred to Colombia, **Strong** (SD 758) transferred to Brazil, **Robert K. Huntington** (DD 781) transferred to Venezuela, all on 31 Oct 1973; **De Haven** (DD 727) transferred to South Korea on 3 Dec 1973; **Wallace L. Lind** (DD 703) to South Korea on 4 Dec 1973; **Charles S. Sperry** (DD 697), **Douglas H. Fox** (DD 779) transferred to Chile on 8 Jan 1974; **Walke** (DD 723), **Mansfield** (DD 728), **Collett** (DD 730), **Blue** (DD 744), **Alfred A. Cunningham** (DD 752) stricken on 1 Feb 1974; **Lyman K. Swenson** (DD 729), **John A. Bole** (DD 755), **Lofberg** (DD 759), **John W. Thomason** (DD 760) stricken on 1 Apr 1974.

"ALLEN M. SUMNER" CLASS

All non-modernised destroyers of the "Allen M. Sumner" class were to have been stricken or transferred by 1973. See 1972-1973 and previous editions for characteristics. A photograph of the *Purdy* (DD 724) appears on the following page; note absence of secondary gun battery; six 5 inch guns as in ships of this type modernised under the FRAM II programme.

DISPOSALS AND TRANSFERS since 1 Jan 1970: **Soley** (DD 707) stricken on 13 Feb 1970; **Haynsworth** (DD 700) transferred to Taiwan China on 12 May 1970; **English** (DD 696) to Taiwan China on 11 Aug 1970; **John W. Weeks** (DD 701) stricken on 12 Aug 1970; **Gainard** (DD 706) transferred to Iran on 19 Mar 1971; **Harlan R. Dickson** (DD 708) stricken on 1 July 1972; **Hank** (DD 702) transferred to Argentina on 1 July 1972; **Willard Keith** (DD 775) transferred to Colombia on 1 July 1972; **Maddox** (DD 731) transferred to Taiwan China on 6 July 1972; **Beatty** (DD 756) transferred to Venezuela on 14 July 1972; **Compton** (DD 705) transferred to Brazil on 27 Sep 1972; **Purdy** (DD 734), **John R. Pierce** (DD 753), **Henley** (DD 762) stricken on 2 July 1973.

Surface Combatants—*continued*

16 DESTROYERS (DD): LATER "FLETCHER" CLASS

Displacement, tons	2 050 standard; 3 500 full load
Length, feet (*metres*)	376·5 (*114·7*) oa
Beam, feet (*metres*)	39·5 (*11·9*)
Draft, feet (*metres*)	18 (*5·5*)
Guns	4 or 5—5 inch (*127 mm*) 38 calibre DP (single) 10—40 mm AA (twin) or 6—3 in (*76 mm*) AA (twin) see *Armament* notes
A/S weapons	depth charges; 2 fixed hedgehogs 2 triple torpedo tubes (Mk 32) in some ships.
Torpedo tubes	5 or 10—21 inch (*533 mm*) quintuple (removed from some ships)
Main engines	2 geared turbines; 60 000 shp; 2 shafts
Boilers	4
Speed, knots	35
Complement	250 (14 officers, 236 enlisted men) (designed wartime 329)

Name	*No.*	*Builder*	*Launched*	*Commisisoned*
BEARSS (4 guns)	DD 654	Gulf SB Corpn	25 July 1943	12 Apr 1944
CAPERTON (4)	DD 650	Bath Iron Works Corpn	24 July 1943	30 July 1943
CASSIN YOUNG	DD 793	Bethlehem Co San Pedro	12 Sep 1943	31 Dec 1943
COTTEN (4)	DD 669	Federal SB & DD Co	12 June 1943	24 July 1943
DASHIELL (4)	DD 659	Federal SB & DD Co	6 Feb 1943	20 Mar 1943
GATLING	DD 671	Federal SB & DD Co	20 June 1943	19 Aug 1943
HEALY (4)	DD 672	Federal SB & DD Co	4 July 1943	3 Sep 1943
HUNT (4)	DD 674	Federal SB & DD Co.	1 Aug 1943	22 Sep 1943
JOHN HOOD (4)	DD 655	Gulf SB Corpn	23 Oct 1943	7 June 1944
KIDD	DD 661	Federal SB & DD Co	28 Feb 1943	23 Apr 1944
McNAIR (4)	DD 679	Federal SB & DD Co	14 Nov 1943	30 Dec 1943
MELVIN	DD 680	Federal SB & DD Co	17 Oct 1943	24 Nov 1943
PICKING (4)	DD 685	Bethlehem Co Staten Island	31 May 1943	21 Sep 1943
PORTERFIELD	DD 682	Bethlehem Co San Pedro	13 June 1943	30 Oct 1943
REMEY	DD 688	Bath Iron Works Corpn	24 July 1943	30 Sep 1943
STOCKHAM	DD 683	Bethlehem Co San Francisco	25 June 1943	11 Feb 1944

Fifty-six destroyers of this class were completed in 1943-1944. They are essentially the same as the original "Fletcher" class. All surviving ships of this class are in reserve.

ARMAMENT-DESIGN. As built, these ships each mounted five 5 inch guns, ten 40 mm AA guns, several 20 mm guns, and ten 21 inch torpedo tubes. The twin 40 mm gun mounts were installed just forward of and below the bridge, alongside the second funnel, and atop the after deckhouse.

All secondary guns have been removed from some ships (see photograph of *Porterfield*).

After World War II a large number of these ships had their pole mast replaced by a tripod mast and five torpedo tubes between funnels were removed. All 20 mm guns also were removed. Twenty ships had their No. 3 ("Q") 5 inch mount removed and the 40 mm guns replaced by six 3 inch guns (twin), the latter installed between funnels and atop after deckhouse.

All ships active during the 1960s were fitted with triple Mk 32 tubes for ASW torpedoes.

TRANSFERS. Ships of this class serve in the navies of Argentina, Brazil, Chile, South Korea, Japan, Peru, Spain and Turkey.

DISPOSALS AND TRANSFERS (since 1 Jan 1970)
Hopewell (DD 681) stricken on 2 Jan 1970; **Mertz** (DD 691) stricken on 1 Oct 1970; **Albert W. Grant** (DD 649) stricken on 14 Apr 1971; **Bennion** (DD 662) stricken on 15 Apr 1971; **Knapp** (DD 653) stricken on 6 Mar 1972; **Uhlmann** (DD 687) stricken on 15 July 1972; **Chauncey** (DD 667), **Porter** (DD 800) stricken on 1 Oct 1972; **Bullard** (DD 660) stricken on 1 Dec 1972; **Norman Scott** (DD 690) stricken on 15 Apr 1973; **Charles J. Badger** (DD 657) stricken on 1 Feb 1974.

PICKING (DD 685) — *1964, United States Navy*

PORTERFIELD (DD 682) — ***1965, United States Navy***

LOFBERG (DD 759)—see previous page — *1970, United States Navy*

Surface Combatants—*continued*

16 DESTROYERS (DD): "FLETCHER" CLASS

Displacement, tons	2 100 standard; 3 050 full load
Length, feet (*metres*)	376·5 (*114·7*) oa
Beam, feet (*metres*)	39·5 (*11·9*)
Draft, feet (*metres*)	18 (*5·5*)
Guns	4 or 5—5 inch (*127 mm*) 38 calibre DP (single) except 3 guns in *Hazelwood* 6—40 mm AA (twin) or 6—3 inch (*76 mm*) AA (twin) (see *Armament* notes)
A/S weapons	depth charges 2 fixed hedgehogs 2 triple torpedo tubes (Mk 32) in some ships
Torpedo tubes	5 or 10—21 inch (*533 mm*) quintuple (removed from some ships)
Main engines	2 geared turbines; 60 000 shp; 2 shafts
Boilers	4
Speed, knots	35
Complement	249 (14 officers, 235 enlisted men) (designed wartime 329)

		Builder	Laid down	Launched	Commissioned
ABBOT (4 guns)	DD 629	Bath Iron Works Corpn	21 Sep 1942	17 Feb 1943	23 Apr 1943
DALY (4)	DD 519	Bethlehem Co, Staten Island	29 Apr 1942	24 Oct 1942	10 Mar 1943
HAZELWOOD (3)	DD 531	Bethlehem Co, San Francisco	11 Apr 1942	20 Nov 1942	18 June 1943
LA VALLETTE	DD 448	Federal SB & DD Co	27 Nov 1941	21 June 1942	12 Aug 1942
JAMES MILLAR	DD 535	Bethlehem Co, San Francisco	18 Aug 1942	7 Mar 1943	31 Aug 1943
ROBINSON	DD 562	Seattle-Tacoma SB Corpn	12 Aug 1942	28 Aug 1943	31 Jan 1944
ROSS (4)	DD 563	Seattle-Tacoma SB Corpn	7 Sep 1942	10 Sep 1943	21 Feb 1944
ROWE (4)	DD 564	Seattle-Tacoma SB Corpn	7 Dec 1942	30 Sep 1943	13 Mar 1944
SIGOURNEY	DD 543	Bath Iron Works Corpn	7 Dec 1942	24 Apr 1943	29 June 1943
SIGSBEE	DD 502	Federal SB & DD Co	22 July 1942	7 Dec 1942	23 Jan 1943
STODDARD (4)	DD 566	Seattle-Tacoma SB Corpn	10 Mar 1943	19 Nov 1943	15 Apr 1944
TERRY	DD 513	Bath Iron Works Corpn	8 June 1942	22 Nov 1942	26 Jan 1943
THE SULLIVANS (4)	DD 537	Bethlehem Co, San Francisco	10 Oct 1942	4 Apr 1943	30 Sep 1943
WATTS	DD 567	Seattle-Tacoma SB Corpn	26 Mar 1943	31 Dec 1943	29 Apr 1944
WREN	DD 568	Seattle-Tacoma SB Corpn	24 Apr 1943	29 Jan 1944	22 May 1944

One hundred ninteen ships of this class were completed in 1942-1945.
Eleven ships of this class were cancelled: DD 505, 506, 523-525, 542, 543, 548, 549, *Percival* (DD 542), and *Watson* (DD 482). The last two were to have been 2 100-ton destroyers with experimental power plants. (The experimental ships DD 503 and DD 504, of an unspecified type, were cancelled in 1941.)
All surviving ships of this class are in reserve. The last active ship was the *Shields* (DD 596), in continuous commission from 1945 to 1972.

THE SULLIVANS (DD 537) *United States Navy*

ARMAMENT-DESIGN. These ships marked reversion to flush-deck destroyers by the US Navy after several broken-deck designs built during the 1930s and early 1940s. This design was extremely successful and 56 additional ships of this class were constructed (listed separately).
As built, these ships mounted five 5 inch guns, six to ten 40 mm AA guns, several 20 mm AA guns, and ten 21 inch torpedo tubes. The twin 40 mm gun mounts were installed on each side of the second funnel and atop the after deckhouse.
After World War II a large number of these ships had their pole mast replaced by a tripod mast and the five torpedo tubes between funnels were removed. All 20 mm guns also removed. Twenty-one ships had their No. 3 ("Q") 5 inch mount removed and the 40 mm guns replaced by six 3 inch guns (twin), the latter installed between funnels and atop after deckhouse.
Ships in commission during the 1960s were fitted with triple Mk 32 launchers for ASW torpedoes.

HELICOPTERS. The *Hazelwood* was extensively modified to serve as test ship for the Drone Anti-Submarine Helicopter (DASH) programme.

HAZELWOOD (DD 531) *United States Navy*

NOMENCLATURE. Ships renamed while building: DD 537 ex-*Putnam*, DD 594 ex-*Mansfield*.
The DD 535 was renamed *James Miller* on 5 Aug 1971 to permit the name *Miller* to be assigned to DE 1091.

TRANSFERS. Ships of this class serve in the navies of Argentina, Brazil, Colombia, West Germany, Greece, Italy, South Korea, Mexico, Peru, Spain, and Taiwan China.

DISPOSALS AND TRANSFERS (since 1 Jan 1970)
Pritchett (DD 561) transferred to Italy on 10 Jan 1970; **Stanley** (DD 478) stricken on 1 Dec 1970; **Metcalf** (DD 595) stricken on 2 Jan 1971; **Twining** (DD 540) transferred to Taiwan China on 1 July 1971; **Cowell** (DD 547), **Braine** (DD 630) transferred to Argentina on 17 Aug 1971; **Mullany** (DD 528) transferred to Taiwan China on 6 Oct 1971; **Shields** (DD 596) transferred to Brazil on 6 July 1972; **Schroeder** (DD 501), **Foote** (DD 511), **McCord** (DD 534), **McKee** (DD 575) stricken on 1 Oct 1972; **Trathen** (DD 530), **Wickes** (DD 578), **Haraden** (DD 585), **Bell** (DD 587), **Burns** (DD 588) stricken on 1 Nov 1972 (all targets); **Hudson** (DD 475), **Stevens** (DD 479), **Stephen Potter** (DD 538), **Franks** (DD 554) stricken on 1 Dec 1972; **Owen** (DD 536), **Laws** (DD 558) **Hart** (DD 594) stricken on 15 Apr 1973.

"BENSON" AND "GLEAVES" CLASSES

All destroyers of the "Benson" and "Gleaves" classes completed 1940-1943 have been stricken or transferred to other navies. See 1971-1972 and previous editions for characteristics. Several ships of these classes serve in the navies of Greece, Italy, Taiwan China, and Turkey. The **Niblack** (DD 424) stricken in 1968, has been retained as a test hull for floating dry dock experiments at Davisville, Rhode Island.

ABBOT (DD 629) *United States Navy*

OCEAN ESCORTS

The US Navy is completing the last ships of the controversial "Knox" class ocean escorts. These ships will provide the Navy with 65 "first-line" ocean escorts in the mid-1970s (ie, ships with long-range SQS-26 sonar, ASROC anti-submarine rocket launcher, and helicopter capability): 46 "Knox" class, 6 "Brooke" class, 10 "Garcia" class, 2 "Bronstein" class, and the escort research ship *Glover* (AGDE 1).

To provide the additional escort-type ships the Navy has requested a new escort class known as the patrol frigate (PF). The new ships will emphasise anti-missile and anti-ship capabilities with some reduction in anti-submarine sensors and weapons (SQS-56 sonar vice the larger SQS-26 and no ASROC). The PF programme calls for 50 ships to be completed between 1977 and 1983. Despite its misleading PF designation, the ship is an ocean escort or destroyer escort by US Navy classification criteria. The PF will be slightly longer than the previous "Knox" class ships although having slightly less displacement. The PF's varied weapons capability and the wide use of equipment already proven in US or foreign service give promise of a highly effective warship.

LOCKWOOD (DE 1064) — *1973, McDonnell Douglas*

DSX PROGRAMME. The US Navy is pursuing the development of the surface effect ship (SES) for the surface combat role in the more distant future. Although the DSX concept is being addressed as a "destroyer-type" ship, the proposed 2 000-ton ship now in preliminary design will be more like an escort ship in size.

The SES development effort to date has concentrated on testing of two 100-tonne research craft completed in 1972 (listed under Experimental, Research and Surveying Ships), the preliminary design of the 2 000-ton DSX, and development of certain subsystems for the larger ship.

According to official statements, the SES development programme is a high risk venture from a technological point of view, but it could have a high payoff in terms of combat effectiveness. The central problem is to develop an ocean-going version of the SES with sufficient range, payload capacity, and sea-keeping to warrant the cost. The key technical areas which must be addressed are the air cushion seals, waterjet inlets, and ride control systems. Also, a practical combat SES with a trans-ocean operating range may be possible only with the development of a light weight nuclear power plant, an area of development that has not been encouraged in the US Navy.

A final factor is the question of specific requirements for a trans-ocean SES with a sustained speed of 80 to 100 knots. Additional analysis is required to ascertain the actual (rather than perceived) value of such speeds in anti-submarine, troop transport, and other naval operations. This is not to imply that speeds of this order will not be valuable in certain operations, but the SES may not be a panacea for future surface warships requirements.

NOMENCLATURE. Escort ships generally are named for deceased US Navy, Marine Corps, and Coast Guard personnel.

PHOTOGRAPHS. The "Knox" class escort ship *Lockwood* (DE 1064) is shown firing a Harpoon surface-to-surface missile from a modified ASROC launcher evaluation of the RGM-84A variant of the weapon.

The *Downes* (DE 1070) of the same class is shown below fitted with the NATO Sea Sparrow surface-to-air missile system. This is a close-in defence weapon scheduled to go aboard several US and NATO ships. Note the eight-cell launcher on the fantail; smaller and a slightly different configuration than the BPDMS firing Sea Sparrow on other "Knox" class ships. The *Downes* also has two missile directors (one atop the enlarged bridge structure and one atop the hangar) and an SPS-58 radar (on lattice mast atop hangar). The ship does not have the enlarged hangar and helicopter deck to accommodate LAMPS.

The bottom photograph is an artist's concept of one possible configuration of a 2 000-ton combat surface effect ship (DS). The domes would house search and fire control radar antennas; an SH-3 Sea King helicopter is illustrated on the after deck.

DOWNES (DE 1070) with NATO Sea Sparrow — *1973, United States Navy*

2 000-ton SES Design (DSX) — *Bell Aerospace*

Ocean Escorts—*continued*

2 000-ton SURFACE EFFECT SHIP (DSX): PROPOSED

Weight, tons	2 000 gross
Length, feet	approx 240
Beam, feet	approx 100
Missile launchers	(tentatively) Harpoon surface-to-surface launchers (tentatively) Sea Sparrow surface-to-air launchers
Guns	(tentatively) 20 mm Vulcan Phalanx rapid-fire CIWS
A/S weapons	helicopters
Main/lift engines	gas turbines
Speed, knots	80-100

The above are preliminary characteristics of a 2 000-ton combat-capable surface effect ship (SES). The Navy tentatively plans to construct two such craft, now designated DSX, for the evaluation of large SES platforms in possible combat roles.
Detailed design is being undertaken by the Bell Aerospace Division of Textron and by Lockheed Missiles & Space Co.
Through Fiscal Year 1974 costs of studies and design efforts related to a 2 000-ton SES have been $114 200 000; reportedly, the cost to develop, construct, and test two SES of this size would be $507 300 000.
The FY 1975 combat SES programme provides $58 000 000 for further testing of the two 100-ton test craft and further development of technology related to a larger SES.
An artist's concept of a possible 2 000-ton SES configuration appears on the previous page and another in the 1973-1974 edition (under Patrol Ships and Craft).

1+7 PATROL FRIGATES (PF): NEW DESIGN

Displacement, tons	3 500 full load
Length, feet	445 overall
Beam, feet	45
Draft, feet	24·5
Missile launchers	1 single launcher for Standard/Harpoon missiles (Mk 13 Mod 4)
Guns	1—76 mm 62 calibre dual-purpose (Mk 75) 1—20 mm Vulcan/Phalanx rapid-fire CIWS
A/S weapons	2 SH-2D LAMPS 2 triple torpedo tubes (Mk 32)
Main engines	2 gas turbines (General Electric); 40 000 shp; 1 shaft
Speed, knots	approx 28
Complement	approx 175

	Builder	Commission
one PF authorised FY 1973 programme	Bath Iron Works Corp	1977
seven PF proposed FY 1975 programme		
11 PF planned FY 1976 programme		1978-1983
31 PF planned FY 1977-1979 programme		

PATROL FRIGATE (PF)

The Navy plans to construct a class of 50 ships of this type for the escort of amphibious forces, underway replenishment groups, and merchantile convoys. They are follow-on ships to the large numbers of ocean escorts (DE) built in the 1960s and early 1970s, but with emphasis on anti-missile/anti-ship defences to complement the ocean escorts which emphasise anti-submarine capabilities (eg, large SQS-25 sonar and ASROC). The patrol frigates will have a viable A/S role, employing a "medium" sonar and two helicopters, plus the ever present Mk 32 torpedo tubes for close-in defence.

The lead ship was authorised in the Fiscal Year 1973 new construction programme, with the additional ships to be requested on the schedule listed above. The lead ship is expected to be constructed by Bath Iron Works Corp, Bath, Maine, with the remaining ships to be broken into three contract groupings and probably allocated to one or two other yards in addition to Bath. Construction of the first ship was to begin late in 1974.
Reportedly, the Australian Navy has expressed an interest in procuring ships of this class.

DESIGN. These ships are slightly longer but lighter than the preceding "Knox" class escort ships. There has been special emphasis on interior design for efficiency to reduce manning requirements and noise levels. The original single-hangar design (see drawing in 1973-1974 edition) has been changed to provide a larger hangar structure to house two SH-2D or follow on-LAMPS (Light Airborne Multi-Purpose System) helicopters.
The engineering plant, weapons, and sensors planned for the patrol frigate are based largely on equipment that is already in use in US and foreign ships. In addition, several systems are being evaluated at sea in the escort ship *Talbot* (DEG 4).

DESIGNATION. These ships officially are referred to as "patrol frigates" with the designation PF. However, according to an official statement, this "is not necessarily the designation these ships will be assigned when they become reality".
The PF designation is most confusing: These ships are similar in size and function to the US ocean escorts (DE). For the past two decades the term "frigates" has been applied by the US Navy to highly capable ships of the destroyer leader/cruiser size (designated DL/DLG/DLGN). Previously the US Navy used the term "frigate" for a series of World War II-built escort ships (PF 1-102) and subsequently for coastal escorts built specifically for transfer to foreign navies (PF 103-108). Artist's concepts of the new patrol frigate display the hull number (PF) 109.

PATROL FRIGATE (PF)

ELECTRONICS. These ships will have the new SQS-56 hull-mounted sonar. This replaces the earlier planned SQS-23 PAIR.
The principal radars will be the SPS-49 for long-range search, SPS-55 for surface search and navigation, and a Separate Track and Illumination Radar (STIR), the last located between the second lattice mast and the 76 mm gun mount. A Mk 92 Mod 2 fire control system will be provided (Americanised version of the WM-28 system developed by N. V. Hollandse Signaalapparaten).

ENGINEERING. Each patrol frigate will be powered by two General Electric LM 2500 marine gas turbines. This is the same engine being used in the "Spruance" class destroyers, the sea control ships, and the PHM hydrofoil missile craft.
Range is unofficially estimated at 4 500 miles at 20 knots.

FISCAL. The Navy requested reallocation of $51 600 000 of Fiscal Year 1972 funds on 30 July 1971 for initiation of this programme; however, the Congress did not act on this request. Approximately $12 000 000 was spent in FY 1971-1972 for studies and preliminary design. The FY 1973 new construction programme provided $193 000 000 to complete the design, fund "start-up" efforts for ship equipment, and fund the lead ship. Estimated cost of follow-on ships is $50 000 000 each (in FY 1973 dollars).

GUNNERY. The principal gun in this ship will be the single 76 mm OTO Melara with a 90-round-per-minute firing rate (designated Mk 75 in US service). Apparently the ship also will have a 20 mm Vulcan/Phalanx rapid-fire gun (shown at the after end of the superstructure). This is a Close-In Weapons System (CIWS) for use as a terminal defence against anti-ship missile attack.

MISSILES. The single-arm Tartar-type missile launcher will be capable of firing both Standard (MR) surface-to-air and Harpoon surface-to-surface missiles. "Mixed" missile magazines will be provided.

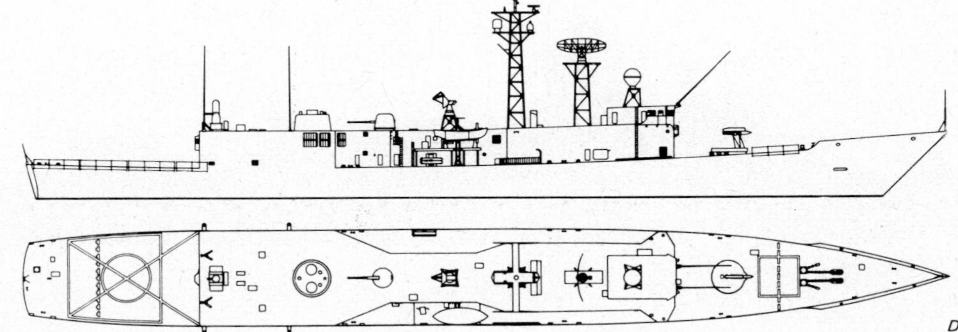

PATROL FRIGATE (PF)

Drawing by A. D. Baker

Ocean Escorts—*continued*

6 GUIDED MISSILE ESCORT SHIPS (DEG): "BROOKE" CLASS

Displacement, tons	2 640 standard; 3 425 full load
Length, feet (*metres*)	414·5 (*126·3*) oa
Beam, feet (*metres*)	44·2 (*13·5*)
Draft, feet (*metres*)	24 (*7·3*)
Missile launchers	1 single Tartar surface-to-air launcher
Guns	1—5 inch (*127 mm*) 38 calibre dual-purpose except 1—76 mm 62 calibre in *Talbot* (see notes)
A/S weapons	1 ASROC 8-tube launcher 2 triple torpedo tubes (Mk 32) 2 fixed torpedo tubes (stern) (Mk 25) 1 SH-2D LAMPS helicopter being provided

Name	*No.*	*Builder*	*Laid down*	*Launched*	*Commissioned*
***BROOKE**	DEG 1	Lockheed SB & Construction Co	10 Dec 1962	19 July 1963	12 Mar 1966
***RAMSEY**	DEG 2	Lockheed SB & Construction Co	4 Feb 1963	15 Oct 1963	3 June 1967
***SCHOFIELD**	DEG 3	Lockheed SB & Construction Co.	15 Apr 1963	7 Dec 1963	20 Apr 1968
***TALBOT**	DEG 4	Bath Iron Works Corp	4 May 1964	6 Jan 1966	22 Apr 1967
***RICHARD L. PAGE**	DEG 5	Bath Iron Works Corp	4 Jan 1965	4 Apr 1966	5 Aug 1967
***JULIUS A. FURER**	DEG 6	Bath Iron Works Corp	12 July 1965	22 July 1966	11 Nov 1967

These ships are identical to the "Garcia" class escorts except for the Tartar missile system in lieu of a second 5 inch gun mount and different electronic equipment. DEG 1-3 were authorised in the Fiscal Year 1962 new construction programme and the DEG 4-6 in the FY 1963 programme. Plans for ten additional DEGs in FY 1964 and possibly three more DEGs in a later programme were dropped because of the $11 000 000 additional cost of a DEG over DE. See "Garcia" class for additional notes.

The *Talbot* also is test ship for the SQS-56 sonar planned for the PF patrol frigates.

CLASSIFICATION. DEG 7-11 are guided missile "frigates" built in Spain with US assistance.

ELECTRONICS. SQS-26AX bow mounted sonar installed. SPS-52 three-dimensional search radar is mounted on the "mack" (combination mast and stack) and SPS-10 search radar is installed on the mast. SPG-52 missile fire control radar is installed aft of the "mack" The advanced Mk 92 fire control system (Americanised version of the WM-28 radar and weapon control system) was installed in the *Talbot* in August 1974 for test and evaluation. The Mk 92 is scheduled for use in the PF patrol frigates and the PHM missile boats.

GUNNERY. A single 76 mm/62 calibre OTO Melara rapid-fire gun (designated Mk 75 in US service) was installed in the *Talbot* in August 1974 for test and evaluation. The gun is scheduled for use in the PF patrol frigates and the PHM missile boats.

HELICOPTERS. These ships were designed to operate Drone Anti-Submarine Helicopters (DASH), but the programme was cut back before helicopters were provided to these ships. Small hangar aft.
These ships are scheduled to be fitted to operate the Light Airborne Multi-Purpose System (LAMPS), now the SH-2D helicopter.

MISSILES. These ships have a single Tartar Mk 22 launching system which weighs 92 395 pounds. Reportedly, the system has a rate of fire similar to the larger Mk 11 and Mk 13 systems installed in guided missile destroyers, but the DEG system has a considerably smaller magazine capacity (16 missiles according to unofficial sources).

The DEGs have a single Mk 74 missile fire control system whereas the larger DDGs have two such systems, providing a considerably greater anti-air warfare capability. The DEG 4-6 have automatic ASROC loading system (note angled base of bridge structure aft of ASROC "pepper box" in these ships.)

PHOTOGRAPHS. Note stem anchor and second anchor on port side near 5 inch gun in view of *Schofield*; stern tube openings in *Brooke*.

SCHOFIELD (DEG 3)

BROOKE (DEG 1) *1969, United States Navy.*

RICHARD L. PAGE (DEG 5) *1973, Giorgio Arra*

Ocean Escorts—*continued*

46 ESCORT SHIPS (DE): "KNOX" CLASS

Displacement, tons	3 011 standard; 4 100 full load
Length, feet (*metres*)	438 (*133·5*) oa
Beam, feet (*metres*)	46·75 (*14·25*)
Draft, feet (*metres*)	24·75 (*7·55*)
Guns	1—5 inch (*127 mm*) 54 calibre dual purpose
A/S weapons	1 ASROC 8-tube launcher 4 fixed torpedo tubes (Mk 32) 1 SH-2D LAMPS helicopter being provided (see notes)
Main engines	1 geared turbine (Westinghouse) 35 000 shp; 1 shaft
Boilers	2—1 200 psi (*83·4 kg/cm²*)
Speed, knots	27+
Complement	245 (17 officers, 228 enlisted men); increased to 283 (22 officers, 261 enlisted men) with BPDMS and LAMPS installation; as built 12 ships had accommodations for 2 staff officers
	1—20 mm Vulcan/Phalanx CIWS in *Lockwood*;
Missile launchers	1 Sea Sparrow BPDMS multiple launcher in 30 ships; 1 NATO Sea Sparrow multiple launcher in *Downes*

Name	*No.*	*Builder*	*Laid down*	*Launched*	*Commissioned*
*KNOX	DE 1052	Todd Shipyards (Seattle)	5 Oct 1965	19 Nov 1966	12 Apr 1969
*ROARK	DE 1053	Todd Shipyards (Seattle)	2 Feb 1966	24 Apr 1967	22 Nov 1969
*GRAY	DE 1054	Todd Shipyards (Seattle)	19 Nov 1966	3 Nov 1967	4 Apr 1970
*HEPBURN	DE 1055	Todd Shipyards (San Pedro)	1 June 1966	25 Mar 1967	3 July 1969
*CONNOLE	DE 1056	Avondale Shipyards	23 Mar 1967	20 July 1968	30 Aug 1969
*RATHBURNE	DE 1057	Lockheed SB & Constn Co	8 Jan 1968	2 May 1969	16 May 1970
*MEYERKORD	DE 1058	Todd Shipyards (San Pedro)	1 Sep 1966	15 July 1967	28 Nov 1969
*W. S. SIMS	DE 1059	Avondale Shipyards	10 Apr 1967	4 Jan 1969	3 Jan 1970
*LANG	DE 1060	Todd Shipyards (San Pedro)	25 Mar 1967	17 Feb 1968	28 Mar 1970
*PATTERSON	DE 1061	Avondale Shipyards	12 Oct 1967	3 May 1969	14 Mar 1970
*WHIPPLE	DE 1062	Todd Shipyards (Seattle)	24 Apr 1967	12 Apr 1968	22 Aug 1970
*REASONER	DE 1063	Lockheed SB & Constn Co	6 Jan 1969	1 Aug 1970	31 July 1971
*LOCKWOOD	DE 1064	Todd Shipyards (Seattle)	3 Nov 1967	5 Sep 1964	5 Dec 1970
*STEIN	DE 1065	Lockheed SB & Constn Co	1 June 1970	19 Dec 1970	8 Jan 1972
*MARVIN SHIELDS	DE 1066	Todd Shipyards (Seattle)	12 Apr 1968	23 Oct 1969	10 Apr 1971
*FRANCIS HAMMOND	DE 1067	Todd Shipyards (San Pedro)	15 July 1967	11 May 1968	25 July 1970
*VREELAND	DE 1068	Avondale Shipyards	20 Mar 1968	14 June 1969	13 June 1970
*BAGLEY	DE 1069	Lockheed SB & Constn Co	22 Sep 1970	24 Apr 1971	6 May 1972
*DOWNES	DE 1070	Todd Shipyards (Seattle)	5 Sep 1968	13 Dec 1969	28 Aug 1971
*BADGER	DE 1071	Todd Shipyards (Seattle)	17 Feb 1968	7 Dec 1968	1 Dec 1970
*BLAKELY	DE 1072	Avondale Shipyards	3 June 1968	23 Aug 1969	18 July 1970
*ROBERT E. PEARY	DE 1073	Lockheed SB & Constn Co	20 Dec 1970	23 June 1971	23 Sep 1972
*HAROLD E. HOLT	DE 1074	Todd Shipyards (San Pedro)	11 May 1968	3 May 1969	26 Mar 1971
*TRIPPE	DE 1075	Avondale Shipyards	29 July 1968	1 Nov 1969	19 Sep 1970
*FANNING	DE 1076	Todd Shipyards (San Pedro)	7 Dec 1968	24 Jan 1970	23 July 1971
*OUELLET	DE 1077	Avondale Shipyards	15 Jan 1969	17 Jan 1970	12 Dec 1970
*JOSEPH HEWES	DE 1078	Avondale Shipyards	15 May 1969	7 Mar 1970	27 Feb 1971
*BOWEN	DE 1079	Avondale Shipyards	11 July 1969	2 May 1970	22 May 1971
*PAUL	DE 1080	Avondale Shipyards	12 Sep 1969	20 June 1970	14 Aug 1971
*AYLWIN	DE 1081	Avondale Shipyards	13 Nov 1969	29 Aug 1970	18 Sep 1971
*ELMER MONTGOMERY	DE 1082	Avondale Shipyards	23 Jan 1970	21 Nov 1970	30 Oct 1971
*COOK	DE 1083	Avondale Shipyards	20 Mar 1970	23 Jan 1971	18 Dec 1971
*McCANDLESS	DE 1084	Avondale Shipyards	4 June 1970	20 Mar 1971	18 Mar 1972
*DONALD B. BEARY	DE 1085	Avondale Shipyards	24 July 1970	22 May 1971	22 July 1972
*BREWTON	DE 1086	Avondale Shipyards	2 Oct 1970	24 July 1971	8 July 1972
*KIRK	DE 1087	Avondale Shipyards	4 Dec 1970	25 Sep 1971	9 Sep 1972
*BARBEY	DE 1088	Avondale Shipyards	5 Feb 1971	4 Dec 1971	11 Nov 1972
*JESSE L. BROWN	DE 1089	Avondale Shipyards	8 Apr 1971	18 Mar 1972	17 Feb 1973
*AINSWORTH	DE 1090	Avondale Shipyards	11 June 1971	15 Apr 1972	31 Mar 1973
*MILLER	DE 1091	Avondale Shipyards	6 Aug 1971	3 June 1972	30 June 1973
*THOMAS S. HART	DE 1092	Avondale Shipyards	8 Oct 1971	12 Aug 1972	28 July 1973
*CAPODANNO	DE 1093	Avondale Shipyards	12 Oct 1971	21 Oct 1972	17 Nov 1973
*PHARRIS	DE 1094	Avondale Shipyards	11 Feb 1972	16 Dec 1972	26 Jan 1974
*TRUETT	DE 1095	Avondale Shipyards	27 Apr 1972	3 Feb 1973	May 1974
VALDEZ	DE 1096	Avondale Shipyards	30 June 1972	24 Mar 1973	July 1974
MOINESTER	DE 1097	Avondale Shipyards	25 Aug 1972	12 May 1973	Sep 1974

The 46 "Knox" class escort ships comprise the largest group of destroyer-type warships built to the same design in the West since the end of World War II. These ships are almost identical in design to the previous "Garcia" and "Brooke" classes, but slightly larger primarily because of use of non-pressure-fired boilers. DE 1052-1061 (10 ships) were authorised in the Fiscal Year 1964 new construction programme, DE 1062-1077 (16 ships) in FY 1965, DE 1078-1087 (10 ships) in FY 1966, DE 1088-1097 (10 ships) in FY 1967, and DE 1098-1107 (10 ships) in FY 1968. However, construction of six ships (DE 1102-1107) was deferred in 1968 as US Navy emphasis shifted to the more versatile and faster DX DXG ships; three additional ships (DE 1099-1101) were deferred late in 1968 to finance cost overruns of FY 1968 nuclear-powered attack submarines and to comply with a Congressional mandate to reduce expenditures; the last ship of the FY 1968 programme (DE 1098) was deferred early in 1969.

These ships have cost considerably more than originally estimated. Contract cost of early ships was $10 800 000 each; actual cost unofficially estimated at approximately $18 000 000 per ship.
The DEG 7-11 guided missile "frigates" constructed in Spain are similar to this design.

CONSTRUCTION. The ships built at Avondale Shipyards in Westwego, Louisiana, were assembled with a mass production technique of fabricating the hulls by using structural carbon steel tees split from wide-flange beams as longitudinal members. The hulls are built keel-up to permit downhand welding with the force of gravity allowing the molten weld to follow the contour of the hull and flow more easily between hull plates. Prefabricated, inverted hull modules first are assembled on a permanent platen, then lifted by hydraulic units and moved laterally into giant turning rings which rotate the hull into an upright position. Avondale, which also builds the "Hamilton" class cutters for the Coast Guard, side launches these ships.

DESIGN. These ships have a very large superstructure and a distinctive, cylindrical "mack" structure combining masts and engine exhaust stacks.

ELECTRONICS. SQS-26CX bow-mounted sonar; installation of SQS-35 Independent Variable Depth Sonar (IVDS) on 36 ships began in 1971.
These ships have SPS-40 and SPS-10 search radar antennas on their "mack" structures.
The DE 1078-1097 (20 ships) are being fitted with SSM-5 Test Evaluation and Monitoring System (TEAMS) which continuously checks shipboard radar and sonar systems. If TEAMS detects a malfunction an automatic search will be conducted throughout the subsystems until the fault is found and the defective component identified for repair or replacement.

ENGINEERING. DE 1101 was to have had gas turbine propulsion; construction of the ship was cancelled when decision was made to provide gas turbine propulsion in "Spruance" class (DD 963).
The *Patterson* is fitted with a Baldwin-Lima-Hamilton controllable-pitch propeller being evaluated for use in the "Spruance" class destroyers; her shafts are non-reversible. Another DE is being fitted to evaluate the Propulsion System Inc design controllable-pitch propeller.

GUNNERY. Gun armament for these ships consists of a single 5 inch/54 calibre Mk 42 mount forward with local anti-surface control (portside "bubble" or "frog-eye") but no local anti-aircraft control capability.
Lockwood fitted with 20 mm rapid-fire Close In Weapon System (CIWS) in 1972 for operational evaluation.

HELICOPTERS. These ships were designed to operate the now-discarded DASH unmanned helicopter. Beginning in 1972 they are being modified to accommodate the Light Airborne Multi-Purpose System, the SH-2D anti-submarine helicopter; hangar and flight deck

AYLWIN (DE 1081) *1973, Giorgio Arra*

are enlarged. Cost is approximately $1 000 000 per ship for LAMPS modification.

MISSILES. Sea Sparrow Basic Point Defence Missile System (BPDMS) launcher installed in 30 ships from 1971-1974 (DE 1052-1067, 1069, 1071-1083); also will be installed in DE 1068 during 1975.
Modified NATO Sea Sparrow installed in *Downes* for evaluation.
The remaining 14 ships of this class are scheduled to be fitted with the Chaparral short-range missile system which, like the BPDMS and NATO Sea Sparrow are anti-aircraft weapons.
In addition, some ships are being fitted with the Standard interim surface-to-surface missile which is fired from the ASROC launcher forward of the bridge.
Two of the eight "cells" in the launcher are modified to fire a single Standard. Cost is approximately $400 000 per ship for BPDMS and $750 000 for Standard missile modification.
The *Downes* and *Lockwood* have been used in at-sea firing tests and shipboard compatability for the Harpoon ship-to-ship missiles.

NOMENCLATURE. The lead ship of this class is named for naval historian Dudley W. Knox (the DD 742 was named for Frank Knox who was secretary of the Navy from 1940 to 1944). The *Harold E. Holt* honours the late Prime Minister of Australia, a firm supporter of U.S. policy in Southeast Asia during the Vietnam War. The *Jesse L. Brown* remembers the first US naval aviator of the Negro race; he was killed in action during the Korean War.
The DE 1073 originally was named *Conolly*; changed on 12 May 1971.

STATUS. These ships were considerably behind schedule partially because of shipyard labour strikes and delays in Navy acceptance.
These ships have been criticised by some authorities as being inferior to their foreign contemporaries. Critics note the delay in providing variable depth sonar and a helicopter capability, the minimal gun armament, and the use of conventional propulsion vice gas turbines or combination diesel-gas turbines.

TORPEDOES. Improved ASROC-torpedo reloading capability as in some ships of previous "Garcia" class (note slanting face of bridge structure immediately behind ASROC "pepper box"). Four Mk 32 torpedo tubes are fixed in the amidships structure, two to a side angled out at 45 degrees. The arrangement provides improved loading capability over exposed triple Mk 32 torpedo tubes.

Ocean Escorts—*continued*

ROBERT E. PEARY (DE 1073) *1972, United States Navy*

Sea Sparrow BPDMS and SQS-35 sonar in HAMMOND (DE 1067) *1972, US Navy*

SH-2D LAMPS helicopter *1972, United States Navy*

AYLWIN (DE 1081) firing ASROC *1972, United States Navy, PH1 James A. Warren*

SAMPLE (DE 1048)—see following page *1970, United States Navy*

Ocean Escorts—*continued*

10 ESCORT SHIPS (DE): "GARCIA" CLASS

Displacement, tons: 2 620 standard; 3 400 full load
Length, feet (*metres*): 414·5 (*126·3*) oa
Beam, feet (*metres*): 44·2 (*13·5*)
Draft, feet (*metres*): 24 (*7·3*)
Guns: 2—5 inch (*127 mm*) 38 calibre DP
A/S weapons: 1 ASROC 8-tube launcher; 2 triple torpedo tubes (Mk 32); facilities for small helicopter
Main engines: 1 geared turbine (Westinghouse); 35 000 shp; 1 shaft
Boilers: 2—1 200 psi (*83·4 kg/cm²*) (Foster Wheeler)
Speed, knots: 27
Complement: 247

These ships exceed many of the world's destroyers in size and ASW capability, but are designated escort ships by virtue of their single propeller shaft and limited speed.
The DE 1040 and DE 1041 were authorised in the Fiscal Year 1961 new construction programme DE 1043-1045 in FY 1962, and DE 1047-1051 in FY 1963.
All ten ships are active.

CLASSIFICATION. Hull numbers DE 1039, DE 1042, and 1046 were assigned to frigates built overseas for Portugal.

DESIGN. These ships are an enlargement of the previous "Bronstein" design. They have a flush deck, radically raked stem, stem anchor, and mast and stack combined into a "mack" structure. Anchors are mounted at stem and on portside, just forward of 5 inch gun. Fitted with gyrostabilising fins.

Name	*No*	*Builder*	*Laid down*	*Launched*	*Commissioned*
•GARCIA	DE 1040	Bethlehem Steel (San Francisco)	16 Oct 1962	31 Oct 1963	21 Dec 1964
•BRADLEY	DE 1041	Bethlehem Steel (San Francisco)	17 Jan 1963	26 Mar 1964	15 May 1965
•EDWARD McDONNELL	DE 1043	Avondale Shipyards	1 Apr 1963	15 Feb 1964	15 Feb 1965
•BRUMBY	DE 1044	Avondale Shipyards	1 Aug 1963	6 June 1964	5 Aug 1965
•DAVIDSON	DE 1045	Avondale Shipyards	30 Sep 1963	2 Oct 1964	7 Dec 1965
•VOGE	DE 1047	Defoe Shipbuilding Co	21 Nov 1963	4 Feb 1965	25 Nov 1966
•SAMPLE	DE 1048	Lockheed SB & Construction Co	19 July 1963	28 Apr 1964	23 Mar 1968
•KOELSCH	DE 1049	Defoe Shipbuilding Co	19 Feb 1964	8 June 1965	10 June 1967
•ALBERT DAVID	DE 1050	Lockheed SB & Construction Co	29 Apr 1964	19 Dec 1964	19 Oct 1968
•O'CALLAHAN	DE 1051	Defoe Shipbuilding Co	19 Feb 1964	20 Oct 1965	13 July 1968

Hangar structure of this class modified during the early 1970s. Compare *Garcia*, below, with photograph on previous page and views in earlier editions.

ELECTRONICS. Bow-mounted SQS-26 AXR sonar in DE 1040-1045; SQS-26 BX sonar in DE 1046-1051. SPS-40 and SPS-10 search radar antennas on "mack". The *Voge* and *Koelsch* have been fitted with a specialised ASW Naval Tactical Data System (NTDS).

ENGINEERING. These ships have an advanced "pressure-fired steam generating plant" which generates 70 percent more power than previous steam plants of the same size and weight. Each boiler has an integrated supercharger and associated control system which provides automatic regulation of fuel, air, and water. The boilers can use JP-5 jet fuel or diesel oil which facilitates boiler maintenance and cleaning, and ballasting empty fuel tanks with sea water. Finally, fewer engineering personnel are required to operate the plant.
A small auxiliary boiler is provided to supply steam when in port. Special noise-reduction features are provided.

HELICOPTERS. The Drone Anti-Submarine Helicopter (DASH) programme was cut back before these ships were provided with helicopters. Reportedly only the *Bradley* actually operated with DASH.
These ships are scheduled to be eventually fitted to operate the Light Airborne Multi-Purpose System (LAMPS), now the SH-2D helicopter.

MISSILES. The *Bradley* was fitted with a Sea Sparrow Basic Point Defense Missile System (BPDMS) in 1967-1968; removed for installation in the carrier *Forrestal*. The BPDMS "pepperbox" was fitted between funnel and after 5 inch mount.

TORPEDOES. Most of these ships were built with two Mk 25 torpedo tubes built into their transom for launching wire-guided ASW torpedoes. However, they have been removed from the earlier ships and deleted in the later ships. The *Voge* and later ships have automatic ASROC reload system (note angled base of bridge structure behind ASROC "pepper box" in these ships).

GARCIA (DE 1040) — *1972, United States Navy, PHC Frederick Gotavco*

1 ESCORT RESEARCH SHIP (AGDE): "GLOVER" TYPE

Name	*No*	*Builder*	*Laid down*	*Launched*	*Commissioned*
•GLOVER	AGDE 1 (ex-AG 163)	Bath Iron Works	29 July 1963	17 Apr 1965	13 Nov 1965

Displacement, tons: 2 643 standard; 3 426 full load
Length, feet (*metres*): 414·5 (*126·3*) oa
Beam, feet (*metres*): 44·2 (*13·5*)
Draft, feet (*metres*): 14·5 (*4·3*)
Guns: 1—5 inch (*127 mm*) 38 calibre DP
A/S weapons: 1 ASROC 8-tube launcher; 2 triple torpedo tubes (Mk 32); facilities for small helicopter
Main engines: 1 geared turbine (Westinghouse); 35 000 shp; 1 shaft
Boilers: 2—1 200 psi (*83·4 kg/cm²*) (Foster Wheeler)
Speed, knots: 27
Complement: 236 plus 38 civilian technicians

The *Glover* was built to test an advanced hull design and propulsion system, much the same as the *Albacore* (AGSS 569) embodied advanced submarine design concepts. However, unlike the *Albacore* the *Glover* has a full combat capability.
The ship was originally authorised in the Fiscal Year 1960 new construction programme, but was postponed and re-introduced in the FY 1961 programme. Estimated construction cost was $29 330 000.

DESIGN. The *Glover* has a massive bow sonar dome integral with her hull and extending well forward underwater.
No reload capability for ASROC because of space requirements for equipment and technical personnel.

GLOVER (AGDE 1) — *1969, United States Navy*

Ocean Escorts—*continued*

"GLOVER" TYPE—*continued*

ELECTRONICS. The *Glover* has bow-mounted SQS-26 AXR active sonar, hull-mounted SQR-13 Passive/Active Detection and Location (PADLOC) sonar, and SQS-35 Independent Variable Depth Sonar (IVDS) lowered from the stern. SPS-40 and SPS-10 search radars are fitted on the "mack" structure.
The ship has a prototype tactical assignment console that integrates signals from the three sonars and radars to present combined and coordinated tactical situation presentations in the Combat Information Centre (CIC). Reportedly, the tactical assignment console increases the combat effectiveness of the ship to a considerable extent.

PHOTOGRAPH. Stern configuration differs from "Garcia" class escort ships. Covered door in stern for retractable variable depth sonar.

2 ESCORT SHIPS (DE): "BRONSTEIN" CLASS

Displacement, tons	2 360 standard; 2 650 full load
Length, feet (*metres*)	371·5 (*113·2*) oa
Beam, feet (*metres*)	40·5 (*12·3*)
Draft, feet (*metres*)	23 (*7·0*)
Guns	3—3 inch (*76 mm*) 50 calibre AA (twin forward, single aft)
A/S weapons	1 ASROC 8-tube launcher 2 triple torpedo tubes (Mk 32) facilities for small helicopter
Main engines	1 geared turbine (De Lavel); 20 000 shp; 1 shaft
Boilers	2 (Foster Wheeler)
Speed, knots	26
Complement	220

Name	*No.*	*Builder*	*Laid down*	*Launched*	*Commissioned*
*BRONSTEIN	DE 1037	Avondale Shipyards	16 May 1961	31 Mar 1962	15 June 1963
*McCLOY	DE 1038	Avondale Shipyards	15 Sep 1961	9 June 1962	21 Oct 1963

These two ships may be considered the first of the "second generation" of post-World War II escort ships which are comparable in size and ASW capabilities to conventional destroyers. The *Bronstein* and *McCloy* have several features such as hull design, large sonar and ASW weapons that subsequently were incorporated into the mass-produced "Garcia", "Brooke", and "Knox" classes.
Both ships were built under the Fiscal Year 1960 new construction programme by Avondale Shipyards in Westwego, Louisiana.

DESIGN. These ships have a sharply raked stem, stem anchor, and mast and stacks combined in a "mack" structure. Position of stem anchor and portside anchor (just forward of gun mount) necessitated by large bow sonar dome. Note the deckhouse adjacent to "mack" in photograph of *McCloy*.

ELECTRONICS. SQS-26 bow-mounted sonar installed. SPS-40 and SPS-10 search radars mounted on "mack".

McCLOY (DE 1038) *1971, United States Navy, PHC F. W. Gotauco*

McCLOY (DE 1038) *1972, United States Navy*

McMORRIS (DE 1036)—see following page *1969, United States Navy*

Ocean Escorts—*continued*

2 ESCORT SHIPS (DE): "CLAUD JONES" CLASS

Displacement, tons	1 450 standard; 1 750 full load
Length, feet (*metres*)	310 (*95·0*) oa
Beam, feet (*metres*)	37 (*11·3*)
Draft, feet (*metres*)	18 (*5·5*)
Guns	2—3 inch (*76 mm*) 50 cal AA
A/S weapons	2 triple torpedo tubes (Mk 32) depth charges
Main engines	4 diesels (Fairbanks Morse); 9 200 bhp; 1 shaft
Speed, knots	22
Complement	175 (15 officers, 160 enlisted men)

Name	*No.*	*Builder*	*Laid down*	*Launched*	*Commissioned*
***CLAUD JONES**	DE 1033	Avondale Marine Ways, Inc.	1 June 1957	27 May 1958	10 Feb 1959
***McMORRIS**	DE 1036	Avondale Marine Ways, Inc.	5 Nov 1958	26 May 1959	4 Mar 1960

These diesel powered escorts were built in an effort to develop an economical DE suitable for mass production, however, they cannot carry the sonar and weapons necessary to cope with modern submarines.
The *Claud Jones* was authorised in the Fiscal Year 1956 shipbuilding programme and the *McMorris* in the FY 1957 programme.
The two surviving ships of this class will be transferred to Indonesia in the near future.

ARMAMENT. As built these ships each had two 3 inch guns (single closed mount forward and open mount aft), two ahead-firing hedgehog launchers, two torpedo tubes (Mk 32), and one depth charge rack. Fixed torpedo tubes removed from all ships and triple torpedo launchers installe.d

DESIGN. These are the only diesel-powered destroyer-type ships built by the US Navy since World War II. They have aluminium superstructure, tripod mast forward and pole mast amidships, and two funnels. Note that *McMorris* has a deckhouse between funnels.

ELECTRONICS. These ships have SPS-10 and SPS-6 search radars. SQS-29/32 hull-mounted sonars; variable depth sonar has been removed.

CLAUD JONES (DE 1033) — *1971, United States Navy, PH1 D. M. Dreher*

TRANSFERS
John R. Perry (DE 1034) transferred to Indonesia on 20 Feb 1973; **Charles Berry** (DE 1035) transferred to Indonesia on 31 Jan 1974.

PHOTOGRAPHS. Note unusual twin stack configuration, unique to US ocean escort ships. Both ships now have built-up section between funnels as in *McMorris*. Note small after mast and the electronic antennas between funnels.

"DEALY" AND "COURTNEY" CLASSES

All 13 ships of these near-similar classes have been stricken or transferred to foreign navies. These were the US Navy's first escort ships of post-World War II design. See 1973-1974 and previous editions for characteristics.

DISPOSALS AND TRANSFERS
Van Voorhis (DE 1028), **Joseph K. Taussig** (DE 1030) stricken on 1 July 1972; **Cromwell** (DE 1014) stricken on 5 July 1972; **Dealey** (DE 1006) transferred to Uruguay on 5 July 1972; **John Willis** (DE 1027) stricken on 7 July 1972; **Hartley** (DE 1029) transferred to Colombia on 8 July 1972; **Hooper** (DE 1026) stricken on 6 July 1973; **Bridget** (DE 1024) stricken on 12 Nov 1973; **Evans** (DE 1023), **Bauer** (DE 1025) stricken on 3 Dec 1973; **Hammerberg** (DE 1015), **Courtney** (DE 1021), **Lester** (DE 1022) stricken on 14 Dec 1973.

"JOHN C. BUTLER" CLASS

All ships of this class have been stricken. See 1973-1974 and previous editions for characteristics.

DISPOSALS (since 1 Jan 1970)
John C. Butler (DE 339), **Joseph E. Connolly** (DE 450) stricken on 1 June 1970; **John L. Williamson** (DE 370) stricken on 15 Sep 1970; **Conklin** (DE 439) stricken on 1 Oct 1970; **Gentry** (DE 349), **Lloyd E. Acree** (DE 356), **La Prade** (DE 409), **Kendall C. Campbell** (DE 443) stricken on 15 Jan 1972; **Key** (DE 348), **Rombach** (DE 364), **Goss** (DE 444), **Gilligan** (DE 508) stricken on 1 Mar 1972; **Richard W. Suesens** (DE 342), **Mack** (DE 358), **Pratt** (DE 363), **Stafford** (DE 411), **Oliver Mitchell** (DE 417) stricken on 15 Mar 1972.
French (DE 367), **Edmonds** (DE 406), **Le Ray Wilson** (DE 414), **Howard F. Clark** (DE 533) stricken on 15 May 1972.
Raymond (DE 341), **Kenneth Willett** (DE 354), **Johnnie Hutchins** (DE 360), **Melvin Norman** (DE 416), **Tabberer** (DE 418), **Robert F. Keller** (DE 419), **Chester T. O'Brien** (DE 421), **Edward H. Allen** (DE 531), stricken on 1 July 1972; **Rizzi** (DE 537), **Osberg** (DE 538), stricken on 1 Aug 1972; **O'Flaherty** (DE 340), **Edwin A. Howard** (DE 346), **Doyle C. Barnes** (DE 353), **George E. Davies** (DE 357), **Rolf** (DE 362), **Dennis** (DE 405), **Lawrence C. Taylor** (DE 415), **Leland E. Thomas** (DE 420), **Corbesier** (DE 438), **William Seiverling** (DE 441), **Hanna** (DE 449), **Silverstein** (DE 534), **Dufilho** (DE 423) stricken on 1 Dec 1972.

"RUDDEROW" CLASS

All escort ships of the "Rudderow" class have been stricken. See 1972-1973 and previous editions for characteristics. Ships of this class serve in the navies of South Korea and Taiwan China.

DISPOSALS (since 1 Jan 1970)
Coates (DE 685) stricken on 30 Jan 1970; **Parle** (DE 708) stricken on 1 July 1970; **Leslie L. B. Knox** (DE 580) stricken on 15 Jan 1972; **McNulty** (DE 581) stricken on 11 Feb 1972; **Tinsman** (DE 589) stricken on 15 May 1972; **Hodges** (DE 231), **Thomas F. Nickel** (DE 587) stricken on 1 Dec 1972.

"BOSTWICK" CLASS

All ships of this class have been stricken. Originally known as the "Cannon" class, but referred to as the "Bostwick" class after the first four ships (DE 99-102) were transferred to other navies. See 1973-1974 and previous editions for characteristics.

TRANSFERS. Ships of this class currently serve in the navies of Brazil, France, Greece, Italy, Japan, South Korea, Peru, the Philippines, Taiwan China, Thailand, and Uruguay.
DISPOSALS (since 1 Jan 1970)
Parks (DE 165), **Acree** (DE 167), **Cooner** (DE 172), **Coffman** (DE 191) stricken on 1 July 1972; **McConnell** (DE 163) stricken on 1 Oct 1972; **Osterhaus** (DE 164) stricken on 1 Nov 1972; **Levy** (DE 162), **Trumpeter** (DE 180), **Straub** (DE 181) stricken on 1 Aug 1973.

"BUCKLEY' CLASS

All ships of this class have been stricken. See 1973-1974 and previous editions for characteristics.
DISPOSALS (since 1 Jan 1970)
J. Douglas Blackwood (DE 219) stricken on 30 Jan 1970; **Alexander J. Luke** (DE/DER 577) stricken on 1 May 1970 (target); **Cronin** (DE 704) stricken on 1 June 1970 (target); **Fieberling** (DE 640), **William C. Cole** (DE 641), **Damon M. Cummings** (DE 643), **Splanger** (DE 696) stricken on 1 Mar 1972; **Coolbaugh** (DE 217), **Frank M. Robinson** (DE 220) stricken on 1 July 1972; **Jack W. Wilke** (DE 800) stricken on 1 Aug 1972; **Holton** (DE 703) stricken on 1 Nov 1972; **Eichenberger** (DE 202), **Gillette** (DE 681), **Osmus** (DE 701), **Frybarger** (DE 705), **Major** (DE 796), **Varian** (DE 798), **Gendreau** (DE 639) stricken on 1 Dec 1972; **Marsh** (DE 699), **Wiseman** (DE 667) stricken on 15 Apr 1973; **Gunason** (DE 795) stricken on 1 Sep 1973.

"EDSALL" CLASS

All ships of this class have been stricken except for the survivors of the 36 units converted to radar picket escorts (DER) and listed separately. See 1973-1974 and previous editions for characteristics.
DISPOSALS (since 1 Jan 1970)
Stanton (DE 247) stricken on 1 Dec 1970; **Jacob Jones** (DE 130), **Pope** (DE 134), **J. R. Y. Blakeley** (DE 140), **Poole** (DE 151), **J. Richard Ward** (DE 243), **Sloat** (DE 245), **Marchland** (DE 249), **Menges** (DE 320), **Mosley** (DE 321), **Pride** (DE 323), **Dale W. Peterson** (DE 337) stricken on 2 Jan 1971; **O'Reilly** (DE 330), **Daniel** (DE 335) stricken on 15 Jan 1971; **Merrill** (DE 392) stricken on 2 Apr 1972; **Herbert C. Jones** (DE 137), **Neunzer** (DE 150), **Swenning** (DE 394(, **Willis** (DE 395), **Janssen** (DE 396), **Stockdale** (DE 399 stricken on 1 July 1972; **Hammann** (DE 131), **Douglas L. Howard** (DE 138), **Farquhar** (DE 139), **Hill** (DE 141), **Inch** (DE 146), **Stewart** (DE 238), stricken on 1 Oct 1972; **Keith** (DE 241), **Tomich** (DE 242), **Swasey** (DE 248), **Ricketts** (DE 254) stricken on 1 Nov 1972; **Hurst** (DE 250) stricken on 1 Dec 1972 and transferred to Mexico on 1 Oct 1973; **Huse** (DE 145), **Chatelain** (DE 149), **Peterson** (DE 152), **Moore** (DE 240), **Pettit** (DE 253), **Cockrill** (DE 398) stricken on 1 Aug 1973.

Ocean Escorts—*continued*

13 RADAR PICKET ESCORT SHIPS (DER): CONVERTED "EDSALL" CLASS

Displacement, tons: 1 590 standard; 1 850 full load
Length, feet (*metres*): 306 (*93·3*) oa
Beam, feet (*metres*): 36·6 (*11·1*)
Draft, feet (*metres*): 14 (*4·3*)
Guns: 2—3 inch (*76 mm*) 50 cal AA
A/S weapons: 2 triple torpedo tubes (Mk 32) in most ships; 1 trainable hedgehog (Mk 15) depth charges
Main engines: 4 diesels (Fairbanks Morse), 6 000 bhp; 2 shafts
Speed, knots: 21
Complement: 169 (19 officers, 150 enlisted men)

Name	*No.*	*Builder*	*Launched*	*Commissioned*
CHAMBERS	DER 391	Brown SB Co, Houston	17 Aug 1943	22 Nov 1943
DURANT	DER 389	Brown SB Co, Houston	3 Aug 1943	16 Nov 1943
FALGOUT	DER 324	Consliodated Steel Corpn	24 July 1943	15 Nov 1943
HISSEM	DER 400	Brown SB Co, Houston	26 Dec 1943	13 Jan 1944
KIRKPATRICK	DER 318	Consolidated Steel Cpron	5 June 1943	23 Oct 1943
MILLS	DER 383	Brown SB Co, Houston	26 May 1943	12 Oct 1943
OTTERSTETTER	DER 244	Brown SB Co, Houston	19 Jan 1943	6 Aug 1943
PRICE	DER 332	Consolidated Steel Corpn	30 Oct 1943	12 Jan 1944
RAMSDEN	DER 382	Brown SB Co, Houston	24 May 1943	19 Oct 1943
RHODES	DER 384	Brown SB Co, Houston	29 June 1943	25 Oct 1943
ROY O. HALE	DER 336	Consolidated Steel Corpn	20 Nov 1943	3 Feb 1944
SAVAGE	DER 386	Brown SB Co, Houston	15 July 1943	29 Oct 1943
VANCE	DRE 387	Brown SB Co, Houston	16 July 1943	1 Nov 1943

Thirty-six ships of this type were converted to radar picket ships between 1951 and 1958; redesignated DER (See *Conversion* notes). Eleven of these ships were on loan to the US Coast Guard from 1951 to 1954 (they retained Navy names and were designated WDE with hull numbers upped by one hundred to avoid confusion with Coast Guard numbering series: DE 322-325, 328, 331, 334, 382, 387-389 and 391).
Several ships were used in Operation MARKET TIME in the South China Sea and Gulf of Tonkin to halt Communist infiltration of men and arms to South Vietnam; while engaged in MARKET TIME several ·50 calibre machineguns are mounted.
All surviving ships of this class are in reserve, the last being the *Calcaterra* (DER 390), decommissioned in 1973.

ARMAMENT. Upon conversion to radar picket ships these ships were fitted with six 20 mm guns; subsequently removed.
Forward 3 inch mount is enclosed; after mount open or enclosed, depending upon availability.

CONVERSION. Conversion to radar picket escorts included removal of conventional torpedo tubes and 40 mm guns; installation of mess compartment on main deck and other habitability improvements; fitting of two tripod masts to support radar antennas and TACAN navigation "bee-hive" antenna; installation of SPS-8 height-finding radar antenna atop after deckhouse; combat information centre (CIC) expanded and improved; and aluminium superstructure installed. Note trainable hedgehog fitted in "B" position in place of second 3 inch mount. TACAN and SPS-8 removed from active ships when seaward radar picket barrier was ended in 1965. The DERs in service during the latter 1960s had SPS-28 and SPS-10 or SPS-8 radar antennas on their forward mast; and electronic warfare "pods" on after mast.

ENGINEERING. Maximum operational speed for remaining ships is about 19 knots.

PHOTOGRAPHS. The *Mills* is shown with full DER electronics suite; the *Savage* has lost her SPS-8 radar antenna and TACAN.

DISPOSALS AND TRANSFERS (since 1 Jan 1970)
Camp (DER 251) transferred to South Vietnam on 13 Feb 1971; **Forster** (DER 334) transferred to South Vietnam on 25 Sep 1971. **Blair** (DER 317), **Sturtevant** (DER 239), **Joyce** (DER 317), **Strickland** (DER 313) stricken on 1 Dec 1972; **Calcaterra** (DER 390) stricken on 2 July 1973; **Kretchmer** (DER 329) stricken on 30 Sep 1973; **Thomas J. Gary** (DER 326) transferred to Tunisia on 22 Oct 1973; **Finch** (DER 328), **Lansing** (DER 388) stricken on 1 Feb 1974.

SAVAGE (DER 386) — *1968, United States Navy*

MILLS (DER 383) — *1964, United States Navy*

2 RADAR PICKET ESCORT SHIPS (DER): CONVERTED "JOHN C. BUTLER" CLASS

Displacement, tons: 1 745 standard; 2 100 full load
Length, feet (*metres*): 306 (*93·3*) oa
Beam, feet (*metres*): 36·6 (*11·2*)
Draft, feet (*metres*): 11 (*3·4*)
Guns: 2—5 in (*127 mm*) 38 cal DP
A S weapons: 1 trainable hedgehog (Mk 15) depth charge rack
Main engines: 2 geared turbines (Westinghouse) 12 000 shp; 2 shafts
Boilers: 2 (Babcock & Wilcox)
Speed, knots: 24
Complement: 187

Name	*No*	*Builder*	*Laid down*	*Launched*	*Commissioned*
VANDIVIER	DER 540	Boston Naval Shipyard	8 Nov 1943	27 Dec 1943	1 Dec 1955
WAGNER	DER 539	Boston Naval Shipyard	8 Nov 1943	27 Dec 1943	31 Dec 1955

These two ships were begun as standard Destroyer Escorts (DE); construction suspended in 1946. Work resumed in 1954 and they were completed as Radar Picket Escort Ships (DER) at the Boston Naval Shipyard. Both ships are in reserve.

ENGINEERING. These are the US Navy's only steam-driven radar picket escort ships; all others have diesel propulsion.

PHOTOGRAPH. Note tripod masts, TACAN navigation "bee-hive" antenna on after mast and SPS-8 height-finding radar antenna atop after deckhouse.

VANDIVIER (DER 540) — *United States Navy*

FIRE SUPPORT SHIPS

The US Navy retains several ships with large calibre guns for possible future use in the role of gunfire support for amphibious operations. They lack anti-aircraft, anti-submarine, and command and control facilities for other big-ship roles.
As of mid-1974 only one of these ships remained in active service, the heavy cruiser *Newport News* (CA 148). Plans to decommission the ship have been delayed for several years; tentatively she is scheduled for layup in the reserve during 1975. The only other US ships in service with guns larger than 5-inch calibre are the converted "Cleveland" class guided missile light cruisers (CLG), which will be decommissioned in the near future.

BATTLESHIPS. The largest fire support ships retained in reserve are the four "Iowa" class dreadnoughts of World War II construction. These are the last battleships officially retained by any navy. The *New Jersey*, which made one deployment to the western Pacific during the Vietnam War, and the *Missouri* are moored at the Puget Sound Naval Shipyard in Bermerton, Washington, the *Iowa* and *Wisconsin* are at the Philadelphia Naval Shipyard.

CRUISERS. Three all-gun cruisers armed with 8-inch guns remain in reserve plus the gun-missile cruiser *Canberra* (CA 70, ex-CAG 2). The *Canberra* and now-stricken *Boston* (CA 69, ex-CAG 1) were reclassified as heavy cruisers vice guided missile cruisers because of the limited effectiveness of their Terrier BW missiles for task force defense.
The all-gun cruisers retained in reserve are two "Salem" class ships and one "Baltimore" class ship. In addition, the all-gun *Newport News* and three heavy crusiers that have been converted to missile ships (CG) are in active service, with the latter ships being listed in an earlier section of this edition.
All light cruisers (CL) and light anti-aircraft cruisers (CLAA) have been stricken from the Navy List. See 1971-1972 edition for compilation of strike dates of the CL-CLAA ships retained into the post-war period. Six "Cleveland" class cruisers converted to a guided missile configuration (CLG) are described in an earlier section. Several light cruisers of the pre-World War II "Brooklyn" and "St. Louis" classes remain in service with Argentina, Brazil, and Chile.

FIRE SUPPORT SHIPS. All inshore fire support ships (LFR, ex-LSMR and ex-IFS) have been stricken. See listing for Amphibious Warfare Ships for strike data.
Plans developed during the mid-1960s to design and construct a new class of landing force support ships (designated LFS) have been deferred. A request for funding of contract definition under the Fiscal Year 1970 budget was denied by the Congress.
The proposed LFS would have combined in one hull an armament of large calibre guns and possibly rocket launchers. The guns were to provide long-range, accurate, and high destructive fire while the rockets would provide saturation fire. The LFS main battery would be three 8 inch Major Calibre Light Weight Guns (MCLWG) that would fire conventional and rocket-assisted projectiles. the latter expected to have a range of more than 50 miles. The ship would have had a relatively large magazine capacity, probably 750 to 800 rounds per 8 inch gun barrel. Secondary gun armament was to be two 5 inch rapid fire guns for close-in support missions and self-defebce (possibly supplemented in the latter role) by point-defence missiles).

The design of the "Spruance" class destroyers provides for installation of a single 8 inch light-weight gun in place of the forward 5-inch gun.
Such a gun is being installed for evoluation in the destroyer *Hull* (DD 945).

PHOTOGRAPHS. The photograph below shows the battleship *New Jersey* in action off the coast of South Vietnam in April 1969, firing some of the last rounds to be fired by a battleship. Additional photographs of "Iowa" class ships appear in the 1973-1974 and previous editions.

4 BATTLESHIPS (BB): "IOWA" CLASS

Name	No.	Builder	Laid down	Launched	Commissioned
IOWA	BB 61	New York Navy Yard	27 June 1940	27 Aug 1942	22 Feb 1943
NEW JERSEY	BB 62	Philadelphia Navy Yard	16 Sep 1940	7 Dec 1942	23 May 1943
MISSOURI	BB 63	New York Navy Yard	6 Jan 1941	29 Jan 1944	11 June 1944
WISCONSIN	BB 64	Philadelphia Navy Yard	25 Jan 1941	7 Dec 1943	16 Apr 1944

Displacement, tons	45 000 standard; 59 000 full load
Length, feet (*metres*)	860 (*262·1*) wl; 887·2 (*270·4*) oa except *New Jersey* 887·6 (*270·5*)
Beam, feet (*metres*)	108·2 (*33·0*)
Draft, feet (*metres*)	38 (*11·6*)
Guns	9—16 inch (*406 mm*) 50 cal. 20—5 inch (*127 mm*) 38 cal. dual purpose. several 40 mm guns in all except *New Jersey*
Main engines	4 geared turbines (General Electric in BB 61 and BB 63; Westinghouse in BB 62 and BB 64; 212 000 shp; 4 shafts
Boilers	8 (Babcock & Wilcox)
Speed, knots	33 (all have reached 35 knots in service)
Complement	designed complement varied, averaging 169 officers and 2 689 enlisted men in wartime; *New Jersey* was manned by 70 officers and 1 556 enlisted men (requirements reduced with removal of all light anti-aircraft weapons, floatplanes, and reduced operational requirements) in 1968-1969

NEW JERSEY (BB 63) — *1969, United States Navy*

These ships were the largest battleships ever built except for the Japanese *Yamato* and *Musashi* (64 170 tons standard, 863 feet overall, 9—18·1 inch guns.) All four "Iowa" class ships were in action in the Pacific during World War II, primarily screening fast carriers and bombarding amphibious invasion objectives. Three were mothballed after the war with the *Missouri* being retained in service as a training ship. All four ships again were in service during the Korean War (1950-1953) as shore-bombardment ships; all mothballed 1954-1958.
The *New Jersey* began reactivation in mid-1967 at a cost of approximately $21 000 000; recommissioned on 6 Apr 1968. The *Iowa* and *Wisconsin* remained in reserve at the Philadelphia Naval Shipyard where the *New Jersey* had been berthed and reactivated; and the mothballed *Missouri* at the Puget Sound Naval Shipyard, Bremerton, Washington.
The *New Jersey* was again decommissioned on 17 Dec 1969 and mothballed at Bremerton with the *Missouri*.
Two additional ships of this class were laid down, but never completed: *Illinois* (BB 65), laid down 15 Jan 1945, and *Kentucky* (BB 66), laid down 6 Dec 1944. The *Illinois* was 22 percent complete when cancelled on 11 Aug 1945. The *Kentucky* was 69·2 percent complete when construction was suspended late in the war; floated from its building dock on 20 Jan 1950. Conversion to a missile ship (BBG) was proposed, but no work was undertaken and she was stricken on 9 June 1958 and broken up for scrap.
Approximate construction cost was $114 485 000 for *Missouri*; other ships cost slightly less.

AIRCRAFT. As built, each ship carried three floatplanes for scouting and gunfire spotting and had two quarterdeck catapults. Catapults removed and helicopters carried during the Korean War.

ARMOUR. These battleships are the most heavily armoured US warships ever constructed, being designed to survive ship-to-ship combat with enemy ships armed with 16 inch guns. The main armour belt consists of Class A steel armour 12·1 inches thick tapering vertically to 1·62 inches; a lower armour belt aft of Turret No. 3 to protect propeller shafts is 13·5 inches; turret faces are 17 inches; turret tops are 7·25 inches; turret backs are 12 inches; barbetts have a maximum of 11·6 inches of armour; second deck armour is 6 inches; and the three-level conning tower sides are 17·3 inches with an armoured roof 7·25 inches (the conning tower levels are pilot house, navigation bridge, and flag-signal bridge).

DESIGN. These ships carried heavier armament than previous US battleships and had increased protection and larger engines, accounting for additional displacement and increased speed. Design includes clipper bow and long foredeck, with graceful sheer (see photographs).
All fitted as fleet flagships with additional accommodations and bridge level for admiral and staff.

ELECTRONICS. During 1968-1969 the *New Jersey* was fitted with SPS-10 and SPS-6 search radars.

GUNNERY. The Mk VII 16 inch guns in these ships fire projectiles weighing up to 2 700 pounds (*1 225 kg*) (armour piercing) a maximum distance of 23 miles (*39 km*). As built, these ships had 80—40 mm and 49 to 60—20 mm anti-aircraft guns (except *Iowa*, only 19 quad 40 mm mounts); all 20 mm guns removed and a reduced number of 40 mm weapons remain on the mothballed ships. During 1968-1969 the *New Jersey* was fitted with two Mk 34 fire control directors in addition to the two Mk 56 and four Mk 37 previously installed. Mk 48 shore bombardment computer installed when reactivated.

NOMENCLATURE. US battleships are generally named for states; the exception was the *Kearsarge*, BB 5 launched in 1899 (later *Crane Ship No. 1*, AB 1). Beginning in 1969 the Navy has named frigates for states.

OPERATIONAL. The *New Jersey* made one deployment to the western Pacific during her third commission (1968-1969).
During the deployment she was on the "gun line" off South Vietnam for a total of 120 days with 47 days being the longest sustained period at sea.
While on the "gun line" the *New Jersey* fired 5 688 rounds of ammunition from her 16 inch main battery guns and a total of 6 200 rounds during the commission, the additional firings being for tests and training. While off Vietnam she also fired some 15 000 rounds from her 5 inch secondary battery guns.
(In comparison, during World War II the *New Jersey* fired 771 main battery rounds and during two deployments in the Korean War and midshipmen training cruises she fired 6 671 main battery rounds.)

Fire Support Ships—*continued*

NEW JERSEY (BB 62) — *1968, United States Navy*

3 HEAVY CRUISERS (CA): "SALEM" CLASS

Displacement, tons	17 000 standard; 21 500 full load
Length, feet (*metres*)	700 (*213·4*) wl; 716·5 (*218·4*) oa
Beam, feet (*metres*)	76·3 (*23·3*)
Draft, feet (*metres*)	26 (*7·9*)
Guns	9—8 inch (*203 mm*) 55 cal (triple) 12—5 inch (*127 mm*) 38 cal DP (twin) 20—3 inch (*76 mm*) 50 cal AA (twin); removed from *Newport News*
Main engines	4 geared turbines (General Electric); 120 000 shp; 4 shafts
Boilers	4 (Babcock & Wilcox)
Speed, knots	33
Complement	approx 1 300 in *Newport News*

Name	*No*	*Builder*	*Laid down*	*Launched*	*Commissioned*
DES MOINES	CA 134	Bethlehem Steel Co (Quincy)	28 May 1945	27 Sep 1946	17 Nov 1948
SALEM	CA 139	Bethlehem Steel Co (Quincy)	4 June 1945	25 Mar 1947	9 May 1949
• **NEWPORT NEWS**	CA 148	Newport News SB & DD Co	1 Oct 1945	6 Mar 1947	29 Jan 1949

These ships were the largest and most powerful 8 inch gun cruisers ever built. Completed too late for World War II, they were employed primarily as flagships for the Sixth Fleet in the Mediterranean and the Second Fleet in the Atlantic. The *Salem* was decommissioned on 30 Jan 1959 and the *Des Moines* on 14 July 1961. The *Newport News*, normally flagship of the second Fleet was employed as a fire support ship off Vietnam in 1967-1968; with the Spanish *Canarias* thus is the only heavy cruiser in service in any western navy.
Periodic plans to decommission the *Newport News* during the past few years have been delayed to retain the ship's "big gun" capability in the Fleet.
The ship's No. 2 main battery was damaged in an accidental explosion in October 1972; not repaired, giving the ship only six useable 8-inch guns.

AIRCRAFT. As completed the *Des Moines* had two stern catapults and carried four floatplanes; catapults removed.

DESIGN. These ships are an improved version of the previous "Oregon City" class. The newer cruisers have automatic main batteries, larger main turrets, taller fire control towers, and larger bridges. The *Des Moines* and *Newport News* are fully air conditioned.
Additional ships of this class were cancelled: the *Dallas* (CA 140) and the unnamed CA 141-142, CA 149-153.

ELECTRONICS. The *Newport News* has an SPS-37 search radar antenna and TACAN on her forward mast, and SPS-8 and SPS-6 antennas on her after mast. (The small antenna on the forward mast is an SPS-10).

GUNNERY. These cruisers were the first ships to be armed with fully automatic 8 inch guns firing cased ammunition. The guns can be loaded at any elevation from —5 to +41 degrees; rate of fire is four times faster than earlier 8 inch guns. Mk XVI 8-inch guns in these ships; other heavy cruisers remaining on Navy List have Mk XV guns.
As built these ships mounted 12·5 inch guns, 24·3 inch guns (in twin mounts), and 12 20 mm guns (single mounts). The 20 mm guns were removed almost immediately and the 3 inch battery was reduced gradually as ships were overhauled. Last 3-inch guns removed from *Newport News* in 1973 (two twin mounts amidships). With full armament the designed wartime complement was 1 860.

MODERNISATION. The *Newport News* has been extensively modified to provide improved flagship facilities; note elaborate antennas on masts, forecastle, atop turrets, and on stern crane.

NEWPORT NEWS (CA 148) — *1967, United States Navy*

NEWPORT NEWS (CA 148) — *1967, United States Navy*

Fire Support Ships—*continued*

SALEM (CA 139) *United States Navy*

DES MOINES (CA 134) *United States Navy*

1 HEAVY CRUISER (CA): "CANBERRA" TYPE (Ex-CAG)

Name	*No.*	*Builder*	*Laid down*	*Launched*	*Commissioned*	*CAG Comm.*
CANBERRA	CA 70 (ex-CAG 2)	Bethlehem Steel Co (Quincy)	3 Sep 1941	19 Apr 1943	14 Oct 1943	15 June 1956

Displacement, tons	13 300 standard; 17 500 full load
Length, feet (*metres*)	664 (*222·3*) wl; 673·5 (*205·3*) oa
Beam, feet (*metres*)	70·8 (*21·6*)
Draft, feet (*metres*)	26 (*7·9*)
Missile launchers	2 twin Terrier surface-to-air launchers
Guns	6—8 inch (*203 mm*) 55 cal (triple) 10—5 inch (*127 mm*) 38 DP (twin) 8—3 inch (*76 mm*) 50 cal AA (twin)
Main engines	4 geared turbines (General Electric), 120 000 shp; 4 shafts
Boilers	4 (Babcock & Wilcox)
Speed, knots	33
Complement	1 273 (73 officers; 1 200 enlisted men)

The *Canberra* and her sister ship *Boston* (CA 69 ex-CAG 1) were the US Navy's first guided missile surface ships. They originally were heavy cruisers (CA) of the "Baltimore" class. The *Canberra* was converted 1952-1956 to a combination gun-missile configuration and reclassified CAG 2 on 4 Jan 1952. Subsequently reverted to original classification of CA 70 on 1 May 1968; as a CA the *Canberra* retained the Terrier missile systems.

Retention of 8 inch guns forward made the *Boston* and *Canberra* valuable in the fire support role during the Vietnam War.

The *Canberra* was decommissioned on 16 Feb 1970 and placed in reserve.

CONVERSION. The *Canberra* was converted to a missile configuration at the New York Shipbuilding Corp, Camden, New Jersey. Conversion included removal of after 8-inch gun turret (143 tons) and after twin 5-inch gun mount; all 40 mm and 20 mm guns replaced by six 3-inch twin mounts (subsequently reduced to four mounts). Original superstructure modified and twin funnels replaced by single large funnel as in "Oregon City" class. Forward pole mast replaced by lattice radar mast and radar platform fitted aft of pole mast. Missile systems include rotating magazine below decks, loading and check-out equipment, two large directors, and two launchers.

ELECTRONICS. The *Canberra* has an SPS-43 search radar antenna atop the pole mast and an SPS-30 antenna on the platform aft of the pole mast. The experimental radar atop the lattice mast has been removed (see photograph of *Boston* in the 1973-1974 and previous editions). TACAN antenna is mounted on the forward mast.

MISSILES. Reportedly, the *Canberra* carries 144 Terrier missiles in two rotating magazines. Each launcher can load and fire two missiles every 30 seconds; loading is completely automatic with the missiles sliding up onto the launchers when in the vertical positions.

NOMENCLATURE. The *Canberra* was originally named *Pittsburgh*; renamed while under construction to honour an Australian cruiser of that name which was sunk at the Battle of Savo Island with several US Navy ships in August 1942. She is the only US warship named for a foreign capital city.

PHOTOGRAPHS. Note that the *Canberra* helicopter platform is angled in on the starboard side to provide for boat stowage.

DISPOSAL
Boston (CAG 1/CA 69) stricken on 1 Nov 1973.

CANBERRA (CA 70) *1968 United States Navy*

Fire Support Ships—*continued*

1 HEAVY CRUISER (CA): "BALTIMORE" CLASS

Displacement, tons	13 600 standard; 17 200 full load
Length, feet (*metres*)	664 (*204·4*) wl; 673·5 (*205·3*) oa
Beam, feet (*metres*)	70·9 (*21·6*)
Draft, feet (*metres*)	26 (*7·9*)
Guns	9—8 inch (*203 mm*) 55 cal (triple) 10—5 inch (*127 mm*) 38 cal DP (twin) 12—3 inch (*76 mm*) 50 cal AA (twin)
Main engines	4 geared turbines (General Electric); 120 000 shp; 4 shafts
Boilers	4 (Babcock & Wilcox)
Speed, knots	33
Complement	1 146 (61 officers, 1 085 enlisted men); designed wartime complement 1 969

Name	*No.*	*Builder*	*Laid down*	*Launched*	*Commissioned*
SAINT PAUL	CA 73	Bethlehem Steel Company, Quincy	3 Feb 1943	16 Sep 1944	17 Feb 1945

SAINT PAUL (CA 73) *1967, United States Navy*

The *Saint Paul* is the last all-gun cruiser of the "Baltimore" class. Fourteen of these ships were completed 1943-1945. This was the largest class of heavy (8-inch gun) cruisers built by any navy. Three missile ship conversions remain on the Navy List (see *Conversion* notes). The *Saint Paul* was the US Navy's last all-gun cruiser in commission except for the *Newport News*; the former ship was decommissioned in 1971 and placed in reserve.

AIRCRAFT. As completed the "Baltimore" class ships had two stern catapults and carried four floatplanes; catapults removed after World War II. Note helicopter on fantail in overhead view of *Saint Paul*.

CONVERSIONS. Two ships of this class were converted to partial missile configurations, the *Boston* (CA 69/CAG 1) and *Canberra* (CA 70/CAG 2); and two ships were converted to all-missile configurations, the *Columbus* (CA 74 now CG 12) and *Chicago* (CA 136 now CG 11). The *Canberra* and the two latter ships remain on the Navy List.

ELECTRONICS. The *Saint Paul's* principal radar antennas when decommissioned were an SPS-37 on the forward pylon mast and an SPS-8 on the after mast; a "bee-hive" TACAN (Tactical Air Navigation system to guide aircraft) was installed atop the forward mast.

Paul also lost the twin 5 inch mount forward of her bridge. Prior to being decommissioned the *Saint Paul* used rocket-assisted 8 inch projectiles during shore bombardment firing in the Vietnam conflict; reportedly, her guns attained a range of 34 miles (approx 60 000 yards), believed to be the longest distance ever fired by a naval gun. It can not be ascertained if this is the maximum range possible with the ship's guns that have been modified to fire the rocket-assisted projectiles that weigh some 113 pounds.

GUNNERY. As built the "Baltimore" class cruisers were armed with nine 8 inch guns, 12—5 inch DP guns, 48—40 mm AA guns, and 23—20 mm AA guns. After World War II all 20 mm weapons were removed and the 40 mm guns were replaced by 20—3 inch AA guns (except in one ship). Subsequently the 5 inch twin mount forward of the bridge was removed from the *Saint Paul* and the number of 3 inch twin gun mounts was reduced.

MODERNISATION. The *Saint Paul* was extensively modified to serve as flagship for the Seventh Fleet in the western Pacific; advanced communications equipment installed and amidships structure built up to provide more office space.

NOMENCLATURE. *Saint Paul* renamed during construction; ex-*Rochester*.

DISPOSALS
Macon (CA 132) stricken on 1 Nov 1969; **Baltimore** (CA 68) stricken on 15 Feb 1971; **Fall River** (CA 131) stricken on 19 Feb 1971; **Pittsburg** (CA 72) stricken on 1 July 1973; **Quincy** (CA 71), **Bremerton** (CA 130) stricken on 1 Oct 1973; **Helena** (CA 75), **Toledo** (CA 133), **Los Angeles** (CA 135) stricken on 1 Jan 1974.

SAINT PAUL (CA 73) *United States Navy*

SAINT PAUL (CA 73) *United States Navy*

COMMAND AND COMMUNICATION SHIPS

This category consists of the command and communication ships operated in support of national and joint US commands. These are different functions than fleet and amphibious command ships that support essentially Navy or Navy-Marine Corp activities.

The only joint command flagship now in commission is the *La Salle* which serves as flagship for the Commander, US Middle East Force who represents US military interests "East of Suez" to the Straits of Malacca. The Commander US Middle East Force is generally a Rear Admiral.

In reserve are two ships configured to serve as afloat command posts for the President or other national authorities and two communication relay ships. The command ships *Northampton* and *Wright* were designated as National Emergency Command Posts Afloat (NECPA) and operated off the Atlantic coast of the United States, prepared to receive the President or other national authorities.

The major communication relay ships *Arlington* and *Annapolis* were operated by the Navy to provide mobile communication facilities for Navy and other service commanders where shore-based communication facilities were inadequate or did not exist. While the command ships *Northampton* and *Wright* are floating command headquarters and their communication facilities are for transmitting and receiving large volumes of voice and teletype communications (as well as electronic data), the communication relay ships *Annapolis* and *Arlington* are equipped to relay large volumes of teletype communications. Further, the two radio relay ships do not have the command centres, theatres, data display facilities, message centres, and staff accommodations that are the keys to the command ships' capabilities.

1 MISCELLANEOUS FLAGSHIP (AGF): CONVERTED AMPHIBIOUS TRANSPORT DOCK

Name	*No.*	*Builder*	*Laid down*	*Launched*	*Commissioned*
***LA SALLE**	AGF 3 (ex-LPD 3)	New York Naval Shipyard	2 Apr 1962	3 Aug 1963	22 Feb 1964

Displacement, tons	8 040 light; 13 900 full load
Length, feet (*metres*)	500 (*152·0*) wl; 521·8 (*158·4*) oa
Beam, feet (*metres*)	84 (*25·6*)
Draft, feet (*metres*)	21 (*6·4*)
Guns	8—3 inch (*76 mm*) 50 cal AA (*twin*)
Main engines	Steam turbines; 24 000 shp; 2 shafts
Boilers	2
Speed, knots	20 sustained; 23 maximum
Complement	387 (18 officers, 369 enlisted men)
Flag accommodations	59 (12 officers, 47 enlisted men)

The *La Salle* serves as flagship for the US Commander Middle East Force, operating in the Persian Gulf, Arabian Sea, and Indian Ocean; the ship is based at Bahrain. She replaced the *Valcour* (AGF 1) in 1972.

Converted in 1972 with elaborate command and communications facilities being installed; accommodations provided for admiral and staff; additional air conditioning fitted; painted white to help retard heat of Persian Gulf area. Reclassified as a flagship and designated AGF 3 on 1 July 1972 (the designation AGF 2 not used because of ship's previous "3" hull number).

DESIGN. The *La Salle* is a former amphibious transport dock (LPD) of the "Raleigh" class. Authorised in Fiscal Year 1961 new construction programme she served as an amphibious ship from completion until 1972.

DISPOSAL

Valcour (AGF 1, ex-AVP 55) stricken in 1972. All other AVP-type ships stricken from Navy List (see 1971-1972 and previous editions for description and disposals); two ships of this type remain in service with the US Coast Guard.

LA SALLE (AGF 3) — *1972, United States Navy*

LA SALLE (AGF 3) — *1972, United States Navy*

1 COMMAND SHIP (CC): CONVERTED HEAVY CRUISER

Name	*No.*	*Builder*	*Laid down*	*Launched*	*Commissioned*
NORTHAMPTON	CC 1 (ex-CLC 1, ex-CA 125)	Bethlehem Steel Co (Quincy)	31 Aug 1944	27 Jan 1951	7 Mar 1953

Displacement, tons	14 700 standard; 17 200 full load
Length, feet (*metres*)	664 (*202·4*) wl; 676 (*206·0*) oa
Beam, feet (*metres*)	71 (*21·6*)
Draft, feet (*metres*)	29 (*8·8*)
Guns	1—5 in (*127 mm*) 54 cal dual-purpose (see *Gunnery* notes)
Helicopters	2 normally carried
Armour	Side 6 in (*152 mm*); Decks 3 in + 2 in (*76 + 51 mm*)
Main engines	4 geared turbines (General Electric); 120 000 shp; 4 shafts
Boilers	4 (Babcock & Wilcox)
Speed, knots	33
Complement	1 191 (68 officers, 1 123 enlisted men)
Flag accommodations	approx 450

The *Northampton* was begun as a heavy cruiser of the "Oregon City" class, numbered CA 125. She was cancelled on 11 Aug 1945 when 56·2 per cent complete. She was re-ordered as a command ship on 1 July 1948 and designated CLC 1 (Task Force Command Ship and later Tactical Command Ship). As CLC 1 she was configured for use primarily by fast carrier force commanders and fitted with an elaborate combat information centre (CIC), electronic equipment, and flag accommodations. She was largely employed as flagship for Commander Second Fleet in the Atlantic prior to her being made available for use by national authorities. Her designation was changed to CC (Command Ship) on 15 April 1961 and she was relieved as Second Fleet flagship on October 1961.

Decommissioned on 8 April 1970 and placed in reserve.

DESIGN. The *Northampton* is one deck higher than other US heavy cruisers to provide additional office and equipment space. Her foremast is the tallest unsupported mast afloat (125 feet). All living and working spaces are air-conditioned. Helicopter landing area aft, but no hangar.

ELECTRONICS. Advanced communications, electronic data processing equipment, and data displays are installed; tropospheric scatter and satellite relay communications facilities. As CLC 1 the *Northampton* carried what was believed the largest radar antenna afloat (see 1968-69 and earlier editions); designated SPS-2; removed in 1963. SPS-37 and SPS-8A search radar antennas on after tower.

Command and Communication Ships—*continued*

"NORTHAMPTON" Type—*continued*

GUNNERY. As built the *Northampton* mounted 4—5 inch and 8—3 inch weapons. The 5 inch guns were Mk 16 54 calibre weapons capable of firing up to 45 rounds per minute. (Similar weapons are installed in US destroyer-type ships built since World War II.) The original 3 inch 50 calibre guns in open twin mounts were replaced by twin 3 inch/70 calibre rapid-fire guns in closed mounts. The latter were removed in 1962 because of high maintenance requirements; removal of the guns and their ammunition hoists, *et cetera*, provided additional space for berthing, offices, and electronic equipment. When decommissioned she was armed with only one 5 inch gun in the "X" position.

OPERATIONAL. The *Northampton* served as flagship of the US Sixth Fleet in the Mediterranean in 1954-1955, and as flagship of the US Second Fleet in the Western Atlantic from 1955 to 1961.

PHOTOGRAPHS. Penultimate configuration shown below; forward 5 inch gun and gun director above bridge subsequently removed. See 1972-1973 edition for later photograph.

NORTHAMPTON (CC 1) *United States Navy*

1 COMMAND SHIP (CC)
1 MAJOR COMMUNICATIONS RELAY SHIP (AGMR) } CONVERTED AIRCRAFT CARRIERS

Name	*No.*	*Builder*	*Laid down*	*Launched*	*CVL Comm*	*CC-AGMR Comm*
WRIGHT	CC 2 (ex-AVT 7, ex-CVL 49)	New York SB Corp	21 Aug 1944	1 Sep 1945	9 Feb 1947	11 May 1963
ARLINGTON (ex-*Saipan*)	AGMR 2 (ex-CC 3, ex-AVT 6, ex-CVL 48)	New York SB Corp	10 July 1944	8 July 1944	14 July 1945	27 Aug 1966

Displacement, tons	14 500 standard; 19 600 full load
Length, feet (*metres*)	664 (*202·4*) wl; 683·6 (*208·4*) oa
Beam, feet (*metres*)	76·8 (*23·6*)
Draft, feet (*metres*)	28 (*8·5*)
Flight deck width, feet (*metres*)	109 (*33·2*)
Guns	*Wright* 8—40 mm anti-aircraft (twin); *Arlington* 8—3 in (*76 mm*) 50 calibre (twin)
Helicopters	5 or 6 carried by *Wright*
Main engines	4 geared turbines (General Electric); 120 000 shp; 4 shafts
Boilers	4 (Babcock & Wilcox)
Speed, knots	33
Complement	746 plus approx 1 000 on command or communications staff

These ships were built as the light carriers *Saipan* (CVL 48) and *Wright* (CVL 49), respectively. They served as experimental and training carriers for a decade before being mothballed in 1967. Both were reclassified as Auxiliary Aircraft Transports on 15 May 1959, being designated AVT 6 (*Saipan*) and AVT 7 (*Wright*). The *Wright* was converted to a command ship at the Puget Sound Naval Shipyard, 1962-1963; the *Saipan* was to have been similarly converted, but the requirement for an additional ship of this category was cancelled. The *Saipan* subsequently was converted to a major communications relay ship at the Alabama Drydock and Shipbuilding Company in 1953-1965, and renamed *Arlington*. See Conversion and Nomenclature notes. The *Arlington* was decommissioned on 14 Jan 1970 and placed in reserve; the *Wright* was similarly decommissioned on 22 May 1970 and placed in reserve.

CONVERSION. The *Wright* was converted to a command ship under the Fiscal Year 1962 authorisation at a cost of $25 000 000. Like the *Northampton*, she is fitted with elaborate communications, data processing, and display facilities for use by national authorities. The command spaces include presentation theatres similar to those at command posts ashore. The *Wright* has the most powerful transmitting antennas ever installed on a ship. They are mounted on plastic-glass masts to reduce interference with electronic transmissions. The tallest mast is 83 feet high and is designed to withstand 100-mph winds. She was reclassified from AVT 7 to CC 2 on 1 Sep 1962.

The *Saipan* was converted to a major communications relay ship at a cost of $26 886 424. She actually began conversion to a command ship (CC 3) and work was halted in February 1964. Work was resumed for her conversion to a communications ship later that year. She is fitted with elaborate communications relay equipment for the support of major commands afloat or ashore. The *Saipan* was reclassified from AVT 6 to CC 3 on 1 Jan 1964, and to AGMR 2 on 3 Sep 1964; she was renamed *Arlington* in April 1965.

WRIGHT (CC 2) *1968, United States Navy*

The flat unencumbered deck of an aircraft carrier-type ship facilitates antenna placement for optimum electromagnetic wave propagation. The new "Blue Ridge" class of amphibious command ships has a similar appearance.

NOMENCLATURE. The Navy's two communications ships are named for the naval radio stations at Arlington, Virginia, and Annapolis, Maryland.

Command and Communication Ships—*continued*

ARLINGTON (AGMR 2)—See previous page *1967, United States Navy*

1 MAJOR COMMUNICATIONS RELAY SHIP (AGMR): CONVERTED ESCORT CARRIER

Name	*No.*	*Builder*	*Laid down*	*Launched*	*CVE Comm.*	*AGMR Comm.*
ANNAPOLIS	AGMR 1 (ex-AKV 39, ex-CVE 107)	Todd Shipyards (Tacoma)	29 Nov 1943	20 July 1944	5 Feb 1945	7 Mar 1964

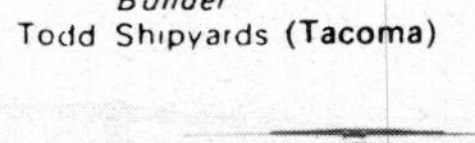

Displacement, tons	11 473 standard; 22 500 full load
Length, feet (*metres*)	525 (*160·0*) wl; 563 (*171·6*) oa
Beam, feet (*metres*)	75 (*22·9*)
Draft, feet (*metres*)	30·6 (*9·3*)
Flight deck width, feet (*metres*)	106 (*32·5*)
Guns	8—3 in (*76 mm*) 50 calibre anti-aircraft (twin)
Main engines	2 turbines (Allis Chalmers); 16 000 shp; 2 shafts
Boilers	4 (Combustion Engineering)
Speed, knots	18
Complement	710 (44 officers, 666 enlisted men)

The *Annapolis* was built as the escort aircraft carrier *Gilbert Islands* (CVE 107). She was decommissioned on 21 May 1946 and placed in reserve; again active as a CVE from Sep 1951 to Jan 1955 when she was again decommissioned. While in reserve, on 7 May 1959 she was reclassified as a Cargo Ship and Aircraft Ferry (AKV 39). Converted into a communications ship by the New York Naval Shipyard, 1962-1964.
Decommissioned on 20 Dec 1969 and placed in reserve.

CONVERSION. During conversion the ship was fitted with elaborate communications relay equipment including approximately 30 transmitters providing frequency band coverage from low frequency to ultra-high frequency. The power outputs of the transmitters vary from 10 to 10 000 watts. Numerous radio receivers also were installed as were five large antenna towers. The ship was renamed *Annapolis* and reclassified AGMR 1 on 1 June 1963.
The former escort carrier, *Vella Gulf* (AKV 11, ex-CVHE 111, ex-CVE 111) was to have been converted to the AGMR 2; her conversion never began because of the availability of the larger carrier *Saipan* for use in this role.

DESIGN. The *Gilbert Islands* was one of 19 "Commencement Bay" class escort carriers built during the latter part of World War II. This ship is the last escort or "jeep" aircraft carrier on the Navy List.

ANNAPOLIS (AGMR 1) *1964, United States Navy*

PHOTOGRAPHS. Note enclosed "hurricane bow" installed during conversion to AGMR to improve rough-sea operation. She has a small helicopter landing area on the port side of the former flight deck.

ANNAPOLIS (AGMR 1) *1966, United States Navy*

AMPHIBIOUS WARFARE SHIPS

The US Navy currently maintains an amphibious force of 65 active ships with the capability of lifting just over one Marine Amphibious Force (MAF) consisting of a re-inforced division/wing team (over 30 000 troops). Normally the amphibious ships are organized into squadrons to deploy two reinforced battalions of Marines afloat in the Pacific and one battalion in the Mediterranean. A fourth battalion is deployed on an intermittent basis to the Caribbean.

All active amphibious ships have a speed of 20 knots or more and all are fitted with helicopter decks.

Five large amphibious assault ships (LHA) are under construction and, with seven older amphibious ships of the LPH type, will provide 12 helicopter carriers. However, some arguments are being advanced for employing up to six of the LPHs in the "sea control" role when the more capable ships become available. Although this would cut in half the number of large helicopter decks available for amphibious operations, one LHA/LPH could be maintained at all times in the western Pacific and one in the Mediterranean.

FIRE SUPPORT SHIPS. The various Surface Combatant Ships (battleships and heavy cruisers) suitable only for gunfire support are listed in a previous section of this edition (Fire Support Ships). The rocket support ships (LFR) are listed in this section because of their L-designations.

TRANSPORT SUBMARINES. The transport submarines of the US Navy are listed in the Submarine section of this edition, in their normal place in the Navy's sequence of hull numbers.

2 AMPHIBIOUS COMMAND SHIPS (LCC): "BLUE RIDGE" CLASS

Displacement, tons	19 290 full load
Length, feet (*metres*)	620 (*188·5*) oa
Beam, feet (*metres*)	82 (*25·3*)
Main deck width, feet (*metres*)	108 (*33*)
Draft, feet (*metres*)	27 (*8·2*)
Missile launchers	2 Basic Point Defense Missile System (BPDMS) launchers for Sea Sparrow missiles
Guns	4—3 inch (*76 mm*) 50 cal AA (twin)
Helicopters	Utility helicopter can be carried
Main engines	1 geared turbine (General Electric); 22 000 shp; 1 shaft
Boilers	2 (Foster Wheeler)
Speed, knots	20
Complement	720 (40 officers, 680 enlisted men)
Flag accommodations	700 (200 officers, 500 enlisted men)

Name	*No.*	*Builder*	*Laid down*	*Launched*	*Commissioned*
* **BLUE RIDGE**	LCC 19	Philadelphia Naval Shipyard	27 Feb 1967	4 Jan 1969	14 Nov 1970
* **MOUNT WHITNEY**	LCC 20	Newport News SB & DD Co	8 Jan 1969	8 Jan 1970	16 Jan 1971

BLUE RIDGE (LCC 19) *1971, United States Navy*

These are the first amphibious force flagships of post-World War II design. They can provide integrated command and control facilities for sea, air and land commanders in amphibious operations. The *Blue Ridge* was authorised in the Fiscal Year 1965 new construction programme, the AGC 20 in FY 1966. An AGC 21 was planned for the FY 1970 programme but cancelled late in 1968. It was proposed that the last ship combine fleet as well as amphibious force command-control facilities.

The phasing out of the converted "Cleveland" class (CLG) fleet flagships has fostered discussion of the potential use of these ships in that role. Their capabilities are greater than would be required by a fleet commander.

Both ships are active, *Blue Ridge* in the Pacific and *Mount Whitney* in the Atlantic.

CLASSIFICATION. Originally designated Amphibious Force Flagships (AGC); redesignated Amphibious Command Ships (LCC) on 1 Jan 1969.

DESIGN. General hull design and machinery arrangement are similar to the "Iwo Jima" class assault ships.

ELECTRONICS. Fitted with SPS-48 three-dimensional search radar, SPS-40 and SPS-10 search radars on "island" structure. After "tower" does not have large antenna sphere originally intended for these ships. (See model photo in 1970-1971 edition.) Tactical Aircraft Navigation (TACAN) pod tops mast.

These ships have three computer systems to support their Naval Tactical Data System (NTDS), Amphibious Command Information System (ACIS), and Naval Intelligence Processing System (NIPS).

GUNNERY. At one stage of design two additional twin 3 inch mounts were provided on forecastle; subsequently deleted from final designs. Antennas and their supports severely restrict firing arcs of guns.

MISSILES. Two BPDMS launchers installed on each ship during 1974 (on antenna deck, aft of superstructure).

PERSONNEL. The ships' complements includes one Marine officer and 12 enlisted men to maintain communications equipment.

PHOTOGRAPHS. The antennas adjacent to the helicopter landing area swing out during flight operations.

MOUNT WHITNEY (LCC 20) *1970, Newport News Shipbuilding & Dry Dock Co*

Amphibious Warfare Ships—*continued*

4 AMPHIBIOUS COMMAND SHIPS (LCC): "MOUNT McKINLEY" CLASS

Displacement, tons	7 510 light; 12 560 full load
Length, feet (*metres*)	435 (*132·2*) wl; 495·3 (*150·5*) oa
Beam, feet (*metres*)	63 (*19·2*)
Draft, feet (*metres*)	28·2 (*8·5*)
Draft, feet (*metres*)	28·2 (*8·5*)
Guns	1—5 inch (*127 mm*) 38 cal DP 4—40 mm AA (twin)
Helicopters	Utility helicopter carried
Main engines	1 turbine (General Electric) 6 000 shp; 1 shaft
Boilers	2 (Babcock & Wilcox in AGC 7; Combustion Engineering in others)
Speed, knots	16·4
Complement (ship)	517 (36 officers, 486 enlisted men)

Name	*No.*	*Builder*	*Launched*	*Commissioned*
MOUNT McKINLEY	LCC 7	North Carolina SB Co	27 Sep 1943	1 May 1944
ESTES	LCC 12	North Carolina SB Co	1 Nov 1943	9 Oct 1944
POCONO	LCC 16	North Carolina SB Co	25 Jan 1945	29 Dec 1945
TACONIC	LCC 17	North Carolina SB Co	10 Feb 1945	17 Jan 1946

Acquired by the Navy in 1943-1944 while under construction to Maritime Commission C2-S-AJ1 design. After 5 inch gun and two twin 40 mm mounts replaced by helicopter platform. The *Pocono* and *Taconic* have a single mast aft in lieu of after king post in earlier ships. All survivors transferred to Maritime Administration reserve (remain on Navy List). They were unable to provide the communication facilities or personnel accommodations required for modern amphibious operations.

CLASSIFICATION. Originally referred to as Auxiliary Combined Operations and Communications Headquarters Ships, but designated Amphibious Force Flagships (AGC); five surviving ships redesignated Amphibious Command Ships (LCC) on 1 Jan 1969.

ELECTRONICS. The *Mount McKinley* and *Estes* had an SPS-37 search radar antenna on the forward king post SPS-30 and SPS-10 antennas on the lattice mast atop the superstructure, and a TACAN antenna installed on the after king post; the *Pocono* and *Taconic* had a TACAN antenna on the forward king post, SPS-30 and SPS-10 antennas on the lattice mast atop the superstructure, and an SPS-37 antenna on the after pole mast.

DISPOSALS
Fourteen World War II amphibious force flagships have been stricken from the Navy List: **Appalachian** (AGC 1) on 1 Mar 1959; **Blue Ridge** (AGC 2), **Rocky Mount** (AGC 3) on 1 Jan 1960; **Ancon** (AGC 4) on 25 Feb 1946; **Catoctin** (AGC 5) on 1 Mar 1959; **Mount Olympus** (AGC 8) in 1961; **Wasatch** (AGC 9) on 1 Jan 1960; **Auburn** (AGC 10), **Panamint** (AGC 13) in late 1960; **Teton** (AGC 14), **Adirondack** (AGC 15) in 1961; **Biscayne** (AGC 18, ex-AVP 11) transferred to US Coast Guard on 19 July 1946. **Eldorado** (AGC/LCC 11) stricken on 16 Nov 1972.
The **Duane** (AGC 6) was retained by the Coast Guard. All except the **Ancon, Duane,** and **Biscayne** were converted C2 merchants hull. Several other Coast Guard cutters served as amphibious command ships with WAGC designations (see "Campbell" class).
The yacht **Williamsburg** (ex-*Aras*, ex-PG 56) was designated AGC 369 in 1945, served as presidential yacht until stricken in 1962 (converted to oceanographic research ship, renamed *Anton Bruun*).

ESTES (LCC 12) *1969, United States Navy*

MOUNT WHITNEY (LCC 20)—see previous page *1973, Giorgio Arra*

MOUNT WHITNEY (LCC 20)—See previous page *1970, United States Navy*

Amphibious Warfare Ships—*continued*

5 AMPHIBIOUS ASSAULT SHIPS (LHA): "TARAWA" CLASS

Displacement, tons	39 300 full load
Length feet (*metres*)	778 (*237·8*) wl; 820 (*250*) oa
Beam, feet (*metres*)	106 (*32·3*)
Draft, feet (*metres*)	27·5 (*8·5*)
Guns	3—5 inch (*127 mm*) 54 cal DP (single) 6—20 mm AA (single)
Missile launchers	2 Basic Point Defence Missile System (BPDMS) launchers firing Sea Sparrow missiles
Aircraft	approx 30 troop helicopters; possibly AV-8 V/STOL close support aircraft in place of some helicopters
Main engines	Geared turbines; 70 000 shp; 2 shafts
Boilers	2
Speed, knots	approx 22 sustained; approx 24 max
Troops	1 825 (163 officers, 1 662 enlisted men)

Name	*No.*	*Erection of First Module*	*Launch*	*Commission*
TARAWA	LHA 1	15 Nov 1973	1 Dec 1973	Mar 1975
SAIPAN	LHA 2	21 July 1972	July 1974	Sep 1975
DA NANG	LHA 3	5 Mar 1973	Dec 1974	Mar 1976
BELLEAU WOOD	LHA 4	23 May 1973	June 1975	Aug 1976
NASSAU	LHA 5	May 1974	Nov 1975	Dec 1976

AMPHIBIOUS ASSAULT SHIP *Artist's concept by G. Meyer*

This is a new class of large amphibious warfare ships combining the characteristics of several previous designs including a full-length flight deck, a landing craft docking well, a large garage for trucks and armoured vehicles, and troop berthing for a reinforced battalion. The LHA 1 was authorised in the Fiscal Year 1969 new construction programme, the LHA 2 and LHA 3 in FY 1970, with two additional ships being authorised in FY 1971. The Navy announced on Jan 20, 1971 that four additional ships of this type previously planned would not be constructed. When the contract was awarded for the LHA programme it included a provision that if the last four ships were not built the government would be charged "cancellation fees" of $109 700 000; this charge—more than half the cost of an LHA—was provided in the FY 1972 budget.

All ships of this class are under construction by Litton Industries at a new ship production facility known as "Ingalls West". The new yard, located at Pasagoula, Mississippi, was developed specifically for multi-ship construction of the same design.

Late in 1971 the Navy announced that the LHA design work was behind schedule. Subsequently the Secretary of Defense announced that the ships would be delayed 12 to 16 months.

CONTRACT. These were the first ships to be procured by the US Navy with the acquisition processes known as Concept Formulation, Contract Definition, and Total Package Procurement. The proposals of Litton Systems Inc and two other shipbuilding firms were submitted in response to specific performance criteria related to the ships' mission. The firms submitted detailed designs and cost estimates for series production of not less than five ships of this type. This procurement process subsequently has been abandoned.

DESIGN. The LHA is intended to combine the features of an amphibious assault ship (LPH), amphibious cargo ship (LKA), and amphibious transport dock (LPD) into a single hull. Beneath the flight deck is a half-length hangar deck, the two being connected by an elevator amidships on the port side and a stern lift; beneath the after elevator is a floodable docking well measuring 268 feet in length and 78 feet in width which is capable of accommodating four LCU 1610 type landing craft.

A 900-hp bow thruster is provided for holding position while offloading landing craft.

ELECTRONICS. Radars planned for these ships are the SPS-52 three-dimensional search, and SPS-10 and SPS-40; advanced communications and helicopter navigation equipment provided. Each ship also will have an Integrated Tactical Amphibious Warfare Data System (ITAWDS) to provide computerised support in control of helicopters and aircraft, shipboard weapons and sensors, navigation, landing craft control, and electronic warfare. SPN 35-aircraft navigation radar fitted on after end of "island" structure.

Chaff Rocket (CHAFROC) launchers fitted on superstructure

FISCAL. In early 1974 the estimated total cost to the government of the five LHAs was $1·145 *billion* or an average of $229 000 000 per ship. See 1973-1974 and previous editions for additional funding information.

GUNNERY. These ships will be armed with three 5 inch/54 calibre Mk 45 light-weight, rapid-fire guns. Six 20 mm guns will be fitted for close-in defense (not Close-in Weapon System).

MEDICAL. These ships are to be fitted with extensive medical facilities including operating rooms, X-ray room, hospital ward, isolation ward, laboratories, pharmacy, dental operating room and medical store rooms.

TARAWA (LHA 1) *Litton Industries*

Amphibious Warfare Ships—*continued*

NOMENCLATURE. These ships are named for actions involving US Marines, with four of the names having previously been carried by aircraft carriers. *Tarawa* (previously honoured by CV 40) and *Saipan* (CVL 48) were World War II landings in the Pacific; *Da Nang* was a battle of the Vietnam War; *Belleau Wood* (CVL 24) was a bitter World War I action in France; and *Nassau* (CVE 16) was a Marine landing during the American Revolution. Note that the tentative names previously listed for LHA 3-5 in *Jane's Fighting Ships* have not been approved and the above names now are reported.

PHOTOGRAPHS. The photographs of the *Tarawa* show the ship being floated in a floating "launch platform" at the time of christening ceremonies. Note the openings for the ship's elevators and docking well stern gate. The photograph at right, with the ship riding high in the water, reveals the ducted thruster near the bow just below the waterline.

TARAWA (LHA 1) *1973, United States Navy*

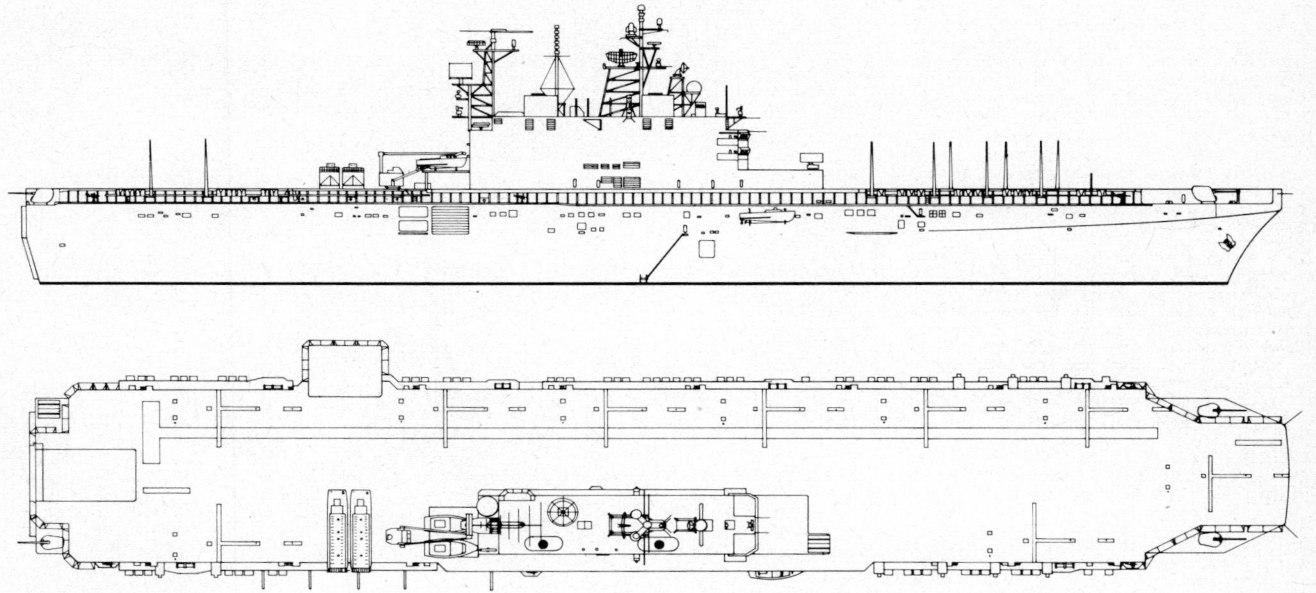

TARAWA (LHA 1) *Litton Industries*

Amphibious Warfare Ships—*continued*

6 AMPHIBIOUS ASSAULT SHIPS (LPH): "IWO JIMA" CLASS

Displacement, tons	17 000 light; 18 300 full load
Length, feet (*metres*)	592 (*180·0*) oa
Beam, feet (*metres*)	84 (*25·6*)
Draft, feet (*metres*)	26 (*7·9*)
Flight deck width, feet (*metres*)	104 (*31·9*) *maximum*
Helicopters	20-24 medium (CH-46) 4 heavy (CH-53) 4 observation (HU-1)
Guns	4—3 inch (*76 mm*) 50 cal AA (twin)
Missile launchers	2 Basic Point Defence Missile System (BPDMS) launchers firing Sea Sparrow missiles
Main engines	1 geared turbine; 23 000 shp; 1 shaft
Boilers	2—655 psi (Combustion Engineering or Babcock & Wilcox)
Speed, knots	20 (sustained)
Complement	528 (48 officers, 480 enlisted men)
Troops	2 090 (190 officers, 1 900 enlisted men)

Name	*No*	*Builder*	*Laid down*	*Launched*	*Commissioned*
*IWO JIMA	LPH 2	Puget Sound Naval Shipyard	2 Apr 1959	17 Sep 1960	26 Aug 1961
*OKINAWA	LPH 3	Philadelphia Naval Shipyard	1 Apr 1960	19 Aug 1961	14 Apr 1962
*GUADALCANAL	LPH 7	Philadelphia Naval Shipyard	1 Sep 1961	16 Mar 1963	20 July 1963
*TRIPOLI	LPH 10	Ingalls Shipbuilding Corp	15 June 1964	31 July 1965	6 Aug 1966
*NEW ORLEANS	LPH 11	Philadelphia Naval Shipyard	1 Mar 1966	3 Feb 1968	16 Nov 1968
*INCHON	LPH 12	Ingalls Shipbuilding Corp	8 Apr 1968	24 May 1969	20 June 1970

INCHON (LPH 12) *1973, United States Navy*

The *Iwo Jima* was the world's first ship designed and constructed specifically to operate helicopters. These ships correspond to Commando Ships in the Royal Navy except that the US ships do not carry landing craft save for the *Inchon* which has davits aft for two LCVPs. Each LPH can carry a Marine battalion landing team, its guns, vehicles, and equipment, plus a reinforced squadron of transport helicopters and various support personnel.

The *Iwo Jima* was authorised in the Fiscal Year 1958 new construction programme, the *Okinawa* in FY 1959, *Guadalcanal* in FY 1960, *Guam* in FY 1962, *Tripoli* in FY 1963, *New Orleans* in FY 1965, and *Inchon* in FY 1966. Estimated cost of the *Iwo Jima* is $40 000 000

The *Guam* was modified late in 1971 and began operations in January 1972 as an interim sea control ship. See section on Surface Combatant section for details. She retains her LPH designation.

DESIGN. These ships resemble World War II-era escort carriers in size but have massive bridge structures, hull continued up to flight deck providing enclosed bows, and rounded flight decks. Each ship has two deck-edge lifts, one to port opposite the bridge and one to starboard aft of island. Full hangars are provided; no arresting wires or catapults. Two small elevators carry cargo from holds to flight deck. Storage provided for 6 500 gallons (US) of vehicle petrol and 405 000 gallons (US) of JP-5 helicopter petrol.

ELECTRONICS. These ships have SPS-40 and SPS-10 search radars, and SPN-10 navigation radar; TACAN pod tops mast; advanced electronic warfare equipment fitted.

GUNNERY. As built each ship had eight 3 inch guns in twin mounts, two forward of the island structure and two at stern "notched" into flight deck. Gun battery reduced by half with substitution of BPDMS launchers (see *Missile* notes).

HELICOPTERS. The flight decks of these ships provides for simultaneous take off or landing of seven CH-46 Sea Knight or four CH-53 Sea Stallion helicopters during normal operations. The hangar decks can accommodate 19 CH-46 Sea Knight or 11 CH-53 Sea Stallion helicopters, or various combinations of helicopters.

MEDICAL. These ships are fitted with extensive medical facilities including operating room, X-ray room, hospital ward, isolation ward, laboratory, pharmacy, dental operating room, and medical store rooms.

MISSILES. All of these ships have been rearmed with two BPDMS launchers for the Sea Sparrow missile, one launcher forward of island structure and one on the port quarter. The *Okinawa* had one BPDMS launcher fitted in 1970 and the second in 1973; *Tripoli* and *Inchon* rearmed in 1972, *Iwo Jima* and *New Orleans* in 1973, and *Guadalcanal* in 1974.

NOMENCLATURE. Amphibious assault ships are named for US Marine combat actions. *Iwo Jima, Okinawa, Guadalcanal,* and *Guam* were World War II campaigns. (The name *Iwo Jima* previously was assigned to the unfinished aircraft carrier CV 46). Marines fought Barbary pirates at Tripoli in 1801 and helped stop the British at New Orleans in 1814. There was also a naval battle at New Orleans during the American Civil War. *Inchon* was the near-perfect 1950 amphibious assault in Korea.

PHOTOGRAPHS. The *Inchon* is shown after operation "End Sweep", the minesweeping of North Vietnamese ports. On her flight deck are a dozen large RH-53 minesweeping helicopters and a smaller CH-46 Sea Knight. The stern view of the *Tripoli*, also taken on her return to Subic Bay in the Philippines from "End Sweep", shows her with CH-46 Sea Knight helicopters and three small, UH-1 "Huey "helicopters (alongside island structure). Note the *Tripoli's* Sea Sparrow BPDMS launchers forward of the island and on the port quarter. The photograph of the *Inchon* on the following page shows her port deck-edge elevator folded against the hull; note her LCVP in davits at stern. The *Inchon* is the only LPH with davits for LCVPs (port and starboard).

NEW ORLEANS (LPH 11) *1973, United States Navy, PH2 T. Ahlgrim*

TRIPOLI (LPH 10) *1973, United States Navy*

Amphibious Warfare Ships—*continued*

DISPOSALS
The **Thetis Bay** (LPH 6, ex-CVHA 1, ex-CVE 90) was stricken on 1 Mar 1964. The **Block Island** (originally CVE 106) was reclassified LPH 1 on 22 Dec 1957 but conversion was cancelled and she reverted to CVE status on 17 Jan 1959; subsequently stricken (as AKV 38) and scrapped.

"ESSEX" CLASS

All three "Essex" class fast carriers employed as amphibious assault ships have been discarded: **Boxer** (LPH 4, ex-CVS 21) stricken on 1 Dec 1969, **Princeton** (LPH 5, ex-CVS 37) stricken on 30 Jan 1970, and **Valley Forge** (LPH 8, ex-CVS 45) stricken on 15 Jan 1970.

INCHON (LPH 12) *1972, Stefan Terzibaschitsch*

5 AMPHIBIOUS CARGO SHIPS (LKA): "CHARLESTON" CLASS

Name	*No.*	*Laid down*	*Launched*	*Commissioned*
***CHARLESTON**	LKA 113	5 Dec 1966	2 Dec 1967	14 Dec 1968
***DURHAM**	LKA 114	10 July 1967	29 Mar 1968	24 May 1969
***MOBILE**	LKA 115	15 Jan 1968	19 Oct 1968	20 Sep 1969
***ST. LOUIS**	LKA 116	3 Apr 1968	4 Jan 1969	22 Nov 1969
***EL PASO**	LKA 117	22 Oct 1968	17 May 1969	17 Jan 1970

Displacement, tons	20 700 full load
Dimensions, feet	575·5 oa × 82 × 25·5
Guns	8—3 inch (*76 mm*) 50 cal AA (twin)
Main engines	1 steam turbine; 22 000 shp; 1 shaft = 20+ knots
Boilers	2 (Combustion Engineering)
Complement	334 (24 officers, 310 enlisted men)
Troops	226 (15 officers, 211 enlisted men)

These ships are designed specifically for the attack cargo ship role; they carry 18 landing craft (LCM) and supplies for amphibious operations. Design includes two heavy-lift cranes with a 78·4-ton capacity, two 40-ton capacity booms, and eight 15-ton capacity booms; helicopter deck aft.
The LKA 113-116 were authorised in the Fiscal Year 1965 shipbuilding programme; LKA 117 in FY 1966 programme.
All built by Newport News Shipbuilding and Dry Dock Co, Virginia. Cost was approximately $21 000 000 per ship.
CLASSIFICATION. Originally designated Attack Cargo Ship (AKA). *Charleston* redesignated Amphibious Cargo Ship (LKA) on 14 Dec 1968; others to LKA on 1 Jan 1969.
ENGINEERING. These are among the first US Navy ships with a fully automated main propulsion plant; control of plant is from bridge or central machinery space console. This automation permitted a 45-man reduction in complement.

NOMENCLATURE. Amphibious cargo ships are named for counties.

DURHAM (LKA 114) *1970, United States Navy*

MOBILE (LKA 115) *1971, US Navy, PH3 E. Larsson*

1 AMPHIBIOUS CARGO SHIP (LKA): "TULARE" TYPE

***TULARE** (ex- *Evergreen Mariner*) LKA 112

Displacement, tons	12 000 light; 16 800 full load
Dimensions, feet	564 oa × 76 × 26
Guns	12—3 inch 50 cal AA (twin)
Main engines	Turbine (De Laval); 22 000 shp; 1 shaft = 23 knots
Boilers	2 (Combustion Engineering)
Complement	437 (38 officers, 399 enlisted men)
Troops	319 (18 officers, 301 enlisted men)

Built by Bethlehem, San Fracisco. Laid down on 16 Feb 1953, launched on 22 Dec 1953. Acquired by Navy during construction. Commissioned on 13 Jan 1956. C4-S-1 type. Has helicopter landing platform and booms capable of lifting 60-ton landing craft. Carries 9 LCM-6 landing craft. Designation changed from AKA 112 to LKA 112 on 1 Jan 1969.
The *Tulare* is expected to be decommissioned when the LHAs are completed.
CLASS. Thirty-five "Mariner" design C4-S-1 merchant ships built during the early 1950s; five acquired by Navy, three for conversion to amphibious ships (AKA-APA) and two for support of Polaris-Poseidon programme (designated AG).

TULARE (LKA 112) *1969, US Navy.*

5 AMPHIBIOUS CARGO SHIPS (LKA): "RANKIN" CLASS

Name	*No.*	*Launched*	*Commissioned*
RANKIN	LKA 103	22 Dec 1944	25 Feb 1945
SEMINOLE	LKA 104	28 Dec 1944	8 Mar 1945
UNION	LKA 106	23 Nov 1944	25 Apr 1945
VERMILION	LKA 107	12 Dec 1944	23 June 1945
WASHBURN	LKA 108	12 Dec 1944	17 May 1945

Displacement, tons	6 456 light; 14 160 full load
Dimensions, feet	459·2 oa × 63 × 26·3
Guns	1—5 inch 38 cal DP (removed from some ships); 8—40 mm AA (twin)
Main engines	Geared turbine (General Electric); 1 shaft; 6 000 shp = 16·5 knots
Boilers	2 (Combustion Engineering)
Complement	247
Troops	138

All built by North Carolina SB Co, Wilmington, North Carolina. Maritime Commission C2-S-AJ3 type. Ten 20 mm AA guns removed. Designation changed from AKA to LKA on 1 Jan 1969.
All of the above ships are in Maritime Administration reserve (remain on the Navy List).

VERMILION LKA 107) *1970, United States Navy*

Amphibious Warfare Ships—*continued*

7 AMPHIBIOUS CARGO SHIPS (LKA): "ANDROMEDA" CLASS

Name	*No.*	*Launched*	*Commissioned*
THUBAN (ex-AK 68)	LKA 19	26 Apr 1943	10 June 1943
ALGOL (ex-*James Baines*)	LKA 54	17 Feb 1943	21 July 1944
CAPRICORNUS (ex-*Spitfire*)	LKA 57	14 Aug 1943	31 May 1944
MULIPHEN	LKA 61	26 Aug 1944	23 Oct 1944
YANCEY	LKA 93	8 July 1944	11 Oct 1944
WINSTON	LKA 94	30 Nov 1944	19 Jan 1945
MERRICK	LKA 97	28 Jan 1945	31 Mar 1945

Displacement, tons	7 430 light; 14 000 full load
Dimensions, feet	435 wl; 495·2 oa × 63 × 24 max
Guns	1—5 inch, 38 cal (removed from some ships); 8—40 mm AA (twin) except *Thuban* 4—3 inch 50 cal AA in lieu of 40 mm
Main engines	Geared turbines (General Electric); 1 shaft; 6 000 shp = 16·5 knots
Boilers	2 (Foster Wheeler)
Complement	247
Troops	414

Algol, *Capricornus*, and *Yancey* built by Moore DD Co, Oakland, California; others by Federal SB & Co, DD Kearney, New Jersey. C2-S-B1 type. Can carry over 5 200 tons of cargo and 2 200 tons of tanks. *Wyandot*, AK A92, assigned to the Navy's Military Sea Transportation Service and manned by a civilian crew since 1963, was redesignated T-AK 283 on 1 Jan 1969. Designation of other ships remaining on Navy List changed from AKA to LKA on 1 Jan 1969.

All of the above ships are in Maritime Administration reserve (remain on the Navy List).

DISPOSALS (since 1 Jan 1970)
Arneb LKA 56 stricken on 13 Aug 1971.

MULIPHEN (LKA 61) *1968, United States Navy*

MULIPHEN (LKA 61) *1968, United States Navy*

2 AMPHIBIOUS TRANSPORTS (LPA): "PAUL REVERE" CLASS

Name	*No.*	*Launched*	*Commissioned*
***PAUL REVERE** (ex-*Diamond Mariner*)	LPA 248	13 Feb 1954	3 Sep 1958
***FRANCIS MARION** (ex-*Prairie Mariner*)	LPA 249	11 Apr 1953	6 July 1961

Displacement, tons	10 709 light; 16 838 full load
Dimensions, feet	563·5 oa × 76 × 27
Guns	8—3 inch 50 cal AA (twin)
Main engines	geared turbines (General Electric); 22 000 shp; 1 shaft = 22 knots
Boiler	2 (Foster Wheeler)
Complement	414 (35 officers, 379 enlisted men)
Troops	1 657 (96 officers, 1 561 enlisted men)

Paul Revere is a C4-S-1 type cargo vessel converted into an Attack Transport by Todd Shipyard Corp, San Pedro, Calif under the Fiscal Year 1957 Conversion programme. Fitted with helicopter platform. *Francis Marion* was a similar "Mariner" type hull converted into an APA by Bethlehem Steel, Key Highway Yard, Baltimore Md, under the Fiscal Year 1959 programme. Both ships were built by New York Shipbuilding Corporation Camden, New Jersey. Designation changed from APA to LPA on 1 Jan 1969. Fitted to serve as force flagships.

These are the only attack transports in active US service. They will be phased out of service when the LHAs are completed.

PAUL REVERE (LPA 248) *1969, United States Navy*

FRANCIS MARION (LPA 249) *1969, Anthony and Joseph Pavia*

7 AMPHIBIOUS TRANSPORTS (LPA): "HASKELL" CLASS

Name	*No.*	*Launched*	*Commissioned*
SANDOVAL	LPA 194	11 Sep 1944	7 Oct 1944
MAGODFFIN	LPA 199	4 Oct 1944	25 Oct 1944
TALLADEGA	LPA 208	17 Aug 1944	31 Oct 1944
MOUNTRAIL	LPA 213	20 Sep 1944	6 Nov 1944
NAVARRO	LPA 215	3 Oct 1944	15 Nov 1944
PICKAWAY	LPA 222	5 Nov 1944	12 Dec 1944
BEXAR	LPA 237	25 July 1945	9 Oct 1945

Displacement, tons	6 720 light; 10 470 fullload
Dimensions, ffee	435·6 wl; 455 oa × 62 × 24
Guns	12—40 mm AA (1 quad, 4 twin) forward quad 40 mm mount removed from some ships
Main engines	Geared turbine; 8 500 shp; 1 shaft = 17·7 knots
Boilers	2 (Babcock & Wilcox)
Complement	536
Troops	1 560

VC2-S-AP5 "Victory" type, all launched in 1944-1945. All have county names. 3 000 tons cargo. All in Maritime Administration reserve (on Navy List). Designation of ships remaining on Navy List changed from APA to LPA on 1 Jan 1969.

The 5-inch gun was removed. *Sherburne* APA 205 converted to missile range instrumentation ship for Poseidon programme; redesignated AGM 22.

DISPOSALS (since 1 Jan 1970)
Okanogan LPA 220 stricken on 1 June 1973.

"BAYFIELD" CLASS

All amphibious transports of the C3-S-A2 type have been stricken.
Cambria LPA 36 stricken on 14 Sep 1970; **Chilton** LPA 38 stricken on 1 July 1972; **Fremont** LPA 44, **Henrico** LPA 45 stricken on 1 June 1973.

SANDOVAL (LPA 194) *1970, United States Navy*

BEVERLY W. REID (LPR 119)—Modernised *1968, United States Navy*

Amphibious Warfare Ships—*continued*

10 AMPHIBIOUS TRANSPORTS (SMALL) (LPR): CONVERTED DE TYPE

Name	*No*	*Launched*	*Commissioned*
LANING	LPR 55 ex-DE 159	4 July 1943	1 Aug 1943
HOLLIS	LPR 86 ex-DE 794	11 Sep 1943	24 Jan 1943
KIRWIN	LPR 90 ex-DE 229	16 June 1944	4 Nov 1945
RINGNESS	LPR 100 ex-DE 590	5 Feb 1944	25 Oct 1944
BEVERLY W. REID	LPR 119 ex-DE 722	4 Mar 1944	25 June 1945
DIACHENKO	LPR 123 ex-DE 690	15 Aug 1944	8 Dec 1944
HORACE A. BASS	LPR 124 ex-DE 691	12 Sep 1944	21 Dec 1944
BEGOR	LPR 127 ex-DE 711	25 May 1944	14 Mar 1945
BALDUCK	LPR 132 ex DE 716	27 Oct 1944	7 May 1945
WEISS	LPR 135 ex-DE 719	17 Feb 1945	7 July 1945

Displacement, tons	1 400 standard; 2 130 full load
Dimensions, feet	300 wl; 306 oa × 37 × 12·6
Guns	1—5 inch (*127 mm*) 38 cal DP; 4—40 mm AA (twin) in modernised ships; 8—40 mm AA (twin) in others
A/S weapons	2 triple torpedo tubes (Mk 32) in modernised ships; depth charges in others
Main engines	Geared turbines (General Electric) with electric drive; 12 000 shp; 2 shafts = 23·6 knots
Boilers	2 ("D" Express)
Complement	204 (designed wartime; 12 or 15 officers, 189 or 192 enlisted men, depending upon DE type)
Troops	162 (12 officers, 150 enlisted men)

These ships are former Destroyer Escorts (DE) converted or completed during World War II to transports for carrying commandoes, reconnaissance troops or frogmen. Fifty-six DEs were completed to this configuration and an additional 38 ships were converted after service as destroyer escorts.
Originally designated as High Speed Transports (APD); designation of 13 ships remaining on Navy List as of 1 Jan 1969 changed to Amphibious Transports (Small) (LPR). Converted from TE and TEV type destroyer escorts with troop quarters being provided, single 5 inch gun and six to eight 40 mm guns (twin) replacing previous armament, davits installed amidships for four LCVPs, and 10-ton capacity boom placed aft.
All surviving ships of this type in the US Navy are in reserve, the last to be decommissioned being the *Beverly W. Reid, Diechenko,* and *Weiss,* all in 1969.
See 1971-1972 edition for detailed disposal and transfer notes.

MODERNISATION. All except *Ringness* and *Begor* were modernised during the 1960s as part of the FRAM II programme. They have new bridge configurations, additional electronic equipment, tripod mast (in some ships place of forward pole mast), improved habitability, ASW torpedo launchers, and retain only two 40 mm twin mounts (aft).

TRANSFERS. Ships of this class serve in the navies of Chile, Colombia, Ecuador, South Korea, Mexico and Taiwan China.

PHOTOGRAPHS. The *Beverly W. Reid* and *Kirwin* have undergone Fleet Rehabilitation and Modernisation (FRAM) process; note enlarged structure between 5 inch gun mount and bridge, modified bridge, additional whip antennas. Both ships retain pole mast (see 1970-1971 edition for photographs of *Ruchamkin* with tripod mast). Neither of these ships has Mk 32 anti-submarine torpedo tubes in these views: normally installed in FRAM transports just forward of boat davits.

DISPOSALS (since 1 Jan 1970)
Knudson LPR 101 stricken on 15 July 1972.

KIRWIN (LPR 90)—Modernised *1963, United States Navy*

12 AMPHIBIOUS TRANSPORT DOCKS (LPD): "AUSTIN" CLASS

Name	*No.*	*Laid down*	*Launched*	*Commissioned*
***AUSTIN**	LPD 4	4 Feb 1963	27 June 1964	6 Feb 1965
***OGDEN**	LPD 5	4 Feb 1963	27 June 1964	19 June 1965
***DULUTH**	LPD 6	18 Dec 1963	14 Aug 1965	12 Apr 1966
***CLEVELAND**	LPD 7	30 Nov 1964	7 May 1966	21 Apr 1967
***DUBUQUE**	LPD 8	25 Jan 1965	6 Aug 1966	1 Sep 1967
***DENVER**	LPD 9	7 Feb 1964	23 Jan 1965	26 Oct 1968
***JUNEAU**	LPD 10	23 Jan 1965	12 Feb 1966	12 July 1969
***CORONADO**	LPD 11	3 May 1965	30 July 1966	23 May 1970
***SHREVEPORT**	LPD 12	27 Dec 1965	22 Oct 1966	12 Dec 1970
***NASHVILLE**	LPD 13	14 Mar 1966	7 Oct 1967	14 Feb 1970
***TRENTON**	LPD 14	8 Aug 1966	3 Aug 1968	6 Mar 1971
***PONCE**	LPD 15	31 Oct 1966	20 May 1970	10 July 1971

"AUSTIN" CLASS—*continued*

Displacement, tons	10 000 light; 16 900 full load
Length, feet (*metres*)	570 (*173·3*) oa
Beam, feet (*metres*)	84 (*25·6*)
Draft, feet (*metres*)	23 (*7·0*)
Guns	8—3 inch (*76 mm*) 50 cal AA (twin)
Helicopters	up to 6 UH-34 or CH-46
Main engines	2 steam turbines (De Laval); 24 000 shp; 2 shafts = 20 knots sustained
Boilers	2 (Babcock & Wilcox)
Complement	490 (30 officers, 460 enlisted men)
Ttoops	930 in LPD 4-6 and LPD 14-16; 840 in LPD 7-13
Flag accommodations	Approx 90 in LPD 7-13

These ships are enlarged versions of the previous "Raleigh" class; most notes for the "Raleigh" class apply to these ships. All 12 of these ships are officially considered in a single class; earlier references to separate classes were based on contract awards to builders.
The LPD 4-6 were authorised in the Fiscal Year 1962 new construction programme, LPD 7-10 in FY 1963, LPD 11-13 in FY 1964, LPD 14 and LPD 15 in FY 1965, and LPD 16 in FY 1966. LPD 16 was deferred in favour of LHA programme; formerly cancelled in Feb 1969. No additional ships of this type are planned in view of the LHA capabilities.
LPD 4-6 built by New York Naval Shipyard; LPD 7-8 built by Ingalls Shipbuilding Corp; LPD 9-15 built by Lockheed Shipbuilding & Construction Co, Seattle, Washington. Completion of later ships has been delayed.

PONCE (LPD 15) *1973, Giorgio Arra*

AUSTIN (LPD) 4 *1973, Giorgio Arra*

SHREVEPORT (LPD 12) *1973, Giorgio Arra*

SHREVEPORT (LPD 12)—see previous page *1973, Giorgio Arra*

RALEIGH (LPD 1)—see following page *1972, United States Navy, PH2 John Smith*

PORTLAND (LSD 37)—see following page *1972, Giorgio Arra*

HERMITAGE (LDS 34)—see following page *1971, Giorgio Arra*

Amphibious Warfare Ships—*continued*

2 AMPHIBIOUS TRANSPORT DOCKS (LPD): "RALEIGH" CLASS

Name	*No.*	*Laid down*	*Launched*	*Commissioned*
•RALEIGH	LPD 1	23 June 1960	17 Mar 1962	8 Sep 1962
•VANCOUVER	LPD 2	19 Nov 1960	15 Sep 1962	11 May 1963

Displacement, tons	8 040 light; 13 900 full load
Length, feet (*metres*)	500 (*152·0*) wl; 521·8 (*158·4*) oa
Beam, feet (*metres*)	84 (*25·6*)
Draft, feet (*metres*)	21 (*6·4*)
Guns	8—3 inch (*76 mm*) 50 cal AA
Helicopters	up to 6 UH-34 or CH-46 (see *Helicopter* notes)
Main engines	2 steam turbines; (De Laval); 24 000 shp; 2 shafts = 20 knots sustained
Boilers	2 (Babcock & Wilcox)
Complement	490 (30 officers, 460 enlisted men)
Troops	930

The amphibious transport dock was developed from the dock landing ship (LSD) concept but provides more versatility. The LPD replaces the Amphibious Transport (LPA) and, in part, the Amphibious Cargo Ship (LKA) and dock landing ship. The LPD can carry a "balanced load" of assault troops and their equipment, has a docking well for landing craft, a helicopter deck, cargo holds and vehicle garages. The *Raleigh* was authorised in the Fiscal Year 1959 new construction programme, the *Vancouver* in FY 1960. Built by New York Naval Shipyard. Approximate construction cost was $29 000 000 per ship.
A third ship of this class, *La Salle* (LPD 3), was reclassified as a command ship (AGF 3) on 1 July 1972.

DESIGN. These ships resemble dock landing ships (LSD) but have fully enclosed docking well with the roof forming a permanent helicopter platform. The docking well is 168 feet long and 50 feet wide, less than half the length of wells in newer LSDs; the LPD design provides more space for vehicles, cargo and troops. Ramps allow vehicles to be driven between helicopter deck, parking area and docking well. side ports provide roll-on/roll off capability when docks are available. An overhead monorail in the docking well with six cranes facilitates loading landing craft.

HELICOPTERS. These ships are not normally assigned helicopters because they lack integral hangars and maintenance facilities. It is intended that helicopters from a nearby amphibious assault ship (LHA or LPH) would provide helicopters during an amphibious operation. Hangars have been fitted (see "Austin" class notes).

LANDING CRAFT. The docking well in these ships can hold one LCU and three LCM-6s or four LCM-8s or 20 LVTs (amphibious tractors). In addition, two LCM-6s or four LCPLs are carried on the boat deck which are lowered by crane.

PHOTOGRAPHS. There are four LCPLs nested on the *Raleigh* between her superstructure and helicopter deck on the 02 level. LPD flight decks extend to stern counter while LSDs have a significant opening where flight deck ends short of stern.

5 DOCK LANDING SHIPS (LSD): "ANCHORAGE" CLASS

Name	*No.*	*Laid down*	*Launched*	*Commissioned*
***ANCHORAGE**	LSD 36	13 Mar 1967	5 May 1968	15 Mar 1969
***PORTLAND**	LSD 37	21 Sep 1967	20 Dec 1969	3 Oct 1970
***PENSACOLA**	LSD 38	12 Mar 1969	11 July 1970	27 Mar 1971
***MOUNT VERNON**	LSD 39	29 Jan 1970	17 Apr 1971	13 May 1972
***FORT FISHER**	LSD 40	15 July 1970	22 Apr 1972	9 Dec 1972

Displacement, tons	8 600 light; 13 700 full load
Dimensions, feet	553·33 oa × 84 × 18·66
Guns	8—3 inch (*76 mm*) 50 cal AA (twin)
Main engines	Geared turbines (De Laval); 24 000 shp; 2 shafts = 20 knots sustained
Boilers	2 (Foster Wheeler except Combustion Engineering in *Anchorage*)
Complement	397 (21 officers, 376 enlisted men)
Troops	376 (28 officers, 348 enlisted men)

Improved dock landing ships, slightly larger than previous class; designed to replace earlier LSDs which are unable to meet 20-knot amphibious lift requirement. Similar in appearance to earlier classes but with a tripod mast. Helicopter platform aft with docking well partially open; helicopter platform can be removed. Docking well approximately 430 × 50 feet can accommodate three LCU-type landing craft. Space on deck for one LCM, and davits for one LCPL and one LCVP. Two 50-ton capacity cranes.
LSD 36 was authorised in Fiscal Year 1965 shipbuilding programme; LSD 37-39 in FY 1966 programme; LSD 40 in FY 1967 programme. *Anchorage* built by Ingalls Shipbuilding; LSD 37-40 by General Dynamics (Quincy).
Estimated construction cost is $11 500 000 per ship.

PENSACOLA (LSD 38) *1971, General Dynamics Corp*

FORT FISHER (LSD 40) *1972, General Dynamics Corp.*

PORTLAND (LDS 37) *1973, Giorgio Arra*

8 DOCK LANDING SHIPS (LSD): "THOMASTON" CLASS

Name	*No*	*Launched*	*Commissioned*
***THOMASTON**	LSD 28	9 Feb 1954	17 Sep 1954
***PLYMOUTH ROCK**	LSD 29	7 May 1954	24 Jan 1955
***FORT SNELLING**	LSD 30	16 July 1954	24 Jan 1955
***POINT DEFIANCE**	LSD 31	28 Sep 1954	31 Mar 1955
***SPIEGEL GROVE**	LSD 32	10 Nov 1955	8 June 1956
***ALAMO**	LSD 33	20 Jan 1956	24 Aug 1956
***HERMITAGE**	LSD 34	12 June 1956	17 Dec 1956
***MONTICELLO**	LSD 35	10 Aug 1956	29 Mar 1957

Displacement, tons	6 880 light; 11 270 full load, *Alamo, Hermitage, Monticello, Spiegel Grove:* 12 150 full load
Dimensions, feet	510 oa × 84 × 19 max
Guns	12—3 inch (*76 mm*) 50 cal AA (twin)
Main engines	Steam turbines (General Electric); 24 000 shp; 2 shafts = 22·5 knots
Boilers	2 (Babcock & Wilcox)
Complement	400
Troops	340

Built by Ingalls Shipbuilding Corp, Pascagoula, Mississippi. Constructed to provide 20-knot LSD capability. Fitted with helicopter platform over docking well; two 5-ton capacity cranes; can carry 21 LCM (6) or 3 LCU and 6 LCM landing craft or approximately 50 LVTs (amphibious tractors) in docking well plus 30 LVTs on mezzanine and super decks (with helicopter landing area clear).
As built each ship had 16—3 inch AA guns; twin mount on each side wall (aft of boats davits) has been removed.
Note pole mast compared to tripod mast of subsequent "Anchorage" class for rapid identification; later class has enclosed 3 inch gun mounts forward of bridge.

NOMENCLATURE. Dock landing ships are named for historic sites in the United States except that the *Anchorage, Portland,* and *Pensacola* primarily honour cities.

Amphibious Warfare Ships—*continued*

SPIEGEL GROVE (LSD 32) *1968. United States Navy*

FORT SNELLING (LSD 30)

SPIEGEL GROVE (LSD 32) *1968, United States Navy*

11 DOCK LANDING SHIPS (LSD): "CASA GRANDE" CLASS

Name	*No*	*Launched*	*Commissioned*
CASA GRANDE	LSD 13	11 Apr 1944	5 June 1944
RUSHMORE	LSD 14	10 May 1944	3 July 1944
SHADWELL	LSD 15	24 May 1944	24 July 1944
CABILDO	LSD 16	28 Dec 1944	15 Mar 1945
CATAMOUNT	LSD 17	27 Jan 1945	9 Apr 1945
COLONIAL	LSD 18	28 Feb 1945	15 May 1945
COMSTOCK	LSD 19	28 Apr 1945	2 July 1945
DONNER	LSD 20	6 Apr 1945	31 July 1945
FORT MARION	LSD 22	22 May 1945	29 Jan 1946
TORTUGA	LSD 26	21 Jan 1945	8 June 1945
WHETSTONE	LSD 27	18 July 1945	12 Feb 1946

Displacement, tons	4 790 standard; 9 375 full load
Dimensions, feet	475·4 oa × 76·2 × 18 max
Guns	8— or 12—40 mm AA (2 quad plus 2 twin in some ships)

CASA GRANDE CLASS—*cont.*

Main engines	Geared turbines (Newport News except Westinghouse in *Fort Marion*); 2 shafts; 7 000 shp except 9 000 in *Fort Marion* = 15·4 knots except 15·6 knots in *Fort Marion*
Boilers	2
Complement	265 (15 officers, 250 men)

LSD 13-19 built by Newport News SB & DD Co, Virginia; LSD 20, 26, 27 built by Boston Navy Yard; LSD 22 by Gulf SB Corp, Chickasaw, Alabama; *Fort Snelling*, LSD 23, and *Point Defiance*, LSD 24, cancelled in 1945; former ship completed for merchant service, reacquired by Navy as cargo ship *Taurus*, T-AK 273, T-AKR 8 (stricken in 1968). LSD 9-12 of this class transferred to Britain in 1943-1944.

Docking well is 392 × 44 feet; can carry 3 LCUs or 18 LSMs or 32 LVTs (amphibious tractors) in docking well. All ships are fitted with helicopter platform.

Catamount, *Colonial*, *Donner* and *Fort Marion*, were modernised under the FRAM II programme in 1960-1962.

All surviving ships of this class are in Navy or Maritime Administration reserve (the latter ships remain on the Navy List).

ARMAMENT. Arrangement differs; all ships have two quad 40 mm mounts on forward superstructure; some have two twin 40 mm mounts on dock walls aft.

As built, each ship had a single 5 inch DP gun, 12—40 mm AA guns, and several 20 mm AA guns.

TRANSFERS

Fort Mandan LSD 21 to Greece on 23 Jan 1971, **San Marcos** LSD 25 to Spain on 1 July 1971

DOCK LANDING SHIPS (LSD): "ASHLAND" CLASS

All ships of this class have been stricken or transferred to foreign navies; see 1972-1973 and previous editions for characteristics.

DONNER (LSD 20) *1968, United States Navy*

COMSTOCK (LSD 19) *1965, United States Navy*

SAN BERNARDINO

Amphibious Warfare Ships—*continued*

20 TANK LANDING SHIPS (LST): "NEWPORT" CLASS

Name	*No.*	*Laid down*	*Launched*	*Commissioned*
***NEWPORT**	LST 1179	1 Nov 1966	3 Feb 1968	7 June 1969
***MANITOWOC**	LST 1180	1 Feb 1967	4 June 1969	24 Jan 1970
***SUMTER**	LST 1181	14 Nov 1967	13 Dec 1969	20 June 1970
***FRESNO**	LST 1182	16 Dec 1967	28 Sep 1968	22 Nov 1969
***PEORIA**	LST 1183	22 Feb 1968	23 Nov 1968	21 Feb 1970
***FREDERICK**	LST 1184	13 Apr 1968	8 Mar 1969	11 Apr 1970
***SCHENECTADY**	LST 1185	2 Aug 1968	24 May 1969	13 June 1970
***CAYUGA**	LST 1186	28 Sep 1968	12 July 1969	8 Aug 1970
***TUSCALOOSA**	LST 1187	23 Nov 1968	6 Sep 1969	24 Oct 1970
***SAGINAW**	LST 1188	24 May 1969	7 Feb 1970	23 Jan 1971
***SAN BERNARDINO**	LST 1189	12 July 1969	28 Mar 1970	27 Mar 1971
***BOULDER**	LST 1190	6 Sep 1969	22 May 1970	30 Apr 1971
***RACINE**	LST 1191	13 Dec 1969	15 Aug 1970	9 July 1971
***SPARTANBURG COUNTY**	LST 1192	7 Feb 1970	11 Nov 1970	1 Sep 1971
***FAIRFAX COUNTY**	LST 1193	28 Mar 1970	19 Dec 1970	16 Oct 1971
***LA MOURE COUNTY**	LST 1194	22 May 1970	13 Feb 1971	18 Dec 1971
***BARBOUR COUNTY**	LST 1195	15 Aug 1970	15 May 1971	12 Feb 1972
***HARLAN COUNTY**	LST 1196	7 Nov 1970	24 July 1971	8 Apr 1972
***BARNSTABLE COUNTY**	LST 1197	19 Dec 1970	2 Oct 1971	27 May 1972
***BRISTOL COUNTY**	LST 1198	13 Feb 1971	4 Dec 1971	5 Aug 1972

Displacement, tons	8 342 full load
Dimensions, feet (*metres*)	522·3 (*158·7*) oa × 69·5 (*21·0*) × 15 (*4·5*) (aft)
Guns	4—3 inch (*76 mm*) 50 cal AA (twin)
Main engines	6 diesels (Alco); 2 shafts, 16 000 hp = 20 knots (sustained)
Complement	213 (11 officers, 202 enlisted men)
Troops	379 (20 officers, 359 enlisted men)

These ships are of an entirely new design larger, and faster than previous tank landing ships. They operate with 20-knot amphibious squadrons to transport tanks, other heavy vehicles, engineer equipment, and supplies which cannot be readily landed by helicopters or landing craft.
The *Newport* was authorised in the Fiscal Year 1965 new construction programme. LST 1180-1187 (8 ships) in FY 1966, and LST 1188-1198 (11 ships) in FY 1967. LST 1179-1181 built by Philadelphia Naval Shipyard, LST 1182-1198 built by National Steel & Shipbuilding Co, San Diego, California. Seven additional ships of this type that were planned for the Fiscal Year 1971 new construction programme have been deferred.

DESIGN. These ships are the first LSTs to depart from the bow-door design developed by the British early in World War II. The hull form required to achieve 20 knots would not permit bow doors, thus these ships unload by a 112-foot ramp over their bow. The ramp is supported by twin derrick arms. A ramp just forward of the superstructure connects the lower tank deck with the main deck and a vehicle passage through the superstructure provides access to the parking area amidships. A stern gate to the tank deck permits unloading of amphibious tractors into the water, or unloading of other vehicles into an LCU or onto a pier. Vehicle stowage is rated at 500 tons and 19 000 square feet (5 000 sq ft more than previous LSTs). Full load draft is 15 feet aft and six feet forward.

NOMENCLATURE. LSTs are named for counties and parishes. In accord with the contemporary US Navy confusion over naming ships, some do not have county or parish suffix.

PHOTOGRAPHS. Note uneven, staggered funnels, bow opening when ramp is lowered, anchors on starboard side forward and at stern, funnel opening in superstructure, and helicopter spots marked aft of funnels. Twin 3 inch closed gun mounts are difficult to distinguish in clutter atop superstructure. *Saginaw* is shown in Mediterranean carrying four pontoon barges lashed amidships.

SPARTANBURG COUNTY (LST 1192) *1972, US Navy, PHAN A. M. Page*

NEWPORT (LST 1179) *1970, United States Navy*

SAGINAW (LST 1188) *1972, Giorgio Arra*

SAGINAW (LST 1188) *1972, Giorgio Arra*

3 TANK LANDING SHIPS (LST): "SUFFOLK COUNTY" CLASS

Name	*No.*	*Builder*	*Launched*
SUFFOLK COUNTY	LST 1173	Boston Navy Yard	5 Sep 1956
LORAIN COUNTY	LST 1177	American SB Co, Lorrain, Ohio	22 June 1957
WOOD COUNTY	LST 1178	American SB Co, Lorrain, Ohio	14 Dec 1957

Displacement, tons	4 164 light; 8 000 full load
Dimensions, feet	445 o a × 62 × 16·5
Guns	6—3 inch (*76 mm*) 50 cal AA (twin)
Main engines	Diesels; 14 400 bhp; 2 shafts; (controllable pitch propellers) = 17·5 knots
Complement	184 (10 officers, 174 men)
Troops	approx 575

Originally a class of seven tank landing ships (LST 1171, 1173-1178 with LST 1172 not built). They were faster and had a greater troop capacity than earlier LSTs; considered the "ultimate" design attainable with the traditional LST bow-door configuration. *Suffolk County* commissioned on 15 Aug 1957, *Lorain County* on 3 Oct 1859, and *Wood County* on 5 Aug 1969.
The surviving ships were decommissioned in 1972 and are in reserve; they probably will be transferred to foreign navies or assigned to the Military Sealift Command for use as cargo ships.
The *Graham County* (LST 1176) has been converted to a gunboat support ship (AGP); see description under Fleet Support Ships.

DESIGN. High degree of habitability with all crew and troop living spaces air conditioned. Can carry 23 medium tanks or vehicles up to 75 tons on 288-foot-long (lower) tank deck. Davits for four LCVP-type landing craft. Liquid cargo capacity of 170 000 gallons (US) diesel or jet fuel plus 7 000 gallons (US) of petrol for embarked vehicles; some ships have reduced troop spaces and carry additional 250 000 gallons (US) of aviation petrol for pumping ashore or to other ships.

ENGINEERING. All built with six Nordburg diesels. *Suffolk County* refitted with six Fairbanks Morse diesels, electric couplings and reduction gears; *Lorain County* and *Wood County* refitted with six Cooper Bessemer diesels, electric couplings and reduction gears.

TRANSFERS
De Soto County LST 1171, **York County** LST 1175 transferred to Italy on 17 July 1972; **Grant County** LST 1174 transferred to Brazil on 15 Jan 1973.

PHOTOGRAPHS. The "Suffolk County" class LSTs are identified by their twin fire control towers forward.

Amphibious Warfare Ships—*continued*

WOOD COUNTY (LST 1178) *1971, J. S. Kinross*

3 TANK LANDING SHIPS (LST): "TERREBONNE PARISH" CLASS

Name	*No.*	*Launched*	*Commissioned*
TERRELL COUNTY	LST 1157	6 Dec 1952	19 Mar 1953
WESTCHESTER COUNTY	LST 1167	18 Apr 1953	10 Mar 1954
WHITFIELD COUNTY	LST 1169	22 Aug 1953	14 Sep 1954

Displacement, tons	2 580 light; 5 800 full load
Dimensions, feet	384 oa × 55 × 17
Guns	6—3 inch (*76 mm*) 50 cal AA (twin)
Main engines	4 diesels (General Motors); 6 000 bhp 2 shafts (controllable pitch propellers) = 15 knots
Complement	115
Troops	395

Originally a class of 15 tank landing ships (LST 1156-1170). *Terrell County* built by Bath Iron Works Corp, Bath Maine; others by Christy Corp.
Six ships were transferred from reserve to the Military Sealift Command in 1972 for use as cargo ships: *Tioga County* LST 1158, *Traverse County* LST 1160, *Wahkiakum County* LST 1162, *Waldo County* LST 1163, *Walworth County*, LST 1164 and *Washoe County* LST 1165. The ships listed above were to transfer to the Military Sealift Command during 1973 but transfer delayed and they were decommissioned. (See Sealift Ships).

DISPOSALS AND TRANSFERS
Terrebonne Parish LST 1156, **Wexford County** LST 1168 transferred to Spain on 29 Oct 1971; **Tom Green County** LST 1159 transferred to Spain on 6 Jan 1972; **Windham County** LST 1170 transferred to Turkey on 1 June 1973; **Vernon County** LST 1161 transferred to Venezuela on 29 June 1973; **Washtenaw County** MSS 2, ex-LST 1166 stricken on 30 Aug 1973.

TERRELL COUNTY (LST 1157) *1969, United States Navy*

"TALBOT COUNTY" CLASS

Both ships of the "Talbot County" class have been stricken; see 1973-1974 and previous editions for characteristics and photographs.
Talbot County LST 1153 stricken on 1 June 1973; **Tallahatchie County** LST 1154 converted to aviation base ship (AVB 2)—stricken in 1970.

SUMNER COUNTY (LST 1148) *1968, United States Navy*

17 TANK LANDING SHIPS (LST): 511-1152 SERIES

Name	*No.*	*Launched*	*Commissioned*
CAROLINE COUNTY	LST 525	20 Dec 1943	14 Feb 1944
CHEBOYGAN COUNTY	LST 533	1 Dec 1943	27 Jan 1944
CHURCHILL COUNTY	LST 583	5 July 1944	2 Aug 1944
DODGE COUNTY	LST 722	21 Aug 1944	13 Sep 1944
DUVAL COUNTY	LST 758	25 July 1944	19 Aug 1944
FLOYD COUNTY	LST 762	1 Aug 1944	5 Sep 1944
HAMPSHIRE COUNTY	LST 819	21 Oct 1944	14 Nov 1944
KEMPER COUNTY	LST 854	20 Nov 1944	14 Dec 1944
LITCHFIELD COUNTY	LST 901	9 Dec 1944	11 Jan 1945
MEEKER COUNTY	LST 980	27 Jan 1944	26 Feb 1944
MIDDLESEX COUNTY	LST 983	10 Feb 1944	25 Mar 1944
PITKIN COUNTY	LST 1082	26 Jan 1945	7 Feb 1954
POLK COUNTY	LST 1084	19 Jan 1945	19 Feb 1945
ST. CLAIR COUNTY	LST 1096	10 Jan 1945	2 Feb 1945
SEDGWICK COUNTY	LST 1123	29 Jan 1945	19 Feb 1945
SUMNER COUNTY	LST 1148	23 May 1945	9 June 1945
SUTTER COUNTY	LST 1150	30 May 1945	20 June 1945

Displacement, tons	1 653 standard; 2 366 beaching; 4 080 full load
Dimensions, feet	316 wl; 328 × oa × 50 × 14
Guns	6—40 mm AA (2 twin and 2 single); reduced in some ships
Main engines	Diesels (General Motors); 1 700 bhp 2 shafts = 11·6 knots
Complement	119
Troops	147

The US Navy built 1 052 LSTs during World War II in two series: LST 1-150 and LST 511-1152; an even 100 ships were cancelled: LST 85-116, 142-156, 182-196, 232-236, 248-260, 296-300, 431-445. Forty-one were lost during the war. Hundreds of these ships have been transferred to foreign navies or converted to auxiliary configurations.
County or Parish names were assigned to 158 LSTs on the Navy List as of 1 July 1955; 36 Japanese-manned LSTs assigned to the Military Sea Transportation Service (MSTS) at that time were not named.
All of the surviving ships of this series are in reserve except for those operated by the Military Sealift Command (listed separately). The latter ships are used as cargo carriers and are no longer suitable for amphibious operations.

DESIGN. These ships are of the classical LST design developed early in World War II by the British; fitted with bow doors, tunnel-like tank deck with trucks, cargo, or landing craft carried on upper deck; small "island" structure aft with davits for two LCVP-type landing craft. Cargo capacity 2 100 tons. Fitted with tripod masts during postwar period.

TRANSFERS. Ships of this class serve in the navies of Brazil, Greece, Indonesia, Japan, South Korea, Malaysia, Mexico, Philippines, Singapore, Spain, Thailand, Taiwan China, Mainland China, and South Vietnam.

DISPOSALS AND TRANSFERS (Since 1 Jan 1970)
Jerome County LST 848 to South Vietnam on 1 Apr 1970; **Snohomish County** LST 1126 stricken on 1 July 1970; **Clarke County** LST 601, **Iredell County** LST 839 to Indonesia on 15 July 1970; **Luzerne County** LST 902, **Monmouth County** LST 1032 stricken on 12 Aug 1970; **Jennings County** LST 846 stricken on 25 Sep 1970; **Harnett County** LST/AGP 821 to South Vietnam on 12 Oct 1970; **Summit County** LST 1146 transferred to Maritime Administration reserve on 16 Mar 1970. **Page County** LST 1076 to Greece on 5 Mar 1971; **Holmes County** LST 836 to Singapore on 1 July 1971; **Outagamie County** LST 1073 to Brazil on 24 May 1971; **Garrett County** LST/AGP 786 to South Vietnam on 24 April 1971; **Hunterdon County** LST/AGP 838 to Malaysia on 1 July 1971; **Park County** LST 1077 to Mexico on 20 Sep 1971; **San Jaoquin County** LST 1122 stricken on 1 May 1972.

1 TANK LANDING SHIP (LST): 1-510 SERIES

BLANCO COUNTY LST 344

Displacement, tons	1 625 light; 2 366 beaching; 4 050 full load
Dimensions, feet	328 oa × 50 × 14·3
Guns	8—40 mm AA (2 twin and 4 single)
Main engines	diesels; (General Motors); 1 700 bhp; 2 shafts = 11·6 knots
Complement	119
Troops	147

Built by Norfolk (Virginia) Navy Yard; launched on 15 Oct 1942; commissioned on 29 Nov 1942.

TRANSFERS (since 1 Jan 1970)
Bulloch County LST 509 transferred to South Vietnam on 1 Apr 1970.

BLANCO COUNTY (LST 344) *courtesy "Our Navy"*

INSHORE FIRE SUPPORT SHIPS (LFR)

All inshore fire support ships have been stricken; see 1973-1974 and previous editions for characteristics and photographs. The converted *Elk River* (ex-LSMR 501) survives as an ocean engineering range support ship (IX 501).
Carronade LFR/IFS 1, **Big Black River** LFR/LSMR 401, **Broadkill River** LFR/LSMR 405, **Lamoille River** LFR/LSMR 512, **Laramie River** LFR/LSMR 513, **Owyhee River** LFR/LSMR 515, **Red River** LFR/LSMR 522, **Smokey Hill River** LFR/LSMR 531 stricken on 1 May 1973.

LANDING CRAFT

1 AMPHIBIOUS ASSAULT LANDING CRAFT: AEROJET-GENERAL DESIGN (JEFF-A)

Weight, tons	85·8 empty; 166·4 gross
Dimensions, feet	99 *oa* × 48 × (height) 23
Main engines	4 gas turbines (Avco-Lycoming T40); 11 200 hp; 4 aircraft type propellers in rotating shrouds for propulsive thrust = approx 50 knots cruise
Lift engines	2 gas turbines (Avco-Lycoming T40); 5 600 hp; 8 horizontal fans (2 sets) for cushion lift
Complement	6

This is an Air Cushion Vehicle (ACV) landing craft being developed by the Aerojet-General Corp and being built by Todd Shipyards, Seattle, Washington, under Navy contract. Construction scheduled to be completed in February 1975 with one year of contractor testing before delivery to Navy in February 1976. (Construction shifted from Tacoma Boatbuilding Co after financial failure of that firm).
Above dimensions are for craft on air cushion; when at rest dimensions will be 97 × 44 × 19. Designed to carry 120 000 pound payload at a design speed of 50 knots (same as Jeff-B). Design features include aluminium construction, bow and stern ramps, cargo deck area of 2 100 square feet; two sound-insulated compartments each hold four persons; three engines housed in each side structure; two propellers in rotating shrouds provide horizontal propulsion and steering.
Performance parameters include four-hour endurance (200 n mile range), four foot obstacle clearance, and capability to maintain cruise speed in Sea State 2 with 25-knot headwind.

PROJECT. Aerojet-General and Bell Aerosystems were awarded contracts in January 1969 to design competitive assault landing craft employing ACV technology. Subsequently, awards were made to both companies in March 1971 to build and test one craft per company.
These are air cushion or bubble craft, supported above the land or water surface by a continuously generated cushion or bubble of air held by flexible "skirts" that surround the base of the vehicle. According to US Navy usage, they differ from surface effect ships (SES) which have rigid sidewalls that penetrate the water surface to help hold the cushion or bubble. Official designation of these craft is Amphibious Assault Landing Craft (AALC), with the Aerojet-General design being referred to as AALC—Jeff(A) and the Bell Aerosystems craft as AALC—Jeff(B)
The two SES constructed for the US Navy are listed with Experimental, Research, and Surveying Ships; also see listing for Patrol Ships and Craft in this edition for additional SES programme details.

AEROJET-GENERAL DESIGN (Model)

1 AMPHIBIOUS ASSAULT LANDING CRAFT: BELL DESIGN (JEFF-B)

Weight, tons	162·5 gross
Dimensions, feet	86·75 *oa* × 47 × (height) 23·5
Main/lift engines	6 gas turbines (Avco-Lycoming T40); 16 800 hp; interconnected with 2 aircraft-type propellers in rotating shrouds for propulsive thrust and 4 horizontal fans for cushion lift = approx 50 knots cruise
Complement	6

ACV landing craft being built by Bell Aerosystems. Scheduled for completion in February 1975 with delivery to Navy in February 1976 after extensive builder's trials.
Above dimensions are for craft on air cushion; when at rest dimensions are 80 × 43 × 19.
Aluminium construction; bow and stern ramps; cargo area of 1 738 square feet; three engines housed in each side structure with raised pilot house on starboard side. Performance parameters similar to Jeff (A).
Distinguished form Aerojet-General craft by having only two shrouded propellers for thrust and steering.

BELL AEROSYSTEMS DESIGN (Model)

46 UTILITY LANDING CRAFT: LCU 1610 SERIES

LCU 1613	**LCU 1627**	**LCU 1641**	**LCU 1651**	**LCU 1661**
LCU 1614	**LCU 1628**	**LCU 1644**	**LCU 1653**	**LCU 1662**
LCU 1616	**LCU 1629**	**LCU 1645**	**LCU 1654**	**LCU 1663**
LCU 1617	**LCU 1630**	**LCU 1646**	**LCU 1655**	**LCU 1664**
LCU 1618	**LCU 1631**	**LCU 1647**	**LCU 1656**	**LCU 1665**
LCU 1619	**LCU 1632**	**LCU 1648**	**LCU 1657**	**LCU 1666**
LCU 1621	**LCU 1633**	**LCU 1649**	**LCU 1658**	**LCU 1667**
LCU 1623	**LCU 1634**	**LCU 1650**	**LCU 1659**	**LCU 1668**
LCU 1624	**LCU 1637**	**LCU 1651**	**LCU 1660**	**LCU 1669**
				LCU 1670

Displacement, tons	200 light; 375 full load
Dimensions, feet	134·9 *oa* × 29 × 6·1
Guns	2—50 cal machine guns
Main engines	Diesels (Detroit); 1 000 bhp; 2 shafts = 11 knots (see *Engineering* notes)
Complement	12 to 14 (enlisted men)

Improved landing craft, larger than previous series; can carry three M-103 or M-48 tanks (approx 64 tons and 48 tons respectively). Cargo capacity 170 tons.
LCU 1610-1612 built by Christy Corp, Sturgeon Bay, Wisconsin; LCU 1613-1619, 1623, 1624 built by Gunderson Bros Engineering Corp, Portland, Oregon; LCU 1620, 1621,1625,1626,1629,1630 built by Southern Shipbuilding Corp, Slidell, Louisiana; LCU 1622 built by Weaver Shipyards, Texas; LCU 1627, 1628, 1631-1636 built by General Ship and Engine Works (last six units completed in 1968). LCU 1638-1645 built by Marinette Marine Corp, Marinette, Wisconsin (completed 1969-1970); LCU 1646-1666 built by Defoe Shipbuilding Co, Bay City, Michigan (completed 1970-1791). The one-of-a-kind aluminium hull, 133·8 ft LCU 1637 built by Pacific Coast Engineering Co, Alameda, California. LCU 1667-1670 built by General Ship & Engine Works, East Boston, in 1973-1974.
LCU 1636, 1638, 1639, 1640 reclassified as YFB 88-91 in October 1969 LCU 1620 and 1625 to YFU 92 and 93 respectively, in April 1971; LCU 1611, 1615 1622 to YFU 97-99 in Feb 1972; LCU 1610,1612 to YFU 100 and 101 respectively, in Aug 1972.

**ENGINEERING. These landing craft have four 250 bhp diesel engines with Kort-nozzle propellers on twin shafts except for the LCU 1620, 1621, and 1625 which have two 500-bhp diesel engines on vertical shafts fitted with vertical-axis, cycloidal six-bladed propellers. The cycloidal propellers provide thrust in any horizontal direction alleviating the need for rudders. The LCU 1622 was to have been fitted with gas-turbine propulsion machinery, but this project was cancelled.
Endurance is 1 200 miles at eight knots.**

TRANSFERS. LCU 1626 was transferred to Burma in 1967.

PHOTOGRAPHS. Note amidships, right-side "Island" structure of LCU 1649; LCU 1625 differs with built up-structure aft. All except LCU 1621, and 1625 have bow and stern ramps.

LCU 1649 *1970, Defoe Shipbuilding*

25 UTILITY LANDING CRAFT: LCU 1466 SERIES

LCU 1466	**LCU 1472**	**LCU 1485**	**LCU 1490**	**LCU 1537**
LCU 1467	**LCU 1473**	**LCU 1486**	**LCU 1492**	**LCU 1539**
LCU 1468	**LCU 1477**	**LCU 1487**	**LCU 1525**	**LCU 1547**
LCU 1469	**LCU 1482**	**LCU 1488**	**LCU 1535**	**LCU 1548**
LCU 1470	**LCU 1484**	**LCU 1489**	**LCU 1536**	**LCU 1559**

Displacement, tons	180 light; 360 full load
Dimensions, feet	115 wl; 119 *oa* × 34 × 6 max
Guns	2—20 mm
Main engines	3 diesels (Gray Marine); 675 bhp; 3 shafts = 18 knots
Complement	14

These are enlarged versions of the World War II-built LCTs; constructed during the early 1950s. LCU 1608 and 1609 have modified propulsion systems; LCU 1582 and later craft have Kort nozzle propellers. LCU 1496 reclassified as YFU 70 on 1 Mar 1966; LCU 1471 to YFU 88 in May 1968; LCU 1576, 1582 and 1608 to YFU 89-91, respectively, in June 1970; LCU 1488, 1491, and 1609 to YFU 94-96 on 1 June 1971; YFU 94 reverted to LCU 1488 on 1 Feb 1972.

CLASSIFICATION. The earlier craft of this series were initially designated as Utility Landing Ships (LSU); redesignated Utility Landing Craft (LCU) on 15 Apr 1952 and classified as sevice craft.

DISPOSALS, TRANSFERS AND LOSSES
LCU 1478 was transferred to Norway and **LCU 1479, 1480, 1501, 1502** were transferred to South Vietnam upon completion; **LCU 1504-1593** were built under US Navy contract for US Army; **LCU 1594-1607** were built in Japan for the Japanese and Nationalist Chinese navies; **LCU 1503** lost accidentally in Aug 1953; **LCU 1476, 1483, 1495, 1497, 1499** to Department of the Interior in 1960-1979; **LCU 1475** to South Vietnam in 1969; **LCU 1493 1494** to South Vietnam in 1970; **LCU 1500** sunk in Vietnam in Mar 1969; **LCU 1481, 1498** to South Vietnam in 1972.

Landing Craft—*continued*

LCU 1468 with mast lowered *United States Navy*

LCU 1488 *1965, United States Navy*

21 UTILITY LANDING CRAFT: LCU 501 SERIES

LCU 539	**LCU 660**	**LCU 768**	**LCU 1124**	**LCU 1430**
LCU 588	**LCU 666**	**LCU 803**	**LCU 1241**	**LCU 1451**
LCU 599	**LCU 667**	**LCU 871**	**LCU 1348**	**LCU 1462**
LCU 608	**LCU 674**	**LCU 893**	**LCU 1348**	
LCU 654	**LCU 742**	**LCU 1045**	**LCU 1387**	

Displacement, tons 143 160 light; 309 to 320 full load
Dimensions, feet 105 wl; 119 oa × 32·7 × 5 max
Guns 2—20 mm
Main engines Diesels (Gray Marine); 675 bhp; 3 shafts = 10 knots
Complement 13 (enlisted men)

Formerly LCT(6) 501-1465 series; built in 1943-1944. Can carry four tanks or 200 tons of cargo. LCU 524, 529, 550, 562, 592, 600, 629, 664, 666, 668, 677, 686, 742, 764, 776, 788, 840, 869, 877, 960, 973, 974, 979, 980, 1056, 1082, 1086, 1124, 1136, 1156, 1159, 1162, 1195, 1224, 1236, 1250, 1283, 1286, 1363, 1376, 1378, 1384, 1386, 1398, 1411, and 1430 reclassified as YFU 1 through 46, respectively, on 18 May 1958; LCU 1040 reclassified YFB 82 on 18 May 1958; LCU 1446 reclassified YFU 53 in 1964; LCU 509, 637, 646, 709, 716, 776, 851, 916, 973, 989, 1126, 1165, 1203, 1232, 1385, and 1388 reclassified as YFU 54 through 69, respectively, on 1 Mar 1966; LCU 780 reclassified as YFU 87. YFU 9 reverted to LCU 666 on 1 Jan 1962; LCU 1459 converted to YLLC 4; LCU 1462 to YFU 102 on 1 Aug 1973 changes reflect employment as general cargo craft assigned to shore commands (see section on Service Craft).

CLASSIFICATION. Originally rated as Landing Craft, Tank (LCT(6)); redesignated Utility Landing Ships (LSU) in 1949 to reflect varied employment; designation changed to Utility Landing Craft (LCU) on 15 Apr 1952 and classified as service craft.

See 1970-1971 edition for war losses, disposals, and transfers prior to 1965.

MECHANISED LANDING CRAFT: LCM 8 TYPE

Displacement, tons 115 full load (steel) or 105 full load (aluminium)
Dimensions, feet 75·6 × 73·7 oa or 21 × 5·2
Main engines 2 diesels (Detroit or General Motors); 650 bhp; 2 shafts = 9 knots
Complement 5 (enlisted men)

Constructed of welded-steel and (later units) aluminium. Can carry one M-48 or M-60 tank (both approx 48 tons) or 60 tons cargo; range is 150 nautical miles at full load. Also operated in large numbers by the US Army.

LCM-8 carrying M-48 tank *United States Navy*

MECHANISED LANDING CRAFT: LCM 6 TYPE

Displacement, tons 60 to 62 full load
Dimensions, feet 56·2 oa × 14 × 3·9
Main engines 2 diesels; 450 bhp; 2 shafts = 9 knots

Welded-steel construction. Cargo capacity is 34 tons or 80 troops.

LANDING CRAFT VEHICLE AND PERSONNEL (LCVP)

Displacement, tons 13·5 full load
Dimensions, feet 35·8 oa × 10·5 × 3·5
Main engines diesel; 1 shaft; 325 bhp = 9 knots

Constructed of wood or fibreglass-reinforced plastic. Fitted with 30-calibre machine guns when in combat areas. Cargo capacity, 8 000 lbs; range, 110 nautical miles at full load.

LCVP from LST 1157 *1969, United States Navy*

2 WARPING TUGS (LWT); NEW CONSTRUCTION

LWT 1 **LWT 2**

Displacement, tons 61 (hoisting weight)
Dimensions, feet 85 oa × 22 × 6·75
Main engines 2 diesels (Harbourmaster); 420 bhp; 2 steerable shafts = 9 knots
Complement 6 (enlisted men)

These craft are employed in amphibious landings to handle pontoon causeways. The LWT 1 and 2 are prototypes of a new, all-aluminium design completed in 1970. A collapsable A-frame is fitted forward to facilitate handling causeway anchors and ship-to-shore fuel lines. They can be "side loaded" on the main deck of an LST 1179 class ship or carried in an LPD/LSD type ship.
The propulsion motors are similar to outboard motors, providing both steering and thrust, alleviating the need for rudders.
Built by Campbell Machine, San Diego, California,

LWT 2 *United States Navy*

WARPING TUGS (LWT)

Displacement, tons approx 120
Dimensions, feet 92·9 oa × 23 × 6·5
Main engines 2 outboard propulsion units = 6·5 knots

These craft are fabricated from pontoon sections and are assembled by the major amphibious commands as required.

LWT 85 *United States Navy*

PATROL SHIPS AND CRAFT

The US Navy has begun construction of a series of 30 hydrofoil missile "ships". These craft are intended to perform a variety of functions, in some instances replacing larger escort ships and destroyers in the severely reduced force levels of the post-Vietnam fleet. In addition, the Navy is continuing to develop advanced coastal and riverine craft for limited US use and for transfer to foreign navies.

SURFACE EFFECT SHIPS. The Navy's combat Surface Effect Ship (SES) programme is described in the listing for Ocean Escorts in this edition of *Jane's Fighting Ships* because of their tentative designation (DS-DSX) and 2 000-ton size.

PATROL FRIGATES. The Navy's patrol frigate (PF) programme is described in the listing for Ocean Escorts because of the size and mission of these ships.

NAVAL RESERVE FORCE. A large number of the Navy's coastal patrol and riverine craft have been assigned to the Naval Reserve Force which are composed of active duty and Naval Reserve personnel.

PHOTOGRAPHS. The artist's concept at right shows the hydrofoil missile craft *Hercules* underway at high speed. Note the four-tube Harpoon missile launchers at the stern, giving the craft twice the missile firepower originally planned.

HERCULES (PHM 2) *Drawing by John J. Olson*

2+4 PATROL HYDROFOILS—GUIDED MISSILE

Name	*No.*	*Laid down*	*Launch*	*Commission*
PEGASUS	PHM 1	10 May 1973	Sep 1974	June 1975
HERCULES	PHM 2	30 May 1974	Mar 1975	June 1975
Four	**PHM**	Proposed Fiscal Year 1975 programme		

Displacement, tons	220 full load
Dimensions, ft (*m*)	foils extended: 131 (*40·0*) oa × 29 (*8·9*) hull × 23·2 (*7·1*) foils retracted: 147·5 (*45·0*) oa × 29 (*8·9*) hull × 9·5 (*2·9*)
Missile launchers	8 launchers (quad) for Harpoon surface-to-surface missile
Guns	1—76 mm 62 calibre AA (Mk 75)
Main engines	foil borne; 1 gas turbine (General Electric); 18 000 shp; waterjet propulsion = 20+ knots hull borne; 2 diesels (Mercedes-Benz); 1 600 bhp; 2 waterjet propulsion units = 12 knots
Complement	approx 21 (accommodations for 4 officers, 17 enlisted men)

The Navy plans to construct 30 "ships" of this design for "shadowing" Soviet naval forces in restricted sea areas, as well as surveillance, screening of amphibious forces, and special missions. The PHM 1 and PHM 2 are being built by the Boeing Company, Seattle, Washington.
The PHM is being developed in conjunction with other NATO navies in an effort to develop a basic design that would be universally acceptable with minor modifications. Germany and Italy have joined the PHM effort with financial support of the ship's development.
The PHM 1 and PHM 2 were authorised in the Fiscal Year 1973 new construction programme. Estimated cost of the two ships is $77 000 000 with subsequent ships having a planned cost of $18 000 000 each (1973 dollars).
DESIGN. The PHM design is based in part on the late hydrofoil gunboat *Tucumcari* (PGH 2). The PHM has fully submerged foils; the forward foil assembly provides steering by rotating the strut about its vertical axis. The foil-borne operation is automatic with a wave-height sensing system to maintain the hull clear of the sea. For displacement operation the forward foil rotates forward and the after foil back and up over the stern. The "span" of the main (after) foil is 47·5 feet. Aluminium construction.

ELECTRONICS. Fitted with the Mk 92 Mod 1 fire control system (Americanised version of the WM-28 radar and weapons control system develcped by N. V. Hollandse Signaalapparaten). The Mk 92 also will be used in the patrol frigate (PF).

ENGINEERING. The PHM's foil-borne propulsion system is an LM 2500 marine gas turbine which drives a waterjet pump displacing 100 000 gallons (US) or 390 tons of water per minute. Hull-borne propulsion is provided by two lightweight diesel engines that power two waterjet pumps in the hull (displacing 33 000 gallons of water each per minute at full power).
The LM 2500 marine gas turbine also is used in the "Spruance" class destroyers, sea control ship (SCS), and patrol frigate (PF).
Foil-borne range at 40+ knots is 600+ nautical miles; hull borne range at 10+ knots is 1 000+ nautical miles.

GUNNERY. Gun armament is a single 76 mm OTO Melara rapid-fire weapon (designated Mk 75 Mod 1 in US service). The same gun also will be used in the PF. No secondary gun armament is planned in US units

MISSILES. Each PHM will have two four-tube lightweight cannister launchers for the Harpoon surface-to-surface missile. No reloads will be carried. This is double the Harpoon armament originally planned.

NOMENCLATURE. PHMs will be named for mythological terms. The PHM 1 originally was named *Delphinus:* renamed *Pegasus* on 26 Apr 1974.

OPERATIONAL. It is planned that these ships will be "in commission" and have commanding officers vice being "in service" with officers-in-charge. Normally they will have an operational endurance of five days, after which they will require refuelIng and resupply.

PEGASUS (PHM 1) *Boeing Company*

PEGASUS (PHM 1) *Boeing Company*

PEGASUS (PHM 1) *Boeing Company*

Patrol Ships and Craft—*continued*

10 PATROL GUNBOATS (PG) } "ASHEVILLE" CLASS
4 PATROL MISSILE BOATS }

Name	*No.*	*Builder*	*Commissioned*
***ASHEVILLE** (NRF)	PG 84	Tacoma Boatbuilding	6 Aug 1966
***GALLUP** (NRF)	PG 85	Tacoma Boatbuilding	22 Oct 1966
***ANTELOPE**	PG 86	Tacoma Boatbuilding	4 Nov 1967
***READY**	PG 87	Tacoma Boatbuilding	6 Jan 1968
***CROCKETT** (NRF)	PG 88	Tacoma Boatbuilding	24 June 1967
***MARATHAN** (NRF)	PG 89	Tacoma Boatbuilding	11 May 1968
***CANON** (NRF)	PG 90	Tacoma Boatbuilding	26 July 1968
***TACOMA** (NRF)	PG 92	Tacoma Boatbuilding	14 July 1969
***WELCH** (NRF)	PG 93	Peterson Builders	8 Sep 1969
***CHEHALIS** (NRF)	PG 94	Tacoma Boatbuilding	11 Aug 1969
***GRAND RAPIDS**	PG 98	Tacoma Boatbuilding	5 Sep 1970
***BEACON**	PG 99	Peterson Builders	21 Nov 1969
***DOUGLAS**	PG 100	Tacoma Boatbuilding	6 Feb 1971
***GREEN BAY**	PG 101	Peterson Builders	5 Dec 1969

Displacement, tons	225 standard; 245 full load
Dimensions, feet	164·5 oa × 23·8 × 9·5
Missile launchers	2 launchers for Standard surface-to-surface missile in *Antelope, Ready, Grand Rapids, Douglas*
Guns	1—3 in (*76 mm*) 50 cal (forward); 1—40 mm (aft); 4—50 cal MG (twin) except 40 mm gun removed from ships with Standard missile
Main engines	CODAG: 2 diesels (Cummins); 1 450 shp; 2 shafts = 16 knots 1 gas turbine (General Electric); 13 300 shp; 2 shafts = 40+ knots
Complement	24 to 27 (3 officers, 21 to 24 enlisted men)

Originally a class of 17 patrol gunboats (PG ex-PGM) designed to perform patrol, blockade, surveillance, and support missions. No anti-submarine capability. Requirement for these craft was based on the volatile Cuban situation in the early 1960s. They are the largest patrol-type craft built by the US Navy since World War II and the first US Navy ships with gas-turbine propulsion.
Built by Tacoma Boatbuilding Co of Tacoma, Washington, and Petersen Builders of Sturgeon Bay, Wisconsin. PG 84 and PG 85 authorised in Fiscal Year 1963 new construction programme; PG 86 and PG 87 in FY 1964; PG 88-90 in FY 1965; PG 92-101 in FY 1966. *Asheville* was laid down on 15 Apr 1964 and launched on 1 May 1965; later ships approximately 18 months from keel laying to completion. Cost per ship approximately $5 000 000.

Eight units have been assigned to the Naval Reserve Force and are manned by composite active—Naval Reserve crews. Four of six units in active Navy service have been fitted with Standard anti-ship missiles and are based in the Mediterranean. Two PGs expected to be transferred to Saudi Arabia,

CLASSIFICATION. These ships originally were classified as motor gunboats (PGM); reclassified as patrol boats (PG) with same hull numbers on 1 Apr 1967. This created a duplication of hull numbers used by the US Navy during World War II for designating ex-British "Arabis" or "Flower" class corvettes acquired under "reverse" lend lease in early 1942 and similar ships built in Canada with US funds (the Canadian-built ships serving in the US or Royal Navy); the first PG 101 was the Canadian-built *Asheville* the first of the US Navy's World War II "frigates" (subsequently redesignated PF 1).
PGM 1-32 were submarine chasers modified during World War II with additional guns; PGM 33-83, 91, 102-121 assigned to gunboats built since 1955 for transfer to foreign navies.

DESIGN. All-aluminium hull and aluminium-fibreglass superstructure. Because of the heat-transmitting qualities of the aluminium hull and the amount of waste heat produced by a gas turbine engine the ships are completely air conditioned.

ENGINEERING. These ships have a Combination Diesel and Gas Turbine (CODAG) propulsion system with twin diesel engines for cruising and a gas turbine for high-speed operations. The gas turbine is an LM1500 with the gas generator essentially the same as the J-79-8 aircraft engine (used in the F-4 Phantom and other aircraft). The transfer from diesel to gas turbine propulsion (or vica versa) can be accomplished while underway with no loss of speed. From full stop these ships can attain 40 knots in one minute; manoeuvrability is exellent due in part to controllable pitch-propellers. Speed and propeller pitch is controlled directly from the pilot house console. Either JP-5 or diesel fuel can be used for both the gas turbine and diesels.
Arrangement of gas turbine intake differs on later ships.

GUNNERY. The *Antelope* and *Ready* have the Mk 87 weapons control system for rapid acquisition and tracking of fast-moving targets; the system can also direct and fire appropriate weapons automatically. The Mk 87 can operate in a radar mode or with a stabilised optical sight on the weather decks. No further procurement of this advanced fire control system is planned in the Navy although it is being fitted to a number of foreign warships. (The Mk 87 is an American-produced copy of the Hollandse Signaalapparaten M22 weapons control system). Other ships have Mk 63 Mod 29 Gunfire Control System with SPG-50 fire control radar.

MISSILES. The *Benica* (PG 96) was experimentally fitted with a single launcher aft for the Standard interim anti-ship missile in 1971; removed prior to transfer to South Korea later that year.
During the latter part of 1971 the *Antelope* and *Ready* were provided with two standard missile launchers. The box-like missile launchers are fitted at the stern (40 mm gun removed); a reload is provided in an adjacent magazine for each launcher; subsequently *Grand Rapids* and *Douglas* fitted with missiles.

NOMENCLATURE. Patrol gunboats are named for small American cities; however, the *Surprise* remembers several earlier US naval ships.

TRANSFERS
Benecia (PG 96) transferred to South Korea on 2 Oct 1971; **Surprise** (PG 97) transferred to Turkey on 28 Feb 1973. **Defiance** (PG 95) transferred to Turkey on 11 June 1973.

PHOTOGRAPHS. Note Mk 87 antenna sphere on the ***Ready.*** **The gas turbine air intake is immediately aft of the bridge structure; the adjacent large funnel is the turbine exhaust with a smaller diesel exhaust stack to either side. The** ***Antelope*** **and** ***Ready*** **are shown at Monaco and the** ***Antelope*** **firing an RIM-66A Standard missile.**

READY (PG 87) *1973, Giorgio Arra*

ANTELOPE (PG 86) *1973, Giorgio Arra*

ANTELOPE (PG 86) firing standard missile *1972, United States Navy*

DOUGLAS (PG 100) *1971, Tacoma Boatbuilding*

MARATHON (PG 89) *1968, United States Navy*

Patrol Ships and Craft—*continued*

1 HYDROFOIL GUNBOAT (PGH): "FLAGSTAFF" TYPE

Name	*No.*	*Laid down*	*Launched*	*In service*
***FLAGSTAFF**	PGH 1	15 July 1966	9 Jan 1968	July 1968

Displacement, tons	56·8 full load
Dimensions, feet	74·4 oa × 21·4 × 4·5 (hull borne) or 13·5 (foils down)
Guns	removed
Main engines	foil borne: 1 gas turbine (Rolls Royce); 3 620 hp; controllable pitch propeller = 40+ knots hull borne; 2 diesels (General Motors); 300 bhp water-jet propulsion = 8 knots
Complement	13 (1 officer, 12 enlisted men)

The *Flagstaff* was a competitive prototype evaluated with the *Tucumcari* (PGH 2). Built by Grumman Aircraft Corporation in Stuart, Florida. Construction cost was $3 600 000. The *Flagstaff* has conducted sea trials with a 152 mm howitzer (see *Gunnery* notes), foil-mounted sonars, and towed shapes representing variable depth sonar (VDS).

DESIGN. The *Flagstaff* has a conventional foil arrangement with 70 per cent of the craft's weight supported by the forward set of foils and 30 per cent of the weight supported by the stern foils. Steering is accomplished by movement of the stern strut about its vertical axis. Foil-borne operation is automatically controlled by a wave-height sensing system. The foils are fully retractable for hull-borne operations. Aluminium construction.

ENGINEERING. During foil-borne operations the propeller is driven by a geared transmission system contained in the tail strut and in the pod located at the strut-foil connection. During hull-borne operation two diessel engines drive a water-jet propulsion system. Water enters the pump inlets through openings in the hull and the thrust is exerted by water flow through nozzles in the transome. Steering in the hull-borne mode is by deflection vanes in the water stream. Rolls-Royce Tyne Mk 621 gas turbine engine.

GUNNERY. Originally armed with one 40 mm gun forward, four ·50 cal MG amidships, and an 81 mm mortar aft. Rearmed in 1971 with a 152 mm gun forward. The weapon was the same used on the Army's Sheridan armoured reconnaissance vehicle; low-velocity firing a fully combustible cartridge. After firing trials in 1971 the gun was removed.

1 EXPERIMENTAL HYDROFOIL (PCH): "HIGH POINT" TYPE

Name	*No.*	*Laid down*	*Launched*	*In service*
***HIGH POINT**	PCH 1	27 Feb 1961	17 Aug 1962	3 Sep 1963

Displacement, tons	100 full load
Dimensions, feet	115 oa × 31 × 6 (hull borne) or 17 (foils down)
Guns	removed
A/S weapons	4 torpedo tubes (twin)
Main engines	foil borne; 2 gas turbines (Bristol Siddeley Marine Proteus); 6 200 shp; 2 paired counter-rotating propellers = 48 knots hull borne; diesel (Curtis Wright); 600 bhp; retractable outdrive with 1 propeller = 12 knots
Complement	13 (1officer, 12 enlisted men)

Experimental hydrofoil submarine chaser. Authorised under Fiscal Year 1960 programme. Built jointly by Boeing Aircraft Corpn, Seattle, Washington, and J. M. Martinac, Tacoma, Washington, at Martinac's Tacoma Yard. Employed in experimental hydrofoil work.

DESIGN. The *High Point's* forward foil is supported by a single strut and the after foil by twin struts. Twin underwater nacelles at the junction of the vertical struts and main full housed contra-rotating, super-cavitating propellers for foil-borne propulsion. After foils modified in 1973 and nacelles repositioned to improve performance in heavy sea states, Also, forward foil strut made steerable to improve manoeuvrability.

GUNNERY. A single 40 mm gun was mounted forward in 1968; subsequently removed.

MISSILES. During 1973-1974 the *High Point* was employed as a test ship for the lightweight cannister launchers for the Harpoon surface-to-surface missile intended for the PHM.

LOSSES
The hydrofoil gunboat **Tucumcari** (PGH 2) ran aground on 16 Nov 1972 and wrecked; plans to restore the craft were dropped due to high costs and she was scrapped in October 1973.

FLAGSTAFF *United States Navy*

FLAGSTAFF (PGH 1) with 152 mm howitzer *1971, US Navy*

FLAGSTAFF (PGH 1) ***Grumman***

HIGH POINT (PCH 1) firing Harpoon *1973, McDonnell Douglas*

HIGH POINT (PCH 1) firing Harpoon *1973, McDonnell Douglas*

HIGH POINT (PCH 1) on early trials *United States Navy*

Patrol Ships and Craft—*continued*

4 FAST PATROL BOATS (PTF): PTF 23 TYPE

• PTF 23 **• PTF 24** **• PTF 25** **• PTF 26**

Displacement, tons	105 full load
Dimensions, feet	94·66 oa × 23·2 × 7
Guns	1—81 mm mortar; 1—50 cal MG (mounted over mortar); 1—40 mm (aft); 2—20 mm (single)
Main engines	2 diesels (Napier Deltic); 6 200 bhp; 2 shafts = approx 40 knots
Complement	approx 20

PTF 23-26 built by Sewart Seacraft Division of Teledyne Inc of Berwick, Louisiana. First unit completed in 1967, others in 1968. Aluminium hulls. Commercial name is "Osprey".

All four units are in service. Several of the Navy's PTFs are assigned to the Naval Reserve Force.

PTF 23 TYPE *United States Navy*

6 FAST PATROL BOATS (PTF): PTF 17 TYPE

• PTF 17 **• PTF 18** **• PTF 19** **• PTF 20** **• PTF 21** **• PTF 22**

Displacement, tons	85 full load
Dimensions, feet	80·3 oa × 24·5 × 6·8
Guns (may vary)	1—81 mm mortar; 1—40 mm; 2—20 mm (single); 1—50 cal MG (mounted over mortar)
Main engines	2 diesels (Napier-Deltic); 6 200 bhp; 2 shafts = approx 45 knots
Complement	19 (3 officers, 16 enlisted men)

PTF 17-22 built by John Trumpy & Sons, Annapolis, Maryland; lead boat completed in late 1967, others 1968-1970. Based on "Nasty" design.

All six units are in service (PTF 21 and 22 were given "commissioned" status on 14 May 1969 but subsequently returned to "in service" on 23 Sep 1970).

PTF 17 Type *1972, Courtesy Ships of the World*

7 FAST PATROL BOATS (PTF): "NASTY" TYPE

• PTF 3 **• PTF 5** **• PTF 6** **• PTF 7** **• PTF 10** **• PTF 11** **• PTF 12**

Displacement, tons	85 full load
Dimensions, feet	80·3 oa × 24·5 × 6·8
Guns (may vary)	1—81 mm mortar; 1—40 mm; 2—20 mm (single); 1—50 cal MG (mounted over mortar)
Main engines	2 diesels (Napier-Deltic); 6 200 bhp; 2 shafts = 45 knots
Complement	19 (3 officers, 16 enlisted men)

PTF 3-16 of the "Nasty" type were built by Boatservice Ltd A/S of Mandal, Norway. Same design as the Norwegian Navy's "Tjeld" class torpedo boats. PTF 3 and PTF 4 delivered to USA in December 1962, PTF 5-8 in April 1964, and PTF 9-16 in September 1964. Hulls made of two layers of mahogany which sandwich a layer of fibreglass. British engines. Endurance is 450 miles at 41 knots or 600 miles at 25 knots.

DISPOSALS AND LOSSES

PTF 1 (ex-PT 810) and **PTF 2** (ex-PT 811) stricken from the Navy list on 1 Aug 1955 (sunk as targets). Sunk in Vietnam: **PTF 4** on Nov 4 1965, **PTF 8** on 16 June 1966, **PTF 9** on 7 Mar 1966, **PTF 14** on 22 Apr 1966, **PTF 15** on 22 Apr 1966, and **PTF 16** on 19 Aug 1966; **PTF 13** disposed of in 1972.

PTF 6 *1973, United States Navy*

1 COASTAL PATROL AND INTERDICTION CRAFT

Displacement, tons	71·25 full load
Dimensions, feet	99·2 oa × 18 × 6
Guns	2—30 mm MG (twin)
Main engines	3 gas turbines (Avco-Lycoming TF-25); 5 400 hp; water-jet propulsion = 45 knots; 2 auxiliary outboard drive diesels; 300 bhp
Complement	approx 15 (varies with armament)

The US Navy has developed the Coastal Patrol and Interdiction Craft (CPIC) for coastal/inshore operations, succeeding the PTF types. The CPIC is capable of operating in rougher water than the PTFs and is more adaptable for cold and hot weather operating areas.

The prototype CPIC was built by Tacoma Boatbuilding Co, Tacoma, Washington; completed in 1973. The prototype will be transferred to South Korea after trials and evaluation. Additional units may be built in South Korea. US Navy requirements for these craft are being studied.

Basic CPIC design provides for two 30 mm twin gun mounts, one forward and one amidships on 01 deck level aft of bridge. Other weapons may be carried as required for specific operations including possibly the Harpoon missile in light weight canister launcher.

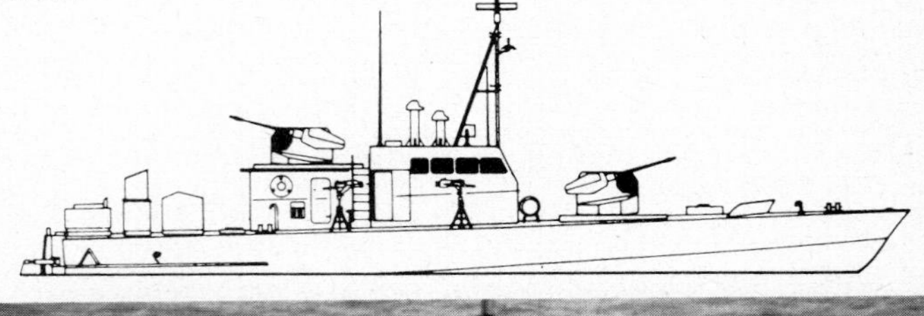

CPIC on trials *1974, United States Navy*

RIVERINE WARFARE CRAFT

2+ PATROL BOATS (PB): NEW DESIGN

two **PB** Mark I series
several **PB** Mark III series

Displacement, tons	Mk I: 26·9 light; 36·3 full load Mk III: 31·5 light; 41·25 full load
Dimensions, feet	Mk I: 65 oa × 16 × 4·9 Mk III: 65 oa × 18 × 5·9
Guns	6—20 mm or ·50 cal MG (1 twin, 4 single)
Main engines	Diesel (Detroit); 1 635 bhp; 3 shafts = 26 knots

The PB series is being developed as replacements for the "Swift" type inshore patrol craft (PCF). Mk I built by Sewart Seacraft, Berwick, Louisiana; Mk III by Peterson Builders Sturgeon Bay, Wisconsin. Two Mark I prototypes completed in 1972 and delivered to the Navy in 1973 for evaluation; assigned to Naval Reserve Force. Additional units of the Mk III design are being constructed for the Philippine Navy. Procurement of the PB Mk III for the US Navy is under consideration. (The PB Mark II design was not built).

Basic weapons arrangement provides for a twin gun mounting above the pilot house and four single mountings on the main deck. The Mk III design has the pilot house offset to starboard to provide space on port side for installation of additional weapons (see drawing).

PB Mk I on trials *1972, Sewart Seacraft*

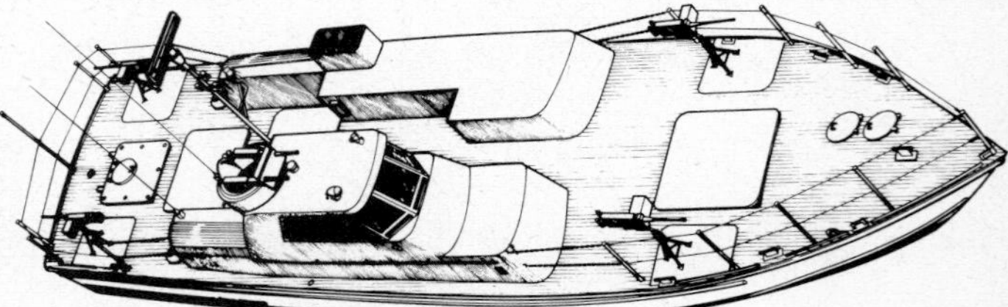

PB Mk III

Riverine Warfare Craft—*continued*

5 INSHORE PATROL CRAFT (PCF): "SWIFT" TYPE

five **PCF** Mark 1 series

Displacement, tons	22·5 full load
Dimensions, feet	50·1 oa × 13 × 3·5
Guns	1—81 mm mortar, 3—50 cal MG (twin MG mount atop pilot house and single MG mounted over mortar)
Main engines	2 geared diesels (General Motors); 960 shp; 2 shafts = 28 knots
Complement	6 (1 officer, 5 enlisted men)

The "Swift" design is adapted from the all-metal crew boat which is used to support off-shore drilling rigs in the Gulf of Mexico. Approximately 125 built since 1965. Most transferred to South Vietnam (see below).
Designation changed from Fast Patrol Craft (PCF) to Inshore Patrol Craft on 14 Aug 1968.

TRANSFERS. PCF 33, 34, and 83-86 transferred to the Philippines in 1966. Additional PCFs of this type constructed specifically for transfer to Thailand, the Philippines, and South Korea; not assigned US hull numbers in the PCF series. 104 PCFs formerly manned by US Navy personnel transferred to South Vietnam in 1968-1970.

PCF MARK 1 TYPE *1969, United States Navy*

21 RIVER PATROL BOATS (PBR)

21 **PBR** Mk II series

Displacement, tons	8
Dimensions, feet	32 oa × 11 × 2·6
Guns	3—·50 cal MG (twin mount forward; single aft); 1—40 mm grenade launcher; 1—60 mm mortar in some boats
Main engines	2 geared diesels (General Motors); water jets = 25+ knots
Complement	4 or 5 (enlisted men)

Fibreglass hull river patrol boats. Approximately 500 built 1967-1973; most transferred to South Vietnam.

PBR Mk II Type *United States Navy*

2 ASSAULT SUPPORT PATROL BOATS (ASPB)

Displacement, tons	36·25 full load
Dimensions, feet	50 oa × 15·6 × 3·75
Guns (varies)	1 or 2—20 mm (with 2—·50 cal MG in boats with one 20 mm) 2—30 cal MG; 2—40 mm high-velocity grenade launchers
Main engines	2 diesels (General Motors); 2 shafts = 14 knots sustained
Complement	6 (enlisted)

The ASPB was designed specifically for riverine operations to escort other river craft, provide mine countermeasures during river operations, and interrupt enemy river traffic. Welded-steel hulls. Armament changed to above configuration in 1968; some boats have twin—50 cal MG "turret" forward in place of single 20 mm gun.
Note that open stern well is plated over in the ASPB pictured here (A-131-2); a view of an ASPB with 81 mm mortar/·50 cal MG aft appears in the 1968-1969 editions.

ASSAULT SUPPORT PATROL BOAT (ASPB) *1968, United States Navy*

13 "MINI" ARMOURED TROOP CARRIERS (ATC)

Dimensions feet	36 oa × 12·66 × 3·5
Main engines	2 diesels (General Motors); water-jet propulsion = 28 knots except one unit with gas turbines.
Complement	2
Troops	15 to 20

A small troop carrier for riverine and swimmer delivery operations; aluminium hull; ceramic armour. Draft is one foot when underway at high speed. The last of the Vietnam-era ATCs have been disposed of along with several hundred riverine warfare craft.

"MINI" ARMOURED TROOP CARRIER (36-ft)

1 COMMAND AND CONTROL BOAT (CCB)

Displacement, tons	80 full load
Dimensions, feet	61 oa × 17·5 × 3·4
Guns	3—20 mm; 2—·30 cal MG; 2—40 mm high velocity-grenade launchers
Main engines	2 diesels (Detroit); 2 shafts = 8·5 knots max (6 knots sustained)
Complement	11

These craft serve as afloat command posts providing command and communications facilities for ground force and boat group commanders. Heavily armoured. Armament changed to above configuration in 1968. Converted from LCM-6 landing craft.

COMMAND CONTROL BOAT *United States Navy*

SWIMMER SUPPORT CRAFT

The US Navy operates several specialised craft in support of "frogmen" (combat swimmers) assigned to SEAL (Sea-Air-Land) teams, Underwater Demolition Teams (UDT), and Explosive Ordenance Disposal (EOD) teams. Most of the craft listed in previous editions have been discarded and the primary craft in service today is the 36-foot Medium SEAL Support Craft (MSSC). A new craft for this role probably will be developed in the near future.

MEDIUM SEAL SUPPORT CRAFT(MSSC) *United States Navy*

MINE WARFARE SHIPS

The US Navy's mine warfare forces have undergone substantial reductions during the past few years. With respect to the numbers of minesweepers in the active fleet, the reduction was from a peak strength of 86 ocean minesweepers (MSO) in 1968 to only some five active units in mid-1974. However, 29 additional ocean and coastal (MSC) minesweepers are operated by the Naval Reserve Force with composite active duty-reserve crews. This reduction has been offset in part by the greater use of mine countermeasure helicopters. By mid-1974 there were some 20 RH-53D Sea Stallion helicopters assigned to Mine Countermeasures Squadron One. The squadron had six months of experience in mine countermeasure operations off North Vietnamese ports and harbours during Operation "Endsweep" in 1973. Subsequently, the squadron has deployed to the Middle East to assist in clearing the Suez Canal.

These helicopters can operate from amphibious ships and are air transportable in Air Force C-5A long-range transports. Thus, if land bases are available in the vicinity of an amphibious group assembling for an assault operation, the minesweeping helicopters could be flown to the area and embarked aboard ship. This capability can, in some situations, overcome the slow-speed (15-knot maximum) of the ocean minesweepers that prevented their accompanying 20-knot amphibious ships.

The capabilities of helicopters to locate and sweep certain types of advanced mines is severely limited. However, there is no effort currently underway in the US Navy to develop an advanced mine-hunting craft similar to recent craft of this type in the British, French and Soviet navies.

The US Navy also is limited in its minelaying capabilities. The Navy's minelaying capabilities are vested in attack aircraft on board aircraft carriers (which were employed in the 1972 mining of North Vietnames ports and harbours), and in attack submarines. Although the covert operation characteristics of nuclear-propelled submarines are preferable in certain mining operations, modern US Navy SSNs have only four torpedo tubes and a limited number of reload spaces; thus, with possible requirements to carry long-range torpedoes, short anti-submarine torpedoes, SUBROC submarine missiles, and tube-launched decoy devices, the feasibility of providing tube-launched mines to a submarine is limited.

Mines also can be laid by the Navy's P-3 Orion patrol aircraft and the Air Force's B-52 strategic bombers (with minelaying being a secondary mission of the Strategic Air Command). The use of these aircraft presuppose the availability of aircraft for this purpose, the proximity of air bases, and no interference from hostile aircraft in the mining area.

NOMENCLATURE. Minesweepers are named for birds and terms indicating action or aggressiveness.

OCEAN MINESWEEPER (MSO): "ABILITY" CLASS

The two surviving minesweepers of this class, **Alacrity** (MSO 520) and **Assurance** (MSO 521), have been allocated to sonar test programmes and redesignated as auxiliary ships AG 520 and AG 521, respectively. See listing under Experimental, Research, and Surveying Ships. **Ability** (MSO 519) of this class stricken on 1 Feb 1971.

4 OCEAN MINESWEEPERS (MSO): "ACME" CLASS

Name	*No.*	*Launched*	*Commissioned*
ACME	MSO 508	23 June 1955	27 Sep 1956
***ADROIT** (NRF)	MSO 509	20 Aug 1955	4 Mar 1957
ADVANCE	MSO 510	12 July 1957	16 June 1958
***AFFRAY** (NRF)	MSO 511	18 Dec 1956	8 Dec 1958

Displacement, tons	720 light; 780 full load
Dimensions, feet	173 oa × 35 × 10
Guns	1—20 mm AA or 1—40 mm AA; 2—50 cal MG
Main engines	4 diesels (Packard); 2 800 bhp; 2 shafts = 14 knots
Complement	78 (8 officers, 70 enlisted men); 86 in NRF ships (3 officers, 36 enlisted active duty; 3 officers, 44 enlisted reserve)

This class is different from the "Agile" type but has similar basic particulars. All built by Frank L. Sample, Jnr, Inc, Boothbay Harbour, Maine. Plans to modernise these ships were cancelled (see notes under "Agile" class).

Two ships were decommissioned and placed in reserve late in 1970. *Adroit* and *Affray* are assigned to Naval Reserve training, manned partially by active and partially by reserve personnel (see notes under "Agile" class).

PHOTOGRAPHS. Note 40 mm gun in *Affray* and 20 mm gun visible in *Advance*.

AFFRAY (MSO 511) *1969, United States Navy*

ADVANCE (MSO 510) *1968, United States Navy*

40 OCEAN MINESWEEPERS (MSO): "AGILE" CLASS

Name	*No.*	*Launched*	*Commissioned*
AGILE	MSO 421	19 Nov 1955	21 June 1956
AGGRESSIVE	MSO 422	4 Oct 1952	25 Nov 1953
BOLD	MSO 424	14 Mar 1953	25 Sep 1953
BULWARK	MSO 425	14 Mar 1953	12 Nov 1953
***CONSTANT** (NRF)	MSO 427	14 Feb 1952	8 Sep 1954
***DASH** (NRF)	MSO 428	20 Sep 1952	14 Aug 1953
***DETECTOR** (NRF)	MSO 429	5 Dec 1952	26 Jan 1954
***DIRECT** (NRF)	MSO 430	27 May 1953	9 July 1954
***DOMINANT** (NRF)	MSO 431	5 Nov 1953	8 Nov 1954
***ENGAGE** (NRF)	MSO 433	18 June 1953	29 June 1954
EMBATTLE	MSO 434	27 Aug 1953	16 Nov 1954
***ENHANCE**	MSO 437	11 Oct 1952	16 Apr 1955
***ESTEEM** (NRF)	MSO 438	20 Dec 1952	10 Sep 1955
***EXCEL** (NRF)	MSO 439	25 Sep 1953	24 Feb 1955
***EXPLOIT** (NRF)	MSO 440	10 Apr 1953	31 Mar 1954
***EXULTANT** (NRF)	MSO 441	6 June 1953	22 June 1954
***FEARLESS**	MSO 442	17 July 1953	22 Sep 1954
***FIDELITY**	MSO 443	21 Aug 1953	19 Jan 1955
FIRM	MSO 444	15 Apr 1953	12 Oct 1954
***FORTIFY** (NRF)	MSO 446	14 Feb 1953	16 July 1954
***ILLUSIVE**	MSO 448	12 July 1952	14 Nov 1953
***IMPERVIOUS** (NRF)	MSO 449	29 Aug 1952	15 July 1954
***IMPLICIT** (NRF)	MSO 455	1 Aug 1953	10 Mar 1954
***INFLICT** (NRF)	MSO 456	6 Oct 1953	11 May 1954
LUCID	MSO 458	14 Nov 1953	4 May 1955
NIMBLE	MSO 459	6 Aug 1954	11 May 1955
OBSERVER	MSO 461	19 Oct 1954	31 Aug 1955
PINNACLE	MSO 462	3 Jan 1955	21 Oct 1955
***PLUCK** (NRF)	MSO 464	6 Feb 1954	11 Aug 1954
PRIME	MSO 466	27 May 1954	11 Oct 1954
REAPER	MSO 467	25 June 1954	10 Nov 1954
SKILL	MSO 471	23 Apr 1955	7 Nov 1955
VITAL	MSO 474	12 Aug 1953	9 June 1955
***CONQUEST** (NRF)	MSO 488	20 May 1954	20 July 1955
***GALLANT** (NRF)	MSO 489	4 June 1954	14 Sep 1955
***LEADER**	MSO 490	15 Sep 1954	16 Nov 1955
***PLEDGE** (NRF)	MSO 492	20 July 1955	20 Apr 1956
STURDY	MSO 494	28 Jan 1956	23 Oct 1957
SWERVE	MSO 495	1 Nov 1955	27 July 1957
VENTURE	MSO 496	27 Nov 1956	3 Feb 1958

Displacement, tons	665 light; 750 full load
Dimensions, feet	165 wl; 172 × 36 × 13·6
Guns	1—40 mm AA; 2—·50 cal MG (replaced by 2—20 mm AA in several ships); some modernised ships are unarmed
Main engines	4 diesels (Packard); 2 shafts; controllable pitch propellers; 2 280 bhp = 15·5 knots; *Dash, Detector, Direct* and *Dominant*, have 4 diesels (General Motors); 1 520 bhp (see *Modernisation* notes)
Complement	78 (8 officers, 70 enlisted men); 86 in NRF ships (3 officers, 36 enlisted active duty; 3 officers, 44 enlisted reserve)

These ships were built on the basis of mine warfare experience in the Korean War (1950-1953); they have wooden hulls and non-magnetic equipment. *Bold* and *Bulwark* were built by the Norfolk (Virginia) Naval Shipyard; others by private yards.

Thirty-six ships of this class transferred to NATO navies upon completion.
Initially designated as minesweepers (AM); reclassified as ocean minesweepers (MSO) in Feb 1955. Originally fitted with UQS-1 mine detecting sonar.

Beginning in 1970 a number of these ships were decommissioned and placed in reserve or assigned to Naval Reserve training; see *Status* notes.

ENGINEERING. Diesel engines are fabricated of non-magnetic stainless steel alloy to help reduce possibility of detonating magnetic mines. Range is 2 400 miles at ten knots.

MODERNISATION. The 62 ocean minesweepers in commission during the mid-1960s all were to have been modernised; estimated cost and schedule per ship were $5 000 000 and ten months in shipyard. However, some of the early modernisations took as long as 26 months which, coupled with changes in mine countermeasure techniques, led to cancellation of programme after 13 ships were modernised: MSO 433, 437, 438, 441-443, 445, 446, 448, 449, 456, 488, and 490.

The modernisation provided improvements in mine detection, engines, communications, and habitability: four Waukesha Motor Co diesel engines installed (plus two or three

Mine Warfare Ships—*continued*

"AGILE" CLASS—*continued*

diesel generators for sweep gear), SQQ-14 sonar with mine classification as well as detection capability provided, twin 20 mm AA in some ships (replacing single 40 mm because of space requirements for sonar hoist mechanism), habitability improved, and advanced communications equipment fitted; bridge structure in modernised ships extended around mast and aft to funnel. Complement in active modernised ships is 6 officers and 70 enlisted men.
Some MSOs have received SQQ-14 sonar but not full modernisation.

STATUS. Of the surviving ships of this class, only five were to be in active commission as of 1 Aug 1974; *Enhance, Fearless, Fidelity, Illusive,* and *Leader.* On that date four MSOs were to have transferred to the Naval Reserve Force: *Engage, Impervious, Fortify,* and *Inflict.* These units bring to 18 the number of "Agile" class MSOs assigned to the Naval Reserve Force (in addition to two MSOs of the "Acme" class). Seventeen "Agile" class ships (and two "Acme" class ships) are laid up in reserve.

TRANSFERS. Ships of this class serve in the navies of Belgium, France, Italy, Netherlands, Norway, Philippines, Portugal, Spain and Uruguay.

DISPOSALS AND TRANSFERS (since 1 Jan 1970)
Avenge MSO 423 stricken on 1 Feb 1970 (fire); **Sagacity** MSO 469 stricken on 1 Oct 1970 (grounding); **Notable** MSO 460, **Rival** MSO 468, **Salute** MSO 470, **Valor** MSO 472 stricken on 1 Feb 1971; **Vigor** MSO 473 transferred to Spain on 5 Apr 1972; **Conflict** MSO 426, **Guide** MSO 447 stricken on 9 June 1972; **Dynamic** MSO 432; **Pivot** MSO 463, **Persistent** MSO 491 to Spain on 1 July 1972; **Endurance** MSO 435, **Loyalty** MSO 457 stricken on 1 July 1972; **Energy** MSO 436, **Firm** MSO 444 transferred to the Philippines on 5 July 1972; **Force** MSO 445 sunk 24 April 1973 (Fire).

LEADER (MSO 490) no gun *1972, Harbor Boat Building Co*

EXCEL (MSO 439) no gun *1971, United States Navy*

EXPLOIT (MSO 440) with 40 mm gun *1969, United States Navy*

ENHANCE (MSO 437) no guns *1971, Harbor Boat Building Co*

11 COASTAL MINESWEEPERS (MSC): "BLUEBIRD" CLASS

Name	*No.*	*Launched*	*Commissioned*
BLUEBIRD	MSC 121	11 May 1953	24 July 1953
CORMORANT	MSC 122	8 June 1953	14 Aug 1953
***PEACOCK**	MSC 198	19 June 1954	7 Feb 1955
***PHOEBE**	MSC 199	21 Aug 1954	29 Apr 1955
***SHRIKE**	MSC 201	21 July 1954	21 Mar 1955
***THRASHER**	MSC 203	6 Oct 1954	16 Aug 1955
***THRUSH**	MSC 204	5 Jan 1955	8 Nov 1955
***VIREO**	MSC 205	30 Apr 1954	7 June 1955
***WARBLER**	MSC 206	18 June 1954	16 July 1955
***WHIPPOORWILL**	MSC 207	13 Aug 1954	20 Oct 1955
***WOODPECKER**	MSC 209	7 Jan 1955	3 Feb 1956

Displacement, tons	320 light; 370 full load
Dimensions, feet	144 oa × 28 × 8·2
Guns	2—20 mm AA (twin)
Main engines	2 diesels (Packard); 1 200 bhp; 2 shafts = 12·5 knots (MSC 201-209 2 diesels (General Motors); 880 bhp; 2 shafts = 12 knots)
Complement	39-40 (4 or 5 officers, 35 enlisted men); 38 in NRF ships (1 officer, 11 enlisted active duty; 4 officers, 22 enlisted reserve)

Constructed throughout of wood and other materials with the lowest possible magnetic attraction to attain the greatest possible safety factor when sweeping for magnetic mines. Fitted with UQS-1 sonar. Range is 2 500 miles at ten knots.
Only named vessels AMS 121, 122, 190-209 were commissioned into US Navy with MSC 200 and 202 being transferred to Spain in 1959 (replaced by MSC 298 and 290 in US Navy)
An additional 167 coastal minesweepers of this design were built in US private shipyards for NATO and other allied navies (see *Transfers*).
Bluebird decommissioned in 1971 and *Cormorant* in 1970 and placed in reserve. The nine other ships are manned jointly by active and reserve crews and assigned to Naval Reserve training/Naval Reserve Force.

TRANSFERS. Minesweepers of this class serve in the navies of Belgium, Denmark, France, Greece, Indonesia, Japan, South Korea, Netherlands, Norway, Pakistan, Philippines, Portugal, Spain, Taiwan China, Thailand, Tunisia, Turkey, and South Korea. (See 1971-1972 and previous editions for details of earlier transfers).

DISPOSALS AND TRANSFERS (since 1 Jan 1970)
Jacana MSC 193, **Meadow Lark** MSC 196 transferred to Indonesia on 7 Apr 1971; **Falcon** MSC 190, **Limpkin** MSC 195 to Indonesia on 24 June 1971; **Hummingbird** MSC 192 to Indonesia on 12 July 1971; **Frigate Bird** MSC 191 to Indonesia on 11 Aug 1971; **Kingbird** MSC 194 stricken on 1 July 1972 (collision); **Parrot** MSC 197 stricken in Aug 1972; **Widgeon** MSC 208 stricken on 2 July 1973; **Parrot** MSC 197 stricken on 22 Aug 1973 (employed as training ship for Navy League Sea Cadets in Washington, DC).
Albatross MSC 289 and **Gannet** MSC 290 of a modified design were stricken on 1 Apr 1970.

PEACOCK (MSC 198) *United States Navy*

Mine Warfare Ships—*continued*

ILLUSIVE (MSO 4488) alongside WESTCHESTER COUNTY (LST 1167) *1973, US Navy, JOC J.J. Gravat*

BLUEBIRD (MSC 121) *1967, United States Navy*

FLEET MINESWEEPERS (MSF): "AUK" AND "ADMIRABLE" CLASSES

The 29 surviving fleet minesweepers (MSF) of the "Auk" and "Admirable" classes were stricken by the US Navy on 1 July 1972. See 1972-1973 and previous editions for names, hull numbers, and characteristics. Subsequently, 21 of these ships were transferred to Mexico on 19 Sep 1972 and in Feb 1973, with 10 ships intended for active service and the remainder for parts cannibalisation.

TRANSFERS. Ships of the "Auk" class serve in the navies of South Korea, Mexico, Norway, Peru, Philippines, Taiwan China, and Uruguay; ships of the "Admirable" class serve in the navies of Burma, Dominican Republic, Mexico, Taiwan China, and South Vietnam.

Bittern MHC 43, a prototype coastal mine hunter built in 1955-1957, has been on loan to a commercial operator since July 1966; officially stricken by US Navy on 1 Feb 1972.

MINE COUNTERMEASURES SHIPS (MCS)

The large mine countermeasures ship **Ozark** MCS 2 (ex-LSV 2, ex-CM 7, ex-AP 107) stricken in 1974, reportedly for transfer to Turkey.
All other mine countermeasure ships, fleet minelayers (MMF), and fast minelayers (MMD) have been stricken or transferred to other navies. See 1973-1974 and previous editions for MCS characteristics and ship lists.

MINE COUNTERMEASURES CRAFT

16 MINESWEEPING BOATS (MSB)

MSB 6	**MSB 16**	**MSB 28**	**MSB 40**
MSB 7	**MSB 17**	**MSB 29**	**MSB 41**
MSB 13	**MSB 25**	**MSB 35**	**MSB 51**
MSB 15	**MSB 26**	**MSB 36**	**MSB 52**

Displacement, tons	30 light; 39 full load except MSB 29, 80 full load
Dimensions, feet	57·2 × 15·5 × 4 except MSB 29, 82 × 19 × 5·5
Guns	several MG (Vietnam configuration)
Main engines	2 geared diesels (Packard); 2 shafts; 600 bhp = 12 knots
Complement	6 (enlisted)

Wooden-hull minesweepers intended to be carried to theatre of operations by large assault ships; however, they are too large to be easily handled by cranes and assigned to sweeping harbours. From 1966 to Sep 1970 they were used extensively in Vietnam for river operations.

Of 49 minesweeping boats of this type built only 16 remain in active service all based at Charleston, South Carolina. (See 1971-1972 and previous editions for details of earlier disposals and additional data).

MSB 1-4 were ex-Army minesweepers built in 1946 (since discarded), MSB 5-54 (less MSB 24) were completed in 1952-1956. MSB 24 was not built. MSB 29 built to enlarged design by John Trumpy & Sons, Annapolis, Maryland in an effort to improve seakeeping ability.
Normally commanded by chief petty officer or petty officer first class.

GUNNERY. MSBs serving in South Vietnam were fitted with several machineguns and removable fibreglass armour. Note machineguns in tub amidships and on bow of MSB 17; shown below sweeping on the Long Tao river in South Vietnam.

MSB 17 *1966, United States Navy*

1 INSHORE MINESWEEPER (MSI): "COVE" CLASS

***CAPE** MSI 2

Displacement, tons	120 light; 240 full load
Dimensions, feet	105 × 22 × 10
Main engines	2 GM diesels; 1 shaft; 650 bhp = 12 knots
Complement	21 (3 officers, 18 men)
Guns	removed

The *Cape* and a sister ship *Cove* (MSI 1) were prototype inshore minesweepers authorised under the Fiscal Year 1956 new construction programme. Both built at Bethlehem Shipyards Co, Bellingham, Washington. *Cape* laid down on 1 May 1957, launched on 5 Apr 1968, and placed in service on 27 Feb 1959.
The *Cape* is operated by the Naval Undersea Research Development Center, San Diego, California; neither in service nor in commission.
Cove MSI 1 transferred to Johns Hopkins Applied Physics Laboratory on 31 July 1970; technically she remains on the Navy List.
MSI 3-10 were built in the Netherlands for the Dutch Navy under US Military Assistance Programme; MSI 11 and MSI 12 built in Denmark under MAP; MSI 13 and MSI 14 built in United States for Iran; MSI 15-19 built in United States for Turkey.

CAPE MSI 2 *1968, United States Navy*

SPECIAL MINESWEEPERS (MSS)

The special minesweeper **MSS 1** (ex-SS *Harry L. Gluckman*) was stricken in 1974. See 1973-1974 and previous editions for characteristics and photographs.

MINESWEEPING LAUNCHES (MSL)

None of the 36-foot minesweeping launches remain in service. See 1973-1974 and previous editions for characteristics and photographs.

RIVERINE MINE COUNTERMEASURE CRAFT

None of the riverine minecountermeasure craft developed by the US Navy during the Vietnam War remain in service; they have been transferred to South Vietnam or scrapped, except for a few laid up in reserve. These craft were patrol minesweepers (MSR), modified ASPB patrol craft; river minesweepers (MSM), converted from LCM-6 landing craft; and small drone minesweepers (MSD). See 1972-1973 and previous editions for characteristics and photographs.

UNDERWAY REPLENISHMENT SHIPS

Underway replenishment (UNREP) ships provide fuel, munitions, provisions, spare parts, and other materiel to warships in forward areas.

In addition, most US Navy replenishment ships are fitted with helicopter platforms to permit helicopters to transfer supplies by vertical replenishment (VERTREP). Virtually all materiel except fuel oil can be transferred by helicopter, reducing, or if fuel oil is not required alleviating, the need for the replenishment ship and warship to steam in close company. Helicopters are carried specifically for this purpose by the newer ammunition ships (AE), the combat store ships (AFS), and the fast combat support ships (AOE). Carrier-based helicopters are sometimes employed in this role when an aircraft carrier is in the area.

Planned UNREP ship force levels provide a wartime capability to support deployed carrier and amphibious task groups in up to four or five locations simultaneously. This plan is based on the availability of some storage depots on foreign territory, and the use of Military Sealift Ships to carry fuels, munitions, and stores from the United States or overseas sources for transfer to UNREP ships in overseas areas.

During peacetime some 16 to 18 UNREP ships normally are deployed in the Mediterranean and western Pacific areas in support of the 6th and 7th Fleets, respectively.

Early in 1974 the Secretary of Defense announced plans for modernisation of the UNREP force, with two ammunition ships (AE), three combat stores ships (AFS), and ten fleet oilers (AO) planned for the Fiscal Year 1975-1979 new construction programmes.

Most UNREP ships are Navy manned and armed; however, beginning in 1972, an increasing number of these ships are being operated by the Military Sealift Command (MSC) with civilian crews. The latter ships are not armed and have T- designations.

8 AMMUNITION SHIPS (AE): "KILAUEA" CLASS

Name	*No.*	*Laid down*	*Launched*	*Commissioned*
***KILAUEA**	AE 26	10 Mar 1966	9 Aug 1967	10 Aug 1968
***BUTTE**	AE 27	21 July 1966	9 Aug 1967	29 Nov 1968
***SANTA BARBARA**	AE 28	20 Dec 1966	23 Jan 1968	11 July 1970
***MOUNT HOOD**	AE 29	8 May 1967	17 July 1968	1 May 1971
***FLINT**	AE 32	4 Aug 1969	9 Nov 1970	20 Nov 1971
***SHASTA**	AE 33	10 Nov 1969	3 Apr 1971	26 Feb 1972
***MOUNT BAKER**	AE 34	10 May 1970	23 Oct 1971	22 July 1972
***KISKA**	AE 35	4 Aug 1971	11 Mar 1972	16 Dec 1972

Displacement, tons	20 500 full load
Dimensions, feet	564 oa × 81 × 25·7
Guns	8—3 inch (*76 mm*) 50 cal AA (twin)
Helicopters	2 UH-46 Sea Knight cargo helicopters normally assigned
Main engines	Geared turbines (General Electric); 22 000 shp; 1 shaft = 20 knots
Boilers	3 (Foster Wheeler)
Complement	401 (28 officers, 373 enlisted men)

Ammunition ships of an advanced design. Fitted for rapid transfer of missiles and other munitions to ships alongside or with helicopters in vertical replenishment operations (VERTREP). Helicopter platform and hangar aft. AE 26 and 27 authorised in Fiscal Year 1965 new construction programme, AE 28 and 29 in FY 1966, AE 32 and 33 in FY 1967, and AE 34 and 35 in FY 1968. AE 26 and 27 built by General Dynamics Corp, Quincy, Massachusetts; AE 28 and 29 Bethlehem Steel Corp, Sparrows Point, Maryland; and AE 32-35 by Ingalls Shipbuilding Corp, Pascagoula, Mississippi.

The 3 inch guns are arranged in twin closed mounts forward and twin open mounts aft, atop superstructure, between funnel and after booms.

All of these ships are active.

KISKA (AE 35) *1972, Ingalls Shipbuilding*

BUTTE (AE 27) *1972, Giorgio Arra*

5 AMMUNITION SHIPS (AE): "SURIBACHI" CLASS

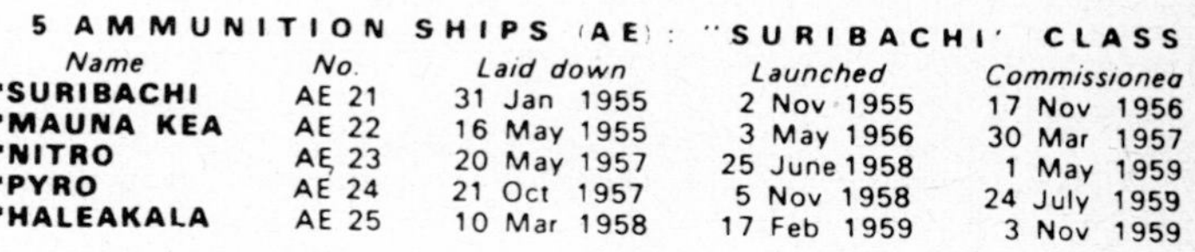

Name	*No.*	*Laid down*	*Launched*	*Commissioned*
***SURIBACHI**	AE 21	31 Jan 1955	2 Nov 1955	17 Nov 1956
***MAUNA KEA**	AE 22	16 May 1955	3 May 1956	30 Mar 1957
***NITRO**	AE 23	20 May 1957	25 June 1958	1 May 1959
***PYRO**	AE 24	21 Oct 1957	5 Nov 1958	24 July 1959
***HALEAKALA**	AE 25	10 Mar 1958	17 Feb 1959	3 Nov 1959

Displacement, tons	7 470 light; 10 000 standard; 17 500 full load
Dimensions, feet	512 oa × 72 × 29
Guns	4—3 inch (*76 mm*) 50 cal AA (twin)
Main engines	Geared turbines (Bethlehem); 16 000 shp; 1 shaft = 20·6 knots
Boilers	2 (Combustion Engineering)
Complement	316 (18 officers, 298 enlisted men)

Ammunition ships designed specifically for underway replenishment. All built by Bethlehem Steel Corp, Sparrows Point Maryland. A sixth ship of this class to have been built under the FY 1959 programme was cancelled.

All ships modernised in 1960s, being fitted with high-speed transfer equipment, three holds configured for stowage of missiles up to and including the 33-foot Talos, and helicopter platform fitted aft (two after twin 3 inch gun mounts removed).

Arrangements of twin 3 inch gun mounts differ, some ships have them in tandem and and others side-by-side.

All of these ships are active.

NOMENCLATURE. Ammunition ships are named for volcanoes and explosives (eg *Nitro* for nitroglycerine and *Pyro* for pyrotechnic).

PYRO (AE 24) *1971, US Navy, PH 2, Brian L. Chandler*

HALEAKALA (AE 25) *1968, United States Navy*

FLINT (AE 32) *1971, Ingalls Shipbuiding*

Underway Replenishment Ships—*continued*

2 AMMUNITION SHIPS (AE): "WRANGELL" CLASS

Name	No.	Launched	Commissioned
WRANGELL (*ex-Midnight*)	AE 12	14 Apr 1944	28 May 1944
FIREDRAKE (*ex-Winged Racer*)	AE 14	12 May 1944	27 Dec 1944

Displacement, tons: 6 350 light; 15 295 full load
Dimensions, feet: 435 wl; 459·2 oa × 63 × 28·2
Guns: 2 or 4—3 inch (*76 mm*) 50 cal AA (single)
Main engines: Geared turbine (General Electric); 6 000 shp; 1 shaft = 16·4 knots
Boilers: 2 (Babcock & Wilcox or Combustion Engineering)
Complement: approx 265

C2 type cargo ships built by North Carolina Shipbuilding Co, Wilmington, NC. Officially the "Mount Hood" class, the *Mount Hood* AE 11 of this type being sunk in World War II. One 5 inch gun and four 40 mm AA guns removed; the *Firedrake* has a helicopter platform installed aft in place of two after 3 inch guns. Both ships are in reserve.

DISPOSALS
Diamond Head AE 19 stricken on 1 Mar 1973; **Paricutin** AE 18 stricken on 1 June 1973; **Great Sitkin** AE 17 stricken on 2 July 1973; **Vesuvius** AE 15, **Mount Katmai** AE 16 stricken on 14 Aug 1973.

WRANGELL (AE 12) — *1968, United States Navy*

FIREDRAKE (AE 14) — *1969, United States Navy*

1 AMMUNITION SHIP (AE): "LASSEN" CLASS

Name	No.	Launched	Commissioned
MAUNA LOA	AE 8	14 Apr 1943	27 Oct 1943

Displacement, tons: 5 220 light; 14 225 full load
Dimensions, feet: 435 wl; 459 oa × 63 × 26·5
Guns: 2—3 inch (*76 mm*) 50 cal AA (single)
Main engines: Diesel (Nordberg); 6 000 bhp; 1 shaft = 15·3 knots
Complement: 281

Built by the Tampa Shipbuilding Co, Tampa, Florida. Modified C2 type, converted by Navy. Original armament was one 5 inch gun, four 3 inch guns, and four 40 mm AA AA guns. *Mauna Loa* transferred to Maritime Administration reserve in 1960; re-acquired and returned to the Navy in Sep 1961 and recommissioned on 27 Nov 1961; fitted with helicopter platform aft. Decommissioned and placed in reserve in 1970.

DISPOSALS
Akutan AE 13 stricken in 1961, **Lassen** AE 3 stricken on 1 July 1961, **Mount Baker** AE 4 stricken on 2 Dec 1969, **Shasta** AE 6 stricken on 1 July 1969, **Rainier** AE 5 stricken on 7 Aug 1970, **Mazama** AE 9 stricken on 1 Sep 1970.
"Sangay" class: **Sangay**, AE 10, stricken in 1961 and **Formalhaut**, AE 20 ex-AK 22 transferred to Maritime Administration in Sep 1962.
Converted AKA type: **Virgo** AE 30 ex-AKA 20, ex-AK 69, stricken on 18 Feb 1971; **Chara** AE 31 ex-AKA 58 stricken on 10 Mar 1972.

MAUNA LOA (AE 8) — *1965 United States Navy*

5 STORE SHIPS (AF): R2-S-BV1 TYPE

Name	No.	Launched	Commissioned
ZELIMA (*ex-Golden Rocket*)	AF 49	2 Mar 1945	27 July 1946
ARCTURUS (*ex-Golden Eagle*)	AF 52	15 Mar 1942	18 Nov 1961
PICTOR (*ex-Great Republic*)	AF 54	4 June 1942	13 Sep 1950
ALUDRA (*ex-Matchless*)	AF 55	14 Oct 1944	7 July 1952
PROCYON (*ex-Flying Scud*)	AF 61	1 July 1942	24 Nov 1961

Displacement, tons: 6 914 light; 15 500 full load
Dimensions, feet: 459·2 oa × 63 × 28
Guns: 8—3 inch (*76 mm*) 50 cal AA (twin) in *Aludra*; most of others are unarmed
Main engines: Geared turbine; 6 000 shp; 1 shaft = 16 knots
Boilers: 2

All built by Moore Dry Dock Co, Oakland, California. R2-S-BV1 type refrigerated cargo ships; similar to C2-S-B1 design but built as "reefers".
Arcturus is formerly USNS *Golden Eagle*, transferred from Military Sea Transportation Service to active Navy; renamed on 13 Sep 1961 and commissioned as USS on 18 Nov 1961 after modification for underway replenishment at the New York Naval Shipyard. These ships have been fitted with helicopter platforms.
All have been decommissioned and are in Navy or Maritime Administration reserve fleets; last active ship was *Arcturus*, decommissioned in 1973.

NOMENCLATURE. Store ships are named for stars and constellations.

DISPOSALS
Sirius AF 60 stricken in 1965, **Bellatrix** AF 62 stricken on 1 Oct 1968, **Alstede** AF 48 stricken on 31 Oct 1969.

PROCYON (AF 61) — *1970, United States Navy*

ALUDRA (AF 55) — *1967, United States Navy*

ARCTURUS (AF 52) — *United States Navy*

2 STORE SHIPS (AF): R3-S-4A TYPE

Name	No.	Launched	Commissioned
•**RIGEL**	AF 58	15 Mar 1955	2 Sep 1955
•**VEGA**	AF 59	26 Apr 1955	10 Nov 1955

Displacement, tons: 7 950 light; 15 540 full load
Dimensions, feet: 475 wl; 502 oa × 72 × 29 max
Guns: 4—3 inch (*76 mm*) 50 cal AA (twin)
Main engines: Geared turbine (General Electric); 16 000 shp; 1 shaft = 20 knots
Boilers: 2 (Combustion Engineering)
Complement: approx 350

Built by Ingalls Shipbuilding Co, Pascagoula. R3-S-4A type. Helicopter platform fitted (two after twin 3 inch mounts removed). Both of these ships are active.

Underway Replenishment Ships—*continued*

RIGEL (AF 58) *1968, United States Navy*

1 STORE SHIP (AF): "VICTORY" TYPE

Name	No.	Launched	Commissioned
***DENEBOLA** (ex-*Hibbing Victory*)	AF 56	10 June 1944	20 Jan 1954

Displacement, tons	6 700 light; 12 130 full load
Dimensions, feet	455·2 × 62 × 28·5
Guns	4—3 inch (*76 mm*) 50 cal AA (twin)
Main engines	Geared turbine (Westinghouse); 8 500 shp; 1 shaft = 18 knots
Boilers	2 (Combustion Engineering)
Complement	225

Built by Oregon Shipbuilding Co, Portland, Oregon. Originally VC2-S-AP3 "Victory" type. Acquired by the Navy on 1 May 1952 and converted to underway replenishment ship at New York Naval Shipyard.
Two after twin 3 inch gun mounts removed and helicopter platform fitted.

The *Denebola* was to be assigned to the Military Sealift Command late in 1974 and operated by a civilian crew (redesignated T-AF and disarmed).

DISPOSALS
Regulus AF 57 driven aground and wrecked by a typhoon in Hong Kong harbour on 18 Aug 1971; subsequently scrapped.

DENEBOLA (AF 56) *1971, United States Navy*

1 STORE SHIP (AF): C2-S-E1 TYPE

Name	No.	Launched	Commissioned
HYADES (ex-*Iberville*)	AF 28	12 June 1943	30 Sep 1943

Displacement, tons	6 313 light; 15 300 full load
Dimensions, feet	468·66 oa × 63 × 28
Guns	2—3 inch (*76 mm*) 50 cal AA (single)
Main engines	Geared turbine (General Electric); 6 000 shp; 1 shaft = 15·5 knots
Boilers	2 (Babcock & Wilcox)
Complement	252

Built by Gulf Shipbuilding Co, Chickensaw, Alabama. Original armament included one 5 inch gun. Helicopter deck fitted aft in place of two single 3 inch guns during 1962. Decommissioned and placed in reserve in 1969.

DISPOSALS
Graffias AF 29 stricken on 19 Dec 1969.

HYADES (AF 28) *Ing Augusti Nani*

7 COMBAT STORE SHIPS (AFS): "MARS" CLASS

Name	No	Laid down	Launched	Commissioned
***MARS**	AFS 1	5 May 1962	15 June 1963	21 Dec 1963
***SYLVANIA**	AFS 2	18 Aug 1962	15 Aug 1963	11 July 1964
***NIAGARA FALLS**	AFS 3	22 May 1965	26 Mar 1966	29 Apr 1967
***WHITE PLAINS**	AFS 4	2 Oct 1965	23 July 1966	23 Nov 1968
***CONCORD**	AFS 5	26 Mar 1966	17 Dec 1966	27 Nov 1968
***SAN DIEGO**	AFS 6	11 Mar 1965	13 Apr 1968	24 May 1969
***SAN JOSE**	AFS 7	8 Mar 1969	13 Dec 1969	23 Oct 1970

Displacement, tons	16 500 full load
Dimensions, feet	581 oa × 79 × 24
Guns	8—3 in, 50 cal AA (twin)
Helicopters	2 UH-46 Sea Knight helicopters normally assigned
Main engines	Steam turbines; 22 000 shp; 1 shaft = 20 knots
Boilers	3 (Babcock & Wilcox) (one spare)
Complement	430 (30 officers, 400 enlisted men)

All built by National Steel & Shipbuilding, San Diego, California. Of a new design with a completely new replenishment at sea system. "M" frames replace conventional king posts and booms, which are equipped with automatic tensioning devices to maintain transfer lines taut between the ship and the warships being replenished despite rolling and yawing. Computers provide up-to-the-minute data on stock status with data displayed by closed-circuit television. Five holds (one refrigerated).
Cargo capacity 2 625 tons dry stores and 1 300 tons refrigerated stores (varies with specific loadings).
Automatic propulsion system with full controls on bridge. SPS-40 radar fitted in *Mars* and *Sylvania*, later ships have smaller radar; some ships have TACAN (tactical aircraft navigation radar).
Mars authorised in Fiscal Year 1961 shipbuilding programme. *Sylvania* in FY 1962 *Niagara Falls* in FY 1964, *White Plains* and *Concord* in FY 1965, *San Diego* in FY 1966 *San Jose* in FY 1967.

NOMENCLATURE. Combat store ships are named for American cities.

SYLVANIA (AFS 2) *1972, Giorgio Arra*

Underway Replenishment Ships—*continued*

"MARS" Class—*continued*

PHOTOGRAPHS. The *Niagara Falls* is shown in the Gulf of Tonkin as the aircraft carrier *Bon Homme Richard* (CVA 31) makes an approach to take on stores during an underway replenishment operation. Note the store ship's two-door hangar, capable of accommodating two UH-46 Sea Knight cargo helicopters. A large TACAN "bee hive" antenna tops her mast, facilitating night helicopter flights.

SAN JOSE (AFS 7) *1971, US Navy, PH1 John Lucas*

NIAGARA FALLS (AFS 3) *1970, United States Navy*

STORES ISSUE SHIPS (AKS)

The last AKS on the Navy List, the **Altair** AKS 32 (ex-AK 257) stricken on 1 June 1973. See 1973-1974 and previous edition for characteristics.

1 OILER (AO): NEW DESIGN

	AO 166	Proposed Fiscal Year 1975 programme
Nine oilers	**AO**	Planned

Displacement, tons	27 500 full load
Dimensions, feet	586·5 oa × 88 × 33·5
Main engines	Geared turbines; 2 shafts = 20 knots
Boilers	2
Complement	approx 140

A new class of fleet oilers planned for construction in the Fiscal Year 1975-1979 new construction programmes. Approximate cargo capacity 120 000 barrels of liquid fuels.

6 OILERS (AO): "NEOSHO" CLASS

Name	No.	Launched	Commissioned
***NEOSHO**	AO 143	10 Nov 1953	24 Sep 1954
***MISSISSINEWA**	AO 144	12 June 1954	18 Jan 1955
***HASSAYAMPA**	AO 145	12 Sep 1954	19 Apr 1955
***KAWISHIWI**	AO 146	11 Dec 1954	6 July 1955
***TRUCKEE**	AO 147	10 Mar 1955	23 Nov 1955
***PONCHATOULA**	AO 148	9 July 1955	12 Jan 1956

Displacement, tons	11 600 light; 38 000 to 40 000 full load
Dimensions, feet	640 wl; 655 oa × 86 × 35
Guns	8 or 12—3 inch (*76 mm*) 50 cal AA (twin)
Main engines	Geared turbines (General Electric); 28 000 shp; 2 shafts = 20 knots
Boilers	2 (Babcock & Wilcox)
Complement	approx 360 (30 officers and 330 enlisted men including staff)

Neosho built by Bethlehem Steel Co, Quincy, Massachusetts; others by New York Shipbuilding Corp, Camden, New Jersey. These are the largest "straight" oilers (AO) constructed for the Navy. Cargo capacity is approximately 180 000 barrels of liquid fuels.
Original armament was two 5 inch DP guns and 12 3 inch AA guns; former removed in 1969. Two twin 3 inch gun mounts removed from *Neosho, Mississinewa*, and *Truckee* and helicopter platform installed. Those ships also have additional superstructure installed forward of after "island" structure. All fitted to carry a service force commander and staff (12 officers). All of these ships are active.

NOMENCLATURE. Oilers are named after American rivers with Indian names.

PONCHATOULA (AO 148) *1970, United States Navy*

TRUCKEE (AO 147) *1972, Giorgio Arra*

5 OILERS (AO): "JUMBOISED" T3-S2-A3 TYPE

Name	No.	Launched	Commissioned
***MISPILLION**	T-AO 105	10 Aug 1945	29 Dec 1945
***NAVASOTA**	AO 106	30 Aug 1945	27 Feb 1946
***PASSUMPSIC**	AO 107	31 Oct 1945	1 Apr 1946
***PAWCATUCK**	AO 108	19 Feb 1945	10 May 1946
***WACCAMAW**	AO 109	30 Mar 1946	25 June 1946

Displacement, tons	11 000 light; 34 750 full load
Dimensions, feet	646 oa × 75 × 35·5
Guns	4—3 inch (*76 mm*) 50 cal AA (single)
Main engines	Geared turbines (Westinghouse); 13 500 shp; 2 shafts = 16 knots
Boilers	4 (Babcock & Wilcox)
Complement	290 (16 officers, 274 men)

All built by Sun Shipbuilding & Dry Dock Co, Chester, Pennsylvania. Originally T3-S2-A-3 oilers; converted during mid-1960s under "jumbo" programme. Enlarged midsections added to increase cargo capacity to approximately 150 000 barrels. Helicopter platform fitted **forward**. All of these ships are active.
The *Mispillion* was assigned to the Military Sealift Command in 1974 and provided with a civilian crew (guns removed); the *Waccamaw* was to be assigned to MSC early in 1975.
Note two funnels on *Navasota*.

NAVASOTA (AO 106) *1970, United States Navy*

3 OILERS (AO): "JUMBOISED" T3-S2-A1 TYPE

Name	No.	Launched	Commissioned
***ASHTABULA**	AO 51	22 May 1943	7 Aug 1943
***CALOOSAHATCHEE**	AO 98	2 June 1945	10 Oct 1945
***CANISTEO**	AO 99	6 July 1945	3 Dec 1945

Displacement, tons	34 750 full load
Dimensions, feet	644 oa × 75 × 31·5
Guns	4—3 inch (*76 mm*) 50 cal AA (single)
Main engines	Geared turbines; 13 500 shp; 2 shafts = 18 knots
Boilers	4 (Foster Wheeler)
Complement	300 (13 officers and 287 enlisted men)

All built by Bethlehem Steel Co, Sparrows Point, Maryland. Originally T3-S2-A1 oilers; converted during mid-1960s under "jumbo" programme. Enlarged midsections added to increase cargo capacity to approximately 143 000 barrels plus 175 tons of munitions and 100 tons refrigerated stores. No helicopter platform fitted.

Underway Replenishment Ships—*continued*

ASHTABULA (AO 51) *1970, United States Navy*

2 OILERS (AO): T2-A TYPE

Name	*No.*	*Launched*	*Commissioned*
KENNEBEC (ex-*Corsicana*)	AO 36	19 Apr 1941	4 Feb 1942
TAPPAHANNOCK (ex-*Jorkay*)	AO 43	18 Apr 1942	22 June 1942

Displacement, tons	21 580 full load
Dimensions, feet	501·4 oa × 68 × 30·75
Guns	2 or 4—3 inch (*76 mm*) 50 cal AA (single)
Main engines	Geared turbine (Westinghouse); 12 000 shp = 16·7 knots
Boilers	2 (Foster Wheeler in *Kennebec*, Babcock & Wilcox in *Tappahannock*)

Fleet oilers of World War II construction but smaller and less capable than the contemporary T-3 series. *Tappahannock* built by Sun Shipbuilding and Dry Dock Co. Chester, Pennsylvania; *Kennebec* by Bethlehem Steel Co, Sparrows Point, Maryland. Cargo capacity approximately 130 000 barrels.

Original armament for this class was one 5 inch DP gun, four 3 inch AA guns, and with 40 mm AA guns; subsequently reduced as above.

The *Tappahannock* is in Navy reserve; *Kennebec* is in Maritime Administration reserve fleet but remains on the Navy List.

DISPOSALS (since 1 Jan 1970)
Neches AO 47 stricken on 1 Oct 1970, **Mattaponi** AO 41 stricken on 15 Oct 1970, **Chukawan** AO 100 stricken on 1 July 1972, **Kankakee** AO 39 stricken on 1 June 1973.

KENNEBEC (AO 36) *1965, United States Navy*

MARIAS (T-AO 57)—see following page *1965, United States Navy*

TRUCKEE (AO 147) *1972, United States Navy*

MISPILLION (AO 105) *1970, United States Navy, PH2 Brian L. Chandler*

Underway Replenishment Ships—*continued*

7 OILERS (AO): T3-S-2A1 TYPE

Name	No.	Launched	Commissioned
SABINE (ex-*Esso Albany*)	AO 25	27 Apr 1940	25 Sep 1940
***GUADALUPE** (ex-*Esso Raleigh*)	AO 32	26 Jan 1940	5 June 1941
CHIKASKIA	AO 54	2 Oct 1943	10 Nov 1943
AUCILLA (ex-*Escanaba*)	AO 56	20 Nov 1943	22 Dec 1943
***MARIAS**	T-AO 57	21 Dec 1943	12 Feb 1944
***TALUGA**	T-AO 62	10 July 1944	25 Aug 1944
***TOLOVANA**	AO 64	6 Jan 1945	24 Feb 1945

Displacement, tons	25 525 full load
Dimensions, feet	553 oa × 75 × 31·5
Guns	4—3 inch (*76 mm* 50 cal AA (single) in most ships; a few ships retain 5 inch guns of original armament (see notes); guns removed from T-AO ships
Main engines	Geared turbines; 13 500 shp; 2 shafts = 18 knots
Boilers	4 (Foster/Wheeler)
Complement	274 (14 officers, 260 enlisted men)

Several ships of this type have been enlarged through the "jumbo" process and are listed separately on a previous page. The *Marias* and *Taluga* have been transferred to the Military Sealift Command for operation and have civilian crews; the two other ships of this type in active service are Navy manned. All provide underway replenishment of Navy ships and are not point-to-point "tankers" (AO). Three ships of this type are in reserve.

All built by Bethlehem Steel Co, Sparrows Point, Maryland, except *Guadalupe* by Newport News Shipbuilding & Dry Dock Co, Virginia. Original armament varied from one to four 5 inch DP guns; up to four 3 inch AA guns, and eight 40 mm AA guns. Cargo capacity approximately 145 000 barrels.

DISPOSALS (since 1 Jan 1970)
Elokomin AO 55 stricken on 17 Mar 1970; **Chemung** AO 30 stricken on 18 Sep 1970; **Platte** AO 24 stricken on 25 Sep 1970; **Allagash** AO 97 stricken on 1 June 1973; **Nantahala** AO 60 stricken on 1 July 1973; **Cacapon** AO 52, **Manatee** AO 58, **Chipola** AO 63 stricken on 14 Aug 1973; **Caliente** AO 53 stricken on 1 Dec 1973; **Severn** AO 61 stricken on 1 July 1974.

4 FAST COMBAT SUPPORT SHIPS (AOE): "SACRAMENTO" CLASS

Name	No.	Laid down	Launched	Commissioned
• **SACRAMENTO**	AOE 1	30 June 1961	14 Sep 1963	14 Mar 1964
• **CAMDEN**	AOE 2	17 Feb 1964	29 May 1965	1 Apr 1967
• **SEATTLE**	AOE 3	1 Oct 1965	2 Mar 1968	5 Apr 1969
• **DETROIT**	AOE 4	29 Nov 1966	21 June 1969	28 Mar 1970

Displacement, tons	19 200 light; 53 600 full load
Dimensions, feet	793 oa × 107 × 39·3
Guns	8—3 inch (*76 mm*) 50 cal AA (twin)
Helicopters	2 UH-46 Sea Knight helicopters normally assigned
Main engines	Geared turbines (General Electric); 100 000 shp; 2 shafts = 26 knots
Boilers	4 (Combustion Engineering)
Complement	600 (33 officers, 567 enlisted men)

These ships operate primarily with fast carrier task forces to provide rapid replenishment at sea of petroleum, munitions, provisions, and fleet freight. Fitted with helicopter platform, internal arrangements, and large hangar for vertical replenishment operations (VERTREP). Cargo capacity 177 000 barrels plus 2 150 tons munitions, 500 tons dry stores, 250 tons refrigerated stores (varies with specific loadings).

Built by Puget Sound Naval Shipyard except *Camden* by New York Shipbuilding Corp, Camden, New Jersey. *Sacramento* authorised in Fiscal Year 1961 new construction programme; *Camden* in FY 1963, *Seattle* in FY 1965, and *Detroit* in FY 1966. Construction of AOE 5 in FY 1968 was deferred and then cancelled in November 1969. No additional ships of this type are planned because of high cost, the availability of new-construction ammunition ships, and the great success of the smaller "Wichita" class replenishment oilers. Approximate cost of the *Camden* was $70 000 000.

ENGINEERING. *Sacramento* and *Camden* have machinery intended for the cancelled battleship *Kentucky* (BB 66).

PHOTOGRAPHS. These ships can be distinguished from the smaller "Wichita" class replenishment oilers by their larger superstructures and funnel, helicopter deck at higher level, and hangar structure aft of funnel.

NOMENCLATURE. Fast combat support ships are named for American cities.

DETROIT (AOE 4) — *1972, United States Navy, Joseph Andrews*

TALUGA (T-AO 62)—Navy manned and armed — *1970, United States Navy*

Underway Replenishment Ships—*continued*

SEATTLE (AOE 3) *1972, Giorgio Arra*

3 GASOLINE TANKERS (AOG): "PATAPSCO" CLASS

Name	*No.*	*Launched*	*Commissioned*
***CHEWAUCAN**	AOG 50	22 July 1944	19 Feb 1945
***NESPELEN**	AOG 55	10 Apr 1945	9 Aug 1945
***NOXUBEE**	AOG 56	3 Apr 1945	19 Oct 1945

Displacement, tons	1 850 light; 4 570 full load
Dimensions, feet	292 wl; 310·8 oa × 48·5 × 15·7
Guns	2 or 3—3 inch (*76 mm*) 50 cal AA (single)
Main engines	Diesel-electric; 3 100 bhp; 2 shafts = 14 knots
Complement	81 (6 officers, 75 enlisted men)

Navy designed small fuel ships originally intended to carry diesel and aviation fuels. All built by Cargill Inc, Savage, Minnesota. Cargo capacity 17 775 barrels. *Noxubee* reacquired from the Maritime Administration and recommissioned in 1966. Only three ships survive on the Navy List; several AOGs are in foreign service. All three ships listed above are active.

PHOTOGRAPHS. The *Chewaucan* is shown entering Malta. Note big tanker configuration; single 3 inch gun mounts forward and aft.

DISPOSALS AND TRANSFERS (since 1 Jan 1970)
Namakagon AOG 53 transferred to Taiwan China on 29 June 1971; **Elkhorn** AOG 7 transferred to Taiwan China on 1 July 1972; **Genesee** AOG 8 transferred to Chile on 1 July 1972; **Tombigbee** AOG 11 transferred to Greece on 7 July 1972; **Patapsco** AOG 1, **Kishwaukee** AOG 9 stricken in May 1974.

7 REPLENISHMENT OILERS (AOR): "WICHITA" CLASS

Name	*No.*	*Laid down*	*Launched*	*Commissioned*
***WICHITA**	AOR 1	18 June 1966	18 Mar 1968	7 June 1969
***MILWAUKEE**	AOR 2	29 Nov 1966	17 Jan 1969	1 Nov 1969
***KANSAS CITY**	AOR 3	20 Apr 1968	28 June 1969	6 June 1970
***SAVANNAH**	AOR 4	22 Jan 1969	25 Apr 1970	5 Dec 1970
***WABASH**	AOR 5	21 Jan 1970	6 Feb 1971	20 Nov 1971
***KALAMAZOO**	AOR 6	28 Oct 1970	11 Nov 1972	11 Aug 1973
ROANOKE	AOR 7	19 Jan 1974	late 1974	1975

Displacement, tons	38 100 full load
Dimensions, feet	659 oa × 96 × 33·3
Guns	4—3 inch (*76 mm*) 50 cal AA (twin)
Main engines	Geared turbines; 32 000 shp; 2 shafts = 20 knots (18 knots on 2 boilers)
Boilers	3 (Foster Wheeler)
Complement	345 (20 officers, 325 enlisted men)
Missile launchers	1 NATO Sea Sparrow multiple launcher

These ships provide rapid replenishment at sea of petroleum and munitions with a limited capacity for provision and fleet freight. Fitted with helicopter platform and internal arrangement for vertical replenishment operations (VERTREP), but no hangar. Cargo capacity 175 000 barrels plus 600 tons munitions, 425 tons dry stores, 150 tons refrigerated stores.

All built by General Dynamics Corp, Quincy, Massachusetts except AOR 7 by National Steel and Shipbuilding Co, San Diego, California. *Wichita* and *Milwaukee* authorised in Fiscal Year 1965 new construction programme *Kansas City* and *Savannah* in FY 1966, *Wabash* and *Kalamazoo* in FY 1967, and AOR 7 in FY 1972. Approximate cost of *Milwaukee* was $27 700 000.

NOMENCLATURE. Replenishment oilers are named after American cities. The port city of Savannah, Georgia, also is honoured by the world's first nuclear-propelled merchant ship, the NS *Savannah*, which is now laid up out of service at that city.

CHEWAUCAN (AOG 50) *1970, Anthony & Joseph Pavia*

MILWAUKEE (AOR 2) *1972, Giorgio Arra*

KALAMAZOO (AOR 6) *1973, United States Navy*

FLEET SUPPORT SHIPS

Fleet support ships provide primarily maintenance and related towing and salvage services at advanced bases and at ports in the United States. These ships normally do not provide fuel, munitions, or other supplies except when ships are alongside for maintenance. Two notable exceptions are the self-propelled barrack ships (APB), that serve as semi-autonomous advanced bases for small landing craft or riverine craft in advanced areas, and the dependant support ship (see hospital ship, AH) which provides services for US civilian dependants in overseas areas.

Most fleet support ships operate from bases in the United States. The five Polaris/Poseidon submarine tenders (AS) are based at Holy Loch, Scotland; Rota, Spain; Charleston, South Carolina; and Apra harbour, Guam, with one ship generally in transit or overhaul. In addition, two support ships (AD/AR/AS type) generally are forward deployed in the Mediterranean and two in the western Pacific. Early in 1974 the Secretary of Defense announced plans for modernisation of the support ship forces, with five destroyer tenders (AD), two submarine tenders (AS), and ten fleet tugs (ATF) planned for the Fiscal Year 1975-1979 new construction programmes.

Fleet support ships are mainly Navy manned and armed; however, an increasing number are being operated by the Military Sealift Command (MSC) with civilian crews. The latter ships are not armed and have T- designations.

3+1 DESTROYER TENDERS (AD): "GOMPERS" CLASS

Name	No.	Laid down	Launched	Commissioned
•**SAMUEL GOMPERS**	AD 37	9 July 1964	14 May 1966	1 July 1967
•**PUGET SOUND**	AD 38	15 Feb 1965	16 Sep 1966	27 Apr 1968

No.		Commissioned
AD 40	Fiscal Year 1973 programme	1978
AD 41	Proposed FY 1975 programme	1979
AD 42	Planned FY 1976 programme	1980
AD 43	Planned FY 1977 programme	1981
AD 44	Planned FY 1978 programme	1982
AD 45	Planned FY 1979 programme	

Displacement, tons	22 260 full load
Dimensions, feet	643 oa × 85 × 22·5
Guns	1—5 inch (*127 mm*) 38 cal DP in *Samuel Gompers* and *Puget Sound*
Missile launchers	1 NATO Sea Sparrow system planned for AD 40 and later ships
Main engines	Geared turbines (De Laval); 20 000 shp; 1 shaft = 20 knots
Boilers	2 (Combustion Engineering)
Complement	1 806 (135 officers, 1 671 enlisted men)

These are the first US destroyer tenders of post-World War II design; capable of providing repair and supply services to new destroyer-type ships which have advanced missile, anti-submarine, and electronic systems. The tenders also have facilities for servicing nuclear power plants. Services can be provided simultaneously to six guided-missile destroyers moored alongside. Basic hull design similar to "L. Y. Spear" and "Simon Lake" submarine tenders. Provided with helicopter platform and hangar; two 7 000-pound capacity cranes.

Samuel Gompers authorised in Fiscal Year 1964 new construction programme and *Puget Sound* in FY 1965 programme. Both ships built by Puget Sound Naval Shipyard, Bremerton, Washington.

AD 39 of FY 1969 programme cancelled prior to start of construction to provide funds for overruns in other new ship programmes. AD 40 authorised in FY 1973 new construction programme. AD 41 requested in FY 1975 programme with four additional ships planned (AD 41 and later ships of a slightly modified design); estimated cost of AD 41 is $116 700 000.

NOMENCLATURE. Destroyer tenders generally are named for geographic areas. Samuel Gompers was an American labour leader.

SAMUEL GOMPERS (AD 37) — *1968, United States Navy*

5 DESTROYER TENDERS (AD): "KLONDIKE" CLASS

Name	No.	Launched	Commissioned
EVERGLADES	AD 24	28 Jan 1945	25 May 1951
***SHENANDOAH**	AD 26	29 Mar 1945	13 Aug 1945
***YELLOWSTONE**	AD 27	12 Apr 1945	15 Jan 1946
ISLE ROYAL	AD 29	19 Sep 1945	9 June 1962
***BRYCE CANYON**	AD 36	7 Mar 1946	15 Sep 1950

Displacement, tons	8 165 standard; 16 635 to 16 900 full load
Dimensions, feet	465 wl; 492 oa × 69·5 × 27·2
Guns	1—5 inch (*127 mm*) 38 cal DP; removed from some ships including *Shenandoah*
Main engines	Geared turbines; 8 500 shp 1 shaft = 18·4 knots
Boilers	2 (Foster-Wheeler or Babcock & Wilcox)
Complement	778 to 918

These ships are of modified C-3 design completed as destroyer tenders. Officially considered two classes (see below). *Arcadia*, *Shenandoah*, *Yellowstone* built by Todd Shipyards, Los Angeles, Calif; *Bryce Canyon* by Charleston Navy Yard; *Everglades* by Los Angeles SB & DD Co; and *Isle Royal* by Todd Pacific Shipyards, Seattle, Wash. *Isle Royal* first commissioned on 26 Mar 1946 and placed in reserve before being completely outfitted; recommissioned for service on 9 June 1962 and commenced operations in January 1963.

Originally 14 ships of two similar designs, the "Klondike" class of AD 22-25 and "Shenandoah" class of AD 26-33, 35, and 36. *Great Lakes* (AD 30), *New England* (AD 32), *Canopus* (AD 33, ex-AS 27), *Arrow Head* (AD 35, ex-AV 19) cancelled before completion; *Klondike* (AD 22) reclassified AR 22; *Grand Canyon* (AD 28) reclassified AR 28. Also see *Disposals* and *Transfers*.

Three ships remain in active service; others in reserve. *Yellowstone* was scheduled to be decommissioned early in 1975.

ARMAMENT. Original armament for "Klondike" class was 1—5 in gun, 4—3 in guns, and 4—40 mm guns; for "Shenandoah" class was 2—5 in guns and 8—40 mm guns.

MODERNISATION. Most of these ships have been modernised under the FRAM II programme to service modernised destroyers fitted with ASROC, improved electronics, helicopters etc.

DISPOSALS AND TRANSFERS

Tidewater AD 31 transferred to Indonesia in Jan 1971 for use as tender to off-shore oil operations (Navy manned); **Frontier** AD 25 stricken on 1 Dec 1972; **Arcadia** AD 24 stricken on 1 July 1973.

ISLE ROYAL (AD 29) — *1970, United States Navy*

PUGET SOUND (AD 38) — *1972, United States Navy*

Fleet Support Ships—*continued*

SHENANDOAH (AD 26) *1973, US Navy, PH2 G. T. Leidy*

ISLE ROYAL (AD 29) *1970, United States Navy*

1 DESTROYER TENDER (AD): "CASCADE" TYPE

Name	*No.*	*Launched*	*Commissioned*
***CASCADE**	AD 16	7 June 1942	12 Mar 1943

Displacement, tons	9 800 standard; 16 600 full load
Dimensions, feet	492 oa × 69·5 × 27·2
Guns	1—5 inch (*127 mm*) 38 cal DP
Main engines	Turbines General Electric; 8 500 shp 1 shaft = 18·4 knots
Boilers	2 (Foster-Wheeler)
Complement	857

Built by Western Pipe & Steel Co, San Francisco, C3-S1-N2 type. Modernised to service FRAM destroyers.
The *Cascade* was scheduled to be decommissioned early in 1975.

CASCADE (AD 16) *1971, United States Navy*

PIEDMONT (AD 17) *1970, United States Navy*

5 DESTROYER TENDERS (AD): "DIXIE" CLASS

Name	*No.*	*Launched*	*Commissioned*
***DIXIE**	AD 14	27 May 1939	25 Apr 1940
***PRAIRIE**	AD 15	9 Dec 1939	5 Aug 1940
***PIEDMONT**	AD 17	7 Dec 1942	5 Jan 1944
***SIERRA**	AD 18	23 Feb 1943	20 Mar 1944
***YOSEMITE**	AD 19	16 May 1943	25 May 1944

Displacement, tons	9 450 standard; 17 176 full load
Dimensions, feet	520 wl; 530·5 oa × 73·3 × 25·5
Guns	1 or 2—5 inch (*127 mm*) 38 cal DP
Main engines	Geared turbines; 11 000 shp; 2 shafts = 19·6 knots
Boilers	4 (Babcock & Wilcox "A")
Complement	1 076 to 1 698 (total accommodation)

Dixie and *Prairie* built by New York Shipbuilding Corp, Camden, New Jersey; others by Tampa Shipbuilding Co, Florida. All five ships are active. The two after 5 inch guns and the eight 40 mm AA guns were removed.
All five ships are active, amongst the oldest ships remaining in service with the US Navy.

MODERNISATION. All of these ships have been modernised under the FRAM II programme to service destroyers fitted with ASROC, improved electronics, helicopters, etc. Two or three 5 inch guns and eight 40 mm guns removed during modernisation.

YOSEMITE (AD 19) *1968, United States Navy*

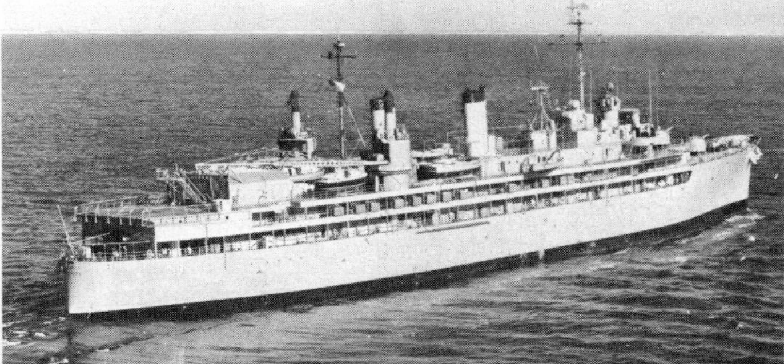

YOSEMITE (AD 19) *1968 United States Navy*

1 DEGAUSSING SHIP (ADG): Ex-MINESWEEPER

Name	*No.*	*Launched*	*Commissioned*
SURFBIRD	ADG 383 (ex-MSF 383)	31 Aug 1944	25 Nov 1944

Displacement, tons	890 standard; 1 250 full load
Dimensions, feet	215 wl; 221·2 oa × 32·2 × 10·8
Guns	removed
Main engines	Diesel electric; 3 532 bhp; 2 shafts = 18 knots
Complement	70

Built by American Shipbuilding Co, Lorain, Ohio. Laid down on 15 Feb 1944. Former Fleet Minesweeper of the steel-hulled type, MSF (ex-AM), reclassified as ADG on 18 May 1957. Decommissioned on 18 Dec 1970 and placed in reserve.

SURFBIRD (ADG 383) *United States Navy*

Fleet Support Ships—*continued*

3 DEGAUSSING SHIPS (ADG): Ex-PCE

Name	No.	Launched
LODESTONE (ex-*PCE* 876)	ADG 8	30 Sep 1943
MAGNET (ex-*PCE* 879)	ADG 9	1 Sep 1943
DEPERM (ex-*PCE* 883)	ADG 10	14 Jan 1944

Displacement, tons	640 standard; 900 full load
Dimensions, feet	184·5 oa × 33 × 9·5
Guns	removed
Main engines	Diesels (General Motors); 1 800 bhp except 2 000 bhp in *Deperm*; 2 shafts = 15·7 knots

Patrol Vessels—Escort (PCE) completed as degaussing craft YDG 8-10; changed to ADG on 1 Nov 1947; named on 1 Feb 1955. In reserve since 1946-1947.

1 AUXILIARY DEEP SUBMERGENCE SUPPORT VEHICLE (AGDS): Ex-DOCK CARGO SHIP

Name	No.	Launched
***POINT LOMA** (ex-*Point Barrow*)	AGDS 2 (ex-AKD 1)	25 May 1957

Displacement, tons	9 415 standard; 14 094 full load
Dimensions, feet	475 wl; 492 oa × 78 × 22
Main engines	Steam turbines; 6 000 shp; 2 shafts = 18 knots
Boilers	2
Complement	160 (including scientific personnel and submersible operators)

A docking or "wet" well ship designed to carry cargo, vehicles, and landing craft (designated AKD). Built by Maryland Shipbuilding & Dry Dock Co, for the Military Sea Transportation Service (now Military Sealift Command); commissioned on 28 Feb 1958 and delivered to MSTS on 29 May 1958. Maritime Administration S2-ST-23A design; winterised for arctic service. Fitted with internal ramp and garage system. Subsequently refitted with hangar over docking well and employed in transport of large booster rockets to Cape Kennedy Space Center. Primarily used to carry the second stage of the Saturn V moon rocket and Lunar Modules. Placed out of service in reserve on 1 Jan 1971 with reduction of US space programme.
Reactivated in mid-1972 for cargo work; transferred from Military Sealift Command to Navy on 28 Feb 1974 for modification to support deep submergence vehicles, especially the bathyscaph *Trieste II*. Placed in commission "special" on 8 Mar 1974 as the AGDS 2; renamed *Point Loma* for the location of the San Diego submarine base where Submarine Development Group 2 operates most of the Navy's submersibles. The *Point Loma* was scheduled to be placed in full commission in November 1974. Aviation gas capacity increased to approx 100 000 gallons (US) to support *Trieste II* which uses lighter-than-water avgas for flotation.

DESIGNATION. The designation AGDS was established on 3 Jan 1974; technically it is a service craft designation vice ship. The AGDS 1 was assigned briefly to the floating dry dock *White Sands* (ARD 20), the previous *Trieste II* support ship.

POINT LOMA (AGDS 2 as T-AKD 1) *1970, United States Navy*

POINT LOMA (AGDS 2 as T-AKD 1) *1970, United States Navy*

1 GUNBOAT SUPPORT SHIP (AGP): CONVERTED LST

Name	No.	Launched	Commissioned
***GRAHAM COUNTY**	AGP 1176 (ex-LST 1176)	19 Sep 1957	17 Apr 1958

Displacement, tons	approx 8 000 full load
Dimensions, feet	445 oa × 62 × 16·5
Guns	6—3 inch (*76 mm*) 50 cal AA (twin)
Main engines	Diesels (Fairbanks-Morse); 9 600 bhp; 2 shafts (controllable-pitch-propellers) = 14·5 knots

Originally an LST of the "Suffolk" County class built by Newport News SB & DD Co, Newport News, Virginia. Converted in 1972 to support US patrol gunboats (PG) and hydrofoil gunboats (PHM) deployed to Mediterranean area. Redesignated gunboat support ship (AGP) on 1 Aug 1972. Fitted with repair shops and spare parts storage.

Four earlier LSTs modified to support riverine craft in Vietnam also were designated AGP (with LST hull numbers); see listing for Amphibious Warfare Ships in 1971-1972 and previous editions. AGP 1-20 were converted yachts, seaplane tenders, cargo ships, and LSTs employed during World War II to service motor torpedo boats.

GRAHAM COUNTY

1 DEPENDENT SUPPORT SHIP (AH): "HAVEN" CLASS

Name	No.	Launched	Commissioned
***SANCTUARY** (ex-*Marine Owl*)	AH 17	15 Aug 1944	20 June 1945

Displacement, tons	11 141 standard; 15 400 full load
Dimensions, feet	496 wl; 529 oa × 71·5 × 24
Main engines	Geared turbines (General Electric); 9 000 shp; 1 shaft = 18·33
Boilers	2 (Babcock & Wilcox)
Complement	530 (70 officers, 460 enlisted)

The *Sanctuary* is the last of six hospital ships (AH) of the "Haven" class in active naval service. Built by Sun Shipbuilding & Dry Dock Co, Chester, Pennsylvania, on C4-S-B2 merchant hull. *Sanctuary* recommissioned from reserve in 1966 for service off Vietnam; decommissioned as a hospital ship on 15 Dec 1971 for modification to "dependent support ship" at Hunter's Point Naval Shipyard, San Francisco, California. Subsequently recommissioned on 18 Nov 1972.
As a dependent support ship the *Sanctuary* has special facilities for obstetrics, gynaecology, maternity, and nursery services. Currently fitted as a 74-bed hospital which can be expanded to 300 beds in 72 hours. She is the first US Navy ship with mixed male-female crew (although previously female nurses have been assigned to hospital ships and transports). The medical personnel consist of 50 officers and approx 120 enlisted men including several female nurse officers; the ship's company consists of 20 officers (including two women) and approx 330 enlisted (including 60 women).
The ship was modified to support US dependents of ships homeported in Pireaus, Greece. The photograph below shows the ship off Danang, South Vietnam; note TACAN pod on forward kingpost and helicopter platform aft.
Constellation (AH 15) of this class was chartered by a private group and operated under the name *Hope* as a floating hospital and medical school from 1961 to 1973; taken out of service at Philadelphia Naval Shipyard in 1974 and stripped of medical facilities.

DISPOSALS (since 1 Jan 1970)
Repose AH 16 stricken on 15 Mar 1974.

SANCTUARY (AH 17) *1970, United States Navy*

NET LAYING SHIPS

All US Navy net laying ships (ANL) have been discarded except for the *Naubuc* (ex-AN 84), in service as a salvage craft tender (designated YRST 4); see listing under Service Craft. *Naubuc* is a former "Cohoes" class net laying ship.
Cohoes (ANL 78, ex-AN 78) stricken on 30 June 1972. See 1972-1973 edition for characteristics and photograph.
All net laying ships of the "Tree" class have been stricken; last unit in US Navy service was *Butternut* (ex-ANL 9, ex-AN 9, ex-YN 4), lately employed in experimental work as YAG 60 until stricken on 1 July 1971.

4 SELF-PROPELLED BARRACKS SHIPS (APB)

Name	No.	Launched
ECHOLS	APB 37 (ex-APL 37)	30 July 1945
MERCER	APB 39 (ex-APL 39)	17 Nov 1944
NUECES	APB 40 (ex-APL 40)	6 May 1945
KINGMAN	APB 47 (ex-AKS 18, ex-LST 1113)	17 Apr 1945

Displacement, tons	2 189 light; 4 080 full load
Dimensions, feet	136 wl; 328 oa × 50 × 11
Guns	Vary (see notes)
Main engines	Diesels (General Motors); 1 600 to 1 800 bhp; 2 shafts = 12 (APB 41-50) or 10 knots (APB 35-40)
Complement	193 (13 officers, 180 enlisted men)
Troops	1 226 (26 officers, 1 200 enlisted men)

Self-propelled barracks ships (APB) that provide support and accommodations for small craft and riverine forces. All ex-LST type ships of the same basic characteristics. *Mercer* and *Nueces* recommissioned in 1968 for service in Vietnam; decommissioned in 1969-1971 as US riverine forces in South Vietnam were reduced.
These most useful ships supported the joint Army-Navy Mobile Riverine Force in the Mekong Delta region of South Vietnam (Navy River Assault Flotilla 1/Task Force 117/ River Support Squadron 7). Complement of each ship in this role was 12 officers and 186 enlisted men, and 900 troops and boat crew personnel were carried. Recommissioned ships had an armament of two 3 inch guns (single) eight 40 mm guns (two quad mounts), eight ·50 cal MG, and ten ·30 cal MG. They each have troop berthing and messing facilities, evaporators which produce up to 40 000 gallons of fresh water per day, a 16-bed hospital, X-ray room, dental room, bacteriological laboratory, pharmacy, laundry, library, and tailor shop; living and most working spaces are air conditioned. Most ships not activated for Vietnam have eight 40 mm AA guns (quad).
Colleton shown below with 12 riverine craft alongside; ships reactivated for Vietnam provide with helicopter platform; 3 inch guns installed at after end of helicopter platform with quad 40 mm mounts at bow and stern.

DISPOSALS (since 1 Jan 1970)
Vandenburgh APB 48 (ex-AKS 19, ex-LST 1114) stricken on 1 Apr 1972; **Benewah** APB 35 (ex-APL 35, changed to IX 311 on 26 Feb 1971) stricken on 1 Sep 1973; **Colleton** APB 36 (ex-APL 36), **Dorchester** APB 46 (ex-AKS 17, ex-LST 1112) stricken on 1 June 1973.

Fleet Support Ships—*continued*

MERCER (APB 39) *1968, United States Navy*

2 REPAIR SHIPS (AR): Ex-DETROYER TENDERS

Name	*No.*	*Launched*	*Commissioned*
KLONDIKE	AR 22 (ex-AD 22)	12 Aug 1944	30 July 1945
***GRAND CANYON**	AR 28 (ex-AD 28)	27 Apr 1945	5 Apr 1946

Displacement, tons	8 165 standard; 16 635 full load
Dimensions, feet	465 wl; 492 oa × 69·5 × 27·2
Guns	2—3 inch (*76 mm*) 50 cal AA (single) in *Klondike* 1—5 inch (*127 mm*) 38 cal DP in *Grand Canyon*
Main engines	Geared turbines (General Electric in *Klondike* Westinghouse in *Grand Canyon*); 8 500 shp; 1 shaft = 18·4 knots
Boilers	2 (Babcock & Wilcox in *Klondike;* Foster-Wheeler in *Grand Canyon*)
Complement	826 (48 officers, 778 enlisted men) and 977 (59 officers, 918 enlisted men) designed wartime for *Klondike* and *Grand Canyon* respectively

These ships are modified C-3 designs completed as destroyer tenders and subsequently reclassified as repair ships, the *Klondike* being redesignated AR 22 on 20 Feb 1960 and the *Grand Canyon* on 10 Mar 1971.
Klondike built by Los Angeles Shipbuilding Corp and *Grand Canyon* by Todd Shipyards, also Los Angeles, Calif. These ships differ in detail, being of slightly different designs; note mast and kingpost arrangements. The *Grand Canyon* has been modernised; note helicopter platform and hangar aft. *Klondike's* designed armament was 1—5 in gun, 4—3 in guns, and 4—40 mm guns; *Grand Canyon's* designed armament was 2—5 in guns and 8—40 mm guns.
Klondike decommissioned on 15 Dec 1970 and placed in service in reserve as station ship at San Diego, Calif; *Grand Canyon* is active.

NOMENCLATURE. Repair ships normally are named for mythological characters.

KLONDIKE (AR 22) *1969, United States Navy*

GRAND CANYON (AR 28) *1968, United States Navy*

1 REPAIR SHIP (AR): Ex-DESTROYER TENDER

Name	*No.*	*Commissioned*
MARKAB (ex-*Mormacpenn*)	AR 23 (ex-AD 21, ex-AK 31)	15 June 1941

Displacement, tons	8 560 standard; 14 800 full load
Dimensions, feet	465 wl; 492·5 oa × 69·8 × 24·8
Guns	4—3 inch (*76 mm*) 50 cal AA (single)
Main engines	Geared turbines (General Electric); 8 500 shp; 1 shaft = 18·4 knots
Boilers	2 (Foster-Wheeler)

Built by Ingalls SB Co, Pascagoula, Miss; launched on 21 Dec 1940. Former destroyer tender, reclassified as repair ship on 15 Apr 1960 and designation changed from AD to AR. One 5 inch gun and 4—40 mm guns were removed. The *Markab* was decommissioned on 19 Dec 1969 but remains in service in reserve as station ship at Mare Island, Calif.

MARKAB (AR 23) *United States Navy*

2 REPAIR SHIPS AR): "DELTA" CLASS

Name	*No.*	*Commissioned*
DELTA (ex-*Hawaiian Packer*)	AR 9 (ex-AK 29)	16 June 1941
BRIAREUS (ex-*Hawaiian Planter*)	AR 12	16 Nov 1943

Displacement, tons	8 975 standard; 14 500 full load
Dimensions, feet	465·5 wl; 490·5 oa × 69·5 × 24·3
Guns	4—3 inch (*76 mm*) 50 cal AA (single)
Main engines	Geared turbines (Newport News); 8 500 shp; 1 shaft = 17 knots
Boilers	2 (Foster-Wheeler and Babcock & Wilcox, respectively)
Complement	688 (29 officers, 559 enlisted men); 903 and 924, respectively, designed wartime

C-3 type built by Newport News SB & DD Co, Newport News, Va. Both launched in 1941 with *Briareus* serving as a merchant ship before being acquired by the Navy. The 5 inch and 4—40 mm guns removed. *Briareus* decommissioned in 1955 and placed in reserve; *Delta* decommissioned in 1970 remains in service in reserve as station ship at Bremerton, Wash.

DISPOSALS (since 1 Jan 1970)
Amphion AR 13 transferred to Iran on 1 Oct 1971; **Cadmus** AR 14 transferred to Taiwan China on 15 Jan 1973.

DELTA (AR 9) *1969, United States Navy*

4 REPAIR SHIPS (AR): "VULCAN" CLASS

Name	*No.*	*Launched*	*Commissioned*
***VULCAN**	AR 5	14 Dec 1940	16 June 1941
***AJAX**	AR 6	22 Aug 1942	30 Oct 1942
***HECTOR**	AR 7	11 Nov 1942	7 Feb 1944
***JASON**	AR 8	3 Apr 1943	19 June 1944

Displacement, tons	9 140 standard; 16 200 full load
Dimensions, feet	520 wl; 529·3 oa × 73·3 × 23·3
Guns	4—5 inch (*127 mm*) 38 cal DP (single)
Main engines	Geared turbines; 11 000 shp; 2 shafts = 19·2 knots
Boilers	4 (Babcock & Wilcox 3-drum)
Complement	715 (23 officers, 692 enlisted men); 950 designed wartime

Vulcan was built by New York SB Corpn under the 1939 programme and the other three by Los Angeles SB & DD Corpn under the 1940 Programme. All carry a most elaborate equipment of machine tools to undertake repairs of every description. *Jason*, originally designated ARH 1 and rated as heavy hull repair ship, was reclassified AR 8 on 9 Sep 1957. Eight 40 mm AA guns (twin) have been removed.
All of these ships are active.

AJAX (AR 6) *1970, United States Navy*

Fleet Support Ships—*continued*

AJAX (AR 6) *1970, United States Navy*

NEW CONSTRUCTION CABLE SHIPS

The Navy plans to underwrite the financing of two new construction cable ships that would be long-term chartered to the Military Sealift Command. These ships could be operational by the late 1970s, when the four existing Navy cable ships are more than 30 years old. In addition to the cable ships listed here, the Military Sealift Command periodically charters the services of three commercial ships to support Navy requirements, the American-flag *Long Lines*, the Liberian-flag and German crewed *Neptun*, and the Canadian-owned and manned *John Cabot*. These are the only three commercial ships considered suitable for U.S. defence needs.

2 CABLE SHIPS (ARC): "AEOLUS" CLASS

Name	*No.*	*Commissioned*
***AEOLUS** (ex-*Turandot*)	T-ARC 3 (ex-AKA 47)	18 June 1945
***THOR** (ex-*Vanadis*)	T-ARC 4 (ex-AKA 49)	9 July 1945

Displacement, tons	7 040 full load
Dimensions, feet	400 wl; 438 oa × 58·2 × 19·25
Guns	None
Main engines	Turbo-electric (Westinghouse); 6 000 shp; 2 shafts = 16·9 knots
Boilers	2 (Wickes)

Built as S4-SE2-BE1 attack cargo ships by Walsh-Kaiser Co, Providence, Rhode Island. Transferred to Maritime Administration and laid up in reserve from 1946 until reacquired by Navy for conversion to cable ships in 1955-1956. Converted to cable ships at the Key Highway Plant of Bethlehem Steel Corp, Baltimore, Maryland, being recommissioned on 14 May 1955 and 3 Jan 1956, respectively. Fitted with cable-laying bow sheaves, cable stowage tanks, cable repair facilities, and helicopter platform aft.

Both ships are employed in hydrographic and cable operations. They were both Navy manned until 1973 when transferred to Military Sealift Command and provided with civilian crews.

AEOLUS (T-ARC 3) *1970, United States Navy*

AEOLUS (T-ARC 3) *United States Navy*

THOR (T-ARC 4) *United States Navy*

2 CABLE SHIPS (ARC): "NEPTUNE" CLASS

***NEPTUNE** (ex-*William H. G. Bullard*)	T-ARC 2
***ALBERT J. MYER**	T-ARC 6

Displacement, tons	7 400 full load
Dimensions, feet	322 wl; 370 oa × 47 × 18
Guns	removed
Main engines	Reciprocating (Skinner); 4 800 ihp; 2 shafts = 14 knots
Boilers	2 (Combustion Engineering)

Built as S3-S2-BP1 type cable ships for Maritime Administration. Both ships built by Pusey & Jones Corp, Wilmington, Delaware, completed 1945-1946.

Neptune acquired by Navy from Maritime Administration in 1953 and sister ship *Albert J. Myer* from US Army in 1966, latter ship for operation by Military Sea Transportation Service (now Military Sealift Command). They have been fitted with electric cable handling machinery (in place of steam equipment) and precision navigation equipment; helicopter platform in *Neptune*.

Both ships are operated by the Military Sealift Command with civilian crews; *Neptune* was Navy manned until 1973 when transferred to MSC.

The USNS *Neptune* (T-ARC 2) should not be confused with the commercial cable ship *Neptun* of the United States Undersea Cable Corp.

See 1971-1972 edition for disposals of other cable ships.

NEPTUNE (T-ARC 2) *United States Navy*

ALBERT J. MYER (T-ARC 6) *United States Navy*

5 REPAIR SHIPS (ARB-ARL): CONVERTED LST TYPE

Name	*No.*	*Commissioned*
MIDAS	ARB 5 (ex-LST 514)	23 May 1944
SARPEDON	ARB 7 (ex-LST 596)	20 Mar 1945
EGERIA	ARL 8 (ex-LST 136)	18 Dec 1943
SPHINX	ARL 24 (ex-LST 963)	12 Dec 1944
INDRA	ARL 37 (ex-LST 1147)	28 May 1945

Displacement, tons	1 625 light; 4 100 full load
Dimensions, feet	316 wl; 328 oa × 50 × 11
Guns	8—40 mm AA (quad); several 20 mm AA in some ships
Main engines	Diesels (General Motors); 1 800 bhp; 2 shafts = 11·6 knots
Complement	251 to 286

LST-type ships converted during construction to battle damage repair ships (ARB) and landing craft repair ships (ARL). All launched 1943-1945. Fitted with machine shops, material and parts storage, lifting gear, etc; the battle damage ships have 50-ton capacity booms and the landing craft ships have 50-ton (ARL 2 and 8) and 60-ton ((ARL 24 and 37) capacities. The ARLs cater to small amphibious, minesweeping, and riverine craft. Most units have pole masts; note tripod mast in *Sphinx*, reactivated during Vietnam War.

Photographs of ARLs active in Vietnamese waters appear in the 1972-1973 and previous editions.

DISPOSALS AND TRANSFERS (since 1 June 1970)

Amycus ARL 2 (ex-LST 489) stricken on 1 June 1970; **Askari** ARL 30 (ex-LST 1131) transferred to Indonesia on 31 Aug 1971; **Satyr** ARL 23 (ex-LST 852) transferred to South Vietnam on 15 Oct 1971; **Krishna** ARL 38 (ex-LST 1148) transferred to the Philippines on 30 Oct 1971; **Atlas** ARL 7 (ex-LST 231), **Endymion** ARL 9 (ex-LST 513) stricken on 1 June 1972; **Zeus** ARB 4 (ex-LSR 132), **Telamon** ARB 8 (ex-LST 976), **Achelous** ARL 1 (ex-LST 10), **Fabius** ARVA 5 (ex-LST 1093), **Chloris** ARVE 4 (ex-LST 1094) stricken on 1 June 1973; **Megara** ARVA 6 (ex-LST 1095) transferred to Mexico on 1 Oct 1973.

"LIBERTY" TYPE

Tutuila ARG 4 transferred to Taiwan China on 21 Feb 1972.

SPHINX (ARL 24) *1968, United States Navy*

Fleet Support Ships—*continued*

14 SALVAGE SHIPS (ARS): "DIVER" CLASS

Name	*No.*	*Launched*	*Commissioned*
***ESCAPE**	ARS 6	22 Nov 1942	20 Nov 1943
***GRAPPLE**	ARS 7	31 Dec 1942	16 Dec 1943
***PRESERVER**	ARS 8	1 Apr 1943	11 Jan 1944
***DELIVER**	ARS 23	25 Sep 1943	18 July 1944
***GRASP**	ARS 24	31 July 1943	22 Aug 1944
***SAFEGUARD**	ARS 25	20 Nov 1943	31 Oct 1944
***CLAMP**	ARS 33	24 Oct 1942	23 Aug 1943
***GEAR**	ARS 34	24 Oct 1942	24 Sep 1943
***BOLSTER**	ARS 38	23 Dec 1944	1 May 1945
***CONSERVER**	ARS 39	27 Jan 1945	9 June 1945
***HOIST**	ARS 40	31 Mar 1945	21 July 1945
***OPPORTUNE**	ARS 41	31 Mar 1945	5 Oct 1945
***RECLAIMER**	ARS 42	25 June 1945	20 Dec 1945
***RECOVERY**	ARS 43	4 Aug 1945	15 May 1946

Displacement, tons	1 530 standard; 1 900 full load
Dimensions, feet	207 wl; 213·5 oa × 39 except later ships 43 × 13
Guns	1—40 mm AA (removed from some ships); 2—50 cal MG or 2—20 mm AA fitted in some ships
Main engines	Diesel-electric (Cooper Bessemer); 3 000 shp; 2 shafts = 14·8 knots except 16 knots in later ships
Complement	85 (120 designed wartime)

These ships are fitted for salvage and towing; equipped with compressed air diving equipment. All built by Basalt Rock Co, Napa, California. Most have a single 40 mm gun fitted atop the superstructure forward of the funnel; replaced in several ships by smaller weapons on bridge wings. Early ships have 8-ton and 10-ton capacity booms; later ships have 10-ton and 20-ton booms.
ARS 38 and later ships are of a slightly different design, sometimes known as the "Bolster" class; however, generally considered to be the same class.
The *Gear* is operated by a commercial firm in support of Navy activities; two additional ships are on loan to private salvage firms, the *Cable* ARS 19 and *Curb* ARS 21, and support naval requirements as needed. The *Clamp* was stricken from the Navy List in 1963 but reacquired in 1973 and returned to service.

CONVERSIONS. *Chain* ARS 20 and *Snatch* ARS 27 converted to oceanographic research ships, designated AGOR 17 and AGOR 18, respectively.

DISPOSALS (since 1 Jan 1970)
Current ARS 22 stricken on 1 June 1973.

OPPORTUNE (ARS 41) *1973, Giorgio Arra*

RECOVERY (ARS 43) *1969, United States Navy*

GRAPPLE (ARS 7) *1970, United States Navy*

SALVAGE LIFTING SHIPS (ARSD)

Gypsy ARSD 1 (ex-LSM 549), **Mender** ARSD 2 (ex-LSM 550) stricken on 1 June 1973. See 1973-1974 and previous editions for characteristics.

SALVAGE TENDERS (ARST)

Laysan Island ARST 1 (ex-LST 1098), **Palmyra** ARST 3 (ex-LST 1100) stricken on 1 June 1973. See 1973-1974 and previous editions for characteristics.

NOMENCLATURE. Salvage ships are named for terms related to salvage activity.

1 HELICOPTER REPAIR SHIP (ARVH): CONVERTED SEAPLANE TENDER

CORPUS CHRISTI BAY (ex-*Albermarle*) T-ARVH 1 (ex-AV 5)

Displacement, tons	8 671 standard; 13 475 full load
Dimensions, feet	508 wl; 537 oa × 69·2 × 21·3
Guns	None
Main engines	Geared turbines (Parsons); 12 000 shp; 2 shafts = 19·7 knots
Boilers	4 (Babcock & Wilcox)
Complement	130 (25 officers, 105 men) plus 310 Army personnel

Built as a large seaplane tender by the New York Shipbuilding Corp, Camden, New Jersey, under the Fiscal Year 1937 shipbuilding Programme; laid down on 12 June 1939, launched on 13 July 1940, commissioned on 20 Dec 1940. She was modernised in 1956-1957 and subsequently converted to a helicopter repair ship in 1964-1965 (see *Conversion* notes).

All other US Navy seaplane tenders have been stricken or transferred to foreign navies; see 1972-1973 and previous editions for ship lists, descriptions, and dispositions.

In service the *Corpus Christi Bay* was operated by the Military Sealift Command (formerly MSTS) and manned by a civilian operating crew and army helicopter maintenance battalion. Placed in ready reserve in 1973.

CONVERSION. The *Albermarle* was converted under the Fiscal Year 1956 programme at the Philadelphia Naval Shipyard to support the P6M Seamaster jet-propelled seaplane. Recommissioned on 21 Oct 1957. Decommissioned in 1960 and placed in the Maritime Administration Reserve Fleet. Stricken from the Navy List in Sep 1962. Reacquired by the Navy in Aug 1964 for conversion to a helicopter repair ship.
The *Albermarle* was converted to an aircraft repair ship (helicopter) at the Charleston Naval Shipyard in 1964-1965; fitted with 33 maintenance shops specialising in helicopter repairs, closed-circuit television provided for rapid transmission of drawings and blueprints from central technical library, automatic boiler controls to reduce operating crew, flight control tower (installed on flying bridge), and improved habitability features; amidships hangar structure extended aft and topped with a 50 × 150 ft helicopter platform with four-part steel hatch to permit helicopters to be lowered into hangars; two 20-ton capacity cranes installed aft of second funnel; smaller helicopter deck installed forward. All armament removed. Renamed *Corpus Christi Bay* and designated T-ARVH 1 on 27 Mar 1965. Deployed to South Vietnam to repair Army light fixed-wing aircraft and helicopters.

DESIGN. As built the *Albermarle* and her sister ship *Curtiss* (AV 4) resembled the "Currituck" class configuration, but with twin funnels. Both of these large seaplane tender designs provided extensive maintenance shops and spare parts, munition, and petrol stowage to support seaplane squadrons; space provided for squadron flight crews and Fleet Air Wing staff; aircraft hangar amidships, open deck aft, and two large aircraft cranes (20-ton capacity in "Curtiss" class; 30-ton capacity in "Currituck" class). As built the *Albermarle* had an armament of 4 5 inch DP guns and 16 40 mm AA guns.

NOMENCLATURE. Seaplane tenders were named after bays and harbours.

CORPUS CHRISTI BAY (T-ARVH 1) *United States Navy*

CORPUS CHRISTI BAY (T-ARVH 1)

Fleet Support Ships—*continued*

4 SUBMARINE TENDERS (AS): "L. Y. SPEAR" CLASS

Name	*No.*	*Laid down*	*Launched*	*Commissioned*
***L. Y. SPEAR**	AS 36	5 May 1966	7 Sep 1967	28 Feb 1970
***DIXON**	AS 37	7 Sep 1967	20 June 1970	7 Aug 1971
	AS 39	Fiscal Year 1972 programme		1978
	AS 40	Fiscal Year 1973 programme		1978
	AS 41	Planned FY 1976 programme		
	AS 42	Planned		

Displacement, tons	13 000 standard; AS 36 and AS 37 23 350 full load; AS 39 and AS 40 24 000 full load
Dimensions, feet	643·6 oa × 85 × 25·3 (AS 39 and AS 40 28·6)
Guns	2—5 inch (*127 mm*) 38 cal DP in *L. Y. Spear* and *Dixon*; 4—20 mm AA planned for AS 39 and AS 40
Missile launchers	NATO Sea Sparrow missile launcher planned for AS 39 and later ships
Main engines	Geared turbines (General Electric); 20 000 shp; 1 shaft = 20 knots
Boilers	2 (Foster Wheeler)
Complement	1 072 (42 officers, 1 030 enlisted men)

These ships are the first US submarine tenders designed specifically for servicing nuclear-propelled attack submarines with latter ships built to a modified design to support SSN-688 class submarines. (Four previous submarine tenders of post-World War II construction are configured to support ballistic missile submarines.) Basic hull design similar to "Samuel Gompers" class destroyer tenders. Provided with helicopter deck but no hangar. Each ship can simultaneously provide services to four submarines moored alongside.

L. Y. Spear authorised in Fiscal Year 1965 new construction programme and *Dixon* in FY 1966 programme. Both ships built by General Dynamics Corp, Quincy, Massachusetts.

AS 38 of FY 1969 programme cancelled prior to start of construction to provide funds for overruns in other new ship programmes.

AS 39 authorised in FY 1972 new construction programme and AS 40 in FY 1973 programme; AS 41 planned for FY 1976 programme request with a sixth unit also planned.

NOMENCLATURE. Submarine tenders generally are named after pioneers in submarine development and mythological characters.

DIXON (AS 37) *1971, US Navy, PH1 Robert L. Varney*

CANOPUS (AS 34) servicing SSBN *1970, United States Navy*

SIMON LAKE (AS 33) *1965 United States Navy*

2 SUBMARINE TENDERS (AS): "SIMON LAKE" CLASS

Name	*No.*	*Laid down*	*Launched*	*Commissioned*
***SIMON LAKE**	AS 33	7 Jan 1963	8 Feb 1964	7 Nov 1964
***CANOPUS**	AS 34	2 Mar 1964	12 Feb 1965	4 Nov 1965

Displacement, tons	21 500 full load
Dimensions, feet	643·7 × 85 × 30
Guns	4—3 inch (*76 mm*) 50 cal AA (twin)
Main engines	Geared turbines; 20 000 shp; 1 shaft = 18 knots
Boilers	2 (Combustion Engineering)
Complement	1 075 (55 officers, 1 020 men)

These ships are designed specifically to service fleet ballistic missile submarines (SSBN), with as many as three submarines alongside being supported simultaneously.

The *Simon Lake* was authorised in the Fiscal Year 1963 new construction programme and built by the Puget Soubd Naval Shipyard, the *Canopus* was authorised in FY 1964 and built by Ignalls Shipbuilding Corp. AS 35 was authorised in FY 1965 programme, but her construction was deferred. The last ship would have permitted one tender to be assigned to each of five FBM submarine squadrons with a sixth ship available to rotate when another was in overhaul, however; only four SSBN squadrons were established.

Note cranes amidships, funnel location (flanked by gun mounts, and helicopter platform).

2 SUBMARINE TENDERS (AS): "HUNLEY" CLASS

Name	*No*	*Laid down*	*Launched*	*Commissioned*
***HUNLEY**	AS 31	28 Nov 1960	28 Sep 1961	16 June 1962
***HOLLAND**	AS 32	5 Mar 1962	19 Jan 1963	7 Sep 1963

Displacement, tons	10 500 standard; 18 300 full load
Dimensions, feet	599 × 83 × 24
Guns	4—3 inch (*76 mm*) 50 cal AA (twin)
Main engines	Diesel-electric (10 Fairbanks-Morse diesels); 15 000 bhp; 1 shaft = 19 knots
Complement	1 081 (58 officers, 1 023 men) plus accommodation for 30 officers and 270 men from submarines

These ships are the first US submarine tenders of post-World War II construction; designed specifically to provide repairs and supply services to fleet ballistic missile submarines (SSBN). Provided with 52 separate workshops to provide complete support to nuclear plants, electronic and navigation systems, missiles, and other submarine systems. Helicopter platform fitted aft but no hangar. Both ships originally fitted with a 32-ton-capacity hammerhead crane (see 1972-1973 and previous editions for photographs); subsequently refitted with two amidships cranes as in "Simon Lake" class (see accompanying photographs).

Hunley authorised in Fiscal Year 1960 shipbuilding programme and built by Newport News Shipbuilding & Dry Dock Co, Virginia; *Holland* authorised in FY 1962 programme and built by Ingalls Shipbuilding Corp, Pascagoula, Mississippi. Former ship cost $24 359 800.

NOMENCLATURE. ***Holland* is named after John Philip Holland, an Irish emigrant to the United States, and submarine designer and builder. One of his submarines was accepted by the US Navy in 1900 and became Submarine Torpedo Boat No 1, named *Holland*, the first officially accepted US Navy submarine.**

OPERATIONS. One FBM submarine tender is assigned to each of the four Polaris/Poseidon squadrons, Submarine Squadron 14 at Holy Loch, Scotland; SubRon 15 at Apra harbour, Guam; SubRon 16 at Rota, Spain; and SubRon 18 at Charleston, South Carolina. A floating dry dock and several service craft also are assigned to each of these bases.

L. Y. SPEAR (AS 36) *1970, United States Navy*

Fleet Support Ships—*continued*

HUNLEY (AS 31) *United States Navy*

HOLLAND (AS 32) *United States Navy*

HOWARD W. GILMORE (AS 16) *1973, Giorgio Arra*

HOWARD W. GILMORE (AS 16) *1971, United States Navy*

7 SUBMARINE TENDERS (AS): "FULTON" CLASS

Name	No.	Launched	Commissioned
***FULTON**	AS 11	27 Dec 1940	12 Sep 1941
***SPERRY**	AS 12	17 Dec 1941	1 May 1942
BUSHNELL	AS 15	14 Sep 1942	10 Apr 1943
***HOWARD W. GILMORE** (*Neptune*)	AS 16	16 Sep 1943	24 May 1944
NEREUS	AS 17	12 Feb 1945	27 Oct 1945
***ORION**	AS 18	14 Oct 1942	30 Sep 1943
***PROTEUS**	AS 19	12 Nov 1942	31 Jan 1944

Displacement, tons	9 734 standard; 18 000 full load except *Proteus:* 10 234 standard; 18 500 full load
Dimensions, feet	530·5 except *Proteus* 574·5 oa × 73·3 × 25·5
Guns	2—5 inch (*127 mm*) 38 cal DP except one gun in *Proteus*
Main engines	Diesel-electric (General Motors); 11 200 to 11 800 bhp; 2 shafts = 15·4 knots
Complement	917 (34 officers, 883 enlisted men); except *Proteus* 1 121 (51 officers, 1 070 enlisted men)

These venerable ships are contemporaries of the similar-design "Dixie" class destroyer tenders. Four ships built by Mare Island Navy Yard, Vallejo, California; *Sperry, Orion,* and *Proteus* built by Moore Shipbuilding & Dry Dock Co, Oakland, California. As built they carried the then-standard large auxiliary armament of four 5 inch guns plus 8—40 mm AA guns (twin). The original 20-ton capacity cylinder cranes have been replaced in the *Howard W. Gilmore.*

CONVERSION. *Proteus* AS 19 was converted at the Charleston Naval Shipyard, under the Fiscal Year 1959 conversion programme, at a cost of $23 000 000 to service nuclear-powered fleet ballistic missile submarines (SSBN). Conversion was begun on 19 Jan 1959 and she was recommissioned on 8 July 1960. She was lengthened by adding a section amidships 44 feet in length, and the bare hull weight of this 6-deck high insertion was approximately 500 tons. Three 5 inch guns were removed and her upper decks extended aft to provide additional workshops. Storage tubes for Polaris missiles installed; bridge crane amidships loads and unloads missiles for alongside submarines.

MODERNISATION. *Bushnell, Fulton, Howard W. Gilmore, Nereus, Orion* and *Sperry* have undergone FRAM II modernisation to service nuclear powered attack submarines. Additional maintenance shops provided to service nuclear plant components and advanced electronic equipment and weapons. After two 5 inch guns and eight 40 mm guns (twin) removed.

NOMENCLATURE. *Howard W. Gilmore* remembers the commanding officer of a World War II submarine who, lying on the bridge wounded, ordered the boat to dive; he was posthumously awarded the Medal of Honour, the highest US military decoration.

DISPOSALS AND TRANSFERS

C-3 type: **Pelias** AS 14 stricken on 1 Aug 1971, **Griffin** AS 13 stricken on 1 Aug 1972. C3-S-A2 type: **Anthendon** AS 24 and **Clytie** AS 26 stricken on 1 Sep 1961 (former ship subsequently transferred on 7 Sep 1969 from Maritime Administration reserve to Turkey), **Apollo** AS 25 stricken on 1 July 1963, **Aegir** AS 23 stricken on 25 Jan 1971. Modified C-3 type: **Euryale** AS 22 stricken on 1 Dec 1971.

FULTON (AS 11) *1971, US Navy, Joseph R. Andrews*

ORION (AS 18) *United States Navy*

Fleet Support Ships—*continued*

2 SUBMARINE RESCUE SHIPS (ASR): "PIGEON" CLASS

Name	*No.*	*Builder*	*Launched*	*Comm.*
***PIGEON**	ASR 21	Alabama DD & SB Co (Mobile)	13 Aug 1969	28 Apr 1973
***ORTOLAN**	ASR 22	Alabama DD & SB Co (Mobile)	10 Sep 1969	June 1973

Displacement tons	4 200 full load
Dimensions, feet	251 oa × 86 (see *Design* notes) × 21·25
Guns	2—3 inch (*76 mm*) 50 cal AA (single) in *Pigeon*; 2—20 mm AA (single) in *Ortolan*; 4—·50 cal MG
Main engines	4 diesels; 6 000 bhp; 2 shafts = 15 knots
Complement	115 (6 officers, 109 enlisted men)
Staff accommodation	14 (4 officers, 10 enlisted men)
Submersible operators	24 (4 officers, 20 enlisted men)

These are the world's first ships designed specifically for this role, all other ASR designs being adaptations of tug types. The ASR 21 class ships will serve as (1) surface support ships for the Deep Submergence Rescue Vehicles (DSRV), (2) rescue ships employing the existing McCann rescue chamber, (3) major deep-sea diving support ships, and (4) operational control ships for salvage operations.

The Navy had planned in the 1960s to replace the 10-ship ASR force with new construction ASRs. However, only two ships have been funded with procurement of others deferred.

ASR 21 authorised in Fiscal Year 1967 new construction programme and ASR 22 in FY 1968 programme. Both ships built by Alabama Dry Dock and Shipbuilding Co, Mobile, Alabama; they have been delayed more than two years by a shipyard strike and technical difficulties; additional delays encountered in special equipment installation.

DESIGN. These ships have twin, catamaran hulls, the first ocean-going catamaran ships to be built for the US Navy since Robert Fulton's steam gunboat *Demologus* of 1812. The design provides a large deck working area, facilities for raising and lowering submersibles and underwater equipment, and improved stability when operating equipment at great depths. Each of the twin hulls is 251 feet long and 26 feet wide. The well between the hulls is 34 feet across, giving the ASR a maximum beam of 86 feet. Fitted with helicopter platform.

DIVING. These ships have been fitted with the Mk II Deep Diving System to support conventional or saturation divers operating at depths to 850 feet. The system consists of two decompression chambers, two personnel transfer capsules to transport divers between the ship and ocean floor, and the associated controls, winches, cables, gas supplies *et cetera*. Submarine rescue ships are the US Navy's primary diving ships and the only ones fitted for helium-oxygen diving.

ELECTRONICS. Fitted with precision three-dimensional sonar system for tracking submersibles.

ENGINEERING. Space and weight are reserved for future installation of a ducted thruster in each bow to enable the ship to maintain precise position while stopped or at slow speeds. Range is 8 500 miles at 13 knots.

GUNNERY. Note only the *Pigeon* has the two 3 inch single gun mounts originally planned for this class; the *Ortolan* has four large mooring buoys or "spuds" in place of the gun mounts. (The *Pigeon* has two buoys forward of the bridge and one on the stern of *each* hull; the *Ortolan* also has carried two buoys aft).

NOMENCLATURE. Submarine rescue ships traditionally have carried bird names (the US Navy's first six ASRs were converted "Bird" class minesweepers).

SUBMERSIBLES. Each ASR is capable of transporting, servicing, lowering, and raising two Deep Submergence Rescue Vehicles (DSRV) (see section on Deep Submergence Vehicles).

PIGEON (ASR 21) *1972, Alabama DD & SB Co*

"PENGUIN" CLASS

The three submarine rescue ships of the "Penguin" class, converted from fleet tugs (ATF), have been stricken; see 1973-1974 and previous editions for characteristics. **Bluebird** ASR 19 transferred to Turkey on 15 Aug 1950; **Penguin** ASR 12 stricken on 30 June 1970; **Skylark** ASR 20 transferred to Brazil on 30 June 1973.

PIGEON (ASR 21) *1972, Alabama DD & SB Co.*

ORTOLAN (ASR 22) *1973, United States Navy*

6 SUBMARINE RESCUE SHIPS (ASR): "CHANTICLEER" CLASS

	ASR	*Launched*		ASR	*Launched*
***COUCAL**	8	29 May 1942	***PETREL**	14	26 Sep 1945
***FLORIKAN**	9	14 June 1942	***SUNBIRD**	15	3 Apr 1945
***KITTIWAKE**	13	10 July 1945	***TRINGA**	16	25 June 1945

Displacement, tons	1 653 standard; 2 290 full load
Dimensions, feet	240 wl; 251·5 oa × 42 × 14·9
Guns	2—20 mm AA in some ships
Main engines	Diesel-electric (Alco in first 4 ships, GM in others); 1 shaft; 3 000 bhp = 14·9 knots
Complement	85 (102 designed wartime)

Large tug-type ships equipped with powerful pumps, heavy air compressors, and rescue chambers for submarine salvage and rescue operations. ASR 7-9 built by Moore SB & DD Co, Oakland, Calif, and ASR 13-16 by Savannah Machine & Foundry Co, Savannah, Ga. Fitted for helium-oxygen diving equipment (submarine rescue ships are the principal deep-sea diving ships in the Navy and the only ones with a built-in helium capability).

As built each ship was armed with two 3 inch AA guns; removed 1957-1958. Some ships subsequently fitted with two 20 mm AA guns.

OPERATIONAL. One ASR normally is deployed to the western Pacific and one in the Mediterranean with the others at US submarine bases in the continental United States and Hawaii.

DISPOSALS AND TRANSFERS

Greenlet ASR 10 transferred to Turkey on 12 June 1970; **Chanticleer** ASR 7 stricken 1 June 1973.

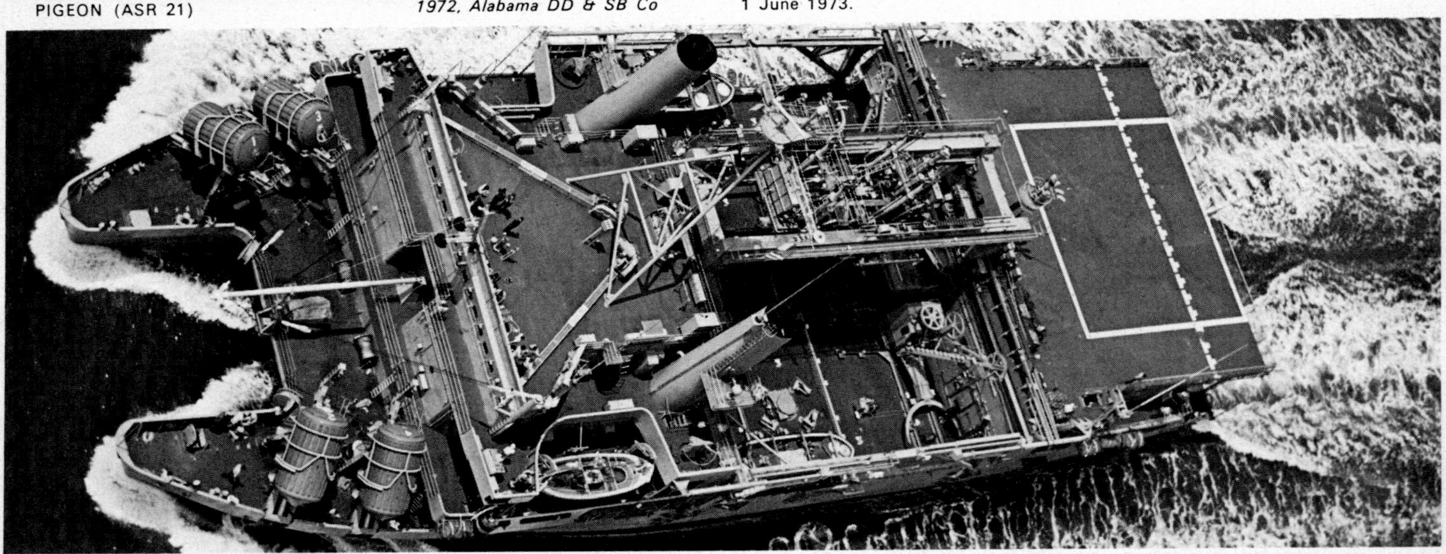

ORTOLAN (ASR 22) *1973, United States Navy, Albert E. Flournoy*

Fleet Support Ships—*continued*

FLORIKAN (ASR 9) *1970, United States Navy*

FLORIKAN (ASR 9) *1971, United States Navy*

PETREL (ASR 14) *United States Navy*

6 AUXILIARY TUGS (ATA): "MARICOPA" CLASS

	ATA	Launched		ATA	Launched
ACCOKEEK	181	27 July 1944	**TATNUCK**	195	14 Dec 1944
PENOBSCOT	188	12 Oct 1944	**STALLION**	193	24 Nov 1944
SAMOSET	190	26 Oct 1944	**KEYWADIN**	213	9 Apr 1945

Displacement, tons	534 standard; 835 full load
Dimensions, feet	134·5 wl; 143 oa × 33·9 × 13
Guns	1—3 inch (*76 mm*) 50 cal AA or 4—20 mm AA (twin); all guns removed from some ships
Main engines	Diesel-electric (General Motors diesels); 1 500 bhp; 1 shaft = 13 knots
Complement	45 (5 officers, 40 enlisted men)

Steel-hulled tugs formerly designated as rescue tugs (ATR); renumbered in same series as larger fleet tugs (ATF) when designation changed to ATA in 1944. All above ships built by Livingston SB Corp, Orange, Texas, or Gulfport Boiler & Welding Works, Port Arthur, Texas. During 1948 they were assigned names that had been carried by discarded fleet and yard tugs.
All of the surviving ships were decommissioned in 1970-1971 and placed in reserve. Two ships of this class serve in the Coast Guard.

NOMENCLATURE. US tugs of World War II construction and previous classes were named for Indian tribes and words.

DISPOSALS AND TRANSFERS (since 1 Jan 1970)
Kalmia ATA 184, **Umpqua** ATA 209 transferred to Colombia on 1 July 1971; **Mahopac** ATA 196 transferred to Taiwan China on 1 July 1971; **Tillamook** ATA 192 transferred to South Korea on 25 July 1971; **Sagamore** ATA 208 transferred to Dominican Republic on 1 Feb 1972; **Salish** ATA 187, **Catawba** ATA 210 transferred to Argentina on 10 Feb 1972; **Cahokia** ATA 186 (loan to US Air Force in 1971) transferred to Taiwan China on 29 Mar 1972; **Koka** ATA 185 to US Department of Health, Education and Welfare on 3 Dec 1973; **Wandank** ATA 204 to US Department of Interior on 1 Aug 1973 (corrections to previous editions).

"MARICOPA" Class—*continued*

ACCOKEEK (ATA 181) *1970, United States Navy*

1 FLEET TUG (ATF): NEW DESIGN

Nine fleet tugs	**ATF 166**	Proposed Fiscal Year 1975 programme
	ATF	Planned FY 1976-1979 programmes

Displacement, tons	2 000 full load
Dimensions, feet	208 oa × 42 × 15
Guns	2—20 mm AA; 2—50 cal MG
Main engines	Diesels; 4 500 bhp; 2 shafts = 15 knots

Construction is planned of ten fleet tugs, the first US ocean-going tugs to be constructed since World War II except for the three larger salvage and rescue ships (ATS).

23 FLEET TUGS (ATF): "APACHE" CLASS

	ATF	Launched		ATF	Launched
***UTE**	T-76	24 June 1942	***MOLALA**	106	23 Dec 1942
***CREE**	84	17 Aug 1942	***QUAPAW**	110	15 May 1943
***LIPAN**	T-85	17 Sep 1942	***TAKELMA**	113	18 Sep 1943
***MATACO**	86	14 Oct 1942	***TAWAKONI**	114	28 Oct 1943
SENECA	91	2 Feb 1943	***ATAKAPA**	T-149	11 July 1944
***TAWASA**	92	22 Feb 1943	***LUISENO**	156	17 Mar 1945
***ABNAKI**	96	22 Apr 1943	***NIPMUC**	157	12 Apr 1945
***CHOWANOC**	100	20 Aug 1943	***MOSOSPELEA**	T-158	7 Mar 1945
***COCOPA**	101	5 Oct 1943	***PAIUTE**	159	4 June 1945
***HITCHITI**	103	29 Jan 1944	***PAPAGO**	160	21 June 1945
***MOCTOBI**	105	25 Mar 1944	***SALINAN**	161	20 July 1945
			***SHAKORI**	162	9 Aug 1945

Displacement, tons	1 235 standard; 1 675 full load
Dimensions, feet	195 wl; 205 oa × 38·5 × 15·5 max
Guns	1—3 inch (*76 mm*) 50 cal AA; some ships in forward areas have machine guns in "tubs" aft of bridge; guns removed from T-ATFs

Large ocean tugs fitted with powerful pumps and other salvage equipment. ATF 96 and later ships ("Abnaki" class) have smaller funnel. As built these ships mounted 2—40 mm guns in addition to 3 inch gun. All surviving ships built by Charleston SB & DD Co, or United Engineering Co, Alameda, Calif, except *Seneca* built by Cramp SB Co, Philadelphia, Pa, and *Tawasa* by Commercial Iron Works, Portland, Oreg.

Beginning in 1973 several fleet tugs have been assigned to the Military Sealift Command and provided with civilian crews these ships are designated T-ATF and are unarmed. ATF 85 and ATF 158 assigned to MSC in 1973; ATF 76, and ATF 149 to MSC in 1974; additional ATFs will follow.
Three ships of this class serve with the US Coast Guard.

CONVERSIONS. *Chetco* ATF 99, *Yurok* ATF 164, and *Yustaga* ATF 165 converted to submarine rescue ships ASR 12, 19, and 20, respectively; *Serrano* ATF 112 converted to surveying ship AGS 24.

DISPOSALS AND TRANSFERS (since 1 Jan 1970)
Utina ATF 163 transferred to Venezuela on 30 Sep 1971; **Arikara** ATF 98 transferred to Chile on 1 July 1972; **Kiowa** ATF 72 transferred to Dominican Republic on 16 Oct 1972; **Sioux** ATF 75 transferred to Turkey on 30 Oct 1972; **Apache** ATF 67 stricken on 20 Mar 1974.

TAWASA (ATF 92)—large funnel *1973, US Navy, JOC Warren Grass*

Fleet Support Ships—*continued*

CHOWANOC (ATF 100) *1973, US Navy, JOC Warren Grass*

BEAUFORT (ATS 2) *1971, Brooke Marine*

COCOPA (ATF 101)—small funnel *1970, United States Navy*

EDENTON (ATS 1) *1971, US Navy, PH 2 Brian Erb*

CREE (ATF 84)—large funnel *1970, United States Navy*

BEAUFORT (ATS 2) *1971, Brooke Marine*

3 SALVAGE AND RESCUE SHIPS (ATS): "EDENTON" CLASS

Name	*No.*	*Laid down*	*Launched*	*Commission*
*EDENTON	ATS 1	1 Apr 1967	15 May 1968	23 Jan 1971
*BEAUFORT	ATS 2	19 Feb 1968	20 Dec 1968	22 Jan 1972
*BRUNSWICK	ATS 3	5 June 1968	14 Oct 1969	10 Dec 1972

Displacement, tons	3 117 full load
Dimensions, feet	282·66 *oa* × 50 × 15·1
Guns	2—20 mm AA; 4—·50 cal MG
Main engines	4 diesels (Paxman); 6 000 bhp; 2 shafts = 16 knots
Complement	102 (9 officers and 93 enlisted men)

These tugs are designed specifically for salvage operations and are capable of (1) ocean towing, (2) supporting diver operations to depths of 850 feet, (3) lifting submerged objects weighing as much as 600 000 pounds from a depth of 120 feet by static tidal lift or 30 000 pounds by dynamic lift, (4) fighting ship fires, and (5) performing general salvage operations.

The ATS 1 was authorised in the Fiscal Year 1966 shipbuilding programme; ATS 2 and ATS 3 in the FY 1967 programme. All three ships constructed by Brooke Marine, Lowestoft, England.

ATF 4 was authorised in the FY 1972 new construction programme and ATS 5 in the FY 1973 programme, with several additional ships being planned. However, construction of these ships was deferred in 1973 with the smaller, new-design ATF being substituted in their place.

Designation changed from salvage tug (ATS) to salvage and rescue ship (ATS) on 16 Feb 1971.

DIVING. **These ships can carry the air-transportable Mk I Deep Diving System to support four divers working in two-man shifts at depths to 850 feet. The system** consists of a double-chamber decompression chamber a personnel transfer capsule to transport divers between the ships and ocean floor and the associated controls, winches, cables, gas supplies, *et cetera*. The ships organic diving capability is compressed air.

ENGINEERING. Fitted with controllable-pitch propellers and tunnel bow thruster for precise manoeuvering.

NOMENCLATURE. These three ships are names for small American cities with namesakes in the United Kingdom.

EDENTON (ATS 1) *1971, United States Navy*

SEAPLANE TENDERS (AV) AND ADVANCED AVIATION BASE SHIPS (AVB)

All US Navy seaplane tenders and aviation base ships have been stricken or transferred except for the ex-*Albermarle* AV 5 which remains on the Navy List as a helicopter repair ship, renamed *Corpus Christi Bay* ARVH 1.

See 1972-1973 edition for final disposal and transfer notes for these ship types.

SEALIFT SHIPS

Military Sealift Ships provide ocean transportation for all components of the Department of Defense. These ships are operated by the Navy's Military Sealift Command, renamed on 1 Aug 1970 from Military Sea Transportation Service (MSTS).

The cargo ships, tankers, troop transports and landing ships, listed below carry military cargo and personnel from port to port except that Military Sealift Command tankers do transfer petroleum to Navy oilers in overseas areas. In addition, the Military Sealift Command directs the chartering of merchantmen owned by shipping lines or private parties to carry government cargo.

The Commander, Deputy Commander, and Area Commanders (Atlantic, Pacific, and Far East) are flag officers of the Navy on active duty. All ships are civilian manned with most of their crews being Civil Service employees of the Navy. However, the tankers are operated under contract to commercial tanker lines and are manned by merchant seamen and some ships are manned by Japanese and Korean merchant seamen under the command of US personnel (see notes for specific ships). In addition to the ships listed in this section, the Military Sealift Command also operates a number of underway replenishment (UNREP) ships, fleet support ships, and Special Projects ships that support other defence related activities, mostly research, surveying and missile-range support ships (see Experimental, Research and Surveying Ships listing). Other Special Projects ships are the cable ships and helicopter repair ship *Corpus Christi Bay* (T-ARVH 1) listed in the section on Fleet Support Ships. A few Navy-manned logistic ships are included in this section although they are not under the control of the Military Sealift Command.

In addition to Navy-owned ships, the Military Sealift Command operates the roll-on/roll-off vehicle cargo ship *Admiral William M. Callaghan* and is constructing a series of tankers under long-term charter agreements. These ships are built by private industry and operated by commercial shipping firms under charter to the government. With this charter security private financing is encouraged and the ships are largely amortised after minimum government use, after which they could be used in private service or purchased outright by the government. The ships wear Military Sealift Command's colours but do not have Navy hull designations.

ARMAMENT. No ships of the Military Sealift Command are armed.

CLASSIFICATION. Military Sealift Command ships are assigned standard US Navy hull designations with the added designation prefix "T". Ships in this category are referred to as "USNS" (United States Naval Ship) vice "USS" (United States Ship) which is used for Navy-manned ships.

DISPOSALS

All store ships (AF) and medium landing ships (LSM/AG), light cargo ships (AKL), and transports (AP) operated by the Military Sealift Command in point-to-point operations have been stricken; see 1973-1974 and previous editions for characteristics.

All aircraft transports (AVT) and cargo and aircraft ferry ships (AKV) have been stricken from the Navy List. See 1971-1972 edition for characteristics of the last AKVs in service.

CARGO SHIPS (AG): FORMER DEPOT SHIPS

The former "Victory" class forward depot ships subsequently employed as cargo ships have been stricken; **Phoenix** T-AG 172, **Provo** T-AG 173, **Cheyenne** T-AG 174 stricken on 19 June 1973. See 1973-1974 and previous editions for characteristics.

1 HEAVY LIFT SHIP (AK): "BROSTROM" TYPE

• PVT. LEONARD C. BROSTROM (ex-*Marine Eagle*) T-AK 255

Displacement, tons	13 865 deadweight
Dimensions, feet	520 oa × 71·5 × 33
Main engines	Geared turbine; 9 000 shp; 1 shaft = 15·8 knots
Boilers	2
Complement	57 (14 officers, 43 men)

The *Brostrom* is fitted with 150-ton capacity booms, providing the most powerful lift capability of any US ship. C4-S-B1 type built in 1943. Note the deckloaded tanks and trucks in the photograph of the *Brostrom*.

DISPOSALS

Marine Fiddler T-AK 267 transferred to Maritime Administration on 14 Sep 1973.

MARSHFIELD (T-AK 282) *1970, United States Navy*

4 FBM CARGO SHIPS (AK): "VICTORY" TYPE

***NORWALK** (ex-*Norwalk Victory*)	T-AK 279
***FURMAN** (ex-*Furman Victory*)	T-AK 280
***VICTORIA** (ex-*Ethiopia Victory*)	T-AK 281
***MARSHFIELD** (ex-*Marshfield Victory*)	T-AK 282

Displacement, tons	6 700 light; *Betelgeuse* 15 580 full load; others 11 150 full load
Dimensions, feet	455·25 oa × 62 × 24
Guns	8—40 mm AA (twin) in *Betelgeuse*; others unarmed
Main engines	geared turbine; 8 500 shp; 1 shaft = 17 knots
Boilers	2
Complement	80 to 90 plus Navy detachment

Former merchant ships of the VC2-S-AP3 "Victory" type built during World War II. Extensively converted to supply supply tenders for Fleet Ballistic Missile (FBM) submarines. Fitted to carry torpedoes, spare parts, packaged petroleum products, bottled gas, black oil and diesel fuel, frozen and dry provisions, and general cargo as well as missiles. No. 3 hold converted to carry 16 Polaris missiles in vertical position; tankage provided for 355 000 gallons of diesel oil and 430 000 gallons of fuel oil (for submarine tenders). All subsequently modified to carry Poseidon missiles. All four ships are operated by the Military Sealift Command with civilian operating crews; small Navy detachment in each ship provides security and technical services.

Betelgeuse reactivated by the Navy in 1951 from Maritime Administration reserve fleet. Decommissioned in 1971 and placed in reserve.

Norwalk converted to FBM cargo ship by Boland Machine & Manufacturing Co, and accepted for service on 30 Dec 1963.

Furman converted by American Shipbuilding Co, and accepted in Oct 1964.

Victoria converted by Philadelphia Naval Shipyard, and accepted in Oct 1965.

Marshfield converted by Boland Machine & Manufacturing Co, and accepted in June 1970.

DISPOSALS

Betelgeuse AK 260 stricken on 1 Feb 1974.

1 CARGO SHIP (AK): "BLAND" TYPE

•SCHUYLER OTIS BLAND T-AK 277

Displacement, tons	15 910 full load
Dimensions, feet	478 × 66 × 30
Main engines	Geared turbine; 13 750 shp; 1 shaft; = 18·5 knots
Boilers	2

Acquired from the Maritime Administration by the Military Sea Transportation Service in July 1961. The only ship of the type (C3-S-DX1), built in 1961; prototype of the "Mariner" cargo ship design.

SCHUYLER OTIS BLAND (T-AK 277) *United States Navy*

PVT LEONARD C. BROSTROM (T-AK 255) *United States Navy*

Sealift Ships—*continued*

1 CARGO SHIP (AK): "ELTANIN" TYPE

***MIRFAK** T-AK 271

Displacement, tons	2 036 light; 4 942 full load
Dimensions, feet	256·8 wl; 262·2 oa × 51·5 × 18·7
Main engines	Diesel-electric (ALCO diesels with Westinghouse electric motors); 3 200 bhp; 2 shafts = 13 knots

Built for MSTS by Avondale Marine Ways, New Orleans, La. Designed for Arctic operation with hull strengthened against ice. C1-M E2-13a type. Launched on 5 Aug 1957. Note icebreaking prow in photo.

CONVERSION. Two other ships of this class converted for oceanographic research: *Eltanin*, reclassified from T-AK 270 to T-AGOR 8 on 15 Nov 1962; *Mizar* T-AK 272 was reclassified T-AGOR 11 on 15 Apr 1964 (see Experimental, Research and Surveying Ships).

MIRFAK (T-AK 271) *United States Navy*

9 CARGO SHIPS (AK): "VICTORY" TYPE

***GREENVILLE VICTORY**	T-AK 237
***PVT. JOHN R. TOWLE** (ex-*Appleton Victory*)	T-AK 240
***PVT. FRANCIS X. McGRAW** (ex-*Wabash Victory*)	T-AK 241
***SGT. ANDREW MILLER** (ex-*Radcliffe Victory*)	T-AK 242
***SGT. MORRIS E. CRAIN** (ex-*Mills Victory*)	T-AK 244
***SGT. TRUMAN KIMBRO**	T-AK 254
***LIEUT. JAMES E. ROBINSON** (ex-T-AG 170, ex-T-AK 274, ex-AKV 3, ex-*Czechoslovakia Victory*)	T-AK 274
***PVT. JOSEPH F. MERRELL** (ex-AKV 4, ex-*Grange Victory*)	T-AK 275
***SGT. JACK J. PENDLETON** (ex-AKV 5)	T-AK 276

Displacement, tons	6 700 light; 12 450 full load
Dimensions, feet	455·25 oa × 62 × 28·5
Main engines	Geared turbine; 8 500 shp; 1 shaft = 15 or 17 knots (see notes)
Boilers	2

Former merchant ships of the "Victory" type built during World War II. VC2-S-AP3 type capable of 17 knots except T-AK 245 is VC2-S-AP2 type capable of 15 knots.
Three ships originally acquired by Navy from Maritime Administration as aircraft cargo and ferry ships (AKV); reclassified as "straight" cargo ships (AK) on 7 May 1959. *Lieut. James E. Robinson* modified for special project work and designated T-AG in 1963; reverted to T-AK 274 on 1 July 1964.
Several other "Victory" cargo ships transferred to Navy after World War II have been converted to research (AG) and space/missile support ships (AGM). "Victory" type cargo ships initially configured as forward depot ships and as Fleet Ballistic Missile (FBM) cargo ships are listed separately.
These ships are unarmed and civilian manned by the Military Sealift Command.

RECLASSIFICATION. The former Military Sea Transportation Service Aircraft Cargo and Ferry Ships *Lieut, James E. Robinson, Private Joseph F. Merrel* and *Sergeant Jack J. Pendleton*, AKV 3, AKV 4, and AKV 5, respectively, were reclassified as Cargo Ships, Ak 274, AK 275 and AK 276 on 7 May 1959. *Kingsport Victory* T-AK 239, was renamed and reclassified *Kingsport* T-AG 164 in 1962 (see Experimental, Research and Surveying ships).
Lieut James E. Robinson T-AK 274, was to have been transferred to the Maritime Administration, but was modified for special project work and reclassified as T-AG 170 in 1963, and reverted to the original classification T-AK 274 on 1 July 1964.
Haiti Victory T-AK 238 and *Dalton Victory* T-AK 256 converted to satellite tracking and recovery ships, reclassified and renamed, *Longview* T-AGM 3 and *Sunnyvale* T-AGM 5, respectively.
Pvt. Joe E. Mann T-AK 253, ex-*Owensboro Victory*, was fitted out as a range instrumentation and telemetry ship for the Pacific Missile Range in Oct 1958 and renamed *Richfield* T-AGM 4.
The ship intended for designation AK 278 became the *Sea Lift*, T-LSV 9, subsequently changed to T-AKR 9.

DISPOSALS
Sgt. Archer T. Gammon T-AK 243 transferred to Maritime Administration in 1973 for scrapping; **Lieut Robert Craig** T-AK 252 stricken on 27 July 1973; **Lieut. George W. G. Boyce** stricken on 30 July 1973.

PVT JOSEPH F. MERRELL (T-AK 275) *United States Navy*

PVT JOHN R. TOWLE (T-AK 240) in Antarctic *1961, US Navy*

SGT MORRIS E CRAIN (T-AK 244) *United States Navy*

1 CARGO SHIP (AK): Ex-AKA TYPE

***WYANDOT** T-AK 283 (ex-T-AKA 92)

Displacement, tons	7 430 light; 14 000 full load
Dimensions	435 wl; 459·2 oa × 63 × 24
Main engines	Geared turbines (General Electric); 6 000 shp; 1 shaft = 16·5 knots
Boilers	2 (Combustion Engineering)

Former attack cargo ship (AKA) of the "Andromeda" class; C2-S-B1 type. Built by Moore Dry Dock Co, Oakland, California; launched on 28 June 1944; commissioned on 30 Sep 1944 as AKA 92. Assigned to MSTS and manned by a civilian crew since 1963. Designation changed to T-AK 283 on 1 Jan 1969. Winterised for arctic service.

1 VEHICLE CARGO SHIP: "CALLAGHAN" TYPE

Name	*Builder*	*Launched*
***ADMIRAL WM. M. CALLAGHAN**	SUN SB & DD	17 Oct 1967

Displacement, tons	24 000 full load
Dimensions, feet	694
Main engines	2 gas turbines (General Electric LM 2500); 50 000 shp; 2 shafts = 26 knots
Complement	33

Roll-on/roll-off vehicle cargo ship built specifically for long-term charter to Military Sealift Command. Internal parking decks and ramps for carrying 750, employing four side ramps and stern ramp, the *Callaghan* can off load and reload full vehicle capacity in 27 hours.
Named for first commander of Military Sea Transportation Service.

ADM WM. M. CALLAGHAN *United States Navy*

Sealift Ships—*continued*

C1-M-AV1 TYPE

All surviving small cargo ships of this type have been stricken: **Herkimer** T-AK 188, **Muskingum** T-AK 198 transferred to US Department of the Interior on 15 June 1973; **Short Splice** T-AK 249 stricken on 15 June 1973; **Col. William J. O'Brien** T-AK 246 stricken on 1 Sep 1973; **Fentress** T-AK 180, **Pvt. Frank J. Petrarca** T-AK 250 stricken on 15 Oct 1973. See 1973-1974 and previous editions for characteristics.

1 VEHICLE CARGO SHIP (AKR): "SEA LIFT" TYPE

***SEA LIFT** T-KAR 9 (ex-T-LSV 9)

Displacement, tons	11 130 light; 16 940 standard; 21 700 full load
Measurement, tons	15 750 gross; 12 100 deadweight
Dimensions, feet	540 oa × 83 × 29
Main engines	Geared steam turbines; 2 shafts; 19 400 shp = 20 knots
Boilers	2
Complement	62 plus 12 Passengers

Improved roll-on/roll-off vehicle cargo ship. Maritime Administration C4-ST-67a type. Built by the Puget Sound Bridge & Dry Dock Co, (now Lockheed Shipbuilding and Construction Co), Seattle, Wash, at a cost of $15 895 500. Authorised under the Fiscal Year 1963 programme. Laid down on 19 May 1964 and launched on 18 Apr 1965. Delivered to Navy on 25 Apr 1967 and to MSTS on 19 May 1967. Designed for point-to-point sea transportation of Department of Defense self-propelled, fully loaded, wheeled, tracked and amphibious vehicles and general cargo. Internal ramps, stern ramp and side openings provide for quick loading and unloading. Designation changed from T-LSV to T-AKR on 1 Jan 1969.

SEA LIFT (T-AKR 9) *1966, Lockheed Shipbuilding*

SEA LIFT (T-AKR 9) *1966, Lockheed Shipbuilding*

1 VEHICLE CARGO SHIP (AKR): "COMET" TYPE

***COMET** T-AKR 7 (ex-T-LSV 7, ex-T-AK 269)

Displacement, tons	7 605 light; 18 150 full load
Measurement, tons	12 750 gross; 6 500 deadweight
Dimensions, feet	465 pp; 499 oa × 78 × 28·8
Main engines	Geared turbines (General Electric); 2 shafts; 13 200 shp = 18 knots
Boilers	2 (Babcock & Wilcox)
Complement	73

Roll-on/roll-off vehicle carrier built for MSTS by Sun Shipbuilding & Dry Dock Co. C3-ST-14A type. Laid down on 15 May 1956. Launched on 31 July 1957. Completed on 27 Jan 1958. Has ramp system for loading and discharging. The hull is strengthened against ice. Can accommodate 700 vehicles in two after holds; the forward holds are for general cargo. Equipped with Denny-Brown Stabilisers. Reclassified from T-AK to T-LSV on 1 June 1963, and changed to T-AKR on 1 Jan 1969. LSV 1-6 were World War II-built amphibious ships; subsequently redesignated as mine warfare ships (MCS) and net cargo ship (AKN).

COMET (T-AKR 7) *United States Navy*

DISPOSALS

Taurus (T-AKR 8, ex-T-LSV 8, ex-AK 273, ex-LSD 23) deactivated in 1968 and subsequently scrapped; officially stricken on 22 June 1971 (almost two years after being sold for scrap).

Galilea AKN 6, ex-LSV 6, ex-AP 161 stricken from the Navy List on 1 Sep 1961 and transferred to Maritime Administration.

9 TANKERS: "SEALIFT" CLASS

Name	Builder	Launched
***SEALIFT PACIFIC**	Todd Shipyards	13 Oct 1973
***SEALIFT ATLANTIC**	Bath Iron Works	26 Jan 1974
***SEALIFT ARABIAN SEA**	Todd Shipyards	26 Jan 1974
SEALIFT MEDITERRANEAN	Bath Iron Works	9 Mar 1974
SEALIFT CHINA SEA	Todd Shipyards	20 Apr 1974
SEALIFT CARIBBEAN	Bath Iron Works	1974
SEALIFT INDIAN OCEAN	Todd Shipyards	1974
SEALIFT ARCTIC	Bath Iron Works	1974
SEALIFT ANTARCTIC	Bath Iron Works	1974

Dimensions, feet	587 oa × 84 × 45·5
Main engines	2 diesels; 14 000 bhp; 1 shaft = 16 knots
Complement	26 + 2 Maritime Academy cadets

Relatively small tankers built specifically for long term-charter by the Military Sealift Command. Four ships built by Todd Shipyards Corp, San Pedro, California; five by Bath Iron Works Corp, Bath, Maine. Operated for MSC by commercial firms with civilian crews. Not assigned Navy hull numbers, but carry MSC colours.
Fitted with bow thruster to assist docking; automated engine room. Approximately 25 000 tons deadweight; cargo capacity 220 000 barrels. Estimated cost $146 500 000 for the nine-ship class.

SEALIFT ARABIAN SEA *1974, Todd Shipyards Corp*

1 TANKER (AO): "EXPLORER" TYPE

*** AMERICAN EXPLORER** T-AO 165

Displacement, tons	16 500 gross; 22 525 deadweight
Dimensions, feet	615 oa × 80 × 44·5
Main engines	Steam turbines; 22 000 shp; 1 shaft = 20 knots

T5-S-RM2a type. Laid down on 9 July 1957; launched on 11 Apr 1958. Built by Ingalls Shipbuilding Corporation, Pascagoula, for the Maritime Administration, but acquired by Military Sea Transportation Service. Cargo capacity 190 300 barrels. Operated for Military Sealift Command by commercial firm.

AMERICAN EXPLORER (T-AO 165) *United States Navy*

3 TANKERS (AO): "MAUMEE" CLASS

		Launched
***MAUMEE**	T-AO 149	16 Feb 1956
***SHOSHONE**	T-AO 151	17 Jan 1957
***YUKON**	T-AO 152	16 Mar 1956

Displacement, tons	25 000 deadweight
Measurement, tons	16 500 gross; 25 000 deadweight
Dimensions, feet	591 wl; 620 oa × 83·5 × 32
Main engines	Geared turbine; 20 460 shp; 1 shaft = 18 knots

Yukon laid down 16 May 1955 by Ingalls, Pascagoula, delivered May 1957. *Maumee* laid down 8 Mar 1955, delivered Dec 1956. *Shoshone* laid down 15 Aug 1955 by Sun Shipbuilding, Chester, delivered Apr 1957. T5-S-12A type. *Potomac* T-AO 150 sank at Morehead, North Carolina, after explosion on 26-27 Sep 1961, but was rebuilt in 1963-1964, renamed SS *Shenandoah* and chartered to MSTS. Cargo capacity 203 216 barrels.
Maumee provided with ice-strengthened bow during 1969-1970 modification at Norfolk SB & DD Co; employed in transporting petroleum products to Antarctica in support of US scientific endeavours.
These ships are operated for the Military Sealift Command by commercial firms.

Sealift Ships—*continued*

SHOSHONE (T-AO 151) *United States Navy*

MISSION SANTA YNEZ (T-AD 134) *United States Navy*

8 TANKERS (AO): "MISSION" CLASS

Name	No.	Launched	Commissioned
***SUAMICO** (ex-*Harlem Heights*)	T-AO 49	30 May 1942	10 Aug 1942
***TALLULAH** (ex-*Valley Forge*)	T-AO 50	25 June 1942	5 Sep 1942
***PECOS** (ex-*Corsicana*)	T-AO 65	17 Aug 1942	5 Oct 1942
***MILLICOMA** (ex-*Conastoga*, ex-*King's Mountain*)	T-AO 73	21 Jan 1943	5 Mar 1943
***SAUGATUCK** (ex-*Newton*)	T-AO 75	7 Dec 1942	19 Feb 1943
***SCHUYLKILL** (ex-*Louisburg*)	T-AO 76	16 Feb 1943	9 Apr 1943
***COSSATOT** (ex-*Fort Necessity*)	T-AO 77	28 Feb 1943	20 Apr 1943
***MISSION SANTA YNEZ**	T-AO 134	19 Dec 1943	(see notes)

Displacement, tons: 5 730 light; 22 380 full load
Dimensions, feet: 503 wl; 523·5 oa × 68 × approx 30
Main engines: Turbo-electric drive; 6 000 shp (except *Mission Santa Ynez* 10 000 shp); 1 shaft = 15 knots (except *Mission Santa Ynez* 16 knots)
Boilers: 2 (Babcock & Wilcox)

T2-SE-A1 tankers begun as merchant ships but acquired by Navy and completed as fleet oilers (AO) except the *Mission Santa Ynez* of T2-SE-A2 type delivered as merchant tanker on 13 March 1944 and subsequently acquired by Navy on 22 Oct 1947. During the post World War II period all of these ships were employed in the tanker role, carrying petroleum point-to-point.
All built by Sun Shipbuilding & Dry Dock Co, Chester, Pennsylvania, except *Mission Santa Ynez* built by Marine Ship Corp, Sausalito, California. Cargo capacity approximately 134 000 barrels.

DISPOSALS AND TRANSFERS (since 1 Jan 1970)
Mission San Rafael T-AO 130 stricken on 28 Apr 1970, **Mission Santa Cruz** T-AO 133 stricken on 15 Sep 1970, **Shawnee Trail** T-AO 142 stricken on 29 Feb 1972, **Chepachet** T-AO 78 stricken on 13 Mar 1972, **Mission Buenaventura** T-AO 111 stricken on 31 Mar 1972, **Cache** T-AO 67 stricken on 6 May 1972, **Cowanesque** T-AO 67 stricken on 1 June 1972, **Pioneer Valley** T-AO 140 stricken on 15 Aug 1972 (not transferred to Columbia). Some ships technically remain on the Navy List but have been "permanently" transferred to Maritime Administration reserve fleet and are expected to be disposed of in the near future.

SCHUYLKILL (T-AO 76) *United States Navy*

TRANSPORTS (AP)

All US troop transports (AP) have been stricken or transferred; these ships differed from amphibious transports (LPA, formerly attack transports, APA) by being point-to-point carriers, operating between ports and not capable of unloading assault troops into landing craft.
The last transports on the Navy List were the three "Barrett" class ships; see 1973-1974 and previous editions for characteristics. **Geiger** T-AP 197 stricken on 27 Apr 1971 and transferred to Maritime Administration reserve; **Upshur** T-AP 198 stricken on 2 Apr 1973 and transferred to the State of Maine as a merchant training ship; **Barrett** T-AP 196 stricken on 2 July 1973 and transferred to Maritime Administration reserve fleet.

4 GASOLINE TANKERS (AOG): "PECONIC" CLASS

Name	No.	Launched
***RINCON**	T-AOG 77	5 Jan 1945
***NODAWAY** (ex-*Belridge*)	T-AOG 78	15 May 1945
***PETALUMA** (ex-*Raccoon Bend*, ex-*Tavispan*)	T-AOG 79	9 Aug 1945
***PISCATAQUA** (ex-*Cisne*, ex-*Taveta*)	T-AOG 80	10 Sep 1945

Displacement, tons: 2 060 light; 6 000 full load
Dimensions, feet: 325·2 oa × 48·2 × 19·1
Main engines: diesel; 1 400 bhp; 1 shaft = 10 knots

T1-M-BT2 gasoline tankers built by Todd Shipyards Corp, Houston, Texas, as merchant tankers. All acquired by Navy in 1950 and assigned to Military Sea Transportation Service and employed in point-to-point carrying of petroleum. Cargo capacity approximately 30 000 barrels.

DISPOSALS
T1-MET-24a type: **Chattahooche** T-AOG 82 stricken on 22 Feb 1972, **Alatna** T-AOG 81 permanently transferred to Maritime Administration reserve fleet on 8 Aug 1972.

RINCON (T-AOG 77) *United States Navy*

PETALUMA (T-AOG 79) *United States Navy*

16 CARGO SHIPS: LST TYPE

Sixteen LSTs configured for point-to-point cargo operations remain on the Navy List, all in Military Sealift Command reserve. They are expected to be stricken or transferred in the near future. See 1973-1974 and previous editions for ship characteristics.
T-LSTs remaining on Navy/MSC List:
LST 47, 176, 230, 287, 491, 566, 579, 607, 613, 623, 629, 649, Daviess County T-LST, 692, Harris County T-LST 822, Orleans Parish T-LST 1069 (ex-MCS 6), and **LST 1072.**

DISPOSALS
LST 600 stricken on 1 June 1969; **Chesterfield County,** T-LST 551 stricken on 1 June 1970; **Clearwater County** LST 602 (operated by US Air Force) transferred to Mexico on 25 May 1972; **LST 581, 626, Plumas County,** T-LST 1083 stricken on 1 June 1972; **LST 222, 488, 546** transferred to Philippines on 15 July 1972; **LST 277** transferred to Chile on 2 February 1973; **LST 117, 276, Chase County** T-LST 532 transferred to Singapore on 10 June 1973; **LST 456, 530, 572, 587, 590, 630, 643, 664** stricken on 15 June 1973; **New London County** T-LST 1066, **Nye County,** T-LST 1067 transferred to Chile on 29 Aug 1973; **LST 399, 550, De Kalb County** T-LST 715, **LST 1088, Traverse County** T-LST 1160, **Wahkiakum County** T-LST 1162, **Waldo County** T-LST 1163, **Walworth County** T-LST 1164, **Washoe County** T-LST 1165 transferred to Maritime administration in 1974.

EXPERIMENTAL, RESEARCH AND SURVEYING SHIPS

1 EXPERIMENTAL SURFACE EFFECT SHIP: AEROJET-GENERAL DESIGN

SES-100A

Weight, tons	100 gross
Dimensions, feet	81·9 oa × 41·9
Main/lift engines	4 gas turbines (Avco-Lycoming) 12 000 hp; three fans for lift and two water-jet propulsion systems = 80+ knots

Surface effects ship developed by Aerojet-General Corp, and built by Tacoma Boatbuilding Co, Tacoma, Washington, to test feasibility of large SES for naval missions. Christened in July 1971; underway in mid-1972 in competition with the Bell design described below. Aluminium construction with rigid sidewalls to hold cushion or bubble of air. Cargo capacity ten tons (instrumentation during evaluation); provision for crew of four and six observers. Fitted with four TF-35 gas turbine engines, marine version of the T55-L-11A developed for the CH-47C helicopter.

PROGRAMME. Two other types of ocean-going "air support" platforms are being developed for the US Navy at this time; air cushion vehicle (ACV) landing craft described in the section on Landing Craft and an armed SES design listed with Patrol Ships and Craft.

SES-100A *1972, Aerojet General*

1 EXPERIMENTAL SURFACE EFFECT SHIP: BELL AEROSYSTEMS DESIGN

SES-100B

Weight, tons	100 gross
Dimensions, feet	78 oa × 35
Main engines	3 gas turbines (Pratt & Whitney); 13 500 hp; 2 semi-submerged, super cavitating propellers = 80+ knots
Lift engines	3 gas turgines (United Aircraft of Canada); 1 500 hp; eight lift fans

Surface effects ship developed by Bell Aerospace Division of the Textron Corp; built Bell facility in Michoud, Louisiana. Christened on March 6, 1971; underway in Feb 1972 as competitive development platform for Navy.
Aluminium hull with rigid sidewalls to hold cushion or bubble of air. Cargo capacity ten tons (instrumentation during evaluation); provision for crew of four and six observers.
Fitted with three Pratt & Whitney FT-12 gas turbine engines and three United Aircraft of Canada ST-6J-70 gas turbine engines.
The SES-100B is credited with having set an SES speed record of more than 80 knots during trials in April 1974.

SES-100B *1974, Bell Aerosystems*

2 SONAR TEST SHIPS (AG): Ex-MINESWEEPERS

Name	*No.*	*Launched*	*Commissioned*
***ALACRITY**	AG 520 (ex-MSO 520)	8 June 1957	2 Oct 1958
***ASSURANCE**	AG 521 (ex-MSO 521)	31 Aug 1957	22 Nov 1958

Displacement, tons	810 light; 934 full load
Dimensions, feet	190 oa × 36 × 14·5
Guns	1—40 mm AA (as MSO)
Main engines	2 diesels (General Motors); 2 700 bhp; 2 shafts (controllable pitch propellers) = 15 knots

Former ocean minesweepers. Both built by Peterson Builders Inc., Sturgeon Bay, Wisconsin. Wood-hulled with non-magnetic engines and fittings. Both ships modified for sonar test activities and redesignated as miscellaneous auxiliaries (AG) on 1 June 1973 and 1 Mar 1973, respectively.

DISPOSALS
Ability MSO 519 stricken in 1 Feb 1971

ALACRITY (AG 520) *1969, United States Navy*

1 HYDROGRAPHIC RESEARCH SHIP (AG)

***FLYER** (ex-*American Flyer*, ex-*Water Witch*) T-AG 178

Displacement, tons	7 360 light; 11 000 full load
Dimensions, feet	459·2 oa × 63 × 28
Main engines	Turbines; 6 000 shp; 1 shaft = 17 knots
Boilers	2
Complement	55 (14 officers, 41 men)

Acquired from Maritime Administration on 9 Feb 1965. C2-S-B1 type built in 1945. Operated by Military Sealift Command for Naval Electronic Systems Command, civilian manned.

FLYER (T-AG 178) *United States Navy*

1 HYDROGRAPHIC RESEARCH SHIP (AG): "VICTORY" TYPE

***KINGSPORT** (ex-*Kingsport Victory*) T-AG 164

Displacement, tons	7 190 light; 10 680 full load
Dimensions, feet	455 oa × 62 × 22
Main engines	Geared turbines; 8 500 shp; 1 shaft = 15·2 knots
Boilers	2
Complement	73 (13 officers, 42 men, 15 technicians)

VC2-S-AP3. Built in 1944 by the California Shipbuiding Corp, Los Angeles. Former cargo ship in the MSTS fleet. Name shortened, ship reclassified and converted in 1961-1962 by Willamette Iron & Steel Co, Portland, Oregon, into the world's first satellite communications ship, for Project Advent, involving the promotion of a terminal to meet the required military capability for high capacity, world-wide radio communications using high altitude hovering satellites, and the installation of ship-to-shore communications, facilities, additional electric power generating equipment, a helicopter landing platform, aerological facilities, and a 30-foot parabolic communication antenna housed in a 53-ft diameter plastic radome abaft the superstructure. Painted white for operations in the tropics. Project Advent Syncom satellite relay operations were completed in 1966, and *Kingsport* was reassigned to hydrographic research. Antenna sphere now removed.
Operated by Military Sealift Command for Naval Electronic Systems Command; civilian manned.
Broadside view appears in 1968-1969 edition; note antenna mast on helicopter platform in photograph; exhaust ducts fitted to funnel.

KINGSPORT (T-AG 164) *United States Navy*

Experimental, Research and Surveying Ships—*continued*

1 POSEIDON TEST SHIP (AG): "MARINER" TYPE

OBSERVATION ISLAND (ex-*YAG* 57, ex-*Empire State Mariner*) AG 154

Displacement, tons	17 600 full load
Dimensions, feet	529·5 wl; 563 oa × 76·2 × 29
Main engines	Geared turbines (General Electric); 19 250 shp; 1 shaft = 20 knots
Boilers	2
Complement	350

Built as a "Mariner" class merchant ship (C4-S-1a type) by the New York Shipbuilding Corp, Camden, New Jersey; launched on 15 Aug 1953; acquired by the Navy on 10 Sep 1956 for use as a Fleet Ballistic Missile (FBM) test ship. Converted at Norfolk Naval Shipyard; commissioned on 5 Dec 1958.

Employed to test fire Polaris and later Poseidon missiles. Navy manned. Decommissioned on 25 Sep 1972 and placed in Maritime Administration reserve; remains on Navy List.

MISSILE TESTING. The ship is fitted with complete missile testing, servicing and firing systems. She fired the first ship-launched Polaris missile at sea on 27 Aug 1959. Refitted to fire the improved Poseidon missile in 1969 and launched the first Poseidon test missile fired afloat on 16 Dec 1969.

OBSERVATION ISLAND (AG 154) *1971, US Navy, PH3, T. F. Ahlgrim*

1 EXPERIMENTAL NAVIGATION SHIP (AG): "MARINER" TYPE

***COMPASS ISLAND** (ex-*YAG* 56, ex-*Garden Mariner*) AG 153

Displacement, tons	16 076 full load
Dimensions, feet	529·5 pp; 563 oa × 76·3 × 29
Main engines	Geared turbines (General Electric); 19 250 shp; 1 shaft = 20 knots
Boilers	2

Originally a "Mariner" class merchant ship (C4-S-1a type); built by New York Shipbuilding Corp, Camden, New Jersey; launched on 24 Oct 1953 and acquired by the Navy on 29 Mar 1956.

Converted by New York Naval Shipyard; commissioned on 3 Dec 1956 for the development of the Fleet Balistic Missile guidance and ship navigation systems. Her mission is to assist in the development and valuation of a navigation system independant of shore-based aids. Navy manned.

COMPASS ISLAND (AG 153) *United States Navy*

DISPOSALS AND RECLASSIFICATIONS

Acquisition of **AG 155** (C-4 cargo ship) was cancelled; **Hunting** AG 156 (ex-EAG 398, ex-LSM 398) sonar test ship, strcken in 1962; **King County** AG 157 (ex-LST 857) Regulus missile test ship, stricken in 1961; acquisition of research ship **AG 158** was cancelled; **Oxford** AG 159 reclassified AGTR 1; **AG 160** and **AG 161** reclassified AGM 1 and AGM 22, respectively; **Mission Capistrano** AG 162 (ex-AO 112) sound test ship stricken on 19 Oct 1971; **Glover** AG 163 reclassified AGDE 1. **AG 165-168** reclassified AGTR 2-5, respectively; **Private J. E. Valdez** AG 169 (ex-APC 119) special mission ship, stricken in 1970; **Lieutenant J. E. Robinson** AG 170 (ex-AK 274) reclassified AK-274; **Seargent Joseph E. Muller** AG 171 (ex-APC 118) special mission ship, stricken in 1970; **AG 172-174** are in service as cargo ships.

Sergeant Curtis F. Shoup AG 175, survey support ship, stricken in 1970; **Peregine** AG 176 (ex-MSF 373) experimental ship, stricken in 1969; **Shearwater** AG 177 (ex-FS 411) special mission ship, returned to US Army in 1967. **AG 179-190** assigned to 12 "Victory" cargo ship to have been used as floating depot ships; project cancelled; **Spokane** AG 191 (ex-CLAA 120) was to be converted to sonar test ship; project cancelled and ship stricken 15 Apr 1972 (see 1970-1971 edition for details).

1 HYDROFOIL RESEARCH SHIP (AGEH)

***PLAINVIEW** AGEH 1

Displacement, tons	320 full load
Dimensions, feet	212 oa × 40·5 × 10 (hull borne) or 26 (with foils down)
A/S weapons	2 triple torpedo tubes (Mk 32)
Main engines	2 gas turbines (General Electric); 30 000 hp; 2 diesels; 1 200 = 50 knots
Complement	20 (6 officers, 14 men)

Aluminium hull experimental hydrofoil. Three retractable foils, 25 ft in height, each weighing 7 tons, fitted port and starboard and on stern, and used in waves up to 15 feet. Initial maximum speed of about 50 knots, with later modifications expected to raise the speed to 80 knots. Fitted with the largest titanium propellers made. The two 15 000 hp gas turbines are General Electric J-79 jet aircraft engines modified for marine use. Power plant and transmission designed to permit future investigation of various types of foils. Built by Lockheed Shipbuilding & Construction Co, Seattle, Washington. Laid down on 8 May 1964, launched on 28 June 1965, and placed in service on 1 May 1969. Delayed because of engineering difficulties. In service vice being in commission.

The photographs of the *Plainview* show the ship on foils and in displacement condition during experimental transfer of personnel from a CH-46A helicopter.

DISPOSALS

The hydrofoil test craft **Denison**, briefly operated by the Navy, has been returned to the Maritime Administration and subsequently sold commercially. Photographs and description appear in the 1970-1971 edition.

PLAINVIEW (AGEH 1) *1972, US Navy, PH2, E. E. Murphy*

PLAINVIEW (AGEH 2) *1972, US Navy, PH2, E. E. Murphy*

1 RANGE INSTRUMENTATION SHIP (AGM): "VICTORY" TYPE

***RANGE SENTINEL** (ex-*Sherburne*) T-AGM 22 (ex-APA 205)

Displacement, tons	11 860 full load
Main engines	Turbine (Westinghouse); 8 500 hp; 1 sha t = 17·7 knots
Boilers	2 (Combustion Engineering)
Complement	95 (14 officers, 54 men, 27 technical personnel)

Former attack transport converted specifically to serve as a range instrumentation ship in support of the Poseidon Fleet Ballistic Missile (FBM) programme. Built by Permanente Metals Corp, Richmond, California; commissioned on 20 Sep 1944. VC2-S-AP5 type.

Stricken from the Navy List on 1 Oct 1958 and transferred to Maritime Administration reserve fleet; reacquired by the Navy on 22 Oct 1969 for AGM conversion. Converted from Oct 1969 to Oct 1971; placed in service as T-AGM 22 on 14 Oct 1971. Operated by Military Sealift Command and civilian manned.

RANGE SENTINEL (T-AGM 22) *1973, United States Navy*

Experimental Research and Surveying Ships—*continued*

2 RANGE INSTRUMENTATION SHIPS (AGM): "JUMBOISED" T2-SE-A2 TYPE

***VANGUARD** (ex-*Muscel Shoals*, ex-*Mission San Fernando*) T-AGM 19 (ex-T-AO 122)
***REDSTONE** (ex-*Johnstown*, ex-*Mission de Pala*) T-AGM 20 (ex-T-AO 114)

Displacement, tons	21 626 full load
Dimensions, feet	595 oa × 75 × 25
Main engines	Turbine-electric; 1 shaft; 10 000 shp = 16 knots
Boilers	2 (Babcock & Wilcox)
Complement	*Vanguard* 19 officers, 71 enlisted men, 108 technical personnel; *Redstone* 20 officers, 71 enlisted men, 120 technical personnel.

Former "Mission" class tankers converted in 1964-1966 to serve as mid-ocean communications and tracking ships in support of the Apollo manned lunar flights. A third ship of this type has been stricken (see *Disposal* notes below).
All built in 1944 by Marinship, Sausalito, California, as tankers. T2-SE-A2 type. Converted to Range Instrumentation Ships (RIS) by General Dynamics, Quincy Division, Massachusetts; each ship was cut in half and a 72-foot mid-section was inserted, increasing length, beam, and displacement; approximately 450 tons of electronic equipment installed for support of lunar flight operations, including communications and tracking systems; balloon hangar and platform fitted aft. Cost of converting the three ships was $90 000 000. Operated by Military Sealift Command for Air Force Eastern Test Range in Atlantic (*Vanguard*) and for NASA Goddard Space Flight Centre (*Redstone*). Civilian crews.

DISPOSALS
Mercury (ex-*Flagstaff*, *Mission San Juan*) T-AGM 21 (ex-T-AO 126) transferred to Maritime Administration in 1969 (converted to merchant configuration).

VANGUARD (T-AGM 19) *1966, General Dynamics*

REDSTONE (T-AGM 20) *1970, United States Air Force*

GEN. HOYT S. VANDENBERG (T-AGM 10) *United States Navy*

2 RANGE INSTRUMENTATION SHIPS (AGM): C4-S-A1 TYPE

***GENERAL H. H. ARNOLD** (ex-USNS *General R. E. Caollan*) T-AGM 9 (ex-T-AP 139)
***GENERAL HOYT S. VANDENBERG** (ex-USNS *General Harry Taylor*) T-AGM 10 (ex-T-AP 145)

Displacement, tons	16 600 full load
Dimensions, feet	552·9 oa × 71·5 × 26·3
Main engines	Geared turbines (Westinghouse); 9 000 shp; 1 shaft = 15 knots
Boilers	2 (Babcock & Wilcox)
Complement	205 (21 officers, 71 men, 113 technical personnel)

Former transports converted in 1962-1963 for monitoring Air Force missiles firing and satellite launches. Both ships built in 1944 by Kaiser Co. Richmond, California, as large troop transports. C4-S-A1 type. Upon conversion to Range Instrumentation Ships (RIS) they were placed in service in 1963 under Air Force operation, however assigned to MSTS for operation on 1 July 1964 (*Arnold*) and 13 July 1964 (*Vandenberg*).
Both ships are operated by Military Sealift Command for Air Force Eastern Test Range in Atlantic. Civilian manned.

DISPOSALS
C1-M-AV1 type: **Sword Knot** T-AGM 13 stricken on 1 Apr 1971, **Rose Knot** T-AGM 14 stricken on 26 Mar 1968, **Coastal Sentry** T-AGM 15 ex-AK 212 stricken on 11 July 1968, **Timber Hitch** T-AGM 17 stricken on 5 Feb 1968, **Sampan Hitch** T-AGM 18 stricken on 24 June 1968.
EC2 "Liberty" type: **American Mariner** T-AGM 12 stricken on 1 July 1965; employed as target hulk in Chesapeake Bay.

4 RANGE INSTRUMENTATION SHIPS (AGM): "VICTORY" TYPE

***LONGVIEW** (ex-*Haiti Victory*) T-AGM 3 (ex-T-AK 238)
***SUNNYVALE** (ex-*Dalton Victory*) T-AGM 5 (ex-T-AK 256)
HUNTSVILLE (ex-SS *Knox Victory*) T-AGM 7
***WHEELING** (ex-*Seton Hall Victory*) T-AGM 8

Displacement, tons	10 680 full load
Dimensions, feet	T-AGM 7: 455·8 oa × 62 × 28·6 T-AMG 3, 5, 8: 455·3 oa × 62·2 × 28 (draft varies)
Main engines	geared turbines; 8 500 shp; 1 shaft = 16·2 knots for T-AGM 6 and 7; 17 knots for others
Boilers	2

All VC2-S-AP3 type; details vary. All extensively modified to serve as Range Instrumentation Ships (RIS) in support of American military and National Aeronautics and Space Administration (NASA) missile and space programmes.
Longview built in 1944 by Permanente Metals Corp, Richmond, California. Assigned to MSTs on 1 Mar 1950 (as T-AK 238); operated in support of Air Force Western Test Range in Pacific; civilian crew of 12 officers, 41 men, plus 20 technical personnel Fitted with helicopter hangar and platform aft. Decommissioned on 1 July 1974.
Sunnyvale built in 1944 by California SB Corp, Los Angeles. Assigned to MSTS on 6 Aug 1950 (as T-AK 256); operated in support of Air Force Western Test Range in Pacific; civilian crew of 12 officers, 41 men, plus 20 technical personnel. Fitted with helicopter hangar and platform aft. Scheduled to decommission in October 1974.
Huntsville built in 1954 by Oregon SB Corp, Portland, Oregon. Assigned to MSTS on 1 Mar 1960; operated in support of Air Force Western Test Range in Pacific and NASA until taken out of service in Jan 1973; will be stricken in the near future Civilian crew of 14 officers, 55 men, plus 72 technical personnel.
Wheeling built in 1954 by Oregon SB Corp, Portland Oregon. Assigned to MSTS on 28 May 1964; operated in support of Navy Pacific Missile Range; civilian crew of 13 officers, 46 men, plus 48 technical personnel (accomodation for 64). Fitted with helicopter hangar and platform aft. *Wheeling* used as test platform for AWG-9 fire control system (for use in F-14 fighter aircraft).

HELICOPTERS. These ships fitted with helicopter platforms and hangars periodically carry helicopters

DISPOSALS
Richfield T-AGM 4, ex-T-AK 253; **Range Tracker** T-AGM 1, ex-T-AG 160, stricken on 28 Apr 1970; **Twin Falls** T-AGM II stricken on 28 Apr 1970 but subsequently reacquired by Navy for conversion to surveying ship (T-AGS 37); conversion subsequently cancelled and again stricken on 1 Sep 1972. Transferred to New York City for use as trade school facility; **Watertown** T-AGM 6 stricken on 16 Feb 1973.

LONGVIEW (T-AGM 3) *1970, United States Navy, PH3 J. B. Land*

Experimental, Research and Surveying Ships—*continued*

HUNTSVILLE (T-AGM 7) *1967, NASA*

SUNNYVALE (T-AGM 5) *United States Navy*

WHEELING (T-AGM 8) *United States Navy*

2 UTILITY RESEARCH SHIPS (AGOR)

Name	*No.*	*Laid down*	*Launched*	*Delivered*
***GYRE**	AGOR 21	9 Oct 1972	25 May 1973	14 Nov 1973
***MOANA WAVE**	AGOR 22	10 Oct 1972	18 June 1973	16 Jan 1974

Displacement, tons	950 full load
Dimensions, feet	176 oa × 36 × 14·5
Main engines	2 turbo-charged diesels (Caterpillar); 1 700 bhp; 2 shafts (controllable pitch propellers) = 13 knots maximum; 12 knots cruising
Complement	21 (10 crew, 11 scientists)

Both ships built by Halter Marine Services Inc, New Orleans, Louisiana. They are based on a commercial ship design. Fitted with a 150 hp retractable propeller pod for low-speed or station keeping with main machinery shut down.

Open deck aft provides space for equipment vans to permit rapid change of mission capabilities. Each ship cost approximately $1 900 000.
The Navy plans to construct several of these small, utility"" oceanographic research ships to replace older and obsolescent ships now operated by civilian research and educational institutions in support of Navy programmes. The above ships are assigned to Texas A & M University and the University of Hawaii, respectively.

CANCELLATION. The planned AGOR 19 and AGOR 20 of a larger design were cancelled in Feb 1969.

GYRE (AGOR 21) *1973, Halter Marine Service*

GYRE (AGOR 21) *1973, Halter Marine Service*

1 OCEANOGRAPHIC RESEARCH SHIP (AGOR): "HAYES" TYPE

***HAYES** T-AGOR 16

Displacement, tons	3 080 full load
Dimensions, feet	220 wl; 246·5 oa × 75 (see *Design* notes) × 18·8
Main engines	Geared diesels; 5 400 bhp; 2 shafts = 15 knots
Complement	74 (11 officers, 33 men, 30 scientists)

Authorised in Fiscal Year 1967 new construction programme. The T-AGOR 16 is one of two classes of modern US naval ships to have a catamaran hull, the other being the ASR 21 class submarine rescue ships. Built by Todd Shipyards, Seattle, Washington; completed in late 1971. Estimated cost is $15 900 000. Laid down 12 Nov 1969; launched 2 July 1970.
Operated by the Military Sealift Command for the Office of Naval Research under the technical control of the Oceanographer of the Navy; civilian crew.

DESIGN. Catamaran hull design provides large deck working area, centre well for operating equipment at great depths, and removes laboratory areas from main propulsion machinery. Each hull is 246·5 feet long and 24 feet wide (maximum). There are three 36-inch diameter instrument wells in addition to the main centre well.
The T-AGOR 16 differs in appearance from the ASR 21 class ships by the oceanographic ship having a small deck working space aft of the bridge structure and the absence of stern helicopter platform of the rescue ships.

ENGINEERING. Fitted with controllable pitch propellers. An auxiliary 165-shp diesel is fitted in each hull to provide "creeping" speed of 2 to 4 knots.
Separation of controllable pitch propellers by catamaran hull separation provides high degree of manoeuverability eliminating the need for bow thrusters.
Range is 6 000 miles at 13·5 knots.

NOMENCLATURE. Oceanographic research ships and surveying ships generally are named for naval oceanographers, hydrographers, and explorers. (Converted ships generally retain original names).
The AGOR 16 is named for Dr. Harvey C. Hayes of the Naval Research Laboratory, known as the "father of sonar in the US Navy".

TRANSFERS
Josiah Willard Gibbs T-AGOR 1 ex-AVP 51 transferred to Greece on 7 Dec 1971.

HAYES (T-AGOR 16) *1971, Todd Shipyards Corp*

HAYES (T-AGOR 16) *1971, Camera Craft*

Experimental, Research and Surveying Ships—*continued*

HAYES (T-AGOR 16) *1971, Todd Shipyards Corp*

2 OCEANOGRAPHIC RESEARCH SHIPS (AGOR): "MELVILLE" CLASS

Name	*No.*	*Laid down*	*Launched*	*Delivered*
***MELVILLE**	AGOR 14	12 July 1967	10 July 1968	27 Aug 1969
***KNORR**	AGOR 15	9 Aug 1967	21 Aug 1968	14 Jan 1970

Displacement, tons	1 915 standard; 2 080 full load
Dimensions, feet	244·9 × 46·3 × 15
Main engines	Diesel 2 500 bhp; 2 cycloidal propellers = 12 knots
Complement	50 (9 officers, 16 men, 25 scientists)

Oceanographic research ships of an advanced design. AGOR 14 and AGOR 15 authorised in Fiscal Year 1966 new construction programme; AGOR 19 and AGOR 20 of this type in FY 1968 programme, but construction of the latter ships was cancelled. These ships are fitted with internal wells for lowering equipment; underwater lights and observation ports. Facilities for handling small research submersibles.

The *Melville* and *Knorr* built by Defoe Shipbuilding Co, Bay City, Michigan. *Melville* operated by Scripps Institution of Oceanography and *Knorr* by Woods Hole Oceanography Institution for the Office of Naval Research; under technical control of the Oceanographer of the Navy.

ENGINEERING. First US Navy ocean-going ships with cycloidal propellers permitting the ships to turn 360 degrees in their own length. One propeller is fitted at each end of the ship, providing movement in any direction and optimum station keeping without use of thrusters. They have experienced engineering difficulties.

MELVILLE (AGOR 14) *1969, Defoe Shipbuilding*

7 OCEANOGRAPHIC RESEARCH SHIPS (AGOR): "CONRAD" CLASS

Name	*No.*	*Laid down*	*Launched*	*Delivered*
***ROBERT D. CONRAD**	AGOR 3	19 Jan 1961	26 May 1962	29 Nov 1962
***JAMES M. GILLISS**	T-AGOR 4	31 May 1961	19 May 1962	5 Nov 1962
***LYNCH**	T-AGOR 7	7 Sep 1962	17 Mar 1964	22 Oct 1965
***THOMAS G. THOMPSON**	AGOR 9	12 Sep 1963	18 July 1964	4 Sep 1965
***THOMAS WASHINGTON**	AGOR 10	12 Sep 1963	1 Aug 1964	17 Sep 1965
***DE STEIGUER**	T-AGOR 12	12 Nov 1965	21 Mar 1966	28 Feb 1969
***BARTLETT**	T-AGOR 13	18 Nov 1965	24 May 1966	15 Apr 1969

Displacement, tons	varies; approx 1 200 standard; 1 380 full load
Dimensions, feet	191·5 wl; 208·9 oa × 37·4 × 15·3
Main engines	Diesel-electric (Caterpillar Tractor Co diesels); 10 000 bhp; 1 shaft = 13·5 knots
Complement	41 (9 officers, 17 men, 15 scientists except *De Steigeur* and *Bartlett*, 8 officers, 18 men)

This is the first class of ships designed and built by the US Navy for oceanographic research. Fitted with instrumentation and laboratories to measure the earth's gravity and magnetic fields, water temperature, sound transmission in water, and the geological profile of the ocean floor.

Special features include 10 ton capacity boom and winches for handling over-the-side equipment; bow thruster propulsion unit for precise manoeuvrability and station keeping; 620 hp gas turbine (housed in funnel structure) for providing "quiet" power when conducting operations in which use of main engines would generate too high a noise level (gas turbine also can drive the ship at 6·5 knots); endurance of 12 000 miles at 12 knots.

"CONRAD" CLASS—*continued*

Robert D. Conrad built by Gibbs Corp, Jacksonville, Florida. Operated by Lamont Geological Observatory of Columbia University under technical control of the Oceanographer of the Navy.

James H. Gilliss built by Christy Corp, Sturgeon Bay, Wisconsin. Operated by the University of Miami (Florida) since 1970 in support of Navy programmes.

Lynch built by Marietta Manufacturing Co, Point Pleasant, West Virginia. Operated by Military Sealift Command under the technical control of the Oceanographer of the Navy. Civilian crew.

Thomas G. Thompson built by Marinette Marine Corp, Marinette, Wisconsin. Operated by University of Washington (state) under technical control of the Oceanographer of the Navy; civilian crew.

Thomas Washington built by Marinette Marine Corp, Marinette, Wisconsin. Operated by Scripps Institution of Oceanography (University of California) under technical control of the Oceanographer on the Navy; civilian crew.

De Steiguer and *Bartlett* built by Northwest Marine Iron Works, Portland, Oregon Operated by Military Sealift Command under the technical control of the Oceanographer of the Navy; civilian crew.

TRANSFERS
Charles H. Davis AGOR 5 of this type was transferred to New Zealand on 10 Aug 1970; **Sands** AGOR 6 was to be transferred to Brazil during 1974.

PHOTOGRAPHS. Note built-up structure amidships on *De Steiguer*; the *Thomas D. Thompson* has side structure built up amidships.

JAMES M. GILLISS (T-AGOR 4) *United States Navy*

THOMAS G. THOMPSON (AGOR 9) *United States Navy*

DE STEIGUER (T-AGOR 12) *United States Navy*

BARTLETT (T-AGOR 13) *United States Navy*

Experimental, Research and Surveying Ships—*continued*

1 OCEANOGRAPHIC RESEARCH SHIP (AGOR): Ex-SALVAGE SHIP

Name	*No.*	*Launched*	*Commissioned*
***CHAIN**	AGOR 17 (ex-ARS 20)	3 June 1943	31 Mar 1944

Displacement, tons	2 100 full load
Dimensions, feet	207 wl; 213·5 oa × 39 × 15
Main engines	Diesel electric (4 Cooper Bessemer diesels); approx 3 000 bhp; 2 shafts = 14 knots
Complement	29 + 26 scientists

Converted from a salvage ship for oceanographic research. Built by Basalt Rock Co, Napa, California. Commission date as ARS. Converted to an oceanographic research ship by Savannah Machine & Foundry in 1958. The *Chain* is operated by the Woods Hole Oceanographic Institution for the Office of Naval Research under the technical control of the Oceanographer of the Navy. Civilian crew.

ENGINEERING. Fitted with an auxiliary 250 hp outboard propulsion unit for manoeuvering at low speeds (up to 4·5 knots).

DISPOSALS
Argo AGOR 18 (ex-*Snatch*, ARS 27) similarly converted; stricken on 1 May 1970. 1970.

1 OCEANOGRAPHIC RESEARCH SHIP (AGOR): Ex-CARGO SHIP

Name	*No.*	*Launched*	*Delivered*
* **MIZAR**	T-AGOR 11 (ex-T-AK 272)	7 Oct 1957	22 Nov 1957

Displacement, tons	2 036 light; 4 942 full load
Dimensions, feet	256·8 wl; 262·2 oa × 51·5 × 22·8
Main engines	Diesel-electric (ALCO diesels, Westinghouse electric motors) 3 200 bhp; 2 shafts = 12 knots
Complement	56 (11 officers, 30 enlisted men, 15 scientists)

Built for Military Sea Transportation Service by Avondale Marine Ways, New Orleans, La. Designed for Arctic operation with hull strengthened against ice. C1-ME2-13a type. Delivered as cargo ship to MSTS (now Military Sealift Command) and subsequently converted to oceanographic research ship.
As research ship the *Mizar* is operated by Military Sealift Command for Naval Research Laboratory, under technical control of the Oceanographer of the Navy; civilian crew.
CONVERSION. *Mizar* converted in 1962 into deep sea research ship. Equipped with centre well for lowering oceanographic equipment including towed sensor platforms, fitted with laboratories and elaborate photographic facilities, hydrophone system and computer for seafloor navigation and tracking towed vehicles. The *Mizar* had key roles in the searches for the US nuclear submarines *Thresher* and *Scorpion*; the French submarine *Eurydice*: and recovery of the H-bomb lost at sea off Palomares, Spain.

TRANSFERS
Eltanin T-AGOR 8 (ex-T-AK 270) transferred to Argentina on 19 Feb 1974.

MIZAR (T-AGOR 11) *United States Navy*

OCEANOGRPAHIC RESEARCH CRAFT

The Navy also owns a number of smaller oceanographic research craft that are operated by various educational and research institutions in support of Navy programmes; under technical control of the Oceanographer of the Navy; no Navy hull numbers are assigned; all are 100 feet in length or smaller except for the *Lamb*, a converted 136-foot minesweeper (YMS/AMS type) operated by the Lamont Geophysical Laboratory.

HYDROGRAPHIC SURVEYING SHIPS (AGS): PROJECT HYSURCH

An advanced class of hydrographic surveying ships is planned which will be capable of surveying 1 000 square miles and produce finished charts within a five-day period. Each ship would serve as a "mother" ship for several 20-foot launches to provide capability of mapping 50 square miles of ocean floor in two days. HYSURCH stands for Hydrographic Survey and Mapping System.
Ship construction tentatively is planned for late 1970s new construction programmes.

DISPOSALS
All Navy-manned surveying ships have been stricken:
Pursuit (AGS 17, ex-AM 108) stricken in 1960, **Prevail** (AGS 20, ex-AM 107), **Requisite** (AGS 18, ex-AM 109) stricken in 1964, **Towhee** (AGS 28, ex-AM 388) stricken on 1 May 1969, **San Pablo** (AGS 30, ex-AVP 30) stricken on 1 June 1969, **Tanner** (AGSS 15, ex-AKA 34) stricken on 1 Aug 1969, **Maury** (AGS 16, ex-AKA 36) stricken on 19 Dec 1969, **Serrano** (AGS 24, ex-ATF 112) stricken on 2 Jan 1970, **Rehoboth** (AGS 50, ex-AVP 50) stricken on 15 Apr 1970, **Sheldrake** (AGS 19, ex-AM 62) stricken on 30 June 1968.
Littlehales (AGSC 15, ex-YF 854), the Navy's last coastal surveying ship, was stricken on 20 Feb 1968 (but not decommissioned until 1 Apr 1968, more than a month after she was struck.

COASTAL CRUSADER (T-AGS 36 as T-AGM 16) *United States Navy*

1 SURVEYING SHIP (AGS): C1-M-AV1 TYPE

COASTAL CRUSADER T-AGS 36 (ex-T-AGM 16)

Dimensions, feet	338·8 oa × 50·3 × 12
Main engines	Diesel; 1 750 bhp; 1 shaft = 11·5 knots

Built in 1945 by Leatham D. Smith SB Co, Sturgeon Bay, Wisconsin. Acquired for conversion to a missile range tracking ship by US Air Force; transferred to Military Sea Transportation service as T-AGM 16 on 1 July 1964.
Reclassified as a surveying ship (T-AGS 36) on 1 Dec 1969 but taken out of service and placed in reserve prior to operation as an AGS; laid up in Maritime Administration reserve but remains on Navy List.

DISPOSALS
Sgt. George D. Keathley T-AGS 35 ex-T-APC 117 of this type transferred to Taiwan China on 29 Mar 1972.

"S. P. LEE" CLASS

Both ships of this design, the first US Navy ships designed and constructed specifically for surveying operations, have been transferred from the Navy List: **Kellar** T-AGS 25 transferred to Portugal on 21 Jan 1972; **S. P. Lee** T-AG 192 (ex-T-AGS 31) transferred to the US Department of the Interior for geological survey on 27 Feb 1974.
See 1973-1974 and previous editions for characteristics.

2 SURVEYING SHIPS (AGS): "CHAUVENET" CLASS

Name	*No.*	*Laid Down*	*Launched*	*Delivered*
***CHAUVENET**	T-AGS 29	24 May 1967	13 May 1968	13 Nov 1970
***HARKNESS**	T-AGS 32	30 June 1967	12 June1968	29 Jan 1971

Displacement, tons	4 200 full load
Dimensions feet,	393·2 oa × 54 × 16
Main engines	Diesel (Westinghouse); 3 600 bhp; 1 shaft = 15 knots
Complement	175 (13 officers, approx 150 men and technical personnel, 12 scientists)

A class of large research ships capable of extensive military hydrographic and oceanographic surveys, supporting coastal surveying craft, amphibious survey teams and helicopters. Fitted with heplicoter hangar and platform.
Chauvenet authorised in Fiscal Year 1965 new construction programme; *Harkness*: in FY 1966 programme. Both ships built by Upper Clyde Shipbuilders, Govan Division, Glasgow, Scotland.
These ships are operated by the Military Sealift Command for the Oceanographer of the Navy with Navy detachments on board. Civilian crews.

CHAUVENET (T-AGS 29) *1971, United States Navy*

HARKNESS (T-AGS 32) *United States Navy*

Experimental, Research, and Surveying Ships—*continued*

4 SURVEYING SHIPS (AGS): "BENT" CLASS

Name	No.	Laid down	Launched	Delivered
*SILAS BENT	T-AGS 26	2 Mar 1964	16 May 1964	23 July 1965
*KANE	T-AGS 27	19 Dec 1964	20 Nov 1965	19 May 1967
*WILKES	T-AGS 33	18 July 1968	31 July 1969	28 June 1971
*WYMAN	T-AGS 34	18 July 1968	30 Oct 1969	3 Nov 1971

Displacement, tons	1 935 standard; *Silas Bent* and *Kane* 2 558 full load; *Wilkes* 2 540 full load; *Wyman* 2 420 full load
Dimensions, feet	285·3 oa × 48 × 15·1
Main engines	Diesel-electric (Westinghouse diesels); 3 600 bhp; 1 shaft = 14 knots
Complement	77 to 79 (12 or 13 officers, 35 or 36 men, 30 scientists)

Designed specifically for surveying operations. Special features include seafloor mapping equipment; bow propulsion unit for precise manoeuvrability and station keeping. All four ships operated by Military Sealift Command for the Oceanographer of the Navy; civilian crews.
Silas Bent built by American SB Co, Lorain, Ohio; *Kane* built by Christy Corp, Sturgeon Bay, Wisconsin; *Wilkes* and *Wyman* built by Defoe SB Co, Bay City, Michigan.

WILKES (T-AGS 33) *1971, United States Navy*

WYMAN (T-AGS 34) *1971, United States Navy*

WILKES (T-AGS 33) *1971, United States Navy*

3 SURVEYING SHIPS (AGS): "VICTORY" TYPE

*BOWDITCH (ex-SS *South Bend Victory*) T-AGS 21
*DUTTON (ex-SS *Tuskegee Victory*) T-AGS 22
*MICHELSON (ex-SS *Joliet Victory* T-AGS 23

Displacement, tons	4 512 full load
Dimensions, feet	455·2 oa × 62·2 × 25
Main engines	Turbine; 8 500 shp; 1 shaft = 15 knots
Boilers	2
Complement	100 to 101 (13 or 14 officers, 47 men, approx 40 technical personnel)

VC2-S-AP3 type built in 1945, *Bowditch* and *Michelson* by Oregon Shipbuilding Co; *Dutton* by South Coast Co. Newport Beach, California. All converted to support the Fleet Ballistic Missile Programme, *Dutton* and *Michelson* at Philadelphia Naval Shipyard 8 Nov 1957 to 16 Nov 1958 and 1 Mar 1958 to 31 Dec 1968, respectively, and *Bowditch* at Charleston Naval Shipyard 10 Oct 1957 to 30 Sep 1958.
Designed to chart the ocean floor and to record magnetic fields and gravity.
Operated by Military Sealift Command for the Oceanographer of the Navy; civilian crews.

MICHELSON (T-AGS 23) *United States Navy*

DUTTON (T-AGS 22) *United States Navy*

1 GUNNERY AND GUIDED MISSILE TEST SHIP (AVM): CONVERTED SEAPLANE TENDER

***NORTON SOUND** AVM 1 (ex-AV 11)

Displacement, tons	9 106 standard; 15 170 full load
Length, feet (*metres*)	543·25 (*165·2*) oa
Beam, feet (*metres*)	71·6 (*21·5*)
Draft, feet (*metres*)	23·5 (*7·15*)
Guns	1—5 inch (*127 mm*) 54 calibre DP experimental (see *Gunnery* notes)
Missile launchers	1 twin launcher for Standard testing 1 Basic Point Defence Missile System (BPDMS) launcher for Sea Sparrow missiles (see *Missile* notes)
Main engines	2 geared turbines (Allis-Chalmers) 12 000 shp; 2 shafts
Boilers	4 (Babcock & Wilcox)
Speed, knots	19·2
Complement	292 (22 officers, 270 enlisted men)

The *Norton Sound* serves as a seagoing weapons laboratory and test centre under the operational control of Commander, Cruiser-Destroyer Force, Pacific Fleet. She was originally a seaplane tender (AV 11) of the "Currituck" class.
Assigned to Operational Development Force as experimental rocket ship on 28 Nov 1947; modified at Philadelphia Naval Shipyard Mar-Sep 1948 and fitted with helicopter platform forward and missile launching ramp aft during late 1940s and reclassified as guided missile test ship (AVM 1) on 8 Aug 1951. Subsequently served as test ship for several guided missile systems and, lately, for advanced gun systems.
Modified in 1974 to serve as test ship for electronic components of **AEGIS** fleet air defence systems.

NORTON SOUND (AVM 1) *1969, United States Navy*

CONSTRUCTION. Built by Los Angeles Shipbuilding & Dry Dock Co, San Pedro, Calif. Laid down 7 Sep 1942; launched 28 Nov 1943; commissioned 8 Jan 1945. As built the *Norton Sound* had a 30-ton capacity boom atop her large, amidships aircraft hangar and a second 30-ton boom on her fantail; second boom removed when fitted with missile launching ramp. Original armament consisted of four 5 inch guns, two in single mounts forward and two in single mounts atop hangar, and 20 40 mm AA guns; forward 5 inch guns removed to make space for helicopter platform; all other original armament subsequently removed.

GUNNERY. Fitted in 1969 with light-weight 5 inch 54 cal gun and associated Mark 86 Gunfire Control System for operational test and evaluation. The light weight Mark 45 gun is intended for new-construction ships.

MISSILES. The *Norton Sound* has served as a test platform for several ship-launched rockets and missiles. In the photo a twin surface-to-air missile launcher is installed aft for testing the Standard missile as is a "pepper box" BPDMS launcher for the Sea Sparrow missile.

Experimental, Research and Surveying Ships—*continued*

1 TEST RANGE SUPPORT SHIP (IX): CONVERTED LSMR

Name	*No.*	*Launched*	*Commissioned*
***ELK RIVER**	IX 501 (ex-LSMR 501)	21 Apr 1954	27 May 1945

Displacement, tons	1 100 full load
Dimensions, feet	225 oa × 50 × 9·2
Main engines	Diesels; 1 400 bhp ; 2 shafts = 11 knots
Complement	25 + 20 technical personnel

The *Elk River* is a former rocket landing ship specifically converted to support Navy deep submergence activities on the San Clemente Island Range off the coast of Southern California. Built by Brown Shipbuilding Co, Houstan, Texas
The ship is capable of supporting the following activities: (1) deep diving for man-in-the-sea programmes, (2) deep diving for salvage programmes, (3) submersible test and evaluation, (4) underwater equipment testing, and (5) deep mooring operations. Operated by combined Navy-civilian crew.
CONVERSION. The *Elk River* was withdrawn from the Reserve Fleet and converted to a range support ship in 1967-1968 at Avondale Shipyards Inc, Westwego, Louisiana, and the San Francisco Bay Naval Shipyard.
The basic LSMR hull was lengthened and eight-foot sponsons were added to either side to increase deck working space and stability; superstructure added forward. An open centre well was provided to facilitate lowering and raising equipment; also fitted with 65-ton-capacity gantry crane (on tracks) to handle submersibles and active positioning mooring system to hold ship in precise location without elaborate mooring and permit shifting within the moor. Five anchors including bow anchor.
DIVING. Fitted with prototype Mk 2 Deep Diving System (see "Pigeon class" submarine rescue ships).

ELK RIVER (IX 501) — *1968, United States Navy*

ELK RIVER (IX 501) — *1968, United States Navy*

1 TORPEDO TEST SHIP (IX)

***NEW BEDFORD** IX 308 (ex-AKL 17, ex-FS 289)

Displacement, tons	approx 700
Dimensions, feet	176·5 oa × 32·8 × 10
Main engines	Diesel; 1 000 bhp; 1 shaft = 10 knots

Small Army cargo ship (freight and supply) acquired by Navy on 1 Mar 1950 for cargo work and subsequently converted to support torpedo testing. Operated by Naval Torpedo Station, Keyport, Washington. Other craft serving in this role are described in the section on Service Craft (YFRT type).

NEW BEDFORD (IX 308) — *1966, United States Navy*

1 INSTRUMENTATION PLATFORM (IX)

***BRIER** IX 307 (ex-WLI 299)

Displacement, tons	178
Dimensions, feet	100 × 24 × 4·5
Machinery	Diesel with electric drive; 300 bhp ; 2 shafts = 8·5 knots

Former Coast Guard buoy tender built in 1943; acquired by Navy on 10 Mar 1969 for use as instrument platform for explosive testing; redesignated IX 307 on 29 Aug 1970.

1 WEAPON TEST SHIP (IX)

***IX 306** (ex-FS 221)

Displacement, tons	906 full load
Dimensions, feet	179 oa × 33 × 10
Main engines	Diesel ; 1 shaft = 12 knots

Former Army cargo ship (freight and supply) acquired by the Navy in January 1966 and subsequently converted to a weapon test ship, being placed in service late in 1969. Conducts research for the Naval Underwater Weapons Research and Engineering Station, Newport, Rhode Island; operates in Atlantic Underwater Test and Evaluation Centre (AUTEC) range in Caribbean. Manned by Navy and civilian RCA personnel. Note white hull with blue bow and torpedo tube opening on starboard side just aft of hull number.

IX 306 — *1969, United States Navy*

DISPOSALS AND RECLASSIFICATIONS

Target ship **Atlanta** IX 304 (ex-CL 104), a converted light cruiser employed in explosive tests, was stricken from the Navy List on 1 Apr 1970 (sunk as target).
Mobile listening barge **MONOB I** IX 309 (ex-YW 87) reclassified as YAG 61 on 1 July 1970 (see Service Craft listing).
Hydrographic research ships **Rexburg** PCER 855 and **Marysville** PCER 857 stricken on 7 Mar 1970 and 15 July 1970, respectively.
Ex-aircraft carrier **Bunker Hill** AVT 9 (ex-CVS 17) stricken on 1 Nov 1966 served as a stationary electronic test ship from 1965 until late 1972. (See 1971-1972 edition for characteristics and photographs).
(The research ships *George Eastman* YAG 39 and *Granville S. Hall* YAG 40 are listed with service Craft; the experimental hydrofoil ships *Plainview* AGEH 1 and *High Point* PCH 1 are listed with Patrol Ships and Craft; the research escort ship *Glover* AGDE 1 is listed with Ocean Escorts).

MISCELLANEOUS

1 PRESIDENTIAL YACHT

***SEQUOIA** AG 23

Displacement, tons	approx 110
Dimensions, feet	99 wl; 104 oa × 18·2
Main engines	2 diesels ; 450 bhp; 2 shafts = 11·5 knots
Complement	21 (1 officer, 20 enlisted men; accommodation for only 14 of crew)
Passengers	accommodation for 7 under normal conditions

Built by Mathis Yacht & Shipbuilding Co, Camden, New Jersey, in 1925. Acquired by Navy and placed in commission on 25 Mar 1933; no longer in commission but remains in service. Assigned as presidential yacht in 1968; previously assigned to the Secretary of the Navy. Based in Washington, DC.

1 SAIL FRIGATE

***CONSTITUTION** IX 21 launched 21 Oct 1797

The oldest ship of the US Navy remaining on the Navy List. "In service" status as a relic at Boston. Periodically she is taken out into Boston Harbour and "turned around". The *Constitution* began an extensive, $4 200 000 overhaul in April 1973 at the Boston Naval Shipyard; to complete in early 1975.
Characteristics and photograph appear in the 1970-1971 edition.

SEQUOIA (AG 23) — *United States Navy*

MISCELLANEOUS

The sailing ship *Constellation* which survives under private ownership at Baltimore, Maryland, is apparently the last sailing man of-war-built for the US Navy; she was constructed at the Norfolk (Virginia) Navy Yard in 1853-1854, built in part with material from the sail frigate *Constallation* (launched 1797).
The self-propelled barracks ship **Benewah** (APB 35) was reclassified IX 311 on 1 Apr 1971 ; stricken on 1 Sep 1973.
The classification **IX 310** has been assigned to a group of barges used at the Naval Underwater Sound Laboratory, Newport, Rhode Island.
The former PT 809 is employed as guard boat for the presidential Yacht; named **Guardian.** Not officially on Navy List, but Navy manned with Secret Service personnel carried. Based at the Navy Yard in Washington, D.C.

SERVICE CRAFT

The US Navy operates several hundred service craft, primarily small craft that provide services to the Fleet in harbours and ports. Only the self-propelled craft are listed here. In addition, there are hundreds of non-self-propelled barge-like craft for carrying cargo, floating cranes, dredges, workshops, power barges, berthing barges, water and fuel barges, garbage scows, *et cetera*. In addition, a few "ships", and the nuclear-propelled research submersible NR-1 officially are designated as service craft. Only the Y- prefix ships and craft are listed in this section (the "Y" originally indicating yardcraft).

The specific type strengths are as of 1 Jan 1973. Asterisks are used to indicate only those active service craft with names.

1 MOBILE LISTENING BARGE (YAG)

***MONOB I** YAG 61 (ex-IX 309, ex-YW 87)

Displacement, tons	1 390 full load
Dimensions, feet	174 oa × 33

The *Monob I* is a mobile listening barge converted from a self-propelled water barge. Built in 1943 and converted for acoustic research in 1969, being placed in service in May 1969. Conducts research for the Naval Ship Research and Development Centre; based at Port Everglades, Florida.
Designation changed from IX 301 to YAG 61 on 1 July 1970.

MONOB I — *United States Navy*

1 RESEARCH SHIP (YAG): "LIBERTY" TYPE

GEORGE EASTMAN YAG 39

Displacement, tons	6 000 light; 11 600 full load
Dimensions, feet	422·7 oa × 57 × 34·7
Main engines	Steam reciprocating; 2 500 ihp; 1 shaft = 11 knots
Boilers	2
Accommodation	169 (19 officers, 150 enlisted men)

EC2-S-C1 "Liberty" ship built by Permanente Metals Corp, Richmond, California; launched on 20 Apr 1943 and delivered as merchant ship on 5 May 1943. The ship was acquired by the Navy on 2 Apr 1953 for use as a nuclear effects research ship (designated YAG 39); not employed as minesweeping ship as were other "Liberty" type ships. The now-stricken *Granville S. Hall* was employed in a similar role.
As a research ship the *George Eastman* was fitted with instrumentation to detect nuclear fallout and radiation; ship controls enclosed in a specially protected compartment; also equipped for remote control for unmanned operation in contaminated areas. Also used in ship biological and chemical defence research. Now in reserve.

DISPOSALS

Granville S. Hall YAG 40 of the "Liberty" type was stricken in 1971.

The experimental minefield sweeper **YAG 37** (ex-*John L. Sullivan*) was scrapped in 1958, **YAG 36** (ex-*Floyd W. Spencer*) and **YAG 38** (ex-*Edward Kavanagh*) were stricken in 1960. The Fleet X-ray examination ship **Whidbey** AG 141, was stricken on 1 May 1959.
The former netlaying ship **Butternut** (ex-ANL 9, ex-AN 9, ex-YN 4) was reinstated on the Navy List as YAG 60 on 28 Oct 1969; after brief service in support of the Pacific Missile Range, she was taken out of service in late 1970 and stricken on 1 July 1971.
Sailing Yacht **Salude** YAG 87 stricken on 15 Apr 1974 (see 1973-1974 edition for characteristics).

GEORGE EASTMAN (YAG 39) — *1966, United States Navy*

2 DIVING TENDERS (YDT)

Tenders used to support shallow-water diving operations. Three self-propelled diving tenders are on the Navy List: **Phoebus** YDT 14 ex-YF 294, and **Suitland** YDT 15 ex-YF 336. (Two non-self-propelled YDTs are in service).

9 COVERED LIGHTERS (YF)

Lighters used to transport material in harbours; self-propelled; nine are on the Navy List, three of which are named: **Lynnhaven** (YF 328), **Keyport** (YF 885), and **Kodiak** (YF 886).

7 FERRYBOATS (YFB)

Ferryboats used to transport personnel and vehicles in large harbours; self-propelled; one is under construction and seven are on the Navy List, one of which is named: **Aquidneck** (YFB 14). The YFB 88-91 are the former LCU 1636, 1638-1640, all reclassified on 1 Sep 1969.

YFB 88 (ex-LCU 1636) — *United States Navy*

YFB 87 — *1970, United States Navy*

2 REFRIGERATED COVERED LIGHTERS (YFR)

Lighters used to store and transport food and other materials which require refrigeration; two remain on the Navy List.

YFR 890 — *United States Navy*

9 COVERED LIGHTERS (RANGE TENDER) (YFRT)

Lighters used for miscellaneous purposes; 11 are on the Navy List. The YFRT 520 is employed in torpedo testing and is fitted with a triple Mk 32 launcher. The **Range Recoverer** YFRT 524 (ex-T-AGM 2, ex-T-AG 161, ex-US Army FS 278), is a former missile range instrumentation ship (RIS); redesignated YFRT 524 on 16 May 1972; see description under Experimental, Research and Surveying Ships in 1972-1973 edition.

YFRT 520 — *1969, United States Navy*

RANGE RECOVERER (YFRT 524) — *United States Navy*

Service Craft—*continued*

11 HARBOUR UTILITY CRAFT (YFU)

YFU 71	**YFU 73**	**YFU 75**	**YFU 77**	**YFU 81**
YFU 72	**YFU 74**	**YFU 76**	**YFU 79**	**YFU 82**
			YFU 80	

Dimensions, feet	125 oa × 36 × 7·5
Main engines	diesels = 8 knots
Guns	2—50 cal MG

Militarised versions of a commercial lighter design. Used for off-loading large ships in harbours and ferrying cargo from one coastal port to another. Built by Pacific Coast Engineering Co. Alameda, California; completed 1967-1968. Can carry more than 300 tons cargo; considerable cruising range.

YFU 71-77 and YFU 80-82 loaned to US Army in 1970 for use in South Vietnam; returned to Navy control in 1973.

LOSSES
YFU 78 sunk in Vietnam in March 1969.

YFU 75 — *1968, United States Navy*

YFU 74 — *1969, United States Navy*

19 HARBOUR UTILITY CRAFT (YFU):

YFU 4 (ex-LCU 562)	**YFU 67** (ex-LCU 1232)	**YFU 97** (ex-LCU 1611)
YFU 24 (ex-LCU 980)	**YFU 83** (new; see notes)	**YFU 98** (ex-LCU 1615)
YFU 44 (ex-LCU 1398)	**YFU 89** (ex-U 1576)	**YFU 99** (ex-LCU 1622)
YFU 50 (ex-LCU 1486)	**YFU 91** (ex-LCU 1608)	**YFU 100** (ex-LCU 1610)
YFU 53 (ex-LCU 1446)	**YFU 93** (ex-LCU 1625)	**YFU 101** (ex-LCU 1612)
YFU 55 (ex-LCU 637)	**YFU 96** (ex-LCU 1609)	**YFU 102** (ex-LCU 1462)
YFU 57 (ex-LCU) 709		

Former utility landing craft employed primarily as harbour and coastal cargo craft (see section on Landing Craft for basic characteristics). The YFU 44 and YFU 53 have open centre wells for lowering research equipment into the water; both are assigned to the Naval Undersea Research and Development Centre in Long Beach, California.
YFU 83 built by Defoe Shipbuilding Co (same design as LCU 1646). Several YFUs were loaned to the US Army in 1970 for use in Vietnam after withdrawal of US Navy riverine and coastal forces.

CLASSIFICATIONS. YFU 1-70 and 84-102 all are former utility landing craft. Several reverted to LCU designations and three were modified for salvage work: YFU 2, 16, and 33 to YLLC 5, 2, and 3, respectively.

DISPOSALS AND TRANSFERS (since 1 Jan 1970)
YFU 5, 7, 20, 36, 37 stricken in 1970; **YFU** 8, 45, 47, 58, 60, 92 stricken in 1971; **YFU** 90 transferred to South Vietnam in 1971; **YFU** 25, 61, 87 stricken in 1972; **YFU** 56, 68 transferred to Khmer Republic (Cambodia) on 19 May 1972; **YFU** 88, 95 transferred to Spain on 28 June 1972; **YFU** 39, 59 stricken in 1973.

YFU 83 — *1971, Defoe Shipbuilding*

9 GARBAGE LIGHTERS (YG)

Lighters used to collect garbage and refuse from ships in port, sepecially those not moored to a pier; popularly known as "honey barges"; self-propelled; nine are on the Navy List.

LIGHT SALVAGE LIFT CRAFT (YLLC)

YLLC 1 (ex-LCU 1388), **YLLC 3** (ex-LCU 1195), **YLLC 5** (ex-LCU 529) transferred to South Vietnam; **YLLC 2** (ex-YFU 16, ex-LCU 788) stricken on 1 May 1972 for sale to commercial firms; **YLLC 4** (ex-LCU 1459) sunk in Vietnam on 15 Nov 1968.

GATE CRAFT (YNG)

No self-propelled gate craft are on the Navy List.

48 FUEL BARGES (YO)

Small liquid fuel carriers inteneded to fuel ships where no pierside fueling facilities are available; self-propelled; 48 are on the Navy List. Three are named: **Casing Head** YO 47, **Crownbrock** YO 48, **Whipstock** YO 49.

YO 130 — *1970, United States Navy*

20 GASOLINE BARGES (YOG)

Similar to the fuel barges (YO), but carry gasoline and aviation fuels; self-propelled; 20 are on the Navy List. One is named: **Lieut. Thomas W. Fowler** YOG 107.

26 SEAMANSHIP TRAINING CRAFT (YP)

YP 584	**YP 589**	**YP 655**	**YP 658**	**YP 662**	**YP 666**	**YP 670**
YP 585	**YP 590**	**YP 656**	**YP 659**	**YP 664**	**YP 667**	**YP 671**
YP 586	**YP 591**	**YP 657**	**YP 660**	**YP 664**	**YP 668**	**YP 672**
YP 587			**YP 661**	**YP 665**	**YP 669**	

YP 584 series:

Displacement, tons	50
Dimensions, feet	75 oa × 16 × 4·5
Main engines	2 diesels (Superior); 400 bhp; 2 shafts = 12 knots

YP 654 series:

Displacement, tons	69·5 full load
Dimensions, feet	80·4 oa × 18·75 × 5·3
Main engines	4 diesels (General Motors); 660 bhp; 2 shafts = 13·5 knots

These craft are used for instruction in seamanship and navigation at the Naval Academy, Annapolis, Maryland, and Naval Officer Candidate School, Newport, Rhode Island. Fitted with surface search radar, Fathometer, gyro compass, and UHF and MF radio; the YP 655 additionally fitted for instruction in oceanographic research.
YPs numbered below 654 are older craft of a once-numerous type employed for training and utility work. YP 654-663 built by Stephens Bros, Inc, Stockton, Calif. completed in 1958; YP 664 and 665 built by Elizabeth City Shipbuilders, Inc, Elizabeth City, North Carolina; YP 666 and 667 built by Stephens Bros; YP 668 built by Peterson Boatbuilding Co, Tacoma, Washington, completed in 1968; YP 669-672 built by Peterson completed in 1971-1972.
These craft are of wooden construction with aluminium deck houses. YP 584 and YP 585 laid up in reserve during 1974.

YP 588 stricken in 1972.

YP 654 type — ***United States Navy***

Service Craft—*continued*

YP 669 — *1971, Peterson Builders*

SALVAGE CRAFT TENDERS (YRST)

No self-propelled salvage craft tenders are on the Navy List. (Propulsion machinery removed from the **Naubuc** YRST 4, ex-AN 84).

83 LARGE HARBOUR TUGS (YTB)

EDENSHAW	YTB 752
MARIN	YTB 753
PONTIAC	YTB 756
OSHKOSH	YTB 757
PADUCAH	YTB 758
BOGALUSA	YTB 759
NATICK	YTB 760
OTTUMWA	YTB 761
TUSCUMBIA	YTB 762
MUSKEGON	YTB 763
MISHAWAKA	YTB 764
OKMULGEE	YTB 765
WAPOAKINETA	YTB 766
APALACHICOLA	YTB 767
ARCATA	YTB 768
CHESANING	YTB 769
DAHLONEGA	YTB 770
KEOKUK	YTB 771
NASHUA	YTB 774
WAUWATOSA	YTB 775
WEEHAWKEN	YTB 776
NOGALES	YTB 777
APOPKA	YTB 778
MANHATTAN	YTB 779
SAUGUS	YTB 780
NIANTIC	YTB 781
MANISTEE	YTB 782
REDWING	YTB 783
KALISPELL	YTB 784
WINNEMUCCA	YTB 785
TONKAWA	YTB 786
KITTANNING	YTB 787
WAPATO	YTB 788
TOMAHAWK	YTB 789
MENOMINEE	YTB 790
MARINETTE	YTB 791
ANTIGO	YTB 792
PIQUA	YTB 793
MANDAN	YTB 794
KETCHIKAN	YTB 795
SACO	YTB 796
TAMAQUA	YTB 797
OPELIKA	YTB 789
NATCHITOCHES	YTB 799
EFAULA	YTB 800
PALATKA	YTB 801
CHERAW	YTB 802
NANTICOKE	YTB 803
AHOSKIE	YTB 804
OCALA	YTB 805
TUSKEGEE	YTB 806
MASSAPEQUA	YTB 807
WENATCHEE	YTB 808
AGAWAN	YTB 809
ANOKA	YTB 810
HOUMA	YTB 811
ACCONAC	YTB 812
POUGHKEEPSIE	YTB 813
WAXAHATCHIE	YTB 814
NEODESHA	YTB 815
CAMPTI	YTB 816
HAYANNIS	YTB 817
MECOSTA	YTB 818
IUKA	YTB 819
WANAMASSA	YTB 820
TONTOGANY	YTB 821
PAWHUSKA	YTB 822
CANONCHET	YTB 823
SANTAQUIN	YTB 824
WATHENA	YTB 825
WASHTUCNA	YTB 826
CHETEK	YTB 827
CATAHECASSA	YTB 828
METACOM	YTB 829
PUSHMATHA	YTB 830
DEKANAWIDA	YTB 831
PETALESHARO	YTB 832
SHABONEE	YTB 833
NEWGAGON	YTB 834
SKENANDOA	YTB 835
POKAGON	YTB 836

LARGE HARBOUR TUGS—*continued*

Displacement, tons	350 full load
Dimensions, feet	109 oa × 30 × 13·8
Machinery	2 diesels; 2 000 bhp; 2 shafts
Complement	10 to 12 (enlisted)

Large harbour tugs; 83 are in service or under construction. YTB 752 completed in 1959, YTB 753 in 1960, YTB 756-762 in 1961, YTB 763-766 in 1963, YTB 770 and YTB 771 in 1964, YTB 767-769, 776 in 1965, YTB 774, 775, 777-789 in 1966, YTB 790-793 in 1967, YTB 794 and 795 in 1968, YTB 796-803 in 1969, and YTB 804-815 completed in 1970-1972, YTB 816-827 completed 1972-1973, YTB 828-836 completed 1974-1975.
Navy tugs have Indian names.

PADUCAH (YTB 758) — *United States Navy*

TUSKEGEE (YTB 806) — *1970, Peterson Builders*

16 SMALL HARBOUR TUGS (YTL)

Sixteen of these craft are on the Navy List; unnamed.

103 MEDIUM HARBOUR TUGS (YTM)

Numbered in YTM 128-779 series; several formerly designated YTB or are former US Army tugs. The YTM 759 fitted with triple Mk 32 torpedo tubes. Most have names.

MASCOUTAN (YTM 760) — *1971, US Navy, PH2 C. Velasquez*

26 WATER BARGES (YW)

Barges modified to carry water to ships in harbour; self-propelled; 26 of these craft are on the Navy List.

RICHLAND (AFDM 8) — *1969, Robert Fudge*

FLOATING DRY DOCKS

The US Navy operates a number of floating dry docks to supplement dry dock facilities at major naval activities, to support fleet ballistic missile submarines (SSBN) at advanced bases, and to provide repair capabilities in forward combat areas.

The larger floating dry docks are made sectional to facilitate movement overseas and to render them self docking. The ARD-type docks have the forward end of their docking well closed by a structure resembling the bow of a ship to facilitate towing. Berthing facilities, repair shops, and machinery are housed in sides of larger docks. None is self-propelled.

Seventeen floating dry docks are in Navy service (including two partial docks), 12 are out of service in reserve (including two partial docks), and 27 are on lease to commercial firms for private use. Several are on loan to other US services and foreign navies (including one partial dock). Asterisks indicate docks in active US service.

LARGE AUXILIARY FLOATING DRY DOCKS

Name-No.	Completed	Capacity	Construction	Notes
***AFDL 1**	1943	1 000 tons	Steel	Guantanamo Bay, Cuba
AFDL 2	1943	1 000 tons	Steel	Commercial lease
***AFDL 6**	1944	1 000 tons	Steel	Little Creek, Virginia
AFDL 7	1944	1 900 tons	Steel	Reserve
AFDL 8	1943	1 000 tons	Steel	Commercial lease
AFDL 9	1943	1 000 tons	Steel	Commercial lease
***AFDL 10**	1943	1 000 tons	Steel	Subic Bay, Philippines
AFDL 12	1943	1 000 tons	Steel	Reserve
AFDL 15	1943	1 000 tons	Steel	Commercial lease
AFDL 16	1943	1 000 tons	Steel	Commercial lease
AFDL 19	1944	1 000 tons	Steel	Commercial lease
***AFDL 21**	1944	1 000 tons	Steel	Guam, Marianas
***AFDL 23**	1944	1 900 tons	Steel	Danang, South Vietnam
AFDL 29	1943	1 000 tons	Steel	Commercial lease
AFDL 30	1944	1 000 tons	Steel	Commercial lease
AFDL 35	1944	2,800 tons	Concrete	Reserve
AFDL 37	1944	2 800 tons	Concrete	Commercial lease
AFDL 38	1944	2 800 tons	Concrete	Commercial lease
AFDL 40	1944	2 800 tons	Concrete	Commercial lease
AFDL 41	1944	2 800 tons	Concrete	Commercial lease
AFDL 43	1944	2 800 tons	Concrete	Commercial lease
AFDL 45	1944	2 800 tons	Concrete	Commercial lease
AFDL 47		6 500 tons	Steel	Commercial lease
***AFDL 48**		4 000 tons	Concrete	Long Beach Nav Shipyard

AUXILIARY REPAIR DRY DOCKS AND MEDIUM AUXILIARY REPAIR DRY DOCKS

Name-No.	Completed	Capacity	Construction	Notes
***ARD 5**	1942	3 000 tons	Steel	New London, Connecticut
***ARD 7**	1943	3 000 tons	Steel	New London, Connecticut
ARDM 3 (ex ARD 18)	1944	3 000 tons	Steel	Reserve
***OAK RIDGE** ARDM 1 (ex-ARD 19)	1944	3 000 tons	Steel	Rota, Spain
ARD 24	1944	3 000 tons	Steel	Reserve
***ALAMAGORDO** ARDM 2 (ex-ARD 26)	1944	3 000 tons	Steel	Charleston South Carolina
***ARD 30**	1944	3 000 tons	Steel	Pearl Harbour Nav Shipyard
***ARD 31**		3 000 tons	Steel	US Air Force

YARD FLOATING DRY DOCKS

Name-No.	Completed	Capacity	Construction	Notes
YFD 7	1943	18 000 tons	Steel (3)	Commercial lease
YFD 8	1942	20 000 tons	Wood	Commercial lease
YFD 9	1942	16 000 tons	Wood	Commercial lease
YFD 23	1943	10 500 tons	Wood	Commercial lease
YFD 54	1943	5 000 tons	Wood	Commercial lease
YFD 68	1945	14 000 tons	Steel (3)	Commercial lease
YFD 69	1945	14 000 tons	Steel (3)	Commercial lease
YFD 70		14 000 tons	Steel (3)	Commercial lease
***YFD 71**		14 000 tons	Steel (3)	San Diego Naval Base
***YFD 83** (ex-AFDL 31)	1943	1 000 tons	Steel	US Coast Guard

LARGE AUXILIARY FLOATING DRY DOCKS

Name-No.	Completed	Capacity	Construction	Notes
***AFDB 1** (partial)	1943	40 000 tons	Steel (4)	Subic Bay, Philippines
AFDB 1 (partial)	——	60 000 tons	Steel (6)	Reserve
AFDB 2	1944	90 000 tons	Steel (10)	Reserve
AFDB 3	1944	81 000 tons	Steel (9)	Reserve
AFDB 4	1944	55 000 tons	Steel (7)	Reserve
AFDB 5	1944	55 000 tons	Steel (7)	Reserve
AFDB 6	1944	55 000 tons	Steel (7)	Reserve
AFDB 7 (partial)	1944		Steel (2)	Reserve
***AFDB 7** (partial)	1945	10 000 tons	Steel (1)	US Army
***LOS ALAMOS** AFDB 7 (partial)	——	40 000 tons	Steel (4)	Holy Loch, Scotland

MEDIUM AUXILIARY FLOATING DRY DOCKS

Name-No.	Completed	Capacity	Construction	Notes
AFDM 1 (ex-YFD 3)	1942	15 000 tons	Steel (3)	Commercial lease
AFDM 2 (ex-YFD 4)	1942	15 000 tons	Steel (3)	Commercial lease
AFDM 3 (ex-YFD 6)	1943	18 000 tons	Steel (3)	Commercial lease
***AFDM 5** (ex-YFD 21)	1943	18 000 tons	Steel (3)	Subic Bay, Philippines
***AFDM 6** (ex-YFD 62)	1944	18 000 tons	Steel (3)	Subic Bay, Philippines
***AFDM 7** (ex-YFD 63)	1945	18 000 tons	Steel (3)	Davisville, Rhode Island
***RICHLAND** AFDM 8 (ex-YFD 64)	1944	18 000 tons	Steel (3)	Guam, Marianas
AFDM 9 (ex-YFD 65)	1945	18 000 tons	Steel (3)	Commercial lease
AFDM 10		18 000 tons	Steel (3)	Commercial lease

Figures in parenthesis indicate the number of sections for sectional docks. Each section of the AFDB docks has a lifting capacity of about 10 000 tons. Four sections of the AFDB 7 form the floating dry dock *Los Alamos* at Holy Loch, Scotland, one section is used at Kwajalein atoll by the US Army in support of the Nike-X missile project and two sections are in reserve. (The AFDB sections each are 256 feet long, 80 feet in width, with wing walls 83 feet high; the wing walls, which contain compartments, fold down when the sections are towed).

The *White Sands* (ARD 20) was employed in support of the deep-diving bathyscaph *Trieste II* (see section on Deep Submergence Vehicles). Early in 1969 the *White Sands*, with *Trieste II* on board, was towed to the Azores to support investigation of the remains of the nuclear-powered submarine *Scorpion* (SSN 589). Reclassified as auxiliary deep submergence support vehicle (AGDS 1) on 1 Aug 1973; subsequently stricken.

All remaining floating dry docks were built during World War II.

TRANSFERS. The following floating dry docks are on foreign loan: ARD 23 to Argentina; AFDL 39, ARD 14 to Brazil; ARD 32 to Chile; ARD 28 to Columbia; ARD 13 to Ecuador; AFDL 11 to Khmer Republic (Cambodia); ARD 15, AFDL 28 to Mexico; ARD 6 to Pakistan; AFDL 26 to Paraguay; AFDL 33, ARD 8 to Peru; AFDL 20, AFDL 44 to Philippines; ARD 9, *Windsor* (ARD 22) to Taiwan China; ARD 13 to Venezuela; AFDL 22 to South Vietnam; ARD 12 to Turkey; *Arco* (ARD 29) to Iran; ARD 25 to to Chile; AFDL 25 to Khmer Republic (Cambodia).

DISPOSALS
ARD 16 stricken on 1 Oct 1972; **ARD 27** stricken on 1 Apr 1973; **AFDL 35** stricken on 1 Aug 1973; **White Sands** AGDS 1 (ex-ARD 20) stricken on 1 Apr 1974; ARD 11 stricken on 15 Apr 1974; **AFDL 42** stricken on 1 May 1974.

AFDL 21 under tow — *1965, United States Navy*

SSBN in OAK RIDGE (ARDM 1) — *1964, United States Navy*

SSBN in OAK RIDGE (ARDM 1) — *United States Navy*

DEEP SUBMERGENCE VEHICLES

The US Navy operates several deep submergence vehicles for scientific, military research, and operational military missions.

The US Navy acquired its first deep submergence vehicle with the purchase of the bathyscaph *Trieste* in 1958. The *Trieste* was designed and constructed by Professor Auguste Piccard, the noted Swiss physicist and aeronaut. The US Navy sponsored research dives in the Mediterranean Sea with the *Trieste* in 1957 after which the bathyscaph was purchased outright and brought to the United States.
The *Trieste* reached a record depth of 35 800 feet (*10 910 metres*) in the Challenger Deep off the Marianas on 23 Jan 1960, being piloted by Lieutenant Don Walsh, USN, and Jacques Piccard (son of Auguste). Rebuilt and designated *Trieste II*, the craft was subsequently used in the search for wreckage of the nuclear-powered submarine *Thresher* (SSN 593) was lost in 1963 and the *Scorpion* (SSN 589) lost in 1968.

After the loss of the *Thresher* the US Navy initiated an extensive deep submergence programme that led to construction of two Deep Submergence Rescue Vehicles (DSRV); however, other vehicles proposed in the recommended programme were not built because of a lack of interest, changing operational concepts, and funding limitations.
Several of these deep submergence vehicles and other craft and support ships are operated by Submarine Development Group One at San Diego, California. The Group is a major operational command that includes advanced diving equipment; divers trained in "saturation" techniques; the DSVs *Trieste II*, *Turtle*, *Sea Cliff*, DSRV-1, DSRV-2; the submarine *Dolphin* (AGSS 555); several submarine rescue ships.
The hull of the original *Trieste* and Krupp sphere are in the Navy Yard in Washington, D.C.

MIDGET SUBMARINES

The US Navy's only "Midget" submarine, the 50-foot long **X-I** was stricken on 16 Feb 1973. See 1972-1973 edition for characteristics and photographs.

NUCLEAR POWERED RESEARCH VEHICLE: PROPOSED

A second nuclear-powered submersible research vehicle has been proposed by Admiral H. G. Rickover, US Navy (Retired), Deputy Commander for Nuclear Propulsion, Naval Ship Systems Command. The craft would have a greater depth capability than the NR-1 (described below) and would employ a nuclear plant similar to that of the earlier craft.
Reportedly, Adm, Rickover began development of the so-called "NR-2" in 1971. Estimated construction time would be 2½ years; however, construction has not yet been approved.

1 NUCLEAR POWERED OCEAN ENGINEERING AND RESEARCH VEHICLE

Name	*Builder*	*Launched*
NR-1	General Dynamics (Electric Boat)	25 Jan 1969

Displacement, tons	400 submerged
Length, feet	136·4 oa × 12·4 × 14·6
Diameter, feet	12 maximum
Machinery	Electric motors, 2 propellers; four ducted thrusters
Reactor	1 pressurised-water cooled
Complement	3 officers, 2 enlisted men, 2 scientists

The NR-1 was built primarily to serve as a test platform for a small nuclear propulsion plant; however, the craft additionally provides an advanced deep submergence ocean engineering and research capability. Vice Admiral Rickover conceived and initiated the NR-1 in 1964-1965 (the craft was not proposed in a Navy research or shipbuilding budget).
Built by Electric Boat Division of General Dynamics Corp, Groton, Connecticut; laid down on 10 June 1967; launched on 25 Jan 1969; completed late in 1969. Commanded by an officer-in-charge vice commanding officer.

Describing the craft Admiral Rickover has stated: "The (NR-1) will be able to perform detailed studies and mapping of the ocean bottom, temperature, currents, and other oceanographic parameters for military, commercial, and scientific use. The development of a nuclear propulsion plant for an oceanographic research vehicle will result in greater independence from surface support ships and essentially unlimited endurance of propulsion and auxiliary power for detailed exploration of the ocean.
"The submarine (NR-1) will have viewing ports for visual observation of its surroundings and the ocean bottom. In addition, a remote grapple will be installed to permit collection of marine samples and other items. With its depth capability, the NR-1 is expected to be capable of exploring areas of the Continental Shelf, an area which appears to contain most accessible wealth in mineral and food resources in the seas. Such exploratory charting may also help the United States in establishing sovereignty over parts of the Continental Shelf".

CONSTRUCTION. Admiral Rickover originally planned to construct the NR-1 using "state of the art" equipment, with the cost of such a vehicle estimated to be $30 000 000 in March 1965. During detailed design of the NR-1 the Navy determined that improved equipment had to be developed and a larger hull than originally planned would be required. Consequently, in July 1967 the Navy obtained Congressional approval to proceed with construction of the NR-1 at an estimated cost of $58 000 300. The final estimated ship construction cost at time of launching was $67 500 000 plus $19 900 000 for oceanographic equipment and sensors, and $11 800 000 for research and development (mainly related to the nuclear propulsion plant), for a total estimated cost of $99 200 000.

DESIGN. The NR-1 is fitted with wheels beneath the hull to permit "bottom crawling". This will obviate the necessity of hovering while exploring the ocean floor. Submarine wheels, a concept proposed as early as the first decade of this century by submarine inventor Simon Lake, were tested in the small submarine *Mackerel* (SST 1).
The NR-1 is fitted with external lights, external television cameras, a remote-controlled manipulator, and various recovery devices. No periscopes, but fixed television mast. Credited with a 30 day endurance.

NR-1 — *1969, General Dynamics, Electric Boat*

NR-1 — *1969, General Dynamics Electric Boat*

ENGINEERING. The NR-1 reactor plant was designed by the Atomic Energy Commission's Knolls Atomic Power Laboratory. She is propelled by two propellers driven by electric motors outside the pressure hull with power provided by a turbine generator within the pressure hull. Four ducted thrusters, two horizontal and two vertical, are provided for precise manoeuvring.

PHOTOGRAPHS. No photographs of the NR-1 have been released for publication since the craft's sea trials in 1969. Note fixed TV mast at after end of sail structure.

2 DEEP SUBMERGENCE RESCUE VEHICLES

No.	*Builder*	*Launched*
DSRV-1	Lockheed Missiles and Space Co. (Sunnyvale, Calif)	24 Jan 1970
DSRV-2		1 May 1971

Weight in air, tons	35
Length, feet	49·2 oa
Diameter, feet	8
Propulsion	Electric motors, propeller mounted in control shroud and four ducted thrusters
Speed, knots	5 (maximum)
Endurance	12 hours at 3 knots
Operating depth, feet	5 000
Complement	3 (pilot, co-pilot, rescue sphere operator) +24 rescuees

The Deep Submergence Rescue Vehicle is intended to provide a quick-reaction, world-wide, all-weather capability for the rescue of survivors in a disabled submarine. The DSRV will be transportable by road, aircraft (in C-141 and C-5 jet cargo aircraft), surface ship (on ASR 21 class submarine rescue ships), and specially modified submarines (SSN type).
Upon notification that a submarine is disabled on the ocean floor the DSRV and its support equipment (all necessary check-out equipment and spare parts being housed in a mobile van) will be loaded in cargo aircraft and flown to a port near the disabled submarine. The DSRV and van will then be towed to a pier and loaded aboard a "mother" submarine, which had proceeded to the port upon notification that a submarine was disabled.

The mother submarine, with the DSRV attached to her main deck (aft of the sail structure), will then proceed to the disabled submarine and serve as an underwater base for the DSRV which will shuttle back and forth between the disabled submarine and the mother submarine. On each trip the DSRV will carry up to 24 survivors from the disabled submarine. The mother submarine will launch and recover the DSRV while submerged and, if necessary, while under ice. A total of six DSRVs were planned, but only two were funded.
The operational effectiveness of the craft is limited severely by the lack of large numbers of ships and submarines that air transport and support the craft. They will be used for the foreseeable future for evaluation and research.

Deep Submergence Vehicles—*continued*

DEEP SUBMERGENCE RESCUE VEHICLES—*Continued*

COST. The estimated construction cost for the DSRV-1 is $41 000 000 and for the DSRV-2 $23 000 000. The development, construction, test, and support of both vehicles through Fiscal Year 1975 is now estimated at $220 000 000. This expenditure includes the design and construction of both vehicles, specific research and development associated with the rescue programme, surface support equipment, modifications to "mother" submarines, test and evaluation programmes, procurement of replacement and spare parts, and training of the DSRV operators and support personnel. The DSRV programme has been forced to support research and development into deep-ocean materials equipment, and other technology-related areas not envisioned in earlier programme cost estimates.

DESIGN. The DSRV outer hull is constructed of formed fibreglass. Within this outer hull are three interconnected spheres which form the main pressure capsule. Each sphere is 7·5 feet in diameter and is constructed of HY-140 steel. The forward sphere contains the vehicle's control equipment and is manned by the pilot and co-pilot, the centre and after spheres accommodate 24 passengers and a third crewman. Under the DSRVs centre sphere is a hemispherical protrusion or "skirt" which seals over the disabled submarine's hatch. During the mating operation the skirt is pumped dry to enable personnel to transfer between the DSRV and disabled or mother submarine.

ELECTRONICS. Elaborate search and navigational sonar, and closed-circuit television (supplemented by optical devices) are installed in the DSRV to determine the exact location of a disabled submarine within a given area and for pinpointing the submarine's escape hatches. Side-looking sonar will be fitted for search missions.

ENGINEERING. Propulsion and control of the DSRV are achieved by a stern propeller in a movable control shroud and four ducted thrusters, two forward and two aft. These, plus a mercury trim system, permit the DSRV to manoeuver and hover with great precision and to mate with submarines lying at angles up to 45 degrees from the horizontal. An elaborate Integrated Control and Display (ICAD) system employs computers to present sensor data to the pilots and transmit their commands to the vehicle's control and propulsion system.

PHOTOGRAPHS. An artist's concept of a DSRV "landing" on a submarine hatch appears in the 1971-1972 edition; a view of the DSRV-1 being assembled appears in the 1970-1971 edition.

DSRV-1 on Hawkbill (SSN 666) *1971, US Navy*

2 RESEARCH VEHICLES: MODIFIED "ALVIN" TYPE

Name	*No.*	*Launched*
SEA CLIFF (ex-*Autec I*)	DSV 4	11 Dec 1968
TURTLE (ex-*Autec II*)	DSV 3	11 Dec 1968

Weight, tons	21
Length, feet	25 oa
Beam, feet	8
Propulsion	Electric motors, trainable stern propeller; 2 rotating propeller pods
Speed, knots	2·5
Endurance	8 hours at 2 knots
Operating depth, feet	6 500
Complement	2 (pilot, observer)

Both submersibles built by Electric Boat Division of General Dynamic Corp, Groton Connecticut. Intended for deep submergence research and work tasks. Designated *Autec I* and *Autec II* during construction, but assigned above names in dual launching on 11 Dec 1968. Completed in 1969.
Designated DSV 4 and DSV 3, respectively, on 1 June 1971.

CONSTRUCTION. Three pressure spheres were fabricated for the *Alvin* submersible programme, one for installation in the *Alvin*, a spare, and one for testing. The second and third spheres subsequently were allocated to these later submersibles.

DESIGN. Twin-arm manipulator fitted to each submersible. Propulsion by stem propeller and two smaller, manoeuvering propeller "pods" on sides of vehicles; no thrusters.

SEA CLIFF *United States Navy*

1 RESEARCH VEHICLE: "ALVIN" TYPE

Name	*No.*
ALVIN	DSV 2

Weight, tons	16
Length, feet	22·5 oa
Beam, feet	8·5
Propulsion	Electric motors; trainable stern propeller; 2 rotating propeller pods
Speed, knots	2
Endurance	8 hours at 1 knot
Operating depth, feet	12 000
Complement	3 1 pilot, 2 observers)

The *Alvin* was built by General Mills, Inc, Minneapolis, Minnesota, for operation by the Woods Hole Oceanographic Institution for the Office of Naval Research. Original configuration had an operating depth of 6 000 feet. Named for Allyn C. Vine of Woods Hole Oceanographic Institution.
The *Alvin* accidentally sank in 5 051 feet of water on 16 Oct 1968; subsequently raised in August 1969; refurbished from May 1971 to Oct 1972 in essentially original configuration; subsequently refitted with titanium pressure sphere to provide increased depth capability and again operational in November 1973. See 1968-1969 edition for photographs of original configuration.

1 BATHYSCAPH RESEARCH VEHICLE: "TRIESTE" TYPE

Name	*No.*
TRIESTE II	DSV 1 (ex-X-2)

Weight in air, tons	84
Displacement, tons	303 submerged
Length, feet	78·6
Beam, feet	15·3
Propulsion	Electric motors, 3 propellers aft, ducted thruster forward (see *Design* notes)
Speed, knots	2
Endurance	10-12 hours at 2 knots
Operating depth, feet	12 000 (see *Design* notes)
Complement	3 (2 operators, 1 observer)

The *Trieste II* is the extensively rebuilt *Trieste I* which the US Navy purchased in 1958 from professor Auguste Piccard. Several "modernisations" have resulted in the current vehicle being essentially a "new" craft, the third to be named *Trieste*. (The original *Trieste* was built at Castellammare, Italy; launched on 1 Aug 1953).
The vehicle is operated by Submarine Development Group One at San Diego, California, and is used primarily as a test bed for underwater equipment and to train deep submergence vehicle operators (hydronauts).
Designated as a "submersible craft" and assigned the designation X-2 on 1 Sep 1969; subsequently changed to DSV 1 on 1 June 1971.

DESIGN. The *Trieste II* is essentially a large float with a small pressure sphere attached to the underside. The float, which is filled with aviation petrol, provides buoyancy. Designed operating depth is 20 000 feet but dives have been limited to approximately 12 000 feet. (The record-setting Challenger Deep dive was made with a Krupp sphere which has a virtually unlimited depth capability).
The bathyscaph was essentially rebuilt for a second time at the Mare Island Naval Shipyard in Sep 1965-Aug 1966 with a modified float, pressure sphere, propulsion system, and mission equipment being fitted. In the broadside view the sphere is now largely hidden by protective supports to keep the sphere clear of the welldeck when the craft rests in a floating dry dock. (Compare with photographs of the earlier *Trieste II* configuration in the 1969-1970 edition).
Fitted with external television cameras and mechanical manipulator; computerised digital navigation system installed.

PHOTOGRAPHS. Note forward "Legs" to prevent pressure sphere from sinking into ocean floor when craft is resting on the bottom. Lights, manipulators, cameras, and and other devices are mounted forward of the sphere, partially in view of sphere's viewpoint.

TRIESTE II *1970, United States Navy*

COAST GUARD

Command

Commandant, United States Coast Guard: Admiral Owen W. Siler
Assistant Commandant: Vice Admiral Ellis L. Perry
Chief of Staff: Rear Admiral Edward D. Scheiderer
Commander, Atlantic Area: Vice Admiral Benjamin F. Engel
Commander, Pacific Area: Vice Admiral Mark A. Whalen

Establishment

The United States Coast Guard was established by an Act of Congress approved Jan 28, 1915, which consolidated the Revenue Cutter Service (founded in 1790) and the Life Saving Service (founded in 1878). The act of establishment stated the Coast Guard "shall be a military service and branch of the armed forces of the United States at all times. The Coast Guard shall be a service in the Treasury Department except when operating as a service in the Navy".
The Congress further legislated that in time of national emergency or when the President so directs, the Coast Guard operates as a part of the Navy. The Coast Guard did operate as a part of the Navy during the First and Second World Wars.
The Lighthouse Service (founded in 1789) was transferred to the Coast Guard on July 1, 1939.
The Coast Guard was transferred to the newly established Department of Transportation on April 1, 1967.

Missions

The current missions of the Coast Guard are to (1) enforce or assist in the enforcement of applicable Federal laws upon the high seas and waters subject to the jurisdiction of the United States including environmental protection; (2) administer all Federal laws regarding safety of life and property on the high seas and on waters subject to the jurisdiction of the United States, except those laws specifically entrusted to other Federal agencies; (3) develop, establish, maintain, operate, and conduct aids to maritime navigation, ocean stations, icebreaking activities, oceanographic research, and rescue facilities; and (4) maintain a state of readiness to function as a specialised service in the Navy when so directed by the President.

Cutters

All Coast Guard vessels are referred to as "cutters". Cutter names are preceded by USCGC. Cutter serial numbers are prefixed with letter designations, the first letter being "W". The first two digits of serial numbers for cutters less than 100 feet in length indicate their approximate length over all. All Coast Guard cutters are active unless otherwise indicated.
Approximately 650 small rescue and utility craft also are in service.

Cutter Strengths

23 High Endurance Cutters
16 Medium Endurance Cutters
2 Oceanographic Cutters
75 Patrol Boats
8 Icebreakers
3 Training Cutters
35 Seagoing Buoy Tenders
67 Coastal-River-Inland Tenders
6 Oceangoing Tugs
29 Harbour Tugs

Personnel

July 1974: 4 505 officers, 1 236 warrant officers, 29 850 enlisted men.

Aviation

The Coast Guard operates a small air arm to support Coast Guard operations. As of 1 July 1974, the Coast Guard operated 20 HC-130 and 1 EC-130E Hercules, 31 HU-16 Albatross, 1 VC-4A Gulfstream I, and 1 VC-11A Gulfstream II fixed-wing aircraft, 39 HH-3F and 72 HH-52A helicopters. The procurement of medium-range, jet-propelled aircraft is being considered to replace the HU-16 Albatross seaplanes for the search and rescue and pollution detection roles.

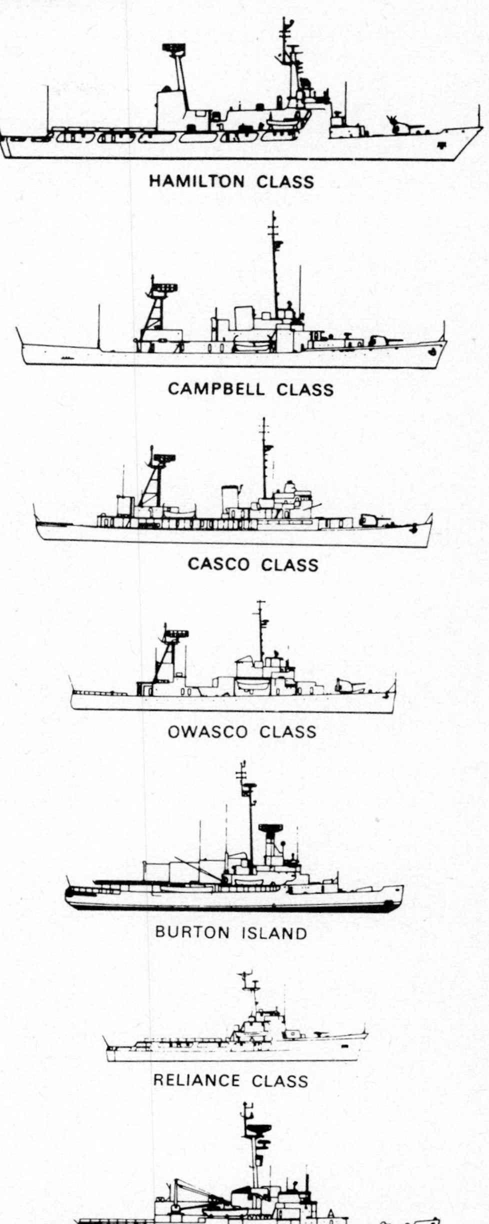

Scale: 1 inch = 150 feet (1 : 1 800) *Drawings by A. D. Baker*

MELLON (WHEC 717), PONCHATOULA (AO 148), JARVIS (WHEC 725) *1972, United States Coast Guard*

HIGH ENDURANCE CUTTERS

12 HIGH ENDURANCE CUTTERS (WHEC): "HAMILTON" (378) CLASS

Displacement, tons	2 716 standard; 3 050 full load
Length, feet	350 wl; 378 oa
Beam, feet	42·8
Draft, feet	20
Guns	1—5 inch (*127 mm*) 38 cal dual-purpose 2—81 mm mortars 4—·50 cal MG
A/S weapons	2 fixed hedgehogs (removed from some ships, see notes) 2 triple torpedo tubes (Mk 32)
Helicopters	1 HH-52 or HH-3 helicopter
Main engines	Combined Diesel and Gas turbine (CODAG): 2 diesels (Fairbanks-Morse) 7 000 hp; 2 gas turbines (Pratt & Whitney), 28 000 hp; aggregate 35 000 hp; 2 shafts
Speed	29
Complement	155 (15 officers, 140 enlisted men)

Name	*No*	*Laid down*	*Launched*	*Completed*
HAMILTON	WHEC 715	Jan 1965	18 Dec 1965	20 Feb 1967
DALLAS	WHEC 716	7 Feb 1966	1 Oct 1966	1 Oct 1967
MELLON	WHEC 717	25 July 1966	11 Feb 1967	22 Dec 1967
CHASE	WHEC 718	15 Oct 1966	20 May 1967	1 Mar 1968
BOUTWELL	WHEC 719	12 Dec 1966	17 June 1967	14 June 1968
SHERMAN	WHEC 720	13 Feb 1967	23 Sep 1967	23 Aug 1968
GALLANTIN	WHEC 721	17 Apr 1967	18 Nov 1967	20 Dec 1968
MORGENTHAU	WHEC 722	17 July 1967	10 Feb 1968	14 Feb 1969
RUSH	WHEC 723	23 Oct 1967	16 Nov 1968	3 July 1969
MUNRO	WHEC 724	18 Feb 1970	5 Dec 1970	10 Sep 1971
JARVIS	WHEC 725	9 Sep 1970	24 Apr 1971	30 Dec 1971
MIDGETT	WHEC 726	5 Apr 1971	4 Sep 1971	17 Mar 1972

These are large, attractive, multi-purpose cutters. All built by Avondale Shipyards, Inc, New Orleans, Louisiana. All these ships are in active service.

ANTI-SUBMARINE ARMAMENT. Hedgehog anti-submarine weapons are being removed from earlier ships during overhaul and Mk 309 fire control system for Mk 32 torpedo launchers installed. Hedgehogs deleted in later ships. *Hamilton* was first to drop hedgehogs and receive Mk 309 during 1970 overhaul.

DESIGN. These ships have clipper bows, twin funnels enclosing a helicopter hangar, helicopter platform aft. All are fitted with oceanographic laboratories, elaborate communications equipment, and meteorological data gathering facilities. Superstructure is largely of aluminium construction. Bridge control of manoeuvring is by aircraft-type "joy stick" rather than wheel.

ELECTRONICS. Original SQS-36 sonar has been replaced by more-capable SQS-38. Fitted with SPS-29 and SPS-51 search radars.

ENGINEERING. The "Hamilton" are the largest US "military" ships with gas turbine propulsion pending completion of the Navy's "Spruance" class destroyers.
The Pratt & Whitney gas turbines are FT-4A, marine variant of the J75 aircraft engine used in the Boeing 707 transport and F-105 fighter-bomber; the Fairbanks Morse diesels are 12 cylinder; variable pitch propellers fitted. Engine and propeller pitch consoles are located in wheelhouse and at bridge wing stations as well as engine room control booth.
A retractable bow propulsion unit is provided for station keeping and precise manoeuvring. (Unit is located directly below hedgehogs, immediately aft of sonar dome).
Range is 14 000 miles at 11 knots on diesels and 2 400 miles at 29 knots on gas turbines.

NOMENCLATURE. The first nine ships of this class were named for secretaries of the Treasury Department reflecting the Coast Guard being a part of that department from 1915 to 1967, when it was transferred to the newly formed Department of Transportation. Subsequent ships of this class honour Coast Guard heroes.
Later ships are referred to as "Hero" class.

PHOTOGRAPHS. Coast Guard cutters are often seen in "troubled waters": the *Rush* was photographed in Southeast Asia and the *Sherman* off Cuba. The *Boutwell* is shown in more tranquil waters off Genoa, Italy. The *Sherman* and *Boutwell* have hedgehogs in "B" position; Mk 32 torpedo tubes amidships. On the previous page two "Hamiltons" refuel from a Navy oiler off Oahu.

RUSH (WHEC 723) — *1970, United States Navy*

MIDGETT (WHEC) 726 with HH-3F and Hovercraft — *1972, United States Coast Guard*

BOUTWELL (WHEC 719) — *1971, Giorgio Arra*

Icebreakers—*continued*

1 ICEBREAKER (WAGB): "GLACIER" TYPE

Name	*No.*	*Launched*	*Commissioned*
GLACIER	WAGB 4 (ex-AGB 4)	27 Aug 1954	27 May 1955

Displacement, tons	8 449 full load
Dimensions, feet	309·6 oa × 74 × 29
Guns	4—·50 cal MG
Helicopters	2 helicopters normally embarked
Main engines	Diesel-electric (10 Fairbanks-Morse diesels and 2 Westinghouse electric motors); 2 shafts; 21 000 hp = 17·6 knots
Complement	229 (14 officers, 215 enlisted men)

The largest icebreaker in US service; designed and built by Ingalls Shipbuilding Corp, Pascagoula, Mississippi laid down on 3 Aug 1953. Transferred from Navy (AGB 4) to Coast Guard on 30 June 1966. During 1972 the *Glacier* and assigned helicopters were painted red to improve visibility in Arctic regions. All other icebreakers painted red during 1973.

ENGINEERING. When built the *Glacier* had the largest capacity single-armature DC motors ever built and installed in a ship. Range is 29 200 miles at 12 knots or 12 000 miles at 17·6 knots.

GUNNERY. As built the *Glacier* was armed with two 5 inch AA guns (twin), six 3 inch AA guns (twin), and four 20 mm AA guns; lighter weapons removed prior to transfer to Coast Guard; 5 inch guns removed in 1969.

GLACIER (WAGB 4)—with guns *1968, US Coast Guard*

GLACIER (WAGB 4) *1972, US Coast Guard*

5 ICEBREAKERS (WAGB): "WIND" CLASS

Name	*No.*	*Launched*
STATEN ISLAND (ex-*Northwind*)	WAGB 278 (ex-AGB 5)	28 Dec 1942
WESTWIND	WAGB 281	31 Mar 1943
NORTHWIND	WAGB 282	25 Feb 1945
BURTON ISLAND	WAGB 283 (ex-AGB 1, ex-AG 88)	30 Apr 1946
EDISTO	WAGB 284 (ex-AGB 2, ex-AG 89)	29 May 1946

Displacement, tons	3 500 standard; 6 515 full load
Dimensions, feet	250 pp; 269 oa × 63·5 × 29
Helicopters	2 helicopters normally embarked
Guns	4—·50 cal MG (see *Gunnery* notes)
Main engines	Diesel-electric (6 diesels); 2 shafts; 10 000 hp = 16 knots
Complement	181 (14 officers, 167 enlisted men)

Originally seven ships in this class built by Western Pipe & Steel Co, San Pedro, California. Five ships were delivered to the US Coast Guard during World War II and two to the US Navy in 1956.
Three of the Coast Guard ships were transferred to the Soviet Navy in 1945: *Northwind* (first of name, WAGB 278) renamed *Severni Veter* and returned to US Navy in 1951 and commissioned as *Staten Island* (AGB 5); *Southwind* renamed *Kapitan Belusov* and returned to US Navy in 1950 and commissioned as *Atka* (AGB 3); *Westwind* renamed *Severni Polius* and returned to US Coast Guard in 1951.
The four "Wind" class ships in the US Navy were transferred to the Coast Guard: *Edisto* on 20 Oct 1965, *Staten Island* on 1 Feb 1966, *Atka* on 20 Oct 1966 (renamed *Southwind* in January 1967), and *Burton Island* on 15 Dec 1966.
The *Westwind* operates on the Great Lakes.

ENGINEERING. These ships were built with a bow propeller shaft in addition to the two stern shafts; bow shaft removed from all units because it would continually break in hard storis ice. Main engines are Fairbanks Morse 38D81/8. Range is 38 000 miles at 10·5 knots or 16 000 miles at 16 knots.

"WIND" CLASS—*continued*

GUNNERY. As built the five Coast Guard ships each mounted four 5 inch guns (one twin mount forward and one twin mount aft on 01 level) and 12 40 mm anti-aircraft guns (quad); the two Navy Ships were completed with only forward twin 5 inch mount (as built a catapult and cranes were fitted immediately behind the funnel and one floatplane was carried). Armament reduced after war and helicopter platform eventually installed in all ships.

During the 1960s the *Northwind* carried two 5 inch guns (twin), and the three other ships each mounted one 5 inch gun; all armament removed in 1969-1970.

DISPOSALS
Eastwind WAGB 279 stricken in 1972; **Southwind** WAGB 280 (ex-AGB 3) stricken in 1974.

STATEN ISLAND (WAGB 278) *1970, US Coast Guard*

BURTON ISLAND (WAGB 283) *US Coast Guard*

NORTHWIND (WAGB 282) ***1969, US Coast Guard***

BURTON ISLAND (WAGB 283) ***1971, US Navy, PH2 J. J. Carmerrale***

Icebreakers—*continued*

1 ICEBREAKER (WAGB): "MACKINAW" TYPE

Name	*No.*	*Launched*	*Commissioned*
MACKINAW (ex-*Manitowac*)	WAGB 83	6 Mar 1944	20 Dec 1944

Displacement, tons	5 252
Dimensions, feet	290 oa × 74 × 19
Helicopters	1 helicopter
Main engines	Diesel; with electric drive; 3 shafts (1 forward, 2 aft); 10 000 bhp = 18·7 knots
Complement	127 (10 officers, 117 enlisted men)

Built by Toledo Shipbuilding Co, Ohio. Laid down on 20 Mar 1943. Completed in Jan 1945. Specially designed and constructed for service as icebreaker on the great Lakes. Equipped with two 12-ton capacity cranes. Clear area for helicopter is provided on the quarter deck.
Range is 60 000 miles at 12 knots.

MACINAW (WAGB 83) *United States Coast Guard*

1 ICEBREAKER (WMEC): "STORIS" TYPE

Name	*No.*
STORIS (ex-*Eskimo*)	WMEC 38 (ex-WAGB 38)

Displacement, tons	1 715 standard; 1 925 full load
Dimensions, feet	230 oa × 43 × 15
Guns	1—3 in, 50 cal; 2—·50 cal MG
Main engines	Diesel-electric; 1 shaft; 1 800 bhp = 14 knots
Complement	106 (10 officers, 96 enlisted men)

Built by Toledo Shipbuilding Co, Ohio. Laid down 14 July 1941; launched on 4 Apr 1942; completed on 30 Sep 1942. Ice patrol tender. Strengthened for ice navigation. Employed on Alaskan service. Search, rescue and law enforcement are primary duties.

Makes supply runs to isolated Coast Guard installations within her patrol area. Her designation changed from WAG to WAGB on 1 May 1966, redesignated as medium endurance cutter (WMEC) on 1 July 1972.
Range is 22 000 miles at 8 knots or 12 000 miles at 14 knots.

STORIS (WMEC, 38) *1968, US Coast Guard*

TRAINING CUTTERS

1 TRAINING CUTTER (WTR): "CASCO" CLASS

Name	*No.*	*Launched*	*Navy Comm.*
UNIMAK	WTR 379 (ex-WHEC 379, ex-AVP 31)	27 May 1942	31 Dec 1943

Displacement, tons	1 766 standard; 2 800 full load
Dimensions, feet	300 wl; 310·75 oa × 41 × 13·5
Guns	1—5 inch (*127 mm*) 38 cal dual-purpose
A/S weapons	removed
Main engines	Diesels (Fairbanks Morse); 6 080 bhp; 2 shafts = 18 knots
Complement	101 (12 officers, 89 enlisted men)

The *Unimak* is the sole survivor of 18 former Navy seaplane tenders (AVP) transferred to the Coast Guard in 1946-1948 (WAVP/WMEC 370-384 initially on loan and WAVP/WMEC 385-387 on permanent transfer).
The *Unimak* was built by Associated Shipbuilders, Seattle, Washington; laid down on 15 Feb 1942. She is employed as a reserve training cutter.

ANTI-SUBMARINE ARMAMENT. All A/S weapons have been removed from the *Unimak*. (The accompanying photograph, taken in 1970, shows the cutter with a fixed hedgehog behind the 5 inch gun mount and triple Mk 32 torpedo tubes on the same 01 level alongside the funnel).

DESIGNATION. The former Navy AVPs were designated WAVP in Coast Guard service until changed to high endurance cutters (WHEC) on 1 May 1966. *Unimak* changed to WTR on 28 Nov 1969.

ENGINEERING. Range is rated at 22 000 miles at 11 knots and 8 000 miles at 19 knots.

Training Cutters —*continued*

DISPOSALS. See 1973-1974 and previous editions for disposals of "Casco" class of cutters except the **Gresham** WAGW 387 (ex-WHEC 387, ex-AGP 9, ex-AVP 57) decommissioned on 1 May 1973 and transferred to Maritime Administration for disposal. Seven ships of this class (former Coast Guard cutters) serve in the South Vietnamese Navy.

Courier WTR 410 (ex-WAGR 410, ex-AK 176) stricken in 1973; **Tanager** WTR 885 (ex-WTR 385, ex-MSF 385) stricken in 1972; **Lamar** WTR 899 (ex-PCE 899) stricken in 1971. See 1973-1974 and previous editions for characteristics.

UNIMAK (WTR 379) *1970, US Coast Guard*

1 TRAINING CUTTER (IX): "ACTIVE" CLASS

CUYAHOGA WIX 157 (ex-WMEC 157, ex-WPC 157, ex-WAG 26)

Dimensions, feet	125 oa × 24 × 8
Guns	Removed
Main engines	Diesel; 2 shafts; 800 bhp = 13·2 knots
Complement	11 (1 officer, 10 enlisted men)

Built in 1926 as one of the 33 "Active" class steel patrol boats. The *Cuyahoga* is the only cutter of this type remaining on the Coast Guard list. She is based at Yorktown, Virginia.

CUYAHOGA (WIX 157) *1966, United States Coast Guard*

1 TRAINING CUTTER (IX): "EAGLE" TYPE

EAGLE (ex-*Horst Wessel*) WIX 327

Displacement, tons	1 634; 1 816 full load
Dimensions, feet	265·8 pp; 295·2 oa × 39·3 × 17
Sail area, sq ft	21 351
Height of masts, feet	150
Main engines	Auxiliary diesel; 740 bhp 1 shaft; = 10·5 knots (as high as 18 knots under full sail alone)
Oil fuel, tons	48
Endurance, miles	3 500 at 10 knots with diesel
Complement	280

Former German training ship for 200 naval cadets. Built by Blohm & Vos, Hamburg. Launched on 13 June 1936. Taken by the United States as part of reparations after the Second World War for employment in US Coast Guard Practice Squadron. Taken over at Bremerhaven in Jan 1946; arrived at home port, New London, Connecticut, in July 1946. She has made several cruises to European waters to train Coast Guard cadets.

Sister ship *Albert Leo Schlageter* was also taken by the United States in 1945 but was sold to Brazil in 1948 and re-sold to Portugal in 1962. Another ship of similar design, the *Gorch Foch*, transferred to the Soviet Union in 1946 and survives as the *Tovarisch*.

Training Cutters—*continued*

EAGLE (WIX 327) *United States Coast Guard*

AIR CUSHION VEHICLES

The three Coast Guard-operated Air Cushion Vehicles (ACV) have been discarded or lost: **Hover 02** lost operationally on Lake Michigan on 23 Nov 1971; **Hover 01** and **Hover 02** decommissioned and discarded in 1973.
All three operated by the US Navy from 1965 to 1969 as Patrol Air Cushion Vehicles (PACV). See 1973-1974 and previous editions for characteristics.

SEAGOING TENDERS

35 SEAGOING TENDERS (WLB) / 1 OCEANOGRAPHIC CUTTER (WAGO) "BALSAM" CLASS

Name	No.	Launched	Name	No.	Launched
BALSAM *	WLB 62	1942	**BITTERSWEET**	WLB 389	1944
COWSLIP	WLB 277	1942	**BLACKHAW***	WLB 390	1944
GENTIAN	WLB 290	1942	**BLACKTHORN**	WLB 391	1944
LAUREL	WLB 291	1942	**BRAMBLE ***	WLB 392	1944
CLOVER	WLB 292	1942	**FIREBUSH**	WLB 393	1944
EVERGREEN	WAGO 295	1943	**HORNBEAM**	WLB 394	1944
SORREL *	WLB 296	1943	**IRIS**	WLB 395	1944
IRONWOOD	WLB 297	1944	**MALLOW**	WLB 396	1944
CITRUS *	WLB 300	1943	**MARIPOSA**	WLB 397	1944
CONIFER	WLB 301	1943	**SAGEBRUSH**	WLB 399	1944
MADRONA	WLB 302	1943	**SALVIA**	WLB 400	1944
TUPELO	WLB 303	1943	**SASSAFRAS**	WLB 401	1944
MESQUITE	WLB 305	1943	**SEDGE ***	WLB 402	1944
BUTTONWOOD	WLB 306	1943	**SPAR ***	WLB 403	1944
PLANETREE	WLB 307	1943	**SUNDEW ***	WLB 404	1944
PAPAW	WLB 308	1943	**SWEETBRIER**	WLB 405	1944
SWEETGUM	WLB 309	1943	**ACACIA**	WLB 406	1944
BASSWOOD	WLB 388	1944	**WOODRUSH**	WLB 407	1944

Displacement, tons	935 standard; 1 025 full load
Dimensions, feet	180 oa × 37 × 13
Guns	1—3 inch (*76 mm*) 50 calibre in *Citrus, Cowslip, Hornbeam,* and *Sorrel* (original armament); most others have ·50 calibre MG except *Sedge* has 2—20 mm guns; several ships are unarmed
Main engines	Diesel-electric; 1 000 bhp in tenders numbered WLB 62-303 series, except *Ironwood*; 1 shaft = 12.8 knots; others 1 200 bhp; 1 shaft = 15 knots
Complement	53 (6 officers, 47 enlisted men)

Seagoing buoy tenders. *Ironwood* built by Coast Guard yard at Curtis Bay, Baltimore, Maryland; others by Marine Iron & Shipbuilding Co, Duluth, Minnesota, or Zeneth Dredge, Co, Duluth Minnesota. Eight ships indicated by asterisks are strengthened for icebreaking. Three ships, *Cowslip, Bittersweet,* and *Hornbeam,* have controllable-pitch, bow-thrust propellers to assist in manoeuvring. All WLBs have 20-capacity booms. The *Evergreen* has been refitted as an oceanographic cutter (WAGO) and is painted white; several ships are laid up in reserve.

HORNBEAM (WLB 394) gun aft of funnel *1969, US Coast Guard*

COASTAL TENDERS

5 COASTAL TENDERS (WLM): "RED" CLASS

Name	No.	Launched	Name	No.	Launched
RED WOOD	WLM 685	1964	**RED CEDAR**	WLM 688	1970
RED BEECH	WLM 688	1964	**RED OAK**	WLM 689	1971
RED BIRCH	WLM 687	1965			

Displacement, tons	471 standard; 512 full load
Dimensions, feet	157 oa × 33 × 6
Main engines	2 diesels; 2 shafts; 1 800 hp = 12·8 knots
Complement	31 (4 officers, 27 enlisted men)

All built by Coast Guard yard, Curtis Bay, Baltimore, Maryland. *Red Cedar* completed late in 1970 and *Red Oak* late in 1971.
Fitted with controllable-pitch propellers and bow thrusters; steel hulls strengthened for light icebreaking. Steering and engine controls on each bridge wing as well as in pilot house. Living spaces are air conditioned. Endurance is 3 000 miles at 11·6 knots. Fitted with 10-ton capacity boom.

RED BIRCH (WLM 687) *1968, U.S. Coast Guard*

3 COASTAL TENDERS (WLM): "HOLLYHOCK" CLASS

FIR WLM 212 **HOLLYHOCK** WLM 220 **WALNUT** WLM 252

Displacement, tons	989
Dimensions, feet	175 × 34 × 12
Main engines	Diesel reduction; 2 shafts; 1 350 bhp = 12 knots
Complement	40 (5 officers, 35 enlisted men)

Launched in 1937 (*Hollyhock*) and 1939 (*Fir* and *Walnut*). *Walnut* was re-engined by Willamette Iron & Steel Co, Portland, Oregon, in 1958. Redesignated Coastal Tenders, WLM, instead on Buoy Tenders, WAGL on 1 Jan 1965. Fitted with 20-ton capacity boom.

1 COASTAL TENDER (WLM): "JUNIPER" TYPE

JUNIPER WLM 224

Displacement, tons	794
Dimensions, feet	177 × 33 × 9·2
Main engines	Diesel, with electric drive; 2 shafts; 900 bhp = 10·8 knots
Complement	38 (4 officers, 34 enlisted men)

Launched on 18 May 1940. Redesignated WLM vice WALG on 1 Jan 1965. Fitted with 20-ton capacity boom.

7 COASTAL TENDERS (WLM): "WHITE" CLASS

WHITE BUSH	WLM 542	**WHITE PINE**	WLM 547
WHITE HEATH	WLM 545	**WHITE SAGE**	WLM 544
WHITE HOLLY	WLM 543	**WHITE SUMAC**	WLM 540
WHITE LUPINE	WLM 546		

Displacement, tons	435 standard; 600 full load
Dimensions, feet	133 oa × 31 × 9
Main engines	Diesel: 2 shafts; 600 bhp = 9·8 knots
Complement	21 (1 officer, 20 enlisted men)

All launched in 1943. All seven ships are former US Navy YFs, adapted for the Coast Guard. The *White Alder* (WLM 541) was sunk in a collision on 7 Dec 1968. Fitted with 10-ton capacity boom.

JUNIPER (WLM 224) *1971, US Coast Guard, LT (jg) M. Robinson*

INLAND TENDERS

TERN WLI 80801

Displacement, tons	168 full load
Dimensions, feet	80 oa × 25 × 5
Main engines	Diesels; 2 shafts; 450 hp = 10 knots
Complement	7 (enlisted men)

The *Tern* is prototype for a new design of inland buoy tenders. A cutaway stern and gantry crane (the first installed in a Coast Guard tender) permit lifting buoys aboard from the stern. The crane moves on rails that extend forward to the deck house. Fitted with 125 hp bow thruster to improve manoeuvrability. Air conditioned. Built by Coast Guard yard at Curtis Bay, Baltimore, Maryland. Launched on 15 June 1968 and placed in service on 7 Feb 1969.

Narcissus WLI 238 decommissioned in 1971 and transferred to Guyana; **Zinnia** WLI 255 decommissioned in 1972 and transferred to US Air Force; **Maple** WLI 234 decommissioned in 1973 for disposal.

TAMARACK WLI 248

Displacement, tons	400 full load
Dimensions, feet	124 oa × 30 × 8
Main engines	Diesels; 1 shaft; 520 hp = 10 knots

Launched in 1934. Fitted with 10-ton capacity boom. Out of service.

COSMOS WLI 293 **BARBERRY** WLI 294 **RAMBLER** WLI 298 **BLUEBELL** WLI 313 **SMILAX** WLI 315 **PRIMROSE** WLI 316 **VERBENA** WLI 317

Displacement, tons	178 full load
Dimensions, feet	100 oa × 24 × 5
Main engines	Diesels; 2 shafts 600; hp = 10·5 knots except *Barberry* 11 knots
Complement	15 (1 officer, 14 enlisted men)

Cosmos launched in 1942, *Barberry* in 1943, *Bluebell* in 1945, others in 1944. The *Barberry* has controllable-pitch propellers. The *Barberry* and *Verbena* are fitted with pile drivers. *Barberry* decommissioned in 1970.

AZALEA WLI 641

Displacement, tons	200 full load
Dimensions, feet	100 oa × 24 × 5
Main engines	Diesels; 2 shafts; 440 hp = 9 knots
Complement	14 (1 officer, 13 enlisted men)

Launched in 1958. Fitted with pile driver.

BUCKTHORN WLI 642

Displacement, tons	200 full load
Dimensions, feet	100 oa × 24 × 4
Main engines	Diesels; 2 shafts; 600 hp = 7·3 knots
Complement	14 (1 officer, 13 enlisted men)

Launched in 1963.

CLEMATIS WLI 74286 **SHADBUSH** WLI 74287

Displacement, tons	93 full load
Dimensions, feet	74 oa × 19 × 4
Main engines	Diesels; 2 shafts; 330 hp = 8 knots
Complement	9 (enlisted men)

Launched in 1944.

BLUEBERRY WLI 65302

Displacement, tons	45 full load
Dimensions, feet	65 oa × 17 × 14
Main engines	Diesels; 2 shafts; 330 hp = 10·5 knots
Complement	5 (enlisted men)

Launched in 1942.

BLACKBERRY WLI 65303 **CHOKEBERRY** WLI 65304 **LOGANBERRY** WLI 65305

Displacement, tons	68 full load
Dimensions, feet	65 oa × 17 × 4
Main engines	Diesels; 1 shaft; 220 hp = 9 knots
Complement	5 (enlisted men)

Launched in 1946.

BAYBERRY WLI 65400 **ELDERBERRY** WLI 65401

Displacement, tons	68 full load
Dimensions, feet	65 oa × 17 × 4
Main engines	Diesels; 2 shafts; 400 hp = 11·3 knots
Complement	5 (enlisted men)

Launched in 1954.

TERN (WLI 80801) *1969, United States Coast Guard*

Inland Tenders—*continued*

BUCKTHORN (WLI 642) *1970, US Coast Guard*

CONSTRUCTION TENDERS

ANVIL WLIC 75301 **HAMMER** WLIC 75302 **SLEDGE** WLIC 75303 **MALLET** WLIC 75304 **VISE** WLIC 75305 **CLAMP** WLIC 75306 **WEDGE** WLIC 75307 **SPIKE** WLIC 75308 **HATCHET** WLIC 75309 **AXE** WLIC 75310

Displacement, tons	145 full load
Dimensions, feet	75 oa (WLIC 75306-75310 are 76 oa) × 22 × 4
Main engines	Diesels; 2 shafts; 600 hp = 10 knots
Complement	9 or 10 (1 officer in *Mallet, Sledge* and *Vise*; 9 enlisted men in all)

Launched 1962-1965

SPIKE (WLIC 75308) pushing barge *1971, US Coast Guard*

RIVER TENDERS

SUMAC WLR 311

Displacement, tons	*Sumac* 404 full load
Dimensions, feet	115 oa × 30 × 6
Main engines	Diesels; 3 shafts; 960 hp = 10·6 knots
Complement	23 (1 officer, 22 enlisted men)

Built in 1943. **Fern** WLR 304 stricken.

DOGWOOD WLR 259 **FORSYTHIA** WLR 63 **SYCAMORE** WLR 268

Displacement, tons	230 full load, except *Forsythia* 280
Dimensions, feet	114 oa × 26 × 4
Main engines	Diesels; 2 shafts; 2 800 hp = 11 knots
Complement	21 (1 officer, 20 enlisted men)

Dogwood and *Sycamore* built in 1940; *Forsythia* in 1943.

FOXGLOVE WLR 285.

Displacement, tons	350 full load
Dimensions, feet	114 oa × 30 × 6
Main engines	Diesels; 3 shafts; 8 500 hp = 13·5 knots
Complement	21 (1 officer, 20 enlisted men)

Built in 1945.

Goldenrod WLR 213 and **Poplar** WLR 241 decommissioned in 1973 and transferred to National Science Foundation.

River Tenders—*continued*

LANTANA WLR 80310

Displacement, tons	235 full load
Dimensions, feet	80 oa × 30 × 6
Main engines	Diesels; 3 shafts; 10 000 hp = 10 knots
Complement	20 (1 officer, 19 enlisted men)

Built in 1943.

OSAGE (WLR 65505) *US Coast Guard*

OUACHITA	WLR 65501	**SCIOTO**	WLR 65504
CIMARRON	WLR 65502	**OSAGE**	WLR 65505
OBION	WLR 65503	**SANGAMON**	WLR 65506

Displacement, tons	139 full load
Dimensions, feet	65·6 oa × 21 × 5
Main engines	Diesel; 2 shafts; 600 hp = 12·5 knots
Complement	10 (enlisted men)

Built in 1960-1962.

OCEANGOING TUGS

1 MEDIUM ENDURANCE CUTTER (WMEC) / 1 OCEANOGRAPHIC CUTTER (WAGO) — ARS TYPE

Name	No.	Launched	Navy Comm.
ACUSHNET (ex-*Shackle*)	WAGO 167 (ex-WAT 167, ARS 9)	1 Apr 1943	5 Feb 1944
YOCONA (ex-*Seize*)	WMEC 168 (ex-WAT 168, ARS 26)	8 Apr 1944	3 Nov 1944

Displacement, tons	1 557 standard; 1 745 full load
Dimensions, feet	213·5 oa × 39 × 15
Main engines	Diesels ; 2 shafts ; 3 000 hp = 15·5 knots
Complement	*Acushnet* 64 (7 officers, 57 enlisted men) *Yacona* 72 (7 officers, 65 enlisted men)

Large, steel-hulled tugs transferred from the Navy to the Coast Guard after World War II. Both by Basalt Rock Co, Napa, California. *Acushnet* modified for handling environmental data buoys and reclassified WAGO in 1969; *Yocona* reclassified as WMEC in 1969. Armament removed.

YOCONA (WMEC 168) *1970, United States Coast Guard*

Oceangoing Tugs—*continued*

3 MEDIUM ENDURANCE CUTTERS (WMEC): ATF TYPE

Name	No.	Launched	Navy Comm.
CHILULA	WMEC 153 (ex-WAT 153, ATF 153)	1 Dec 1944	5 Apr 1945
CHEROKEE	WMEC 165 (ex-WAT 165, ATF 66)	10 Nov 1939	26 Apr 1940
TAMAROA (ex-*Zuni*)	WMEC 166 (ex-WAT 166, ATF 95)	13 July 1943	9 Oct 1943

Displacement, tons	1 731 full load
Dimensions, feet	205 oa × 38·5 × 17
Guns	1—3 inch 50 calibre; 2—·50 cal MG
Main engines	Diesel electric (General Motors diesel); 1 shaft; 3 000 hp = 16·2 knots
Complement	72 (7 officers, 65 enlisted men)

Steel-hulled tugs transferred from the Navy to the Coast Guard after World War II; *Chilula* officially on loan since 9 July 1956 until stricken from the Navy List on 1 June 1969. Classification of all three ships changed to WMEC in 1969. *Chilula* built by Charleston Shipbuilding & Dry Dock Co, Charleston, South Carolina; *Cherokee* built by Bethlehem Steel Co, Staten Island, New York; *Tamaroa* built by Commercial Iron Works, Portland, Oregon.

DISPOSALS
Avoyel (WMEC 150, ex-WAT 150, ex-ATF 150) stricken in 1970.

TAMAROA (WMEC 166) *1970, United States Coast Guard*

2 MEDIUM ENDURANCE CUTTERS (WMEC): ATA TYPE

Name	No	Launched	Navy Comm.
MODOC (ex-*Bagaduce*)	WMEC 194 (ex-WATA 194, ATA 194)	4 Dec 1944	14 Feb 1945
COMANCHE (ex-*Wampanoag*)	WMEC 202 (ex-WATA 202, ATA 202)	10 Oct 1944	8 Dec 1944

Displacement, tons	534 standard; 860 full load
Dimensions, feet	143 oa × 33·8 × 14
Armament	2—·50 cal MG
Main engines	Diesel electric (General Motors diesel); 1 shaft; 1 500 hp = 13·5 knots
Complement	47 (5 officers, 42 enlisted men)

Steel-hulled tugs. The *Modoc* was stricken from the Navy List after World War II and transferred to Maritime Administration; transferred to Coast Guard on 15 Apr 1959. *Comanche* transferred on loan from Navy to Coast Guard from 25 Feb 1959 until stricken from Navy List on 1 June 1969. Both ships reclassified as WMEC in 1969. *Modoc* built by Levingston Shipbuilding Co, Orange, Texas; *Comanche* built by Gulfport Boiler & Welding Works, Port Arthur, Texas.

COMANCHE (WMEC 202) *1969, United States Coast Guard*

HARBOUR TUGS

MANITOU	WYTM 60	**MOHICAN**	WYTM 73	**CHINOOK**	WYTM 96		
KAW	WYTM 61	**ARUNDEL**	WYTM 90	**OJIBWA**	WYTM 97		
APALACHEE	WYTM 71	**MAMONING**	WYTM 91	**SNOHOMISH**	WYTM 98		
YANKTON	WYTM 72	**NAUGATUCK**	WYTM 92	**SAUK**	WYTM 99		
		RARITAN	WYTM 93				

Displacement, tons	370 full load
Dimensions, feet	110 oa × 27 × 11
Main engines	Diesel-electric; 1 shaft; 1 000 hp = 11·2 knots
Complement	20 (1 officer, 19 enlisted men)

Built in 1943 except WYTM 90-93 built in 1939.

MESSENGER WYTM 85009

Displacement, tons	230 full load
Dimensions, feet	85 oa × 23 × 9
Main engines	Diesel; 1 shaft; 700 hp = 9·5 knots
Complement	10 (enlisted)

Built in 1944.

CAPSTAN	WYTL 65601	**CATENARY**	WYTL 65606	**LINE**	WYTL 65611
CHOCK	WYTL 65602	**BRIDLE**	WYTL 65607	**WIRE**	WYTL 65612
SWIVEL	WYTL 65603	**PENDANT**	WYTL 65608	**BITT**	WYTL 65613
TACKLE	WYTL 65604	**SHACKLE**	WYTL 65609	**BOLLARD**	WYTL 65614
TOWLINE	WYTL 65605	**HAWSER**	WYTL 65610	**CLEAT**	WYTL 65615

Displacement, tons	72 full load
Dimensions, feet	65 oa × 19 × 7
Main engines	Diesel; 1 shaft; 400 hp = 9·8 knots except WYTL 65601-65606 10·5 knots
Complement	10 (enlisted men)

Built from 1961 to 1967.

SUPPLY SHIPS (WAK)

All Coast Guard supply ships (WAK) have been stricken: **Kukui** WAK 186 ex-AK 174 transferred to Philippines on 1 Mar 1972; see "Balsam" class seagoing tenders for transfer of **Redbud** to Philippines.

NATIONAL OCEANIC AND ATMOSPHERIC ADMINISTRATION

Command

Director, National Ocean Survey: Rear Admiral Allen L. Powell

Associate Director, Office of Fleet Operations: Rear Admiral Eugene A. Taylor

Director, Atlantic Marine Center: Rear Admiral Alfred C. Holmes

Director, Pacific Marine Center: Rear Admiral Herbert R. Lippold Jnr.

Missions

The National Ocean Survey operates the ships of the National Oceanic and Atmospheric Administration (NOAA), a federal agency created in 1970. During 1972-1973 the National Marine Fisheries Service (formerly the Bureau of Commercial Fisheries of the Department of Interior) was consolidated into the NOAA fleet which is operated by the National Ocean Survey. Approximately 15 small ships and craft 65 feet or longer are counted in the National Marine Fisheries Service. The former National Marine Fisheries vessels are not described because of the specialised, non-military nature of their work.

The National Ocean Survey prepares nautical and aeronautical charts; conducts geodetic, geophysical, oceanographic, and marine surveys; predicts tides and currents; tests, evaluates, and calibrates sensing systems for ocean use; and conducts the development and eventually will operate a national system of automated ocean buoys for obtaining environmental information.

The National Ocean Survey is a civilian agency that supports national civilian and military requirements. During time of war the ships and officers of NOAA, can be expected to operate with the Navy, either as a separate service or integrated into the Navy.

Establishment

The "Survey of the Coast" was established by an act of Congress on Feb 10, 1807. Renamed US Coast Survey in 1834 and again renamed Coast and Geodetic Survey in 1878. The commissioned officer corps was established in 1917. The Coast and Geodetic Survey was made a component of the Environmental Science Services Administration on July 13, 1965, when that agency was established within the Department of Commerce. The Environmental Science Services Administration subsequently became the National Oceanic and Atmospheric Administration in October 1970 with the Coast and Geodetic Survey being renamed National Ocean Survey and its jurisdiction expanded to include the US Lake Survey, formerly a part of the US Army Corps of Engineers; the Coast Guard's national data buoy development project; and the Navy's National Oceanographic Instrumentation Centre.

Ships

National Ocean Survey ship designations are: OSS for Ocean Survey Ship, MSS for Medium Survey Ship, CSS for Coastal Survey Ship, and ASV for Auxiliary Survey Vessel. No National Ocean Survey Ships are armed. All ships are active except where noted otherwise.

Personnel

The National Ocean Survey which operates NOAA ships has approximately 225 commissioned officers and 2 250 officers and 2 250 civil service personnel. In addition, another 125 commissioned officers serve elsewhere in NOAA and several US Navy officers are assigned to NOAA, the most senior being Vice Admiral William W. Behrens, Jnr, Assistant Deputy Administrator and Naval Deputy to the Administrator of NOAA.

Aviation

The National Ocean Survey's Coastal Mapping Division operates two aircraft for aerial photographic missions, a twin-engine de Havilland Canada Buffalo and a twin-engine North American Rockwell Aero Commander.

SURVEY SHIPS

1 OCEANOGRAPIC SURVEY SHIP (OSS): "RESEARCHER" TYPE

Name	*No.*	*Launched*	*Commissioned*
RESEARCHER	OSS 03	5 Oct 1968	8 Oct 1970

Displacement, tons	2 875 light
Dimensions, feet	278·25 oa × 51 × 16·25 (*84·7 m × 15·5 m × 4·9 m*)
Main engines	2 geared diesels; 3 200 hp; 2 shafts = 16 knots
Complement	13 officers, 54 crewmen
Scientists	10 to 13

The *Researcher* was designed specifically for deep ocean research; she is ice strengthened. Estimated cost $10 000 000. Fitted with 20-ton capacity crane, 5-ton capacity crane, four $2\frac{1}{2}$-ton capacity cranes, and an A-frame with 10-ton lift capacity. Built by American Shipbuilding Co, Lorain, Ohio.

DESIGN. Fitted with computerised data acquisition system that automatically samples, processes, and records oceanographic, geophysical, hydrographic, and meteorological data. The 20-ton telescoping crane is designed to handle special sampling equipment and small submersible vehicles as well as small boats. S2-MT-MA74a type.

ENGINEERING. Controllable pitch propellers. A 450-horsepower, 360-degree retractable bow thruster provides sustained low speeds up to seven knots and permits precise positioning. Cruising speed is 14·5 knots with a range of 13000 nautical miles.

2 OCEANOGRAPHIC SURVEY SHIPS (OSS): "OCEANOGRAPHER" CLASS

Name	*No.*	*Launched*	*Commissioned*
OCEANOGRAPHER	OSS 01	18 Apr 1964	13 July 1966
DISCOVERER	OSS 02	29 Oct 1964	29 Apr 1967

Displacement, tons	3 959 light
Dimensions, feet	303·3 oa × 52 × 18·5 (*92·4 m × 15·8 m × 5·6 m*)
Main engines	4 diesels with electric drive; 5 000 bhp; 2 shafts = 16+ knots
Complement	13 officers, 80 crewmen
Scientists	20 to 22

Ice strengthened construction. Fitted with a 5-ton capacity crane and a a $3\frac{1}{2}$-ton capacity crane. Built by Aerojet-General Corp, Jacksonville Shipyard, Jacksonville, Florida. *Discoverer* deactivated in 1973 and placed in reserve.

DESIGN. Fitted with computerised data acquisition system. Center well 8 × 6 feet provides sheltered access to sea for SCUBA divers and for lowering research equipment Six ports in submerged bow observation chamber. S2-MET-MA62a type.

ENGINEERING. A 400-horsepower, through-hull bow thruster provides precise manoeuvring. Not equipped for silent operation. Cruising speed is 16 knots with a range of 15 200 nautical miles.

Survey Ships—*continued*

RESEARCHER (OSS 03) *see previous page* *National Ocean Survey*

OCEANOGRAPHER (OSS 01) *see previous page* *National Ocean Survey*

DISCOVERER (OSS 02) *see previous page* *National Ocean Survey*

3 HYDROGRAPHIC SURVEY SHIPS (MSS): "FAIRWEATHER" CLASS

Name	*No.*	*Launched*	*Commissioned*
FAIRWEATHER	MSS 20	15 Mar 1967	2 Oct 1968
RAINIER	MSS 21	15 Mar 1967	2 Oct 1968
MT. MITCHELL	MSS 22	29 Nov 1966	23 Mar 1968

Displacement, tons	1 798 light
Dimensions, feet	231 oa × 42·07 × 13·9 (*70·2 m × 12·8 m × 4·2 m*)
Main engines	2 diesels ; 2 400 bhp ; 2 shafts = 13+ knots
Complement	12 officers, 62 crewmen
Scientists	

Ice strengthened. Built by Aeroiet-General Corp, Jacksonville Shipyard, Jacksonville, Fla. SI-MT-MA72a type.

ENGINEERING. Fitted with a 200-horsepower, through-bow thruster for precise manoeuvring. Controllable-pitch propellers. Cruising speed is 13 knots with a range of 9 000 nautical miles.

DISCOVERER (OSS 02) see previous page *National Ocean Survey*

SURVEYOR (OSS 32) *National Ocean Survey*

1 HYDROGRAPHIC SURVEY SHIP (OSS): "SURVEYOR" TYPE

Name	*No.*	*Launched*	*Commissioned*
SURVEYOR	OSS 32	25 Apr 1959	30 Apr 1960

Displacement, tons	3 150 light
Dimensions, feet	292·3 oa × 46 × 18 (*88·8 m × 14·0 m × 5·5 m*)
Main engines	1 steam turbine (De Laval) ; 3 520 shp ; 1 shaft = 15+ knots
Complement	14 officers, 76 crewmen
Scientists	8

Specially designed for marine charting and geophysical surveys. Fitted with helicopter platform aft. Ice strenghtened. Twin telescoping 2½-ton capacity cargo booms (forward) and 12½-ton capacity crane. Estimated cost $6 000 000. Built by National Steel & Co, San Diego, California. The *Surveyor* was deactivated in 1973 and placed in reserve.

DESIGN. Large bilge keel (18 inches × 70 feet) permits oceanographic observations to be performed up to Sea State 6. S2-S-RM28a type.

ENGINEERING. Retractable outboard motor mounted to stern for precision manoeuvring. Cruising speed is 15 knots with a range of 10 500 nautical miles.

DISPOSALS

Pathfinder OSS 30, ex-US Navy AGS 1 decommissioned in 1972 and stricken. See 1972-1973 edition for description and photograph.

Survey Ships—*continued*

MT MITCHELL (MSS 22) *see previous page* *National Ocean Survey*

2 HYDROGRAPHIC SURVEY SHIPS (CSS): "McARTHUR" CLASS

Name	*No.*	*Launched*	*Commissioned*
McARTHUR	CSS 30	15 Nov 1965	15 Dec 1966
DAVIDSON	CSS 31	7 May 1966	10 Mar 1967

Displacement, tons	995 light
Dimensions, feet	175 oa × 38 × 11·5 (*53·0 m × 11·5 m × 3·5 m*)
Main engines	2 diesels; 1 600 bhp; 2 shafts = 13·5+ knots
Complement	6 officers, 30 crewmen

Designed for nearshore operations. Ice strengthened. Built by Norfolk SB & DD Co, Norfolk, Virginia. SI-MT-MA70a type.

ENGINEERING. Controllable-pitch propellers. Cruising speed is 13·5 knots with a range of 4 500 nautical miles.

RAINIER (MSS 21) *see previous page* *National Ocean Survey*

McARTHUR (CSS 30) *National Ocean Survey*

FAIRWEATHER (MSS 20) *see previous page* *National Ocean Survey*

2 HYDROGRAPHIC SURVEY SHIPS (CSS): "PEIRCE" CLASS

Name	*No.*	*Launched*	*Commissioned*
PEIRCE	CSS 28	15 Oct 1962	6 May 1963
WHITING	CSS 29	20 Nov 1962	8 July 1963

Displacement, tons	760 light
Dimensions, feet	164 oa × 33 × 10·1 (*50·0 m × 10·0 m × 3·1 m*)
Main engines	2 diesels; 1 600 bhp; 2 shafts = 12·5+ knots
Complement	6 officers, 30 crewmen

Designed for nearshore operations. Ice strengthened. Built by Marietta Manufacturing Co, Point Pleasant, West Virginia. SI-MT-59a type.

ENGINEERING. Controllable pitch-propellers. Cruising speed is 12·5 knots with a range of 4 500 nautical miles.

DAVIDSON (CSS 31) *National Ocean Survey*

PEIRCE (CSS 28) *National Ocean Survey*

Survey Ships—*continued*

WHITING (CSS 29) *see previous page* *National Ocean Survey*

COASTAL VESSELS

2 WIRE DRAG VESSELS (ASV); "RUDE" CLASS

Name	*No.*	*Launched*	*Commissioned*
RUDE	ASV 90	17 Aug 1966	29 Mar 1967
HECK	ASV 91	1 Nov 1966	29 Mar 1967

Displacement, tons	214 light
Dimensions, feet	90 oa × 22 × 7 (*27·4 m × 6·7 m × 2·1 m*)
Main engines	2 diesels ; 800 bhp ; 2 shafts = 11·5+ knots
Complement	2 officers, 9 crewmen

Designed to search out underwater navigational hazards along the coast using wire drags. Built by Jacobson Shipyard Inc, Oyster Bay, New York. SI-MT-MA71a type. A single commanding officer is assigned to both vessels; normally he rides one ship and the executive officer the other.

ENGINEERING. Propellers are guarded by shrouds similar to Kort nozzles. Auxiliary propulsion provides 50 horsepower to each propeller for dragging operations. Cruising speed is 11·5 knots with a range of 740 nautical miles (provisions carried for eight days.)

RUDE (ASV 90) *National Ocean Survey*

Coastal Vessels—*continued*

1 CURRENT SURVEY VESSEL (ASV); "FERREL" TYPE

Name	*No.*	*Launched*	*Commissioned*
FERREL	ASV 92	4 Apr 1968	4 June 1968

Displacement, tons	363 light
Dimensions, feet	133·25 × 32 × 7 (*40·5 m × 9·7 m × 2·1 m*)
Main engines	2 diesels ; 820 bhp ; 2 shafts = 10+ knots
Complement	3 officers, 13 crewmen

Specially designed to conduct nearshore and estuarine current surveys. Limited surface meteorological observations also are made. Buoy workshop provided in 450-square feet of enclosed deck area with buoy stowage on open after deck. Built by Zeigler Shipyard, Jennings, Louisiana. SI-MT-MA83a type.

ENGINEERING. Fitted with 100-horsepower, electric-driven bow thruster. Cruising speed is 10 knots (provisions for 15 days carried).

FERREL (ASV 92) *National Ocean Survey*

FERREL (ASV 92) *National Ocean Survey*

UNION OF SOVIET SOCIALIST REPUBLICS

Administration — Flag Officers Soviet Navy

Administration	Flag Officers Soviet Navy
Commander-in-Chief of the Soviet Navy and First Deputy Minister of Defence:	Admiral of the Fleet of the Soviet Union Sergei Georgiyevich Gorshkov
First Deputy Commander-in-Chief of the Soviet Navy:	Admiral of the Fleet Vladimir Afanasevich Kasatonov
Assistant Chief of the General Staff of the Armed Forces:	Admiral of the Fleet S. M. Lobov
Deputy Commander-in-Chief:	Admiral N. N. Amelko
Deputy Commander-in-Chief:	Engineer Admiral P. G. Kotov
Deputy Commander-in-Chief:	Engineer Vice Admiral V. G. Novikov
Commander of Naval Aviation:	Marshall Ivan I. Borzov
Chief of the Political Directorate:	Admiral V. M. Grishanov
Chief of Rear Services:	Admiral G. G. Oleynik
Chief of Naval Training Establishments:	Vice-Admiral I. M. Kuznetsov
Chief of Main Naval Staff:	Admiral of the Fleet N. D. Sergeyev
1st Deputy Chief of the Main Naval Staff:	Admiral V. N. Alekseyev
Chief of the Hydrographic Service:	Admiral A. I. Rassokho
Northern Fleet	
Commander-in-Chief:	Admiral of the Fleet G. M. Yegorov
1st Deputy Commander-in-Chief:	Vice-Admiral N. I. Khovrin
Chief of Staff:	Vice-Admiral V. G. Kichev
In Command of the Political Department:	Admiral F. Ya Sizov
Pacific	
Commander-in-Chief:	Admiral of the Fleet N. I. Smirnov
1st Deputy Commander-in-Chief:	Vice-Admiral V. P. Maslov
Chief of Staff:	Vice-Admiral G. A. Bondarenko
In Command of the Political Department:	Rear-Admiral S. S. Bevz
Black Sea	
Commander-in-Chief:	Admiral V. S. Sysoyev
1st Deputy Commander-in-Chief:	Rear-Admiral V. Samoylov
Chief of Staff:	Vice-Admiral B. Yamkovoy
In Command of the Political Department:	Vice-Admiral I. S. Rudnev
Baltic	
Commander-in-Chief:	Vice-Admiral A. Kosov
1st Deputy Commander-in-Chief:	Rear-Admiral N. I. Shablikov
Chief of Staff:	Rear-Admiral L. D. Ryabtsev
In Command of the Political Department:	Rear-Admiral V. N. Sergeyev
Caspian Flotilla	
Commander-in-Chief:	Rear-Admiral Ya M. Kudelkin
In Command of the Political Department:	Rear-Admiral P. D. Burlachenko
Leningrad Naval Base	
Commanding Officer:	Vice-Admiral V. M. Leonenkov
In Command of the Political Department:	Rear-Admiral A. A. Plekhanov
Head of the Order of Lenin Naval Academy:	Admiral A. Ya Orel
Head of Frunze Naval College:	Vice-Admiral V. A. Khrenov

Diplomatic Representation

Naval Attaché London: Captain V. Z. Khuzhokov

Mercantile Marine

Lloyd's Register of Shipping: 7 123 vessels of 17 396 900 tons gross

SOVIET NAVAL AVIATION

The Soviet Navy operates 1 200 fixed-wing aircraft and helicopters in *Morskaya Aviatsiya*, the world's second largest naval air arm. The primary combat components are
(1) Long range and medium bombers employed in the maritime reconnaissance role
(2) Medium bombers mostly equipped with air-to-surface missiles in the anti-ship strike role.
(3) Land based patrol aircraft, amphibians and helicopters in the anti-submarine role.

The Soviet Navy flies no fixed-wing aircraft from ships, but several medium classes of destroyers and all modern missile armed cruisers, and the cruiser-helicopter ships *Moskva* and *Leningrad* can carry helicopters. The two helicopter ships are the largest built to date by any navy specifically for anti-submarine operations and are the first Soviet warships intended primarily for aviation activities. (A third ship possibly of an improved design is believed to be under construction according to some reports)

Bombers. The Soviet naval air arm has about 55 heavy and 550 medium bombers in the anti-shipping, strike, tanker and reconnaissance roles. The main strike force comprises about 300 "Badger" equipped with "Kipper" and "Kelt" air-to-surface missiles. The reconnaissance aircraft are about 55 "Bear D" (long range recce); 55 "Badger" and a similar number of "Blinder A". The latter and some of the "Badger" have a bombing capability. About 50 "Beagle" light bombers remain in service.

ASW Helicopters. Over 200 anti-submarine helicopters are believed to be in the naval air arm, mostly Ka-25 "Hormone" (a twin-turbine craft known as the "Harp" in the prototype stage) and some of the older Mi-4 "Hound" helicopters. The "Hormone" anti-submarine helicopters, armed with torpedoes or other ASW weapons operate from the large helicopter cruisers *Moskva* and *Leningrad* which can each operate some 15 to 20 helicopters, servicing them in a hangar below the flight deck. They have also been seen in the "Kara", "Kresta" I and "Kresta II" class cruisers which are the first Soviet ships of this type to be fitted with a helicopter hangar. In some of these ships the radar fitted helicopter may also have a reconnaissance role associated with the surface-to-surface missile system. The older MI-4 "Hound" and other "Hormone" helicopters are used in the ASW role from shore bases. Other types of helicopter are also used in the transport role ashore.

ASW Patrol Aircraft. The Soviet Union is the only nation other than Japan maintaining modern military flying boats, about 100 Be-12 "Mail" (turboprop) aircraft of this type being operational. The latter aircraft, an amphibian often photographed on runways, has an advanced anti-submarine capability evidenced by a radome extending forward, a Magnetic Anomaly Detector (MAD) boom extending aft and a weapons bay in the rear fuselage. The numbers of the shore based ASW patrol aircraft IL 38 "May" are growing, some 30 are now in service. They have been seen in northern waters and reported in service with Soviet Units based in Egypt.

The "May", of which some 75 are in service, is a militarised version of the four-turboprop commercial air freighter (code name "Coot") in wide commercial service. The patrol/anti-submarine version has been lengthened and fitted with a MAD boom as well as other electronic equipment and a weapons capability similar to the US Navy's conversion of the Lockheed Electra into the P-3 "Orion" patrol aircraft.

Transports/Training Aircraft. There are also a few hundred transports, utility, and training fixed-wing aircraft and helicopters under Navy control.

*Aircraft names are NATO code names; "B" names indicate bombers, "H" names for helicopters, and "M" names for miscellaneous aircraft.

SOVIET NAVAL RADARS

Code Name	Freq. Band	Function	Ship Application
Ball Gun	S	Surface warning	Kronstadt and older Light Forces
Big Net	L	Long-range air warning	Kresta I, Kashin (some) Dzerzhinski
Boat Sail	S or L	Surveillance	Whisky Canvas Bag
Cross Bird	G	Early warning	Obsolescent older Destroyers
Dead Duck	C	IFF	General
Don-2	X	Navigation	
Drum Tilt	X	Short-range armament Control	General with 30 mm guns
Egg Cup	S	Fire Control	
Fan Song E	C	Control for SA-N-2	Dzerzhinski
Flat Spin	L or S	Air surveillance	Some destroyers
Hair Net	S	Search & Surveillance	Kildins, Kotlins and Frigates
Half Bow		Torpedo fire control	Older destroyers
Hawk Screech/ Owl Screech	C	Acquisition and fire control for main armament	Ships mounting 57—100 mm guns
Head Light	X and C	Missile control	Most modern major surface ships
Head Net A	S	Air surveillance	Kynda, Kashin, Krupny and other destroyers
Head Net B	S	Air surveillance	Krupny (some)
Head Net C	S	Air surveillance and Height Finder	Kiev, Moskva, Kara, Kresta I and II and SAM fitted destroyers
High Lune	S	Height finder	Dzerzhinski (with FanSong E)
High Pole	C	IFF	General
High Sieve	S	Surveillance	
Horn Spoon		Navigation	General
Knife Rest	I	Air warning	Sverdlov's and Kildin's
Long Bow		Torpedo fire control	Destroyers

Code Name	Freq. Band	Function	Ship Application
Low Sieve	S	Surface search	
Muff Cob	C or X	Fire control	Moskva, Kresta I & II, Ugra, Lama, Poti, T58, Polnocny, Light Forces
Neptun	X	Navigation	Light Forces
Owl Screech (see Hawk Screech)			
Peel Group	X	SA-N-1 fire control	Kresta I, Kashin, Kynda, SAM Kotlin, Kanin
Plinth Net		Surface search	Obsolete
Post Lamp	X	Fire Control	Older destroyers
Pot Drum	X	Surface search	Some Light Forces and Kronstadts
Pot Head	X	Surface search	Some Light Forces and Kronstadts
Round Top		Fire control system	Older destroyers
Scoop Pair	E	SS-N-3 guidance	Kresta I and Kynda
Ship Globe	E	Missile Tracking	Instrumentation ships
Skin Head	X	Surface search	Some Light Forces & Krupny
Slim Net	S	Surface search	Some destroyers and frigates
Snoop Plate	X	Surveillance	Submarines
Snoop Slab	X	Surveillance	Submarines
Snoop Tray	X	Surveillance	Submarines
Square Head	C	IFF interrogator	Osa, Kotlin and Skory
Square Tie	X	Surface search	Osa
Strut Curve	S	Medium range search	Poti, Support ships
Sun Visor B	X	Fire control	
Top Bow	X	Fire control	Some cruisers and destroyers
Top Sail	L	Air surveillance	Moskva, Kiev, Kara, Kresta II
Top Trough	S	Surface Search	Sverdlov's
Wasp Head		Fire control system	Older destroyers
Witch Five	C	IFF	Some cruisers and destroyers

SOVIET NAVAL MISSILES

Type	System	Missile Code-Name	Launch Platform	No. of Tubes/ Launchers	Max speed	Max Range (n. miles)	Length (feet)	Notes
SSM (cruise)	SS-N-1	Scrubber	2 "Kildin" destroyers	1	0·9	130	22·5	Subsonic and obsolescent. Limited use after 1975. Operational in 1958. 8-9 reloads per launcher may be carried. "KILDINS" converting to SS-N-11.
			2 "Krupny" destroyers	2				
SSM (cruise)	SS-N-2	Styx	15 "Komar" FAC	2	0·9	23	15	Two versions—A and B. Probably has an active radar homing capability. Operational in 1960.
			65 "Osa" I FAC	4				
SSM (cruise)	SS-N-3	Shaddock	4 "Kynda" cruisers	8	0·9-1·5	150-250	42	In some cases requires external guidance from aircraft. There is evidence that this missile may be pre-programmed for shorter ranges and have an active radar terminal homing capability. Operational in 1961-62.
			4 "Kresta I" cruisers	4				
			16 "Juliet" submarines	4				
			1 "Echo I" submarine	6				
			27 "Echo II" submarines	8				
			7 "Whisky Long Bin" submarines	4				
			5 "Whisky Twin Cylinder" submarines	2				
Strat	SS-N-4	Sark	11 "Golf I" submarines	3	—	300	37·5	An obsolescent system now being phased-out with the submarines carrying it. Operational in 1958-60
			1 "Zulu V" submarine	2				
Strat	SS-N-5	Serb	11 "Golf II" submarines	3	—	700	35	Development of SS-N-4 system. Operational in 1963.
			8 "Hotel II" submarines	3				
Strat	SS-N-6	Sawfly	33 "Yankee" submarines	16	—	1 300	42	Dived launch. Operational in 1969.
SSM (dived cruise)	SS-N-7		11 "Charlie" submarines	8	1·5	30	22	Dived launch. Operational in 1969-70.
Strat	SS-N-8		5+14 "Delta" submarines	12	—	4 200	45 est	Dived launch. Operational in 1973.
SSM	SS-N-9		1 "Delta II" submarine	16 (?)	1·0+	150	30 est	Operational in 1968-69.
SSM	SS-N-10		9 "Nanuchka" missile corvettes	6	1·2	29	25 est	Operational in 1968.
			2 "Kara" cruisers	8				
			6 "Kresta II" cruisers	8				
			7 "Krivak" destroyers	4				
SSM	SS-N-11		55 "Osa II" FAC	4				
			1+2 Modified "Kildin" destroyers	4	0·9	29	21	Probably modified Styx with folding wings. Low altitude capability.
						Slant Range		
SAM	SA-N-1	Goa	8 SAM "Kotlin" destroyers	2 (1 twin)	2	17		
			6 "Kanin" destroyers	2 (1 twin)				
			19 "Kashin" destroyers	4 (2 twin)				
			4 "Kynda" cruisers	2 (1 twin)				
			4 "Kresta I" cruisers	4 (2 twin)				
SAM	SA-N-2	Guideline	1 "Dzerzhinski" cruiser	2 (1 twin)		25		
SAM	SA-N-3	Goblet	1+1 "Kuril" aircraft carriers	4 (2 twin)				
			2 "Moskva" cruisers	4 (2 twin)		20		
			6 "Kresta II" cruisers	4 (2 twin)				
SAM	SA-N-4		2 "Kara" cruisers	4 (2 twin)				
			1+1 "Kuril" aircraft carriers	6 (3 twin)				
			2 "Sverdlov" conversion cruisers	2 (1 twin)		20		
			2 "Kara" cruisers	4 (2 twin)				
			5 "Krivak" destroyers	4 (2 twin)				
			9 "Nanuchka" missile corvettes	2 (1 twin)				
			14 "Grisha" corvettes	2 (1 twin)		*Max Range (n. miles)*		
ASM	AS-1	Kennel	c50 "Badger B" bomber	2	0·9	55		Obsolete.
ASM	AS-2	Kipper	c150 "Badger C" bomber	1	1·0+	115		Obsolescent
ASM	AS-3	Kangaroo	c20 "Bear B" and "C" bomber	2	1·5+	400		
ASM	AS-4	Kitchen	? "Blinder B" bomber	1	2+	185		Inertial Guided.
ASM	AS-5	Kelt	c150 "Badger G"	2	0·9	120		Replacing AS-1 Active homer.
ASM	AS-6	—	c50 "Badger modified" bombers	2	2	300?		Possibly also to be used in "Backfire" Operational in 1970.

NOTE: Numbers of aircraft under AS-1 to AS-6 are approximate.

MISSILE LAUNCHERS—TOTALS

Cruise Missiles (SSM's)

Long Range (50 nm+)	Surface launchers	108
	S/M launchers	324
Short Range (less than 50 nm)	Surface launchers	598
	S/M launchers	88

Strategic Missiles (SLBM's)
(all submarine launched)

Medium Range	90
Long Range ("Yankees" and "Deltas")	604

Surface-to-Air (SAM's) (all surface launched) 258

Air-to-Surface (ASM's) 690

NOTES:—

a). SAM's are now frequently fitted in SSM-carrying ships.

b). Total of ASM's very approximate.

c). Total of missiles carried by surface ships not listed owing to lack of reliable information.

SOVIET NAVAL STRENGTHS

Class	North	Baltic	Black Sea (incl. Caspian)	Pacific	Total
Submarines					
Delta II	1	—	—	—	1
Delta	5	—	—	—	5
Yankee	25	—	—	8	33
Hotel III	1	—	—	—	1
Hotel II	5	—	—	3	8
Charlie	11	—	—	—	11
Echo II	15	—	—	12	27
Echo I	—	—	—	1	1
Victor	12	—	—	2	14
November	9	—	—	5	14
Golf I & II	14	—	—	8	22
Zulu V	1	—	—	—	1
Juliet	11	—	—	5	16
W Twin Cylinder					5
W Long Bin	5	2	1	4	7
Alpha	1	—	—	—	1
Bravo	1	1	1	1	4
Tango	1	—	—	—	1
Foxtrot	31	14	—	11	56
Romeo	—	5	9	—	14
Quebec	—	11	11	—	22
Zulu	9	4	—	4	20
Whisky	20	40	22	28	110
Whisky Canvas Bag	1	—	—	2	3
Surface Ships					
Kuril	—	—	1+1	—	1+1
Kara	—	—	2	—	2

Class	North	Baltic	Black Sea (incl. Caspian)	Pacific	Total
Moskva	—	—	2	—	2
Sverdlov	2	3	4	3	12
Chapaev	1	1	—	—	2
Kirov	—	1	1	—	2
Kresta II	3	2	1	—	6
Kresta I	3	—	—	1	4
Kynda	—	—	2	2	4
Krivak	4	3	—	—	7
Kashin	3	3	8	5	19
Kanin	3	2	—	1	6
Krupny	—	—	—	2	2
SAM Kotlin	2	1	3	2	8
Kidlin	—	1	2	—	3
Kotlin	3	3	4	8	18
Tallin	—	1	—	—	1
Skory	10	10	10	10	40
Nanuchka	—	5	4	—	9
Mirka I and II	4	4	8	4	20
Petya I and II	10	12	13	10	45
Kola	—	1	3	2	6
Riga	10	9	12	9	40
Ugra	4	2	—	2	6
Lama	2	—	1	2	5
Don	3	—	—	3	6
Grisha	3	5	4	2	14
Stenka	—	19	4	7	30
Poti	25	25	5	15	70
SO 1	—	40	30	10	80
Kronstadt	5	7	4	4	20

Class	North	Baltic	Black Sea (incl. Caspian)	Pacific	Total
Fleet Sweepers	40	58	40	50	188 (13 Natya 45 Yurka 20 T 58 10 T 43)
Coastal Sweepers	27	45	25	25	123 (3 Zhenya 70 Vanya 40 Sasha 10 T 301)
Pchela	—	10	15	—	25
Komar	—	5	10	—	15
Osa	25	35	25	35	120 (65 Type I 55 Type II)
FAC—Torpedo	15	70	20	45	150 (40 Shershen 100 P6, 8 P 10 10 P4)
Alligator	2	4	3	3	12
Polnocny	12	15	18	15	60
Landing Craft	10	15	30	20	75 (5 MP 8 15 MP 4 35 Vydra 20 MP 10)
Intelligence Ships (AGIs)	15	8	15	15	53

AIRCRAFT CARRIERS

1+1 "KURIL" CLASS (AIRCRAFT CARRIERS)

KIEV **MINSK**

Displacement, tons	40 000
Length, feet (*metres*)	925 (*282*) oa; 880 (*268*) wl; 100 (*30·5*) (hull)
Beam, feet (*metres*)	200 (*61*) (overall, including flight deck and sponsons)
Aircraft (estimated)	25 fixed wing (? Freehand type) 25 Hormone A or modified Hind A helicopters
Missile launchers	2 twin SA-N-3 for Goblet missiles 1 ASW twin launcher; possibly 3-4 SA-N-4 launchers
Guns	28—57 mm
A/S weapons	2—12 barrelled MBU launchers forward
Speed, knots	At least 30

The *Kiev*, now fitting out at Nikolayev, and her sister building at the same yard, mark an impressive and logical advance by the Soviet Navy. The arrival of these ships has been heralded by Admiral Gorshkov's support for embarked tactical air as a necessity for navies employed in extending political influence far abroad, and by a softening of previous Soviet criticisms of this class of ship.

Kiev appears to be a carrier designed for VTOL aircraft and helicopter operations. There is at present no sign of steam catapults, arrester gear, mirror-landing-sights, and all the expensive gear required for fixed-wing operations. Nor is there yet any evidence of the existence of a fixed-wing aircraft suitable for carrier operations. On the other hand, the Freehand VTOL aircraft or its derivative, the Hormone A helicopter or a modification of the Army's Hind A helicopter could all be embarked. Two examples of the former, designed by Yakovlev, appeared at the 1967 Domodedovo air show, were clearly subsonic and mounted 16-round rocket packs under each wing in one aircraft. They were powered by twin Turbo-jet engines, had a wide fuselage to accommodate these and short delta wings of about 27 ft wing-span. The overall length of the aircraft was about 58 ft. Since 1967 further trials of what is apparently an improved version of Freehand have continued at Ramenskoye airfield near Moscow, culminating in sea-trials from a specially fitted pad on the flight-deck of *Moskva*. These were primarily in the Black Sea—her subsequent deployment to the Mediterranean may have indicated stage two in these trials. The provision of a 550-600 ft angled flight deck in the *Kiev* would allow the VTOL aircraft an increase of up to 25% in their take-off weight.

A rough estimate of her hangar capacity suggests that *Kiev* could carry 25 of each type simultaneously. Her forward lift appears to be adequate to accommodate a Freehand type but until more detailed evidence is available this, with many other deductions, must remain conjectural.

Her armament is of interest, her missiles being, if present estimates are correct, similar to those in *Moskva* with the addition of SAN 4 whilst she may carry a heavy armament of medium calibre guns. The missile systems SAN-3, using Goblet missiles with a slant range of some 20 miles, are possibly to balance the lack of embarked high-performance fighters and are of longer range than the BPDMS's with Sea Sparrow which are fitted in the latest U.S. carriers. The heavy gun armament is a complete break with the latter's armament—neither *Nimitz* nor *Enterprise* carry any guns. But provision of an increasingly heavy conventional gun-armament can be seen throughout the Soviet surface fleet and this class could be a prime example of this trend.

If *Kiev* turns out to have similar A/S weapons to *Moskva* (Twin A/S rocket launchers forward and a possible A/S weapon launcher) another radical change in carrier practice will have been seen. The A/S rocket launchers would presuppose a sonar fit of a hull mounted set and/ or VDS, showing the Soviets have taken the submarine threat seriously. Success with such a system depends very largely on the speed and handling of that ship and the efficiency of the A/S helicopters which, presumably, would work with the weapon launcher.

With world-wide Soviet deployments a pair of ships is clearly insufficient, allowing for maintenance and any refitting required. The design of the carrier must have been on the drawing-board before *Moskva* was commissioned in 1967. Perhaps the decision to build more of the latter was delayed until after the extensive heavy-weather operations which *Moskva* and *Leningrad* carried out. It seems most likely that these were sufficiently successful to encourage the Soviet navy to proceed with the larger ships. A minimum of six would be not unlikely.

They will be a powerful addition to the political impact of the Soviet fleet in peacetime. With ships capable of operating VTOL strike aircraft and troop-lift helicopters their credibility in the intervention role would be increased, and their fleet would be that much more prepared for hostilities. Such ships roles could be changed merely by alterations in the number and type of aircraft enbarked. They are clearly not as enormously expensive as the US nuclear-powered carriers but will greatly enhance the manifest capability of the Soviet fleet to operate effectively world-wide in both peace and war.

RADAR. Top Sail and Headlight,

SONAR. Possibly hull-mounted and VDS.

SOVIET TYPE NAME. Protivo Lodochny Kreyser meaning Anti-submarine cruiser. This is an interesting designation for a ship of this size, suggesting a bias towards A/S in her future employment but more probably aimed at circumventing the restrictions on aircraft carriers in the Montreux Convention, regulating the use of the Turkish Straits.

KIEV *1973, USN Artists Impression*

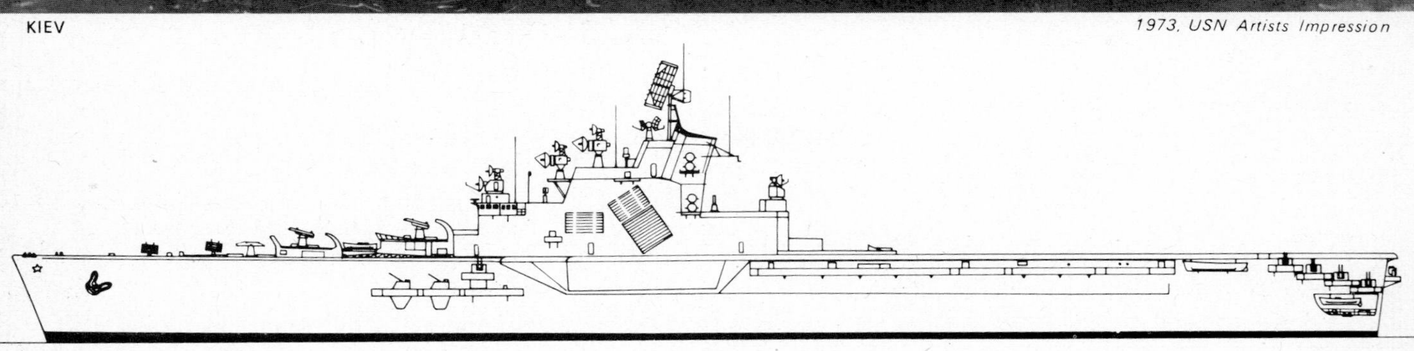

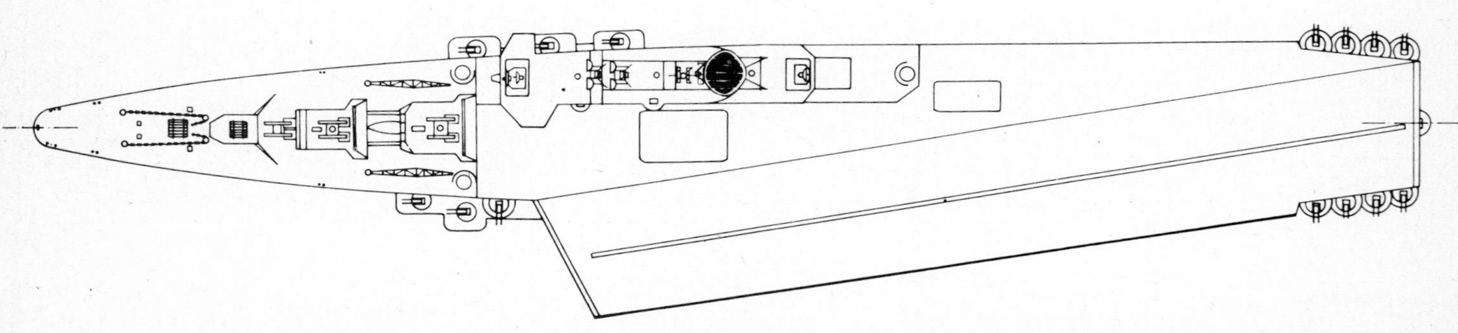

HELICOPTER CRUISERS

2 "MOSKVA" CLASS

LENINGRAD **MOSKVA**

Displacement, tons	15 000 standard; 18 000 full load
Length, feet (*metres*)	624·8 (*190·5*); 644·8 oa (*196·6*)
Flight deck, feet (*m*)	295·3 (*90·0*) aft of superstructure
Width, feet (*metres*)	115·0 (*35·0*)
Beam, feet (*metres*)	75·9 (*23*)
Draught, feet (*metres*)	24·9 (*7·6*)
Aircraft	18 Hormone A ASW helicopters
Missile launchers	2 surface-to-air "SA-N-3" systems of twin launchers (180 reloads) and 1 twin launcher for anti-submarine missiles
Guns, dual purpose	4—57 mm (2 twin mountings)
A/S weapons	2—12 tube MBUs on forecastle
Torpedo tubes	2 quintuple 21 inch
Main engines	Geared turbines; 2 shafts; 100 000 shp
Boilers	4 watertube
Speed, knots	30 max
Complement	800

GENERAL
Both built at Nikolayev, *Moskva* probably being laid down in 1962-3 as she carried out sea-trials in mid-1967. This class represented a radical change of thought in the Soviet fleet. The design must have been completed while the *"November"* class submarines were building and with her heavy A/S armament and efficient sensors (helicopters and VDS) suggests an awareness of the problem of dealing with nuclear submarines. Alongside what is apparently a primary A/S role these ships have a capability for A/A warning and self-defence as well as a command function. With a full fit of radar and ECM equipment they clearly represent good value for money. Both ships handle well in heavy weather and are capable of helicopter-operations under adverse conditions. Why only two were built is discussed earlier in the notes on the *"Kiev"* class aircraft carriers.

MODIFICATION. In early 1973 *Moskva* was seen with a landing pad on the after end of the flight deck, probably for flight tests of VTOL aircraft.

RADAR. Search: Top Sail 3-D and Head Net C 3-D. Fire control: Head Light (2). Muff Cob. Miscellaneous: Electronic warfare equipment.

SONAR. VDS and, probably, hull mounted set. In addition all helicopters have dunking-sonar.

SOVIET TYPE NAME. Protivo Lodochny Kreyser meaning Anti-Submarine Cruiser.

MOSKVA *1972*

MOSKVA *1968, US Navy*

MOSKVA *1968, USNFE*

Helicopter Cruisers—*continued*

MOSKVA with landing pad aft *1973*

MOSKVA *MOD. 1970,*

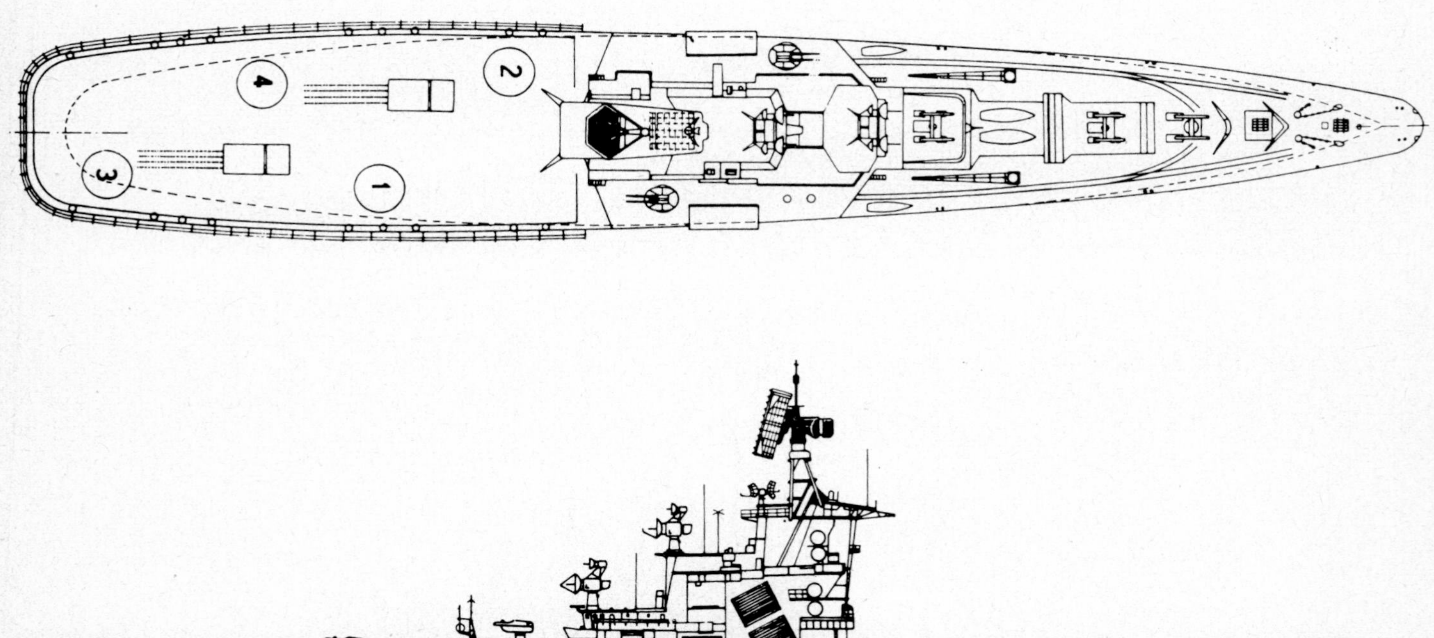

SUBMARINES

Ballistic Missile classes

1+1 "DELTA II" CLASS

(BALLISTIC MISSILE SUBMARINES SSBN's)

This submarine, announced in November 1973, is believed to carry more than the 12 launchers in the Delta class (possibly 16). If this is so this will certainly be the largest submarine ever built.

5+14 "DELTA" CLASS

(BALLISTIC MISSILE SUBMARINES SSBN's)

Displacement, tons	8 000 surfaced; 9 000 dived
Length, feet (*metres*)	426·5 (*130·0*)
Beam, feet (*metres*)	34·8 (*10·6*)
Draught, feet (*metres*)	32·8 (*10·0*)
Missile launchers	12 SSN-8 tubes
Torpedo tubes	8—21 in
Main machinery	Nuclear reactors; Steam turbines; 2 screws; 24 000 shp
Speed, knots	25
Complement	About 120

This reconstruction of the "Yankee" class SSBN's was announced at the end of 1972. The missile armament is twelve SSN-8's with a range of 4 200 nautical miles. at present believed to carry single heads, rather than MRV's. As the SSN-6 has already been tested with MRV warheads, however, it is not unlikely that these missiles will, in due course be similarly armed. Otherwise the details of this class are similar to the "Yankee" class. The longer-range SSN-8 missiles can be assumed to be of greater length than the SSN-6's and, as this length could not be accommodated below the keel, they must stand several feet proud of the after-casing of the "Yankee" class. At the same time their presumed greater diameter and the need to compensate for the additional top-weight would seem to be the reasons for the reduction to twelve missiles in this class.

So far as the "Delta" class building programme is concerned this must be viewed in the light of the SALT agreement signed on May 26 1972 by Mr. Brezhnev and President Nixon. This agreement, once various substitution sums for pre-1964 ICBMs and older submarine-launched missiles have been done, would allow the USSR to maintain 62 SSBNs and a total of 950 missiles in their fleet. Allowing for a building rate of 6-7 SSBNs a year and with 18 "Delta's" carrying a total of 216 missiles it is possible that this might be the total number eventually completed, the remainder of the missiles, allowing for 33 "Yankee's" in commission, being made up with the armament of 12 "Delta II's" if they do, in fact, carry 16 missiles. This assumes that all "Hotel's" and "Golf's" will be phased out by the end of the programme which could be late 1977.

"Delta" Class

"Delta" Class *1973*

Submarines— *continued*
Ballistic Missile classes

33 "YANKEE" CLASS

(BALLISTIC MISSILE SUBMARINES SSBN's)

Displacement, tons	8 000 surface; 9 000 submerged
Length, feet (*metres*)	426·5 (*130·0*)
Beam, feet (*metres*)	34·8 (*10·6*)
Draught, feet (*metres*)	32·8 (*10·0*)
Missile launchers	16 SS-N-6 tubes
Torpedo tubes	8—21 in
Main machinery	Nuclear reactors; steam turbines; 24 000 shp
Speed, knots	25
Complement	About 120

The first units of this class were reported in 1968. The vertical launching tubes are arranged in two rows of eight, and the missiles have a range of 1 500 nautical miles.

The first units of this class were reported in 1968. The vertical launching tubes are arranged in two rows of eight, and the missiles have a range of 1 300 nautical miles. These missiles have been tested with MRV warheads and these, presumably, will soon be operational. At about the time that the USS *George Washington* was laid down (1 Nov 1957) as the world's first SSBN it is likely that the Soviet Navy embarked on its own major SSBN programme. With experience gained from the diesel-propelled "Golf" class and the nuclear-propelled "Hotel" class, both originally carrying three SS-N4 (350 mile) missiles in the fin, the "Yankee" design was compieted mounting 16 SSN-6 (1350 miles) missiles in the hull in two banks of 8.The first of the class was delivered late-1967 and the programme then accelerated from 4 boats in 1968 to 8 in 1971. The original deployment of this class was to the Eastern seaboard of the US giving a coverage at least as far as the Mississippi. Increase in numbers allowed a Pacific patrol to be established off California extending coverage at least as far as the Rockies. To provide greater coverage and more flexible operations a longer range missile system was needed and this is now at sea in the "Delta" class.

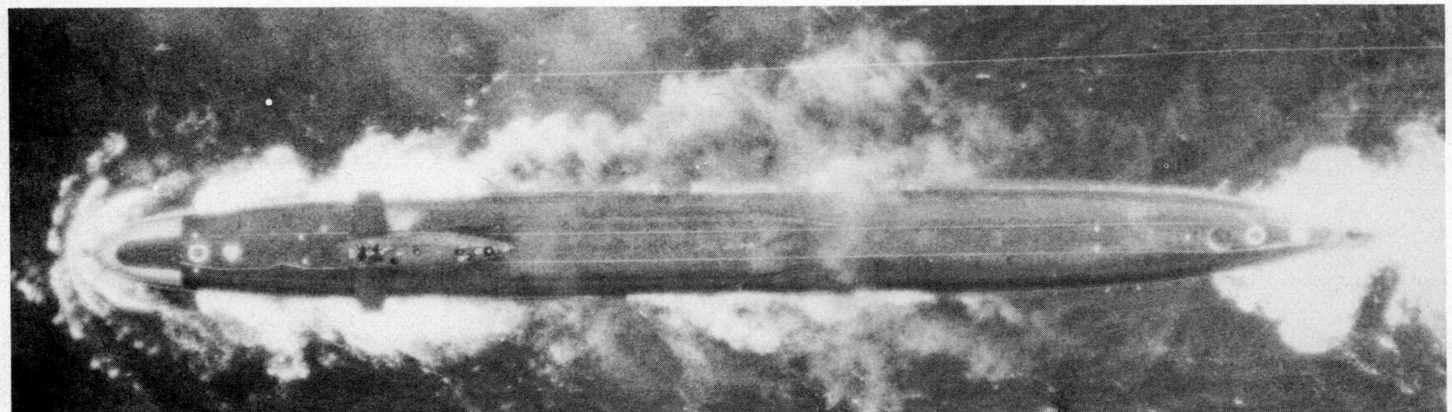

"Yankee" Class *1972*

"Yankee" Class *1970*

"Yankee" Class *1970 S. Breyer*

Guild State Convention at Pepperdine College. His work has been exhibited in many galleries.

To Rittershausen, the Gateway Park entrance to Whittier is a challenge in design that he sees housing

ONE CERAMIC creation of Christoph Rittershausen serves both an aesthetic purpose and a functional one — as a support pillar. (Daily News photos by Howard Lipin)

Soviet Super-Sub Cruising Seas

BRUSSELS, Belgium (UPI) — A new gigantic Soviet submarine of more than 30,000 tons — dwarfing any known U.S. sub and as large as a World War II aircraft carrier — is cruising the high seas, NATO Secretary General Joseph Luns said.

At a news conference Friday following a two-day NATO meeting on nuclear planning, Luns said the "disturbing bit of news about the the new Soviet submarines of more than 30,000 tons ... is being confirmed."

The biggest U.S. submarine is the Ohio, launched in April 1979 and expected to begin sea trials early in the new year. The Ohio, first of the Trident missile firing submarines, is 560 feet long and displaces 18,700 tons.

The biggest operational U.S. submarines are the 425-foot, 8,250-ton Poseidon class missile submarine and the 6,900-ton Los Angeles class attack submarine, all nuclear powered.

"There is now at sea a first (Soviet) submarine of more than 30,000 tons, which is equivalent to the tonnage of American aircraft carriers during the last war (World War II), but the details of the armament and speed are not known ... That they would dive to 4,000 feet and cruise at a speed of 45 knots, although possible, is not being confirmed," Luns said.

U.S. Defense Secretary Harold Brown refused to speculate on the mission of these submarines. "We should be careful about jumping at conclusions about just what these ships do," he said.

Brown said the United States will preserve nuclear parity with the Soviet Union in the coming years. Soviet

expansion of nuclear forces continues, he said, but the Soviets still stand behind the United States in total numbers of warheads, although they are reducing that gap.

Submarines—*continued*

Ballistic Missile classes

1 "HOTEL III" CLASS
8 "HOTEL II" CLASS

(BALLISTIC MISSILE SUBMARINES SSBNs)

Displacement, tons	3 700 surface; 4 100 submerged
Length, feet (*metres*)	377·2 (*115·2*)
Beam, feet (*metres*)	28·2 (*8·6*)
Draught, feet (*metres*)	25 (*7·6*)
Missile launchers	3 SS-N-5 tubes
Torpedo tubes	6—21 in (bow); 4—16 in (aft) (anti-submarine)
Main machinery	Nuclear reactor, steam turbine; 22 500 shp
Speed, knots	20 (dived)
Complement	90

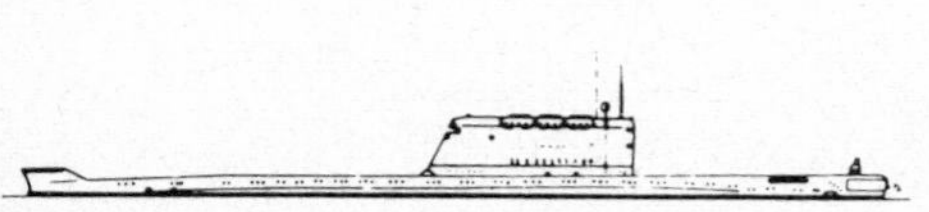

"Hotel" Class

"Hotel II" Class damaged in North Atlantic *Mar 1973*

Long range submarines with three vertical ballistic missile tubes in the large fin. All this class were completed between 1958 and 1962. Originally fitted with SS-N-4 system with "Sark" missiles (350 miles). Between 1963 and 1967 this system was replaced by the SS-N-5 system with "Serb" missiles capable of 650 mile range. Since then these boats have been deployed off both coasts of the USA and Canada. As the limitations of SALT are felt the "Hotel II's" will probably be phased-out to allow the maximum number of "Delta" class to be built.

The "Hotel III" was a single unit converted for the test firings of the SSN-8. The earlier boats of this class, which was of a similar hull and reactor design to the "Echo" class, will, by the late 1970's, be reaching their twentieth year in service.

"Hotel II" Class *1972*

Submarines—*continued*

BALLISTIC MISSILE CLASSES

22 "GOLF I and II" CLASS

(BALLISTIC MISSILE SUBMARINES SSB)

Displacement, tons	2 350 surface; 2 800 submerged
Length, feet (*metres*)	320·0 (*97·5*)
Beam, feet (*metres*)	25·1 (*7·6*)
Draught, feet (*metres*)	22·0 (*6·7*)
Missile launchers	3 SS-N-4 (G 1); 3 SS-N-5 (G II)
Torpedo tubes	10—21 in (6 bow 4 stern)
Main machinery	3 diesels; 3 shafts; 6 000 hp; Electric motors; 6 000 hp
Speed, knots	17·6 surface; 17 submerged
Range, miles	22 700 surface cruising
Complement	86 (12 officers, 74 men)

"Golf" *Class*

"Golf I" Class *1962, US Navy*

This type has a very large fin fitted with three vertically mounted tubes and hatches for launching ballistic missiles. Built at Komsomolsk and Severodvinsk. Building started in 1958 and finished in 1961-62. After the missile conversion of the "Hotel" class was completed in 1967 about half this class was converted to carry the SS-N-5 system with 650 mile Serb missiles in place of the shorter range (350 mile) Sarks. One of this class has been built by China, although apparently lacking missiles.

"Golf I" Class missile Type (side opening hatches open) *1962, US Navy*

1 "ZULU V" CLASS

(Ex-BALLISTIC MISSILE SUBMARINE SSB)

Displacement, tons	2 100 surface; 2 600 submerged
Length, feet (*metres*)	295·3 (*90·0*)
Beam, feet (*metres*)	24·1 (*7·3*)
Draught, feet (*metres*)	19·0 (*5·8*)
Missile launchers	2 tubes for SS-N-4 missiles
Torpedo tubes	10—21 in
Main machinery	3 diesels; 3 shafts; 10 000 bhp; 3 electric motors; 3 500 hp
Range, miles	13 000 surfaced cruising
Speed, knots	18 surface; 15 submerged
Complement	85

These were basically of "Z" class design but converted in 1955-57 to ballistic missile submarines with larger fins and two vertical tubes for launching Sark (350 mile) missiles on the surface. These were the first Soviet ballistic missile submarines. Of the seven converted only one remains and is probably used only for scientific and fishery research being no longer operational.

"Zulu V" Class

"Zulu V" *Class* *1972*

Submarines—*continued*

Cruise Missile classes

1+? "PAPA" CLASS

(CRUISE MISSILE SUBMARINES SSGN)

A new class of nuclear submarine, named "Papa", with a cruise-missile armament is building and some units may already be in service. Details are not yet available but it is unlikely that she would be any less efficient than the "Charlie" class. This suggests an armament of at least eight missiles although whether these are of the SS-N-7 type has yet to be discovered.

11 "CHARLIE" CLASS

(CRUISE MISSILE SUBMARINE SSGN)

Displacement, tons	4 300 surface; 5 100 submerged
Length, feet (*metres*)	295 (*90·0*)
Beam, feet (*metres*)	32·8 (*10·0*)
Draught, feet (*metres*)	24·6 (*7·5*)
Missile launchers	8 tubes for SS-N-7 missile system
Torpedo tubes	8—21 in
Main machinery	Nuclear reactor; steam turbine; 24 000 shp
Speed, knots	30 approx, submerged, 20 surface
Complement	100

A class of cruise-missile submarine building at Gorky at a rate of about 3 per year. The first of class was delivered in 1968, representing a very significant advance in the cruise-missile submarine field. With a speed of at least 30 knots and mounting eight missile tubes for the SSN-7 system (30 miles range) which has a dived launch capability, this is a great advance on the "Echo" class. Having an improved hull and reactor design these boats must be assumed to have an organic control for their missile system and therefore pose a notable threat to any surface force. Their deployment to the Mediterranean, the area of the US 6th Fleet, suggests their probable employment. The only strange thing about them is their comparatively low building rate.

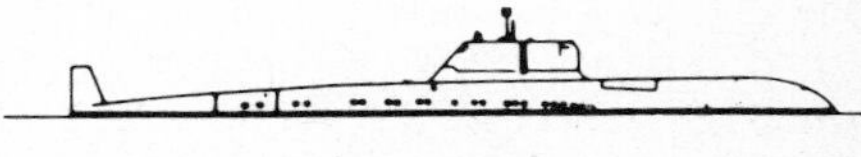

"Charlie Class"

"Charlie" Class 1973

"Charlie" Class 1972

"Charlie" Class 1972

Submarines—*continued*
Cruise Missile classes

1 "ECHO I" CLASS

(CRUISE MISSILE SUBMARINE SSGN)

Displacement, tons	4 600 surface; 5 000 submerged
Length, feet (*metres*)	380·9 (*116·0*)
Beam, feet (*metres*)	28·4 (*8·6*)
Draught, feet (*metres*)	25·9 (*7·9*)
Missile launchers	6 SS-N-3 launching tubes
Torpedo tubes	6—21 in (bow); 4—16 in (aft) A/S
Main machinery	Nuclear reactor; steam turbine; 22 500 shp
Speed, knots	20
Complement	92 (12 officers; 80 men)

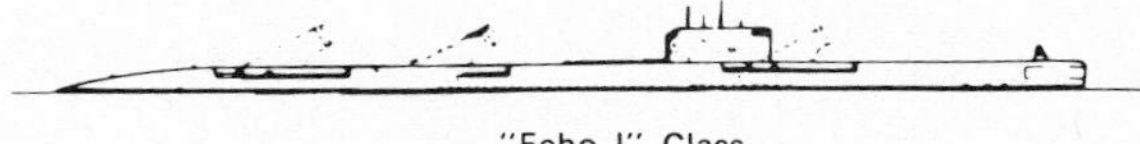
"Echo I" Class

This class was completed in 1960-62. The six SSN-3 launchers for Shaddock missiles are hinged within either side of the casing requiring the submarine to surface for launch.
The hull of this class is very similar to the "Hotel"/"November" type and it is probably powered by similar nuclear plant. This class was started at about the same time as the "Juliet" diesel-driven SSG's, and may have been intended as a nuclear prototype using the same SS-N-3 system. Only five "Echo I's" were built, probably an adequate test for a new weapon system, being followed immediately by the "Echo II's". The Soviet fleet now had a continuing production of SSGN's which with the 250 mile range SS-N-3 system presented a powerful threat to any task force.

27 "ECHO II" CLASS

(CRUISE MISSILE SUBMARINES SSGN)

Displacement, tons	5 000 surface; 5 600 submerged
Length, feet (*metres*)	387·4 (*118*)
Beam, feet (*metres*)	28·4 (*8·6*)
Draught, feet (*metres*)	25·9 (*7·9*)
Missiles, launchers	8 SS-N-3 launching tubes
Torpedo tubes	6—21 in (bow); 4—16 in (aft) A/S
Main machinery	Nuclear reactor; steam turbine; 22 500 shp
Speed, knots	20
Complement	100

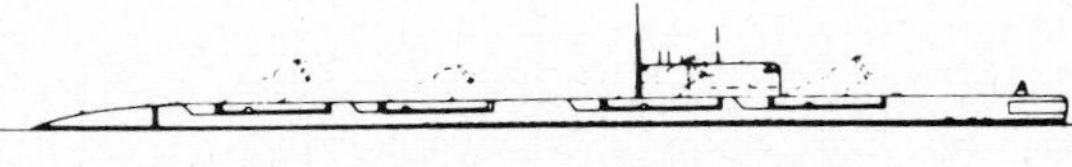
"Echo" II *Class*

The "Echo II" was the natural development of the "Echo I". With a slightly lengthened hull, a fourth pair of launchers was installed and between 1963 and 1967 twenty-seven of this class were built. They are now deployed evenly between the Pacific and Northern fleets and still provide a useful group of boats for operations such as those of the mixed task force which was in the South China Sea in June 1972. As well as surface ships this included 3 "Echo II's" and an "Echo I".

"Echo II" Class *1972*

16 "JULIET" CLASS

(CRUISE MISSILE SUBMARINES SSG)

Displacement, tons	2 200 surface; 2 500 submerged
Length, feet (*metres*)	280·5 (*85·5*)
Beam, feet (*metres*)	31·4 (*9·5*)
Draught, feet (*metres*)	20·0 (*6·1*)
Missile launchers	4 SS-N-3 tubes; 2 before and 2 abaft the fin
Torpedo tubes	6—21 in (bow); 2 or 4—16 in (aft) A/S
Main machinery	Diesels; 6 000 bhp; Electric motors; 6 000 hp
Speed, knots	16 surface; 16 submerged
Range, miles	15 000 surfaced cruising

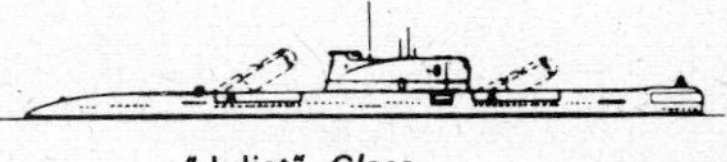
"Juliet" *Class*

Completed between 1962 and 1967. An unmistakable class with a high casing to house the 4 SS-N-3 launchers, one pair either end of the fin which appears to be comparatively low. This class was the logical continuation of the "Whisky" class conversions but was overtaken by the "Echo" class SSGN's. A number of this class has in the past been deployed to the Mediterranean.

"Juliet" Class *1973*

"Juliet" Class *1972, US Navy*

Submarines—*continued*

Cruise Missile classes

7 "WHISKY LONG-BIN" CLASS

(CRUISE MISSILE SUBMARINES SSG)

Displacement, tons 1 300 surface; 1 800 submerged
Length, feet (*metres*) 272·3 (*83·0*)
Beam, feet (*metres*) 19·8 (*6·0*)
Draught, feet (*metres*) 15·7 (*4·8*)
Missile launchers 4 SS-N-3 tubes
Torpedo tubes 6—21 in (4 bow, 2 stern)
Main machinery Diesels; 4 000 bhp; Electric motors; 2 500 hp
Speed, knots 17 surface; 15 submerged
Range, miles 13 000 surfaced, cruising

A more efficient modification of the "Whisky" class than the Twin-Cylinder with four SSN-3 launchers built into a remodelled fin on a hull lengthened by 26 feet. Converted between 1960-63—no organic guidance and therefore reliance must be made on aircraft or surface-ship cooperation. Must still be a very noisy boat when dived.

"Whisky" *Class* Long Bin

"Whisky Long-bin" Class *1970, Niels Gartig*

"Whisky Long-Bin" Class *1968, S. Breyer*

5 "WHISKY TWIN CYLINDER" CLASS

(CRUISE MISSILE SUBMARINES SSG)

Displacement, tons 1 100 surface; 1 600 submerged
Length, feet (*metres*) 247 (*75·3*)
Beam, feet (*metres*) 19 (*5·8*)
Draught, feet (*metres*) 15·1 (*4·6*)
Missile launchers 2 cylinders for SS-N-3
Torpedo tubes 6—21 in (4 bow, 2 stern)
Main machinery Diesels; 4 000 bhp; Electric motors; 2 500 hp
Speed, knots 17 surface; 15 submerged
Range, miles 13 000, surfaced, cruising

A 1958-60 modification of the conventional "Whisky" class designed to test out the SSN-3 system at sea. Probably never truly operational being a thoroughly messy conversion which must make a noise like a train if proceeding at any speed above dead slow when dived.

"Whisky" *Class* Twin Cylinder

The modification consisted of fitting a pair of launchers abaft the fin.

"Whisky" Twin Cylinder Class *1970, Col Borg*

Submarines—*continued*

Fleet Submarine classes

1 "ALPHA" CLASS

(FLEET SUBMARINE SSN)

One unit only of this class was completed in 1970. Her form of propulsion is by no means certain nor is her purpose. It is, however, believed that this is a "one-off" nuclear boat.

14 "VICTOR" CLASS

(FLEET SUBMARINES SSN)

Displacement, tons	3 600 surface; 4 200 submerged
Length, feet (*metres*)	285·4 (*87·0*)
Beam, feet (*metres*)	32·8 (*10·0*)
Draught, feet (*metres*)	26·2 (*8·0*)
Torpedo tubes	8—21 in
Main engines	Nuclear reactors; steam turbines; 24 000 shp
Speed, knots	26 surface; 30 plus submerged

This appears to be a class with great possibilities. Designed purely as a torpedo carrying submarine its much increased speed makes it a menace to all but the fastest ships. The first of class entered service in 1967-8 with a subsequent building rate of about two per year.

The majority is deployed with the Northern Fleet, although two have joined the Pacific Fleet.

1 NEW CONSTRUCTION

(FLEET SUBMARINE SSN)

One unit of a new class of nuclear-propelled submarines has been reported. This tends to suggest that the ALPHA may have been a test-vehicle-perhaps for a more silent class than before.

"Victor" Class *1972*

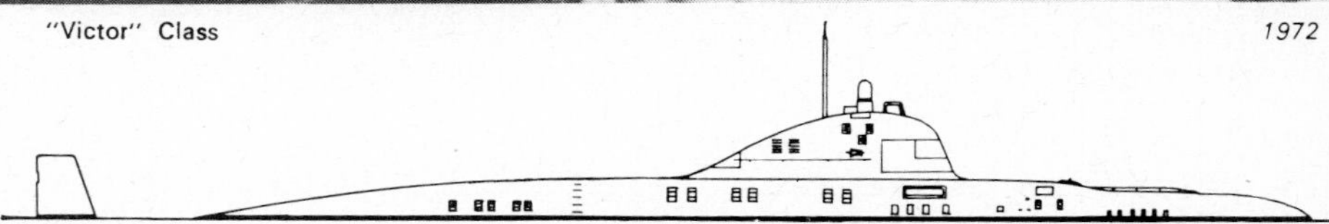

"Victor" Class

"Victor" Class *S. Breyer*

"Victor" Class

Submarines—*continued*

Fleet Submarine classes

13 "NOVEMBER" CLASS

(FLEET SUBMARINES SSN's)

Displacement, tons	3 500 surface; 4 000 submerged
Length, feet (*metres*)	360·9 (*110·0*)
Beam, feet (*metres*)	32·1 (*9·8*)
Draught, feet (*metres*)	24·3 (*7·4*)
Torpedo tubes	6—21 in (bow);
Main engines	Nuclear reactor, steam turbines; 22 500 shp
Speed, knots	20 surface; 25 submerged
Complement	88

The first class of Soviet Fleet Submarines which entered service between 1958 and 1963. The hull form with the great number of free-flood holes in the casing suggests a noisy boat and it is surprising that greater efforts have not been made to supersede this class with the "Victors". In 1970 one of this class sank south-west of the United Kingdom.

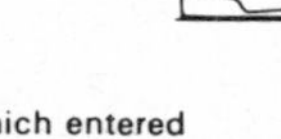

"November" Class

"November" *Class*

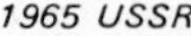

1965 USSR

"November" Class foundering in Atlantic *April 1970*

"November" Class foundering in Atlantic *April 1970*

Patrol Submarine classes

1 "TANGO" CLASS NEW CONSTRUCTION

(PATROL SUBMARINE SS)

This new class was first seen at the Sevastopol review in July 1973. She appears to be comparatively small, in the 1 000/1 500 tons bracket, with a ships company of no more than 50. Notable features are the rise in the fore-casing and a new shape for the snort exhaust. This class, following five years after the **"Bravo"**, shows a continuing commitment to diesel-propelled boats which is of interest in view of the comparatively slow Fleet Submarine building programme.

"Tango" Class

4 "BRAVO" CLASS

(PATROL SUBMARINES SS)

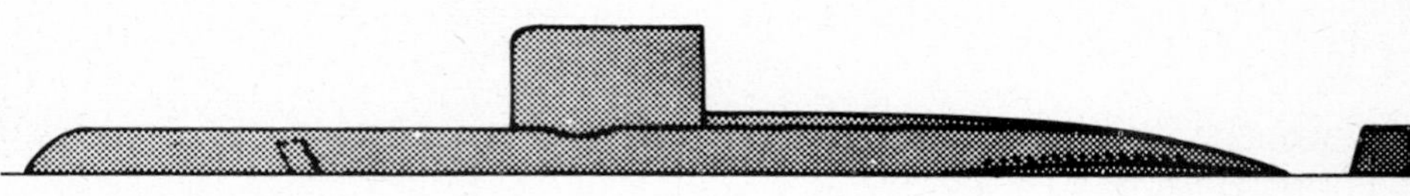

"BRAVO" Class

Displacement, tons	2 500 surface; 2 800 submerged
Length, feet (*metres*)	229·6 (*70*)
Beam, feet (*metres*)	24·8 (*7·5*)
Draught, feet (*metres*)	14·8 (*4·5*)
Torpedo tubes	6—21 in
Main machinery	Diesel-Electric
Speed, knots	16 dived

A class of conventional submarine whose purpose remains unclear. Only a few have been built since 1968 and the drawing is merely an indication of the general form which this class may be expected to have. The beam-to-length ratio is larger than normal in a diesel submarine which would account in part for the large displacement for a comparatively short hull.

The spread of these boats evenly amongst the four fleets suggests an experimental background.

56 "FOXTROT" CLASS

(PATROL SUBMARINES SS)

Displacement, tons	2 000 surface; 2 300 submerged
Length, feet (*metres*)	296·8 (*90·5*)
Beam, feet (*metres*)	24·1 (*7·3*)
Draught, feet (*metres*)	19·0 (*5·8*)
Torpedo tubes	10—21 in (6 bow, 4 stern) (20 torpedoes carried)
Main machinery	Diesels; 3 shafts; 6 000 bhp; 3 electric motors; 6 000 hp
Speed, knots	20 surface; 15 submerged
Complement	70
Range	20 000 miles surface cruising

Built between 1958 and 1967 at Sudomekh and Leningrad. A follow-on of the "Zulu" class with similar propulsion to the "Golf" class. A most successful class which has been deployed world-wide, forming the bulk of the Soviet submarine force in the Mediterranean. Four transferred to India in 1968-69 with a further four new construction following.

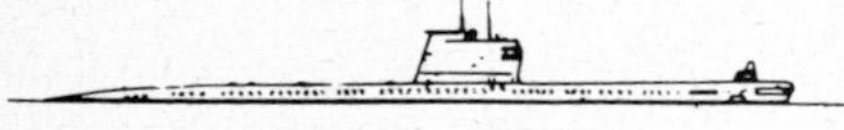

"Foxtrot" *Class*

"Foxtrot" Class — *1972*

"Foxtrot" Class — *1971 USN*

"Foxtrot" *Class* — *1972*

Submarines—*continued*

19+3 "ZULU IV" CLASS

(PATROL SUBMARINES)

Displacement, tons	1 900 surface; 2 200 submerged
Length, feet (*metres*)	259·3 (*90·0*)
Beam, feet (*metres*)	23·9 (*7·3*)
Draught, feet (*metres*)	19·0 (*5·8*)
Torpedo tubes	10—21 in (6 bow, 4 stern); 24 torpedoes carried (or 40 mines)
Main machinery	Diesel-electric; 3 shafts 3 diesels; 10 000 bhp 3 electric motors; 3 500 hp
Speed, knots	18 surface; 15 submerged
Range, miles	20 000 surfaced, cruising
Complement	70

The first large post-war patrol submarines built by USSR. Completed from late 1951 to 1955. General appearance is streamlined with a complete row of free-flood holes along the casing. Eighteen were built by Sudomekh Shipyard, Leningrad, in 1952-55 and others at Severodvinsk. The general external similarity to the later German U-boats of WW II suggests that this was not an entirely indigenous design. All now appear to be of the "Zulu IV" type. This class, although the majority are probably still operational, is obsolescent and will soon be disposed of. Three have been converted for oceanographic research (*Lyra, Orion, Vega*).
The "Zulu V" conversions of this class provided the first Soviet ballistic missile submarines with SS-N-4 systems.

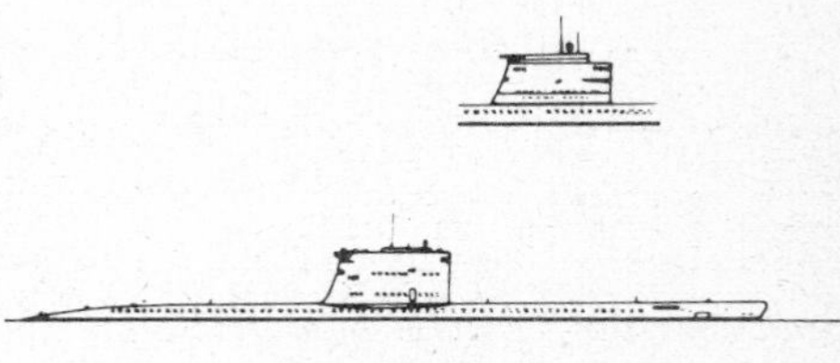
"Zulu IV" Class

"Zulu IV" *Class* *1969, MOD*

12 "ROMEO" CLASS

(PATROL SUBMARINES SS)

"Romeo" *Class*

Displacement, tons	1 100 surface; 1 600 submerged
Length, feet (*metres*)	246·0 (*75·0*)
Beam, feet (*metres*)	24·0 (*7·3*)
Draught, feet (*metres*)	14·5 (*4·4*)
Torpedo tubes	6—21 in bow
Main machinery	Diesels; 4 000 bhp; Electric motors; 4 000 hp; 2 shafts
Speed, knots	17 surfaced; 14 submerged
Complement	65

These are an improved "W" class design with modernised conning tower, and sonar installation. All built in 1958 to 1961. This was presumably an interim class while the **"November"** class of Fleet Submarines was brought into service—an insurance against failure.
Foreign transfers. Six of this class transferred to Egypt in 1966 and the Chinese are building a considerable force of the same class of submarines.

"Romeo" Class *1972*

Submarines—*continued*

110 "WHISKY" CLASS

(PATROL SUBMARINES SS)

Displacement, tons 1 030 surface; 1 180 submerged
Length, feet (*metres*) 240·0 (*73·2*)
Beam, feet (*metres*) 22·0 (*6·7*)
Draught, feet (*metres*) 15·0 (*4·6*)
Torpedo tubes 6—21 in (4 bow, 2 stern); 18 torpedoes carried (or 40 mines)
Main machinery Diesel-electric; 2 shafts
Diesels; 4 000 bhp
Electric motors; 2 500 hp
Speed, knots 17 surface; 15 submerged
Range, miles 13 000 at 8 knots (surfaced)
Complement 60

"Whisky V" Class

This was the first post-war Soviet design for a medium-range submarine. Like its larger contemporary the "Zulu", this class shows considerable German influence. About 240 of the "Whisky's" were built between 1951 and 1957 at yards throughout the USSR. Built in six types—I and IV had guns forward of the conning tower, II had guns both ends, whilst III and V have no guns. V is the most common variant whilst VA has a diver's exit hatch forward of the conning tower. Now being paid-off at possibly 15-20 per year. Up to 50% are probably now in reserve.

FOREIGN TRANSFERS. Has been the most popular export model; currently in service in Albania (4), Bulgaria (2), China (21), Egypt (6), Indonesia (10), North Korea (4) and Poland (4).

CONVERSIONS. Two of this class, named *Severyanka* and *Slavyanka*, were converted for oceanographic and fishery research.

"Whisky V" Class *1970, Niels Gartig*

3 "WHISKY CANVAS-BAG" CLASS

(RADAR PICKET SUBMARINES SSR)

Displacement, tons 1 100 surface; 1 200 submerged
Length, feet (*metres*) 240·0 (*73·2*)
Beam, feet (*metres*) 22·0 (*6·7*)
Draught, feet (*metres*) 15·0 (*4·6*)
Torpedo tubes 6—21 in (4 bow, 2 stern)
Main machinery Diesels; 4 000 bhp
Electric motors; 2 500 hp
Speed, knots 17 surface; 15 submerged
Range, miles 13 000 at 8 knots surfaced
Complement 65

Basically of same design as the "Whisky" class but with long-range Boat-Sail radar aerial mounted on the fin. The coy way in which this is normally covered prompted the title "Canvas Bag". Converted in 1959 to 1963.

"Whisky Canvas Bag" Class *1972, S. Breyer*

22 "QUEBEC" CLASS

(PATROL SUBMARINES SS)

Displacement, tons 650 surface; 740 submerged
Length, feet (*metres*) 185·0 (*56·4*)
Beam, feet (*metres*) 18·0 (*5·5*)
Draught, feet (*metres*) 13·2 (*4·0*)
Torpedo tubes 4—21 in bow
Main machinery 1 diesel; 3 shafts; 3 000 bhp
3 electric motors; 2 500 hp
Speed, knots 18 surface; 16 submerged
Oil fuel, tons 50
Range, miles 7 000 surface cruising
Complement 42

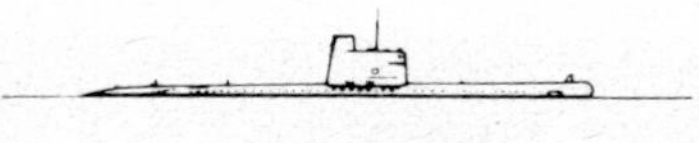
"Quebec" *Class*

Short range, coastal submarines. Built from 1954 to 1957. Thirteen were constructed in 1955 by Sudomekh Shipyard, Leningrad. The earlier boats of this class were fiitted wth what was possibly a closed-cycle propulsion, probably on the third shaft. This may however, have been a Walther HTP turbine but, whatever it was, it is believed to have been unsuccessful and subsequently removed. The majority of this class are now in reserve.

"Quebec" Class *1965, S. Breyer*

CRUISERS

1 "SVERDLOV" CLASS (CG)

2 "SVERDLOV" CLASS (CC)

9 "SVERDLOV" CLASS (CA)

ADMIRAL LAZAREV
ADMIRAL SENYAVIN
ADMIRAL USHAKOV
ALEKSANDR NEVSKI
ALEKSANDR SUVOROV
DMITRI POZHARSKI
DZERZHINSKI
MIKHAIL KUTUSOV
MURMANSK
OKTYABRSKAYA REVOLUTSIYA
SVERDLOV
ZHDANOV

Displacement, tons	15 450 standard; 19 200 full load
Length, feet (*metres*)	656·2 (*200·0*)pp; 689·0 (*210·0*)oa
Beam, feet (*metres*)	72·2 (*22·0*)
Draught, feet (*metres*)	24·5 (*7·5*) max
Aircraft	Helicopter pad in *Zhdanov*. Pad and hangar in *Senyavin*
Armour	Belts 3·9—4·9 in (*100—125 mm*); fwd and aft 1·6—2 in (*40—50 mm*); turrets 4·9 in (*125 mm*); C.T. 5·9 in (*150 mm*); decks 1—2 in (*25—50 mm*) and 2—3 in (*50—75 mm*)
Missile launchers	Twin "SA-N-2" aft in *Dzerzhinski* 2 SAN-4 in *Zhdanov* and *Senyavin* (twin) (see conversions)
Guns	12—6 in (*152 mm*), (4 triple) (9—6 in in *Dzerzhinski* and *Zhdanov*—6—6 in in *Senyavin*) 12—3·9 in (*100 mm*), (6 twin) 16—37 mm (twin), 8—30 mm (twin)
Torpedo tubes	10—21 in (*533 mm*) 2 quintuple (see *Torpedoes*)
Mines	150 capacity—(except *Zhdanov* and *Senyavin*)
Boilers	6 watertube
Main engines	Geared turbines; 2 shafts; 130 000 shp
Speed, knots	34
Range, miles	8 700 at 18 knots
Oil fuel, tons	3 800
Complement	1 000 average

GENERAL

Of the 24 cruisers of this class originally projected, 20 keels were laid and 17 hulls were launched from 1951 onwards, but only 14 ships were completed by 1956. There were two slightly different types. *Sverdlov* and sisters had the 37 mm AA guns near the fore-funnel one deck higher than in later cruisers. All ships except *Zhdanov* and *Senyavin* are fitted for minelaying. Mine stowage is on the second deck. *Zhdanov* and *Senyavin* used as command ships with much increased communications capability.

CONVERSIONS. *Dzerzhinski* has been fitted with an SA-N-2 launcher aft replacing X-Turret. In 1972 *Admiral Senyavin* returned to service with both X and Y turrets removed and replaced by a helicopter pad and a hangar surmounted by four 30 mm mountings and an SA-N-4 mounting. At about the same time *Zhdanov* appeared on the scene with a different outfit. She has had only X-turret removed and replaced by a high deckhouse mounting an SA-N-4 launcher.

RADAR. Search: Head Net A, Strut Curve and some ships fitted with Big Net. (*Dzerzhinski* only.—Fire control: Peel Group and Drum Tilt. High Lune and Fan Song E for SA-N-2 system.
CC's only Big Net and Slim Net.

SOVIET TYPE NAME. Kreyser meaning Cruiser.

TORPEDOES. *Oktyabrskaya Revolutsiya* and *Murmansk* no longer have tubes.

NAMES. The ship first named *Molotovsk* was renamed *Oktyabrskaya Revolutsiya* in 1957.

SVERDLOV *1972*

ADMIRAL USHAKOV *1973, Commander Aldo Fraccorali*

DRAWING. Starboard elevation and plan of *Dzerzhinski*.
Scale: 145 feet = 1 inch

DZERZHINSKI. Twin missile launcher in place of "X" turret

SVERDLOV *Class*

Cruisers—*continued*

DZERZHINSKI with twin SA-N-2 launcher in place of "X" turret *1972*

ZHDANOV *1972*

ADMIRAL SENYAVIN *1973*

ADMIRAL SENYAVIN (after conversion showing hangar and SA-N-4) *1972*

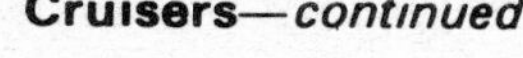

Cruisers—*continued*

2 "CHAPAEV" CLASS (CA)

KOMSOMOLETS (ex-*Chkalov*) **ZHELEZNYAKOV**

Displacement, tons	11 300 standard; 15 000 full load
Length, feet (*metres*)	659·5 (*201·0*) wl; 665 (*202·8*)
Beam, feet (*metres*)	62 (*18·9*)
Draught, feet (*metres*)	24 (*7·3*)
Guns, surface	12—6 in (*152 mm*) 57 cal, (4 triple)
Guns, dual purpose	8—3·9 in (*100 mm*) 70 cal, (4 twin)
Guns, AA	24—37 mm (12 twin)
Mines	200 capacity; 425 ft rails
Boilers	6 watertube
Main engines	Geared turbines, with diesels for cruising speeds; 4 shafts 130 000 shp
Speed, knots	32
Range, miles	5 400 at 15 knots
Oil fuel, tons	2 500
Complement	900

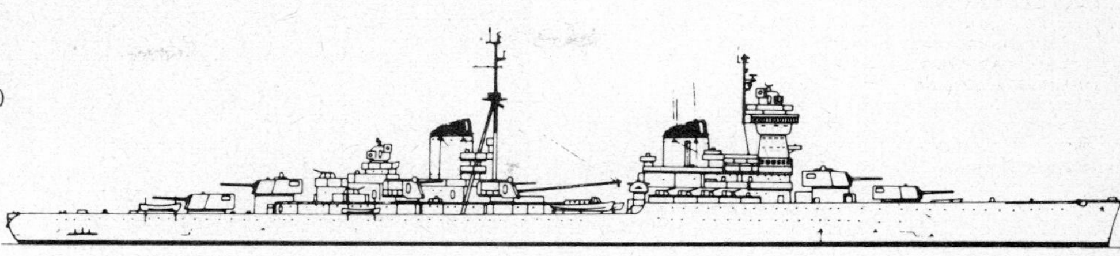

CHAPAEV CLASS

Originally a class of six ships of which one was never completed—show signs of both Italian and German influence. Laid down in 1939-40. Launched during 1941-47. All work on these ships was stopped during the war, but was resumed in 1946-47. Completed in 1948-50 both in Leningrad. Catapults were removed from all ships of this type. Both remaining ships serve as training cruisers.

SOVIET TYPE NAME. Kreyser meaning Cruiser.

RADAR. They have long range surveillance radars and gunfire control tracking radar. *Komsomolets* was fitted with modern radar in 1969-70. Surface—Low Sieve; Early warning—Slim Net and Knife Rest B; Fire control—Top Bow, Sun Visor B, Egg Cup; IFF— High Pole.

GUNNERY. Turret guns fitting allows independent elevation to 45 degrees.

DRAWING. Starboard elevation. Scale: 125 feet = 1 inch (1 : 1 500).

ZHELENYAKOV

1958, Antonov Rogov

2 "KIROV" CLASS (CL)

Name	Builders	Laid down	Launched	Completed
KIROV	Putilov DY	1934	1 Dec 1936	26 Sep 1938
SLAVA (ex-*Molotov*)	Marti Yard, Nikolaye	1935	23 Feb 1939	1944

Displacement, tons	7 780 standard; 9 060 full load
Length, feet (*metres*)	613·5 (*178·0*)pp; 626·7 (*191·0*)oa
Beam, feet (*metres*)	58 (*18*)
Draught, feet (*metres*)	20 (*6·3*)
Armour	Side 3 in (*75 mm*); deck 2 in (*50 mm*); gunhouses 3·9 in (*100 mm*) CT 3 in (*75 mm*)
Guns	9—7·1 in (*180 mm*); 6—3·9 in (*100 mm*) 18—37 *mm* (*Kirov*); 12—37 mm (*Slava*)
Mines	180 capacity; 375 ft rails
Main engines	Geared turbines; with diesels for cruising; 2 shafts; 113 000 shp
Boilers	6 Yarrow
Speed, knots	34
Range, miles	4 000 at 15 knots
Oil fuel, tons	1 280
Complement	734 (training role)

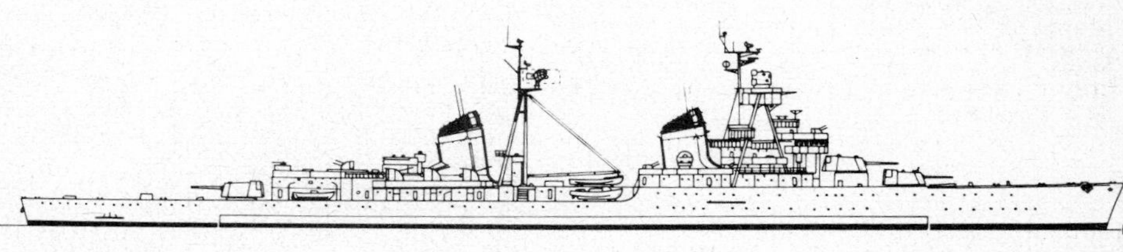

KIROV CLASS

Design and technical direction of construction by Ansaldo. The survivors of a class of six.

APPEARANCE. *Kirov* has very long forecastle, heavy tripod mast stepped abaft forebridge, *Slava* has high director tower on forebridge, light tripod foremast abaft bridge.

RADAR. Search: Hair Net, Seagull, High Sieve. Fire Control: Top Bow, Sun Visor. IFF: High Pole A.

DRAWING. Starboard elevation of *Kirov*. Drawn in 1971. Scale: 125 feet = 1 inch (1 : 1 500).

SOVIET TYPE NAME. Kreyser, meaning Cruiser.

KIROV

1970, Bertil Gard

2 "KARA" CLASS (CLG)

NIKOLAYEV +1 building

Displacement, tons	8 200 standard; 9 500 full load
Length, feet (*metres*)	570 (*173·8*)
Beam, feet (*metres*)	60 (*18·3*)
Draught, feet (*metres*)	20 (*6·2*)
Aircraft	1 Hormone A Helicopter (Hangar aft)
Missile Systems	8—SS-N-10 (Two mounts abreast bridge) 4—SA-N-4 (twins either side of mast) 4—SA-N-3 (Twins for'd and aft)
Guns	4—76 mm (2 Twins abaft bridge) 4—30 mm (abreast funnel) (see *Gunnery* note)
A/S weapons	2—16 barrelled MBU launchers (forward) 2—6 barrelled MBU launchers aft
Torpedo tubes	10—21 in (2 quintuple mountings abaft funnel)
Main engines	Gas-turbine
Speed, knots	Approximately 34

GENERAL
Apart from the specialised "Moskva" class this is the first large cruiser to join the Soviet navy since the "Sverdlov's". Built at Nikolayev, she was first seen in public when she entered the Mediterranean from the Black Sea on 2 March 1973. Clearly capable of prolonged operations overseas

ECM. A full outfit appears to be housed on the bridge and mast.

MISSILES. In addition to the "Kresta II" armament of eight tubes for the SS-N-10 (29 mile) surface-to-surface system and the pair of twin launchers for SA-N-3 system with Goblet missiles, "Kara" mounts the new SA-N-4 system in two silos, either side of the mast. The combination of such a number of systems presents a formidable capability, matched by no other ship.

GUNNERY. The sighting of both main and secondary armament on either beams in the waist follows the precedent of both "Kresta" classes, although the weight of the main armament is increased. The single mountings, classified above as 30 mm, appear to be some form of "Gatling" and are quite different from the usual twin 30 mm mountings.

RADAR. Topsail and Headnet C; Headlight for SA-N-3 system; Owl Screech for 76 mm guns; separate systems for SA-N-4; Drum Tilt for 30 mm guns.

SONAR AND A/S. VDS is mounted below the helicopter pad and is presumably complementary to a hull-mounted set or sets. The presence of the helicopter with dipping-sonar and an A/S weapon load adds to her long-range capability.

SOVIET TYPE NAME. Bolshoy Protivo Lodochny Korabl, meaning Large Anti-Submarine Ship.

NIKOLAYEV *1973*

NIKOLAYEV *1973*

NIKOLAYEV *1973, USN*

Cruisers—*continued*

ACCOMMODATION. Conditions below decks are presumably fairly spartan but certainly must have some form of air-conditioning. Magazine requirements from forward to aft will include:—

(a one amidships for forward MBUs
b) one amidships for forward SA-N-3.
c) one on either beam for SS-N-10 (if fitted).
d) one on either beam for 76 mm ammunition.
e) one on either beam for SA-N-4.
f) one on either beam for 30 mm ammunition.
g) presumably one on either beam for reload torpedoes.
h) one amidships for after SA-N-3.
i) one on either beam for after MBUs.

In addition there are space requirements for all the radar and ECM equipment and associated machines. All this will require a lot of room and produce a lot of heat in a comparatively small ship.

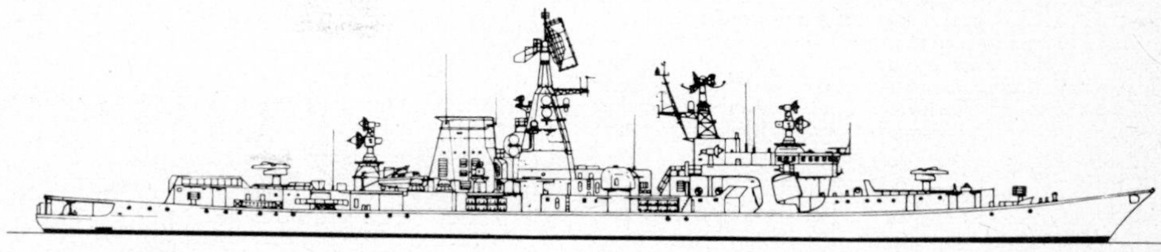

"KARA" CLASS *1974 S. Breyer*

NIKOLAYEV *1973, MOD (UK)*

6 "KRESTA II" CLASS (CLG)

ADMIRAL ISAKOV
ADMIRAL MAKAROV
ADMIRAL NAKHIMOV
ADMIRAL OKTYABRSKY
KRONSTADT
MARSHAL VOROSHILOV

"KRESTA II" Class *1969, S. Breyer*

Displacement, tons	6 000 standard; 7 500 full load
Length, feet (*metres*)	519·9 (*158·5*)
Beam, feet (*metres*)	55·1 (*16·8*)
Draught, feet (*metres*)	19·7 (*6·0*)
Aircraft	1 Hormone A
Missile launchers	2 quadruple for SS-N-10; 2 twin for SA-N-3
A/S weapons	2—12 barrelled MBU forward and 2—6 barrelled MBU aft
Torpedo tubes	10—21 in (two quintuple)
Guns	4—57 mm (2 twin) dual purpose; 8—30 mm (4 twin) anti-aircraft
Main engines	Steam turbines; 2 shafts 100 000 shp
Boilers	4 watertube
Speed, knots	33
Range, miles	5 000 at 18 knots
Complement	500

GENERAL

Multi-0urpose guided missile armed, anti-submarine and

" KRESTA II" Class *1971*

Cruisers—*continued*

helicopter cruisers. The design was developed from that of the "Kresta I" class, but the layout is more sophisticated. The missile armament shows an advance on the "Kresta I" SAM armament and a complete change of practice in the fitting of the SS-N-10 system with 29 mile range missiles. This is a mach 1·2 missile and the fact that it has subsequently been fitted in the "Kara" and "Krivak" classes indicates a possible change in tactical thought. Built at Leningrad from 1968 onwards.

FLIGHT. A flight of two helicopters could be operated, although the normal would appear to be one on the apron aft with adjacent low hangar.

RADAR. The radar installation seems to be similar to that in the "Moskva" class with the same "Top Sail" 3 D and Head Net C 3D for search radar and the Head Light and "Peel Group" (2) fire control radar for surface to air missiles and "Drum Tilt" (2) for guns. Muff Cob also fitted.

SOVIET TYPE NAME. Bolshoy Protivo Lodochny Korabl, meaning Large Anti-Submarine Ship.

"KRESTA II" Class *1971, S. Breyer*

4 "KRESTA I" CLASS (CLG)

VICE-ADMIRAL DROZD
ADMIRAL ZOZULYA
SEVASTOPOL
VLADIVOSTOK

Displacement, tons	5 140 standard; 6 500 full load
Length, feet (*metres*)	510 (*155·5*)
Beam, feet (*metres*)	55·1 (*16·8*)
Draught, feet (*metres*)	18·0 (*5·5*)
Aircraft	1 Hormone A helicopter with hangar aft
Missile launchers	2 twin SS-N-3 for Shaddock 2 twin SA-N-1 for Goa (no reloads)
A/S weapons	2—12 barrelled MBU (60 reloads) forward; 2—6 barrelled MBU aft
Torpedo tubes	10 (two quintuple) 21 in
Guns	4—57 mm (2 twin)
Main engines	Steam turbines; 2 shafts; 100 000 shp
Boilers	4 watertube
Speed, knots	34
Range, miles	4 500 at 18 knots
Complement	400

"KRESTA I" Class

GENERAL
Provided with a helicopter hangar and flight apron aft for the first time in a Soviet ship. This gives an enhanced A/S capability and could certainly provide carried-on-board target-location facilities for the 250 mile SS-N-3 system at a lower, possibly optimum, range. The "Kresta I" was, therefore the first Soviet missile cruiser free to operate alone and distant from own aircraft.
Built at the Zhdanov Shipyard, Leningrad. The prototype ship was laid down in Sep 1964, launched in 1965 and carried out sea trials in the Baltic in Feb 1967. The second ship was launched in 1966 and the others in 1967-68.

KRESTA I Class *1971, US Navy*

Cruisers—*continued*

RADAR. Four pods, or radomes, are fitted to the sides of the superstructure. These are similar to those fitted in the "Moskva" class helicopter missile cruisers and probably contain passive detection and active jamming equipment. Search: Head Net C 3D and Big Net. Fire Control: Scoop Pair for "Shaddock" system and Peel Group (2) for "Goa" system. Muff Cob.

SOVIET TYPE NAME. Bolshoy Protivo Lodochny Korabl, meaning Large Anti-Submarine Ship.

"KRESTA I" Class — *1973, S. Breyer*

4 "KYNDA" CLASS (CLG)

ADMIRAL FOKIN — **GROZNY**
ADMIRAL GOLOVKO — **VARYAG**

Displacement, tons	4 500 standard; 6 000 full load
Length, feet (*metres*)	465·8 (*142·0*)
Beam, feet (*metres*)	51·8 (*15·8*)
Draught, feet (*metres*)	17·4 (*5·3*)
Aircraft	Pad for helicopter on stern
Missile launchers	2 quadruple mounts, 1 fwd, 1 aft, for SS-N-3 system (possible reloads) 1 twin mount on forecastle for SA-N-1 system (30 reloads)
A/S weapons	2—12 barrelled MBUs on forecastle
Guns, AA	4—3 in (*76 mm*) 2 twin
Torpedo tubes	6—21 in (*533 mm*) 2 triple ASW amidships.
Main engines	2 sets geared turbines; 2 shafts; 100 000 shp
Boilers	4 high pressure
Speed, knots	35
Complement	390

"KYNDA" Class

GENERAL
The first ship of this class was laid down in June 1960, launched in Apr 1961 at Zhdanov Shipyard, Leningrad, and completed in June 1962. The second ship was launched in Nov 1961 and fitted out in Aug 1962. The others were completed by 1965. Two enclosed towers, instead of masts, are stepped forward of each raked funnel. In this class there is no helicopter embarked, so guidance, for the SS-N-3 system would be more difficult than in later ships. She will therefore be constrained in her operations compared with the "Kresta I" with her own helicopter.

RADAR. This class showed at an early stage the Soviet ability to match radar availability to weapon capability. The duplicated aerials provide not only a capability for separate target engagement but also provide a reserve in the event of damage. Search: Head Net A. Fire Control: Scoop Pair (2) for "Shaddock" systems, Peel Group for "Goa" systems and Owl Screech for gun.

SOVIET TYPE NAME. Bolshoy Protivo Lodochny Korabl, meaning Large Anti-Submarine Ship.

"KYNDA" Class No. 854 — *1972*

"KYNDA" Class No. 810 — *1972*

DESTROYERS

7 "KRIVAK" CLASS (DDG)

BDITELNY
BODRY
DOSTOYNY
SILNY
SVIREPY
+ 2

"KRIVAK" Class

Displacement, tons	4 800 standard; 5 200 full load
Length, feet (*metres*)	404·8 (*123·4*)
Beam, feet (*metres*)	45·9 (*14·0*)
Draught, feet (*metres*)	16·4 (*5·0*)
Missile launchers	4 for SS-N-10 system, in "A" position; (quadruple); 2 for SA-N-4 system (twins)
A/S weapons	2 twelve-barrelled MBUs forward in "B" position
Torpedo tubes	8—21 in (*533 mm*) in two quadruple banks on either side amidships
Guns	4—3 in (*76 mm*) dual purpose automatic (2 twin) in "X" and "Y" positions; 4—30 mm
Main engines	8 sets Gas turbines; 2 shafts; 112 000 shp
Speed, knots	38

"KRIVAK" Class — *1973, H. W. van Boeijen*

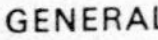

GENERAL
This handsome class, the first ship of which appeared in 1971, appears to be a most successful design incorporating surface and anti-air capability, a VDS with associated MBUs, two banks of tubes, all in a hull designed for both speed and sea-keeping. The use of gas-turbines gives the "Krivak" class a rapid acceleration and an availability which cannot be matched by steam driven ships. Building continues at about 2 per year.

MISSILES. The surface-to-surface missiles of the SS-N-10 system have a range of 29 miles, continuing the short-range trend of the "Kresta II" class and followed by the "Kara" class. The SA-N-4 SAMs are of a new design which is now mounted also in the "Kara", "Nanuchka" and "Grisha" classes. The launcher retracts into the mounting for stowage and protection, rising to fire and retracting to reload. The two mountings are forward of the bridge and abaft the funnel.

RADAR. Head Net C. Drum Tilt and Head Light.

SOVIET TYPE NAME. Bolshoy Protivo Lodochny Korabl, meaning Large Anti-Submarine Ship.

"KRIVAK" Class — *1972*

"KRIVAK" Class — *1972*

Destroyers—*continued*

19 "KASHIN" CLASS (DDG)

"KASHIN" Class

KOMSOMOLETS UKRAINY	**SMELY**
KRASNY-KAVKAZ	**SMETLIVY**
KRASNY-KRIM	**SOOBRAZITELNY**
OBRAZTSOVY	**SPOSOBNY**
ODARENNY	**STEREGUSHCHY**
OTVAZHNY	**STROGNY**
PROVORNY	**STROYNY**
SKORY	**+ 3**
SLAVNY	

Displacement, tons	4 300 standard; 5 200 full load
Length, feet (*metres*)	470·9 (*143·3*) or 481 (*146·5*)
Beam, feet (*metres*)	52·5 (*15·9*)
Draught, feet (*metres*)	19 (*5·8*)
Missile launchers	4 (2 twin) SA-N-1 mounted in "B" and "X" positions for surface-to-air missiles
Guns	4—3 in (*76 mm*), 2 twin, in "A" and "Y" positions
A/S weapons	2—12 barrelled MBU forward; 2—6 barrelled MBU aft
Torpedo tubes	5—21 in (*533 mm*) quintuple, amidships for ASW torpedoes
Main engines	8 sets gas turbines; each 12 000 hp; 2 shafts; 96 000 shp
Speed, knots	35

GENERAL
The first class of warships in the world to rely entirely on gas turbine-propulsion giving them the quick get-away and acceleration necessary for modern tactics. These ships were delivered from 1962 onwards from the Zhdanov Yard, Leningrad and the Nosenko Yard, Nikolayev. Despite their comparative youth the "Kashin's" with a somewhat dated SAM system, no SSM, and neither helicopter nor VDS, have been rapidly out-dated by later classes.

SOVIET TYPE NAME. Bolshoy Protivo Lodochny Korabl, meaning Large Anti-Submarine Ship.

RADAR. Search: Head Net C and Big Net in some ships; Head Net A (2) in others. Fire control: Peel Group (2) for "Goa" system and Owl Screech (2) for guns.

"KASHIN" Class *1972, US Navy*

OTVAZHNY *1973, Commander Aldo Fraccorali*

Destroyers—*continued*

6 "KANIN" CLASS (DDG)

BOYKY
DERZKY
GREMYASHCHYI
ZHGUCHY
ZORKY
+ 1

Displacement, tons	3 700 standard; 4 600 full load
Length, feet (*metres*)	456·9 (*139·3*)
Beam, feet (*metres*)	48·2 (*14·7*)
Draught, feet (*metres*)	16·4 (*5·0*)
Aircraft	Helicopter pad
Missile launchers	1 twin "SA-N-1" mounted aft
A/S weapons	Three 12-barrelled MBU
Guns	8—57 mm (2 quadruple forward) 8—30 mm (twin) (by after funnel)
Torpedo tubes	10—21 in (*533 mm*) A/S (2 quintuple)
Main engines	2 sets geared steam turbines 2 shafts; 80 000 shp
Boilers	4 watertube
Oil fuel, tons	900
Speed, knots	34
Complement	350

GENERAL
All ships of this class have been converted from "Krupny's" at Zhdanov Yard, Leningrad from 1967 onwards, being given a SAM capability instead of the latter's SSM armament.

APPEARANCE. As compared with the "Krupny" class these ships have enlarged bridge, converted bow (probably for a new sonar) and larger helicopter platforms.

GUNNERY. The four twin 30 mm abaft the after funnel were a late addition to the armament.

RADAR. Search: Head Net C or Head Net A. Fire Control: Peel Group for "Goa", Hawk Screech for guns. Drum Tilt for additional 30 mm guns.

SOVIET TYPE NAME. Bolshoy Protivo Lodochny Korabl, meaning Large Anti-Submarine Ship.

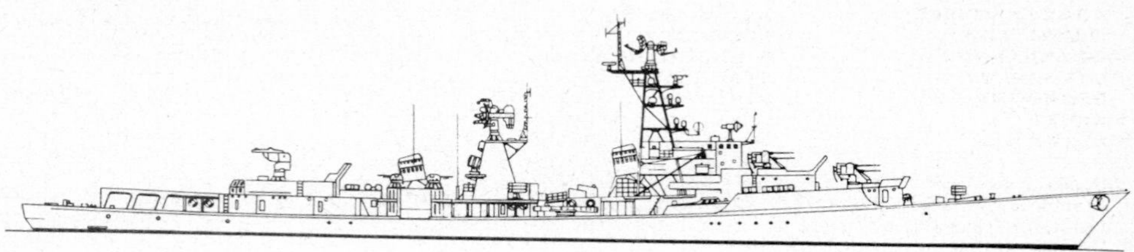

"KANIN" Class with additional 8—30 mm *1973 S. Breyer*

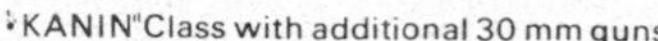

"KANIN" Class with additional 30 mm guns *1973, S. Breyer*

"KANIN" Class, Hull 2, *1972*

"KANIN SAM" Class No. 911 *1972*

2 "KRUPNY" CLASS (DDG)

GNEVNY **GORDY**

Displacement, tons	3 650 standard; 4 650 full load
Length, feet (*metres*)	452 (*137·8*)
Beam, feet (*metres*)	48·2 (*14·7*)
Draught, feet (*metres*)	16·5 (*5·0*)
Missile launchers	2 mountings; 1 forward, 1 aft for "SS-N-1" system
Guns, AA	16—57 mm, (4 quadruple;
A/S weapons	2—16 barrelled MBUs 2 amidships, 1 forward, 1 aft)
Torpedo launchers	6 (2 triple) for 21 in A/S torpedoes
Main engines	Geared steam turbines; 2 shat 80 000 shp
Boilers	4 high pressure water tube
Speed, knots	34
Complement	360

Flush-decked destroyers designed to carry surface-to-surface guided missiles. Helicopter spot landing apron on the stern. Initial construction started in 1958 at Leningrad. Four ships of this class were converted to carry surface-to-air missiles in 1967 to 1971 and are known as the "Kanin" class; two more subsequently converted.

RADAR. Search: Either Head Net C 3D or Head Net A. Fire Control: Hawk Screech (2) for guns, and, probably surface missiles. Skinhead.

SOVIET TYPE NAME. Rated as Raketny Korabl meaning Rocket Ship.

"KRUPNY" Class firing Scrubber missile 1968

"KRUPNY" Class

GNEVNY 1969, MOD, UK

"KRUPNY" Class 1971, USN

Destroyers—*continued*

8 "SAM KOTLIN" CLASS (DDG)

BRAVY
NAKHODCHIVY
NASTOYCHIVY
NESOKRUSHIMY
SKROMNY
SKRYTNY
SOZNATELNY
+ 1

Displacement, tons	2 850 standard; 3 885 full load
Length, feet (*metres*)	414·9 (*126·5*)
Beam, feet (*metres*)	42·6 (*13·0*)
Draught, feet (*metres*)	16·1 (*4·9*)
Missile launchers	1 twin SA-N-1 mounted aft
Guns	2—5·1 in (*130 mm*) dp (1 twin) 4—57 mm AA (1 quadruple) 8—30 mm in later ships
Torpedo tubes	1 quintuple 21 in mounting
Guns	2—3·9 in (100 *mm*) dp (1 twin) 4—57 mm AA (1 quadruple) 4—30 mm in later ships
A/S weapons	6 side thrown DC projectors or 2—12 barrelled ASW rocket launchers
Main engines	Geared turbines; 2 shafts 72 000 shp
Boilers	4 high pressure
Speed, knots	36
Range, miles	5 500 at 16 knots
Complement	285

"SAM KOTLIN" Class

"SAM KOTLIN" Class

Converted "Kotlin" class destroyers with a surface-to-air missile launcher in place of the main twin turret aft and anti-aircraft guns reduced to one quadruple mounting.

The prototype conversion was completed about 1962 and the others since 1966. One ship transferred to Poland.

APPEARANCE. The prototype "Kotlin" SAM class has a different after funnel and different radar pedestal from those in the standard "Kotlin" SAM class.

RADAR. Search: Head Net C 3D or Head Net A. Fire Control: Peel Group for "Goa" system, Hawk Screech for guns. Drum Tilt for 30 mm in later ships.

SOVIET TYPE NAME. Rated as Esminets meaning Destroyer.

SAM KOTLIN Class — *1971, USN*

Later SAM KOTLIN (with 2 extra Drum Tilt and 8—30 mm by after funnel) — *1973*

SAM KOTLIN Class (with different design of midship radar pedestal and after funnel from the prototype). — *1971 MOD (UK)*

"KILDIN" CLASS (DDGS)

BEDOVY **NEULOVIMY** +1

Displacement, tons	3 000 standard; 4 000 full load
Length, feet (*metres*)	414·9 (*126·5*)
Beam, feet (*metres*)	42·6 (*13·0*)
Draught, feet (*metres*)	16·1 (*4·9*)
Missile launchers	4 for SSN—II system
A/S Weapon	2—16 barrel MBU on forcastle
Guns	4—76 mm (twins aft); 16—57 mm (quads—2 forward, 2 between funnels)
Torpedo tubes	4—21 in (2 twin)
Main engines	Geared turbines; 2 shafts 72 000 shp
Boilers	4 high pressure
Speed, knots	36
Range, miles	5 500 at 16 knots
Complement	350 officers and men

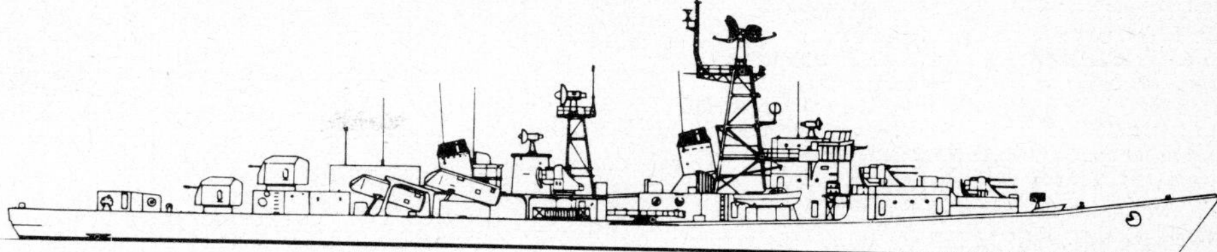

" KILDIN"Class after modernisation *1973 S. Breyer*

Large destroyers with the "Kotlin" type hull, but re-designed as guided missile armed destroyers with a launcher installed in place of the after gun mountings.

MODERNISATION. In 1972 *Neulovimy* was taken in hand for modification. This was completed in mid-1973 and consisted of the replacement of the SSN-1 on the quarterdeck by two super-imposed twin 76 mm turrets, the fitting of four SSN-11 launchers abreast the after funnel and the fitting of new radar. The substitution of the 29 mile SSN-11 system (a modified Styx) for the obsolescent, SSN-1 system and the notable increase in gun armament illustrate two trends in Soviet thought.

SOVIET TYPE NAME. Rated Bolshoy Protivo Lodochny Kerabl meaning Large Anti-Submarine Ship.

RADAR. Search: Head Net A and Slim Net. Fire Control: New outfit at modernisation

NEULOVIMY after modernisation *1973*

NEULOVIMY after modernisation *1973, S. Brexer*

BEDOVY (with KOTLIN type director) *1970*

Destroyers— *continued*

18 "KOTLIN" CLASS (DD)

BESSLEDNY
BLAGORODNY
BLESTYASHCHY
BURLIVY
BYVALY
NAPORISTY
KOMSOMOLETS DALNEVOSTOCHNY
KOMSOMOLETS MOSKOVSKY
PLAMENNY
SVETLY
VDOKHNOVENNY
VOZBUZHDENNY
VOZMUSHCHENNY
VYDERZHANNY
+4

Displacement, tons	2 850 standard; 3 885 full load
Length, feet (*metres*)	414·9 (*126·5*)
Beam, feet (*metres*)	42·6 (*13·0*)
Draught, feet (*metres*)	16·1 (*4·9*) max
Guns	4—5·1 in (*130 mm*) dp (2 twin) 16—57 mm AA (4 quadruple) (8—30 mm in some)
A/S weapons	6 side thrown DC projectors or (2—16 barrelled MBUs in some)
Torpedo tubes	10—21 in (*533 mm*) (5 only in some)
Mines	80 capacity
Main engines	Geared turbines; 2 shafts; 72 000 shp
Boilers	4 high pressure
Speed, knots	36
Range, miles	5 500 at 16 knots
Complement	285

"KOTLIN HELO" Class

" KOTLIN" Class (modification with after TT replaced by deckhouse)

GENERAL
These destroyers, built in 1954-57, were designed for mass production. The last four hulls were converted to "Kildin's".

MODIFICATIONS. (a) Eight converted to "SAM KOTLIN'S" plus one transferred to Poland. (b) *Svetly* and others provided with helicopter pad on stern.

(c) Some had the after torpedo-tubes replaced by a deckhouse. (d) Some ships had two 16-barrelled MBUs fitted. (e) The latest addition in some ships is the fitting of eight 30 mm either side of the after-funnel.

RADAR. Search: Slim Net and Strut Curve. Fire Control: Hawk Screech (2). Hair Net. Square Head. Flat Spin in some.

SOVIET TYPE NAMES. Rated as Esminets meaning Destroyer.

" KOTLIN" Class with 5 torpedo tubes and additional 30 mm guns — *1973, USN*

"KOTLIN" Class — *1970, S. Breyer*

"KOTLIN" Class (helicopter platform aft) — *1969, MOD, (UK)*

Destroyers— *continued*

40 "SKORY" CLASS (DD)

BESSMENNY
BEZUKORIZNENNY
OTCHAYANNY
OTVETSTVENNY
OZHESTOCHENNY
OZHIVLENNY
SERDITY
SERIOZNY
SMOTRYASHCHY
SOKRUSHITELNY
SOLIDNY
SOVERSHENNY
STATNY
STEPENNY
STOJKY
STREMITELNY
SUROVY
SVOBODNY
VDUMCHIVY
VRAZUMITELNY
+20

Displacement, tons	2 600 standard; 3 500 full load
Length, feet	395·2 (*120·5*)
Beam, feet (*metres*)	38.9 (*11·8*)
Draught, feet (*metres*)	15·1 (*4·6*)
Guns	4—5·1 in (*130 mm*), 2 twin 2—3·4 in (*86 mm*) 1 twin 8—37 mm (4 twin), (see *Modernisation* and *Armament Notes*)
A/S weapons	4 DCT (see *Armament Note*)
Torpedo tubes	10—21 in (*533 mm*) (see *Armament Note*)
Mines	80 can be carried
Main engines	Geared turbines; 2 shafts; 60 000 shp
Boilers	4 high pressure
Speed, knots	33
Range, miles	3 900 at 13 knots
Complement	260

There were to have been 85 destroyers of this class, but construction beyond 75 units was discontinued in favour of later types of destroyers, and the number has been further reduced to 40 by transfers to other countries, translations to other types and disposals at an increasing rate.

APPEARANCE. There were three differing types in this class, the anti-aircraft guns varying with twin and single mountings; and two types of foremast, one vertical with all scanners on top and the other with one scanner on top and one on a platform half way.

SVOBODNYJ *1968*

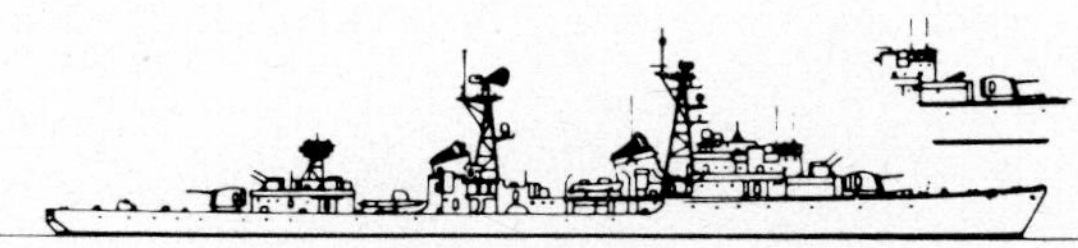

"SKORY" Modified **Class**

"SKORY" Original Class

MODERNISATION. At least six ships, of the "Skory" class were modified from 1959 onwards including extensive alterations to anti-aircraft armament, electronic equipment and anti-submarine weapons. These now have five 57 mm single, five torpedo tubes and two 16-barrelled MBU.

RADAR. Search: Strut Curve and unknown S Band. Fire Control: Obsolescent X Band. Square Head.

TRANSFERS. Of this class *Skory* and *Smeriivy* were transferred to the Polish Navy in 1957-58, two to the Egyptian Navy in 1956, four to the Indonesian Navy in 1959, and two (modernised) to Egypt in 1968.

SOVIET TYPE NAME. Rated as Esminets meaning Destroyer.

1 "TALLIN" CLASS (DD)

NEUSTRASHIMY

Displacement, tons	3 200 standard; 4 300 full load
Length, feet (*metres*)	440·0 (*134·0*) oa
Beam, feet (*metres*)	44·9 (*13·7*)
Draught, feet (*metres*)	16·1 (*4·9*)
Guns	4—5·1 in (*130 mm*) semi-automatic (2 twin) 16—57 mm (4 quadruple)
A/S weapons	2—16 barrelled MBUs and 2 DC launchers
Torpedo tubes	10—21 in (*533 mm*), 2 quintuple
Mines	70
Main engines	Geared turbines; 2 shafts; 80 000 shp
Boilers	4 water tube
Speed, knots	38
Range, miles	2 500 at 18 knots
Oil fuel, tons	850
Complement	340

Built in 1952-54.

"TALLIN" Class

GUNNERY. The 5·1 inch (*130 mm*) guns in two twin turrets, including firing directors, are fully stabilised.

RADAR. Search: Slim Net and Strut Curve. Fire Control: Hawk Screech (2).

SOVIET TYPE NAME. Rated as Esminets meaning Destroyer.

NEUSTRASHIMYJ *Skyfotos*

FRIGATES

6 "KOLA" CLASS

SOVIETSKY AZERBAIDJAN
SOVIETSKY DAGESTAN
SOVIETSKY TURKESTAN
+3

Displacement, tons	1 500 standard; 1 900 full load
Length, feet (*metres*)	315·0 (*96·0*) oa
Beam, feet (*metres*)	35·4 (*10·8*)
Draught, feet (*metres*)	11·5 (*3·5*)
Guns, dual purpose	4—3·9 (*100 mm*) single
Guns, AA	4—37 mm (2 twin)
A/S weapons	DCT's and racks
Torpedo tubes	3—21 in (*533 mm*)
Mines	30
Main engines	Geared turbines; 2 shafts; 30,000 shp
Boilers	2
Speed, knots	31
Complement	190

"KOLA" Class

Built in 1950-52. In design this class of flushdecked frigates appears to be a combination of the former German "Elbing" class destroyers, with a similar hull form, and of the earlier Soviet "Birds" class escorts. At least three are stationed in the Caspian Sea.

GUNNERY. The four 3.9 inch guns were mounted as in the "Gordy" class destroyers. Some also mount 4—25 mm (twins).

RADAR. Navigational and obsolescent type fire control.

SOVIET TYPE NAME. Rated as Storozhevoy Korabl meaning Escort Ship.

"Kola "Class

40 "RIGA" CLASS

Displacement, tons	1 200 standard; 1 600 full load
Length, feet (*metres*)	298·8 (*91·0*)
Beam, feet (*metres*)	33·7 (10·2)
Draught, feet (*metres*)	11 (*3·4*)
Guns, dual purpose	3—3·9 in (*100 mm*) single
Guns, AA	4—37 mm (2 twin)
A/S weapons	2—16 barrelled MBUs; 4 DC projectors
Torpedo tubes	3—21 in (*533 mm*)
Mines	50
Main engines	Geared turbines; 2 shafts; 25 000 shp
Boilers	2
Speed, knots	28
Range, miles	2 500 at 15 knots
Complement	150

"RIGA" Class — *1973, H. W. van Boeijeu*

Built from 1952 to 1959. Successors to the "Kola" class escorts, of which they are lighter and less heavily armed but improved versions. Fitted with mine rails.

ANTI-SUBMARINE. The two 16-barrelled MBU rocket launchers are mounted just before the bridge abreast "B" gun.

RADAR. Search: Slim Net. Fire Control: Obsolescent type.

SOVIET TYPE NAME. Rated as Storozhevoy Korabl meaning Escort Ship.

TRANSFERS. Bulgaria (2), China (4), East Germany (2), Finland (2), Indonesia (6).

"RIGA" Class

20 "MIRKA I AND II" CLASS

Displacement, tons	950 standard; 1 100 full load
Length, feet (*metres*)	269·9 (*82·3*)
Beam, feet (*metres*)	29·9 (*9·1*)
Draught, feet (*metres*)	9·8 (*3·0*)
Guns	4—3 in (*76 mm*) (2 twin) (I)
A/S weapons	4—12 barrel MBUs (2 forward, 2 aft) (1); 2—16 barrel MBUs (II)
Torpedo tubes	5—16 in anti-submarine (I) 10—16 in (II)
Main engines	2 diesels; total 6 000 hp; 2 gas turbines, total 31 000 hp; 2 shafts
Speed, knots	33
Complement	100

MIRKA II Class (with two torpedo mountings)

This class of ships was built in 1964-69 as improved "Petya" class. Some units have the after MBU rocket launchers removed and an additional quintuple 16-inch torpedo mounting fitted between the bridge and the mast. At least one mounts VDS.

RADAR. Search: Slim Net. Fire Control: Hawk Screech.

SOVIET TYPE NAMES. Rated as Storozhevoy Korabl meaning Escort Ship.

"MIRKA" Class

MIRKA II Class No. 876 (with two torpedo mountings) — *1972*

Frigates—*continued*

20 "PETYA I" CLASS
25 "PETYA II" CLASS

Displacement, tons	950 standard; 1 150 full load
Length, feet (*metres*)	270 (*82·3*)
Beam, feet (*metres*)	29·9 (*9·1*)
Draught, feet (*metres*)	10·5 (*3·2*)
Guns, dual purpose	4—3 in (*76 mm*), (2 twin)
A/S weapons	4—16 barrelled MBUs (I) 2—12 barrelled MBUs (II)
Torpedo tubes	5—16 in (*406 mm*) (I) 10—16 in (*406 mm*) (II)
Main engines	2 diesels, total 6 000 hp; 2 gas turbines; total 30 000 hp; 2 shafts
Speed, knots	34
Complement	100

"Petya I" with VDS — *1973, S. Breyer*

"PETYA" Class

Small freeboard with a low wide funnel. The first ship reported to have been built in 1960-61 at Kaliningrad. Construction continued until about 1964. Fitted with two mine rails. "Petya II's" sacrifice MBU's for extra tubes whilst two of the "Petya II's" have lost the after 3 in turret to compensate for VDS.

RADAR. Search: Slim Net. Fire Control: Hawk Screech.

SOVIET TYPE NAME. Rated as Storozhevkoy Korabl meaning Escort Ship.

"PETYA II" Class — *1970, MOD (UK)*

CORVETTES

14 "GRISHA" CLASS

Displacement, tons	750 full load
Dimensions, feet	234·8 × 32·8 × 9·2
Missile launchers	SA-N-4 surface-to-air (twin)
Guns	2—57 mm dual purpose (1 twin)
Torpedo tubes	4—16 in anti-submarine
A/S weapons	2—12 barrelled MBUs
Main engines	2 gas turbines; 2 diesels = 30 knots

This class is the successor to the "Poti". Reported to have started series production in the late 1969-70 period. Five built by end of 1972, with a continuing programme of 3 a year. SA-N-4 launcher mounted on the forecastle.

SOVIET TYPE NAME. Rated as Maly Protivo Lodochny Korabl meaning Small Anti-Submarine Ship.

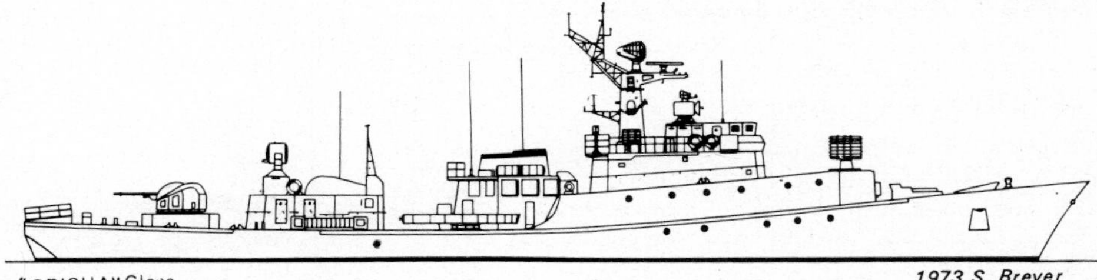
"GRISHA" Class — *1973 S. Breyer*

"GRISHA" Class — *1972*

"GRISHA" Class — *1972*

Corvettes—*continued*

70 "POTI" CLASS

Displacement, tons	550 standard; 650 full load
Dimensions, feet	195·2 × 26·2 × 9·2
Guns	2—57 mm AA (1 twin mounting)
Tubes	4—16 in anti-submarine
A/S weapons	2—12 barrelled MBUs
Main engines	2 gas turbines; 2 diesels; 4 shafts; total 20 000 hp = 28 knots

This class of ships was under series construction from 1961 to 1968. Strut Curve and Muff Cob Radars.

SOVIET TYPE NAME. Rated as Maly Protivo Lodochny Korabl meaning Small Anti-Submarine Ship.

"Poti" Class *1971*

"Poti" Class *1970, S. Breyer*

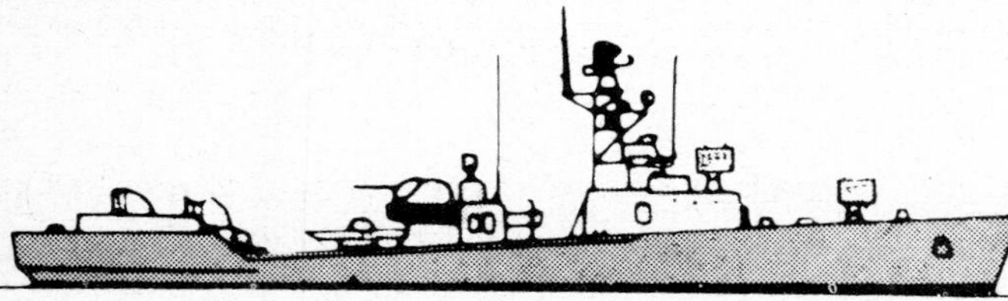

"POTI" Class

20 "KRONSTADT" CLASS

Displacement, tons	310 standard; 380 full load
Dimensions, feet	170·6 × 21·5 × 9·0
Guns	1—3·5 in; 2—37 mm AA; 6 MGs (twins)
A/S weapons	Depth charge projectors (some have 2—5 barrelled MBUs)
Main engines	3 diesels; 3 shafts; 3 300 hp = 24 knots
Range, miles	1 500 at 12 knots
Complement	65

Built in 1948-56. Flush-decked with large squat funnel, slightly raked, and massive block bridge structure. Pot Head radar. Now being phased out of service due to age. About 20 ships were rebuilt as communications relay ships of the "Libau" class.

SOVIET TYPE NAME. Rated as Maly Protivo Lodochny Korabl meaning Small Anti-Submarine Ship.

TRANSFERS. Bulgaria (2), China (24), Cuba (18), Indonesia (14), Poland (8), Romania (3).

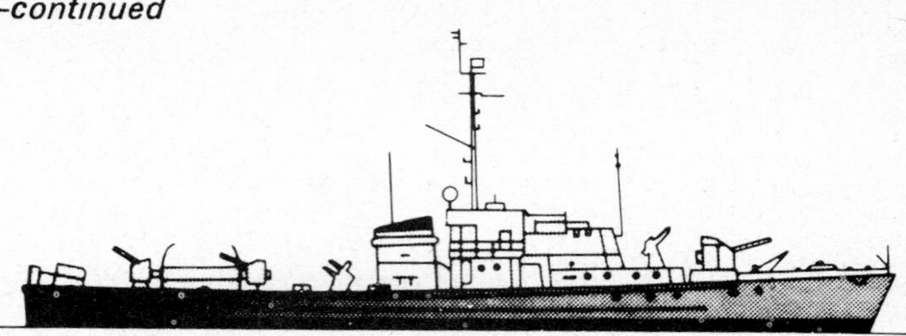

"KRONSTADT" Class

"Kronstadt" Class

"Kronstadt" Class *1970, courtesy, Godfrey H. Walker Esq.*

80 "SO I" CLASS

Displacement, tons	215 light; 250 normal
Dimensions, feet	138·6 × 20·0 × 9·2
Guns	4—25 mm AA (2 twin mountings) see notes
A/S weapons	4 five-barrelled MBUs
Main engines	3 diesels; 6 000 bhp = 29 knots
Range, miles	1 100 at 13 knots
Complement	30

Built since 1957. Steel hulled. Modernised boats of this class have only two 25 mm AA guns but also have four 16 in anti-submarine torpedo tubes. Being phased out of service.

SOVIET TYPE NAME. Rated as Maly Provito Lodochny Korabl meaning small Anti-Submarine ship.

"SO I" Class *1968*

"SOI" Class

9 "NANUCHKA" CLASS

(MISSILE CORVETTE)

Displacement, tons	800 normal (approx)
Length, feet (*metres*)	196·8 (*60·0*)
Beam, feet (*metres*)	39·6 (*12·0*)
Draught, feet (*metres*)	9·9 (*3·0*)
Missile launchers	6 (2 triple) for SS-N-9 surface to-surface system SA-N-4 surface-to-air system forward (twin)
Guns	2—57 mm AA (1 twin)
A/S weapons	1 or 2 MBUs
Main engines	Diesels
Speed, knots	32

A new class of diesel powered craft with SSM launchers as the main armament probably mainly intended for deployment in coastal waters. Reported to have a very high beam to length ratio making her a much steadier firing platform than the *Osas* and *Komars*. Built from 1969 onwards. Has received many type designations including "Missile Cutter". Building continues at rate of about 3 a year at Leningrad.

RADAR. Search: Slim Net. Fire Control: Hawk Screech

"NANUCHKA" Class *S. Breyer*

LIGHT FORCES

120 "OSA I and II" CLASS (65 I and 55 II) (FAST ATTACK CRAFT—MISSILE)

Displacement, tons	165 standard; 200 full load
Dimensions, feet	128·7 × 25·1 × 5·9
Missile launchers	4 in two pairs abreast for "SS-N-2A"
Guns	4—30 mm; (2 twin, 1 forward, 1 aft)
Main engines	3 diesels; 13 000 bhp = 32 knots
Range, miles	800 at 25 knots
Complement	25

These boats, built since 1959, have a larger hull and four launchers in two pairs as compared with one pair in the "Komar" class. They have a surface-to-surface missile range of up to 23 miles. Later boats have cylindrical missile launchers, comprising the "Osa II" class.

This class was a revolution in naval shipbuilding. Although confined by their size and range to coastal operations the lethality and accuracy of the Styx missile have already been proved by the sinking of the Israeli destroyer *Eilat* on 21 Oct 1967 by an Egyptian "Komar". The operations of the Indian "Osa's" in the war with Pakistan in December 1971 were equally successful against merchant vessels by night. These operations surely represent a most important lesson in naval operations and, in light of this, the list of transfers should be noted.

TRANSFERS. Algeria (3), Bulgaria (3), China (17), Cuba (2), Egypt (12), East Germany (12), India (8), Iraq (5), Poland (12), Romania (5), Syria (5), Yugoslavia (10).

"OSA" Class firing missile *1970*

"Osa" I Class *1970*

"Osa II" Class *1970, Godfrey H. Walker*

"Osa I" Class *1970*

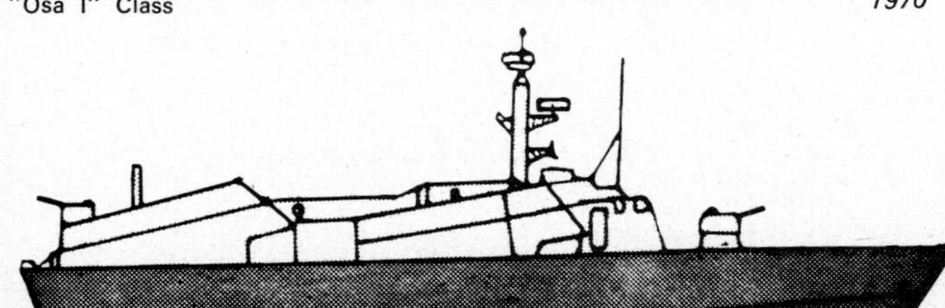

"OSA" *Class*

25 "KOMAR" CLASS (FAST ATTACK CRAFT—MISSILE)

Displacement, tons	70 standard; 80 full load
Dimensions, feet	83·7 × 19·8 × 5·0
Missile launchers	2 for "SS-N-2 A" system
Guns	2—25 mm AA (1 twin forward)
Range, miles	400 at 30 knots
Main engines	4 diesels; 4 shafts; 4 800 bhp = 40 knots

A smaller type of boat converted from "P 6" class torpedo boats. Fitted with two surface-to-surface launchers aft in a hooded casing approximately 45 degrees to the deck line with a range of 23 miles. First units completed 1961. Being phased out of service.

TRANSFERS. Algeria (6), China (10), Cuba (18), Egypt (6), Indonesia (12), Korea (N) (6), Syria (3).

"Komar" Class

35 "STENKA" CLASS (FAST ATTACK CRAFT—PATROL)

Displacement, tons	170 standard; 210 full load
Dimensions, feet	130·7 × 25·1 × 6·0
Guns	4—30 mm AA (2 twin)
Torpedo tubes	4—16 in (*406 mm*) anti-submarine
A/S weapons	2 depth charge racks
Main engines	3 diesels; 10 000 bhp = 40 knots
Complement	25

Based on the hull design of the "Osa" class. Built from 1967-68 onwards.

RADAR. Search: Square Tie. Fire Control: Drum Tilt. Pot Drum.

Stenka" Class *1973, S. Breyer*

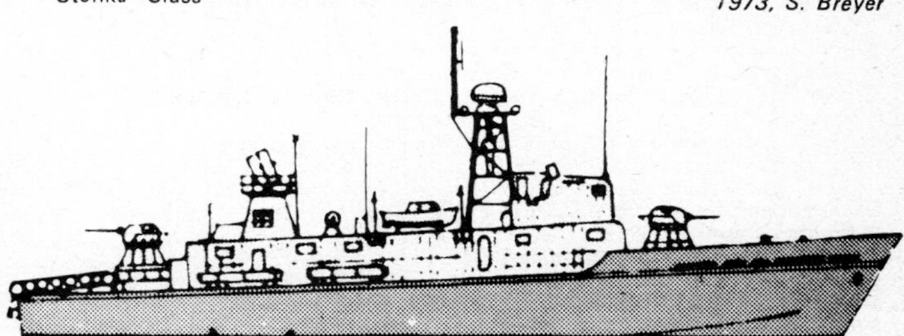

"STENKA" *Class*

15 "MO VI" CLASS (FAST ATTACK CRAFT—PATROL)

Displacement, tons	64 standard; 73 full load
Dimensions, feet	83·6 × 19·7 × 4·0
Guns	4—25 mm AA (2 twin)
A/S weapons	2 depth charge mortars; 2 depth charge racks
Main engines	4 diesels; 4 shafts; 4 800 bhp = 40 knots

Built in 1956 to 1960. Based on the hull design of the "P-6"

"MO VI" Class *1972*

Light Forces—*continued*

25 "PCHELA" CLASS (HYDROFOILS)

Displacement, tons	70 standard; 80 full load
Dimensions, feet	82·0 × 19·7 × ?
Guns	4 MG (2 twin)
Main engines	2 diesels; 6 000 bhp = 50 knots

This class of hydrofoils, is reported to have been built since 1964-65. Also carry depth charges. Used for frontier guard duties by KGB.

"Pchela" Class 1970

40 "SHERSHEN" CLASS (FAST ATTACK CRAFT—TORPEDO)

Displacement, tons	150 standard; 160 full load
Dimensions, feet	115·5 × 23·1 × 5·0
Guns	4—30 mm AA (2 twin)
Tubes	4—21 in (single)
A/S weapons	12 DC
Main engines	Diesels; 3 shafts; 13 000 bhp = 41 knots
Complement	16

TRANSFERS. Bulgaria (4), East Germany (15), Egypt (6), Yugoslavia (13).

"Shershen" Class 1970, S. Breyer

100 "P 6" "P 8" "P 10" CLASSES

(FAST ATTACK CRAFT—TORPEDO)

Displacement, tons	66 standard; 75 full load
Dimensions, feet	84·2 × 20·0 × 6·0
Guns	4—25 mm AA
Tubes	2—21 in (or mines, or depth charges)
Main engines	4 diesels; 4 shafts; 4 800 bhp = 43 knots
Range, miles	450 at 30 knots
Complement	25

The "P 6" class was of a standard medium sized type running into series production. Launched during 1951 to 1960. Known as "MO VI" class in the submarine chaser version. The later versions, known as the "P 8" and "P 10" classes, are powered with gas turbines, and have different bridge and funnel, "P 8" boats have hydrofoils. This class is now being deleted because of old age.

TRANSFERS. Algeria (12), China (80, indigenous construction), Cuba (12), Egypt (24), East Germany (18), Guinea (4), Indonesia (14), Iraq (12), Nigeria (3), Poland (20), North Vietnam (6), Somalia (2).

"P 6" Class

"P 6" Class after modernisation 1972, S. Breyer

"P 8" Class 1969, S. Breyer

"P 10" Class 1968, S. Breyer

10 "P 4" CLASS (FAST ATTACK CRAFT—TORPEDO)

Displacement, tons	22
Dimensions, feet	62·7 × 11·6 × 5·6
Guns	2—15 mm MG (twin)
Tubes	2—18 in
Main engines	2 Diesels; 2 shafts; 2 200 bhp = 50 knots

Originally a numerically large class of boats with aluminium alloy hulls. Launched in 1951-58. The earlier units are being discarded.

TRANSFERS. Albania (12), Bulgaria (8), China (70), Cuba (12), Cyprus (6), North Korea (40), Romania (13), Somalia (4), Syria (17).

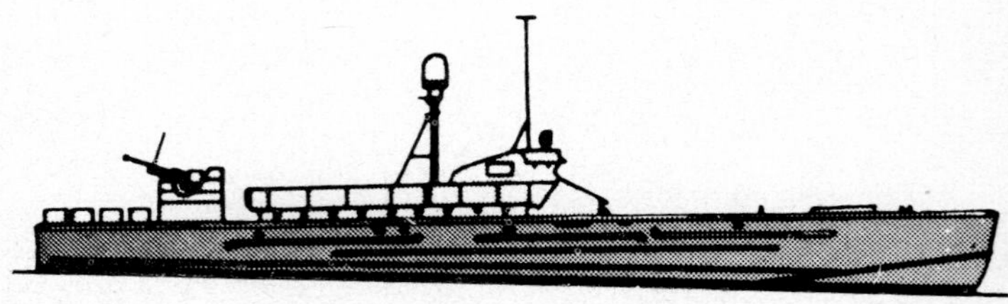

"P 4" Class

"SHMEL" CLASS (RIVER PATROL CRAFT)

Length, feet	92
Guns	1—76 mm; 2—25 mm (twin)
Speed, knots	20
Complement	15

A number of this class is deployed in the Danube and Amur River flotillas.

MINE WARFARE FORCES

NOTE. The "Alesha" class (under Support and Depot Ships) probably has a primary minelaying role.

13 "NATYA" CLASS (MINESWEEPERS—OCEAN)

Displacement, tons	650
Dimensions, feet	200·1 × 34·1 × 7·2
Guns	4—30 mm AA (2 twin); 4—25 mm AA (2 twin)
A/S weapons	2 5-barrelled MBUs
Main engines	2 diesels; 5 000 bhp = 18 knots

A new class of fleet minesweepers first reported in 1971, evidently intended as successors of the "Yurka" class. Building rate of 3 a year.

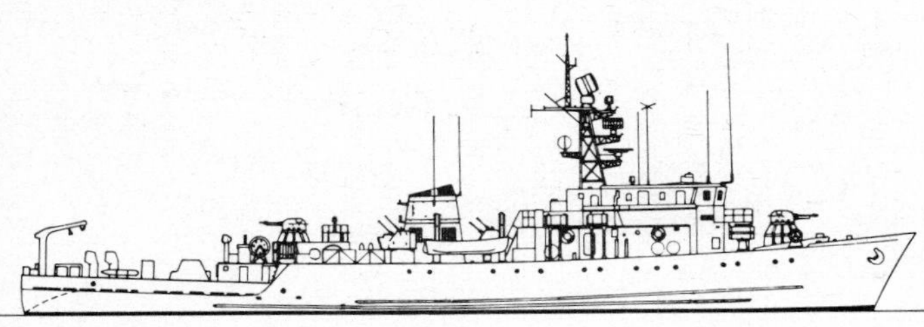

"NATYE" CLASS *1973 S. Breyer*

45 "YURKA" CLASS (MINESWEEPERS—OCEAN)

Displacement, tons	500 standard; 550 full load
Dimensions, feet	171·9 × 31 × 8·9
Guns	4—30 mm AA (2 twin)
Main engines	2 diesels; 4 000 bhp = 18 knots

A class of medium fleet minesweepers with steel hull. Built from 1963 to the late 1960s.

"Yurka" Class *1973, S. Breyer*

20 "T 58" CLASS (MINESWEEPERS—OCEAN)

Displacement, tons	790 standard; 900 full load
Dimensions, feet	229·9 × 29·5 × 7·9
A/S weapons	2—5 barrelled MBUs
Guns	4—57 mm AA (2 twin)
Main engines	2 diesels; 2 shafts; 4 000 bhp = 18 knots

Built from 1957 to 1964. Of this class 14 were converted to submarine rescue ships with armament and sweeping gear removed, see later page ("Valdai" class).

"T 58" with "Muff Cob" fire control radar on bridge *1968*

110 "T 43" CLASS (MINESWEEPERS—OCEAN)

Displacement, tons	500 standard; 610 full load
Dimensions, feet	190·2 × 28·2 × 6·9
Guns	4—37 mm AA (2 twin); 4—25 mm AA (2 twin)
Main engines	2 diesels; 2 shafts; 2 000 bhp = 17 knots
Range, miles	1 600 at 10 knots
Complement	40

Built in 1948-57 in shipyards throughout the Soviet Union. A number of this class was converted into radar pickets. The remainder is gradually being replaced by newer types of fleet minesweepers.

TRANSFERS. Algeria (2), Albania (2), Bulgaria (2), China (20), Egypt (6), Indonesia (6), Poland (12), Syria (2).

"T 43" Class *1972*

3 "ZHENYA" CLASS (MINESWEEPERS—COASTAL)

Displacement, tons	320
Dimensions, feet	141 × 25 × 7
Guns	2—30 mm (twin)
Main engines	2 diesels = ? 18 knots

A recent design presumably the successors of the "Vanya's", although the building rate is low.

"ZHENYA" CLASS

70 "VANYA" CLASS (MINESWEEPERS—COASTAL)

Displacement, tons	250 standard; 275 full load
Dimensions, feet	130·7 × 24 × 6·9
Guns	2—30 mm AA (1 twin)
Main engines	2 diesels; 2 200 bhp = 18 knots
Complement	30

A coastal class with wooden hulls of a type suitable for series production built from 1961 onwards. Basically similar to NATO type coastal minesweepers.

Vanya" Class *1970, S. Breyer*

40 "SASHA" CLASS (MINESWEEPERS—COASTAL)

Displacement, tons	245 standard; 280 full load
Dimensions ,feet	150·9 × 20·5 × 6·6
Guns	1—57mm dp; 4—25 mm AA (2 twin)
Main engines	2 diesels; 2 200 bhp = 18 knots
Complement	25

Basically similar to NATO coastal minesweepers, but of steel construction.

"Sasha" Class *1968, S. Breyer*

10 "T 301" CLASS (MINESWEEPERS—COASTAL)

Displacement, tons	150 standard; 180 full load
Dimensions, feet	128·0 × 18·0 × 4·9
Guns	2—37 mm AA; 4 MG (twin)
Main engines	2 diesels; 2 shafts; 1 440 bhp = 17 knots

Built from 1946 to 1956. Several were converted to survey craft, and many adapted for other purposes or used for port duty and auxiliary service. Now being withdrawn from service due to age.

"T 301" Class

"RT 40" CLASS (MINESWEEPERS—INSHORE)

Displacement, tons	40 standard; 60 full load
Dimensions, feet	55·8 × 11·5 × 4·0
Guns	2—25 mm (twin) 2 MG (twin)
Main engines	Diesels; speed 18 knots

"K 8" CLASS (MINESWEEPERS—INSHORE)

Displacement, tons	50 standard; 70 full load
Dimensions, feet	92·0 × 13·5 × 2·3
Guns	2 MG (twin)
Main engines	Diesels; 600 bhp = 14 knots

Auxiliary motor minesweeping boats of the inshore ("RT 40") and river ("K 8") types. A total of about 100 of both classes in service.

AMPHIBIOUS FORCES

12 "ALLIGATOR" CLASS (LST)

ALEKSANDR TORTSEV
DONETSKY SHAKHTER
KRASNAYA PRESNYA
KRYMSKY KOMSOMOLETS
TOMSKY KOMSOMOLETS
+7

Displacement, tons	4 100 standard; 5 800 full load
Dimensions, feet	374·0 × 50·9 × 12·1
Guns	2—57 mm AA
Main engines	Diesels; 8 000 bhp = 15 knots

Largest type of landing ship built in the USSR to date. First ship built in 1965-66 and commissioned in 1966. These ships have ramps on the bow and stern. Carrying capacity 1 700 tons. There are three variations of rig. In earlier type two or three cranes are carried—later types have only one crane. In the third type the bridge structure has been raised and the forward deck house has been considerably lengthened.

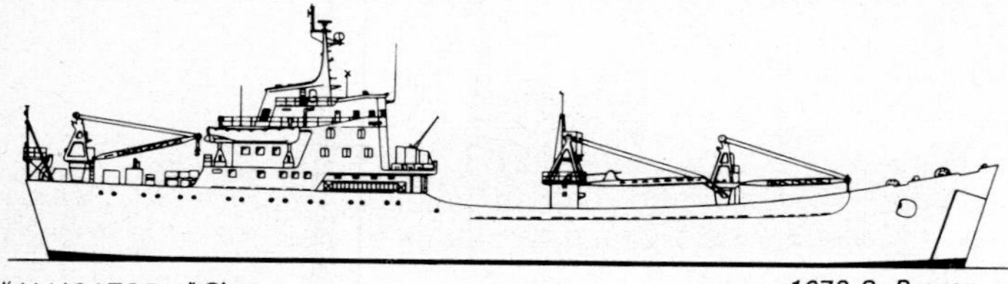

"ALLIGATOR I" Class *1973 S. Breyer*

"ALLIGATOR" Class *1972*

"ALLIGATOR II" Class

1972, H W. Van Boeijen

60 "POLNOCNY" CLASS (LCT)

Displacement, tons	780 standard; 1 000 full load (Type IX 1 300)
Dimensions, feet	246·0 × 29·5 × 9·8 (Type IX 265 × 27·7 × 9·8)
Guns	2—30 mm (twin) in all but earliest ships
A/S weapons	2—18 barrelled MBU
Main engines	2 diesels; 5 000 bhp = 18 knots

A type of amphibious vessel basically similar to the US medium landing ship, rocket (LSMR) type. Carrying capacity 350 tons. Can carry 6 tanks. Up to 9 types of this class have been built. In I to IV the mast and funnel are combined—in V onwards the mast is stepped on the bridge—in VI to VIII there is a redesign of the bow-form—IX is a completely new design of 40 ft greater length and corresponding increase in tonnage and with 4—30 mm (2 twins). Muff Cob radar.

"POLNOCNY" Class with 2—30 mm AA before bridge and fire control radar on bridge

"POLNOCNY" Class

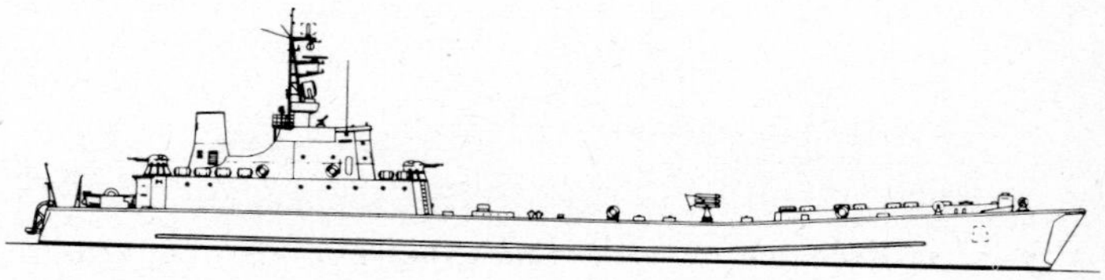

"POLNOCNY" Class with higher funnel *1973, S. Breyer*

"POLNOCNY" Class *1973*

35 "VYDRA" CLASS (LCU)

Displacement, tons 300 standard; 500 full load
Dimensions, feet 157·4 × 24·6 × 7·2
Main engines 2 diesels; 2 shafts; 400 hp = 15 knots

A new class of landing craft of the LCU type. Built from 1967-1969. No armament. Carrying capacity 250 tons.

"Vydra" Type 1971

8 "MP 2" CLASS (LCT)

Displacement, tons 750
Dimensions, feet 190 × 25 × 8·2
Guns 6—25 mm (twins)
Main engines Diesels; 1 200 hp = 16 knots

Built 1956-60. Carrying capacity 200 tons.

15 "MP 4" CLASS (LCT)

Displacement, tons 800 full load
Dimensions, feet 183·7 × 26·2 × 8·9
Guns 4—25 mm (2 twin)
Main engines Diesels; 2 shafts; 1 100 bhp = 12 knots

Built in 1956-58. Of the small freighter type in appearance. Two masts, one abaft the bridge and one in the waist. Gun mountings on poop and forecastle. Can carry 6 to 8 tanks. Several ships now serve as transports.

8 "MP 6" CLASS (LCT)

Displacement, tons 2 000
Dimensions, feet 246 × 40 × 10·5
Guns 4—45 mm (quad)
Main engines Diesels; 2 400 hp = 14 knots

Ex-merchant ship hulls. Carrying capacity 500 tons. Built 1958-61.

5 "MP 8" CLASS (LCT)

Displacement, tons 800 standard; 1 200 full load
Dimensions, feet 239·5 × 34·8 × 15·1
Guns 4—57 mm (2 twin)
Main engines Diesels; 4 000 bhp = 15 knots

Have a short and low quarter deck abaft the funnel. Can carry 6 tanks. Carrying capacity 400 tons. Built 1958-61.

"MP 8" Type 1970, S. Breyer

20 "MP10/SMB 1" CLASS (LCU)

Displacement, tons 200 standard; 420 full load
Dimensions, feet 157·5 × 21·3 × 6·5
Main engines 2 diesels; 2 shafts; 400 hp = 11 knots

A type of landing craft basically similar to the British LCT (4) type in silhouette and layout. Can carry 4 tanks. Loading capacity about 150 tons. Built 1959-66.

"MP 10/SMB 1" Class 1971

"T 4" CLASS (LCM)

Main engines 3 diesels; 3 shafts; 3 300 bhp = 24 knots
Range, miles 1 500 at 12 knots

Formerly corvettes of the "Kronstadt" class rebuilt in 1955-56. Armament removed.

AIR CUSHION VEHICLES

(Numbers in service are not known. The following gives an indication of Soviet capability. Fuller details appear in *Janes Surface Skimmers 1973-74*).

RESEARCH HOVERCRAFT

Operating weight, tons 15
Dimensions, feet 70 × 30
Propulsion 2—350 hp aircraft radial engines;
Lift 1—350 hp aircraft radial with centrifugal fan
Speed, knots 50

In use in the Soviet Navy since 1967 for tests and evaluation.

Military Derivatives of the Skate Passenger Ferry at speed on the Volga *Jane's Surface Skimmers 73/74*

"SKATE" CLASS

Operating weight, tons 27
Dimensions, feet 67·5 × 24
Propulsion 2—780 hp marine gas turbines (VP and reversible propellers)
Lift 1—780 hp marine gas turbine
Speed, knots 58
Range, miles 230 cruising

This is a naval version of a 50-seat passenger carrying craft, probably in use for the Naval Infantry.

This 15 ton research craft has been employed by the Soviet Navy to assess the potential of the skirted Air Cushion Vehicle for Naval applications *Jane's Surface Skimmers 73/74*

ASSAULT CRAFT

Operating weight, tons 200 approx
Dimensions, feet 130 × 80 approx
Speed, knots 70 approx

Currently undergoing trials for Naval Infantry. Is the first large Soviet amphibious hovercraft. Similar to British SR.N4.

EKRANOPLAN CRAFT (WIG)

Dimensions, feet 400 × 170 approx
Propulsion Two gas turbines (one to assist take-off then one for cruising)
Speed, knots 185-200 approx

An experimental craft, a wing-in-ground-effect machine, with a carrying capacity of about 900 troops and with potential for a number of naval applications such as ASW, minesweeping or patrol. Claimed to be capable of operations in heavy weather as well as crossing marshes, ice and low obstacles.

SUPPORT AND DEPOT SHIPS

8 "UGRA" CLASS (SUBMARINE SUPPORT)

BORODINO
GANGUT
IVAN KOLYSHKIN
IVAN KUCHERENKO
TOBOL
+3

Displacement, tons	6 750 standard; 9 500 full load
Length, feet (*metres*)	463·8 (*141·4*)
Beam, feet (*metres*)	57·6 (*17·6*)
Aircraft	1 helicopter
Guns	8—57 mm (twin)
Range, miles	10 000 at 12 knots

Improved versions of the "Don" class. Built from 1961 onwards, all in Nikolayev. Equipped with workshops. Provided with a helicopter platform and, in later versions, a hangar. Carries a large derrick to handle torpedoes. Has mooring points in hull about 100 feet apart, and has baggage ports possibly for coastal craft and submarines. The last pair of this class mount a large superstructure from the mainmast to quarter-deck and are used for training.

RADAR. Search Slim Net. Fire Control: Hawk Screech (2). Strut Curve. Muff Cob.

TRANSFER. The ninth ship, *Amba*, which had four 76 mm guns, was transferred to India.

"Ugra" Class No. 82 — *Skyfotos*

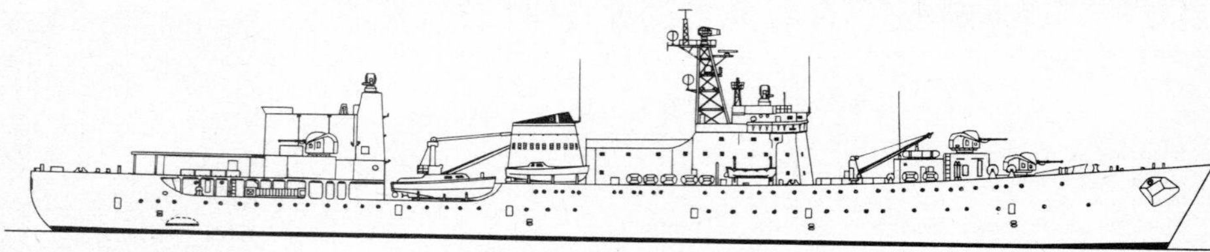

"UGRA" Class with raised helicopter platform and hangar — *1973*

"UGRA" Class — *1971, USN*

"Ugra" Class — *1970, Niels Gartig*

"UGRA" Class — *1972*

Support and Depot Ships—*continued*

6 "DON" CLASS (SUBMARINE SUPPORT)

DMITRI GALKIN
FEDOR VIDYAEV
MAGOMED GADZHIEV
MIKHAIL TUKAEVSKY
NIKOLAY STOLBOV
VIKTOR KOTELNIKOV

Displacement, tons	6 700 standard; 9 000 full load
Length, feet (*metres*)	458·9 (139·9)
Beam, feet (*metres*)	57·7 (*17·6*)
Draught, feet (*metres*)	22·3 (*6·8*)
Aircraft	Provision for helicopter in two ships
Guns	4—3·9 (*100 mm*) 8—57 mm (4 twin) (see *notes*)
Main engines	4 or 6 diesels; 14 000 bhp
Speed, knots	21
Complement	300

MAGOMED GADZHIEV *1970*

Support ships, all named after officers lost in WW II. Built in 1957 to 1962. Originally seven ships were built, all in Nikolaev. One was transferred to Indonesia in 1962. Quarters for about 450 submariners.

GUNNERY. In hull number III only 2—3·9 in. In IV no 3·9 in mounted. In some of class 8—25 mm (twin) are mounted.

RADAR. Search: Slim Net and probably Strut Curve. Fire Control: Hawk Screech (2).

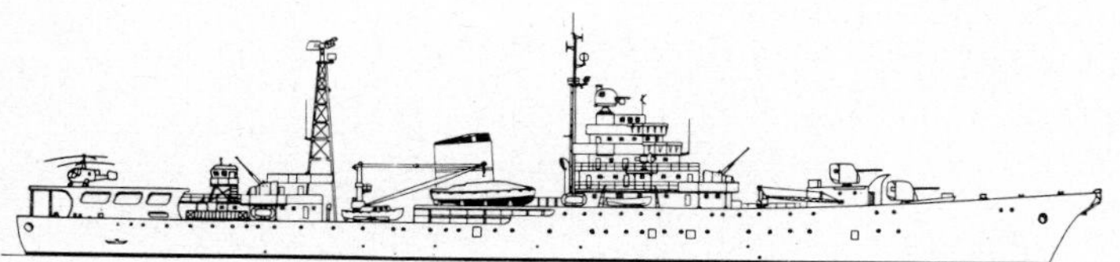
DON with helicopter platform *S. Breyer*

"DON" Class

"DON" Class *1972*

1 "PURGA" CLASS

Displacement, tons	2 250 standard; 3 000 full load
Length, feet (*metres*)	324·8 (*99·0*)
Beam, feet (*metres*)	44·3 (*13·5*)
Draught, feet (*metres*)	17·1 (*5·2*)
Guns, dual purpose	4—3·9 in (*100 mm*) singles
Mines	50 capacity
Main engines	Diesels
Speed, knots	18
Complement	250

Laid down in 1939 in Leningrad and completed in 1948. Sturdy oceangoing general purpose ship equipped as icebreaker, escort, training ship and tender. Fitted with directors similar to those in the "Riga" class frigates. Modernised in 1958-60.

"Purga" Class

Support and Depot Ships—*continued*

5 "LAMA" CLASS (MISSILE SUPPORT)

Displacement, tons	5 000 standard; 7 000 full load
Length, feet (*metres*)	370·0 (*112·8*) oa
Beam, feet (*metres*)	47·2 (*14·4*)
Draught, feet (*metres*)	19·0 (*5·8*)
Guns, dual purpose	8—57 mm, 2 quadruple, 1 on the forecastle; 1 on the break of the quarter deck
Main engines	Diesels; 2 shafts; 5 000 shp
Speed, knots	15

Support and repair ships of the depot and freighting type. Their features indicate a possible missile armed surface ship supply role. The engines are sited aft to allow for a very large and high hangar or hold amidships for carrying missiles or weapons spares. The amidships hold or hangar structure is about 12 feet high above the main deck. There are doors at the forward end with rails leading in. This is surmounted by a turntable gantry or travelling cranes for transferring armaments to combatant ships.

There are mooring points along the hull for low vessels such as submarines to come alongside. The turntable amidships is built up 2 feet above the upper deck. The two cranes are in the stowed position and there appear to be pulleyed lifting arrangements, apparently intended to service the well deck and overside. The well deck is about 40 feet long, enough for a missile to fit horizontally before being lifted vertically for loading in submarines. The ships can apparently be used for salvage and towing.

RADAR. Search: Slim Net and Strut Curve. Fire Control: Hawk Screech. (2).

"Lama" Class *Skyfotos*

LAMA *Class* *S. Breyer*

LAMA Class 1973

2 "ALESHA" CLASS (MINELAYERS)

075 **083**

Displacement, tons	3 600 standard; 4 300 full load
Dimensions, feet	337·9 × 47·6 × 15·7
Guns	4—57 mm AA (1 quadruple forward)
Mines	400
Main engines	4 diesels; 2 shafts; 8 000 bhp = 20 knots
Complement	150

In service since 1965. Fitted with four mine tracks to provide stern launchings. Also have a capability in general support role.

2 "WILHELM BAUER" CLASS (SUBMARINE TENDERS)

KUBAN (ex-*Waldemar Kophamel*) **PECHORA** (ex-*Otto Wünche*)

Displacement, tons	4 726 standard; 5 600 full load
Dimensions, feet	446·0 × 52·5 × 14·5
Main engines	4 MAN diesels; 2 shafts; 12 400 bhp = 20 knots

Former German. Launched in 1939. *Kuban* was salvaged in 1950-51 after being sunk in shallow water by bombing in WW II and was rehabilitated in 1951-57.

ALESHA Class 1972

Support and Depot Ships—*continued*

10 "AMUR" CLASS (DEPOT SHIPS)

Displacement, tons	6 500 full load
Dimensions, feet	377·3 × 57·4 × 18·0
Main engines	Diesels; 2 shafts

A new class of general purpose depot ships built since 1969. Successors to the "Oskol" class. In series production at a rate of about 2 a year.

"AMUR" Class *1972, H. W. Van Boeijen*

" AMUR" Class *1973*

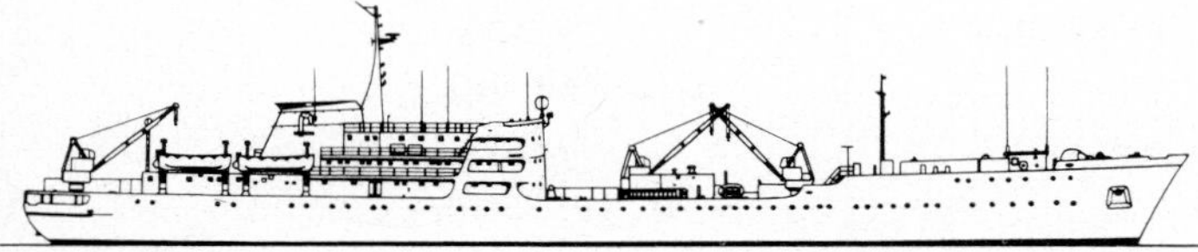

" AMUR" Class *1973 S. Breyer*

10 "OSKOL" CLASS (REPAIR SHIPS)

Displacement, tons	2 500 standard; 3 000 full load
Dimensions, feet	295·2 × 39·4 × 14·8
Main engines	2 diesels; 2 shafts; speed = 16 knots

Three series: "Oskol I" class, well-decked hull, no armament; "Oskol II" Class, well-decked hull, armed with 2—57 mm guns (1 twin) and 4—25 mm guns (2 twin); "Oskol III" class, flush-decked hull. General purpose tenders and repair ships. Built from 1963 to 1970 in Poland.

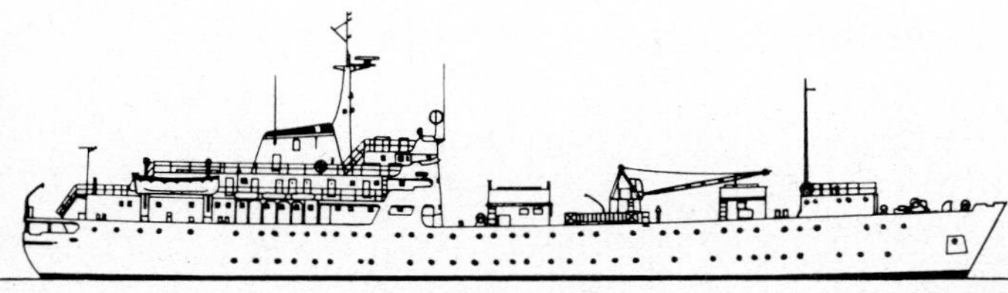

" OSKOL III" Class *1973 S. Breyer*

6 "ATREK" CLASS (SUBMARINE SUPPORT)

ATREK AYAT BAKHMUT DVINA MURMATS OSIPOV

Displacement, tons	3 500 standard; 6 700 full load
Measurement, tons	3 258 gross
Dimensions, feet	336 × 49 × 20
Main engines	Expansion and exhaust turbines; 1 shaft; 2 450 hp = 13 knots
Boilers	2 water tube
Range, miles	3 500 at 13 knots

Built in 1956-58, and converted to naval use from "Kolomna" class freighters. There are six of these vessels employed as submarine tenders and replenishment ships. Some may have up to 6—37 mm (twins).

BAKHMUT *1974*

5 "DNEPR" CLASS (REPAIR SHIPS)

Displacement, tons	4 500 standard; 5 250 full load
Dimensions, feet	370·7 × 54·1 × 14·4
Main engines	Diesels; 2 000 bhp = 12 knots

Bow lift repair ships for fleet support and maintenance. Built in 1957-66 and equipped with workshops and servicing facilities. The last two ships of this class are flushdecked ("Dnepr II" class).

"DNEPR I" Class *1965*

3 "TOVDA" CLASS (REPAIR SHIPS)

INZA (ex-*Novoshaktinsk*) **TOVDA** **VITEGRA**

Displacement, tons	3 000 standard; 4 000 full load
Dimensions, feet	282·1 × 39·4 × 16·0
Guns	6—57 mm AA (3 twin mountings)
Main engines	Triple expansion; 1 300 ihp = 11 knots

Polish built ex-tankers converted in 1958 to 1960. Repair ships. Also known as the "Soldek" class, but the NATO designation is "Tovda" class.

"TOVDA" Class *1959*

Support and Depot Ships—*continued*

53 INTELLIGENCE COLLECTORS (AGI's)

6 "PRIMORYE" CLASS

PRIMORYE **KAVKAZ** **KRYM** **ZABAIKALYE** **ZAPOROZYE** **ZAKARPATYE**

Displacement, tons 5 000
Dimensions, feet 274 × 45 × 26·2

The most modern intelligence collectors in the world, apparently with built-in processing and (?) analysis.

" PRIMORYE"Class 1972

15 "OKEAN" CLASS

ALIDADA **AMPERMETR** **BAROGRAF** **BAROMETR** **DEFLEKTOR** **EKHOLOT** **GIDROFON** **KRENOMETR** **LINZA** **LOTLIN** **REDUKTOR** **REPITER** **TEODOLIT** **TRAVERZ** **ZOND**

REDUKTOR, "Okean" Class AGI *1972, H. W. van Boeijen*

8 "LENTRA" CLASS

GS 34 **GS 36** **GS 41** **GS 43** **GS 46** **GS 47** **GS 55** **GS 59**

"LENTRA" CLASS *1968, Michael D. J. Lennon*

8 "MAYAK" CLASS

ANEROID **GIRORULEVOY** **KHERSONES** **KURS** **KURSOGRAF** **LADOGA** **GS 239** **GS 242**

"MAYAK" Class *1972*

GIRORULEVOY, "Mayak" Class *1972*

4 "MIRNY" CLASS

BAKAN **LOTSMAN** **VAL** **VERTIKAL**

BAKAN "Mirny" Class AGI *1972*

5 "MOMA" CLASS

ARKEPELAG **ILMEN** **NAKHODKA** **PELORUS** **SELIGER**

ARKEPELAG "Moma" Class AGI *1972*

2 "PAMIR" CLASS

GIDROGRAF **PELENG**

2 "DNEPR" CLASS

IZMERITEL **PROTRAKTOR**

1 "T 58" CLASS

GIDROLOG

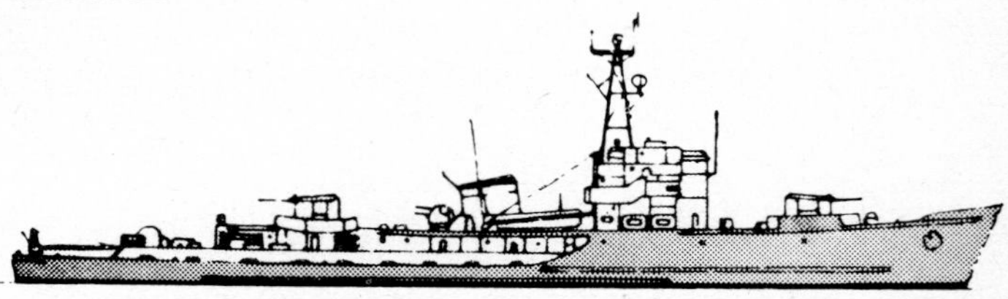

2 "ZUBOV" CLASS

G. SARYCHEV **K. LAPTEV**

"ZUBOV" Class

SURVEY SHIPS

NOTE. Only a fairly small proportion of Survey and Research Ships are naval manne d, the choice apparently varying from time to time for different duties.

22 "MOMA" CLASS (+5 AGI's)

ANADIR
ARTIKA
ASKOLD
BEREZAN
CHELEKEN
EKVATOR
KILDIN
KRILON
KOLGUEV
OKEAN
TAYMYR
ZAPOLARA

+10

Displacement, tons 1 240 standard; 1 800 full load
Dimensions, feet 219·8 × 32·8 × 13·2
Main engines Diesels; speed 16 knots

Eight ships of this class were reported to have been built from 1967 to 1970 and the remainder since.

CHELEKEN, "Moma" Class AGS 1972

8 "KAMENKA" CLASS

Displacement, tons 1 000 standard
Dimensions, feet 180·5 × 31·2 × 11·5
Main engines Diesels; speed 16 knots

The ships of this class are not named but have a number with the prefix letters "GS". All reported to have been built since 1967-68.

5 "TELNOVSK" CLASS

AYTADOR
SVIYAGA

Displacement, tons 1 200 standard
Measurement, tons 1 217 gross, 448 net
Dimensions, feet 229·6 × 32·8 × 13·1
Main engines Diesels; speed 10 knots

Formerly coastal freighters. Built in Bulgaria and Hungary. Refitted and modernised or naval supply and surveying duties.

AYTADOR *1965, Michael D. J. Lennon*

IZUMRUD

Measurement, tons 3 862 gross; 465 net
Main engines Powered by diesel-electric machinery

A new type of research and survey ship built in 1970.

IZUMRUD *1972, Michael D. J. Lennon*

16 "SAMARA" CLASS

AZIMUT
DEVIATOR
GIDROLOG
GIGROMETR
GLOBUS
GLUBOMER
GORIZONT
GRADUS
KOMPAS
PAMYAT MERKURYIA
RUMB
TROPIK
ZENIT
VAGACH
VOSTOK
YUG

Displacement, tons 800 standard; 1 000 full load
Measurement, tons 1 276 gross; 1 000 net
Dimensions, feet 180·4 × 32·8 × 11·5
Main engines Diesels; speed 16 knots

Built at Gdansk, Poland since 1962 for hydrographic surveying and research.

KOMPAS *1970, Michael D. J. Lennon*

GLOBUS *1972, Michael D. J. Lennon*

AZIMUT *1972, Michael D. J. Lennon*

2 "MALYGIN" CLASS

STEFAN MALYGIN
NICOLAI KOLOMEITEY

Both built by Turku, Finland Launched 16 Nov 1970 and 16 Nov 1971 respectively.

Survey Ships—*continued*

MICHAIL LOMONOSOV

Displacement, tons	5 960 normal
Measurement, tons	3 897 gross; 1 195 net
Dimensions, feet	336·0 × 47·2 × 14·0
Main engines	Triple expansion; 2 450 ihp = 13 knots

Built by Neptune, Rostock, in 1957 from the hull of a freighter of the "Kolomna" class. Operated not by the Navy but by the Academy of Science. Equipped with 16 laboratories. Carries a helicopter for survey.

MICHAIL LOMONOSOV *1970, Michael D. J. Lennon*

9 "NIKOLAI ZUBOV" CLASS

A. CHIRIKOV **NIKOLAI ZUBOV** **SEJMEN DEZHNEV**
A. VILKITSKIJ **S. CHELYUSKIN** **T. BELLINSGAUSEN**
BORIS DAVIDOV **V. GOLOVNIN**
F. LITKE

Displacement, tons	2 674 standard; 3 021 full load
Dimensions, feet	295·2 × 42·7 × 15
Main engines	2 diesels; speed = 16·7 knots
Complement	108 to 120, including 70 scientists

Oceanographic research ships built at Szczecin Shipyard, Poland in 1964. *Nikolai Zubov* visited London in 1965. Employed on survey in the Atlantic.

NIKOLAI ZUBOV

GAVRIL SARITSHEV *1966, Michael D. J. Lennon*

DOLINSK

Measurement, tons	10 826 deadweight; 5 419 gross, 2 946 net
Dimensions, feet	456·0 × 58·0 × 15·5
Main engines	2 diesels

Built at Abo in Finland in 1959. Converted for surveying. Fitted with directional aerial between bridge and funnel.

DOLINSK (ex-ARKHANGELSK) *1972, Michael D. J. Lennon*

ZARJA

Measurement, tons	71 net; 333 gross

Auxiliary vessel built in 1952. One of some 50 or so similar schooners built in Finland. Constructed almost entirely of wood. Classed as a research vessel.

NEREY **NOVATOR** **VLADIMIR OBRUCHEV**

All three of these ships are former fleet tugs converted to survey vessels.

PETRODVORETSK

Reported to be a former ferry ship converted for special surveying duties.

RESEARCH SHIPS

3 "POLYUS" CLASS

BAIKAL **BALKHASH** **POLYUS**

Displacement, tons	6 900 standard
Dimensions, feet	365·8 × 47·2 × 20·7
Main engines	Diesel-electric; 3 400 hp = 14 knots

These ships of the "Polyus" class were built in East Germany in 1961-64. Oceanographic research ships.

POLYUS *1972*

VITYAZ (ex-*Mars*)

Displacement, tons	5 700 standard
Main engines	Diesels; 3 000 bhp = 14·5 knots
Range, miles	18 400 at 14 knots
Complement	137 officers and men including 73 scientists

Oceanographic research ship. Formerly a German freighter built at Bremen in 1939 Equipped with 13 laboratories.

VITYAZ *1972, Michael D. J. Lennon*

Research Ships—*continued*

2 "ORBELI" CLASS

AKADEMIK IOSIF ORBELI
PROFESSOR NIKOLAI BARABSKI

Both of 9 727 tons gross built in Warnemünde 1969-71.

7 "AKADEMIK KURCHATOV" CLASS

AKADEMIK KOROLEV
AKADEMIK KURCHATOV
AKADEMIK SHIRSHOV
AKADEMIK VERBADSKIJ
DMITRI MENDELEYEV
PROFESSOR ZUBOV
PROFESSOR VIZE

Displacement, tons	6 681 full load
Measurement, tons	1 387 net; 1 986 deadweight; 5 460 gross
Dimensions, feet	400·3 to 406·8 × 56·1 × 15·0
Main engines	2 Halberstadt 6-cylinder diesels; 2 shafts; 8 000 bhp = 18 to 20 knots

All built by Mathias Thesen Werft at Wismar, East Germany between 1965 and 1968.

PROFESSOR VIZE *1972, H. W. van Boeijen*

DMITRI MENDELEYEV *1973, M. R. Ross*

9 "PASSAT" CLASS

MUSSON
OKEAN
PASSAT
PRIBOJ
PORIV
PRILIV
SHKVAL
VIKHR
VOLNA

Research or weather ships built at Szczecin, Poland, since 1968. Aerials differ in certain ships.

OKEAN *1972, Michael D. J. Lennon*

PASSAT *1970, Michael D. J. Lennon*

2 "LEBEDEV" CLASS

PETR LEBEDEV
SERGEI VAVILOV

Measurement, tons	1 180 net; 3 561 gross
Main engines	Diesels

Research vessels with comprehensive equipment and accommodation. Both built in 1954.

PETR LEBEDEV *1970, Michael D. J. Lennon*

PROFESSOR DERYUGIN
AKADEMIK BERG
AKADEMIK KNIPOUITCH

Fishery research ships of 1 166 tons net; 3 165 gross. Built in the USSR at Nikola v between 1964 and 1968.

AYSBERG **ISSLEDOVATEL** **OKEANOGRAF** **POLIARNIK** **TAMANGO**

Converted trawlers of 265 tons gross; 93 net for research. All M-Research. *Aysberg, Okeanograf* and *Poliarnik* have visited the United Kingdom. Built in 1952 to 1970.

OKEANOGRAF *1970, Michael D. J. Lennon*

SPACE ASSOCIATED SHIPS

1 "GAGARIN" CLASS

KOSMONAUT YURIY GAGARIN

Displacement, tons	45 000
Measurement, tons	32 291 gross; 5 247 net
Dimensions, feet	757·9; 773·3oa × 101·7 × 30·0
Main engines	2 geared steam turbines; 1 shaft; 19 000 shp = 17 knots max

Design based on the "Sofia" or "Akhtubu" (ex-"Hanoi") class steam tanker. Built at Leningrad in 1970, completing in 1971. Used for investigation into conditions in the upper atmosphere, and the control of space vehicles. She is the largest Soviet research vessel. Has bow and stern thrust units for ease of berthing.

KOSMONAUT YURIY GAGARIN *1972, Michael D. J. Lennon*

1 "KOMAROV" CLASS

KOSMONAUT VLADIMIR KOMAROV (ex-*Genichesk*)

Displacement, tons	17 500 full load
Measurement, tons	8 000 approximately
Dimensions, feet	510·8 × 75·5 × 29·5
Main engines	Diesels; 2 shafts; 24 000 bhp = 22 knots

Former freighter of the "Poltava" class, *Kosmonaut Vladimir Komarov* was launched in 1966. Built at the Leningrad Shipyard. Designed for the Soviet Academy of Science as a research vessel to study higher layers of atmosphere in the tropical zone of the western part of the Atlantic Ocean. Prominent features of the ship are the unusual hull sponsons and the radomes, massive plastic spheres enclosing radar arrays. The ship is named in honour of the Soviet astronaut who died when his space craft crashed in 1967.

KOSMONAUT VLADIMIR KOMAROV *1969, Skyfotos*

4 "SIBIR" CLASS

CHUKOTKA **SAKHALIN** **SIBIR** **SUCHAN**

Displacement, tons	4 000 standard; 5 000 full load
Measurement, tons	3 767 gross (*Chukotka* 3 800, *Suchan* 3 710)
Dimensions, feet	354 × 49·2 × 20
Guns	6—45 mm AA; 2 MG
Main engines	Triple expansion; 2 shafts; 3 300 ihp = 15 knots
Range, miles	3 300 at 12 knots

Converted bulk ore carriers employed as Missile Range Ships in the Pacific. *Sakhalin* and *Sibir* have three radomes forward and aft, and carry helicopters. *Suchan* is also equipped with a helicopter flight deck. Launched in 1957-59. Formerly freighters of the Polish "B 31" type. Rebuilt in 1958-59 as missile range ships in Leningrad.

2 "DESNA" CLASS

CHAZHMA **CHUMIKAN**

Displacement, tons	5 300 light; 14 065 full load
Dimensions, feet	457·7 × 59·0 × 25·9
Aircraft	1 helicopter
Main engines	Triple expansion; 4 000 ihp = 18 knots

Formerly freighters of the "Dzankoy" class (7 265 tons gross). Soviet Range Instrumentation Ships (SRIS). The "Desna" class have a larger hull than the "Sibir" class and are better equipped. Active since 1963. Large radome on the bridge.

1 "KOROLEV" TYPE

AKADEMIK SERGEI KOROLEV

Displacement, tons	21 250
Measurement, tons	17 114 gross; 2 185 net
Dimensions, feet	597·1 × 82·0 × 30·0

Built at Nikolaev in 1970, completing in 1971. Equipped with the smaller type radome and two "saucers"

8 "BASKUNCHAK" (ex-VOSTOK) CLASS

APSHERON **DAURIYA** **DONBASS** **TAMAN**
BASKUNCHAK **DIKSON** **SEVAN** **YAMAL**

Measurement, tons	2 215 net; 6 450 deadweight; 4 896 gross
Dimensions, feet	400·3 × 55·1 × 14·0
Main engines	B & W 9-cylinder diesels; speed 15 knots

Standard timber carriers modified with helicopter flight decks. Built at Leningrad between 1963 and 1966. Entirely manned by naval personnel.

BASKUNCHAK *1970, Michael D. J. Lennon*

7 "MORZHOVETS" (ex-VOSTOK *) CLASS

BOROVICHI * **BEZHITSA** **DOLINSK** **MORZHOVETS ***
KEGOSTROV * **NEVEL ***

Former timber carriers but completely modified with a comprehensive array of tracking, direction finding and directional aerials. Additional laboratories built above the forward holds. Same measurements as the "Baskunchak" class, but tonnage increased to 5 277 gross and 967 net. *Bezhitsa* is ex-"Poltava" class, *Dolinsk* is ex-*Arkhangelsk* class and remainder (starred) "Vostok" class.

BEZHITSA *1972, Michael D. J. Lennon*

Ex-"POVOLETS CLASS

RISTNA

Measurement, tons	1 819 net; 4 200 deadweight; 3 724 gross
Dimensions, feet	347·8 × 47·9 × 14·0
Main engines	MAN 6-cylinder diesels; speed = 15 knots

Classed as M Research. Converted from a timber carrier. Built in East Germany at Rostok by Schiffswerft Neptun in 1963. Painted white. Fitted with directional aerials on top of bridge wings. Served as Missile Detection Ship. In the same group as the "Morzhovets" class, see above.

RISTNA (ex-"Povolets" class) *1970, Michael D. J. Lennon*

Space Associated Ships—*continued*

KOSMONAUT YURIY GAGARIN *1972*

KOSMONAUT VLADIMIR KOMAROV *1972, Michael D. J. Lennon*

AKADEMIK SERGEI KOROLEV ***1972, Michael D. J. Lennon***

SERVICE FORCES

NOTE. With the Soviet merchant fleet under State control any ships under their control, including tankers, may be diverted to a fleet support role at any time.

3 "CHILIKIN" CLASS (FLEET REPLENISHMENT SHIPS)

BORIS CHILIKIN **VLADIMIR KOLECHITSKY** +1

Displacement, tons 20 500 full load
Dimensions, feet 531·5 × 70·2 × 28·1 loaded
Guns 4—57 mm (2 twin)

Based on the "Veliky Oktyabr" merchant ship tanker design *Chilikin* was built at Leningrad completing in 1971. This is the first Soviet Navy class of purpose built underway fleet replenishment ships for the supply of both liquids and solids, indicating a growing awareness of the need for afloat support for a widely dispersed fleet.

BORIS CHILIKIN 1972

BORIS CHILIKIN 1972

1 "MANYCH" CLASS

Displacement, tons 7 500
Guns 4—57 mm (2 twin) with Muff Cob radar

Completed 1972, probably in Finland. A smaller edition of the "*Boris Chilikin*" but showing the new interest in custom built replenishment ships. The high point on the single gantry is very similar to that on "*Chilikin's*" third gantry.

MANYCH 1973 S. Breyer

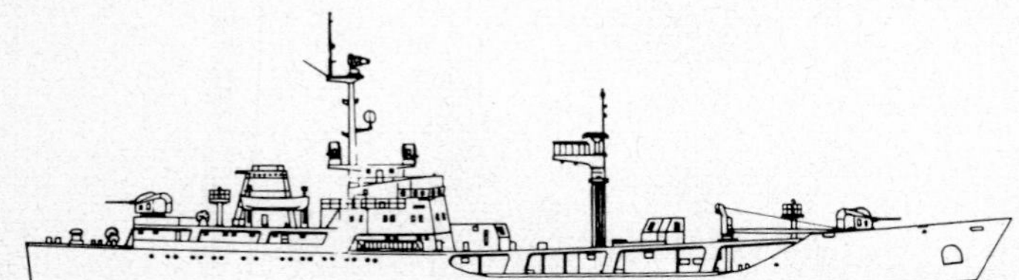

MANYCH 1973

1 "SOFIA" CLASS

AKHTUBA (ex-*Khanoy*)

Displacement, tons 45 000 full load
Measurement, tons 62 000 deadweight, 32 840 gross, 16 383 net
Dimensions, feet 757·9 × 101·7 × 32·8

AKHTUBA *1972, Michael D. J. Lennon*

Built as the merchant tanker *Khanoy* in 1963 at Leningrad, she was taken over by the Navy in 1969 and renamed *Akhtuba*. The hull type was used in the construction of the space associated ship *Kosmonaut Yuriy Gagarin*.

4 "KAZBEK" CLASS

ALATYR **ANDREY** **DESNA** **VOLKHOV**

Displacement, tons 16 250 full load
Measurement, tons 16 250 deadweight; 3 942 gross; 8 229 net
Dimensions, feet 479·0 × 63·0 × 23·0
Main engines 2 diesels driving single screw

Former "Leningrad" class merchant fleet tankers taken over by the Navy as oilers. All built at Leningrad from 1954 to 1957. Sister ship *Kazbec* was returned to the mercantile marine in 1970.

6 "ALTAY" CLASS

ALTAY **ELYENYA** **IZHORA** **KOLA** **YEGORLIK** +1

Displacement, tons 5 500 standard
Dimensions, feet 344·5 × 49·2 × 19·7
Main engines Diesels, speed = 14 knots

"ALTAY Class" 1972

Built from 1967 onwards. Naval oilers with no armament.

6 "UDA" CLASS

DUNAY **KOIDA** **LENA** **SHEKSNA** **TEREK** **VISHERA**

Displacement, tons 5 500 standard; 7 200 full load
Dimensions, feet 400·3 × 51·8 × 20·3
Main engines Diesels; 2 shafts; 8 000 bhp = 17 knots

"UDA Class" *1966, S. Breyer*

A medium type of Soviet supply ships. Built since 1961.

2 "PEVEK" CLASS

PEVEK **ZOLOTOY ROG**

Displacement, tons 4 000 standard
Measurement, tons 4 500 deadweight
Dimensions, feet 344·5 × 47·9 × 20·0
Main engines Diesels; 2 900 bhp = 14 knots

A type similar to the United States AOG gasolene carriers. Built in Finland in 1960.

2 "OLEKMA" CLASS

IMAN **OLEKMA**

Displacement, tons 3 300
Dimensions, feet 344·5 × 49·2 × 20·0

RESCUE LAUNCH

AR 1

Displacement, tons	25 standard; 30 full load
Dimensions, feet	63·0 × 15·0 × 3·8
Guns	4 MG
Main engines	2 Hall-Scott Defender; 1 260 bhp = 33·5 knots
Range, miles	600 at 15 knots
Complement	8

British type rescue launch. Launched on 4 July 1944.

TANKERS

PRESIDENTE ORIBE 1971

PRESIDENTE ORIBE AO 9

Measurement, tons	17 920 gross; 28 267 deadweight
Dimensions, feet	587·2 pp; 620 oa × 84·3 × 33
Main engines	1 Ishikawajima turbine; 12 500 shp = 16·75 knots
Boilers	2 Ishikawajima-Harima Foster Wheeler type
Range, miles	16 100 at 16 knots
Complement	76

Built by Ishikawajima-Harima Ltd, Japan. Delivered to the Uruguayan Navy on 22 Mar 1962.

PRESIDENTE RIVERA

Measurement, tons	19 350
Dimensions, feet	636·3 × 84 × 32
Main engines	15 300 bhp = 15 knots

Built in Spain, completing in 1971.

VIGILANTE (ex-YTL 589)

of 350 tons.

VENEZUELA

Administration

Commander General of the Navy (Chief of Naval Operations):
Rear-Admiral Armando Perez Leefmans

Chief of Naval Staff:
Rear-Admiral Enrique Dominauez Garcia

Diplomatic Representation

Chief of Inspecting Commission (UK):
Captain O. E. Ortega

Naval Attaché in Washington:
Rear Admiral Luis Ramirez Aranda

Personnel

(a) 1974: 7 500 officers and men including 4 000 of the Marine Corps
(b) 2 years National Service

Strength of the Fleet

Type	Active	Building
Destroyers	5	—
Frigates	6	—
Submarines, Patrol	3	2
Fast Attack Craft—Missile	2	4
Large Patrol Craft	10	—
Coastal Patrol Craft (manned by National Guard)	16	21
LST	1	—
LSM	4	—
Transport Landing Ship	1	—
Transports	3	—
Survey Ships	5	—
Ocean Tug	1	—
Harbour Tugs	9	—
Floating Dock	1	—

National Guard

The Fuerzas Armadas de Cooperacion, generally known as the National Guard, is a paramilitary organisation, 10 000 strong. It is concerned, amongst other things, with customs and internal security—the Maritime Wing operates the Coastal Patrol Craft listed under Light Forces, though these nominally belong to the Navy.

Mercantile Marine

Lloyd's Register of Shipping:
137 vessels of 478 643 tons gross

DESTROYERS

3 "ARAGUA" CLASS

Name	*No.*	*Builders*	*Laid down*	*Launched*	*Completed*
ARAGUA	D 31	Vickers Ltd, Barrow	29 June 1953	27 Jan 1955	14 Feb 1956
NUEVA ESPARTA	D 11	Vickers Ltd, Barrow	24 July 1951	19 Nov 1952	8 Dec 1953
ZULIA	D 21	Vickers Ltd, Barrow	24 July 1951	29 June 1953	15 Sep 1954

Displacement, tons	2 600 standard; 3 670 full load
Length, feet (*metres*)	384·0 (*117·0*)wl; 402·0 (*122·5*)oa
Beam, feet (*metres*)	43·0 (*13·1*)
Draught, feet (*metres*)	19·0 (*5·8*)
Missiles	2 quadruple "Seacat" in D 11
Guns, dual purpose	6—4·5 (*114 mm*), 3 twin
Guns, AA	16—40 mm (8 twin) 4—40 mm (2 twin) in D 11 only
A/S weapons	2 Hedgehogs 2 DCT; 2 DC racks ("Squids" in D 11 and D 21)
Torpedo tubes	3—21 in (*533 mm*) triple (none in D 11)
Boilers	2 Yarrow
Main engines	Parsons geared turbines; 2 shafts; 50 000 shp
Speed, knots	34
Range, miles	5 000 at 10 knots
Complement	256 (20 officers, 236 men)

ARAGUA 1969, Venezuelan Navy

All built in Great Britain. *Nueva Esparta* and *Zulia* were ordered in 1950. Air conditioned. Two engine rooms and two boiler rooms served by a single uptake. The 4·5 inch guns are fully automatic. *Nueva Esparta* and *Zulia* refitted at Palmers Hebburn Works, Vickers in 1959, and at New York Navy Yard in 1960 to improve anti-submarine and anti-aircraft capabilities. *Aragua* refitted by Palmers Hebburn in 1964-65, *Nueva Esparta* at Cammell Laird in 1968-69 when "Seacat" launchers were fitted and some 40 mm and the torpedo tubes removed.

RADAR. Search: AWS 2 and (*Nueva Esparta*) SPS 6. Fire Control: X Band.

NUEVA ESPARTA 1970, Venezuelan Navy.

Destroyers—*continued*

1 Ex-US "ALLEN M. SUMNER" CLASS

Name	Builders	Launched	Commissioned
CARABOBO (ex-USS *Beatty* DD 756)	Bethlehem, Staten Is.	30 Nov 1944	31 Mar 1945

Displacement, tons: 2 200 standard; 3 320 full load
Dimensions, ft (*m*): 376·5 × 40·9 × 19·0 (*114·8 × 12·4 × 5·8*)
Guns: 6—5 in dp (twins)
A/S weapons: 2 fixed Hedgehogs, DC's; 2 triple torpedo tubes (Mk 32)
Main engines: 2 geared turbines; 60 000 shp; 2 shafts
Boilers: 4
Speed, knots: 34
Range, miles: 4 600 at 15 knots
Complement: 274

Transferred from USN 14 July 1972.

CARABOBO (as *Beatty*) — *1965, Dr. Giorgio Arra*

1 Ex-US "ALLEN M. SUMNER FRAM II" CLASS

Name	No.	Builders	Launched	Commissioned
FALCON (ex-USS *Robert K. Huntington* DD 781)	D 21	Todd Pacific Shipyards	5 Dec 1944	3 Mar 1945

Displacement, tons: 2 200 standard; 3 320 full load
Dimensions, ft (*m*): 376·5 × 40·9 × 19 (*114·8 × 12·4 × 5·8*)
Guns: 6—5 in 38 cal DP (twins)
A/S weapons: 2 Fixed Hedgehogs; 2 triple torpedo tubes (Mk 32); Facilities for small helicopter
Main engines: 2 geared turbines; 60 000 shp; 2 shafts
Boilers: 4
Speed, knots: 34
Range, miles: 4 600 at 15 knots
Complement: 274

Purchased from USN 31 Oct 1973. Modernised under the FRAM II programme.

RADAR. SPS 40 and SPS 10.

SONAR. Hull mounted; SQS 29 series. VDS.

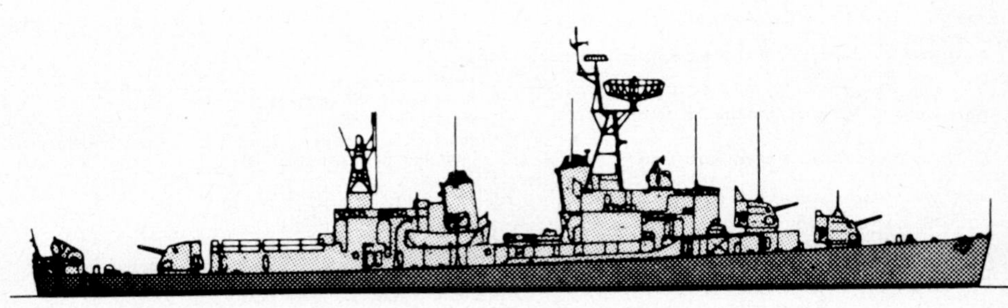

"ALLEN M. SUMNER FRAM II" Class

FRIGATES

6 "ALMIRANTE CLEMENTE" CLASS

Name	No.	Laid down	Launched	Completed
ALMIRANTE CLEMENTE	D 12	5 May 1954	12 Dec 1954	1956
ALMIRANTE JOSE GARCIA	D 33	12 Dec 1954	12 Oct 1956	1957
ALMIRANTE BRION	D 23	12 Dec 1954	4 Sep 1955	1957
GENERAL JOSÉ DE AUSTRIA	D 32	12 Dec 1954	15 July 1956	1957
GENERAL JOSÉ TRINIDAD MORAN	D 22	5 May 1954	12 Dec 1954	1956
GENERAL JUAN JOSÉ FLORES	D 13	5 May 1954	7 Feb 1955	1956

Displacement, tons: 1 300 standard; 1 500 full load
Length, feet (*metres*): 325·11 (*99·1*) oa
Beam, feet (*metres*): 35·5 (*10·8*)
Draught, feet (*metres*): 12·2 (*3·7*)
Guns, dual purpose: 4—4 in (*102 mm*) 2 twin
Guns, AA: 4—40 mm; 8—20 mm (modified group 40 mm only)
A/S weapons: 2 "Hegehogs", 4 DCT and 2 DC racks in original group; 1 A/S Mortar, 4 DCT and 2 DC racks in modified group
Torpedo tubes: 3—21 in (*533 mm*) triple (original group only)
Boilers: 2 Foster Wheeler
Main engines: 2 sets geared turbines; 2 shafts; 24 000 shp
Speed, knots: 32 max, 28 in service
Range, miles: 3 500 at 15 knots
Oil, fuel tons: 350
Complement: 162 (12 officers, 150 men)

All built by Ansaldo, Leghorn. The first three were ordered in 1953. Three more were ordered in 1954. Aluminium alloys were widely employed in the building of all superstructure. All six ships are fitted with Denny-Brown fin stabilisers and air conditioned throughout the living and command spaces.

GUNNERY. The 4 inch anti-aircraft guns are fully automatic and radar controlled.

MODERNISATION. *Almirante José Garcia, Almirante Brion* and *General José de Austria* were refitted by Ansaldo, Leghorn, in 1962 to improve their anti-submarine and anti-aircraft capabilities: this group are known as "Modified Almirante Clemente" type. *Almirante Clemente* and *General José Trinidad Moran* were refitted by the Cammell Laird/Plessey group during 1969.

RADAR. Search: MLA 1. Fire Control: X Band.

GENERAL JOSE TRINIDAD MORAN — *1972, Venezuelan Navy,*

GENERAL JOSE DE AUSTRIA (modified group) — *1972, Venezuelan Navy*

SUBMARINES

2 HOWALDTSWERKE TYPE 209

Displacement, tons	990 surfaced; 1 350 dived
Dimensions, ft (*m*)	177·1 × 20·3 × — (*54·0* × *6·2* × —)
Torpedo tubes	8—21 in (with reloads) bow
Main machinery	Diesel-electric; 4 MTU-Siemens diesel generators; 1 Siemens electric motor 5 000 hp; 1 shaft
Speed, knots	10 surfaced; 22 dived
Range,	50 days
Complement	31

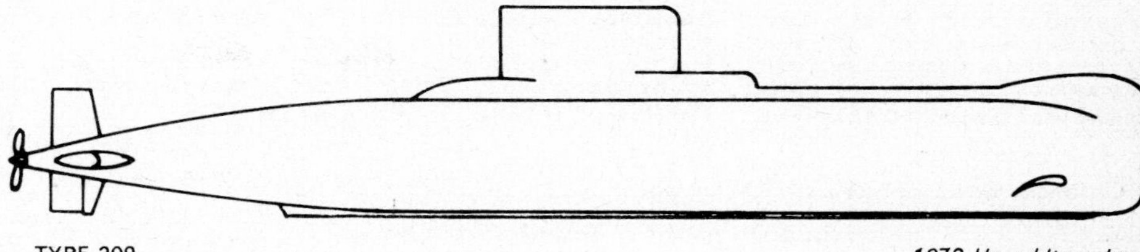
TYPE 209 — *1973 Howaldtswerke*

Type 209, IK81 designed by Ingenieurkontor Lübeck for construction by Howaldtswerke, Kiel and sale by Ferrostaal, Essen, all acting as a consortium.
A single-hull design with two main ballast tanks and forward and after trim tanks. Fitted with snort and remote machinery control. Slow revving single screw. Very high capacity batteries with GRP lead-acid cells and battery-cooling—by W. Hagen and VARTA. Active and passive sonar, sonar detection set, sound-ranging equipment and underwater telephone. Have two periscopes, radar and Omega receiver. Fore-planes retract. Ordered in 1971. Building in Germany for completion 1974-75.

2 Ex-US "GUPPY II" CLASS

Name	*No.*	*Builders*	*Launched*	*Commissioned*
TIBURON (ex-USS *Cubera* SS 347)	S 12	Electric Boat Co, Groton	17 June 1945	19 Dec 1945
PICUDA (ex-USS *Grenadier* SS 525)	S 13	Boston Navy Yard	15 Dec 1944	10 Feb 1951

Displacement, tons	1 870 surface; 2 420 submerged
Length, feet (*metres*)	307·5 (*93·8*)
Beam, feet (*metres*)	27·0 (*8·2*)
Draught, feet (*metres*)	18·0 (*5·5*)
Torpedo tubes	10—21 in (*533 mm*), 6 bow, 4 stern
Main machinery	3 diesels; 4 800 shp; 2 electric motors; 5 400 shp; 2 shafts
Speed, knots	18 on surface; 15 submerged
Range, miles	12 000 at 10 knots
Oil fuel, tons	300
Complement	80

Transferred as follows—*Tiburon* 5 Jan 1972, *Picuda* 15 May 1973.

PICUDA (as GRENADIER) — *US Navy*

1 Ex-US "BALAO" CLASS

Name	*No.*	*Builders*	*Launched*	*Commissioned*
CARITE (ex-USS *Tilefish* SS 307)	S 11	Mare Island Navy Yard	25 Oct 1943	28 Dec 1943

Displacement, tons	1 450 standard; 2 400 dived
Dimensions, ft (*m*)	312 × 27·2 × 17·2 (*95·1* × *8·3* × *5·3*)
Torpedo tubes	10—21 in; 6 bow, 4 stern
Main machinery	4 diesels; 6 400 hp; 2 electric motors; 5 400 shp; 2 shafts
Range, miles	12 000 at 10 knots
Speed, knots	20 surface; 10 dived
Complement	85

Purchased from USN—Transfer 4 May 1960 after 4 month refit. Subsequently refitted with streamlined fin.

CARITE — *1969 Venezuelan Navy.*

LIGHT FORCES

6 VOSPER-THORNYCROFT 121 FT CLASS (FAST ATTACK CRAFT—MISSILE AND GUN)

CONSTITUCION	**LIBERTAD**
FEDERACION	**PATRIA**
INDEPENDENCIA	**VICTORIA**

Displacement, tons	150 (approx)
Length, feet (*metres*)	121·3 (*37*)
Missiles	3 to be armed with Otomat
Guns	Second 3 to be armed with Oto Melara 76 mm
Main engines	2 MTU diesels; 3 600 hp 2 shafts
Speed, knots	27

A £6m, order, the first laid down in Jan 1973. A new design, fitted with Elsag fire-control system NA 10 mod 1 and Selenia radar.
Launch dates—*Constitucion* 1 June 1973, *Independencia* 24 July 1973, *Patria* 27 Sep 1973, *Federacion* 26 Feb 1974, *Libertad* 5 Mar 1974, *Victoria* May 1974.

Vosper Thornycroft 37 m FPB (with missiles) — *1973, Vosper Thornycroft*

Light Forces—*continued*

10 Ex-US PC TYPE (LARGE PATROL CRAFT)

ALBATROS	(ex-USS PC 582)	P-04
ALCATRAZ	(ex-USS PC 565)	P-03
CALAMAR	(ex-USS PC 566)	P-02
CAMARON	(ex-USS PC 483)	P-08
CARACOL	(ex-USS PC 1077)	P-06
GAVIOTA	(ex-USS PC 619)	P-10
PETREL	(ex-USS PC 1176)	P-05
PULPO	(ex-USS PC 465)	P-07
MEJILLON	(ex-USS PC 487)	P-01
TOGOGO	(ex-USS PC 484)	P-09

Displacement, tons	280 standard; 430 full load
Dimensions, feet	170·0 wl; 173·7 oa × 23·0 × 10·8
Guns	1—3 in dp; 2—40 mm AA (1 twin); 2—20 mm AA
A/S weapons	Provision for 4 DCT
Main engines	2 Fairbanks-Morse diesels; 2 shafts; 2 800 bhp = 19 knots
Complement	65

Mejillon was refitted and overhauled by Diques y Astilleros Nacionalis, Venezuela, prior to commissioning in the Venezuelan Navy, and from 1962 onwards more ships of this type underwent similar preparation to join the fleet. Altogether twelve of these former United States PC's of the steel-hulled "173-ft" type were purchased from the USA in Oct 1960. *Camaron, Pulpo* and *Gaviota* were placed in reserve 1968-70.

ALBATROS *1972, Venezuelan Navy*

6 NEW CONSTRUCTION (COASTAL PATROL CRAFT)

Displacement, tons	45
Dimensions, feet (*m*)	88·6 × 16 × 4·9 (*27 × 4·9 × 1·5*)
Guns	1—20 mm; 1 MG
Main engines	2 diesels; 3 300 hp = 30 knots
Range, miles	1 500 at 15 knots
Complement	12

Built at Chantiers Navales d'Estrel. Manned by National Guard.

8 "RIO" CLASS (COASTAL PATROL CRAFT)

RIO APURE, **RIO ARAUCA**, **RIO CABRIALES**, **RIO CARONI**, **RIO GUARICO**, **RIO NEGRO**, **RIO NEVERI**, **RIO TUY**

Displacement, tons	38
Dimensions, feet	82 × 15 × 4
Main engines	2 MTU 12 V 493 diesels; 1 400 rpm; 1 350 bhp = 27 knots

All built by the Chantiers Navales de l'Esterel, Cannes, during 1954-56. Manned by National Guard.

RIO NEGRO *1972, Venezuelan Navy,*

GOLFO DE CARIACO (COASTAL PATROL CRAFT)

Displacement, tons	37
Dimensions, feet	65 × 18 × 9
Main engines	Diesels; speed = 19 knots
Complement	10

Manned by National Guard.

RIO SANTO DOMINGO (COASTAL PATROL CRAFT)

Displacement, tons	40
Dimensions, feet	70 × 15 × 6
Main engines	2 GM diesels; 1 250 bhp = 24 knots
Complement	10

Manned by National Guard.

21 NEW CONSTRUCTION (COASTAL PATROL CRAFT)

21 90 ft Coastal Patrol Craft are under construction. These were ordered from INMA, La Spezia in Mar 1973 and some are probably building in Venezuela.

AMPHIBIOUS FORCES

1 Ex-US "TERREBONNE PARISH" CLASS (LST)

AMAZONAS (ex-USS *Vernon County,* LST 1161) T 21

Displacement, tons	2 590 light; 5 800 full load
Dimensions, feet	384 × 55 × 17
Guns	6—3 in 50 cal (twins)
Main engines	4 GM diesels; 2 shafts; cp propeller; 6 000 bhp = 15 knots
Complement	116
Troops	395

Built by Ingalls Shipbuilding Corpn, 1952-53. Carries four LCVP landing craft. Transferred on loan 29 June 1973.

4 Ex-US LSM TYPE

LOS FRAILES T 15 (ex-USS *LSM* 544)
LOS MONJES T 13 (ex-USS *LSM* 548)
LOS ROQUES T 14 (ex-USS *LSM* 543)
LOS TESTIGOS T 16 (ex-USS *LSM* 545)

Displacement, tons	743 beaching; 1 095 full load
Dimensions, feet	196·5 wl; 203·5 oa × 34·5 × 8·3
Guns	1—40 mm AA; 4—20 mm AA
Main engines	Direct drive diesels; 2 shafts; 2 800 bhp = 12 knots
Range, miles	9 000 at 11 knots
Complement	59

All built by Brown Shipbuilding Co, Houston, Texas, in 1945. The former United States medium landing ships were sold to Venezuela under MAP in Aug 1958.

LOS MONJES *1970, Venezuelan Navy,*

GUAYANA T 18 (ex-USS *Quirinus,* ARL 39, ex-LST 1151) (TRANSPORT)

Displacement, tons	1 625 light; 3 960 trials; 4 100 full load
Dimensions, feet	316 wl; 328 oa × 50 × 11·2 max
Guns	8—40 mm AA (two quadruple mountings)
Main engines	GM diesels; 2 shafts; 1 800 bhp = 11·6 knots
Complement	81 (11 officers 70 men)

Former US Navy landing craft repair ship. Built by Chicago Bridge and Iron Co, Seneca, Illinois. Laid down on 3 Mar 1945. Loaned to Venezuela in June 1962 and now used as a transport in the Venezuelan Navy.

GUAYANA *1970, Venezuelan Navy,*

TRANSPORTS

PUNTA CABANA T 17

Small troop carriers of about 3 000 tons with a speed of 17 knots.

LAS AVES (ex-*Dos de Diciembre*) T 12

Displacement, tons	944
Dimensions, feet	234·2 × 33·5 × 10
Guns	4—20 mm (2 twin)
Main engines	2 diesels; 2 shafts; 1 600 bhp = 15 knots
Radius, miles	2 600 at 11 knots

Launched by Chantiers Dubigeon, Nantes-Chantenay, France in Sept 1954. Light transport for naval personnel. Renamed *Las Aves* in 1961.

LAS AVES *1970, Venezuelan Navy,*

SURVEY SHIPS

3 "PUERTO" CLASS

PUERTO DE NUTRIAS (ex-USS *Tunxis*, AN 90) H 02
PUERTO MIRANDA (ex-USS *Waxsaw*, AN 91) H 03
PUERTO SANTO (ex-USS *Marietta*, AN 82) H 01

Displacement, tons	650 standard; 785 full load
Dimensions, feet	146 wl; 168·5 oa × 33·9 × 10·2 max
Guns	1—20 mm AA
Main engines	Bush-Sulzer diesel-electric; 1 shaft; 1 500 bhp = 12 knots
Complement	46

Former US netlayers of the "Cohoes" class. *Puerto Santo* was built by Commercial Iron Works, Portland, Oregon. Laid down on 17 Feb 1945, launched on 27 Apr 1945. Loaned from USA in Jan 1961 under MAP and converted into hydrographic survey vessel and buoy tender by US Coast Guard Yard, Curtis Bay, Maryland, in Feb 1962. All ships originally carried one 3-inch 50 cal dp gun. *Puerto du Nutrias* and *Puerto Miranda*, built by Zenith Bridge Co, Duluth, Minn. launched in 1944. completed in 1945, were loaned to Venezuela in 1963 under MAP.

PUERTO SANTO *1970, Venezuelan Navy,*

2 RESEARCH CRAFT

GABRIELA **LALY**

Displacement, tons	90
Dimensions, ft (*m*)	88·6 × 18·4 × 4·9 (*27 × 5·6 × 1·5*)
Main engines	2 diesels; 2 300 hp = 20 knots
Complement	16

Built in 1973 by Abeking and Rasmussen, Lemwerder.

TUGS

FELIPE LARRAZABAL R 21 (ex-USS *Utina*, ATF 163) (OCEAN TUG)

Displacement, tons	1 235 standard; 1 675 full load
Dimensions	205 oa × 38·5 × 15·5
Gun	1—3 in 50 cal AA
Main engines	Diesel-electric; 3 000 bhp; 1 shaft
Speed, knots	15
Complement	85

Transferred 3 Sept 1972. This is the third tug of this name. The first (ex-USS *Discoverer*, (ex-USCG *Auk*, AM 38 was deleted in 1962. The second (ex-USS *Tolowa*, ATF 116) was deleted in 1972 after damage when grounded.

FERNANDO GOMEZ (ex-USS *Dudley*, YTM 744, ex-*Diana*, ex-US Army ST 873) R 12 (HARBOUR TUG)

Displacement, tons	161
Dimensions, feet	80 × 19 × 8
Main engines	Clark diesel, 6-cyl, 315 rpm; 380 bhp= 15 knots
Complement	10

GENERAL JOSE FELIX RIBAS R 13 (ex-USS *Oswegatchie*, YTM 778, ex-YTB 515) (HARBOUR TUG)

Large harbour tug. Transferred on 4 June 1965 at San Diego, Calif.

2 Ex-US MEDIUM HARBOUR TUGS

Ex-*Wannalancet* YTM 385, ex-*Sassacus* YTM 193 leased to Venezuela late 1960's.

5 Ex-US SMALL HARBOUR TUGS

80 feet long, leased in Jan 1963.

FLOATING DOCK

DF 1 (ex-USS *ARD* 13)

The ex-USN ARD 13 of 3 000 tons and built of steel was transferred on loan to Venezuela in Feb 1962 as DF 1.

VIETNAM (REPUBLIC OF)

Principal Flag Officers

Commander-in-Chief and Chief of Naval Operations:
Rear Admiral Tran Van Chon
Vice Chief of Naval Operations:
Commodore Larn Nquon Tanh
Fleet Commander:
Captain Nguyen Thanh Chau

Diplomatic Representation

Defence Attaché in Washington D.C.:
Colonel Nguyen Linh Chieu
Defence Attaché in London:
Colonel Cao Xuan Ve

Strength of the Fleet

- 7 Frigates (High Endurance Cutters)
- 2 Frigates (Radar Picket Type)
- 8 Escorts (Including 5 Fleet Minesweepers)
- 1 Patrol Vessel (Submarine Chaser Type)
- 2 Coastal Minesweepers
- 20 Coastal Gunboats (Patrol Type)
- 25 Landing Ships (LST, LSM, LSSL, LSIL)
- 6 Oilers
- 26 Coast Guard Launches
- 850 Patrol, Coastal and Riverine Craft
- 165 Auxiliaries

Personnel

approx 40 000 Navy officers and enlisted men plus 13 800 marines

Ships

All South Vietnamese Navy ships are prefixed by HQ for Hai Quan, meaning "navy".
Some of the patrol, coastal, and riverine craft are believed inoperative because of maintenance and support limitations.

Mercantile Marine

Lloyd's Register of Shipping:
39 vessels of 31 979 tons gross

FRIGATES

7 Ex-US 311-ft COAST GUARD CUTTERS

Name	*No.*	*Builder*	*Launched*	*US Navy Comm*	*Transferred*
TRAN QUANG KHAI (ex-USCGC *Bering Strait*, WHEC 382 ex-AVP 34)	HQ 02	Lake Washington SY	15 Jan 1944	19 July 1944	1 Jan 1971
TRAN NHAT DUAT (ex-USCGC *Yakutat*, WHEC 380 ex-AVP 32)	HQ 03	Associated Shipbuilders	2 July 1942	31 Mar 1944	1 Jan 1971
TRAN BINH TRONG (ex-USCGC *Castle Rock*, WHEC 383, ex-AVP 35)	HQ 05	Lake Washington SY	11 Mar 1944	8 Oct 1944	21 Dec 1971
TRAN QUOC TOAN (ex-USCGC *Cook Inlet*, WHEC 384, ex-AVP 36)	HQ 06	Lake Washington SY	13 May 1944	5 Nov 1944	21 Dec 1971
THAM NGU LAO (ex-USCGC *Absecon*, WHEC 374, ex-AVP 23)	HQ 15	Lake Washington SY	8 Mar 1942	28 Jan 1943	15 July 1972
LY THOUNG KIET (ex-USCGC *Chincoteague*, WHEC 375, ex-AVP 24)	HQ 16	Lake Washington SY	15 Apr 1942	12 Apr 1943	21 June 1972
NGO KUYEN (ex-USCGC *McCulloch*, WHEC 386, ex-USS *Wachapreague*, AGP 8, AVP 56)	HQ 17	Lake Washington SY	10 July 1943	17 May 1944	21 June 1972

Displacement, tons	1 766; standard 2 800 full load
Length, feet	300 wl; 310·75 oa
Beam, feet	41·1
Draught, feet	13·5
Guns	1—5 inch (*127 mm*) .38 cal DP 1 or 2—81 mm mortars in some ships; several MG
Main engines	Diesels (Fairbanks Morse); 6 080 bhp; 2 shafts
Speed, knots	approx 18
Complement	approx 200

TRAN QUANG KHAI *1971, Vietnamese Navy*

Frigates—*continued*

Built as seaplane tenders of the "Barnegat" class for the US Navy; *Tran Nhat Duat* by Associated Shipbuilders, Seattle, Washington; others by Lake Washington Shipyard, Houghton, Washington.
All transferred to US Coast Guard in 1946-1948, initially on loan designated WAVP and then on permanent transfer except ex-*McCulloch* transferred outright from US Navy to Coast Guard; subsequently redesignated as high endurance cutters (WHEC). Transferred from US Coast Guard to South Vietnamese Navy in 1971-1972.
These ships are the largest combatants in the South Vietnamese Navy and the only ones to mount a 5 inch gun battery. All anti-submarine weapons are believed to have been removed prior to transfer.

PHOTOGRAPHS. These ships are distinguished from the former US Navy radar picket escorts of similar size by their pole masts forward, open side passages amidships, and radar antenna on second mast. Note combination ·50 cal MG/81 mm mortar forward of bridge in "B" position.

TRAN NHAT DUAT — *1971, Vietnamese Navy*

2 Ex-US DER TYPE

Name	No.	Launched	US Navy Comm.	Transferred
TRAN HUNG DAO (ex-USS *Camp*, DER 251)	HQ 01	16 Apr 1943	16 Sep 1943	6 Feb 1971
TRAN KHANH DU (ex-USS *Forster*, DER 334)	HQ 04	13 Nov 1943	25 Jan 1944	25 Sep 1971

Displacement, tons	1 590 standard; 1 850 full load
Length, feet	300 wl; 306 oa
Beam, feet	36·6
Draught, feet	14
Guns	2—3 inch (*76 mm*) 50 cal AA (single)
A/S weapons	6—12·75 inch (*324 mm*) torpedo tubes (Mk 32 triple) 1 trainable hedgehog (Mk 15) depth charge rack
Main engines	Diesel (Fairbank Morse); 6 000 bhp; 2 shafts
Speed, knots	21
Complement	approx 170

Former US Navy destroyer escorts, of the FMR design group. *Tran Hung Dao* built by Brown SB Co, Houston, Texas; *Tran Khanh Du* built by Consolidated Steel Corp, Orange, Texas.

After World War II both ships were extensively converted to radar picket configuration to serve as seaward extension of US aircraft attack warning system; redesignated DER with original DE hull numbers. Large SPS-8 search radar and TACAN (tactical aircraft navigation) "pod" removed after radar picket barrier ended in 1965, but ships retained DER designation. Subsequently employed during 1960s in Indochina for coastal patrol and interdiction by US Navy (Operation MARKET TIME). Transferred to South Vietnamese Navy in 1971.
These ships are second in firepower in the South Vietnamese Navy only to the ex-US Coast Guard cutters with respect to gun calibre; however, these ships each mount two guns (forward mount enclosed, after mount open). Also, they are the most-capable anti-submarine ships of the Navy.

ELECTRONICS. SPS-28 and SPS-10 search radars on forward tripod mast. Apparently most electronic warfare equipment was removed prior to transfer (compare after masts with "pods" in photographs of US ships of this class in the United States section.)

TRAN KHANH DU — *1971, Vietnamese Navy*

THAN HUNG DAO — *Vietnamese Navy*

PATROL VESSELS

2 PATROL GUNBOATS: US NEW CONSTRUCTION

Displacement, tons	230 full load
Dimensions, feet	165 oa × 24 × 9·5
Main engines	Diesel; 2 shafts
Guns	1—3 inch (*76 mm*) AA; 1—40 mm AA

The US Navy's Fiscal Year 1975 new construction programme requests funding for two gunboats to be constructed in US shipyards for South Vietnamese use.

Patrol Vessels—*continued*

3 Ex-US PCE TYPE

DONG DA II (ex-USS *Crestview, PCE* 895)	HQ 07	18 May 1943
NGOC HOI (ex-USS *Brattleboro, EPCER* 852)	HQ 12	1 Mar 1944
VAN KIEP II (ex-USS *Amherst, PCER* 853)	HQ 14	18 Mar 1944

Displacement, tons	640 standard; 903 full load
Dimensions, feet	180 wl; 184·5 oa × 33·1 × 9·5
Guns	1—3 inch (*76 mm*) 50 cal AA; 2—40 mm AA (single); 8—20 mm AA (twin)
A/S weapons	1 fixed hedgehog; depth charges
Main engines	Diesel (General Motors); 2 000 bhp; 2 shafts = 15 knots
Complement	approx 90

Former US Navy patrol vessels—escort (PCE), two of which were fitted as rescue ships (PCER) to pickup survivors of convoy sinkings. *Dong Da II* built by Willamette Iron & Steel Corp, Portland, Oregon; others by Pullman Standard Car Manufacturing Co, Chicago, Illinois; launch dates above. After World War II the *Ngoc Hoi* was employed as an experimental ship (designation given "E" prefix); others used for Naval Reserve training.

Dong Da II transferred to South Vietnam on 29 Nov 1961, *Ngoc Hoi* on 11 July 1966, and *Van Kiep II* in June 1970.

These ships are similar in design to the former minesweepers listed below.

NGOC HOI *1971, Vietnamese Navy,*

5 Ex-US MSF TYPE

CHI LANG II (ex-USS *Gayety, MSF* 239)	HQ 08	19 Mar 1944
KY HOA (ex-USS *Sentry, MSF* 299)	HQ 09	15 Aug 1943
NHUT TAO (ex-USS *Serene, MSF* 300)	HQ 10	31 Oct 1943
CHI LINH (ex-USS *Shelter, MSF* 301)	HQ 11	14 Nov 1943
HA HOI (ex-USS *Prowess*, IX 305, ex-MSF 280)	HQ 13	17 Feb 1944

Displacement, tons	650 standard; 945 full load
Dimensions, feet	180 wl; 184·5 oa × 33 × 9·75
Guns	1—3 inch (*76 mm*) 50 cal AA; 2—40 mm AA (single); up to 8—20 mm AA (twin)
A/S weapons	1 fixed hedgehog; depth charges
Main engines	Diesel (Cooper Bessemer); 1 710 bhp; 2 shafts = 14 knots
Complement	approx 80

Former US Navy minesweepers of the "Admirable" class (originally designated AM). Built by Winslow Marine Railway & SB Co, Winslow, Washington, except *Ha Hoi* built by Gulf SB Corp, Chicasaw, Alabama; launch dates above. *Ha Hoi* served as a Naval Reserve training ship from 1962 to 1971 (redesignated as an unclassified auxiliary IX 305 on 1 Mar 1966).

Chi Lang II transferred to South Vietnam in Apr 1962, *Ky Hoa* transferred in Aug 1962, *Nhut Tao* and *Chi Linh* transferred in Jan 1964, and *Ha Hoi* transferred on 4 June 1970. Minesweeping equipment has been removed and two depth charge racks fitted on fantail; employed in patrol and escort roles. All of these ships are believed to have two 20 mm twin mounts at after end of bridge and one or two 20 mm twin mounts on fantail.

NHUT TAO *Vietnamese Navy*

CHI LANG II *1962, Vietnamese Navy*

Patrol Vessels—*continued*

1 Ex-US PC TYPE

VAN DON (ex-USS *Anacortes, PC* 1569) HQ 06 9 Dec 1944

Displacement, tons	280 standard; 450 full load
Dimensions, feet	170 wl; 173·7 oa × 3 × 10·8
Guns	1—3 inch (*76 mm*) 50 cal AA; 1—40 mm AA; 4—20 mm AA (single)
A/S weapons	2 mousetrap launchers; depth charges
Main engines	Diesel; 2 800 bhp; 2 shafts = 19 knots
Complement	approx 50

Van Don was built by Leathem D. Smith SB Co. Launch date above. Laid down on 26 Sep 1944 and completed on 14 Mar 1945. *Van Don* was transferred at Seattle, Washington on 23 Nov 1960. *Dong Da* ex-French *Ardent*, ex-USS PC 1167) was officially stricken from the list in 1961 and *Chi Lang* (ex-French *Mousquet* P 633, ex-USS PC 1144) in 1961, the names allocated to larger vessels, *Tay Ket* HQ 05 (ex-French *Glaive*, ex-USS PC 1146 and *Van Kiep* HQ 02 (ex-French *Intrepide*, ex-USS PC 1130)on 10 July 1965 and July 1965 respectively, and *Tuy Dong* (ex-*Trident*, ex-USS PC 1143) HQ 04, former French *escorteur cotier* transferred in 1956 was officially deleted in 1971.

Reportedly the *Van Don* remains on the Navy List as HQ 06 despite the assignment of that number to a former US 311-ft Coast Guard Cutter.

VAN DON *1971, Vietnamese Navy*

PATROL GUNBOATS

20 100-ft PGM TYPE

Name	*No*	*Transferred*
PHU DU	HQ 600 (PGM 64)	Feb 1963
TIEN MOI	HQ 601 (PGM 65)	Feb 1963
MINH HOA	HQ 602 (PGM 66)	Feb 1963
KIEN VANG	HQ 603 (PGM 67)	Feb 1963
KEO NGUA	HQ 604 (PGM 68)	Feb 1963
KIM QUI	HQ 605 (PGM 60)	May 1963
MAY RUT	HQ 606 (PGM 59)	May 1963
NAM DU	HQ 607 (PGM 61)	May 1963
HOA LU	HQ 608 (PGM 62)	July 1963
TO YEN	HQ 609 (PGM 63)	July 1963
DINH HAI	HQ 610 (PGM 69)	Feb 1964
TRUONG SA	HQ 611 (PGM 70)	Apr 1964
THAI BINH	HQ 612 (PGM 72)	Jan 1966
THI TU	HQ 613 (PGM 73)	Jan 1966
SONG TU	HQ 614 (PGM 74)	Jan 1966
TAT SA	HQ 615 (PGM 80)	Oct 1966
HOANG SA	HQ 616 (PGM 82)	Apr 1967
PHU QUI	HQ 617 (PGM 81)	Apr 1967
HON TROC	HQ 618 (PGM 83)	Apr 1967
THO CHAU	HQ 619 (PGM 91)	Apr 1967

Displacement, tons	117 full load
Dimensions, feet	100·33 oa × 21·1 × 6·9
Guns	1—40 mm AA; 2 or 4—20 mm AA (twin); 2—MG
Main engines	Diesel; 1 900 bhp; 2 shafts = 17 knots
Complement	approx 15

Welded-steel patrol gunboats built in the United States specifically for foreign transfer; assigned PGM numbers for contract purposes. Enlarged version of US Coast Guard 95-foot patrol boats with commercial-type machinery and electronic equipment. HQ 600-605 built by J. M. Martinac SB Corp, Tacoma, Washington; HQ 606-610 built by Marinette Marine Corp, Wisconsin.

All ships have a 20 mm twin mount on after end of deckhouse and some apparently have a second 20 mm mount aft; machineguns are atop deckhouse immediately behind low funnel and forward of 20 mm mount.

KIM QUI *1970, Vietnamese Navy*

DINH HAI *1967, United States Navy*

Patrol Gunboats—*continued*

26 Ex-USCG 82-ft "POINT" CLASS

LE PHUOC DUI	HQ 700 (ex-*Point Garnet* 82310)
LE VAN NGA	HQ 701 (ex-*Point League* 82304)
HUYNH VAN CU	HQ 702 (ex-*Point Clear* 82315)
NGUYEN DAO	HQ 703 (ex-*Point Gammon* 82328)
DAO THUC	HQ 704 (ex-*Point Comfort* 82317)
LE NGOC THANH	HQ 705 (ex-*Point Ellis* 82330)
NGUYEN NGOC THACH	HQ 706 (ex-*Point Slocum* 82313)
DANG VAN HOANH	HQ 707 (ex-*Point Hudson* 82322)
LE DINH HUNG	HQ 708 (ex-*Point White* 82308)
THUONG TIEN	HQ 709 (ex-*Point Dume* 82325)
PHAM NGOC CHAU	HQ 710 (ex-*Point Arden* 82309)
DAO VAN DANG	HQ 711 (ex-*Point Glover* 82307)
LE DGOC AN	HQ 712 (ex-*Point Jefferson* 82306)
HUYNH VAN NGAN	HQ 713 (ex-*Point Kennedy* 82320)
TRAN LO	HQ 714 (ex-*Point Young* 82303)
BUI VIET THANH	HQ 715 (ex-*Point Patrige* 82305)
NGUYEN AN	HQ 716 (ex-*Point Caution* 82301)
NGUYEN HAN	HQ 717 (ex-*Point Welcome* 82329)
NGO VAN QUYEN	HQ 718 (ex-*Point Banks* 82327)
VAN DIEN	HQ 719 (ex-*Point Lomas* 82321)
HO DANG LA	HQ 720 (ex-*Point Grace* 82323)
DAM THOAI	HQ 721 (ex-*Point Mast* 82316)
HUYNH BO	HQ 722 (ex-*Point Grey* 82324)
NGUYEN KIM HUNG	HQ 723 (ex-*Point Orient* 82319)
HO DUY	HQ 724 (ex-*Point Cypress* 82326)
TROUNG BA	HQ 725 (ex-*Point Maromc* 82331)

Displacement, tons	64 standard ; 67 full load
Dimensions, feet	83 oa × 17·2 × 5·8
Guns	1—81 mm/50 cal MG (combination)plus 2 to 4—50 cal MG (single) or 1—20 mm
Main engines	2 diesels ; 1 200 bhp ; 2 shafts = 16·8 knots
Complement	8 to 10

Former US Coast Guard 82-ft patrol boats (designated WPB) ; actual length is 83 feet overall. All served in Vietnamese waters, manned by US personnel, comprising Coast Guard Squadron One. HQ 700-707 transferred to South Vietnamese Navy in 1969, HQ 708-HQ 725 in 1970.
Numerous units of this type are in service with the US Coast Guard.

POINT CLASS — *1970, Vietnamese Navy*

COASTAL MINESWEEPERS

2 Ex-US MSC TYPE

HAM TU II (ex-*MSC* 281)	HQ 114
CHUONG DUONG II (ex-*MSC* 282)	HQ 115

Displacement, tons	320 standard ; 370 full load
Dimensions, feet	144 oa × 28 × 9
Guns	2—20 mm AA
Main engines	2 diesels ; 2 shafts ; 1 200 bhp = 12·5 knots
Complement	45

United States coastal motor minesweepers of the "Bluebird" class, non-magnetic type, of wooden construction, constructed under the Mutual Defence Assistance Programme transferred to South Vietnam in Sep 1959 and Dec 1959, respectively. Sister ship *Bach Dang II* (ex-MSC 283) HQ 116 grounded on 9 Oct 1970 ; stripped and destroyed.

DISPOSALS
Of the three coastal minesweepers of the ex-US YMS type transferred from the French Navy on 11 Feb 1954, *Ham Tu* HQ 211 (ex-*Aubepine*, ex-D 315, ex-TMS 28) was removed from the effective list in 1958. *Bach Bang* HQ 113, (ex-*Belledone*, ex-D 318, ex-YMS 78) in 1963, and *Chu'o'ng-Du'o'ng* HQ 112 (ex-*Digitale*, ex-D 326, ex-YMS 83)in 1964.

CHUONG DUONG II — *1971, Vietnamese Navy*

Coastal Minesweepers—*continued*

HAM TU — *1960, Vietnamese Navy*

LANDING SHIPS

6 Ex-US LST TYPE

CAM RANH (ex-USS *Marion County, LST* 975)	HQ 500	6 Jan 1945
DA NANG (ex-USS *Maricopa County, LST* 938)	HQ 501	15 Aug 1944
THI NAI (ex-USS *Cayuga County, LST* 529)	HQ 502	17 Jan 1944
VUNG TAU (ex-USS *Cochino County, LST* 603)	HQ 503	14 Mar 1944
QUI NHON (ex-USS *Bullock County, LST* 509)	HQ 504	23 Nov 1943
HNA TRANG (ex-USS *Jerome County, LST* 848)	HQ 505	2 Jan 1943

Displacement, tons	2 366 beaching ; 4 080 full load
Dimensions, feet	316 wl ; 328 oa × 50 × 14
Guns	7 or 8—40 mm AA (1 or 2 twin ; 4 or 5 single) ; several 20 mm AA
Main engines	Diesel (General Motors) ; 1 700 bhp ; 2 shafts = 11 knots
Complement	110

Former US Navy tank landing ships ; launch dates above. HQ 500 and 501 built by Bethlehem Steel Co, Hingham, Massachusetts ; HQ 502 and 504 by Jeffersonville B & M Co, Jeffersonville, Indiana ; HQ 3 by Chicago Bridge & Iron Co. Illinois ; HQ 5 by Kaiser Co, Richmond, California. HQ 500 and 502 have pole masts ; others have lattice tripod masts.

QUI NHON — *1971, Vietnamese Navy*

THI NAI — *Vietnamese Navy*

DA NANG — *1962, Vietnamese Navy*

Landing Ships—*continued*

6 Ex-US LSM TYPE

HAT GIANG (ex-LSM 9011, ex-USS LSM 335)	HQ 400	10 Nov 1944
HAN GIANG (ex-LSM 9012, ex-USS LSM 110)	HQ 401	28 Oct 1944
LAM GIANG (ex-USS LSM 226)	HQ 402	4 Sep 1944
NINH GIANG (ex-USS LSM 85)	HQ 403	15 Sep 1944
HUONG GIANG (ex-USS *Oceanside*, LSM 176)	HQ 404	12 Aug 1944
TIEN GIANG (ex-USS LSM 313)	HQ 405	24 May 1944
HAU GIANG (ex-USS LSM 276)	HQ 406	20 Sep 1944

Displacement, tons	743 beaching; 1 095 full load
Dimensions, feet	196·5 wl; 203·5 oa × 34·5 × 8·3
Guns	2—40 mm AA; 4—20 mm AA
Main engines	Diesel; 2 shafts; 2 800 bhp = 12 knots
Complement	73

Former US Navy medium landing ships; launch dates above.
Designed primarily to carry assault troops. First four transfrered to French Navy for use in Indo-China, Jan 1954. *LSM* 9011, 9012 transferred to Vietnam Navy, Dec 1955. LSM 9014, 9017, 9018, returned to USA in 1955. *Oceanside LSM* 175 transferred at Los Angeles on 1 Aug 1961, LSM 313 in 1962, *Hau Giang* (ex-LSM 276) on 10 June 1965.

Hat Giang and *Han Giang* are hospital ships (LSM-H); refitted for treating casualties and assigned political warfare personnel (in addition to normal complement). All are armed.

LAM GIANG *Vietnamese Navy*

HAT GIANG (LSM-H) *Vietnamese Navy*

4 Ex-US LSSL TYPE

DOAN NGOC TANG (ex-USS LSSL 9)	HQ 228	17 Aug 1944
LULU PHU THO (ex-USS LSSL 101)	HQ 229	27 Jan 1945
NGUYEN NGOC LONG (ex-USS LSSL 96)	HQ 230	6 Jan 1945
NIGUYEN DUC BONG (ex-USS LSSL 129)	HQ 231	13 Dec 1944

Displacement, tons	227 standard; 383 full load
Dimensions, feet	158 × 23·7 × 5·7
Guns	1—3 inch; 4—40 mm AA; 4—20 mm AA; 4 MG
Main engines	Diesel; 2 shafts; 1 600 bhp = 14 knots
Complement	60

Former US Navy landing ships support; designed to provide close-in-fire support for amphibious assaults, but suitable for general gunfire missions. Launch dates above.

The *Doan Ngoc Tang* was transferred to France in 1951 (*Hallebarde* L. 9023); transferred to Japan 1956-1964; returned and transferred to South Vietnam in 1965. Three other ships served in Japanese Navy 1953 to 1964; retransfered to South Vietnam in 1965 and 1966.

Three ships of this type sunk; *Le Van Binh* HQ 227, ex-French *Javeline* L 9024, ex-USS LSSL 10 sunk in 1966; *Neuyen Van Tru* HQ 225, ex-French *Framee*, ex-USS LSSL 105 sunk in 1970; *Le Trong Dam* HQ 226, ex-French *Arquesbusei* L 9022, ex-USS LSSL 4 sunk in 1970.

NIGUYEN DUC BONG *Vietnamese Navy*

Landing Ships—*continued*

LE TRONG DAM—sunk in 1970 *Vietnamese Navy*

5 Ex-US LSIL TYPE

LONG DAO (ex-French L 9029, ex-USS LSIL 698)	HQ 327	17 June 1944
THAN TIEN (ex-French L 9035, ex-USS LSIL 702)	HQ 328	28 June 1944
THIEN KICH (ex-French L 9038, ex-USS LSIL 872)	HQ 329	4 Oct 1944
LOI CONG (ex-French L 9034, ex-USS LSIL 699)	HQ 330	21 June 1944
TAM SET (ex-French L 9033, ex-USS LSIL 871)	HQ 331	3 Oct 1944

Displacement, tons	227 standard; 383 full load
Dimensions, feet	158 × 22·7 × 5·3
Guns	1—3 inch; 1—40 mm AA; 2—20 mm AA; 4 MG; and up to 4 army mortars (2—81 mm; 2—60 mm)
Main engines	Diesel; 2 shafts; 1 600 bhp = 14·4 knots
Complement	55

Former US Navy landing ships infantry; launch dates above. Designed to carry 200 troops. *Tam Set* originally transferred to France in 1951 and others in 1953 for use in Indochina; subsequently retransferred in 1956 to South Vietnam.

LONG DAO *1971, Vietnamese Navy*

UTILITY LANDING CRAFT

19 Ex-US LCU TYPE

HQ 533 (ex-US LCU 1479)
HQ 534 (ex-US LCU 1480)
HQ 535 (ex-US LCU 1221)
HQ 536 (ex-US LCU 1446)
HQ 537 (ex-US LCU 1501)
HQ 538 (ex-US LCU 1594)
HQ 539 (ex-US LCU 1502)
HQ 540 (ex-US LCU 1475)
HQ 541 (ex-US LCU 1477)
HQ 542 (ex-US LCU 1494)
HQ 543 (ex-US LCU 1493)
HQ 544 (ex-US LCU 1485)
HQ 545 (ex-US LCU 1484)
HQ 546 (ex-US YFU 90, ex-LCU 1582)
HQ 547 (ex-US LCU 1481)
HQ 548 (ex-US LCU 1498)
HQ 560 (ex-US YLLC 1, LCU 1348)
HQ 561 (ex-US YLLC 5, YFU 2, LCU 529)
HQ 562 (ex-US YLLC 3, YFU 33, LCU 1195)

LCU 501 series

Displacement, tons	309 to 320 full load
Dimensions, feet	105 wl; 119 oa × 32·7 × 5
Main engines	Diesels (Gray Marine); 675 bhp; 3 shafts = 10 knots

LCU 1466 series

Displacement, tons	360 full load
Dimensions, feet	115 wl; 119 oa × 34 × 5·25
Main engines	Diesels (Gray Marine); 675 bhp; 3 shafts = 8 knots

Former US Navy utility landing craft; 501 series built during World War II with LCT (6) designation; 1466 series built during the early 1950s. Transferred to South Vietnam from 1954 to 1971, with some of the earlier craft serving briefly in French Navy in Indichina waters.

Three units (ex-YLLC) converted while in US Navy service for use as salvage lifting craft; fitted with 20-ton capacity "A" frame derrick, special anchors, diver's air compressors, welding equipment, and salvage pumps.
Most units armed with two 20 mm AA guns; armament varies with assignment.

HQ 538 *1971, Vietnamese Navy*

Utility Landing Craft—*continued*

HQ 561 (as YLLC 5) *United States Navy*

RIVERINE CRAFT

The US Navy has transferred approximately 700 armed small craft to South Vietnam since 1965 for use in riverine and coastal areas of Indochina. A few former French riverine craft also survive. The exact number of these craft now in service is not known. The following totals are the offical South Vietnamese Navy listings for 1972.

Some of these craft may not be operational because of maintenance limitations of the South Vietnamese Navy and some are believed to have been lost during the April-May 1972 invasion of South Vietnam by regular forces of the Democratic Republic of (North) Vietnam.

In addition to the armed craft grouped here under the category of Riverine (Warfare) Craft, there are numerous small landing craft which are armed.

107 Ex-US "SWIFT" TYPE

Displacement, tons	22·5 full load
Dimensions, feet	50 oa × 13 × 3·5
Guns	1—81 mm mortar/1—·50 cal mG combination Mount: 2—·50 cal MG (twin)
Main engines	2 geared diesels (General Motors); 960 bhp; 2 shafts = 28 knots
Complement	6

All-metal inshore patrol craft (PCF). Transferred to South Vietnam from 1968 to 1970. Numbered in HQ 3800-3887 and later series.

HQ 3825 *1970, Vietnamese Navy*

293 Ex-US PBR TYPE

Displacement, tons	PBR I series: 7·5 PBR II series: 8
Dimensions, feet	PBR I series: 31 oa × 10·5 × 2·5 PBR II series: 32 oa × 11 × 2·6
Guns	3—·50 cal MG (twin mount forward; single gun aft)
Main engines	2 geared diesels; 440 bhp; water-jet propulsion = 25+ knots
Complement	4 or 5

River patrol boats (PBR) with fibreglass (plastic) hulls. Transferred to South Vietnam from 1968 to 1970. Numbered in HQ 7500-7749 and 7800 series.

PBR TYPE *1970, Vietnamese Navy*

Riverine Craft—*continued*

27 Ex-US RPC TYPE

Displacement, tons	15·6
Dimensions, feet	35·75 oa × 10·3 × 3·6
Guns	varies: 2—·50 cal MG (twin); 3—·30 cal MG (twin mount aft and single gun at conning station); some units have additional twin ·30 cal mount in place of ·50 cal MH
Main engines	2 geared diesels; 2 shafts = 14 knots

River patrol craft (RPC); predecessor to PBR type. Welded-steel hulls. Few used by US Navy as minesweepers, but most of the 34 units built were transferred to South Vietnam upon completion in 1965; others in 1968-1969. Numbered HQ 7000-7028.

RPC TYPE *1970, Vietnamese Navy*

84 Ex-US ASPB TYPE

Displacement, tons	36·25 full load
Dimensions, feet	50 oa × 15·6 × 3·75
Guns	varies: 1 or 2—20 mm (with 2—·50 cal MG in boats with one 20 mm); 2—·30 cal MG; 2—40 mm grenade launchers
Main engines	2 geared diesels; 2 shafts = 14 knots sustained
Complement	6

Assault support patrol boats (ASPB) with welded-steel hulls. Transferred to South Vietnam from 1969 to 1970. Numbered in HQ 5100 series. These craft operate in escort, river interdiction, and minesweeping roles.

ASPB TYPE *1970, Vietnamese Navy*

42 Ex-US MONITORS

Displacement, tons	80 to 90 full load
Dimensions, feet	60·5 oa × 17·5 × 3·5
Guns	1—105 mm howitzer; 2—20 mm; 3—·30 cal MG; 2—40 mm grenade launchers
Main engines	2 geared diesels; 2 shaft = 9 knots
Complement	11

River monitors (MON). Transferred to South Vietnam in 1969-1970. Numbered in HQ 6500 series.

MONITOR *1970, Vietnamese Navy*

Riverine Class—*continued*

22 Ex-US LCM MONITORS

Displacement, tons	75 full load
Dimensions, feet	60 oa × 17
Guns	varies: 1—81 mm mortar or 2 M10-8 flame throwers; 1—40 mm; 1—20 mm; 2—·50 cal MG; possibly 2 to 4—·30 cal MG
Main engines	2 geared diesels; 2 shafts = 8 knots
Complement	approx 10

Twenty-four LCM-6 landing craft converted to this configuration from 1964 to 1967. Predecessor to the "monitor" listed above. Transferred to South Vietnam from 1965 to 1970. Numbered in HQ 1800 series.

LCM MONITOR *1970, Vietnamese Navy*

100 Ex-US ATC TYPE

Displacement, tons	66 full load
Dimensions, feet	65·5 oa × 17·5 × 3·25
Guns	varies: 1 or 2—20 mm; 2—·50 cal MG; several ·30 cal MG; 2—40 mm grenade launchers
Main engines	2 geared diesels; 2 shafts = 8·5 knots (6 knots sustained)

Armoured troop carriers(ATC). Some fitted with steel helicopter platforms or evacuation of wounded. Transferred to South Vietnam in 1969. Numbered in HQ 1200 series. A few additional units of this design are fitted with extra fuel tanks and serve as refuelers.

ATC TYPE *1970, Vietnamese Navy*

9 Ex-US CCB TYPE

Displacement, tons	80 full load
Dimensions, feet	61 oa × 17·5 × 3·4
Guns	3—20 mm; 2—·30 cal MG; 2—40 mm grenade launchers
Main engines	2 geared diesels; 2 shafts = 8·5 knots maximum (6 knots sustained)
Complement	11

Command and control boats (CCB) to provide command and communication facilities for riverine commanders. Transferred to South Vietnam in 1969-1970. Numbered HQ 6100-6108.

4 Ex-US CSB TYPE

Dimensions, feet	56 oa × 18·75 × 6
Guns	4—·50 cal MG (twin)
Main engines	2 geared diesels; 2 shafts = 6 knots
Complement	6

Combat salvage boats (CSB) converted from LCM-6 landing craft; configured for river salvage and to support diving operations. Ten-ton capacity "A" frame forward.

Ex-FRENCH CRAFT

The Vietnamese Navy still lists 43 ex-French STCAN/FOM and 14 LCM Commandament as being in service. The latter are converted LCM-3 landing craft.

STCAN/FOM *Vietnamese Navy*

Riverine Class—*continued*

LCM-COMMANDAMENT *Vietnamese Navy*

MINESWEEPING LAUNCHES

The Vietnamese Navy lists 24 minesweeping launches; ten MLMS 50-foot type transferred in 1963 from US Navy (numbered HQ 150-155, 157-160; HQ 156 and 161 stricken in 1971); eight MSM 56-foot type transferred in 1970 (numbered HQ 1700-1707); six MSR 50-foot type transferred in 1970 (numbered HQ 1900-1905). Other riverine craft had a minesweeping capability (see photograph of ATC type).

MLMS *1971, Vietnamese Navy*

SUPPORT SHIPS

3 Ex-US MODIFIED LST TYPE

MY THO (ex-USS *Harnett County*, AGP 821, ex-LST 821)	HQ 800	27 Oct 1944
CAN THO (ex-USS *Garrett County*, AGP 786, ex-LST 786)	HQ 801	22 July 1944
VINH LONG (ex-USS *Satyr*, ARL 23, ex-LST 852)	HQ 802	13 Nov 1944

Displacement, tons	AGP type: 4 080 full load ARL type: 4 100 full load
Dimensions, feet	316 wl; 328 oa × 50 × 14
Guns	AGP type: 8—40 mm AA (2 twin, 4 single) ARL type: 8—40 mm AA (2 quad)
Main engines	Diesels (General Motors); 1 700 bhp except *Vinh Long* 1 800 bhp; 2 shafts = 11·6 knots

Former US Navy ships of LST design employed in support of coastal and riverine craft. Launch dates above. *Vinh Long* converted during construction to landing craft repair ship (ARL); others completed as standard LSTs but were modified in late 1960s to support US Navy small craft in Vietnamese waters; redesignated as patrol craft tenders (AGP) on 25 Sep 1970. The *Vinh Long* has more extensive repair facilities.

My Tho transferred to South Vietnam on 12 Oct 1970, *Can Tho* on 23 Apr 1971, and *Vinh Long* on 15 Oct 1971.

A photograph of the *Garrett County* supporting PBRs and UH-1B helicopters in Vietnamese waters appears in the 1970-1971 edition.

VINH LONG *Vietnamese Navy*

Support Ships—*continued*

MY THO see previous page *1971, Vietnamese Navy*

TRAINING SHIP

1 Ex-US FS TYPE

HOA GIANG (ex-*Dinh An*, ex-*Ingenieur en Chef Griod*, ex-US Army *FS* 287, ex-*Governor Wright*) HQ 451

Displacement, tons	950
Dimensions, feet	176 × 32·3 × 10·2
Main engines	2 GM diesels; 1 shaft; 1 000 bhp = 10 knots
Complement	4 officers, 36 men

Former French survey vessel (ex-US Army freighter), sold to Vietnam in Dec 1955. Formerly rated as a light cargo ship (AKL), or supply vessel, but adapted and reclassified as training ship in 1966.

HOA GIANG *1971, Vietnamese Navy*

OILERS

6 Ex-US YOG TYPE

HQ 470 (ex-*L'Aulne*, ex-US YOG 80)
HQ 471 (ex-*YOG* 33)
HQ 472 (ex-US *YOG* 67)
HQ 473 (ex-US *YOG* 71)
HQ 474 (ex-*YOG* 131)
HQ 475 (ex-*YOG* 56)

Displacement, tons	450 light; 1 253 full load
Dimensions, feet	174·0 × 32·0 × 10·9
Main engines	Diesels; 1 shaft = 10 knots
Cargo capacity	6 570 barrels

Former US Navy small gasoline tankers. HQ 470 transferred to South Vietnam in Jan 1951, HQ 471 in Aug 1963, HQ 472 in July 1967, HQ 473 in Mar 1970; HQ 474 in Apr 1971, and HQ 475 in June 1972. No Vietnamese names.

HQ 471 *Vietnamese Navy*

Oilers—*continued*

HQ 470 *1971, Vietnamese Navy*

WATER CARRIER

2 Ex-US YW TYPE

HQ 9118 (ex-US YW 152)
HQ 9113 (ex-US YW 153)

Former US Navy self-propelled water carriers. Transferred to South Vietnam in 1956. No Vietnamese name assigned.

HARBOUR TUGS

9 Ex-US YTL TYPE

HQ 9500 (ex-US YTL 152)
HQ 9501 (ex-US YTL 245)
HQ 9503 (ex-US YTL 200)
HQ 9504 (ex-US YTL 206)
HQ 9507 (ex-US YTL 423)
HQ 9508 (ex-US YTL 452)
HQ 9509 (ex-US YTL 456)
HQ 9510 (ex-US YTL 586)
HQ 9511 (ex-US YTL 457)

Former US Navy harbour tugs. HQ 9500 transferred to South Vietnam in 1955; HQ 9501, 9503, 0954 in 1956; others from 1968 to 1970.

JUNK FORCE

There are approximately 250 motor-propelled junks in naval service. The breakdown as of January 1972 included 62 command junks, 31 Kien Giang junks, and 153 Yabuta junks. Some of the Yabuta junks are fabricated of ferrous cement. The Yabuta junk illustrated below has two ·50 cal MG; some also have a 60 mm mortar. Diesel propulsion permits them to overtake and search some of the thousands of coastal sailing craft in Indochina waters. The Vietnamese Navy has discarded the armed sailing junks previously employed in this role.

YABUTA JUNK *1971, Vietnamese Navy*

FERROUS CEMENT JUNK *Vietnamese Navy*

MISCELLANEOUS

Numerous craft are operated by the Vietnamese Navy in addition to those described above. However, details are not available.

The former US Coast Guard lightship WLV-523 was transferred to South Vietnam on 25 Sep 1971 for use as an offshore radar station to supplement 16 coastal radar stations on shore which are operated to detect seaborne infiltration effort; renamed *Da Bong* (304). The shore stations are manned by naval personnel.

VIETNAM (North)

Administration

Commander in Chief of the Navy: Rear Admiral Ta Xuan Thu

Strength of the Fleet

All figures approximate in this section

	Active		Active
Corvettes	3	Tenders	10
Fast Attack Craft—Torpedo	20	MSBs	4
Fast Attack Craft—Gun	28	LSMs	7
Coastal Patrol Craft	30	Landing Ships—various	17

Personnel

1974: Total 4 000 officers and ratings

Mercantile Marine

Lloyd's Register of Shipping: 5 vessels of 5 002 tons

CORVETTES

3 USSR "SOI" TYPE

Displacement, tons	215 light; 250 normal
Dimensions, feet	138·6 × 20 × 9·2
Guns	4—25 mm (2 twin mountings)
A/S weapons	4—5 barrelled MBU; 2 DCT
Range, miles	1 100 at 13 knots
Main engines	3 diesels; 6 000 hp = 29 knots
Complement	30

Four submarine chasers of Soviet "SOI" type were originally transferred to North Vietnam, two in 1960-61 and two in 1964-65, but one was sunk by US Navy aircraft on 1 Feb 1966

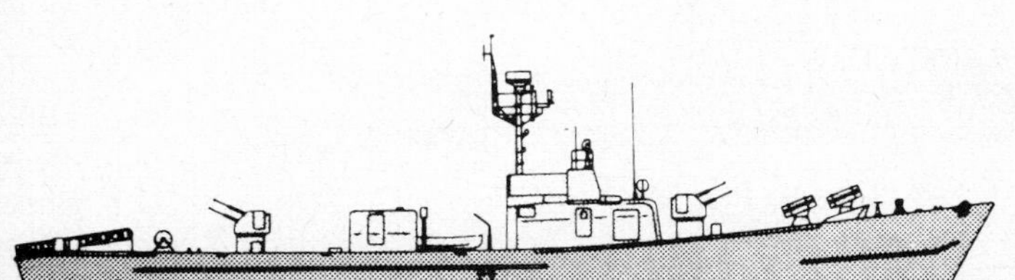

SOI *Class*

LIGHT FORCES

6 USSR "P 6" CLASS (FAST ATTACK CRAFT—TORPEDO)

Displacement, tons	66 standard; 75 full load
Dimensions, feet	84·2 × 20 × 6
Guns	4—25 mm AA (2 twin)
Torpedo tubes	2—21 in (single)
Mines	4
Main engines	4 diesels; 4 800 bhp; 4 shafts = 43 knots
Range, miles	450 at 30 knots
Complement	25

Built in China and transferred in 1967.

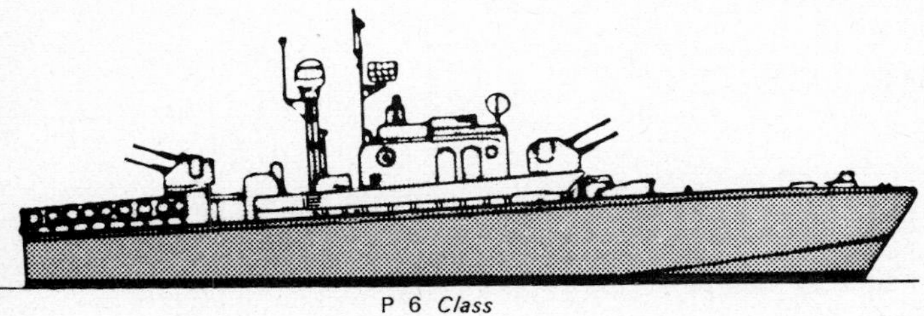

P 6 *Class*

14 USSR "P 4" CLASS (FAST ATTACK CRAFT—TORPEDO)

Displacement, tons	25 standard
Dimensions, feet	62·7 × 11·6 × 5·6
Guns	2 MG (1 twin)
Torpedo tubes	2—18 in
Main engines	2 diesels; 2 200 bhp = 50 knots

Approximately a dozen aluminium hulled motor torpedo boats were transferred from the Soviet Union in 1961 and 1964. and some from China.

P 4 *Class*

Light Forces—*continued*

4 Ex-CHINESE "SHANGHAI" CLASS (FAST ATTACK CRAFT—GUN)

Displacement, tons	120 full load
Dimensions, ft (*m*)	128 × 18 × 5·5 (*39 × 5·5 × 1·7*)
Guns	4—37 mm (2 twin mountings); 4—25 mm (twins)
Main engines	4 diesels; 4 800 bhp = 30 knots
Complement	25

Four motor gunboats were received from the People's Republic of China (Communist) Navy in May 1966.

SHANGHAI II *1972, Aviation Fan*

30 MOTOR LAUNCH TYPES (COASTAL PATROL CRAFT)

Some thirty motor launches were reported to have been incorporated into the North Vietnam Navy before May, 1966, but not all are still in service.

4 PATROL TYPE (MSB)

Four vessels for sweeping, patrol and general purpose duties have been reported delivered in recent years.

14 Ex-CHINESE "SWATOW" CLASS (FAST ATTACK CRAFT—GUN)

Displacement, tons	80 full load
Dimensions, feet	83·5 × 19 × 6·5
Guns	4—37 mm; 2—20 mm
A/S weapons	8 depth charges
Main engines	4 diesels; 4 800 bhp = 40 knots
Range, miles	750 at 15 knots
Complement	17

Approximately 30 "Swatow" class motor gunboats built in China were transferred in 1958, and 20 were delivered in 1964 to replace those lost in action. Pennant numbers run in a 600 series.

10 GENERAL UTILITY TYPES (TENDERS)

Tenders and launches commandeered from private and commercial sources to serve the fleet and naval establishments.

AMPHIBIOUS FORCES

7 US LSM TYPE

Displacement, tons	743 standard; 1 095 full load
Dimensions, feet	196·5 wl; 203·5 oa × 34·5 × 8·3
Guns	2—40 mm AA (1 twin mounting); 4—20 mm AA
Main engines	Diesels; 2 shafts; 2 800 bhp = 12 knots

One or two of these are reported to be out of operational service.

5 US LSSL TYPE

Displacement, tons	250 standard; 430 full load
Dimensions, feet	153·0 wl; 158·5 oa × 23·7 × 5·7
Guns	1—3 in; 4—40 mm AA; 4—20 mm AA
Main engines	Diesels; 2 shafts; 1 800 bhp = 14 knots
Range, miles	3 500 at 12 knots
Complement	71

There are also reported to be five of the LCI/LSIL type, one of the LCT(6) type, and six of the LCT (7) type.

AUXILIARY PATROL CRAFT

There is a substantial number of armed junks and similarly adapted craft.

VIRGIN ISLANDS

Mercantile Marine

Lloyd's Register of Shipping:

5 vessels of 713 tons

1 BROOKE MARINE PATROL CRAFT

VIRGIN CLIPPER

Displacement, tons	15
Dimensions, feet	40 × 12 × 2
Guns	3 MG
Main engines	2 diesels; 370 hp = 22 knots

YEMEN—NORTH (Arab Republic of)

Mercantile Marine

Lloyd's Register of Shipping:
4 vessels of 2 844 tons

Personnel

(a) 1974: 300 officers and men
(b) 3 years National Service
Base Hodeida

5 Ex-USSR "P4" CLASS

(FAST ATTACK CRAFT—TORPEDO)

Displacement, tons	25
Dimensions, feet	62·7 × 11·6 × 5·6
Guns	2 MG
Turpedo Tubes	2—18 in
Main engines	2 diesels; 2 shafts; 2 200 hp = 50 knots

Transferred by USSR in late 1960s.

NOTE. In addition a dozen smaller Patrol Craft and two small landing craft have been reported.

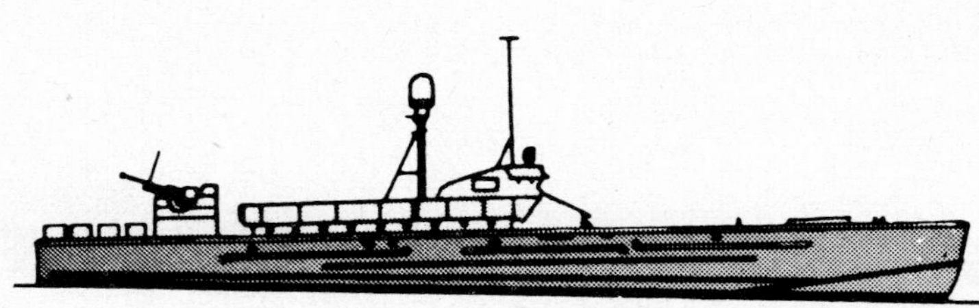

"P 4" Class

YEMEN—SOUTH (People's Democratic Republic of)

Mercantile Marine

Lloyd's Register of Shipping:
6 vessels of 1 680 tons gross

Personnel

(a) 1974: 250 officers and men
(b) Possibly 2 years National Service

CORVETTES

2 Ex-SOVIET "SO I" CLASS

Displacement, tons	215 standard; 250 full load
Dimensions, feet	138·6 × 20·0 × 9·2
Guns	4—25 mm
A/S weapons	4—5 barrelled MBUs
Main engines	3 diesels; 6 000 shp = 29 knots
Range, miles	1 100 at 13 knots
Complement	30

Transferred in late 1960's.

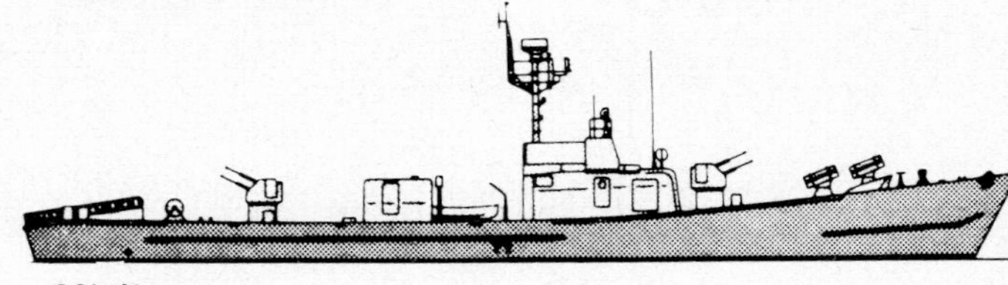

SOI *Class*

AMPHIBIOUS FORCES

2 Ex-USSR "POLNOCNY" CLASS

(LCT)

Displacement, tons	780 standard; 1 000 full load
Dimensions, ft (*m*)	246 × 29·5 × 9·8 (*75 × 9 × 3*)
Guns	2—30 mm (twin)
A/S weapons	2—18 barrelled MBUs
Main engines	2 diesels; 5 000 bhp = 18 knots

Can carry 6 tanks. Transferred early 1970's.

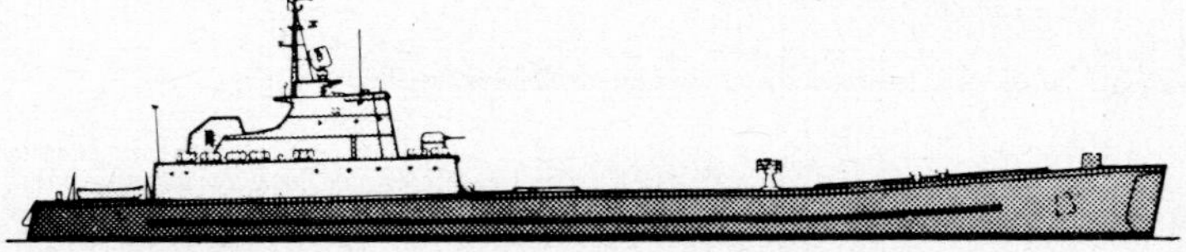

"POLNOCNY" Class

LCM's

Several smaller Soviet LCM's have also been transferred.

INSHORE MINESWEEPERS

3 "HAM" CLASS

Displacement, tons	120 standard; 160 full load
Dimensions, feet	106·5 oa × 21·2 × 5·5
Gun	1—20 mm AA
Main engines	2 Paxman diesels; 1 100 bhp = 14 knots
Oil fuel, tons	15
Complement	15 officers and men

The British inshore minesweepers *Bodenham, Blunham* and *Elsenham* were transferred to the South Arabian Navy established by the Federal Government.

PATROL BOATS

15 COASTAL TYPE

Fifteen small diesel engined patrol boats were bought in the United Kingdom in 1970.

YUGOSLAVIA

Administration

Assistant Secretary of State for National Defence for the Navy:
Vice-Admiral Branko Mamula

Commander-in-Chief of the Fleet:
Vice-Admiral Ivo Purisic

Personnel

(a) 1974: 27 000 (2 500 officers and 24 500 men)
(b) 18 months National Service

Diplomatic Representation

Defence Attaché in London:
Captain Radomir Bogdanovic

Naval, Military and Air Attaché in Washington:
Colonel Milan Mavric

Naval, Military and Air Attaché in Moscow:
Colonel S. Krivokapic

Strength of the Fleet

Type	*Active*	*Building*
Destroyer	1	—
Corvettes	3	—
Submarines—Patrol	5	?
Fast Attack Craft—Missile	10	?
Fast Attack Craft—Torpedo	44	—
Large Patrol Craft	25	—
Minesweepers—Coastal	4	—
Minesweepers—Inshore	12	—
River Minesweepers	14	—
LCT	29(?)	—
Training Ships	2	—
Survey Ship	1	—
Despatch Vessels	2	—
Salvage Vessel	1	—
Tankers—Harbour	7	—
Transports	2	—
Tugs	20	—
Water Carriers	8	—
Yacht	1	—

DISPOSALS

Destroyers

1971 *Kotor* (ex-*Kempenfelt*, ex-*Valentine*)
Pula (ex-*Wager*)

Frigates

1971 *Biokovo* (ex-*Aliseo*)
Triglav (ex-*Indomito*)

Submarines

1971 *Sava* (ex-*Nautilo*)

Mercantile Marine

Lloyd's Register of Shipping:
382 vessels of 1 667 183 tons gross

DESTROYER

1 "SPLIT" CLASS

SPLIT (ex-*Spalato*, ex-*Split*) R 11

Displacement, tons	2 400 standard; 3 000 full load
Length, feet (*metres*)	376·3 (*114·7*) pp; 393·7 (*120·0*) oa
Beam, feet (*metres*)	36·5 (*11·1*)
Draught, feet (*metres*)	12·3 (*3·8*)
Guns, surface	4—5 in (*127 mm*)
Guns, AA	12—40 mm
A/S weapons	2 "Squids", 6 DCT, 2 DC racks
Torpedo tubes	5—21 in (*533 mm*)
Mines	Capacity 40
Boilers	2 watertube type
Main engines	Geared turbines; 2 shafts; 50 000 shp
Speed, knots	31·5
Oil fuel, tons	590 capacity
Complement	240

Built by Brodogradiliste "3 Maj", Rijeka. The original ship was laid down in July 1939 by Chantieres de Loire, Nantes, in 1939 at Split Shipyard. Launched in 1940. Completed on 4 July 1958. Ready for operational service in 1959. The original design provided for an armament of 5—5·5 inch guns, 10—40 mm AA guns and 6—21·7 inch torpedo tubes (tripled), but the plans were subsequently modified.

SPLIT *Aldo Fraccaroli*

CORVETTES

2 "MORNAR" CLASS

MORNAR 551 **BORAC** 552

Displacement, tons	330 standard; 430 full load
Length, feet (*metres*)	170·0 (*51·8*) pp; 174·8 (*53·3*) oa
Beam, feet (*metres*)	23·0 (*7·0*)
Draught, feet (*metres*)	6·6 (*2·0*)
Guns, dual purpose	2—3 in (single)
Guns, AA	2—40 mm single; 2—20 mm single
A/S weapons	2 "Hedgehogs"; 2 DCT; 2 DC racks
Main engines	4 SEMT-Pielstick diesels; 2 shafts 3 240 bhp
Speed, knots	20 max; 16 sustained sea
Range, miles	3 000 at 12 knots; 2 000 at 15 knots
Complement	60

Mornar was completed on 10 Sep 1959. Her design is an improved version of that of PBR 581. *Borac* was launched in 1965.

BORAC *Aldo Fraccaroli*

1 "FOUGUEUX" TYPE

581 (ex-P6)

Displacement, tons	325 standard; 400 full load
Dimensions feet	170 pp × 23 × 6·5
Guns	2—40 mm AA; 2—20 mm AA
A/S weapons	1 Hedgehog; 4 DCT; 2 DC racks
Main engines	4 Pielstick SEMT diesels; 3 240 bhp = 18·7 knots
Range, miles	3 000 at 12 knots; 2 000 at 15 knots
Complement	62

USA offshore procurement. Ordered in France. Built by F. C. Mediterranee (Graville). Launched on 1 June 1954. Transferred to Yugoslavia in 1956.

581 *1972, Yugoslavian Navy*

SUBMARINES

NOTE. There are reports from Yugoslavia of a submarine building programme but it is not known if this is for the Navy or for export.

3 "HEROJ" CLASS (PATROL SUBMARINES)

HEROJ 821 **JUNAK** 822 **USKOK** 823

Displacement, tons	1 068 submerged
Length, feet (*metres*)	210·0 (*64*)
Beam, feet (*metres*)	23·6 (*7·2*)
Draught, feet (*metres*)	16·4 (*5·0*)
Torpedo tubes	6—21 in (*533 mm*)
Main machinery	Diesels; electric motors; 2 400 hp
Speed, knots	16 on surface; 10 submerged
Complement	55

Heroj, the first submarine of this class, was built at the Uljanik Shipyard, Pula in 1968.

JUNAK 1972, S. and DE. Factory, Split

JUNAK 1972, S. and DE. Factory, Split

JUNAK 1972, S. and DE. Factory, Split

2 "SUTJESKA" CLASS (PATROL SUBMARINES)

NERETVA 812 **SUTJESKA** 811

Displacement, tons	820 surfaced; 945 submerged
Length, feet (*metres*)	196·8 (*60·0*)
Beam, feet (*metres*)	22·3 (*6·8*)
Draught, feet (*metres*)	16·1 (*4·9*)
Torpedo tubes	6—21 in (*533 mm*)
Main machinery	Diesels; electric motors; 1 800 hp
Speed, knots	14 on surface; 9 submerged
Range, miles	4 800 at 8 knots
Complement	38

Sutjeska was launched on 28 Sep 1958 at Shipyard Factory, Split. The first submarine to be built in a Yugoslav yard. Commissioned on 16 Sep 1960.

NERETVA 1969, Dr Giorgio Arra

"MALA" CLASS (2 MAN SUBMARINES)

Dimensions, feet	25 × 6 approx
Main motors	1 electric motor; single screw
Complement	2

This class has been given trials by the Navy. It is a free-flood craft with the main motor, battery, navigation-pod and electronic equipment housed in separate watertight cylinders. Constructed of light aluminium it is fitted with fore- and after hydroplanes, the tail being a conventional cruciform with a single rudder abaft the screw. Large perspex windows give a good all-round view.

"MALA" Class 1973, S and DE Factory, Split

LIGHT FORCES

NEW CONSTRUCTION

A number of craft are under construction in Yugoslavia, which may be based on the Swedish "Spica" class. They have two Rolls-Royce Proteus gas-turbines and cruising diesels.

10 USSR "OSA" CLASS (FAST ATTACK CRAFT—MISSILE)

301	**303**	**305**	**307**	**309**
302	**304**	**306**	**308**	**310**

Displacement, tons	165 standard; 200 full load
Dimensions, feet	128·7 × 25·1 × 5·9
Missile launchers	4 for SSN-2 system
Guns	4—30 mm (2 twin, 1 forward, 1 aft)
Main engines	3 diesels; 13 000 bhp = 32 knots
Range, miles	800 at 25 knots
Complement	25

Acquired between 1965 and 1969.

"OSA" Class *1972, Yugoslavian Navy*

"OSA" Class *1972*

14 USSR "SHERSHEN" CLASS (FAST ATTACK CRAFT—TORPEDO)

210	**212**	**214**	**216**	**218**	**221**
211	**213**	**215**	**217**	**219**	**222**
				220	**223**

Displacement, tons	150 standard; 160 full load
Dimensions, feet	115·5 × 23·1 × 5·0
Torpedo tubes	4—21 in single
Guns	4—30 mm (2 twin)
A/S weapons	12 DC
Main engines	3 diesels; 3 shafts; 13 000 bhp = 41 knots
Complement	16

Acquired between 1965 and 1971, some from the USSR whilst the remainder were built in Yugoslavia.

TC 220 *1972*

30 "101" CLASS (FAST ATTACK CRAFT—TORPEDO)

Displacement, tons	55 standard; 60 full load
Dimensions, feet	69 pp; 78 oa × 21·3 × 7·8
Guns	1—40 mm AA; 4—12·7 mm MG
Tubes	2—18 in
Main engines	3 Packard motors; 3 shafts; 5 000 bhp = 36 knots
Complement	14

Of the same class as US "Higgins". Built in Yugoslavia 1951-60. Some have had their torpedo tubes removed. Can be used as FAC-gun when they mount 2—40 mm and either 2 twin 50 cal MG or 2—20 mm (singles). Two of this class were transferred to Ethiopia in 1960 and renamed *Barracuda* P 22 and *Shark* P 21.

No. 174 with torpedo tubes *Yugoslavian Navy*

9 TYPE "133" (LARGE PATROL CRAFT)

132	**133**	**134**	**135**	**137**	**139**
			136	**138**	**140**

Displacement, tons	85 standard; 120 full load
Dimensions, feet	91·9 × 14·8 × 8·3
Guns	2—20 mm AA
Main engines	2 diesels; 900 bhp = 13 knots sea speed

Used for coastguard duties. Armament varies in individual boats. Built in Yugoslavia 1967-68.

No. 134 *1968, Yugoslavian Navy*

16 "KRALJEVICA" CLASS (LARGE PATROL CRAFT)

501-512, 519-521 and 524.

Displacement, tons	195 standard; 250 full load
Dimensions, feet	134·5 × 20·7 × 7·2
Guns	1—3 in; 1—40 mm AA; 4—20 mm AA
A/S weapons	DCs plus Mousetrap in some
Main engines	Diesels; 2 shafts; 3 300 bhp = 20 knots

Built in 1952-58. Six transferred to Indonesia in 1959 and two to Sudan in 1969.

PBR 512 ***Yugoslavian Navy***

10 "131" CLASS (LARGE PATROL CRAFT)

131-140

Displacement, tons	85 standard; 120 full load
Dimensions ft, (*m*)	98·4 × 16·4 × 8·2 (*30 × 5 × 2·5*)
Guns	6—20 mm (triples)
Main engines	2 diesels; 2 500 hp = 20 knots

Built in Yugoslavia 1967.

MINE WARFARE FORCES

4 "HRABRI" CLASS (MINESWEEPERS—COASTAL)

HRABRI M 151 (ex-*D* 25)
SLOBODNI M 153 (ex-*D* 27)
SMELI M 152 (ex-*D* 26)
SNAZNI M 161

Displacement, tons	365 standard; 424 full load
Dimensions, feet	140 ppa; 152 oa × 28 × 8·2
Guns	2—20 mm AA
Main engines	SIGMA free piston generators; 2 shafts; 2 000 bhp = 15 knots
Oil fuel, tons	48
Range, miles	3 000 at 10 knots
Complement	40

Hrabri, *Slobodni* and *Smeli* were built in France by A. Normand as US "off-shore" orders, launched on 27 Feb 1956, 26 May 1956, 26 June 1956, respectively, and allocated to the Yugoslav Navy at Cherbourg in Sep 1957. *Snazni* was built in Yugoslavia in 1960 with French assistance.

SLOBODNI — *1966, Yugoslavian Navy*

6 "ML 117" CLASS (MINESWEEPERS—INSHORE)

M 117 **M 118** **M 119** **M 121** **M 122** **M 123**

Displacement, tons	120 standard; 131 full load
Dimensions, feet	98·4 × 18 × 4·9
Guns	1—40 mm AA; 2—12·7 mm MG
Main engines	2 GM diesels; 1 000 bhp = 12 knots

A small type of inshore minesweeper built in Yugoslav shipyards between 1966 and 1968.

M 121 — *1968, Yugoslavian Navy*

4 BRITISH "HAM" CLASS (MINESWEEPERS—INSHORE)

M 141 **M 142** **M 143** **M 144**

Displacement, tons	123 standard; 164 full load
Dimensions, feet	100 × 21·8 × 5·5
Guns	1—40 mm AA or 1—20 mm AA
Main engines	2 Paxman diesels; 1 100 bhp = 14 knots
Range, miles	2 000 at 9 knots
Complement	22

Built in Yugoslavia 1964-66 under the US Military Aid Programme. Of same design as British "Ham" class.

M 142 — *1968, Yugoslavian Navy*

2 TYPE 101 (MINESWEEPERS—INSHORE)

M 105 **M 106**

Displacement, tons	90 standard; 95 full load
Dimensions, feet	82 × 19·5 × 6·2
Guns	1—40 mm; 1—20 mm
Main engines	Diesel; 135-175 bhp = 12 knots

Built during 1950-56 in Yugoslav shipyards.

Mine Warfare Forces—*continued*

14 RML 300 TYPE (RIVER MINESWEEPERS)

M 301 **M 302** **M 303** **M 304** **M 305** **M 306** **M 307** **M 308** **M 309** **M 310** **M 311** **M 312** **M 313** **M 314**

Displacement, tons	38
Guns	1—20 mm
Main engines	Speed = 12 knots

All launched in 1951-53. Serve on the Danube.

AMPHIBIOUS FORCES

25 DTM 230 TYPE (LCT)

DTM 230 onwards

Displacement, tons	*circa* 220
Guns	4—20 mm AA

Capable of carrying at least two, possibly three of the heaviest tanks. Unlike other tank landing craft in that the lower part of the bow drops to form a ramp down which the tanks go ashore, underneath the prow, which is rigid. It is reported that probably some 25 of these craft are operational. Ex German.

DTM 230 — *B. Hinchcliffe*

DTK 221 TYPE (LCT)

DTK 221

Displacement, tons	410
Dimensions, feet	144·3 × 19·7 × 7
Guns	1—20 mm AA; 2—12·7 mm
Main engines	Speed = 10 knots
Complement	15

DTK 221 — *Yugoslavian Navy*

Ex-ITALIAN MZ TYPE (LCT)

D 206 (ex-*MZ* 713)
D 219 (ex-*MZ* 717)

Displacement, tons	225 and 239
Guns	1—20 mm AA; 2 MG AA
Main engines	Speed = 11 knots

Ex-Italian landing craft. Launched in 1942. Capable of carrying three tanks.

Ex-GERMAN TYPE (LCT)

D 203 **D 204**

Displacement, tons	220
Guns	1—3·4 in (88 mm); 2—20 mm AA
Main engines	Speed = 10 knots

Ex-German landing craft.

CATAMARAN TYPE (LCU)

Displacement, tons	*circa* 50

A smaller craft consisting of two pontoons some feet apart, secured to each other by cross-girders on which stand the bridge and cabins, etc. This vessel appears to be capable of carrying one medium tank, to be put ashore by two bridge members which can be seen quite clearly, folded back on the deck.

Catamaran type — *B. Hinchcliffe*

TRAINING SHIPS

1 "GALEB" CLASS

GALEB (ex-*Kuchuck*, ex-*Ramb III*) M 11

Displacement, tons	5 182 standard
Measurement, tons	3 667 gross
Length, feet (*metres*)	384·8 (*117·3*)
Beam, feet (*metres*)	51·2 (*15·6*)
Draught, feet (*metres*)	18·4 (*5·6*)
Main engines	2 diesels; 2 shafts; 7 200 bhp
Speed, knots	17

Ex-Italian. Built by Ansaldo, Genoa. Launched in 1938. Refloated and completed in 1952. Now training ship. Also Presidential Yacht. Former armament was four 3·5 inch, four 40 mm and 24—20 mm (six quadruple) guns. The guns were landed. Can act as minelayer.

GALEB *1972, Yugoslavian Navy*

JADRAN

Displacement, tons	720
Dimensions, feet	190 × 29·2 × 13·8
Sail area, sq ft	8 600
Main engines	1 Linke-Hofman Diesel; 375 hp = 8 knots

Topsail schooner. Launched in 1932. Accommodation for 150 Cadets. Name means "Adriatic". While in Italian hands she was named *Marco Polo*.

DESPATCH VESSELS

JADRANKA (ex-*Bjeli Orao*)

Displacement, tons	567 standard; 660 full load
Dimensions, feet	213·2 oa × 26·5 × 9·3
Guns	2—40 mm AA; 2 MG
Main engines	2 Sulzer diesels; 1 900 bhp = 18 knots

Built by C. R. dell Adriatico, San Marco, Trieste. Launched on 3 June 1939. Was used as Admiralty yacht and yacht of Marshall Tito. While in Italian hands was named *Alba*, for some days only, then *Zagaria*.

JADRANKA *1970, Yugoslavian Navy*

VIS Also reported in service.

SURVEY SHIP

A. MOHOROVIC PH 33

Displacement, tons	1 475 full load
Dimensions, feet	239·5 × 36·1 × 15·1
Main engines	2 diesels = 15 knots

Built in 1971 at the shipyard in Gdansk, Poland, and added to the Yugoslav Navy List in 1972.

A. MOHOROVICIC *1972, Yugoslavian Navy*

SALVAGE VESSEL

SPASILAC PS II

Displacement, tons	740
Dimensions, feet	174 × 26·2 × 13
Main engines	Triple expansion; 2 000 hp = 15 knots

Built by Howaldt, Kiel. Launched in 1929. Name means "Salvador". While in Italian hands she was called *Intangible*.

SPASILAC *1966, Yugoslavian Navy*

TANKERS

4 PN 13 TYPE (HARBOUR TANKERS)

PN 13 (ex-*Lovcen*) **PN 14** **PN 15** **PN 16**

Displacement, tons	695 standard
Main engines	Speed = 8·5 knots

PN 13 (ex-*Lovcen*) was launched in 1932. PN 17 was transferred to the Sudanese Navy in 1969.

PO 55 (HARBOUR TANKER)

Of 600 tons.

2 "KIT" CLASS (HARBOUR TANKER)

KIT **ULJESURA**

250 ton harbour tankers.

TRANSPORTS

2 PT 71 TYPE

PT 71 **PT 72**

Displacement, tons	310 standard; 428 full load
Dimensions, feet	141·5 × 22·2 × 16
Main engines	300 bhp = 7 knots

The transport *Tuni* PT 21 (ex-*Krk*, ex-*Kt.* 6) was removed from the list in 1963.

TUGS

LR II (ex-*Basiluzzo*)

Displacement, tons	108
Main engines	130 hp = 8 knots

Former Italian tug. Launched in 1915.

PR 51 (ex-*Porto Conte*)

Displacement, tons	226

Former Italian tug. Launched in 1936.

PR 52 (ex-*San Remo*)

Displacement, tons	170
Main engines	350 hp = 9 knots

Former Italian tug and multi-purpose vessel. Launched in 1937.

PR 54 (ex-*Ustrajni*)

Displacement, tons	160
Main engines	250 hp = 9 knots

Launched in 1917.

PR 55 (ex-*Snazi*)

Displacement, tons	100
Main engines	300 hp = 10 knots

Launched in 1917.

PR 58 (ex-*Molara*)

Displacement, tons	118
Main engines	250 hp = 8 knots

Former Italian tug. Launched in 1937.

There are also in service PP 1 (ex-*Marljivi*) of 130 tons, RRM 11, LR 67-74 new construction of 130 tons, BM 29, LD 21, LP 21 and RM 27—the last four being small mooring tugs.

WATER CARRIERS

PV 6 **PV 11** **PV 12**
PT 12 **PO 54** + 3

There are 8 water carriers of various types and of modern construction.

YACHT

ISTRANKA (ex-*Vila*, ex-*Dalmata*)

Displacement, tons	230
Dimensions, feet	40·4 × 5·1 × 2·1
Main engines	325 hp = 12 knots

Built in 1896

ZAIRE

Personnel

(a) 200 officers and men
(b) Voluntary service

Some of the following craft have been deployed on Lake Tanganyika since 1967.

ZAIRE (ex-*President Mobuto*, ex-*General Olsen*), ex-*Congo* (COASTAL PATROL CRAFT)

A 70 ton craft, the first in this naval force.

6 SEWART TYPE (COASTAL PATROL CRAFT)

Displacement, tons	33
Length, feet	65
Guns	6 MG
Main engines	2 GM diesels = 26 knots
Range, miles	1 000 at 18 knots

Purchased in USA in 1971.

1 COASTAL PATROL CRAFT

Of 18 tons, 25 knots and mounting 3 MG. Purchased in USA in 1968.

4 COASTAL PATROL CRAFT

Reported as transferred by China in late 1960's.

ZANZIBAR

Although part of the United Republic of Zanzibar, Tanzania retains a separate Executive and Legislature, the President of Zanzibar being First Vice-President of Tanzania.

4 VOSPER THORNYCROFT 75 FT TYPE

Dimensions, ft (*m*)	75 × 19·5 × 8 (*22·9 × 6·0 × 1·5*)
Guns	2—20 mm
Main engines	2 diesels; 1 840 hp
Speed, knots	24·5
Range, miles	800 at 20 knots
Complement	10

This is one of the first orders for the new Keith Nelson 75 ft craft. First pair delivered 6 July 1973, second pair 1974.

75 FT TYPE *1974, Vosper Thornycroft*

NAVAL AIRCRAFT AND MISSILES

NAVAL AIRCRAFT

Shipborne Aircraft

Helicopters

Land-based Aircraft

NAVAL MISSILES

Surface-to-surface
Air-to-surface
Surface-to-air
Air-to-air
Anti-submarine Systems

NAVAL AIRCRAFT

NOTES.

(a) For those countries using equipment acquired from abroad reference is made to the main supplier.

(b) In each country the equipment listed is split as follows:—

(A) Shipborne aircraft
(B) Helicopters
(C) Land-based aircraft

(c) Where two countries are involved in the production of an aircraft it is listed under the first country alphabetically (e.g. Jaguar, (France/UK)) appears under "France".

ARGENTINA

(A) 15 McDONNELL-DOUGLAS "Skyhawk" (A-4F)
6 GRUMMAN "Tracker" (G-89)
3 GRUMMAN "Albatross" (HU 16)

(B) 9 ALOUETTE II
4 SEA KING SH3-D

(C) 2 WESTLAND "Lynx" (WG-13)
8 AERMACCHI MB 326K (Trainers)
6 LOCKHEED Neptune (P2-H)

CANADA

(B) 41 SIKORSKY CH-SS22

(C) CANADAIR "Argus" (CP-107)

Fifteen-crew long-range maritime reconnaissance aircraft

Max speed at 20 000 ft (*6 100 m*)	**274 knots**
Cruising speed	**150-175 knots**
Service ceiling	**20 000 ft (*6 100 m*) plus**
Max range	**5 124 n. miles at 194 knots**
Equipment	Large nose radome, MAD in tail (for search role), searchlight
Armament	15 600 lb of weapons (bombs, torpedoes, missiles) stowed 8 000 lb internally and 3 800 lb under each wing
T-O weight	148 000 lb (*67 130 kg*)
Wing span	142 ft 3·5 in (*43·38 m*)
Length	**128 ft 9½ in (*39·25 m*)**
Height	36 ft 8·5 in (*11·19 m*)
Power plant	4 × Wright R-3350-EA-1 turbo-Compound radial piston engines of 3 700 hp each

In service with five squadrons (Nos. 404, 405, 407, 415 and 449 training Sqdns) of the Canadian Armed Forces in both Mk 1 and Mk 2 versions which differ in equipment.

CANADAIR CL 215 (Amphibian)

Cruising speed	158 knots
Max range	970 n. miles
T-O weight	43 500 lb (*19 731 kg*) (land)
	37 700 lb (*17 100 kg*) (water)
Wing span	93 ft 10 in (*28·6 m*)
Length	65 ft (*19·82 m*)
Height	29 ft 6 in (*8·98 m*)
Power plant	2 × 2 100 hp Pratt and Whitney

AUSTRALIA

(A) McDONNELL-DOUGLAS "Skyhawk" (A-4E)
FAIREY "Gannet"
GRUMMAN "Tracker" (G-89)

(B) BELL "Iroquois" (UH-IB)
WESTLAND "Wessex" (Mk 3)

BELGIUM

(B) 3 "Alouette III" (HSS-1)
3 SIKORSKY S-58

BRAZIL

(A) 13 GRUMMAN "Tracker" (G-89)

(B) BELL 47 C2 and 47J
4 HILLER FH-1100
10 HUGHES 200
4 SIKORSKY S58
3 SIKORSKY SH 3D (Sea King)
3 WESTLAND "Wasp" UH-2
5 WESTLAND "Whirlwind"
2 WESTLAND "Lynx" (WG 13) (in new destroyers)

operated by Air Force

30 GRUMMAN "Tracker" (G-89)
LOCKHEED "Neptune" (P2V-7)
LOCKHEED "Orion" (P3)

Argus Mk. 2 maritime reconnaissance aircraft *Courtesy, B. M. Service*

CHILE

(B) 4 BELL "Jetranger" (206 A)

(C) 1 GRUMMAN "Albatross" (HU-16)
5 C-45 (Transports)
5 C-47 (Transports)

DENMARK

(B) 8 SUD-AVIATION "Alouette III"

FRANCE

(A)

50 BR 1050 ALIZÉ Breguet

Carrier-borne 3-seat anti-submarine aircraft

Max speed at 10 000 ft (*3 050 m*)	**254 knots**
Patrol speed	**210-320 knots**
Service ceiling	**26 250 ft (*8 000 m*)**
Normal range	**1 350 n. miles**
Normal endurance	**5 hr 10 min**
Max endurance	**7 hr 40 min**
Armament	**Internal Bay: 3 × 353 lb depth charges or one torpedo Inner wing racks for 2 × 353 lb or 385 lb depth charges Outer wing racks: 6 × 5-in rockets or 2 × AS12 ASM's**
Max T-O weight	**18 100 lb (*8 200 kg*)**
Wing span	**51 ft 2 in (*15·60 m*)**
Width folded	**23 ft 0 in (*7·00 m*)**
Length	**45 ft 6 in (*13·86 m*)**
Height	**16 ft 5 in (*5·00 m*)**
Power plant	1 × 2 100 eshp Rolls-Royce Dart R.Da 21 turboprop

75 were built for the French Navy to equip three squadrons; 12 were supplied to the Indian Navy for service on board *Vikrant*.

36 CHANCE VOUGHT "Crusader" F-8E (FN)

These, embarked in *Clemenceau* and *Foch* are fitted to carry 2 MATRA R 500 missiles each.

Alizé of the French Navy, with wings extending

FRANCE (continued)

42 ETENDARD IV-M Dassault

Carrier-borne single-seat interceptor and fighter bomber

Max speed at 36,000 ft (*11 000 m*)	Mach 1·02
Max cruising speed at 25,000 ft (*7 600 m*)	Mach 0·90
Service ceiling	49 200 ft (*15 000 m*)
Range (at 510 mph; 821 kmh with external tanks)	1 520 n. miles
Armament	Fuselage: 2 × 30 mm Cannon Wing Mounts (4): Up to 3 000 lb (*1 060 kg*) of rockets, bombs, Sidewinder AAM's or AS.30 ASM's
Max T-O weight	22 650 lb (*10 275 kg*)
Wing span	31 ft 6 in (*9·60 m*)
Width folded	25 ft 7 in (*7·80 m*)
Length	47 ft 3 in (*14·40 m*)
Height	14 ft 1 in (*4·30 m*)
Power plant	1 × SNECMA Atar 8B turbojet of 9 700 lb (*4 400 kg*) st

Entered service with French Navy for *Clemenceau & Foch* carriers in 1962. 75 aircraft were built. 21 additional aircraft were built as IV-P dual-role tanker and reconnaissance aircraft with nose and ventral camera positions and flight refuelling equipment.

Etendard IV-M of the French Navy, with wing tips folded

70 SEPECAT JAGUAR M Breguet/BAC

Single-seat naval tactical aircraft

Max speed at S/L	729 knots
Range (ferry, with external fuel)	2 270 n. miles
Armament	2 × 30 mm DEFA 553 type cannon in lower fuselage aft of cockpit. One ventral attachment point on fuselage centre-line and two under each wing. Provision for wingtip attachments for air-to-air missiles. The centre-line and inboard wing points can each carry up to 2 000 lb (*900 kg*) of weapons, and outboard underwing points up to 1 000 lb (*450 kg*) each. Typical alternative loads include 2 × Martel AS 37 anti-radar missiles and a drop tank; 8 × 1 000 lb (*450 kg*) bombs; various combinations of freefall bombs, Sidewinder air-to-air missiles, air-to-air or air-to-surface rockets, including the 68 mm SNEB rocket; or a reconnaissance camera pack with two photo-flare pods.
Max T-O weight	29 762 lb (*13 500 kg*)
Wing span	27 ft 10½ in (*8·49 m*)
Length overall	50 ft 11 in (*15·52 m*)
Height overall	16 ft 0½ in (*4·89 m*)
Power plant	2 × Rolls-Royce/Turboméca Ad-our turbofan engines (each 4 620 lb = 2 100 *kg* st dry) and (6 950 lb = *3 150 kg*) with afterburning.

SEPECAT Jaguar M prototype *Courtesy Air Portraits*

Under development for French Navy. Prototype first flew on 14 November 1969.

(B) 16 SA321 SUPER FRELON Aérospatiale

Land-based two crew heavy assault and anti-submarine helicopter

Max (never exceed) speed at S/L	148 knots
Cruising speed	135 knots
Hovering ceiling in ground effect	6 950 ft (*2 120 m*)
Service ceiling	10 325 ft (*3 150 m*)
Range at S/L	442 n. miles
Range, ferry with two 220 imp gallon (*1 000 litre*) auxiliary tanks	549 n. miles
Capacity	30 troops, 15 stretchers and 2 attendants or 11 023 lb (*5 000 kg*) payload
Max T-O weight	28 660 lb (*13 000 kg*)
Main rotor diameter	62 ft 0 in (*18·90 m*)
Length of fuselage, incl tail rotor	65 ft 10¾ in (*20·08 m*)
Width folded	17 ft 0¾ in (*5·20 m*)
Height	21 ft 10¼ in (*6·66 m*)
Power plant	3 × Turbomeca Turmo IIIE6 shaft-turbine engines of 1 570 shp each

SA-321G Super Frelon—French Navy

20 ALOUETTE III Aérospatiale

Seven-seat general-purpose helicopter

Max speed at S/L	114 knots
Max cruising speed at S/L	100 knots
Service ceiling	10 825 ft (3 300 m)
Range	290 n. miles
Armament	2 × AS12 missiles or 2 × Mk 44 torpedoes or 1 × torpedo and MAD equipment
Max T-O weight (standard version)	4 850 lb (*2 200 kg*)
Main rotor diameter	36 ft 1¾ in (*11·02 m*)
Length overall	42 ft 1½ in (*12·84 m*)
Length folded	32 ft 10¾ in (*10·03 m*)
Height	9 ft 10 in (*3·0 m*)
Power plant	1 × Turbomeca Artouste IIIB turboshaft engine of 870 shp derated to 550 shp

Developed from the standard Alouette III, this version is intended for "plane guard", ASW and attack duties aboard various classes of naval vessels.

Alouette III of the French Navy *Courtesy of Peter R. March*

FRANCE (continued)

(C) 38 BR 1150 ATLANTIC Breguet

Twelve-crew long-range maritime reconnaissance aircraft

Max speed at high altitudes	355 knots
Max range	4 854 n. miles
Max endurance at 169 knots (patrol speed)	18 hours
Armament	Fuselage weapons bay: carries standard NATO bombs, 385 lb (*175 kg*) depth charges, homing torpedoes Wing mounts (4): HVAR rockets; or Martel ASM's
Max T-O weight	95 900 lb (*43 500 kg*)
Wing span	119 ft 1 in (*36·3 m*)
Length	104 ft 2 in (*31·75 m*)
Height	37 ft 2 in (*11·33 m*)
Power plant	2 × RR Tyne R.Ty.20 Mk 21 turboprop engines of 6 105 ehp each. (SNECMA built)

In service since 1966 with French Navy (38 aircraft), German Navy (20 aircraft), Netherlands (9 aircraft), Italian (18 aircraft)

Atlantic in French Navy insignia *Courtesy of B. M. Service*

15 N262 Aérospatiale

Light transport aircraft

Max speed	208 knots
Max and econ cruising speed	202 knots
Service ceiling	23 500 ft (*7 160 m*)
Range with max payload, FAA reserves	525 n. miles
Capacity	Max seating for 29
Max T-O weight	23 369 lb (*10 600 kg*)
Wing span	71 ft 10 in (*21·90 m*)
Length overall	63 ft 3 in (*19·28 m*)
Height over tail	20 ft 4 in (*6·21 m*)
Power plant	2 × 1 080 eshp Turboméca Bastan VIC turboprop engines (1 145 ehp Bastan VIIA in Series C and D)

Used by the French Navy as aircrew trainers and light transports.

Aerospatiale N 262 transport of the French Navy

GERMANY (FEDERAL REPUBLIC)

(B) 22 WESTLAND/SIKORSKY "Sea King" (SH-3D)
23 SIKORSKY SH 34J

(C) 20 BREGUET "Atlantic" (1150)
20 DORNIER 28 D-2 SKYSERVANT
121 LOCKHEED Starfighter F104G

INDIA

(A) 12 BREGUET "Alizé" (1050)
10 GRUMMAN "Tracker" (S2-A)

35 SEA HAWK Hawker Siddeley (UK)

Carrier-borne single-seat fighter bomber

Max cruising speed at S/L	512 knots
Radius of action	251 n. miles
Armament	Fuselage: 4 × 20 mm cannon Wing mounts (4): 2 × 500 lb bombs and/or RP
Max gross weight	16 200 lb (*7 355 kg*)
Wing span	39 ft 0 in (*11·89 m*)
Width folded	13 ft 4 in (*4·04 m*)
Length	39 ft 8 in (*12·09 m*)
Height overall	8 ft 8 in (*2·64 m*)
Height folded	16 ft 10 in (*5·13 m*)
Power plant	1 × RR Nene 103 turbojet of 5 400 lb (*2 450 kg*) st

The type is operational with the Indian Navy for the carrier *Vikrant*.

Sea Hawk Mk. 50 of the Indian Navy with underwing rockets

(B) 18 AÉROSPATIALE "Alouette III"
2 AÉROSPATIALE "Alouette II"
6 WESTLAND/SIKORSKY "Sea King" (SH 3D)

(C) HINDUSTAN HT 2
SHORT "Sealand"

NOTE. (a) The Indian Air Force includes a maritime squadron of L-1049 Super Constellations.
(b) The Indian Navy is considering the addition of LRMP aircraft—possibly Breguet "Atlantics".

INDONESIA

(B) 3 AEROSPATIALÉ "Alouette II"

(C) FAIREY "Gannet" (AS 4)
GRUMMAN "Albatross" (HU 16C)
ILYUSHIN "Beagle" (Il-28)

NOTE.
Very few of the above can be considered as operational.

ISRAEL

(B) SIKORSKY S-55

(C) CATALINA PBY-5A

ITALY

(B) (all naval)
9 SIKORSKY SH-34
24 SIKORSKY SH-3D (Sea King)

30 AGUSTA BELL 204B/AS — Agusta

Utility helicopter

Max speed at S/L	104 knots
Cruising speed	96 knots
Hovering ceiling (out of ground effect)	4 500 ft (*1 370 m*)
Max range	340 n. miles
Equipment	Dipping Sonar and special electronic equipment for stabilisation etc (AB 204AS version)
Armament	2 × Mk 44 torpedoes (AB 204AS version)
Max T-O weight	9 500 lb (*4 310 kg*)
Main rotor diameter	48 ft 0 in (*14·63 m*)
Length overall	57 ft 0 in (*17·37 m*)
Power plant	1 × Lycoming T53-11A shaft-turbine engine of 1 100 shp; alternatively 1 × Rolls-Royce Bristol Gnome H.1200 of 1 200 shp or a General Electric T58-GE-3

In service with the navies of Italy, Spain and Holland. A special ASW version of the 204B known as the 204 AS has been built for individual or dual-role search and attack missions and is in service with the navies of Italy and Spain.

NOTE. The Italian Navy and Air Force work together in ASW matters. All aircraft concerned are listed below. Navy personnel fly with the Air Force and the operations and administration of these ASW squadrons are a naval responsibility.

(C) (all Air Force)

18 BREGUET "Atlantic" (1150) (delivery started July 1972)
30 GRUMMAN "Tracker" (S2 F)

Agusta-Bell 204AS anti-submarine helicopter of the Italian Navy

NOTE. The Chinook CH4T is under evaluation for use in the Italian Navy.

JAPAN

(B) 40 SH-SD Seakings
10 SH-34 Seabats
10 S61A
KV 107A

(C) BEECH T-34A Mentors
FUJI KM 2's
GRUMMAN SA-16 Albatross

40 GRUMMAN S-2A Trackers
46 KAWASAKI P2-J (Neptunes)
50 LOCKHEED P2-H Neptunes
2 SHIN-MEIWA PS (STOL flying boat)

MEXICO

(B) 4 AEROSPATIALE "Alouette III"
4 BELL 47-G
1 BELL 47-J

(C) 5 "Catalina" PBY-5

NETHERLANDS

(B) 9 AGUSTA-BELL 204B AS
SIKORSKY H-34J
9 WESTLAND "Wasp" HAS Mk I

(C) 8 BREGUET "Atlantic" (1150)
17 GRUMMAN "Tracker" (S-2N)
18 LOCKHEED "Neptune" (P-2V)

NEW ZEALAND

(B) WESTLAND "Wasp" HAS Mk I (in two frigates)

(C) 5 LOCKHEED "Orion" (P-38) (MP aircraft operated by RNZAF)

NORWAY

(B) WESTLAND/SIKORSKY "Sea King" (SH-3D) (For ASR duties operated by Norwegian Air Force)

(C) 9 LOCKHEED "Orion" (P-SB) (MP aircraft operated by Norwegian Air Force)

PAKISTAN

(B) 2 UH-19 (for ASR duties)
6 WESTLAND/SIKORSKY Sea Kings (SH-3D)

PERU

(B) ALOUETTE II SE 3130
8 BELL 47G

(C) 6 GRUMMAN "Albatross" (HU-16A)
6 LOCKHEED "Harpoon" (PV-2)
(Both LRMP aircraft operated by Peruvian Air Force)

POLAND

(B) MIL "Hound" Mi-4

(C) 10 ILYUSHIN "Beagle" (Il-28)
45 MIKOYAN MiG-17

PORTUGAL

(C) 12 LOCKHEED "Neptune" (P-2V5)
(LRMP aircraft operated by Portuguese Air Force)

SOUTH AFRICA

(B) 6 WESTLAND "Wasp" HAS Mk I
(embarked in destroyers and frigates)

(C) 7 AVRO "Shackleton"
(LRMP aircraft operated by South African Air Force)

SPAIN

(B) AGUSTA-BELL 212
9 AGUSTA-BELL 204 AS
BELL 209 Hueycobra
SIKORSKY Sea Kings (SH-3D)
SIKORSKY S-56
28 SIKORSKY S-61
(For embarkation in *Dedalo*)

(C) 12 GRUMMAN "Albatross" (HU-16B)
(MP Aircraft operated by Spanish Air Force)

SWEDEN

(B) 10 AGUSTA-BELL 204B
10 ALOUETTE II SE 3130
10 BOEING-VERTOL 107-II

TURKEY

(B) 3 AGUSTA-BELL 204B AS
(C) 8 S-2E Trackers

UNITED KINGDOM

(A)

16 BUCCANEER S Mk 2 — Hawker Siddeley

Carrier-borne and land-based 2-seat all-weather strike and reconnaissance aircraft

Max speed at 200 ft (*61 m*)	Mach 0·85 approx.
Tactical radius	1 000 n. miles plus
Armament	Internal Bay: Nuclear or conventional weapons (4 × 1 000 lb *453 kg* bombs) or camera pack; four underwing attachments for Bullpup or Martel missiles, 1 000 lb (453 *kg*) bombs (up to three on each pylon) or rocket packs
Max weapon load	16 000 lb (*7,257 kg*)
Max T-O weight	62 000 lb (*28 123 kg*)
Wing span	44 ft 0 in (*13·41 m*)
Width folded	19 ft 11 in (*6·07 m*)
Length overall	63 ft 5 in (*19·33 m*)
Length folded	51 ft 10 in (*15·79 m*)
Height overall	16 ft 3 in (*4·95 m*)
Height folded	16 ft 8 in (*5·08 m*)

Hawker Siddeley Buccaneer

Power plant	2 × 11 100 lb (*5 035 kg*) st Rolls-Royce Spey turbofans

Only one squadron of the Fleet Air Arm, based on HMS *Ark Royal*, continues to operate the Buccaneer. Former FAA aircraft are operated by the Royal Air Force, for which production was continued. A land-based version, designated S.50, was built for the South African Air Force, to a total of sixteen.

UNITED KINGDOM (continued)

36 SEA VIXEN (AN) Mk 2 — Hawker Siddeley

Carrier-borne two-seat all weather fighter

Max speed at 10 000 ft (*3 050 m*)	560 knots
Service ceiling	Approx 48 000 ft (*14 630 m*)
Armament	Fuselage: 2 pods each containing 14 × 2 in rockets Wing mounts: (6) Combination of Firestreak, Red Top or Bullpup missiles, bombs, rocket pods or air-to-surface rockets.
Max gross weight	35 000 lb (*15 875 kg*) approx
Wing span	50 ft 0 in (*15·24 m*)
Width folded	22 ft 3 in (*6·78 m*)
Length overall	55 ft 7 in (*16·68 m*)
Length folded	50 ft 2·5 in (*15·30 m*)
Height overall	11 ft 0 in (*3·35 m*)
Height folded	14 ft 11 in (*4·55 m*)
Power plant	2 × RR Avon Ra.24 Mk 208 turbojets of 11 250 lb (*5 100 kg*) st

With the Fleet Air Arm since 1959, it is still in first-line service. 4 squadrons.

Sea Vixen FAW Mk. 2 of No. 766 Squadron, Royal Navy — *Courtesy, Peter R. March*

(A) (continued)

15 GANNET AEW Mk 3 — Westland

Carrier-borne three-seat early-warning aircraft

Max speed	220 knots approx
Endurance	5-6 hours at 120 knots
Equipment	Early-warning electronic for long-range ship and aircraft detection
Max loaded weight	24 000 lb (*10 886 kg*)
Wing span	54 ft 6 in (*16·61 m*)
Width folded	19 ft 11 in (*6·07 m*)
Length	44 ft 0 in (*13·41 m*)
Height	16 ft 10 in (*5·13 m*)
Power plant	1 × Rolls-Royce Bristol Double Mamba 102 turboprop of 3 875 ehp

Entered service with the Fleet Air Arm in 1959, equips No. 849 Squadron which provides early-warning flights on each carrier.

Westland Gannet AEW Mk 3

AV-8A HARRIER — Hawker Siddeley

Single-seat V/STOL strike and reconnaissance aircraft

Max speed	over 640 knots
Service ceiling	over 50 000 ft (*15 240 m*)
Range with one in-flight refuelling	over 3 000 n. miles
Ferry range, unrefuelled	nearly 2 000 n. miles
Armament	One under-fuselage and four under-wing attachments for up to 5 000 lb (*2 270 kg*) of bombs, 68 mm SNEB rocket pods etc. Under-fuselage strakes can be replaced by two 30 mm gun pods
Max T-O weight (GR Mk 1)	over 25 000 lb (*11 339 kg*)
Wing span	25 ft 3 in (*7·70 m*)
Length	45 ft 6 in (*13·87 m*)
Height	approx 11 ft 3 in (*3·43 m*)
Power plant	1 × RR Pegasus 10 (first ten aircraft for USMC) or 1 × Pegasus II of 21 500 lb (*9 752 kg*) st on later aircraft

Delivery of 60 aircraft for the USMC began in 1971. Others serve with the RAF.
(This aircraft is included in the hope that the long-delayed decision to use it in the Royal Navy may be reached during this year.)

Hawker Siddeley AV-8A Harrier of the US Marine Corps

28 PHANTOM F4K — McDONNELL-DOUGLAS

Length overall	58·3 ft (*17·8 m*)
Wing span	38·4 ft (*11·7 m*)
Max TO weight	54 600 lbs (*24 765 kg*)
Max level speed (with external stores)	Mach 2+
Combat Radius	781 n. miles (*1 450 km*) (interceptor) 860 n. miles (*1 600 km*) (ground attack)
Ferry range	2 000 n. miles (*3 700 km*)

This is a development of the USN F-4B . To allow its use in HMS *Ark Royal.* Powered by two Rolls-Royce Spey RB-168-25R Mk 201 Turbofans with 70% reheat, a more powerful system than in US models. After receiving four preliminary aircraft, 24 were ordered as Phantom FG Mk 1, the first being delivered in April 1968.

Phantom FG MK 1

UNITED KINGDOM (continued)

(B)

GAZELLE SA 341C — Westland/Aerospatiale

Max speed at S/L	167 knots
Max cruising speed at S/L	139 knots
Range at S/L with max fuel	361 n. miles
Range with 1 crew and 1 000 lbs payload	194 n. miles
Length, overall	39·2 feet
Max TO weight	3 747 lbs

An Anglo-French development being built by Westlands as Gazalle HT Mk 2 as a replacement for Whirlwind 7 and Sioux. A five-seater with one Turboméca Astazou III Turbo shaft engine.

Gazelle

LYNX WG-13 — Westland

Frigate-borne anti-submarine search and strike helicopter

Max speed	179 knots
Hovering ceiling out of ground effect	above 12 000 ft (*3 650 m*)
Mission radius	154 n. miles
Accommodation	Two crew; 12 troops or freight for secondary capability
Armament	2 × Mk 44 torpedoes etc on cabin sides
Max T-O weight	8 550 lb (*3 878 kg*)
Main rotor diameter	42 ft 0 in (*12·80 m*)
Length overall	49 ft 9 in (*15·16 m*)
Width folded	9 ft 7¾ in (*2·93 m*)
Height overall	12 ft 3 in (*3·73 m*)
Power plant	2 × RR BS.360-07-26 turboshaft engines.

The Royal Navy is to receive the Lynx helicopter as a replacement for the Wasp.

Lynx helicopters will also go to the French and Argentine Navies.

Prototype Westland Lynx. Naval version will have wheel landing gear

60 SEA KINGS — Westland

Speed, knots	max permissible diving	124
	normal operating	114
	for max endurance	75
Ceiling, feet	10 000	
Transit range	520 n. miles (normal fuel)	
	750 n. miles (with auxiliary fuel)	
Main rotor diameter	62 ft (*18·9 m*)	
Length overall (rotors turning)	72·7 ft (*22·2 m*)	
Max TO weight	20 500 lbs	

Designed and built by Westland on a basic air frame and rotor-system obtained under licence from Sikorsky in 1959. Powered by two Rolls-Royce Bristol Gnome H 1400 turboshaft engines. Now appears in several forms—A/S, SAR, Missile (with SS II or Kormoran), Troop Transport, Cargo. In service with RN, Federal German Navy (22 SAR), Norwegian Air Force (ISOAR).

Sea King

SIOUX — Bell

These helicopters are attached as Air Troops of two or three aircraft to Royal Marine commandos and Brigade Headquarters. They are piloted by RM officers and serviced by Fleet Air Arm ratings, all of whom have completed a commando course.

Sioux

80 WASP — Westland

Shipborne general purpose and anti-submarine helicopter

Max speed at S/L	104 knots
Cruising speed	96 knots
Hovering ceiling out of ground effect	8 800 ft (*2 682 m*)
Range with max fuel and allowances of 5 min for T-O and landing, 15 min cruising with 4 passengers	234 n. miles
Armament	2 × Mk 44 homing torpedoes
Max T-O weight	5 500 lb (*2 495 kg*)
Main rotor diameter	32 ft 3 in (*9·83 m*)
Length	40 ft 4 in (*12·29 m*)
Width folded	8 ft 8 in (*2·64 m*)
Height, tail rotor turning	11 ft 8 in (*3·56 m*)
Power plant	1 × RR Bristol Nimbus 503 turboshaft engine of 710 shp

In service with the Fleet Air Arm since 1963 aboard anti-submarine frigates. Also with the navies of Brazil, the Netherlands, New Zealand and South Africa.

Westland Wasp

UNITED KINGDOM (continued)

WESSEX — Westland

Ship and carrier-borne two-crew anti-submarine assault and general-purpose helicopter

Max speed at S/L	115 knots
Cruising speed	105 knots
Hovering ceiling out of ground effect	HAS.1: 3 600 ft (*1 100 m*) HU.5: 4 000 ft (*1 220 m*)
Service ceiling	HAS.1: 14 000 ft (*4 300 m*)
Range with max fuel 10% reserves	HAS.1: 560 n. miles HU.5: 415 n. miles
Equipment	HAS.1: Doppler radar and dipping sonar HAS.3: as HAS.1 plus new search radar
Armament	HAS.1, 3: 1 or 2 homing torpedoes on fuselage side mounts, alternatively 4 × SS.11 ASM's, Machine guns or rockets HU.5: 4 × SS.11 ASM's alternatively various gun/rocket combinations
Capacity	In commando role can carry 16 troops or 8 stretchers or 4 000 lb (*1 814 kg*) of freight
Max T-O weight	HAS.1: 12 600 lb (*5 715 kg*) HU.5: 13 500 lb (*6 120 kg*)
Main rotor diameter	56 ft 0 in (*17·07 m*)
Length	65 ft 9 in (*20·03 m*)
Length folded	38 ft 6 in (*11·73 m*)
Width, folded	13 ft 4 in (*4·06 m*)
Height	16 ft 2 in (*4·93 m*)
Power plant	HAS.1: 1 × Napier Gazelle NGa. 13 Mk 161 shaft turbine engine of 1 450 shp HAS.3: 1 × Napier Gazelle NGa. 22 Mk 165 shaft turbine engine of 1 600 shp HU.5: 2 × RR Bristol Gnome 112/113 shaft turbine engines of 775 shp each

Wessex 5 — *1973 MOD (N)*

In service with the Fleet Air Arm on anti-submarine duties since 1961 (HAS.1) and 1966/67 (HAS.3). 8 squadrons.
With Royal Australian Navy as HAS.31, which is similar to the Mk 1 but with Gazelle Mk 162 engine of 1,540 shp. **(27 aircraft, since modified to HAS-31B, with new search radar). The HU.5 version is a Marine Commando assault version, in service since 1964 with the Commando carriers.**

WHIRLWIND — Westland

Land-based and Carrier-borne two-crew rescue and general-purpose helicopter

Max speed	92 knots
Cruising speed	90 knots
Hovering ceiling	6 900 ft (*2 100 m*)
Service ceiling	16 600 ft (*5 060 m*)
Normal range	260 n. miles
Capacity	Up to 10 troops or 6 stretchers or freight
Max T-O weight	8 000 lb (*3 630 kg*)
Main rotor diameter	53 ft 0 in (*16·15 m*)
Length fuselage	44 ft 2 in (*13·46 m*)
Height	13 ft 2·5 in (*4·03 m*)
Power plant	1 × RR Bristol Siddeley Gnome H.1000 shaft turbine of 1 050 shp

This aircraft is in service with the Fleet Air Arm as the HAR.9 for plane guard and SAR duties and with RAF Strike Command as the HAR.10 for SAR duties. Also in service with the Brazilian Navy.

Westland Whirlwind HAR 10—Brazilian Navy

Shore-based maritime reconnaissance aircraft (C)

(All operated by the Royal Air Force)

HS 801 NIMROD MRI — Hawker Siddeley

Eleven-seat long-range maritime-reconnaissance aircraft

Max speed for operational necessity, ISA +20°C	500 knots
Ferry range	4 500-5 000 n. miles
Wing span	114 ft 10 in (*35·00 m*)
Length	126 ft 9 in (*38·63 m*)
Height	29 ft 8·5 in (*9·05 m*)
Power plant	4 × RR RB168 Spey Mk 250 turbofan engines of 11 500 lb st (*5 217 kg*) each
Armament	Forward bay for bombs, mines, depth charges and/or torpedoes 2 wing mounts for Nord AS.12 or Martel ASM Rear weapons bay for active and passive sonobuoys.
Equipment	Elliot nav-attack system, Sonar ASV-21 radar, Autolycus Ionisation detector, ECM gear, MAD and searchlight

Hawker Siddeley Nimrod MR.Mk.1

38 aircraft in service with RAF Strike Command and further orders have been placed.

SHACKLETON MR Mk 3 — Hawker Siddeley/Avro

Ten-seat long range maritime-reconnaissance and rescue aircraft

Max cruising speed	220 knots
Service ceiling	19 200 ft (*5 850 m*)
Range at 150 knots at 1 500 ft (*450 m*)	3 178 n. miles
Armament	2 × 20 mm cannon in nose (optional) Weapons bay for bombs, mines, depth charge torpedoes, etc Wing mounts (8) for unguided rockets on SAAF aircraft only
Gross weight	100 000 lb (*45 360 kg*)
Wing span	119 ft 10 in (*36·52 m*)
Length	92 ft 6 in (*28·19 m*)
Height	23 ft 4 in (*7·11 m*)
Power plant	4 × RR Griffon 57A in-line piston engines of 2 455 hp each RAF Phase 3 versions have additionally 2 × RR Bristol Viper 203 turbojet engines of 2 500 lb (*1 133 kg*) st in outboard nacelles

Hawker Siddeley Shackleton MR Mk 3 Phase 3 of the RAF — ***Courtesy, Peter R. March***

In service with the South African Air Force in the MR Mk 3 version and the RAF in the MR Mk 3 Phase 3 version and MR Mk 2 which is an earlier tail-wheel version with less tankage. Twelve AEW Mk 2 Shackletons have been delivered to the RAF for maritime airborne early-warning duties.

UNITED STATES OF AMERICA

(A)

OV-IOA BRONCO — North American

Two-seat multi-purpose counter-insurgency aircraft

Max speed at S/L without weapons	**244 knots**
Combat radius, with max weapon load	**198 n. miles**
Ferry range	**1 240 n. miles**
Armament	**4 × 0·30 in machine-guns in sponsons, which also carry maximum of 2 400 lb (*1 088 kg*) external ordnance; provision for one Sidewinder AAM under each wing, and for 1 200 lb (*544 kg*) load under fuselsge**
Max weapon load	3 600 lb (*1 633 kg*)
Max T-O weight	14 466 lb (*6 563 kg*)
Wing span	40 ft 0 in (*12·19 m*)
Length	41 ft 7 in (*12·67 m*)
Height	15 ft 2 in (*4·62 m*)
Power plant	2 × Garrett AiResearch T76-G-10/12 turboprops each of 715 shp

96 built for the US Marine Corps, of which 18 were loaned to the US Navy for use in Vietnam. Two converted to YOV-10D configuration, with ventral turret and infra-red sensors, as night observation/gunships.

OV-10A Bronco light armed reconnaissance aircraft — *Courtesy of Duane A. Kasulka*

A7 CORSAIR II — Ling-Temco-Vought (USA)

Carrier-borne single-seat attack aircraft

Data for A-7E

Max speed at S/L	606 knots
Max range (ferry)	2 900 n. miles
Other performance details	Secret
Armament	Fuselage: 1 × 20 mm multi-barrel gun. Six underwing pylons and two fuselage weapon stations. Two outboard pylons on each wing can each accommodate a load of 3 500 lb (*1 587 kg*). Inboard pylon on each wing can carry 2 500 lb (*1,134 kg*). Two fuselage weapons stations, one on each side, can each carry 500 lb (*227 kg*). Weapons include air-to-air and air-to-ground missiles; general-purpose bombs; rockets; gun pods and auxiliary fuel tanks
Max T-O weight	42 000 lb (*19 050 kg*)
Wing span	38 ft 9 in (*11·80 m*)
Width folded	23 ft 9 in (*7·24 m*)
Length	46 ft 1·5 in (*14·06 m*)
Height	16 ft 0 in (*4·88 m*)
Power plant	**A-7A 1 × P. & W. TF30-P-6 of 11 350 lb (*5 150 kg*) st A-7B 1 × P. & W. TF30-P-8 of 12 200 lb (*5 534 kg*) A-7E: 1 × Allison TF41-A-2 of 15 000 lb (*6 800 kg*)**

A-7E Corsair II of squadron VA-195 of the US Navy

A-7A entered service with US Navy in November 1967, followed by A 7B. A-7E is a development of the A-7B, with TF41-A-2 engine. It was preceded by 67 similar aircraft, designated A-7C with TF30-P-8 engine.

F-8 CRUSADER — Ling-Temco-Vought

Carrier-borne single-seat fighter

Max speed	F-8A, B, C: 868 knots plus F-8D, E, H, J: nearly Mach 2
Combat radius (F-8A)	521·05 n. miles (*965 km*)
Other performance details	Secret
Armament	Fuselage: 4 × 20 mm Colt cannon and 2 × Sidewinder missiles (4 on F-8C/K, F-8D/H, F-8E/J) Provision for carrying Matra R 530 AAMs on F-8E(FN). Wing Mounts: (2) on F-8E, E(FN), H, J, K and L: 2 × 2 000 lb (*907 kg*) bombs or Bullpup A or B ASMs or 24 Zuni rockets
Max weight F-8E/J	34 000 lb (*15 420 kg*)
Wing span	35 ft 8 in (*10·87 m*)
Length	F-8E/J: 54 ft 6 in (*16·61 m*) Others: 54 ft 3 in (*16·54 m*)
Width folded	22 ft 6 in (*6·86 m*)
Height	15 ft 9 in (*4·80 m*)
Power plant	F-8A, B: 1 × Pratt & Whitney J57-P-4A turbojet of 16 200 lb (*7 327 kg*) st F-8C: 1 × P. & W. J57-P-16 of 16 900 lb (*7 665 kg*) st F-8D, E, H, J: 1 × P. & W. J-57-P-20 turbojet of 18 000 lb (*8 165 kg*) st

RF-8G Crusader, a remanufactured RF-8A

In service with the US Navy since 1957. F-8H, J, K and L are reworked D's, E's, C's and B's respectively.

F-8E(FN) is version for French Navy. Reconnaissance versions are RF-8A & RF-8G.

C-2A GREYHOUND — Grumman

Carrier-borne COD (Carrier On-board Delivery) Transport Aircraft

Max speed at 11 000 ft (*3 450 m*).	**306 knots**
Cruising speed at 27 300 ft (*8 320 m*)	**258 knots**
Range at cruising speed and height	**1 432 n. miles**
Capacity	**39 troops, 20 litters with 4 attendants or 10 000 lb (*4 535 kg*) of freight**
Max T-O weight	**54 830 lb (*24 870 kg*)**
Wing span	**80 ft 7 in (*24·56 m*)**
Length	**56 ft 8 in (*17·27 m*)**
Width folded	29 ft 4 in (*8·94 m*)
Height	15 ft 11 in (*4·85 m*)
Power plant	2 × Allison T56-A-8A turboprops of 4 050 ehp

A small number (17) of these COD transports were built, developed from the E-2A Hawkeye, for service aboard US Navy carriers. 8 more were ordered in 1970.

Grumman C-2A Greyhound of US Navy squadron VR-24 — ***Courtesy, B.M. Service***

UNITED STATES OF AMERICA (continued)

E-2 HAWKEYE Grumman

Carrier-borne five-seat early-warning aircraft

Max speed	320 knots plus
Service ceiling	31 700 ft (*9 660 m*)
Ferry range	1,654 n. miles
Equipment	Early-warning and command electronics including Airborne Tactical Data System (ATDS)
Max T-O weight	49 638 lb (*22 515 kg*)
Wing span	80 ft 7 in (*24·56 m*)
Length	56 ft 4 in (*17·17 m*)
Height	18 ft 4 in (*5·59 m*)
Power plant	2 × Allison T56-A-8A turboprops of 4 050 ehp

E-2C Hawkeye of the US Navy

59 produced for service with Squadrons VAW-11 and VAW-12 of the US Navy in 1964. A development, designated the E-2B with more advanced avionics, first flew in February, 1969, and E-2A's are being converted to E-2B standard. The E-2C with new electronics flew for the first time on 20 January 1971.

A-6 INTRUDER Grumman

Carrier-borne two-seat strike and reconnaissance aircraft

Max speed at S/L	595 knots
Service ceiling	41 660 ft (*12 700 m*)
Max range (ferry)	2 800 n. miles
Armament	Weapon mounts (5): Each mount is of 3 600 lb (*1 633 kg*) capacity to carry bombs, Bullpup missiles and other stores.
Max T-O weight	60 626 lb (*27 500 kg*)
Wing span	53 ft 0 in (*16·15 m*)
Width folded	25 ft 2 in (*7·67 m*)
Length	54 ft 7 in (*16·64 m*)
Height overall	15 ft 7 in (*4·75 m*)
Height folded	15 ft 10 in (*4·82 m*)
Power plant	2 × P & W J52-P-8A turbojets of 9 300 lb (*4 218 kg*) each

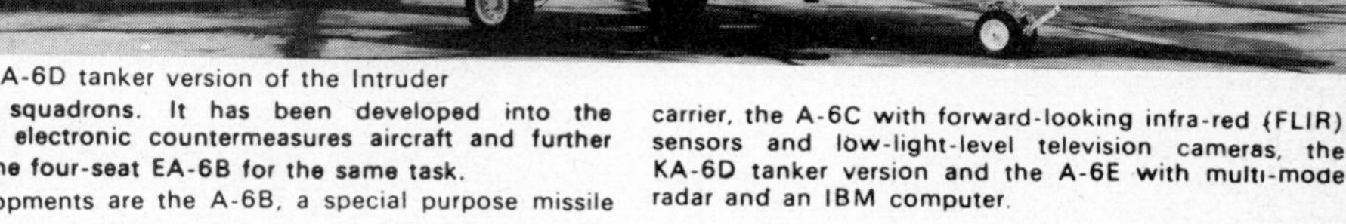

KA-6D tanker version of the Intruder

This attack aircraft uses a digital integrated attack navigation system and serves with US Navy and Marine Corps squadrons. It has been developed into the EA-6A electronic countermeasures aircraft and further into the four-seat EA-6B for the same task. Developments are the A-6B, a special purpose missile carrier, the A-6C with forward-looking infra-red (FLIR) sensors and low-light-level television cameras, the KA-6D tanker version and the A-6E with multi-mode radar and an IBM computer.

F-4B PHANTOM II McDonnell Douglas

Carrier-borne two-seat all-weather fighter

Max speed	Mach 2·5
Combat ceiling	71 000 ft (*21 640 m*)
Combat radius	781 n. miles
Ferry range	1 997 n. miles
Armament	Fuselage: 4 mountings for Sparrow III and/or Sidewinder AAM's Wings: 2 mountings for Sparrow III or Sidewinder AAM's Alternatively, 5 mounts for nuclear or conventional bombs and/or missiles up to 16 000 lb (*7 250 kg*)
Max T-O weight	54 600 lb (*24 765 kg*)
Wing span	38 ft 5 in (*11·70 m*)
Width folded	27 ft 6·5 in (*8·39 m*)
Length	58 ft 3 in (*17·76 m*)
Height	16 ft 3 in (*4·96 m*)
Power plant	F-4B, G: 2 × GE J79-GE-8 turbojets F-4J: 2 × GE J79-GE-10 turbojets of 16 500 lb (*7 485 kg*) st F-4K: 2 × RR Spey RB 168-25R Mk 201 turbofans of 12 500 lb (*5 670 kg*) st dry

Phantom FG.Mk.1 (F-4K) of Royal Navy taking off from HMS *Ark Royal* ***Courtesy, B. M. Service***

In service with the US Navy and Marines since 1962 in the F-4B form, together with the reconnaissance version the RF-4B. The F-4G is a development of the F-4B with AN/ASW-21 data link communications equipment; the F-4J is a developed F-4B with more powerful engines, control improvements and advanced electronics; the F-4K version, a developed F-4B, is in service as the Phantom FG Mk 1 with the British Fleet Air Arm.

A-4 SKYHAWK **McDonnell Douglas**

Carrier-borne single-seat attack bomber

Max speed (with 4 000 lb *814 kg* bombs)	560 knots (A-4M version)
Max ferry range (at max TO weight, with max fuel and standard reserves)	1 785 n. miles (A-4M version)
Armament	Fixed: 2 × 20 mm cannon in wings. Fuselage and Wing Mounts (5): Up to 10 000 lb (*4 535 kg*) assorted bombs, rockets, Sidewinder AAM's Bullpup ASM's, Zuni or Mighty Mouse pods, gun pods, torpedoes or ECM equipment
Max T-O weight	24 500 lb (*11 113 kg*) (A-4M version)
Wing span	27 ft 6 in (*8·38 m*)
Length	40 ft 3·25 in (*12·27 m*) (A-4M version)
Height	15 ft 0 in (*4·57 m*)
Power plant	A-4A: 1 × Wright J-65-W-4 turbojet of 7 700 lb (*3 493 kg*) st A-4B, C: 1 × Wright J65-W-16A of 7 700 lb (*3 493 kg*) st A-4E: 1 × P & W J52-P-6A of 8 500 lb (*3 855 kg*) st A-4F, G: 1 × P & W J52-P-8A of 9 300 lb (*4 218 kg*) st A-4M, J52-P-408A 11,200 lb (*5 080 kg*) st

A-4M Skyhawk of the US Marine Corps

In service with the US Navy since 1956. A-4C and subsequent models have all-weather capability. A-4F inproved controls. A-4G in service with the Royal Australian Navy since 1967. Delivery of about 50 A-4M's for the US Marine Corps with a more powerful J52-P-408A engine began in November 1970. Further orders placed for A-4M's in 1971.

UNITED STATES OF AMERICA (continued)

EA-3B SKYWARRIOR — McDonnell Douglas

Carrier-borne electronic countermeasures aircraft

(Data applies basically to standard A-3B)

Max speed at 10 000 ft (*3 050 m*)	530 knots
Service ceiling	45 000 ft (*13 780 m*)
Range, normal	2 520 n. miles
Armament	Fuselage: Weapons bay for bombs, torpedoes, etc. Tail-mounted barbette with 2 × 20 mm cannon (not always fitted)
Gross weight	73 000 lb (*33 181 kg*)
Wing span	72 ft 6 in (*22·07 m*)
Length	76 ft 4 in (*21·46 m*)
Height	22 ft 8 in (*6·91 m*)
Power plant	2 × P & W J57-P-10 turbojets of 10 500 lb (*4 760 kg*) st

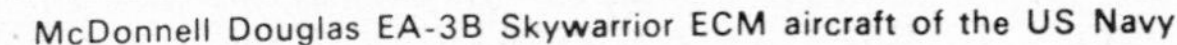

McDonnell Douglas EA-3B Skywarrior ECM aircraft of the US Navy — *Courtesy of AiReview*

Entered service with the US Navy in 1957, the A-3B has provision for flight-refuelling. Electronic countermeasures version (24 built) designated EA-3B with crew compartment in weapons bay and thirty RA-3B's with cameras in the weapons bay entered service. Also in service are KA-3 and EKA-3 tankers which will eventually be replaced by KA-6D's.

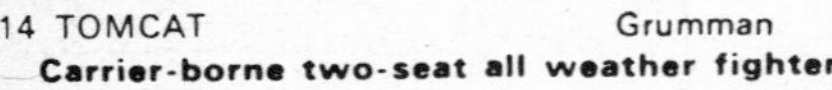

F14 TOMCAT — Grumman

Carrier-borne two-seat all weather fighter

Max speed	Mach 2 plus
Max T-O weight	(with 4 Sparrow missiles) 53 500 lb (*24 262 kg*)
Wing span (max)	64 ft 1½ in (*19·54 m*)
Wing span (min)	32 ft 11½ in (*10·05 m*)
Length	61 ft 10½ in (*18·86 m*)
Height	16 ft 0 in (*4·88 m*)
Armament	1 nose-mounted M-61 six-barrelled cannon, Phoenix, Sidewinder and Sparrow missiles under fuselage and wings
Power plant	F-14A 2 × Pratt & Whitney TF30-P-412 turbofans of 23 000 lb (*10 432 kg*) st F-14B: 2 × P and W F401-P-400 turbofans

Grumman F-14A variable-geometry fighter with its wings fully swept

This aircraft is a replacement for the Phantom II in the US Navy. The prototype F-144A first flew on 2 December 1970. Present orders are for 12 development aircraft and 26 production aircraft, with plans for eventual procurement of 313. From the 67th aircraft, designation will be F-14B with P and W F401-P-400 turbofans.

E-1B TRACER — Grumman

Carrier-borne four-seat early-warning aircraft

Max speed at S/L	230 knots
Endurance at 10 000 ft (*3 050 m*) at 156 knots	8 hr
Equipment	A 20 × 30 ft (*6·1 × 9·1 m*) radar antenna used in conjunction with the APS-82 early-warning system
Gross weight	27 000 lb (*12 250 kg*)
Wing span	72 ft 7 in (*22·04 m*)
Length	45 ft 4 in (*13·82 m*)
Height	16 ft 10 in (*5·13 m*)
Power plant	2 × Wright R-1820-82 piston engines of 1 525 hp

Developed from the S-2 Tracker, the Tracer entered service with the Navy in 1960. 64 aircraft remain in service.

E-1B Tracer early-warning aircraft of Squadron VAW-11, US Navy

S-2 TRACKER — Grumman

Carrier-borne four-seat anti-submarine attack aircraft

Max speed at S/L	230 knots (S-2E)
Patrol speed at 1 500 ft (*450 m*)	130 knots
Service ceiling	21 000 ft (*6 400 m*)
Ferry range	1 128 n. miles
Max endurance	9 hrs
Armament (S-2D version)	Fuselage bomb bay: 2 × homing torpedoes or 4 × 385 lb depth charges or 1 × Mk 101 depth bomb Wing mounts (6): torpedoes or rockets or 250 lb bombs. Sonobuoys and marine markers in rear of engine nacelles.
Max T-O weight	29 150 lb (*13 222 kg*)
Wing span	72 ft 7 in (*22·13 m*)
Width folded	27 ft 4 in (*8·33 m*)
Length	43 ft 6 in (*13·26 m*)
Height	16 ft 7 in (*5·06 m*)
Power plant	**2 × Wright R-1820-82WA piston engines of 1 525 hp each**

Grumman S-2E of the Royal Australian Navy

The original variant, the S-2A, entered production in 1954; a total of about 500 were built including over 100 supplied to Japan, Italy, Brazil, the Royal Netherlands Navy and other countries. The S-2C (60 built) had enlarged weapons bay. The S-2D (215 built) had increased wing span and improved accommodation. The S-2E is an S-2D with improved ASW equipment, 14 of which were supplied to the Royal Australian Navy. This aircraft was built under licence in Canada with the designations CS2F-1 (S-2A equivalent) and CS2F-2, and CS2F-3 which are developed versions. These are in service with the Royal Canadian Navy and the CS2F-1 with the Royal Netherlands Navy. A new version, the S-2G, was being developed in 1972, with changed equipment, as an interim ASW aircraft for the US Navy, pending delivery of the S-3A.

C-1A TRADER

Developed from the S-2 Tracker is the C-1A Trader which is used by the US Navy as a COD transport with accommodation for nine passengers or 3 500 lb (*1 590 kg*) of freight.

UNITED STATES OF AMERICA (continued)

S-3A VIKING Lockheed

Carrier-borne anti-submarine aircraft

Max speed	430 knots plus
Ferry range	3 000 n. miles plus
Normal ASW weight	42 000 lb (*19 050 kg*)
Wing span	68 ft 8 in (*20·93 m*)
Length, overall	53 ft 4 in (*16·26 m*)
Armament	Provision for homing torpedoes, mines, depth charges, rockets, missiles and special weapons in fuselage weapon bay and on underwing pylons
Power plant	2 × General Electric TF34-GE-2 high by-pass ratio turbofan engines of approx 9 000 lb (*4 082 kg*) st

Lockheed S-3A Viking prototype

Lockheed received contracts from US Navy to build 8 prototypes of a new anti-submarine aircraft under the designation S-3A. This four crew-aircraft has improved sonobuoys and MAD equipment, enabling it to find the latest submarines. The first prototype flew on 21 Jan 1972. The aircraft entered squadron service in Spring 1974.

RA-5C VIGILANTE North American Rockwell

Carrier-borne two-seat tactical reconnaissance aircraft

Max speed	Mach 2 (approx)
Service ceiling	64 000 ft (*19 500 m*)
Normal range	2 000 n. miles
Armament	Wing mountings (4): variety of weapons, including thermo-nuclear bombs
Max T-O weight	approx 80 000 lb (*36 285 kg*)
Wing span	53 ft 0 in (*16·15 m*)
Width folded	42 ft 5 in (*12·93 m*)
Length, overall	75 ft 10 in (*23·11 m*)
Length folded	68 ft 0 in (*20·73 m*)
Height	19 ft 5 in (*5·92 m*)
Power plant	2 × GE J79-GE-10 turbojets of 17 859 lb (*8 118 kg*) st

In service as the A-5A with the US Navy from 1961. The A-5B was a long-range version with extra fuel in the enlarged fuselage. The RA-5C is a reconnaissance version, carrying cameras and side-looking radar in a ventral fairing. All A's and most B's have been converted to RA-5C standard.

RA-5C Vigilante reconnaissance aircraft of the US Navy *Courtesy, AiReview (Tokyo)*

S-58 SEABAT, SEAHORSE, CHOCTAW Sikorsky

Carrier-borne and land-based anti-submarine and general-purpose helicopter

Max speed at S/L	107 knots
Cruising speed	85 knots
Hovering ceiling, out of ground effect	2 400 ft (*730 m*)
Service ceiling	9 000 ft (*2 740 m*)
Range with max fuel, 10% reserve	243 n. miles
Capacity	16-18 passengers
Max permissible weight	14 000 lb (*6 350 kg*)
Main rotor diameter	56 ft 0 in (*17·07 m*)
Length	56 ft $8\frac{1}{4}$ in (*17·27 m*)
Height	15 ft 11 in (*4·85 m*)
Power plant	1 × Wright R-1820-84B/D piston engine of 1 525 hp

In service with the US Navy as the SH-34G and SH-34J Seabat, the LH-34D for cold-weather operation, UH-34G and UH-34J utility aircraft. UH-34D is the US Marines version, also UH-34E amphibious version and VH-34D VIP transport. The S-58 is in service with other navies including the Belgian Navy (Sud-built), Federal German Navy, Italian Navy, Indonesian Navy, Royal Netherlands Navy and the French Navy, the latter's aircraft being built in France by Sud-Aviation.

Sikorsky S-58, Royal Netherlands Navy

AH-IJ SEACOBRA Bell

Two-seat close-support helicopter

Max speed	180 knots
Service ceiling	10 550 ft (*3 215 m*)
Hovering ceiling (in ground effect)	12 450 ft (*3 794 m*)
Range	311 n. miles
Armament	XM-197 three-barrel 20 mm cannon in forward lower fuselage turret. Four external attachment points under wings for 7·62 mm minigun pods and rockets
Gross weight	10 000 lb (*4 535 kg*)
Main rotor diameter	44 ft 0 in (*13·41 m*)
Length overall	53 ft 4 in (*16·26 m*)
Power plant	1 × 1 800 shp Pratt and Whitney T400-CP-400 coupled free-turbine turboshaft

The AH-1J SeaCobra is in production for the US Marine Corps, with 49 ordered initially. Also in service with the Marine Corps are 38 single-engined HueyCobras, designated AH-1G.

Bell AH-1J SeaCobra of the US Marine Corps

UNITED STATES OF AMERICA (continued)

SH-3 SEAKING — Sikorsky

Carrier-borne and land-based amphibious all-weather ASW and transport helicopter

Max speed	144 knots
Cruising speed for max range	118 knots
Hovering ceiling (out of ground effect)	8 200 ft (*2 500 m*)
Service ceiling	14 700 ft (*4 480 m*)
Range with max fuel, 10% reserve	542 n. miles
Equipment	Bendix AQS-13 sonar. Hamilton Standard autostabilisation equipment with sonar coupler. Ryan APN-130 Doppler radar
Armament	Up to 840 lb (*381 kg*) of weapons including homing torpedoes, Kormoran missiles
Max T-O weight	**20 500 lb (*9 300 kg*)**
Main rotor diameter	**62 ft 0 in (*18·90 m*)**
Length overall	**72 ft 8 in (*22·15 m*)**
Width folded	**16 ft 4 in (*4·98 m*)**
Height to top of rotor hub	**15 ft 6 in (*4·72 m*)**
Power plant	**2 × GE T58-GE-10 shaft turbines of 1 400 shp each.**

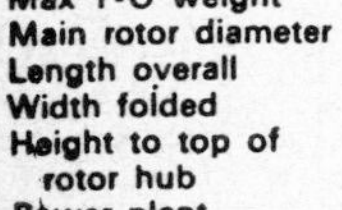

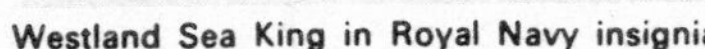

Westland Sea King in Royal Navy insignia

The original versions built by Sikorsky for the US Navy were the SH-3A, with GE T58-GE-8B engines which is also in service with the Japanese MSDF and, under the designation CHSS-2, with the Canadian Armed Forces; and the SH-3D which is in service with the US, Spanish, Brazilian and Italian Navies and built under licence by Westland Aircraft for the Fleet Air Arm, German and Indian navies, this latter using the RR Bristol Gnome 1400 engine. The Italian Sea Kings are built by Agusta. Nine SH-3A's were converted for mine countermeasures duty and designated RH-3A's. Also a number of SH-3A's are being converted into SH-3G Utility helicopters; and a new version of the G, designated the SH-3H, is a multi-purpose version with increased capabilities against submarines and low-flying enemy missiles.

SEA KNIGHT — Boeing-Vertol

Carrier-borne and land-based three-crew transport and utility helicopter

Data for UH-46D

Max speed	144 knots
Cruising speed	143 knots
Hovering ceiling out of ground effect	**5 750 ft (*1 753 m*)**
Service ceiling	**14 000 ft (*4 265 m*)**
Range at AUW of 23 000 lb (*10 433 kg*) with 6 750 lb (*3 062 kg*) payload, 10% fuel reserve	198 n. miles
Capacity	25 troops and troop commander or 15 stretchers plus 2 attendants or up to a 10 000 lb (*4 535 kg*) load
Max T-O weight	23 000 lb (*10 433 kg*)
Main rotor diameter (each)	51 ft 0 in (*15·54 m*)
Length, fuselage	44 ft 10 in (*13·66 m*)
Height to top of rear rotor hub	16 ft 8·5 in (*5·09 m*)
Power plant	2 × GE T58-GE-10 shaft-turbine engines of 1 400 shp each

In service with the US Marine Corps since 1962 as the CH-46A and US Navy for shore to ship and ship to ship duties as the UH-46A, uprated in 1966 to CH-46D and UH-46D. Three in service with the Royal Swedish Navy as the HKP-4 using Bristol Siddeley Gnome H1200, and six with the Japanese MSDF for mine countermeasures duties.

Boeing-Vertol UH-46D Sea Knight of US Navy Squadron HC-6 — *Courtesy, B. M. Service*

SEASPRITE — Kaman

Ship-borne two-crew all-weather rescue, ASW, anti-missile defence and utility helicopter

Data for UH-2A/B

Max speed at S/L	141 knots
Cruising speed	130 knots
Hovering ceiling out of ground effect	5 100 ft (*1 555 m*)
Service ceiling	17 400 ft (*5 300 m*)
Normal range with max fuel	581 n. miles
Capacity	11 passengers or 4 stretcher patients
Max T-O weight	10 000 lb (*4 535 kg*)
Main rotor diameter	44 ft 0 in (*13·41 m*)
Length (blades turning)	52 ft 7 in (*16·03 m*)
Height	15 ft 6 in (*4·72 m*)
Power plant	1 × GE T58-GE-8B shaft turbine engine of 1 250 shp

Entered service with the US Navy in 1962 as the UH-2A, followed by the UH-2B "fair weather" version. A twin-engined version, the UH-2C with two T58 engines, was introduced into service by retrospective modification of UH-2A's and B's. 6 UH-2C's redesignated HH-2C's, were converted into gunships with a chin Minigun, 2 additional machine-guns and additional armour. A total of 67 single-engined models were being converted into HH-2D's, similar to HH-2C but with armament and armour deleted. Ten SH-2D's are interim ship-borne ASW helicopters, with search radar, homing torpedoes and other equipment.

HH-2D Seasprite helicopter of the US Navy

SIKORSKY YCH-53E

A three-engined helicopter undergoing evaluation for USN and USMC in 1974.

UNITED STATES OF AMERICA (continued)

SEA STALLION — Sikorsky

Carrier-borne and land-based three-crew heavy assault and transport helicopter

Max speed	170 knots
Cruising speed	150 knots
Hovering ceiling out of ground effect	6 500 ft (*1 980 m*)
Service ceiling	21 000 ft (*6 400 m*)
Range, with 4 076 lb (*1 849 kg*) payload 10% reserve at cruising speed and 2 min warming up	223 n. miles
Capacity	38 passengers, 24 stretchers and 4 attendants or internal or external cargo
Max T-O weight	42 000 lb (*19 050 kg*)
Main rotor diameter	72 ft 3 in (*22·02 m*)
Length	68 ft 3 in (*26·90 m*)
Width, folded	15 ft 6 in (*4·72 m*)
Height	24 ft 11 in (*7·60 m*)
Power plant	2 × GE T64-GE-6 shaft turbine engines of 2 850 shp each

Entered service with the US Marine Corps as the CH-53A in 1966, becoming operational in Vietnam in January 1967. The later CH-53D has 3 695 shp T64-GE-412 engines or 3 925 shp T64-GE-413 engines. Under development are the RH-53D, for mine countermeasures operations, and the CH-53E, a three-engined version of the CH-53D.

Sikorsky CH-53A of the US Marine Corps

UH-IE

Land-based single-crew assault support helicopter

Max speed	140 knots
Cruising speed	120 knots
Hovering ceiling out of ground effect	11 800 ft (*3 595 m*)
Service ceiling	21 000 ft (*6 400 m*)
Range, max fuel	248 n. miles
Armament	2 × machine guns and 2 × rocket pods, on each side of the cabin
Capacity	8 passengers or 4 000 lb (*1 815 kg*) of freight
Max T-O weight	9 500 lb (*4 309 kg*)
Main rotor diameter	44 ft 0 in (*13·41 m*)
Length	53 ft 0 in (*16·15 m*)
Height	12 ft 7½ in (*3·84 m*)
Power plant	1 × Lycoming T53-L-11 shaft-turbine engine of 1 100 shp

Bell TH-IL trainer of the US Navy

Entered service with the US Marine Corps in 1964; the UH-1E is the Marine version of the Iroquois which is in widespread military service. Nine UH-1D's are in service with the Royal Australian Navy. Licence-built by Dornier, UH-1D's will serve with the German Navy. The US Navy is receiving 45 TH-IL trainers and 8 UH-1L.

QH-50 — Gyrodyne

Max speed	80 knots
Speed for max endurance	55 knots
Service ceiling	QH-50C: 16 400 ft (*5 000 m*) QH-50D: 16 000 ft (*4 875 m*)
Hovering ceiling (in ground effect)	QH-50C: 16 900 ft (*5 150 m*) QH-50D: 16 300 ft (*4 965 m*)
Max range	QH-50C 71 n. miles QH-50D 122 n. miles
Armament	2 × Mk 44 torpedoes or 1 Mk 46 torpedo
Max T-O weight	QH-50C: 2 285 lb (*1 036 kg*) QH-50D: 2 328 lb (*1 056 kg*)
Rotor diameter	20 ft 0 in (*6.10 m*)
Power plant	QH-50C: 1 × Boeing T50-BO-8A shaft-turbine of 300 shp QH-50D: 1 × Boeing T50-BO-12 shaft-turbine of 365 shp

The DASH System (Drone Anti-Submarine Helicopter) of which the QH-50 is the mobile weapon-carrying unit is carried aboard many US Navy vessels. The QH-50C went into service in 1962 and the QH-50D in 1965. Take-off and landing are visually controlled by the Deck Control Officer who hands the helicopter over to the control information centre in the ship which flies the drone to the target, actuates the arming and weapon release switches and returns the drone to the ship.

QH-50C drone helicopter, armed with two Mk. 46 torpedoes

HU-16 ALBATROSS — Grumman

Land-based five-crew general purpose amphibian

Max speed at S/L	205 knots
Max cruising speed	195 knots
Service ceiling	21 500 ft (*6 550 m*)
Range	2 475 n. miles
Equipment (ASW version	MAD gear, nose AS radome, ECM radome in wing, searchlight
Armament (ASW version)	Torpedoes, depth charges or rockets
Max T-O weight	37 500 lb (*12 500 kg*)
Wing span	96 ft 8 in (*29·42 m*)
Length	62 ft 10 in (*19 12 m*)
Power plant	2 × Wright R-1820-76A radial piston engines of 1 425 hp each

In service with the US Navy as HU-16D and Coast Guard as HU-16E, developed from earlier HU-16C, many of which were converted. Supplied to a number of foreign countries including Argentina, Brazil, Chile, Germany (West), Indonesia, Italy, Nationalist China, Japan and the Philippines. Spain, Norway and Greece use the ASW version.

ASW version of Albatross in service with the Greek Air Force — *Courtesy of S. P. Peltz*

UNITED STATES OF AMERICA (continued)

C-130 HERCULES — Lockheed

Medium/long-range transport and reconnaissance aircraft

Max level speed	333 knots
Max cruising speed	320 knots
Service ceiling at 155 000 lb (*70 310 kg*) AUW	23 000 ft (*7 010 m*)
Range with max load	2 101 n. miles
Capacity	92 troops, 64 paratroops, or 74 stretchers and 2 attendants. Cargo of 26 640 lb (*12 080 kg*)
Max normal T-O weight	155 000 lb (*70 310 kg*)
Wing span	132 ft 7 in (*40·41 m*)
Length	97 ft 9 in (*29·78 m*)
Height	38 ft 3 in (*11·66 m*)
Power plant	4 × Allison T56-A-7A turbobrop engines of 4 050 eshp each

This transport is in widespread service with twenty air forces and with the US Navy as C-130E, C-130F and C-130D (for ski operation), the Marine Corps as KC-130F (with flight refuelling equipment) and with the US Coast Guard as HC-130B for SAR duties and EC-130E.

The US Navy has also ordered several LC-130R's which are basically C-130H's with wheel-ski gear and T56-A-16 engines of 4 500 eshp.

Lockheed KC-130F Hercules tanker refuelling two Phantom fighters

P-2 NEPTUNE — Lockheed

Seven-seat long-range maritime patrol aircraft

Max speed at 10,000 ft (*3 050 m*)	309 knots
Patrol speed at 1 000 ft (*305 m*)	150-180 knots
Service ceiling	22 000 ft (*6 700 m*)
Max range	3 200 n. miles
Armament	Fuselage Weapons Bay: Up to 8 000 lb (*5 000 kg*) of bombs, torpedoes, depth charges. Wing mounts (2): 16 × 0·5 in rockets. Optional dorsal turret with 2 × 0·5 guns
Max T-O weight	79 895 lb (*36 497·73 kg*)
Wing span (inc. tiptanks)	103 ft 10 in (*31·65 m*)
Length	91 ft 8 in (*27·94 m*)
Height	29 ft 4 in (*8·94 m*)
Power plant	2 × Wright R-3350-32W radial piston engines of 3 500 hp each Plus 2 × Westinghouse J34 turbojet engines of 3 400 lb st each

This aircraft is in widespread service with the US Navy as the P-2H and with the French Navy, Royal Netherlands Navy and Argentine Navy. With Brazil and Portugal it serves as the P-2E without the auxiliary turbojets.

A highly-modified version, the Kawasaki P-2J serves with the Japanese MSDF. It is powered by two 2 850 shp IHI/General Electric T64-IHI-10 turboprops plus two 3 085 lb st IHI J3-7C auxiliary turbojets. It has an extended front fuselage and new sensor systems.

Kawasaki P-2J of the Japanese MSDF

P-3 ORION — Lockheed

Data apply to P-3C

Twelve-seat anti-submarine reconnaissance aircraft

Max speed at 15 000 ft (*4 570 m*) at AUW of 105 000 lb (*47 625 kg*)	411 knots
Patrol speed at 1 500 ft (*450 m*), same weight as above	206 knots
Max mission radius	2 070 n. miles
Equipment	A-NEW sensors and control equipment, with ASQ-114 digital computer.
Armament	Fuselage weapons bay: accommodates mines, depth bombs, torpedoes. Wing mounts (10): torpedoes, mines or rockets singly or in pods
Max T-O weight	142 000 lb (*64 410 kg*)
Wing span	99 ft 8 in (*30·37 m*)
Length	116 ft 10 in (*35·61 m*)
Height	33 ft 8·5 in (*10·29 m*)
Power plant	4 × Allison T56-A-14 turboprop engines of 4 910 eshp each

EP-3B Orion of the US Navy — *Courtesy T. Matsuzaki*

Produced for US Navy as P-3A (Allison T56-A-10W engines), P-3B and P-3C with A-NEW data processing system. P-3B also serves with Royal Australian Air Force, Royal New Zealand Air Force, Royal Norwegian Air Force, and the Spanish Air Force. Specially-equipped US Navy versions are the WP-3A for weather reconnaissance, the RP-3D for long-range flights to map the earth's magnetic field, and EP-3B/E for electronic warfare duties.

USSR

(A) FREEHAND Yakovlev VTOL Experimental Aircraft

Approximate dimensions:

Length, overall	58 feet
Wing span	27 feet
Height	15 feet
Max speed	400 mph
Armament	Small stores can be carried on external fuselage racks. Main armament possibly depth-charges

The NATO codename for an R & D VTOL aircraft first seen at the Domodedovo air-show in July 1967. The original version was clearly subsonic with a wide fuselage housing two turbojet engines, a stubby delta wing assembly and a high-tail with a fixed tailplane mounted towards its top. Since 1967 development has clearly gone ahead—advanced versions have been flown at Ramenskoye, southeast of Moscow and the helicopter-cruiser *Moskva* has been fitted with a pad on the after-end of her flight deck, suitable for use by VTOL aircraft. The "Freehand" derivative will probably operate from the new Soviet aircraft-carrier *Kiev*.

(B) HOUND MIL Mi-4

Land-based anti-submarine search and strike helicopter.

Max speed	90 knots
Normal cruising speed	75 knots
Service ceiling	18 000 ft (*5 500 m*)
Max range	Probably about 220 n. miles
Equipment	Search radar under nose. MAD (sensors in a towed "bird") Sonobuoys
Max T-O weight	17 200 lbs (*7 800 kg*)
Main rotor diameter	68 ft 11 in (*21·0 m*)
Length of fuselage	55 ft 1 in (*16·8 m*)
Height overall	17 ft (*5·18 m*)
Power plant	1—ASh 82V eighteen cylinder air-cooled radial piston engine — 1 700 hp.

This anti-submarine version of the "Hound" which in its other versions is in service with all Soviet air-forces, Aeroflot and foreign forces is with the Soviet and other Warsaw Pact navies. Has been operating from shore-bases for some years and is probably being replaced by "Hormone".

(B) HORMONE Kamov Ka-25

Shipborne and land-based anti-submarine search and strike helicopter

Max speed	119 knots
Normal cruising speed	104 knots
Service ceiling	11 500 ft (*3 500 m*)
Range with max fuel with reserves	351 n. miles
Equipment	Search radar under nose. Dipping sonar
T-O weight	16 100 lb (*7 300 kg*)
Main rotor diameter	51 ft 8 in (*15·75 m*) (no tail rotor)
Length	32 ft 0 in (*9·75 m*)
Height to top of rotor head	17 ft 7½ in (*5·37 m*)
Power plant	2 × 900 shp Glushenkov GTD-3 shaft-turbine engines
Armament	An internal weapons bay with doors under the fuselage carries stores including A/S torpedoes. Smaller stores such as markers and flares can be carried on external racks, one either side of the fuselage

Kamov Ka-25 "Hormone" anti-submarine helicopters on the cruiser "Moskva"

In service with the Soviet Naval Air Force in a number of roles. The anti-submarine version (A) operates mainly from the "Moskva" class, although hangars are now provided in *Kara*, the "Kresta I" and "II" class and the latest Sverdlov conversion. Helicopter pads are becoming more common now in cruisers and destroyers. There is also believed to be a reconnaissance version of Hormone, presumably intended to operate with cruise-missile ships.

(C) BACKFIRE TUPOLEV

Max speed	Possibly Mach 2·5
Max range	Possibly 4 000 n. miles
Armament	? AS-6 system
Max weight	272 000 lbs
Power plant	Possibly 2 Kuznetsov turbofans

A variable-geometry medium bomber which may shortly be entering squadron service with the Soviet Naval Air Force. Probably V-G only on outer wings and with engines built into fuselage with large air-intake either side of the cockpit.

BADGER TU-16

Long-range medium bomber/maritime reconnaissance aircraft

Max speed at 35 000 ft (*10 700 m*)	510 knots
Cruising speed	417 knots
Service ceiling	42 650 ft (*13 000 m*)
Range, max bomb load	2 605 n. miles
Max range at 417 knots with 6 600 lb (*3 000 kg*) bombs	3 450 n. miles
Armament	Defensive: 2—23 mm cannon in each of the dorsal, ventral and tail turrets. Some versions have one 23 mm cannon in starboard nose position
Bombs/ASM	Badger A. 19 800 lbs (*9 000 kg*) carried internally Badger B. 2 Kennel ASM—No bombs Badger C. 1 Kipper ASM—No bombs Badger G. 2 Kelt ASM—Can carry alternative bomb load
Wing span	110 ft 0 in (*33·5m*)
Length	120 ft 0 in (*36·5 m*)
Height	35 ft 6 in (*10·8 m*)
Power plant	2 × Mikulin AM-3M turbojet engines of 20 950 lb (*9 500 kg*) st each
Normal T-O weight	150 000 lb (*68 000 kg*) approx

The version of the Tu-16 known as Badger-F with underwing electronic pods

Badger A—Basic bomber, some tankers
Badger B—Kennel ASMs.
Badger C—Kipper ASMs.
Badger D, E and F—EW versions.
Badger G—Kelt ASMs or bombs

There are at least seven versions of this bomber serving with the Soviet Naval Air Force, probably more.

First entered service in 1956. Some have been supplied to Egypt, Indonesia and Iraq.

USSR (continued)

BEAR TUPOLEV TU-95

Long-range Bomber and maritime reconnaissance aircraft

Over target speed at 41 000 ft (*12 500 m*)	435 knots
Cruising speed at 32 000 ft (*10 000 m*)	410 knots
Range with max bomb load	6 775 n. miles
Armament	Fuselage weapons bay: 25 000 lb (*11 300 kg*) of bombs (Bear-A) Fuselage external mounts 1 Kangaroo ASM (Bear B and C) 2—23 mm cannon in dorsal, ventral and tail turrets
Loaded weight	340 000 lb (*154 220 kg*)
Wing span	159 ft (*48·5 m*)
Length	156 ft (*47·6 m*)
Power plant	4 × Kuznetsov NK-12M turboprop engines of 14 795 shp each

At least four versions of BEAR are in service with the Soviet Naval Air Force and there are probably others:

Bear A—basic bomber
Bear B—ASM carrier with one Kangaroo
Bear C—As B with additional equipment blisters
Bear D—Maritime reconnaissance version without bomb-bay or ASM pylons

BEAR D—maritime reconnaissance version

BLINDER TUPOLEV TU-22

Medium-range supersonic maritime reconnaissance bomber

Max speed at 40 000 ft (*12 200 m*)	Mach 1·4
Service ceiling	60 000 ft (*18 300 m*) plus
Range	1 215 n. miles
Armament	Fuselage (Blinder B): "Kitchen" ASM part-recessed in bomb bay, alternatively internal bomb load. Blinder A has free-fall bombs only
Max T-O weight	184 970 lb (*83 900 kg*)
Wing span	90 ft 10½ in (*27·70 m*)
Length	132 ft 11½ in (*40·53 m*)
Height	17 ft 0 in (*5·18 m*)
Power plant	2 × unspecified turbojet engines developing 26 000 lb (*11 790 kg*) st with reheat

Blinder B in service with the Soviet Naval Air Force. A version with electronic countermeasures (ECM) equipment is now in service.

Tupolev Tu-22 "Blinder" of the Soviet Naval Airfleet

MAIL BEREIV M-12

Anti-submarine reconnaissance amphibian

Max speed	329 knots
Normal operating speed	172 knots
Max range	2 160 n. miles (*4 000 km*)
Max altitude (record attempt)	39 977 ft (*12 185 m*)
Gross weight	65 035 lb (*29 500 kg*)
Armament	Bomb-bay in bottom of hull, aft of step, and pylons for external stores under outer wings. Main armament probably torpedoes and depth charges.
Equipment	Nose radome and MAD gear in tail. Sonobuoys
Span	97 ft 6 in (*29·72 m*)
Length	99 ft 0 in (*30·18 m*)
Power plant	2 × Ivchenko AI-20D turboprop engines of 4 000 shp each

In service with Soviet Naval Air Force, some operating until recently from bases in Egypt.

Beriev M-12 "Mail" of the Soviet Naval Airfleet *Courtesy, Tass*

MAY ILYUSHIN IL-38

Anti-submarine reconnaissance aircraft

Max cruising speed	365 knots (*675 km/hr*)
Max operating height	32 800 ft (*10 000 m*)
Max operating radius	1 500 n. miles

Increasing numbers of this aircraft are in service with the Soviet Naval Air Force and some with the Polish. It has been encountered whilst operating from bases in Egypt and in the North Atlantic area. The MAY is based on the IL-18 (Coot) transport. The main changes seem to be a lengthened nose and a move forward of the complete wing-assembly. A radome, possibly with a new ASW radar, is placed under the nose and a MAD tail-boom has been added in addition to weapon-carrying equipment. Its A/S detection equipment is probably therefore, similar to that of MAIL (radar, MAD, sonobuoys) whilst its weapons are most likely the same (A/S torpedoes, depth-charges). Few details of performance are available but they are likely to be similar to those of the IL-18D from which the above figures are derived.

VENEZUELA

Helicopters

BELL 47G
SIKORSKY S51

Shore-based

GRUMMAN "Widgeon" (G 44)
GRUMMAN "Avenger" (TBM-IC)
2 MARTIN "Mariner" (PBM-5)

URUGUAY

Helicopters

4 BELL 47

Shore-based

GRUMMAN Albatross (SA 16-A)

NAVAL MISSILES

AUSTRALIA

(D) (vi) IKARA

Anti-Submarine

Length	11 ft 0 in (*3·35 m*)
Wing span	5 ft 0 in (*1·50 m*)
Range	13 miles
Producer	Australian Dept of Supply

The weapon is a dual-thrust, solid-fuel rocket-propelled missile carrying an acoustic homing torpedo launched from a surface ship. It has short cropped-delta wings, elevon control surfaces and upper/lower vertical tail-fins. Target information from a ship's Sonar ot a helicopter's Dunking Sonar feeds into the appropriate computer system which, with radar/radio guidance, ensures that the American Type 44 acoustic homing torpedo, separated from the missile and lowered by a parachute, enters the sea in the immediate vicinity of the target. There are three variants of the control system—(a) The RAN uses an autonomous digital system, (b) The RN feed into the ADA system and (c) The Brazilian "Niteroi" class operates with the Branck system, in which a purpose built missile tracking system feeds a Ferranti FM 1600 B computer. It is operational in three "Perth" class and six "River" class destroyers of the Royal Australian Navy is being fitted in certain "Leander" class ships and HMS *Bristol* and the Brazilian "Niteroi" class.

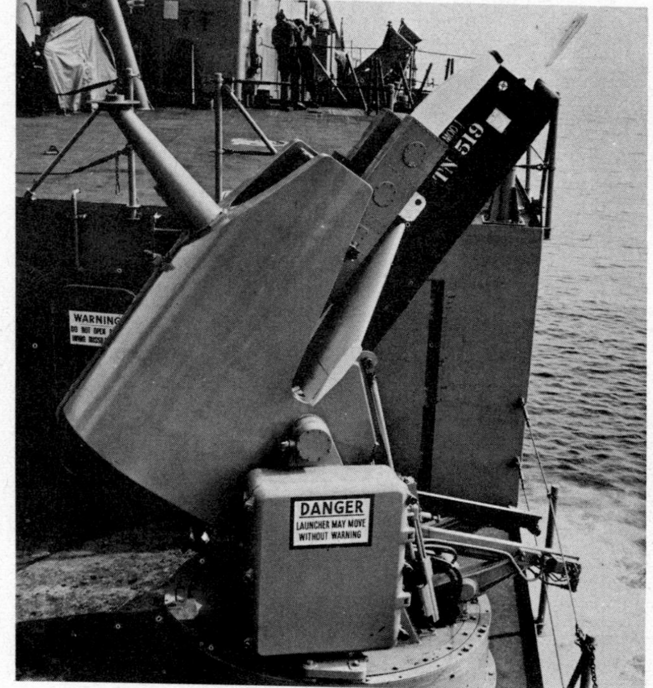

Ikara missile in launcher on HMAS "Perth"

FRANCE

Strategic

MSBS — Aérospatiale

Submarine-borne intermediate range ballistic missile (IRBM)

Length	34 ft 1½ in (*10·40 m*)
Body diameter	4 ft 11 in (*1·50 m*)
Firing weight	39 683 lb (*18 000 kg*)
Range	M1: 1 350 n. miles (*2 500 km*)
	M2: 1 620 n. miles (*3 000 km*)

This two-stage solid-propellant missile with nuclear warhead was developed in France to equip the "Redoubtable" class of nuclear powered submarines from 1969 onwards, each of 5 submarines carrying 16 missiles. The first stage has 22 050 lb (*10 000 kg*) of solid propellant in a PNSM P10 type 904 rocket motor; the second stage has 8 820 lb (*4 000 kg*) of solid propellant in a PNSM P4 Rita rocket motor. The MSBS has inertial guidance. A second generation MSBS called the M2 is now in production and differs from the M1 in the replacement of the second stage Rita I motor by a Rita II. It will be operational in 1974, and by 1976 a thermonuclear charge will be incorporated. A further refinement, either M3 or M4, is expected later in the 1970's with MRV fitted.

MSBS missile

Surface-to-surface

OTOMAT **SA Engines Matra/Oto Melara**

Surface-to-surface missile

Length	15 ft 9½ in (*4·82 m*)
Launch weight	1 543 lb (*700 kg*)
Max range	32 n. miles

This weapon is powered by a Turboméca Arbizon III turbojet. It is launched with aid of two jettisonable booster rockets and flies the last 2 n. miles to its target at 50 ft above S/L, with the aid of a TRT type AHV-7 radio altimeter. It is fitted with an active Thomson-CSF homing head. Delivery began in 1973, and it is to be operated by the Italian Navy in the "Freccia" class of fast patrol boats.

Full-scale test version of Otomat in a wind tunnel

FRANCE (continued)

SURFACE TO SURFACE (continued)

MM-38 EXOCET — **Aérospatiale**

Length	16 ft 9½ in (*5·12 m*)
Body diameter	1 ft 1½ in (*0·344 m*)
Span of wings	3 ft 3½ in (*1·004 m*)
Launch weight	1 587 lb (*719 kg*)
Warhead (over)	220 lb (*100 kg*)
Range	20 n. miles

Designed to provide warships with all-weather attack capability against other surface vessels. It can be fitted in all classes of surface warships, including fast patrol boats.
The Exocet missile is in the form of a streamlined body, fitted with cruciform wings and cruciform tail control surfaces indexed in line with the wings. Propulsion is provided by a tandem two-stage solid-propellant motor, and highly destructive warhead. The launch tubes, which are also used as store containers, can be installed in a fixed position or on rotatable mountings.

For operation of the weapon system, the launch ship must be fitted with surveillance and target indicating radar, a vertical reference plane gyro and a log, indicating its speed through the water. Also required is a fire control installation comprising a control panel, fire control computer and junction box.
The missile flight profile consists of a pre-guidance phase during which it travels towards the target, whose range and bearing have been determined by the fire control computer and set up in the missile pre-guidance circuits before launch, and a final guidance phase during which the missile flies directly towards the target under the control of its active homing head. Throughout the flight the missile is maintained at a very low altitude (reported to be 2 to 3 metres=6·5 to 10 ft) by an FM radio altimeter supplied by TRT. Its range is approximately 20 n. miles (*37 km*), cruising at high subsonic speed, and Exocet is intended to operate efficiently in an ECM environment.

Development firing of Exocet

The French, German, Greek, British Royal Navy and others operate Exocet. A project to adapt Exocet for submarine-launch is in existence but there is no information on its progress.

SS-11-(B1) — **Aérospatiale**

Length	3 ft 11 in (*1·20 m*)
Body diameter	6 in (*0·16 m*)
Wing span	1 ft 7·5 in (*0·50 m*)
Launch weight	66 lb (*30 kg*)
Range	1·6 miles (*3 km*)
Cruising speed	313 knots
Endurance	20-21 secs

Developed from the AS-11 (B.1) ASM this missile is in use by French Navy and Army and differs from the AS-11 in launching systems only. It is powered by two-stage solid propellant rocket with cruciform swept wings on a cylindrical body and can be fitted with a range of warheads for anti-tank, perforating/exploding or anti-personnel work. The guidance is visual/manual, with a gyrostabilised optical sighting system, through wires from the control. Orders totalled 148 000 by the beginning of 1971, with the production at the rate of 600 per month.. France, USA, NATO countries and others use this misslie.

SS-12M — **Aérospatiale**

Length	**6 ft 2 in (*1·875 m*)**
Body diameter	**7·1 in (*0·18 m*)**
Wing span	**2 ft 1·5 in (*0·65 m*)**
Launch weight	**167 lb (*75 kg*)**
Range	**19 650 ft (*6 000 m*)**
Endurance	**32 secs**
Impact speed	**182 knots**

A larger and more powerful derivative of the SS-11, it is used from a twin shipboard launcher. The warhead weighs about 66 lb (*30 kg*), which is four times as much as that of the SSII, and it is powered by a two-stage solid-propellant rocket motor. It is used aboard three Royal Libyan Navy patrol boats. Also used by France and the Royal Netherlands Navy.

SS-11 and SS-12

Surface-to-air

MASURCA Mk 2 — Marine Francaise

Length	28 ft 2·5 in (*8 600 m*)
Body diameter	1 ft 4 in (*0·405 m*)
Launch weight	4 585 lb (*2 079 kg*)
Range	22 n. miles
Max speed	Mach 2·5

Developed to equip *Colbert, Suffren* and *Duquesne* of the French Navy this missile is a two-stage solid-propellant missile, the first stage being jettisonable. The second stage has controllable tail surfaces in cruciform configuration, in line with the low-aspect ratio wings. A high-explosive warhead with a proximity fuse is fitted. There are two versions of this weapon; Masurca Mk 2 Mod 2 (with a beam riding guidance system) and Masurca Mk 2 Mod 3 (with a semi-active homing system). In both cases the guidance systems are produced by CFTH/CFS.

NOTE. In addition the French navy is developing two systems for defence against low-flying aircraft. The first is Hirondelle, a four missile launcher for Super 530 missiles (operational in 1977) and the second is Catulle, a multi-barrelled rocket system firing salvoes of 40 mm projectiles (development).

Two Masurca missiles on the launcher of the French Navy's guided missile frigate Suffren

FRANCE (continued)

SURFACE TO AIR (continued)

CROTALE NAVALE — Thomson/CSF—Matra

Length	9·5 ft (*2·9 m*)
Launch weight	36 lbs (*80 kgs*)
Warhead	6 lbs (*15 kgs*)
Speed	Mach 2·3
Range	5 miles
Control	Infra-red or radar/command

A naval version of the "Crotale"—not yet in service.

Air-to-surface

AS-11 (B1) — Aérospatiale

This is identical with the SS-11 (B.1) (which see) except that it is air-launched and this increases its range. It is carried by 14 different types of aircraft (fixed and rotary-wing) of 19 nations including all the ASW aircraft of the NATO countries.

AS-12 missile under wing of Alize of French Navy

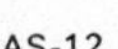

AS-12 — Aérospatiale

This missile is a companion to the SS-12M (which see) and is already supplementing and replacing the AS-11 (B.1). It is being prepared for automatic guidance with the TCA system for the Harpon missile.

AS-30 — Aérospatiale

Length	12 ft 9 in (*3·885 m*)
Body diameter	1 ft 1·4 in (*0·34 m*)
Wing span	3 ft 3·5 in (*1·00 m*)
Launch weight	1 146 lb (*520 kg*)
Speed at impact	1 475/1 640 ft/sec (*450/500 m/sec*)
Range	5·9/6·5 n. miles

This missile has a two-stage solid-propellant power plant and is directed by a pilot-operated radio-command guidance system whereby the pilot steers the missile by means of a small control column in the cockpit. Alternatively this missile can utilise the TCA optical aiming/infra-red automatic guidance system. It is operational with the French Air Force, French Navy, German, Swiss, Israeli and South African air forces and the RAF. It normally carries a 510 lb (*230 kg*) HE warhead.

Aérospatiale AS-30 (inboard) and AS-20 (outboard)

AS-30L — Aérospatiale

Length	11 ft 9·5 in (*3·60 m*)
Body diameter	1 ft 1·5 in (*0·34 m*)
Wing span	2 ft 11·5 in (*0·90 m*)
Launch weight	838 lb (*380 kg*)

A developed lighter version of the AS-30 for smaller, lighter aircraft. Warhead reduced to 253 lb (*115 kg*).

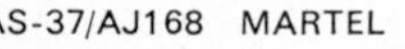

AS-37/AJ168 MARTEL — Matra/Hawker Siddeley Dynamics

Length	12 ft (*3·65 m*) teleguidance
	13 ft 1½ in (*4·00 m*) anti-radar
Wing span	3 ft 8 in (*1·12 m*)
Body diameter	1 ft 3 in (*0·38 m*)
Range	15 n. miles (approx)

Developed jointly by Matra and Hawker Siddeley Dynamics the Martel is in two forms, a passive radar homing missile or a television-guided missile operated by a weapon operator aboard the parent aircraft. The radar version can be launched in a variety of height and mission profiles. Immediately after launch the missile homes automatically on the target radar, the parent aircraft being independent. Its range gives it a stand-off capability. The TV version is guided in the final stages of its run by the weapon operator in the launch aircraft reading from a high brightness monitor in the aircraft displaying the missile's target field.
Martel is operational with the Fleet Air Arm and RAF on Buccaneer aircraft and the French services on Mirage III-E, Jaguar and Atlantic aircraft.

Martel development missiles under wing of Buccaneer aircraft

FRANCE (continued)

Air-to-air

R-550 MAGIC — SA Engins Matra

Length	8·2 feet
Wing span	2·3 feet
Weight	200 lbs
Range	up to 6 miles

The first guided firing of this missile took place on 11th January 1972. The missile itself is powered by a solid-propellant rocket motor and is infra-red guided. The body is cylindrical with cruciform movable foreplanes, fixed wings and tail-fins.

R-550 Magic air-to-air missile

MATRA R-530 — Matra

Length	10 ft 9·25 in (*3·28 m*)
Body diameter	10·25 in (*0·26 m*)
Wing span	3 ft 7·25 in (*1·10 m*)
Launch weight	430 lb (*195 kg*)
Max speed	Mach 2·7
Range	9·5 n. miles
Operational heights	0-69 000 ft (*21 000 m*)

In quantity production for the French Air Force and Navy, which latter uses it on its F-8E (FN) Crusaders; it is also supplied to Israel and the South African and Royal Australian Air Forces. It has a cylindrical body with cruciform delta wings, two with ailerons and cruciform tail controls and is powered by a two-stage Hotchkiss-Brandt solid-propellant motor of 18 740 lb (*8 500 kg*) static thrust.

It has interchangeable Hotchkiss-Brandt warheads, each weighing 60 lb (*27 kg*) and fitted with a proximity fuse; with semi-active radar or infra-red homing heads.

The Super 530 with much enhanced range and acquisition performance is now superseding the R530.

R-530 missile with semi-active radar head

MATRA R-511

A 396 lb weapon with a range of 15 miles. Now obsolescent.

Anti-submarine

MALAFON Mk 2 — Latecoere

Length	19 ft 8 in (*6·00 m*)
Wing span	9 ft 10 in (*3·0 m*)
Launch weight	3 200 lb (*1 500 kg*)
Speed	450 knots
Range	7 n. miles

It comprises a cylindrical body containing a 21 inch (*0·533 m*) acoustic homing torpedo and with wings and tail, this weapon is ramp-launched by two solid propellant rocket boosters which jettison after 3 sec. The weapon then glides at a height fixed by radio-altimeter. Sonar-detected data is fed into the device by radio so that 875 yards short of its target the torpedo is jettisoned by parachute enters the water and homes on its target. It is in service with the French Navy installed in the anti-submarine vessel *La Galisonniere* and subsequently the *Suffren* and *Duquesne*, five T-47 class destroyers and three ships of the "Tourville" class.

Malafon ASW missile on the French destroyer Vauquelin

GERMANY (FEDERAL REPUBLIC)

KORMORAN — Messerschmitt-Bölkow-Blohm

Length, overall (approx)	14 ft 5in (*4·40 m*)
Wing span (approx)	3 ft 3½ in (*1·00 m*)
Launch weight (approx)	1 280 lbs (*580 kg*)
Speed	Mach ·95
Range	20 n. miles

This missile was developed to fulfil a German Navy requirement. Its guidance system has pre-guidance and homing phases, enabling it to approach the target at low altitude. The Kormoran is carried by F-104G Starfighters of the German Naval Air Arm and by Sea King helicopters, but can be employed with all aircraft having modern navigation system.

Kormoran missile under wing of F-104G Starfighter.

ISRAEL

Surface-to-surface

GABRIEL — Israel Aircraft Industries

Length	11 ft 0 in (*3·35 m*)
Max diameter	12·8 in (*32·5 cm*)
Wing span	4 ft 6½ in (*1·385 m*)
Launch weight	882 lb (*400 kg*)
Warhead	330 lb (*150 kg*)
Max range	11 n. miles and 20 n. miles

Operated in the "Saar" class and "Saar IV" class of the Israeli Navy. It is a radar guided weapon with alternative optical control and carries an HE warhead. Terminal guidance is probably semi-active with capability in an ECM environment. Gabriel is subsonic and travels a few metres above S/L to its target. It can be used in rough seas and adverse weather. An improved Gabriel with a 20 mile range is now operational.

Gabriel missile leaving its launcher

ITALY

Surface-to-surface

SEA KILLER Mk 1 (Nettuno) — Sistel

Length	12 ft 3 in (*3·73 m*)
Body diameter	8·1 in (*0·206 m*)
Wing span	2 ft 9·5 in (*0·85 m*)
Launch weight	370 lb (*168 kg*)
Speed at burnout	Mach 1·9
Warhead	77 lbs
Min/max range	1·6/5·4 n. miles (*3/10 km*)

This is a sea-skimmer fired from a five round launcher with alternative optical control. In Italy known as Nettuno. Single-stage solid-propellant rocket of 4 410 lb (*2 000 kg*) st thrust propels this missile which has movable cruciform control surfaces and stabilising tailfins. Guidance is from beam rider/radio command/radar altimeter-systems and the warhead is a high-explosive fragmentation type with proximity impact fuse.

Sea Killer Mk I in flight

SEA KILLER Mk 2 (Vulcano) — Sistel

A two-stage version of Sea Killer Mk I, to increase operational range. The booster and sustainer are both solid-propellant rocket motors. After burn-out the booster is separated by an aerodynamic drag section.
The missile has the same specification as the Mk 1 except for length increased to 15 ft 5 in (*4·7 m*), launching weight to 594 lb (*270 kg*), warhead to 155 lbs, and max effective range to over 13 n. miles. The missile is fully operational.

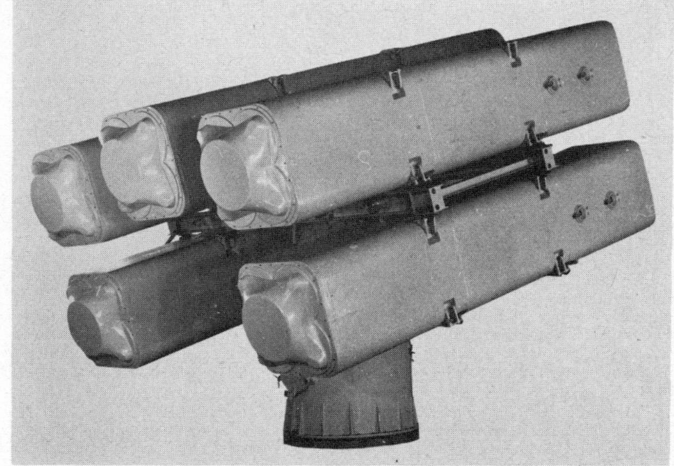

Sea Killer multi-round launcher

SEA KILLER Mk 3 — Sistel

Power plant	1 booster 2 sustainers
Launch weight	1 200 lbs
Range, miles	24+ (*45 km+*)
Warhead	330 lbs

A further advance in this series, currently under development.

Surface-to-air

ALBATROS

The system consists of a Ferranti GA-10 digital gun fire control system or an Elsag NA-10 system; Selenia Orion RTN 10X tracking radar; Sparrow or Aspide missiles and a missile launching system integrated with 1/2 anti-aircraft guns. The Sparrow missiles are modified with folding wings and cropped tail-fins, so as to fit into launcher.
The system gives Naval ships of 100 tons and upwards all-weather defence against aircraft and missiles.

Range (missiles)	5 n. miles

SEA INDIGO — Contraves Italiana/Sistel

This is a marine version of the Indigo. An automatic reloading system is used in ships of more than 500 tons displacement; manual reloading in naval craft of less than 500 tons.

Length	11 feet (*3·32 m*)
Launch weight	266 lbs (*121 kg*)
Warhead	46 lbs (*21 kg*) HE
Speed	Mach 2·5 at burnout
Range	5·5 miles (*10 km*) (slant)
Control	Beam-rider with stand-by radio command and IR

NOTE. Sistel is developing an air-to-surface missile, AIRTOS, for use at medium ranges under all weather conditions. It is 13 feet long with a speed of Mach 1·5, a range of 6 miles and an 80 lb HE warhead. Not yet in service.

NORWAY

Surface-to-surface

PENGUIN **Kongsberg Vaapenfabrikk**

Length	10 ft (*3·05 m*)
Max dia	11 in (*0·28 m*)
Wing span	4 ft 7 in (*1·40 m*)
Launch weight	727 lb (*329 kg*)
Range	11 n. miles

Penguin uses an inertial guidance system with infra-red terminal homing, and has a 264 lb (*119 kg*) warhead. It has two-stage solid-propellant propulsion. 20 "Storm" class gunboats are fitted with 6 launchers on rear deck. 6 "Snogg" class torpedo boats are each fitted with four launchers, with others on the five Oslo class frigates.

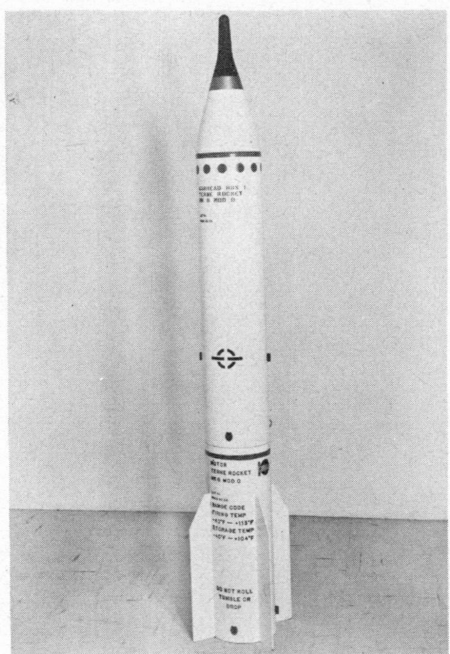

Terne Mk.8 surface-to-surface missile

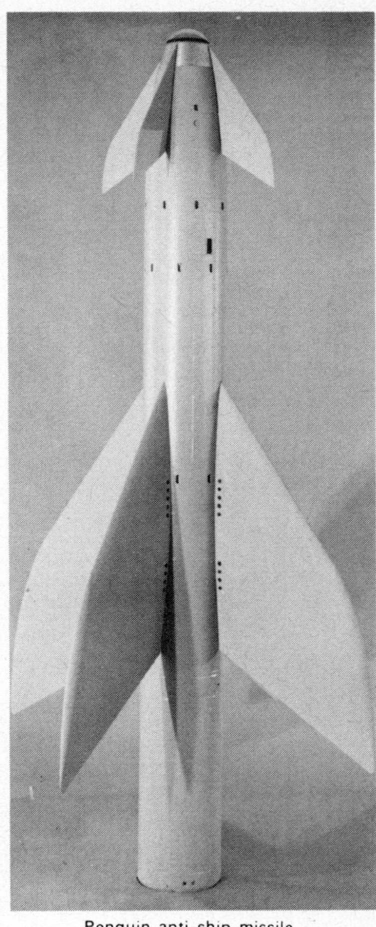

Penguin anti-ship missile

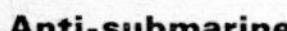

Anti-submarine

TERNE Mk 8 Kongsberg Vaapenfabrikk

Length	6 ft 4·75 in (*1·95 m*)
Body diameter	8·0 in (*20·3 cm*)
Launching weight	298 lb (*135·2 kg*)
Range	about 1·4 miles (*3 km*)

This anti-submarine missile was originated by the Norwegian Defence Research Establishment for the Royal Norwegian Navy, who now use it operationally. It is a rocket-propelled depth charge with a 110 lb (*50 kg*) warhead having an ogival nose cone, and cruciform stabilising fins. Propulsion is by two concentric solid-propellant rocket motors and detonation of the warhead by a combined hydrostatic and impact fuse. A full salvo of six missiles can be fired in 5 seconds. Reloading is automatic and takes 40 seconds.

SWEDEN

Air-to-surface

RBO4 **Robotavdelningen**

Length	14 ft 7¼ in (*4·45 m*)
Body diameter	1 ft 7·75 in (*0·50 m*)
Wing span	6 ft 8 in (*2·04 m*)
Launch weight	1 320 lb (*600 kg*)

This missile has been operational since early 1959 with the Swedish Air Force but has been under a continuous improvement programme to up-date it to modern needs. It equips the four attack wings flying A32A Lansens as the RB.04D and is also used with the Viggen in a later version, the RB.04E. It is powered by a solid-propellant rocket motor giving it a subsonic performance carrying a 660 lb (*300 kg*) warhead. Guidance is by a passive/active radar homing system.

RB.04E anti-shipping missile for the Viggen

Surface-to-surface

RB 08A SAAB

Length	18·8 ft (*5·7 m*)
Wing span	9·9 ft (*3 m*)
Launch weight	2 675 lbs (*1 215 kg*)
Speed	Mach ·85
Range	? 100 n. miles

A cruise-missile for ship borne and Coastal Artillery use which entered service in 1967, production ceased in 1970. After a directional launch auto-pilot control takes over until terminal homing (possibly radar) starts.

RBO5A **SAAB**

Length	**11 ft 10 in (*3·61 m*)**
Body diameter	**1 ft 0 in (*0·30 m*)**
Wing span	**2 ft 8 in (*0·80 m*)**
Launch weight	**675 lb (*306 kg*)**

Being developed for the Viggen and Saab-105, this missile is intended for the strike role but can also be used air-to-air. With long-chord cruciform wings and aft-mounted cruciform control surfaces it is powered by a pre-packed liquid propellant rocket motor built by Volvo-Flygmotor. Guidance is by radio command signals from a pilot-operated micro-wave radio link, based on simultaneous observation of both target and missile by the pilot.

RB.05A missiles under the fuselage of a Draken aircraft used for development trials

UNITED KINGDOM

Strategic

POLARIS

The A3 Polaris missiles carried in the UK's four SSBN's are of American manufacture and details will be found under USA. However the re-entry bodies, warheads, fusing and arming devices have all been developed and manufactured in the UK.

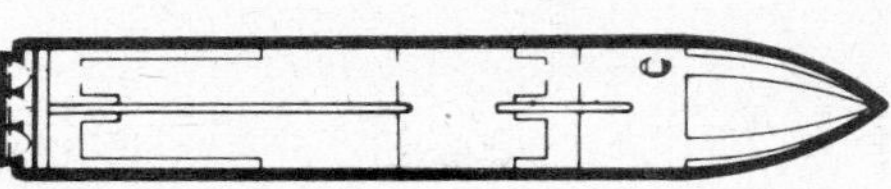

Polaris

Surface-to-air

SEACAT — Short Bros. & Harland

Length	4 ft 10·3 in (*1·48 m*)
Body diameter	7·5 in (*19·05 cm*)
Wing span	2 ft *1·6* in (*0·64 m*)
Range	1·9 n. miles (*3·5 km*)

It is standard armament aboard Royal Navy ships and is also ordered for the Royal Australian Navy, Royal New Zealand Navy, Royal Netherlands Navy, Royal Swedish Navy (with whom it is designated RB 07) Chilean, Brazilian, Federal German, Indian, Argentinian, Libyan, Venezuelan, Iranian, Royal Malaysian and Thailand navies. A light-weight version is also used from fast patrol-boats. It is propelled by a two-stage solid-propellant IMI rocket and has a high-explosive warhead with contact and proximity fuses. A number of different fire control systems are in use.—Mk 20 Visual, Mks 22 and 24 Radar Director, M4/3 Radar director, Signaal M40 and integrated with fire control system of guns. Normally mounted in a four-round launcher. In 1969 Shorts stated that successful trials had been completed of a system that replaces the optical sighting binocular with a closed-circuit TV system produced by Marconi Co. as the 323 Series.

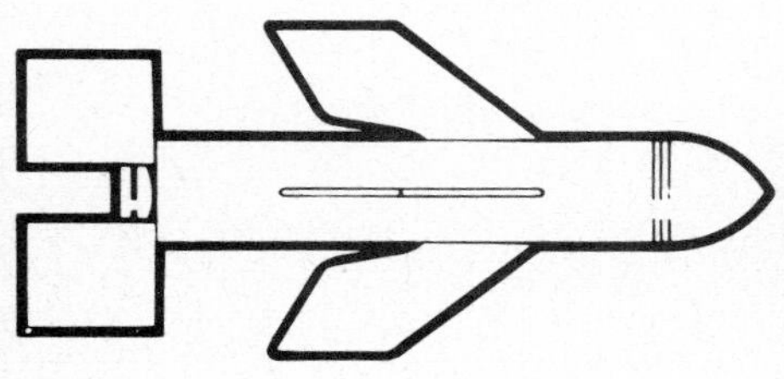

Seacat

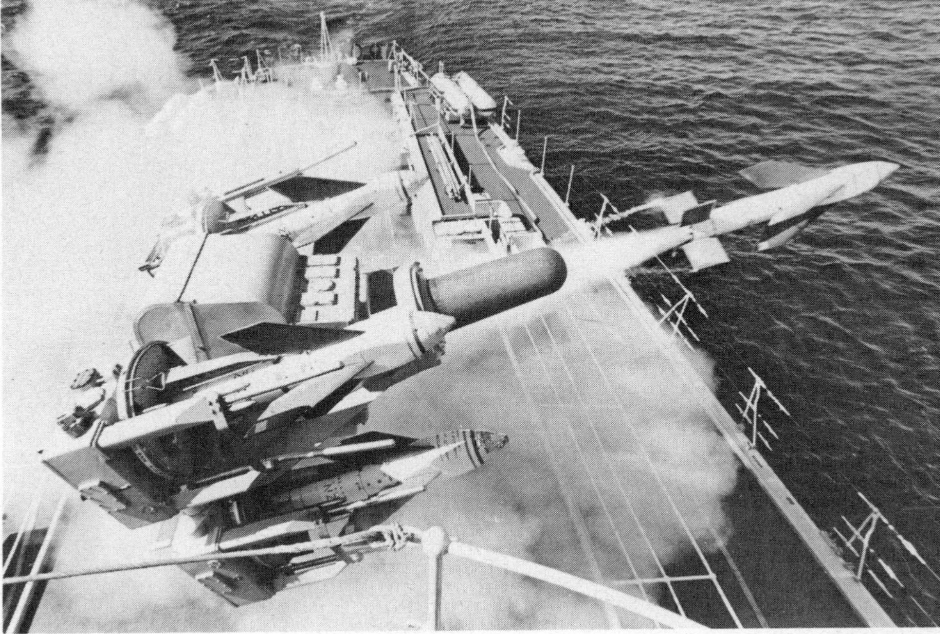

Seacat missile being fired from HMNZS Taranaki

SEADART — Hawker Siddeley

Length	14 ft 3·5 in (*4·36 m*)
Body diameter	1 ft 4·5 in (*0·42 m*)
Wing span (max)	3 ft 0 in (*0·91* m)
Range	20 n. miles
Launch weight	1 220 lbs (*550*) *kg*)

Fitted in the Royal Navy's HMS *Bristol* and Type 42 destroyers, this missile is a two-stage vehicle with an IMI solid propellent first stage booster and a second stage comprising the warhead powered by a Rolls-Royce Bristol Odin ramjet. The air duct is in the nose with interferometer aerials for the guidance systems around it. It employs semi-active radar homing using the Tracker illuminator radar Type 909. Sea Dart will also arm two type 42 destroyers ordered for the Argentine Navy. Has high and low altitude capability against aircraft and missiles and can be used in the surface-to-surface role.

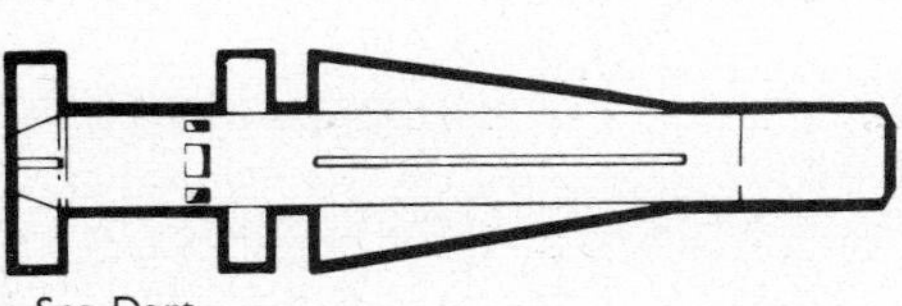

Sea Dart

Hawker Siddeley Sea Dart

SEASLUG Mk 1/Mk 2 — Hawker Siddeley

Length (Mk 2)	20 ft (*6·10 m*)
Body diameter	1 ft 4·1 in (*0·41 m*)
Wing span	4 ft 8·6 in (*1·438 m*)
Tail span	5 ft 6·6 in (*1·69 m*)
Range	24 n. miles (*45 km*) (approx)

The Seaslug, in its Mk 1 and Mk 2 forms, equips the "County" class of the Royal Navy. The Mk 1 was fitted in the first four ships although they will be retrospectively fitted with Mk 2 as are the last four "County" class ships now in service. During test firings a success rate of 90% has been achieved, by the Mk 1, at heights up to 50 000 ft (*15 250 m*) plus. It has a solid-propellant sustainer rocket which is made by ICI, with four solid-propellant booster rockets around the body. Its guidance system is beamriding in conjunction with Type 901M Radar. The Mk 2 also has transistorized electronics, longer range, better low-level capacity and an increase in length of 4 in.

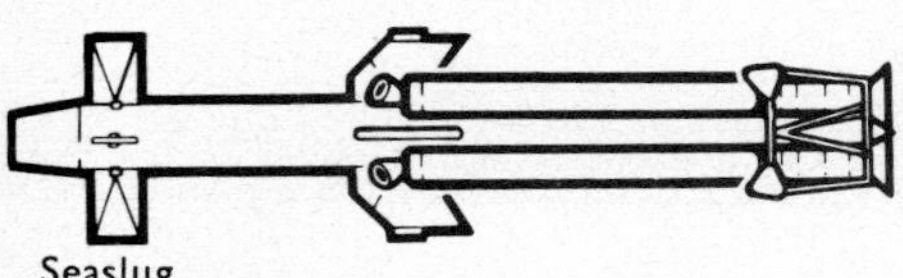

Seaslug

Seaslug being launched from HMS "Kent"

Surface-to-surface

MM38 EXOCET — Aérospatiale

Details under France. Being mounted in some of the "County" and "Leander" class.

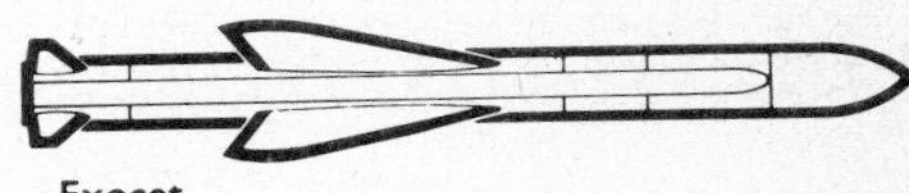

Exocet

UNITED KINGDOM (continued)

SEAWOLF — BAC

This is a point-defence system currently under trial in HMS *Penelope.* Acquisition radars are Marconi Type 967 and 968, tracking is by Marconi Type 910 and missile TV tracking by a Marconi-Elliott system. The launcher is a six-barrelled version made by Vickers with manual reloading. The entire system is known as GWS 25 and is suitable for frigates and above. A light-weight version for smaller ships, known as Seawolt/Omega is under study.

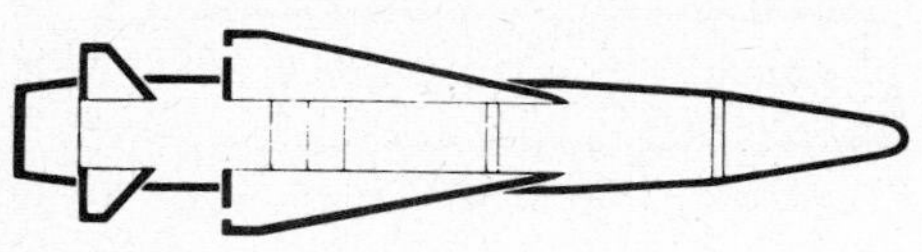

Seawolf

SLAM — Vicker Ltd

Dimensions of Blowpipe missile.

Length	4 ft 5·1 in (*1·35 m*)
Body diameter	3 in (*7·60 cm*)
Span of tail-fins	10·8 in (*27·4 cm*)

The system consists of six Blowpipe missiles in launchers around a central TV camera, gyro-stabiliser and control package.
An operator in the launch ship's control room guides each missile, by means of a joystick, by keeping the target and missile centred on a TV monitor.
It is being developed for close range defence against aircraft and ships, and can be fitted to submarines and surface ships.

Blowpipe defence system for light surface ship

Air-to-surface

BULLPUP — Martin (USA)

Details included in USA section.

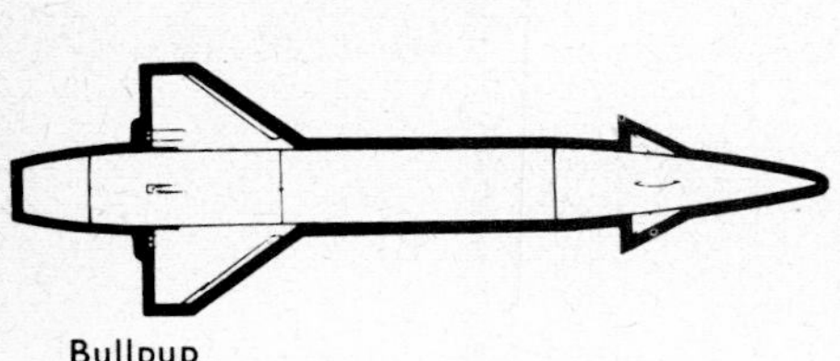

Bullpup

SS-11 — Aérospatiale (France)

Details included in French section.

SS-11

Air-to-air

FIRESTREAK — Hawker Siddeley Dynamics

This British air-to-air weapon is used by the RAF on Lightnings and was used on Sea Vixens by the Fleet Air Arm. It has a cylindrical metal body, cruciform wings and tail. It is propelled by a solid-propellant rocket and is homed by an infra-red guidance system and controlled by a proportional navigation system. The 50 lb (*22·7 kg*) warhead can be detonated at a pre-determined range. Now being replaced by Red Top production having ceased in 1969.

Length	10 ft 5·5 in (*3·19 m*)
Body diameter	8·75 in (*22·5 cm*)
Wing span	2 ft 5·5 in (*0·75 m*)
Launch weight	300 lb (*136 kg*)
Cruising speed	Mach 2 plus
Range	0·65/4·34 n. miles

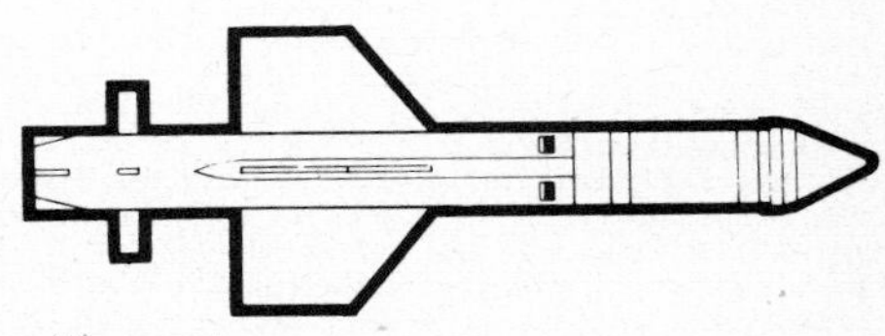

Firestreak

A Firestreak AAM being loaded on a Sea Vixen aboard HMS Victorious

UNITED KINGDOM (continued)

Air-to-air (continued)

RED TOP **Hawker Siddeley Dynamics**

Length	10·8 ft (*3·3 m*)
Body diameter	8·75 in (*22·5 cm*)
Wing span	2 ft 11·75 in (*0·91 m*)
Cruising speed	Mach 3
Range	6 n. miles

This is in effect a vastly-improved Firestreak with larger wings and control surfaces and a new infra-red guidance unit not limited to pursuit-course attack. Warhead is increased in weight to 68 lb (*31 kg*). The rocket motor is increased in power also. This missile is used by the RAF on Lightnings and the Fleet Air Arm on Sea Vixen FAW Mk 2's.

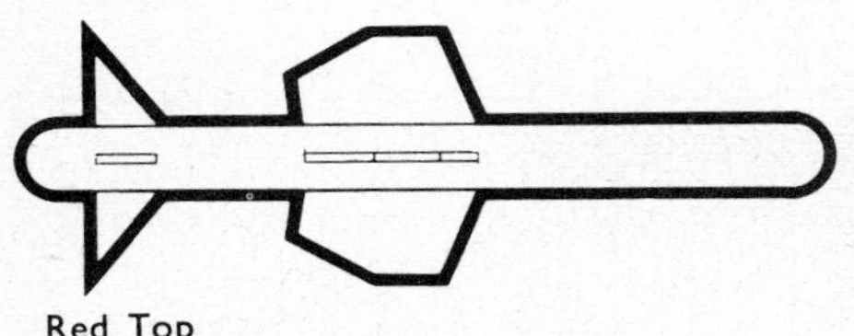

Red Top

Red Top missile

Anti-submarine

IKARA

Details under Australia. Now being fitted in some "Leander" class and *HMS Bristol*.

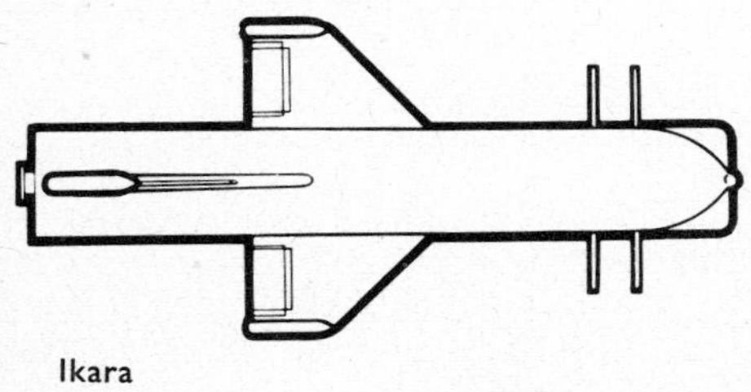

Ikara

UNITED STATES OF AMERICA

Strategic

POLARIS A2 and A3 (UGM-27B and C) Lockheed

Length	A2/3—31 ft (*9·45 m*)
Body diameter	4 ft 6 in (*1·37 m*)
Launch weight	A2—30 000 lb (*13 600 kg*)
	A3—35 000 lb (*15 850 kg*)
Speed at burn-out	Mach 10
Max range	A2—1 500 n. miles
	A3—2 500 n. miles

Both versions are in service as long-range two-stage solid-propellant missiles with thermo-nuclear warhead. In the A2 this is an 8KT head—in the A3 the majority of US missiles are fitted with a triple 200 KT MRV head. The first stage is powered by an Aerojet-General motor and the second stage by a Hercules Inc motor. Initially 41 US Navy nuclear-powered submarines were operational with 16 Polaris missiles, 28 with A3 and 13 with A2. The A3 is carried in 4 Royal Navy submarines. The submarine is positioned by a Ship Inertial Navigation System (SINS), thereafter the missile, after firing relies on its own inertial guidance system. The first stage ignites as the missile breaks surface, having been ejected by a pressure system forcing air or steam into the base of the launch tube. Polaris is no longer in production but a total of 1 452 missiles were built.

POSEIDON CB UGM-73A Lockheed

Length	**34 ft 0 in (*10·36 m*)**
Body diameter	**6 ft 2 in (*1·88 m*)**
Launch weight	**65 000 lb (*29 500 kg*) approx**
Range	**2 500 n. miles**

POSEIDON

This is a larger and twice as powerful missile to replace Polaris with twice the payload and increased accuracy. It became operational in the USS *James Madison* in March 1971 and is to equip 31 existing Polaris submarines of the "Lafayette" class by mid-1976. First test firing, at Cape Kennedy, was on 16 August 1968. The first stage is powered by a Hercules Inc or Thiokol solid propellant motor and the second by a Hercules Inc solid-propellant motor. This missile carries an MIRV head and is directed by the Mk 88 fire control system.

TRIDENT

This is a programme designed to supplant the Poseidon/Polaris deployment. It is in two stages: (a) The replacement of Poseidon by a missile of 3 200 n. miles range, variously designated Expo, ULMS 1, Trident 1 or C4 in late 1978. (b) The fitting in new construction submarines of a missile of 4 500 n. miles range known as Trident II. The submarines will be double the size of the "Lafayette" class and the first should be in commission in 1979-80. Trident II should be available shortly afterwards.

Surface-to-air

AEGIS RCA

This missile will be carried on board new construction destroyers and frigates. The launcher for Aegis is the Mk 26 dual-purpose launcher also used for ASROC. The solid-propellant rocket motor is dual-thrust and guidance is by semi-active radar. The missile itself is the standard SM-2 mod.

The solid-propellant rocket motor is dual-thrust and guidance is by semi-active radar.

An electric (all-direction) scanning radar is part of the Aegis equipment, as well as the UYK-7 naval tactical data system computer and microwave radars for target illumination.

The prime contractor is Radio Corporation of America

SEASPARROW Raytheon

Otherwise known as Point Defence missile system this ship-launched version of the Sparrow AAM is operational with the US Navy. It is a single-stage rocket powered by a Rocketdyne Mk 38 Mod-2 solid-propellant motor and its guidance system is a Raytheon-built continuous-wave semi-active radar homing system. It has a cylindrical body with pivoted cruciform wings and tailfins. Successful test firings have been made from USS *Enterprise*. Canada is installing its close range system with Raytheon Canada Ltd as prime contractor. Norway, Denmark, Italy, Netherlands, Belgium and the US have joined together in the development of a NATO Sea Sparrow system. Raytheon is the prime contractor. Contractors in each European country developed significant portions of the system.

Length	12 ft 0 in (*3·66 m*)
Body diameter	8 in (*0·20 m*)
Wing span	3 ft 4 in (*1·02 m*)
Launch weight	450 lb (*204 kg*)
Speed	**over Mach 3·5**
Range	**7 n. miles plus**

UNITED STATES OF AMERICA (continued)

ADVANCED TERRIER RIM-2 General Dynamics

Supersonic surface-to-air missile

Length	27 ft 0 in (*8·23 m*)
Body diameter, missile	1 ft (*0·305 m*)
Body diameter, boosters	1 ft 4 in (*0·406 m*)
Wing span	1 ft 8 in (*0·51 m*)
Launch weight	3 000 lb (*1 360 kg*)
Range	20 n. miles
Speed	Mach 2·5

Developed from the Terrier the Advanced Terrier is in widespread service. As well as many ships of the US Navy, 3 cruisers of the Italian Navy and one of the Dutch Navy are equipped with this missile which is especially effective against low-flying aicraft. There is a solid-propellant sustainer and booster for this missile and it uses a beam-riding guidance system in conjunction with SPS-48 search radar, the Mk 76 fire control system and the Naval Tactical Data System (NTDS). To be replaced by Standard RIM 67A.

Air-to-air

PHOENIX XAIM-7E Hughes

The F-111B aircraft was in mind when the Phoenix was being developed but now it is specified for the Grumman F-14A. It has a cylindrical body with long-chord cruciform wings and tail controls. It is powered by a Rocketdyne solid-propellant motor. It is radar-guided (AN/AWG-9) and all-weather operation is envisaged with particular application to long-range targets.

Length	**13 ft 0 in (*3·96 m*)**
Span	**3 ft 0 in (*0·91 m*)**
Max dia	**1 ft 3 in (*0·38 m*)**
Launch weight	approx 1 000 lb (*455 kg*)
Range	85 n. miles plus

Phoenix missile (extreme right)

SPARROW AIM-7E Raytheon

The Sparrow is in service with F-4B and F-4C aircraft of the US Navy and USAF respectively and equips the F-4K (Fleet Air Arm) and F-4M (RAF) versions in the UK. It is also carried by the F-104S of the Italian Air Force and will be carried by the McDonnell Douglas F-15 and the Grumman F-14 Tomcat for the USAF and US Navy respectively. Powered by a Rocketdyne Mk 38 Mod-2 solid-propellant motor, it is of standard cylindrical shape with pivoted cruciform wings and tail fins in line with the wings. Homing is by means of a Raytheon continuous-wave semi-active homing system and a 60 lb (*27 kg*) warhead is fitted.

Length	**12 ft 0 in (*3·66 m*)**
Body diameter	**8 in (*0·20 m*)**
Wing span	3 ft 4 in (*1·02 m*)
Launch weight	450 lb (*204 kg*)
Speed	**Mach 3·5**
Range	**7 n. miles plus**

An advanced version, designated AIM-7F, is being developed.

AIM-7E Sparrow IIIB missiles carried by F-4B of US Navy

UNITED STATES OF AMERICA (continued)

STANDARD RIM-66A/67A **General Dynamics**

Length	ER: 27 ft (*8·23 m*)
	MR: 15 ft (*4·57 m*)
Launch weight	ER: 2 300 lb (*1 060 kg*)
	MR: 1 300 lb (*590 kg*)
Range	ER: 30 n. miles
	MR: 10 n. miles

This missile was developed in two versions, medium-range and extended-range, the first in place of Tartar and the second replacing Terrier. Little modification was needed to fit it to the older launchers. The MR version is a single-stage integral dual-thrust rocket whilst the ER version has a two-stage motor with jettisonable booster. Both versions have all-electric controls and solid-state electronics and an adaptive autopilot. Standard Missile has a semi-active homing system.

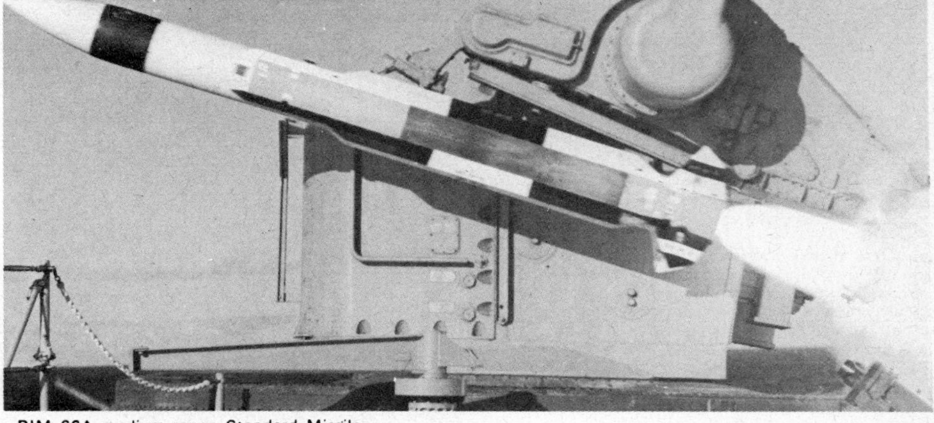

RIM-66A medium-range Standard Missile

Surface-to-surface

HARPOON

Length (with booster)	15·6 ft (*4·75 m*)
Body Diameter	1·1 ft (*·34 m*)
Launch weight (with booster)	1 397 lbs (*635 kilos*)
Warhead	HE
Range	30 n. miles (*55 km*)

This all-weather system is too late to overcome the superiority of the Soviet fleet in SSMs for some time. However within 3-4 years of its introduction in 1975 the USN should have retrieved a lot of the ground which it voluntarily surrendered by putting its reliance on carrier-borne aircraft.

Harpoon is designed for launch from ships, submarines or aircraft. In the first two cases the initial power from the solid fuel booster will place the missile in a ballistic trajectory. After separation the missile will descend to a cruise level, propelled by its turbojet at a height controlled by its altimeter. In the terminal phase radar guidance takes over and with a frequency agile radar and other ECCM devices it should be proof against heavy countermeasures.

NOTE. Until Harpoon is introduced a horizon-limited surface-to-surface ability has been provided by modifications to the Standard I and Standard ARM missiles.

TALOS RIM 8G-AAW and RGM 8 H ARM
Bendix

Long-range ramjet surface-to-air/surface-to-surface missile

Length with booster	31·3 ft (*9·53 m*)
Body diameter	2·5 ft (*0·76 m*)
Wing span	9·5 ft (*2·90 m*)
Launch weight	7 000 lb (*3 175 kg*)
Speed at burn-out	Mach 2·5
Slant range	65 n. miles plus

Entered service in USS *Galveston* in 1959 and has since equipped six other cruisers including USS *"Long Beach"* for which General Electric has developed a special launching and handling system using a computer mechanism by means of which all operations from selecting the particular warhead below decks to the firing of the missile are done automatically. It is a two stage vehicle with a 40 000 hp Bendix 28 inch (*710 mm*) ramjet sustainer and jettisonable solid-propellant booster. It is a beam-riding missile using a semi-active Sperry SPG-49 "lamp" radar and can carry either a nuclear or high-explosive warhead.

It can also be used surface-to-surface. It was reported that the *Long Beach* destroyed two MiG's using Talos over North Vietnam in 1968, with intercepts in the 60 n. mile range.

Talos

TARTAR RIM-24 General Dynamics

Supersonic surface-to-air missile

Length	15 ft 0 in (*4·57 m*)
Body diameter	10 in (*0·30 m*)
Launch weight	1 496 lb (*680 kg*)
Speed	Mach 2
Range	10 n. miles plus
Height effectiveness	1 000 to 40 000 ft (*305* to *12 200 m*)

This weapon is in service with the US Navy, and equips many guided missile destroyers and several heavy cruisers. In addition it is aboard 4 French "Surcouf" destroyers, two Italian destroyers, three destroyers of the Royal Australian Navy and the Japanese destroyer *Amatsukaze*. It is secondary armament on the larger ships and primary on the smaller ships and has a dual-thrust solid-propellant Aerojet-General motor with an initial high-thrust firing followed by a longer low-thrust period maintaining a supersonic speed to the target. It employs a Raytheon guidance system of the homing type. To be replaced by Standard RIM 66A.

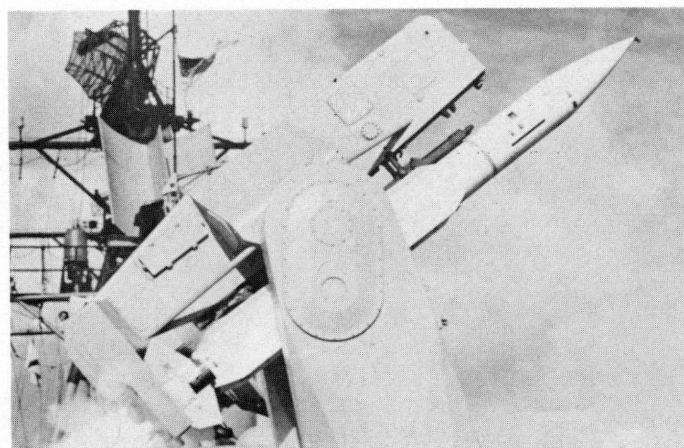

Tartar on a twin-launcher

UNITED STATES OF AMERICA (continued)

Air-to-air (continued)

SIDEWINDER IA AIM-9B and AIM-9H NWC

Sidewinder missile mounted on an F-8 Crusader

Accent in the Sidewinder is on simplicity, with fewer than two dozen moving parts and unsophisticated radio equipment. It is powered by a Naval Propellant Plant solid-propellant rocket and has a 25 lb (*11·4 kg*) warhead. Control surfaces are at the nose in cruciform configuration, indexed by similar tailfins. It has had limited success in action. As well as being used by the USAF and US Navy it has been exported to Nationalist China, Australia, Japan, Philippines, Spain, Sweden and nine NATO countries, the Royal Navy, Royal Canadian and Royal Netherlands Navies, and is under licence production in Germany. The AIM-9H version is under development for the F-14 and other aircraft for the US Navy.

Length	9 ft 3½ in (*2·83 m*)
Body diameter	5 in (*0·13 m*)
Fin span	1 ft 10 in (*0·56 m*)
Launch weight	159 lb (*72 kg*)
Speed	Mach 2·5
Range	1·75 n. miles

SIDEWINDER IC AIM-9C/D **NWC**

Air-to-air missile

Length	9 ft 6·5 in (*2·91 m*)
Body diameter	5 in (*0·13 m*)
Fin span	2 ft 1 in (*0·64 m*)
Launch weight	185 lb (*84 kg*)
Range	2 n. miles plus
Speed	Mach 2·5

All figures relate to AIM-9D version.

A developed version of the 1A the 1C is in production for the US Navy and the UK. Power is from the Rocketdyne Mk 36 Mod-5 solid-propellant motor and the aerofoil surfaces have been revised. The AIM-9D version is equipped with infra-red homing guidance (the US Navy and UK version, in production by Raytheon) and the -9C with semi-active radar guidance, (Produced by Motorola).

Anti-submarine

ASROC RUR-5A **Honeywell**

Surface ship-launched anti-submarine ballistic missile

Length	15 ft 0 in (*4·57 m*)
Diameter	1 ft 0 in (*0·30 m*)
Fin span	2 ft 6 in (*0·76 m*)
Launch weight	1 000 lb (*450 kg*)
Range	1 to 5 n. miles

The complete system comprises a Librascope precision fire control computer fed with data from a Sangamo Electric underwater sonar detector, the Asroc missile and an 8-missile launcher. The missile comprises a ballistic solid propellant-rocket with the weapon (General Electric Mk 44 Model O acoustic homing torpedo; Mk 46 Model O advanced acoustic homing torpedo by Aerojet-General, Honeywell Mk 46 Model 1 or NWC and Honeywell nuclear depth charge) affixed by a frame. After firing, from its 8-tube launcher or a Terrier Mk 10 launcher the rocket is jettisoned at a pre-determined point and the weapon continues to its target. If a torpedo a parachute opens to lower it into the target area and when submerged behaves as any other homing torpedo. If a depth charge it sinks to a pre-determined depth before detonating.

It is operational aboard cruisers, destroyers and escort vessels of the US Navy and the Japanese destroyer *Amatsukaze*.

Asroc anti-submarine missile

UNITED STATES OF AMERICA (continued)

SUBROC UUM-44A Goodyear

Submarine-launched long-range anti-submarine missile

Length	21 ft 0 in (*6·40 m*)
Max diameter	1 ft 9 in (*0·5333 m*)
Launching weight	4 000 lb (*1 815 kg*)
Max range	30 n. miles

Subroc is part of a complex weapons system including advanced long-range detection equipment and a specially designed fire control system for use aboard US Navy submarines. It is fired conventionally from a submarine's torpedo tube, after which the solid-propellant tandem booster ignites under water at a safe distance from the submarine. Thrust-vectoring controls set the missile on its course, its angle of emergence from the water and control its stability in flight. At a pre-determined range the rocket separates from the depth bomb which continues to its target supersonically, controlled by the inertial guidance system. Upon re-entering the water a shock-mitigating device cushions the impact, the bomb sinks and explodes. The production of Subroc is expected to continue until 1978.

Subroc anti-submarine missile.

USSR

NOTES

a) This is the only navy with a full inventory of all types of missiles with the exception of a submarine-launched A/S missile and air-to-air missiles, which reflects their lack of carrier-borne aircraft.

(b) The NATO/US method has been used throughout this section. It should be noted that the numbered missile systems employ code-named missiles which may be used for other systems—e.g. the SA-N-2 system in *Dzerzhinski* uses the Guideline missile which is deployed by the Soviet army in a land-towed system, the SA-2.

(c) In all cases maximum range is given, (optimum and minimum range are given where possible).

(d) The figures in brackets after Launch Platform/Aircraft indicate number of launchers.

Surface-to-surface

SS-N-1

Missiles	Scrubber (Strela)
Launch Platform	2 Kildin's (1), 2 Krupny's (2)
Total launchers available	6
Number of stages	—
Power plant	—
Mach speed	0.9
Max range n. miles	130 (minimum 15)
Length, feet	22·5
Control	Radar with infra-red homing
Operational Date	1958

This obsolescent missile system remains something of an enigma—even whether the Scrubber and Strela are the same missile. Of the launchers two further "Krupny" class have been converted to SAM-carrying "Kanin" class and two "Kildins" have been fitted with SS-N-11. At maximum range external mid-course guidance is required.

SS-N-2

Missile	Styx A and B
Launch platform	15 Komar missile Boats (2), 65 Osa I missile boats (4)
Total launchers available	290
Number of stages	1 booster, 1 sustainer
Power plant	solid fuel
Mach speed	0·9
Max range n. miles	23 (minimum 6)
Length, feet	15
Control	Radar with active radar homing
Operational Date	1960

"Styx" surface-to-surface missile

The Styx missile is in two versions of which A is probably the export model and B used in Warsaw Pact forces. In use by Algeria, China, Cuba, Egypt, East Germany, India, Indonesia, Poland, Romania, Syria, Yugoslavia. A Chinese version may be embarked in their new destroyers and be exported to Pakistan.

The missile itself has short delta wings and a triform tail-unit with control surfaces. It is carried in containers on a twin-rail launcher. This system proved its efficiency when used by the Egyptians to sink the Israeli destroyer *Eilat* on 21 Oct 1967 and by the Indians in a night attack on anchored merchant ships in Pakistan waters in Dec 1971.

USSR (continued)

SS-N-3

Missile	Shaddock
Launch platform	4 Kynda's (8) 4 Kresta I (4) 16 Juliet's (4) 3 Echo I (6) 27 Echo II (8) 7 Whisky Long Bin (4) 5 Whisky Twin Cylinder (2)
Total launchers available	48 (surface), 318 (submarine)
Number of stages	2 Boosters, Ramjet or Turbojet sustainers
Power plant	Ramjet or Turbojet
Mach speed	0·9-1·5
Max range, n. miles	150-250 (optimum probably nearer 100)
Length, feet	42
Control	Radar with external mid-course guidance and, possibly, radar or infra-red homing
Operational date	1961-62

For this medium-range system target information is probably obtained from reconnaissance aircraft or embarked helicopters in the case of cruisers. There is evidence that this missile may be pre-programmed for shorter ranges and have an active radar terminal homing capability. In the cruisers the launchers are trainable. The submarine version is carried in both nuclear boats (Echo I and II) and diesel boats (Juliet and Whisky). A road-mobile system using the Shaddock missile is also used by the Soviet Navy for coast-defence.

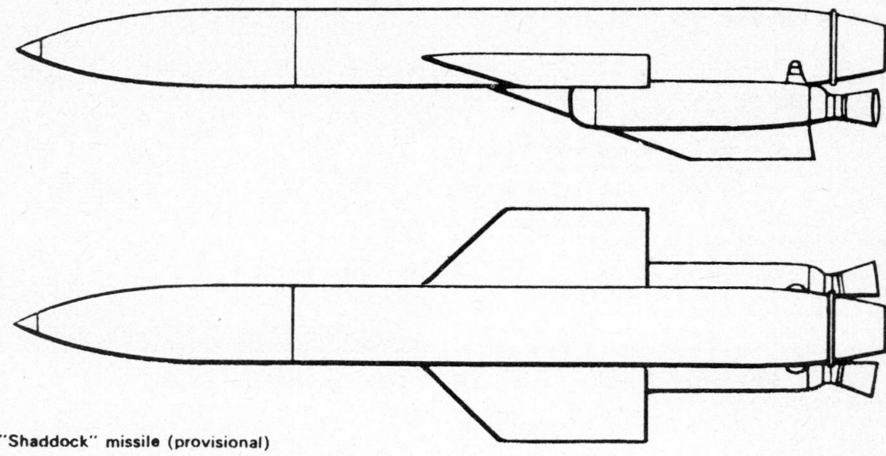

"Shaddock" missile (provisional)

SS-N-7

Missile	—
Launch platform	11 Charlie submarines (8)
Total launchers available	88
Number of stages	—
Power plant	—
Mach speed	1·5
Max range n. miles	26
Length, feet	Possibly 22 max
Control	—
Operational date	1969-70

Eight vertical launch-tubes forward are fitted in the Charlie class for dived launch of this new missile.

SS-N-9

Missile	—
Launch platform	9 Nanuchka (6)
Total launchers available	54
Number of stages	—
Power plant	—
Mach speed	1·0+
Max range n. miles	150 (optimum probably nearer 50)
Length, feet	Possibly about 30
Control	Radar with external mid-course guidance beyond horizon range
Operational date	1968-69

The Nanuchka's carry a triple launcher either side of the bridge. A derivative of the missile used here may be mounted in the Papa class submarine.

SS-C-2

A coastal defence system using an adaptation of the Kennel ASM named Samlet. This has a probable range up to 55 n. miles and a speed of Mach .9 (see section D (iv)).

SS-N-10

Missile	—
Launch platform	2 Kara (8), 6 Kresta II (8), 7 Krivak (4)
Total launchers available	92
Number of stages	—
Power plant	—
Mach speed	1·2
Max range n. miles	29
Length, feet	approx 25
Control	Radar controlled
Operational	1968

This system first appeared in the Kresta II where a group of four launchers was positioned either side of the bridge. In Krivak there is a four-launcher mounting on the forecastle and in Kara the same arrangement as in Kresta II has been adopted.

SS-N-11

Missile	Probably modified Styx
Launch platform	55 Osa II (4), 2 mod "Kildins" (4)
Total launchers available	228
Number of stages	? 1 booster, 1 sustainer
Power plant	? Solid
Mach speed	·9
Max range n. miles	29
Length, feet	21
Control	? Radar with radar terminal homing
Operational date	1968

The above details are conjectural in places, although this must be a very similar missile to Styx, possibly with folding wings.

SS-N-?

Reports have been received of the development of a mach 4 cruise missile with a range of 400 n. miles.

SS-C-?

See remarks under SS-N-3.

Samlet missile on launch ramp

USSR (continued)

Strategic

SS-N-4

Missile	Sark derivative
Launch platform	11 Golf I (3), 1 Zulu V (2)
Total launchers available	35
Number of stages	? 2
Power plant	—
Max range n. miles	300
Length, feet	37·5
Operational date	Test firing 1955. Operational 1958.

The first ballistic system which, in the nuclear Hotel I class and the diesel boats of the Golf I and Zulu V classes, was fitted for surface launch. Now probably obsolete, all Hotel I's having been converted to II's and the Zulu V's almost certainly non-operational.

SS-N-5

Missile	Serb
Launch platform	11 Golf II (3), 8 Hotel II (3)
Total Launchers available	57
Number of stages	Two
Power plant	Solid
Max range n. miles	700
Length, feet (*metres*)	35 (*10.6*)
Diameter (*metres*)	5 (*1·5*)
Operational date	Test fired March 1962. Operational 1963.

Retrofitted to the Golf II and Hotel II classes. Dived launch.

Serb submarine-launched missile *Courtesy Novosti*

SS-N-6

Missile	Sawfly
Launch platform	33 Yankee (16)
Total launchers available	528
Number of stages	Two
Power plant	Solid
Max range n. miles	1 300
Length, feet (*metres*)	42 (*12·8*)
Diameter, feet (*metres*)	5·75 (*1·75*)
Operational date	1969

The first version of the missile was seen in the Moscow parade of 7 Nov 1967.

Sawfly missile

SS-N-8

Missile	—
Launch platfotm	5 Delta (12), 1 Delta II (?16) 1 Hotel III (1)
Total launchers available	77
Number of stages	? 2
Power plant	? Solid
Max range n. miles	4 200
Length, feet (*metres*)	Approx 46 (*14*)
Diameter, feet (*metres*)	approx. 7 (*2·1*)
Operational date	Tested 1971. Operational 1973

First test-fired at sea from the single Hotel III conversion and now operational in the Delta class. The fact of tripling the Sawfly range has brought a totally new problem into Western missile-defence planning.

Surface-to-air

SA-N-1

Missile	Goa
Launch platform	8 Sam Kotlin (2), 6 Kanin (2), 19 Kashin (4), 4 Kynda (2), 4 Kresta I (4)
Total launchers available	128
Number of stages	2
Power plant	Solid with booster
Slant range n. miles	15
Mach speed	2
Max effective ceiling, feet (*metres*)	44 000 (*12 200*)
Length, feet (*metres*)	19·3 (*5·9*)
Wing span, feet (*metres*)	4·0 (*1·2*)
Operational date	1961-62

The first embarked SAM in the Soviet fleet with a low-altitude short-range capability.

GOA in its land-based form

USSR (continued)

Strategic

SS-N-4

Missile	Sark derivative
Launch platform	11 Golf I (3), 1 Zulu V (2)
Total launchers available	35
Number of stages	? 2
Power plant	—
Max range n. miles	300
Length, feet	37·5
Operational date	Test firing 1955. Operational 1958.

The first ballistic system which, in the nuclear Hotel I class and the diesel boats of the Golf I and Zulu V classes, was fitted for surface launch. Now probably obsolete, all Hotel I's having been converted to II's and the Zulu V's almost certainly non-operational.

SS-N-5

Missile	Serb
Launch platform	11 Golf II (3), 8 Hotel II (3)
Total Launchers available	57
Number of stages	Two
Power plant	Solid
Max range n. miles	700
Length, feet (*metres*)	35 (*10.6*)
Diameter (*metres*)	5 (*1·5*)
Operational date	Test fired March 1962. Operational 1963.

Retrofitted to the Golf II and Hotel II classes. Dived launch.

Serb submarine-launched missile *Courtesy Novosti*

SS-N-6

Missile	Sawfly
Launch platform	33 Yankee (16)
Total launchers available	528
Number of stages	Two
Power plant	Solid
Max range n. miles	1 300
Length, feet (*metres*)	42 (*12·8*)
Diameter, feet (*metres*)	5·75 (*1·75*)
Operational date	1969

The first version of the missile was seen in the Moscow parade of 7 Nov 1967.

Sawfly missile

SS-N-8

Missile	—
Launch platfotm	5 Delta (12), 1 Delta II (?16) 1 Hotel III (1)
Total launchers available	77
Number of stages	? 2
Power plant	? Solid
Max range n. miles	4 200
Length, feet (*metres*)	Approx 46 (*14*)
Diameter, feet (*metres*)	approx. 7 (*2·1*)
Operational date	Tested 1971. Operational 1973

First test-fired at sea from the single Hotel III conversion and now operational in the Delta class. The fact of tripling the Sawfly range has brought a totally new problem into Western missile-defence planning.

Surface-to-air

SA-N-1

Missile	Goa
Launch platform	8 Sam Kotlin (2), 6 Kanin (2), 19 Kashin (4), 4 Kynda (2), 4 Kresta I (4)
Total launchers available	128
Number of stages	2
Power plant	Solid with booster
Slant range n. miles	15
Mach speed	2
Max effective ceiling, feet (*metres*)	44 000 (*12 200*)
Length, feet (*metres*)	19·3 (*5·9*)
Wing span, feet (*metres*)	4·0 (*1·2*)
Operational date	1961-62

The first embarked SAM in the Soviet fleet with a low-altitude short-range capability.

GOA in its land-based form

USSR (continued)

SA-N-2

Missile	Guideline
Launch Platform	Dzerzhinski (2)
Total launchers available	2
Number of stages	2
Power plant	Solid booster, liquid sustainer
Slant range n. miles	22
Mach speed	3·5
Max effective ceiling feet (*metres*)	60 000 (*18 300*)
Length, feet (*metres*)	34·7 (*10·6*) (27 (*8·25*) without booster)
Wing span, feet (*metres*)	main body 5·6 (*1·7*)
	Booster 8·5 (*2·6*)
Warhead	288 lbs HE
Guidance	Radar
Operational date	First reported ashore 1957. Fitted in *Dzerzhinski* in 1961-62

As this system went to sea slightly before SA-N-1 and has not been repeated it must be assumed to be unsuitable for maritime operations.

SA-N-3

Missile	Goblet
Launch platform	1+1 Kuril (4), 2 Moskva (4), 6 Kresta II (4), 2 Kara (4)
Total launchers available	48
Slant range n. miles	20

A larger and longer range follow-on of SA-N-1.

SA-N-4

Missile	
Launch platform	1+1 Kuril (6), 2 Sverdlov conversions (2), 2 Kara (4), 5 Krivak (4), 9 Nanuchka (2), 14 Grisha (2)
Total launchers available	90
Slant range, n. miles	20

Normally housed in a silo, is raised to fire and retracted for reloading or stowage. Associated with a new radar.

Air-to-surface

AS-1

Missile	Kennel
Aircraft	Badger B (2)
Total no. of aircraft	About 50
Stages	1
Power plant	Turbojet
Length, feet (*metres*)	27·9 (*8·5*)
Wing span	16·0 (*4·9*)
Max range n. miles	55
Mach speed	0·9
Operational date	? 1958

An obsolete system, possibly beam-riding. And adaptation of the German Komet missile. Launch height below 25 000 ft (*7 600 m*). Has been supplied to Indonesia and Egypt. The shore based version of this missile, Samlet, appears in section D (i) above, under "SS-C-2".

Two "Kennel" anti-ship missiles loaded beneath the wings of a Tu-16 bomber

AS-2

Missile	Kipper
Aircraft	Badger C (1)
Total no. of aircraft	About 150
Stages	1
Power plant	Turbojet
Length, feet	31 (*9·5*)
Wing span feet (*metres*)	16 (*4·9*)
Max range n. miles	115
Mach speed	1·0+
Operational date	1960

This system imposes neither height nor speed restrictions on the parent aircraft. The missile itself has an underslung turbojet power plant.

AS-3

Missile	Kangaroo
Aircraft	Bear B and C (1)
Total no. of aircraft	About 20
Stages	1
Power plant	Turbojet
Length, feet (*metres*)	49·2 (*15·0*)
Wing span feet (*metres*)	29·8 (*9·1*)
Max range n. miles	400
Mach speed	1·5+
Operational date	1961

The missile is very similar to a swept-wing fighter such as "Fitter", and is the largest in the Soviet naval armoury. It gives the Bear a long-range stand-off capability and is probably radar guided.

AS-4

Missile	Kitchen
Aircraft	Blinder B (1)
Stages	1
Power plant	Liquid rocket
Length, feet (*metres*)	37 (*11·3*)
Wing span feet (*metres*)	8·5 (*2·6*)
Max range, n. miles	185
Mach speed	2+

Apparently intended only for the TU-22 Blinder B on which it is belly-slung. Probably fitted with inertial guidance.

AS-5

Missile	Kelt
Aircraft	Badger G (2)
Total no. of aircraft	About 150
Stages	1
Power plant	Liquid rocket
Length, feet (*metres*)	30·8 (*9·4*)
Wing span, feet (*metres*)	15·1 (*4·6*)
Max range, n. miles	120
Mach speed	·9
Operational date	1968

Externally similar missile to Kennel with a variation of the nose and belly lines. The nose houses an active-homing radar.

AS-6

Missile	Unnamed
Aircraft	Badger ? G (2)
Total no. of aircraft	About 50
Stages	1
Max range n. miles	? 300
Mach speed	3
Operational date	1970-71

This system may also be fitted to Backfire.

Anti-submarine

The Moskva and Kuril classes mount a weapon which is probably an A/S launcher.
This suggests either an increase in range of the ship-borne sonar or, more likely, an integration with the Hormone A helicopters embarked. The head could be torpedo or depth-charge.

NAVAL STRENGTHS

NAVAL STRENGTHS

	Aircraft Carriers (L=light)	Cruisers and Light Cruisers	Destroyers	Frigates	Corvettes	Ballistic Missile Sub-marines (N=Nuclear D=Diesel)	Cruise Missile Sub-marines (N=Nuclear D=Diesel)	Fleet Sub-marines	Patrol Sub-marines	FAC Missile	FAC Torpedo	FAC Gun	Patrol Craft	Mine-layers
ARGENTINA	1 (L)	3	8 (2)		1				2 (2)		2	2	3	
AUSTRALIA	1 (L)		5	6					4				19	
BELGIUM													6	
BRAZIL	1 (L)	1	15 (6)	3	10				8 (2)			8	14	
BULGARIA				2	2				4	2	12		6	
BURMA				2	4						5	72	2	
CANADA			4	15					4				6	
CEYLON				1								5	27	
CHILE		3	4	3					1 (2)		4		5	
CHINA			5 (2)	14 (1)	43	1		1 (?)	49 (4)	80 (15)	80	455 (20)	39	
COLOMBIA			5	4					2 (small)			4	25	
CUBA				3	18				(2)	18	24		33	
DENMARK				6 (1)	4				6	(8)	16		38 (2)	7
DOMINICAN REP				3	2 (5)								12	
ECUADOR				3	2						3 (3)		8	
EGYPT			5	3	12				12	12	36			
FINLAND				2	2					1		15	18	2
FRANCE	2 (L)	2	22 (4)	27 (12)	25	4 (1)	(1)		19 (4)	1 (2)			6	
GERMANY (DEM)				2	18					12	55		12	
GERMANY (FED)			11	6 (10)	6				28 (2)	12	29			
GREECE			11	4	5				7	4	12		5	2
INDIA	1 (L)	2	3	23 (4)					4 (4)	8 (?4)			17	
INDONESIA				9	18				10	12	21		65	
IRAN			3	4	4								16	
IRAQ					3						12	4	18	
ISRAEL									2	13	9		30	
ITALY		3	9	11	12				11 (2)		8	4		
JAPAN			29 (5)	16 (5)	20				14 (4)		5		13	2
KOREA (N)					14				4	10	53	47		
KOREA (S)			7	10									36	
MALAYSIA				2						8			24	
MEXICO			2	9									10	
NETHERLANDS		1	(2)	16 (8)	11				6				6	
NEW ZEALAND				4	2								11 (4)	
NORWAY				5	2				15	26	20			5
PAKISTAN		1	4	2					3+6		4	8	3	
PERU		3	4	3	2				4 (2)				26	
PHILLIPINES				1	6							9	18	
POLAND			4		2				4	12	25		46	
PORTUGAL				14 (4)	15				4				36	
ROMANIA					6					6	12		10	
SOUTH AFRICA			2	7	(6)				3				5	
SPAIN	1 (L)	1 (1)	13 (3)	16 (3)	4 (10)				8 (2)	(12?)	3		10 (23)	
SWEDEN			8	5	2				22 (5)	1 (16)	39 (9)		23	48 (4)
TAIWAN			19	12					2		6		4	1
THAILAND			1	9	7							13	10+20	2
TURKEY			14	2	5				13 (2)	(4)	9		52	9
UNITED KINGDOM	1+2 (L)	2+10 (5 bldg)		64		4		8	23				13	3
UNITED STATES	15 (2N) + 8+(2N)	33 (+10 res)	99+23 (+35 res)	66 (+2)		41 (N) (+1 res)	1 res (D)	61 (27 bldg)	13 (+5 res)	3	17	14		
USSR	(2) (L)	34	104	46	74	48 (N) 21 (D)	39 (N) 28 (D)	30 28	230	135	150			
VENEZUELA			5	6					3 (2)	2 (4)			26 (21)	
VIETNAM (N)					3						20	28	30	
YUGOSLAVIA			1		3				5	10	44		25	

* In addition there are 30 Cargo and Transport Ships (amphib), of which 22 are in reserve.

TABLE SHOWING THE NUMERICAL STRENGTH OF EACH COUNTRY

Ocean Mine-sweepers	*Coastal Mine-sweepers/ Mine-hunters*	*Inshore Mine-sweepers*	*Mine-sweeping Boats*	*Assault Ships*	*Landing Ships*	*Landing Craft*	*Depot Repair Main-tenance Ships*	*Survey Research Ships (Large and Small)*	*Supply Ships*	*Large Tankers*	*Small Tankers*	*Hydrofoils and ACVs*	*Misc-ellaneous*	
	4/2				5	20		7 (3)		1	2		21	ARGENTINA
	6					8		4 (1)	2				7	AUSTRALIA
7	9	12						2	2				13	BELGIUM
	6 (2)				2		2	17		1	1		10	BRAZIL
2	4	2	24			20								BULGARIA
								2					11	BURMA
							2	6	3		2	1	63	CANADA
												1	1	CEYLON
					5	2	2	1		1	2		12	CHILE
16	10 (2)				48	465	1	12	20 (?)		8	70	380	CHINA
							1	4			3		22	COLOMBIA
														CUBA
	8	4					2				2		4	DENMARK
	2				1	2		2			2		12	DOMINICAN REP
					2			1	1				7	ECUADOR
	10	2				14							6	EGYPT
						11							15	FINLAND
12	42/5	3		2	5	27	12	13	2	4 (3)	5		112	FRANCE
6	44	10				18		11	1		3		48	GERMANY (DEM)
	18	44			2	50	16	6	14		11		68	GERMANY (FED)
	15			1	14	8	2	5			8		12	GREECE
	4	4			1	4	3	4	1	1	4		1	INDIA
6	20				8	9	5	4			7		58	INDONESIA
	4	2				2	2		(2)		1	12 (2)	4	IRAN
													3	IRAQ
						9							9	ISRAEL
4	36	20			2	64	8	2 (1)	1	1	1	1	125	ITALY
	36 (2)	4	8 (2)		5 (4)	68	2				1		19	JAPAN
														KOREA (N)
	10				20			1	13					KOREA (S)
	6						1	1					24 (Police)	MALAYSIA
	25							2			2		5	MEXICO
	25/4	16				12	2(1 bldg)	2 (1)	1 (1)				16	NETHERLANDS
	2							2					2	NEW ZEALAND
	10					7	1						7	NORWAY
	7							1			2		5	PAKISTAN
	2				4	13		2			6		4	PERU
4					11							4	2	PHILIPPINES
24			20		23			2			6		35	POLAND
	9					67	1	7	1	1			8	PORTUGAL
	4	22	8			10							6	ROMANIA
	10							1	1				10	SOUTH AFRICA
11	12			1	8	8+99	1 (2)	6 (2)	(1)	1	15		113	SPAIN
	18 (6)	18 (2)				123 (15)		5	1		2		26	SWEDEN
	13		9		28	22							24	TAIWAN
	4				7	9		1					20	THAILAND
	16	4			1	53	5	6			8		26	TURKEY
	38	24		2	7	24+33	5	5+5	10	25	6	2	285	UNITED KINGDOM
25 (19 res)	9 (2 res)			8 (5 bldg+4 res)	*47 (+45 res)	100	28 (+24 res)	46 (2 bldg+5 res)	120+9 (+28 res)	54+1 (+13 res)		3 (2 bldg)	84	UNITED STATES
188	123	100			12	60	60	120	4	11	29	25+	200+ 53 AGIs	USSR
					6			5					14	VENEZUELA
			4		24								100	VIETNAM (N)
	4	12	14 (river)			29		1			7		36	YUGOSLAVIA

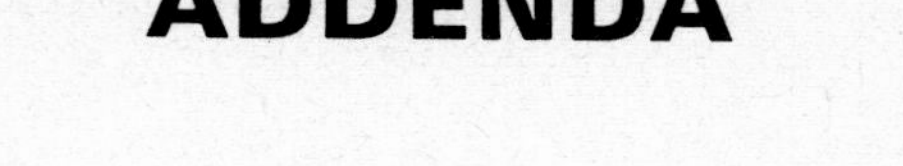

ADDENDA

ABU DHABI

Four "Spear" class 30 ft patrol craft ordered from Fairey Marine Hamble in early 1974.

BANGLADESH

Akshay transferred from India (April 1973) and renamed *Padma.*

BARBADOS

TT Lewis, second "Guardian" patrol boat of four delivered early 1974.

BRAZIL

Four additional "Gearing Fram I" class transferred by USA *Frontier, Greenhalgh, Inhauma, Jacegaui.*
"Aratu" class—additional names announced "Abrolhos" *Albardão.*
New oceanographic ship *Alvaro Alberto* ordered 1973. *Almirante Graça Aranha* laid down 1973. Three 365 ton patrol craft, *Rondonia, Amapa* +1 built by McLaren (Niteroi).

CANADA

Chaudiére paid off late 1973.

CHILE

Riveros and *Williams*—replace 21 in torpedo tubes by triple Mark 32 tubes.

COLOMBIA

Tankers *Covenas, Mamonal* and *Sancho Jimeno* deleted.

DOMINICA

Fourth "Bellatrix" class commissioned 1974.

FINLAND

"Riga" class now armed with single 40 mm gun in place of twin 37 mm with additional twin 30 mm in the eyes.

GERMANY—WEST

U30 named on March 26, 1974.

IRAN

There are reports of an order for four DD 963 class and four PF 109 class from the USA.
Babr and *Palang* now mount two twin 5 in turrets and have an enlarged flight deck and hangar.

INDIA

Twenty 45 ft customs launches ordered from Batservice Verft Mandal Dec 1973.

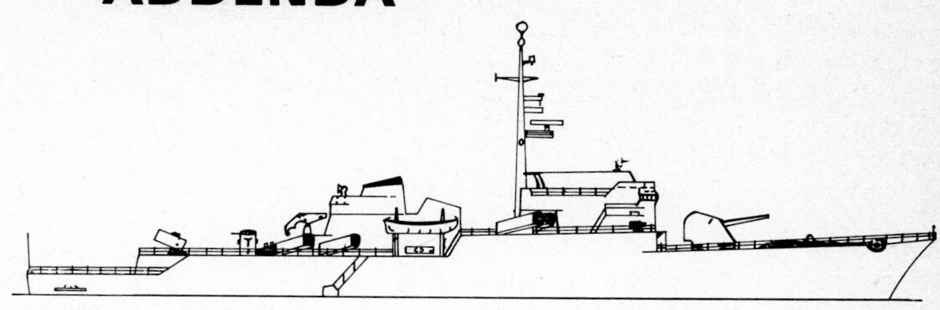

NEW ITALIAN FRIGATE

ISRAEL

The "Ophir" class and "HDML" class have now probably been deleted. 3 Ex-USN PBR type have been acquired.

INDONESIA

"Claude Jones" class *Martadinata* transferred Jan 1974. HMAS *Bandolier* renamed *RI Sibarau* on transfer 16 Nov 1973.

ITALY

4 new missile-armed frigates ordered in early 1974 from Cantieri Navali del Tirreno e Riuniti. Details as follows:

Displacement, tons	2 208 standard; 2 500 full load
Dimensions, ft (*m*)	347·7 × 39·5 × 12·0 (*106 × 12 × 3·7*)
Missiles	Four OTOMAT 2 missile launchers (surface-to-surface) One octuple Albatros (Sea-sparrow) launcher for Point Defence
Guns	1—127 mm OTO MELARA 2—35 mm OTO-Oerlikons (twin)
Rocket launchers	2—105 mm Breda ELSAG multi-purpose 20-barrelled launchers
Torpedo tubes	6 tubes in triple mountings, port and starboard
Main engines	CODOG with 2 GE/Fiat LM 2500 gas turbines; 50 000 hp; 2 Fiat 20 cyl A 230 diesels; 7 800 hp
Speed, knots	35

NOTE: The white paper issued in Spring 1974 foreshadows the building of eight of the above frigates, four 60-ton Swordfish class hydrofoils, six more missile hydrofoils, ten minehunters, one LPD, one supply ship, one salvage ship, all by 1984 plus an additional helicopter cruiser with VSTOL aircraft as well as helicopters to follow in the late 1980's.
This programme, in addition to the provision of extra and replacement helicopters, will be needed to maintain a minimum naval force of lesser tonnage than the present fleet.

JAPAN

New Construction

DDG 168	*Tachikaze*	launching Dec 1974
DD 120	*Akigumo*	completed July 1974
DE 222	*Teshio*	completion Feb 1975
DE 223	*Yoshino*	completion Feb 1975
DE 224	*Kumano*	launching March 1975
SS 570	*Kuroshio*	completion Feb 1975
SS 571	*Takashio*	launching March 1975
LST 4151	*Miura*	launched 13 Aug 1974
LST 4103	*Nemuro*	cancelled
LST 4152	*Ojika*	completion Mar 1976
MSC 640	*Takane*	completed Aug 1974
MSC 641	*Muzuki*	completed Aug 1974
MSC 642	*Yokose*	completion Feb 1976
MSC 643	*Sakate*	completion Mar 1976
MSB 9 & 10		completed Mar 1974
MSB 11 & 12		completion Mar 1975
PT 15		completion Mar 1975

NOTE. DDG 169, DE 225 and SS 572 were not put out for contract in FY 1973 and were delayed to FY 1974.

Conversions

KASADO (MSC 604) converted to AGS 5111.
HABUSHI (MSC 608) converting to AGS by Mar 1975.
MOGAMI altered during special refit (Mar 1974) to carry Bofors rocket launcher in place of Mk 108 and two A/S torpedo tubes in place of two surface torpedo tubes.

Deletions

DD's *Ariake* and *Yuugure* returned to USA 9 Mar 1974
LST's *Oosumi* and 3001 returned to USA 30 Mar 1974
MSB 3 and 4 deleted Mar 1974
PT8 deleted 15 Feb 1974
ASH 2 deleted 30 Mar 1974

MEXICO

Drawing of "Azteca" class building by James Lamont, Ailsa Shipbuilding and Scott and Sons (Bowling). First vessel launched April 1974.

AZTECA

Addenda—*continued*

NETHERLANDS

Drawing of "Standard" or "S" class frigate. Four now ordered with provision in 1974 estimates for long-lead items for a further four. First ship planned to commission in October 1978.

OMAN

Four further 37·5 metre patrol craft ordered from Brooke Marine, Lowestoft on April 26 1974.

PAKISTAN

"Shanghai" class fast-attack-craft. Two of this class recently acquired.

PERU

Four missile-armed frigates ordered from Italy, in early 1974. Two to be built by Cantiere Navale di Tirreno e Riuniti (CNTR) and two, with technical assistance from CNTR, at Servicio Industrial de la Marina at Callao. Details are similar to those listed under "Italy" above with the addition of helicopter facilities.

QATAR

Seven 30 ft "Spear" class patrol boats ordered from Fairey Marine, the first to be delivered in June 1974.

SPAIN

Canarias to reserve 2 Sep 1974. Replacement aircraft carrier of USN Sea Control Ship contemplated. Five new PF frigates to be built by Bazan, El Ferrol. *Andalucia* started sea trials 7 Mar 1974. *Marsopa* started sea trials June 1974.

UNITED KINGDOM

In addition to craft listed the Scottish Dept of Agriculture and Fisheries operates a number of patrol craft the latest of which is *Jura* of 890 tons completed in 1973 by Hall Russell & Co Ltd of Aberdeen.

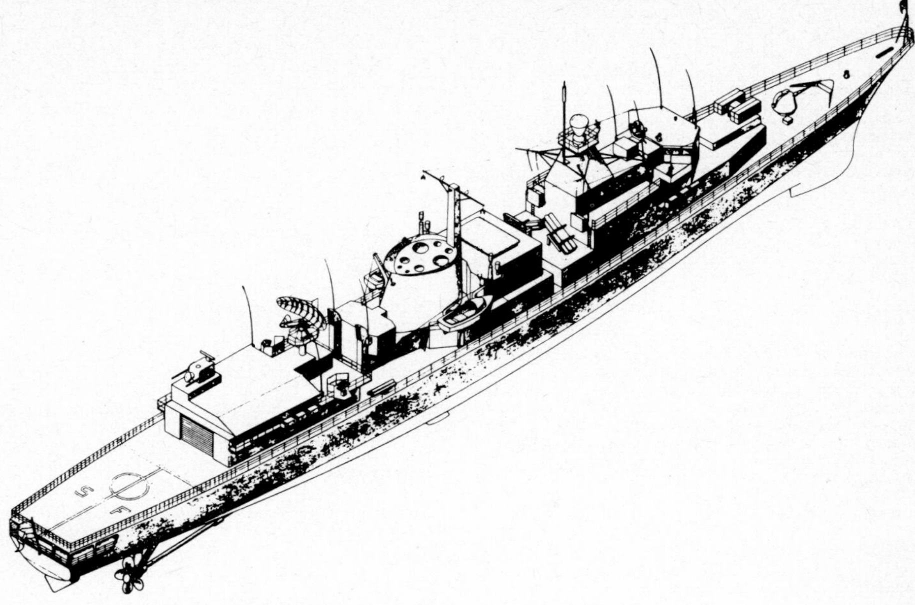

NETHERLANDS STANDARD FRIGATE

PAKISTAN "SHANGHAI" Class

PAKISTAN "HU CHWAN" Class

INDEX OF NAMED SHIPS

INDEX OF NAMED SHIPS

Abbreviations in brackets following the names of the ships indicate the country of origin

AbD	Abu Dhabi
Al	Albania
Alg	Algeria
A	Argentina
Aus	Australia
Au	Austria
B	Bahamas
Bah	Bahrain
Ba	Bangla Desh
Bar	Barbados
Bel	Belgium
Bo	Bolivia
Br	Brazil
Bru	Brunei
Bul	Bulgaria
Bur	Burma
Cam	Cameroon
Can	Canada
Chi	Chile
C	China (People's Republic)
Col	Colombia
Co	Congo
C.R.	Costa Rica
Cu	Cuba
Cy	Cyprus
D	Denmark
Dom	Dominican Republic
Ec	Ecuador
Eg	Egypt
ES	El Salvador
Et	Ethiopia
Fin	Finland
F	France
G	Gabon
Ger	Germany (Federal Republic)
GE	Germany (Democratic Republic)
Gh	Ghana
Gr	Greece
Ga	Grenada
Gu	Guatemala
Gui	Guinea
Guy	Guyana
H	Haiti
Hon	Honduras
HB	Honduras, British
HK	Hong Kong
Hun	Hungary
Ice	Iceland
In	India
Ind	Indonesia
Ir	Iran
Ira	Iraq
Ire	Ireland (Republic of)
Is	Israel
I	Italy
I.C.	Ivory Coast
Jam	Jamaica
J	Japan
Jo	Jordan
Ke	Kenya
Kh	Khmer Republic
Kor	Korea (Republic of)
K.N.	Korea (North)
Ku	Kuwait
L	Laos
Leb	Lebanon
Li	Liberia
Lib	Libya
Ma	Malagasy
Ml	Malawi
M	Malaysia
Mau	Mauritania
Mex	Mexico
Mo	Montserrat
Mor	Morocco
N	Netherlands
N.Z.	New Zealand
Nic	Nicaragua
Nig	Nigeria
Nor	Norway
O	Oman (Sultanate of)
Pak	Pakistan
Pan	Panama
Par	Paraguay
P	Peru
Ph	Philippines
Po	Poland
Por	Portugal
Q	Qatar
R	Romania
S	Sabah
St. L	St. Lucia
St. V	St. Vincent
Sau	Saudi Arabia
Sen	Senegal
S.L.	Sierra Leone
Sin	Singapore
Som	Somalia
S.A.	South Africa
Sp	Spain
Sri	Sri Lanka
Su	Sudan
Sw	Sweden
Sy	Syria
T.C.	Taiwan (Republic of China)
Tan	Tanzania
Th	Thailand
To	Togo
Ton	Tonga
T & T	Trinidad & Tobago
Tu	Tunisia
T	Turkey
U.K.	United Kingdom
U.S.A.	United States of America
Rus	Union of Soviet Socialist Republics
U	Uganda
Ur	Uruguay
Ven	Venezuela
V	Vietnam (Republic of)
V.N.	Vietnam (North)
V.I.	Virgin Islands
Yem	Yemen
YS	Yemen (South)
Y	Yugoslavia
Z	Zaire
Zan	Zanzibar

Page

A

ALMIRANTE GRAU—BAT YAM

CAPITAN QUIÑONES—DAR EL BARKA

FALANGRIN—GUADALUPE

GUADIANA—INDOMITA

INDOMITO—KOOTENAY

L

M

MACORIX—NAN YANG

NANAVA—PARINAS

PARKSVILLE—QUEENFISH

QUEENSVILLE—SANTO DEGOLLADO

SAO GABRIEL—SRI SEMPORNA

TOSHIMA—WENATCHEE

INDEX OF CLASSES

INDEX OF CLASSES

A CLASS—HRABRI

RORAIMA—ZWAARDVIS

Printed in England by Netherwood Dalton & Co. Ltd., Huddersfield